Arctic Geology

Published with financial aid from the
National Science Foundation and from
the DeGolyer Memorial Fund of
the AAPG Foundation.

Memoir 19

ARCTIC GEOLOGY

Proceedings of the Second International Symposium on Arctic Geology,
held February 1–4, 1971, at San Francisco, California.

Edited by *MAX G. PITCHER*

Published by The American Association of Petroleum Geologists,
Tulsa, Oklahoma, U.S.A., 1973

COMPOSED, PRINTED, AND BOUND BY THE COLLEGIATE PRESS,
GEORGE BANTA COMPANY, INC.
MENASHA, WISCONSIN 54952

Contents

Contents

Foreword

Following the discovery of Prudhoe Bay oil field in 1968, much attention was turned to the Arctic in the search for giant hydrocarbon accumulations. The Soviets had already proved giant reserves in their West Siberian Basin, and exploration was moving ahead quickly in the Canadian Arctic. In addition to industry activity, many Surveys and Institutes were independently collecting data on the geology of the Arctic. Chance placed three former Columbia graduate-student acquaintances in diverse employ, each with an interest in the integration of academic and industry interests in Arctic geology. I was involved in exploration for oil and gas with Continental Oil Company, Michael Churkin was with the Alaskan Branch of the United States Geological Survey, and Bill Kerr was with the Geological Survey of Canada. Mike and Bill had already been to Russia and were actively integrating their work with that of Soviet geologists. The three of us discussed the organization of the Second International Symposium on Arctic Geology and invited the AAPG to be the host society. Frank Conselman, then president of AAPG, in February 1969 presented the proposal to the AAPG Executive Committee, who accepted the challenge. The two succeeding AAPG presidents, Ken Crandrall and Bill Curry, continued to support the meeting. The Symposium was held in San Francisco in February 1971, with the Pacific Section of the AAPG as the sponsoring society. Bill Currans, then president of the Pacific Section, invited the Northern California Geological Society to be host and the Pacific Sections of the SEPM and SEG to participate in the symposium organization. Peter Gester, from the Chevron Overseas Petroleum Company in San Francisco, and many of his colleagues on the Pacific Coast did a masterful job of engineering the meeting.

The technical program was organized by regional and topical chairmen, and papers selected from the Symposium for this *Memoir* were solicited by some of those chairmen. George Gryc, from the Alaskan Branch of the USGS, was in charge of the Arctic of the United States and Bill Kerr, of the Canadian Geological Survey in Calgary, was in charge of the Canadian Arctic; Peter Friend, Cambridge University, Cambridge, England, chaired the sessions covering the Nordic Arctic, and Academician V. V. Menner and Nikita Bogdanov, of the Geological Institute of the Academy of Sciences of the USSR, oversaw those on Soviet geology. Mory Adelman, from the Massachusetts Institute of Technology, chaired the session on economics; Michael Churkin and Ned Ostenso chaired the session on origin of the Arctic Ocean basin. The 70 papers of this volume are less than half of those presented at the San Francisco meeting.

Assembling manuscripts from eight countries is complicated by translation problems. To overcome some of these problems with the Russian papers, I went to the USSR, with the aid of National Science Foundation funds, and read through each of the edited 24 Soviet papers with the authors or a designee. I wish to express gratitude to the Academy of Sciences of the USSR, who hosted me, and especially to the tireless efforts of Academician V. V. Menner. The Arctic Institute of the Ministry of Geology hosted me in Leningrad, and the Siberian Branch of the Academy of Sciences was my host in Novosibirsk. Rika Sorkina, Igor Gramberg, and Boris Egiazarov were indispensable to the inclusion of the Leningrad papers. Academician B. Sokolov, Sergei Troitskiy, Alla Bezobrazova, Alexander Obut, and Olga Pavlova were most helpful while I was in Novosibirsk. I wish space would permit me to relate the events of my Soviet trip, but suffice it to say that I have seldom developed such warm feelings for new acquaintances as I did during my 3-week sojourn in Russia.

Two grants from the National Science Foundation have assisted this project. Grant GN-32926 for $25,000, from the office of Science Information Service, has helped to reduce the cost of the publication, and Grant GV-27696 for $14,200, from the office of Polar Programs, has helped cover the excessive expenses of overseas participants.

Paul Nixon, who was affiliated with Brigham Young University at the time of the Symposium, assisted in editing some of the Soviet papers and in writing the Introduction. I express appreciation to many with Continental Oil Company who assisted directly in typing manuscripts and drafting charts, and to those who assisted indirectly by covering my responsibilities within the company while I was involved in the Symposium. Art Meyerhoff and Peggy Rice and others of the Editorial Staff at AAPG have an unfathomable capacity to answer questions and absorb deadline pressures.

It has been a stimulating experience to be associated with so many varied people on this project. In addition to the intellectual and industry achievements of this work, I hope that it has served to draw citizens of all nations surrounding the Arctic a little closer together. Sergei Troitskiy verbalized my dedication to this volume when, on my last night in Novosibirsk, I was expressing my appreciation to him and his colleagues in the Soviet Union. He said, "An international brotherhood exists among geologists; it is my wish that all men might someday feel the warm friendship that you and I feel tonight."

MAX G. PITCHER, *Editor*
Denver, Colorado
August 1, 1972

Introduction

This volume contains papers selected from the technical program presented at the Second International Symposium on Arctic Geology which was held in San Francisco, California, February 1–4, 1971. Sponsoring institutions were the Pacific Sections of The American Association of Petroleum Geologists, the Society of Economic Paleontologists and Mineralogists, and the Society of Exploration Geophysicists. The Northern California Geological Society was host for the event.

The Symposium and this *Memoir* have as a theme "Integration of Regional Geology of the Arctic Provinces." Papers are organized into seven topical groupings. The first four groups of technical papers deal with the regional Arctic geology of Canada, the Nordic countries, the USSR, and Alaska. The fifth section is devoted to comparisons in the North Atlantic borders. Papers in the sixth section are related to the general theme of the evolution of the Arctic Ocean basin. Economics of petroleum exploration and production are the main topics of papers in the seventh, and final, section of the volume.

The following general location map of geologic provinces of the Arctic will help the reader locate the areas discussed in the various papers.

Regional Arctic Geology of Canada

Seven papers in the *Memoir* deal specifically with the geology of Arctic Canada. Structure and tectonic style are emphasized in a series of papers—by Cook and Aitken on the Franklin Mountains and Colville Hills areas, by Norris on the Arctic plateau and Yukon Territory coastal plain, and by Bourne and Pallister on the offshore areas of the Canadian Arctic Islands. Stratigraphy is the general topic of a paper by Yorath on the Beaufort-Mackenzie basin and the eastern part of the northern Interior Plains, as well as a paper by Noble and Ferguson on the South Nahanni River area. Papers by Trettin on the northern Canadian Arctic Islands and by Plauchut on the Sverdrup basin describe the general geologic history of these areas.

Regional Arctic Geology of the Nordic Countries

Harland's study of Svalbard presents data on Mesozoic stratigraphy, and Johnson and Vogt report on the marine geology of the North Atlantic. The rest of the papers in this section are devoted principally to discussions of the geologic history of various areas. In their joint paper, Bridgwater, Escher, Jackson, Taylor, and Windley discuss the Precambrian geology of West Greenland, Labrador, and Baffin Island. Dawes and Soper report on North Greenland. Brooks deals with the Tertiary history of Greenland, and Birkelund describes the Mesozoic geology of East Greenland. Einarsson discusses the geology of Iceland.

Regional Arctic Geology of the USSR

Papers on a variety of subjects and areas have been contributed by Soviet scientists. Emphasis is placed by Krasny on interpretation of the geologic history of the eastern USSR, and by Belyi on the Okhotsk-Chukotsk volcanic belts. Vinogradov *et al.* discuss the geology of north-central Siberia. A discussion of Vendian relations of northern Eurasia is given by Sokolov, and a comparison of zonal scales for warm-water and Arctic areas is made by Menner. Gladenkov considers paleontologic problems in the North Pacific area. Tertiary paleobotanical correlations betweeen Alaska and north-

General location map for geologic provinces of the Arctic. Adapted from Churkin (this volume).

eastern Asia are the subject of the paper by Biske. Sachs *et al.* discuss paleozoogeography of the Arctic area during the Jurassic and Neocomian. Oil and gas possibilities of the Soviet Arctic are examined by Semenovich, Gramberg, and Nesterov. Fourteen other papers from the Arctic Institute in Leningrad deal with the paleontology, paleobotany, stratigraphy, and structural history of the Soviet Arctic. Some of the Russian papers have adequate location maps, but the reader will find the map which was prepared by I. S. Gramberg for the paper by Semenovich *et al.* to be a most useful reference.

The editors have generally followed the American Geological Institute system of Cyrillic transliteration as published in several early volumes of the *International Geology Review*. In some of the Russian papers, the senior author is listed first, but in others the authors are listed in alphabetical order according to the Cyrillic alphabet. Transliterations of geographic names usually are root words with the Russian adjectival endings deleted.

Because some of the terms used in several Russian papers are unfamiliar to many English readers, a short glossary has been assembled. This glossary, printed at the end of this paper, is a result of personal conversations with the Soviet writers and is an attempt to interpret the spirit of the terms as used in their manuscripts.

Regional Arctic Geology of Alaska

All the papers on the regional Arctic geology of Alaska are oriented toward consideration of various aspects of geologic history. Lathram's paper deals with the tectonic framework of northern and central Alaska. Brosgé and Dutro discuss the Paleozoic history of the area, and Detterman describes the Mesozoic history of Arctic Alaska. The geologic history of the Yukon-Tanana upland is the subject of a paper by Foster, Weber, Forbes, and Brabb. Kirschner and Lyon treat the geologic history of the Cook Inlet. Parts of the Alaska Range and the Alaska Peninsula are considered in studies by Richter and Jones and by Reed and Lanphere.

Comparisons in the North Atlantic Borders

Devonian stratigraphy of Greenland and Svalbard is the subject of the paper by Friend. Geologic history is the focal point of the remainder of the papers in this section. Precambrian history of northern Sweden is the subject of the paper by Padget. Henriksen considers the Caledonian geology of central East Greenland, and Gayer summarizes the Caledonian geology of Arctic Norway. The subject of Nilsen's paper is Early and Middle Devonian sedimentation and tectonics of Norway.

Evolution of the Arctic Ocean Basin

Twelve papers included in the *Memoir* are devoted principally to various aspects of the evolution of the Arctic Ocean basin. Origin of the Arctic Ocean basin is discussed in papers by Churkin, Meyerhoff, and Ostenso and Wold. The geologic history of the Canada basin is the subject of Tailleur's manuscript, and Hall discusses the significance of the Alpha Cordillera and the Mendeleyev Ridge in the formation of that basin. The geologic history of Baffin Bay and the Labrador Sea is emphasized by Fahrig, Irving, and Jackson; Kerr; Manchester and Clarke; and Martin. Papers discussing the Barents and Kara Seas were contributed by Harland and by Vogt and Ostenso. Sobczak and Weber report data on the nature of the continental margin along the Canadian Arctic Archipelago.

Economics of Petroleum Exploration and Production in the Arctic

The final seven papers in the *Memoir* are discussions of political and economic aspects of petroleum in the Arctic. Edgington, Campbell, and Cleland consider exploration and production. Bradley and Kaufman have authored two papers on the prediction of risk and reward in petroleum exploration. Norman's paper is a discussion of the economic potential of the Prudhoe Bay field. Meyerhoff and Meyerhoff, Steele, and Ion present data on geopolitics and the impact of petroleum in the Arctic.

DISCUSSION OF PAPERS

The contributions of papers in this volume toward an integration of regional geology of the Arctic may be highlighted in relation to a series of topics which includes (1) origin of Arctic Ocean basin and ridges, (2) geology of Arctic platforms and shields, (3) geology of Arctic sedimentary basins and fold belts, (4) regional geology of Arctic USSR, (5) igneous rocks in the Arctic, (6) Arctic paleontology, (7) petroleum and mineral resources of the Arctic, and (8) petroleum economics in the Arctic. A brief discussion of papers which are devoted to each of these major topics may serve to guide the reader to the wealth of information which is contained in this *Memoir*.

Origin of Arctic Ocean Basin and Ridges

Four papers examine the overall history and evolution of the Arctic Ocean basin. Churkin's discussion suggests that the tectonic history of the basin is too complicated to be explained by an early origin dating to early Paleozoic or Precambrian time, or by a relatively recent origin due to subsidence of continental crust or to continental drift. He postulates a history of development of the basin involving multiple openings and closings of basins in the area, leading to the ultimate formation of the present Arctic basin. Ostenso and Wold cite aeromagnetic data showing magnetic disturbance zones which parallel the Alpha-Mendeleyev and Nansen (Gakkel) ridges. Lomonosov Ridge is shown to be magnetically quiet. These authors also present a hypothesis for the evolution of the Arctic basin. Harland reconstructs the tectonic history and configuration of lithosphere plates as related to the Barents shelf; the structural and geophysical evidence on which he bases this reconstruction has been tested for stratigraphic consistency. Meyerhoff attributes late Proterozoic through Early Permian evaporite deposition to the existence and persistence of the Gulf Stream–North Atlantic Drift system and suggests that continental drift and polar wandering, if either took place, are pre–late Proterozoic events in the Arctic and North Atlantic areas. In a group of papers dealing with selected parts of the Arctic basin, formation of the Canada basin by post-Triassic rifting and rotation is suggested by Tailleur. He indicates that recent spreading from Gakkel Ridge appears to have been preceded by spreading from the Alpha Cordillera; thus, formation of the Canada basin would have been an initial stage. Hall presents geophysical data to support suggestions that the Alpha Cordillera and Mendeleyev Ridge are a fossil center of sea-floor spreading. Sobczak and Weber's investigation of the northern Canadian Arctic Islands indicates that the continental margin in this area consists of a sedimentary layer up to 10 km thick and a crust which has a thickness variation of as much as 17 km. Extensional movements along the Canadian Arctic rift-system branch of the Mid-Atlantic Ridge are postulated by Kerr to have begun in latest Triassic or Early Jurassic time, and substantial movement is thought to have occurred as late as the Oligocene. Vogt reports data from reconnaissance geophysical surveys in the Barents and Kara Seas. Magnetic data do not substantiate a continuation of Caledonian or Precambrian basement under the Barents Sea at shallow depth.

Three papers discuss the formation of Baffin Bay and related depressions. Fahrig indicates that Davis Strait and Baffin Bay originated as a result of late Precambrian regional tension. Martin suggests formation of Baffin Bay by Late Cretaceous–early Tertiary rifting. Manchester and Clarke's analysis of magnetometer and bathymetric data shows no clear northward continuation of the linear magnetic anomalies which are associated with the Mid–Labrador Sea Ridge.

Chronologic evolution of the Norwegian-Greenland sea is examined in the paper by Johnson and Vogt. They suggest that the process of axial accretion along the crest of an active midoceanic ridge is of paramount tectonic importance to the geologic fabric of the northern Atlantic sea floor.

Geology of Arctic Platforms and Shields

Bridgwater *et al.* have determined that Precambrian rocks on either side of Davis Strait show a similar pattern of events and can be interpreted as having formed part of a single shield. Eight major stages in the development of this shield are suggested. Padget's studies of northernmost Sweden have indicated the existence of an ancient cratonic nucleus covered by a thick sequence of geosynclinal sedimentary beds. Two phases of younger orogenic activity and post-orogenic deformation are recognized. Yorath reports that the eastern part of the northern Interior Plains of Arctic Canada is underlain by Paleozoic, Mesozoic, and Cenozoic rocks which dip homoclinally northwestward. Tectonic styles of the Arctic plateau and coastal plain of the Yukon Territory, District of Mackenzie, are described in the paper by Norris.

Geology of Arctic Sedimentary Basins and Fold Belts

Aspects of the sedimentary basins and fold belts in Alaska are the subject of six papers in this volume. Lathram suggests that traditional interpretations of the tectonic framework of northern and central Alaska are inadequate and that many of the newly-proposed hypotheses are contradictory. He discusses the known data concerning the area that must be accommodated in reinterpretations of the region. Brosgé and Dutro interpret the Paleozoic geologic history of northern and central Alaska as revealed by the sedimentary record. The depositional and structural history of Arctic Alaska during the Mesozoic is traced by Detterman. Foster *et al.* point out that recognition of large-scale offset along the Tintina fault necessitates reconsideration of the regional structural and stratigraphic relations of the Yukon-Tanana upland. The Mesozoic and Tertiary history of the Cook Inlet area is discussed in a paper by Kirschner and Lyon. The eastern Alaska Range is believed by Richter and Jones to provide clues to the tectonic development of northwestern North America.

Sedimentary basins and fold belts of Arctic Canada provide important data for the integration of the regional geology of the Arctic. Trettin traces the early Paleozoic evolution of northern parts of the Canadian Arctic Islands. Major events in the development and deformation of the major geosynclines of the area are discussed. Pallister and Bourne suggest that the geology of the inter-island areas of the Canadian Arctic Archipelago is speculative; they believe that interpretations may have to be revised after a review of newly-available geophysical data. Plauchut's paper indicates that the Sverdrup basin, in the northern part of the Canadian Arctic Archipelago, contains a substantial thickness of deposits ranging in age from Carboniferous to early Tertiary. These rocks lie unconformably on deformed Devonian and older rocks. Cook and Aitken report that rocks in the northern Franklin Mountains and Colville Hills, District of Mackenzie, are deformed in structures reflecting shortening of sedimentary cover caused by tangential compression. Noble and Ferguson have investigated facies relations at the edge of an early mid-Devonian carbonate shelf in the South Nahanni River area, Northwest Territories.

The Caledonian orogenic history constitutes an important element of the geology of the Arctic. Henricksen distinguishes four main geologic units in the Caledonian fold belt of central East Greenland. Gayer's paper summarizes the structural and stratigraphic history of the Caledonian orogen in Arctic Norway. Rocks ranging in age from late Precambrian to Silurian have undergone polyphase deformation and metamorphism. Diachronism of orogeny is interpreted to be a result of migration of the point of plate contact.

Post-Caledonian Devonian history is described in papers by Friend and by Nilsen. Friend states that Devonian rocks of Greenland and Svalbard are nonmarine clastic sequences up to 7 km thick which contain vertebrate fossils. These rocks overlie pre-Devonian rocks deformed by Caledonian orogenesis. Lower and Middle Devonian continental redbeds in Norway are reported by Nilsen to reflect fluvial deposition of coarse-grained clastic sediments in a series of separate intermontane basins. The Mesozoic geology of Svalbard is the subject of Harland's paper. He discusses rocks which range in age from Early Triassic through Early Cretaceous. Maximum known thickness of these rocks is about 3 km.

In northern Greenland a geologic section is present, according to Dawes and Soper, in which a Precambrian crystalline basement is overlain by strata of Precambrian, Paleozoic, Mesozoic, and Tertiary age. Events leading to the development of an extensive platform and the North Greenland fold belt are described. Birkelund indicates that, in eastern Greenland, Mesozoic sediments were deposited in fault-bounded basins. The composite thickness of the sequence is 6–7 km, and it is dominated by clastic material which was deposited in shallow water.

Regional Geology of Arctic USSR

Two papers provide an integrated discussion of the shields, platforms, sedimentary basins, and fold belts of this area. Krasny traces the structure and history of geologic development of the eastern USSR in the framework of three major geochrons. Vinogradov *et al.* portray the geologic history of north-central Siberia in their reconstruction of the history of the North Asiatic craton in relation to the evolution of the surrounding belts. In a related paper, Menner discusses the work of Russian geologists in the Arctic. Implicit in many of the Russian papers (*e.g.,* Tkachenko *et al.,* Egiazarov *et al.*) is the existence of a Hyperborean platform which is thought to have been a stable region in the area of the present Arctic Ocean basin. The "Arctides," or circumpolar fold belt, surrounded this shield region. The Hyperborean platform sank in post-Paleozoic time to form the present Arctic Ocean basin. This concept is consistent with their belief that the stratigraphy and structure giving rise to the Prudhoe Bay hydrocarbon accumulation extend across the Bering Sea to Wrangel Island and the New Siberian Islands. Egiazarov *et al.* consider the sigificance of "reentrant angles" which form as a result of the intersection of arcuate fold trends. Such fold systems and associated geosynclines are pronounced along the Pacific borders from Kamchatka to Alaska. Semenovich *et al.* discuss the hydrocarbon potential of most of the sedimentary basins of the Soviet Arctic. Continuing the discussion of sedimentary rocks with hydrocarbon potential, Patrunov describes Devonian reefs up to 2,000 m thick on Vaygach Island.

Igneous Rocks in the Arctic

Papers dealing primarily with various aspects of igneous rocks form an important element of this *Memoir.* Belyi discusses the importance of the structural and tectonic development of the Okhotsk-Chukotsk volcanic belt as it relates to the general problem of andesitic volcanism. Reed and Lanphere have documented three major episodes of plutonism which occurred during the Mesozoic and Tertiary history in central and southern Alaska. Tertiary plateau basalts and a wide spectrum of intrusive rocks are the subject of Brooks' paper. Einarsson describes the Tertiary and younger basalts of Iceland.

Arctic Paleontology

Paleozoogeography of the Arctic during the Jurassic and Neocomian is discussed by Sachs *et al.,* who report that during this time Arctic seas were linked with the Atlantic and Pacific Oceans. Biske suggests that comprehensive paleobotanical studies of major stratigraphic sections of Tertiary nonmarine deposits of Alaska and northeastern Asia indicate that they are possibly correlative. Menner's paper compares zonal scales for warm-water and Arctic areas. According to studies by Gladenkov, stratigraphic scales of the North Pacific area now can be tied to the general world scale. Sokolov's classic paper on the Vendian stratigraphy and paleontology describes Precambrian faunas.

Petroleum and Mineral Resources

Two excellent reviews of the petroleum and mineral resources of the Arctic are included in this volume. Semenovich *et al.* discuss the oil and gas possibilities of the Soviet Arctic. They describe the major platforms with thick sedimentary sections which form the known and prospective areas for oil and gas. Meyerhoff and Meyerhoff emphasize the geopolitical considerations of the known and potential petroleum and mineral resources of the Arctic.

Petroleum Economics in the Arctic

Kaufman and Bradley develop models for examination of aspects of the spatial distribution and probability of finding petroleum reservoirs. In a second paper, Bradley and Kaufman examine the process of estimation of significant variables in the prediction of economic success of petroleum exploration prospects. Ion and Edgington *et al.* consider the impact of Arctic oil on world oil supply and demand patterns. Norman presents an economic model of the Prudhoe Bay field and compares it with a model of the Bell Creek field, Montana. Steele's paper concentrates on the economic potential of petroleum production from Alaska and other possibly productive areas in the North American Arctic.

MAX G. PITCHER
Continental Oil Company
Denver, Colorado

GLOSSARY OF RUSSIAN TERMS USED IN SYMPOSIUM PAPERS

Aleurite—An unconsolidated sedimentary deposit composed of silt-sized grains.

Aleurolite—A consolidated aleurite; commonly used to mean siltstone.

Anticlise—A structure of the craton, usually with a crystalline core and sedimentary flanks; also, a structure of the platform with areal coverage of greater than hundreds or thousands of square kilometers. Sedimentary cover of an anticlise rarely exceeds 3 km.

Arcogenesis—The process of deformation during the uplift of an area; also, deformation that takes place above sea level. It may be accompanied by magmatic intrusions or volcanic extrusions; usually evidenced by the presence of continental deposits and an absence of marine deposits. *E.g.:* Transbaykal area.

Aulacogene—A trough that "burrows" into the craton from the geosynclinal borders. *E.g.:* Ouachita trough of the United States.

Brachyanticline—An anticline with a major axis not longer than two times the minor axis. (The definition in the 1957 edition of the AGI Glossary [J. V. Howell, editor] is incorrect.)

Brachyform structures—Structures with nearly equal major and minor axes.

Disjunctive dislocations—Faults.

Fold phases—Significant orogenic pulses with the following order and ages:

Alpine—end of the Eocene–beginning of the Miocene, 12 ± 1 m.y. ago; end of the Miocene–beginning of the Anthropogene, 1.5–2 m.y. ago.

Mesozoic—early Mesozoic (Kimerides, Nevadides, Audides, Columbides, early Mesozoides), 160 ± 10 m.y. ago; late Mesozoic (Laramides, late Mesozoides), 67 ± 3 m.y. ago.

Hercynian (= Variscan)—early Hercynian, 300 ± 20 m.y. ago; late Hercynian, 270 ± 10 m.y. ago.

Caledonian—early Caledonian, 500 ± 20 m.y. ago; late Caledonian, 400 ± 10 m.y. ago.

Baykalian (= Assinian, Assyntic)—570 ± 30 m.y. ago.

Dalslandian—early Baykalian (Carolinides), 850 ± 50 m.y. ago.

Geoblock—A part of the earth's crust characterized by a similarity of structure and the same type of crust; it is usually bordered by deep fracture zones.

E.g.: Kolyma-Verkhoyansk geoblock, which has gentle, stable structural features and is separate from the Kamchatka geoblock, which has a different tectonic style.

Hydrocarbon traps—**1.** Stratigraphic (Russian term) = unconformity (English term). **2.** Lithologic (Russian term) = pinchout (English term). **3.** Massive (Russian term) is used to describe a trap such as a reef trap or an anticlinal structure with a large oil column and a common oil-water contact across the feature.

Inversion—The change of sign of the structural movement. *E.g.:* Inversion of a geosyncline is the change from subsidence to uplift.

Pericraton—A structural entity on the periphery of the craton. *E.g.:* A basin on the side of the craton.

Planorium—An area characterized by gentle folds with long periods.

Plicative dislocations—Folds.

Pre-Baykal or Pre-Urals, etc.—Terms usually refer to the area west of the Baykal or Urals, *etc.*, but may mean the surrounding area. Synonym is Cis-Baykal or Cis-Urals.

Reentrant angle—Angle formed by the intersection of two fault zones.

Structural stage—A term used in the paper by Demenitskaya *et al.* to depict a complex of sedimentary beds characterized by quite different structural attitude and physical properties from overlying and underlying "structural stages." In that paper, the structural stages are determined on the basis of geophysical data, including reflections and velocities. Stages are numbered in descending order.

Sublatitudinal structure—A structure with a strike nearly paralleling lines of latitude.

Sublongitudinal structure—A structure with a strike nearly paralleling lines of longitude.

Syneclise—A basin of large extent generated on the continental platform by epeirogenic movements rather than orogenic. Dips are of very low order, generally discernible by map pattern.

Thalassocraton—A persistent ocean platform such as the floor of the Pacific Ocean.

Trough—A basin with depositional thicknesses on the borders very much less than in the center.

Keynote Address

Challenge of Resource Development and Environmental Protection in the Arctic[1]

HOLLIS M. DOLE[2]

Washington, D.C. 20240

Abstract Arctic geology, as related to the development of natural resources, is an essential element in man's most critical challenges: (1) to provide mineral and energy resources in amounts adequate for present and developing needs; (2) to provide these resources without degrading the natural environment; and (3) to acquire, organize, communicate, and apply the knowledge on which solutions to the first two challenges depend. The first challenge can be illustrated by reference to the United States, whose energy requirements are projected to be almost doubled by 1985 and to increase threefold by the year 2000. Projected demands for other nonrenewable mineral resources are similar. Exploration for fossil fuel reserves and for nonfuel minerals will intensify in the near future.

Accepting the need for a continuing supply of mineral raw materials, we must make every effort to minimize the potentially adverse effects of resource development and to remedy them when they do occur. The costs of nonrenewable resources necessarily may be increased, but the increased costs represent the purchase of values to be shared and passed on to future generations. The Arctic, being practically unmodified by man's living systems, provides a unique test of our abilities to meet these two challenges. The third challenge, acquiring the data necessary to accomplish the first two challenges, will be difficult because of the natural Arctic environment. Accelerated research and effort will be required.

The three proposed challenges must be met at three levels of involvement: international, national, and individual. The response at the international level is complex, but our responsibilities—as individuals and as scientists—are emerging. At the national level, the U.S. Department of the Interior has a leadership role in Arctic activities through the various agencies and bureaus under its jurisdiction and through cooperation with many other government agencies. The geologist, as an individual, must make an effort to communicate and to apply geology to the service of man in coping with the problems he faces. He must make a commitment and become part of the solutions to the critical challenges.

INTRODUCTION

This symposium focuses specifically on Arctic geology. This subject is of great interest to us as scientists for its own sake, but, more importantly, it relates to what I believe are mankind's most serious and critical challenges. Let me try to define these challenges and to describe the levels at which significant responses

[1] Manuscript received, February 1, 1971.

[2] Assistant Secretary—Mineral Resources, U.S. Department of the Interior.

to them can and must be made. By so doing, we can develop a clearer picture of what we must do to meet them.

Let me first define the environment in which these challenges and response levels exist. We live in a total environment that consists of our living systems, economic systems, and governmental systems superposed on our natural environment. Up to now, the influence of man and his accompanying systems on the natural Arctic environment has been insignificant. Man has not greatly influenced the natural phenomena and processes existing there, nor has his understanding of them been very deep. The breadth of our ignorance is revealed in the wide variety of scientific studies now being directed toward the acquisition of baseline data and the development of hypotheses and theories concerning this relatively untouched part of our earth.

THE CHALLENGES

What are the critical challenges? The first is to provide mineral and energy resources to all mankind in amounts that are adequate for present and developing needs; the second is to provide these resources without degrading the natural environment that sustains and gratifies humans in innumerable ways; and the third is to acquire, organize, communicate, and apply the knowledge on which solutions to the first two challenges depend.

The challenge to provide nonrenewable mineral resources, including energy-producing materials, for the world's demands can be illustrated by reference to the United States. Although the United States is far from typical for the world, because our per capita consumption of mineral raw materials is far greater than that of other nations, the general trend in all nations is in the direction of increased population and increased consumption.

Energy-consumption projections based on gross national product (GNP) indicate that by 1985 the United States will require—at the very least—almost double the amount of energy used last year to heat its homes; to power its factories, mines, and transportation systems;

and, in general, to accomplish the work that supports our high level of living. Similar projections indicate a threefold increase in energy consumption between now and the year 2000.

When we consider the projected demands on the other nonrenewable mineral resources, we find a similar situation. Present estimates suggest that the United States' demand for primary minerals will increase fourfold by the year 2000. Specifically, demands for aluminum and titanium are expected to increase sixfold; tungsten and vanadium, fourfold; and copper, sand and gravel, crushed stone, beryllium, fluorine, tantalum, and magnesium, threefold. Demands for many other minerals will show twofold increases. This staggering projected demand for hard-mineral resources imposes a gigantic task of discovery and development—not only in the United States, but throughout the world.

In speaking of projections, some may ask, why allow ourselves to be swept on to such higher and higher levels of consumption? Why not simply curtail our use of resources, perhaps even return to a lower level of living—one that might make us healthier and happier anyway?

I shall not speculate about how much popular support we might find for such an idea or whether we might be forced to take such a course eventually by reason of resource inadequacy. Instead, without elaboration, I submit that, if we were to attempt such a retrenchment over a short time span, national and world civilization would collapse and millions upon millions of people would starve. Furthermore, a tapering off in our rate of increase in consumption would solve our problem only temporarily. Whether we set as our goal continued growth in level of living or mere survival, for the next few decades we are going to have to find the raw materials to keep our industrial society going!

Accepting these increasing needs for minerals and fuels, how are we going to meet them?

At the present time, United States domestic onshore oil exploration is at a low, all productive capacity is being utilized, and the United States inevitably is becoming more dependent on the rest of the world for crude oil and residual fuel oil supplies. At the same time, oil is being forced to supply more and more of the U.S. energy demand. The role of coal in the energy mix is likely to be curtailed by air quality restrictions for at least the next 5 years. Hydroelectric power will continue to grow, but will be of decreasing relative importance. Nuclear power, though growing, is lagging behind earlier timetables and exceeding cost estimates. In addition to unforeseen technical problems, the nuclear industry has encountered public concern and resistance to thermal pollution and potential radiation hazards. Unconventional energy sources, such as oil derived from shale and gas derived from coal, are not expected to be available commercially before the 1980s, although they, together with nuclear breeder reactors, are the only apparent *real* possibilities for very long-term energy sources.

The situation with regard to hard minerals also calls for new sources, and the needs for hard minerals and for petroleum underscore the importance of Arctic exploration and development.

Although petroleum exploration has been going on in the Arctic for years, it has been accelerated recently. Significant increases in the efforts to find and develop new fossil-fuel reserves probably will take place during the next few years. The search for nonfuel minerals also will intensify as technology provides improved transportation and processing methods. We actually are just starting the exploration phase that will result in discovery of the major nonrenewable-resource accumulations that are present in the Arctic.

The challenge to protect and enhance our natural environment in the face of all the intentional and unintentional influences of man is linked inextricably to the resource challenge I just described. The quest for and utilization of nonrenewable-resource raw materials necessarily results in modification of the natural environment. The path of resource use—with its extraction, beneficiation, refining, transportation, fabrication, consumption, and disposal elements—is inevitably marked by blazes—and sometimes with ugly scars or worse effects—on our natural environment.

If we accept, *as we must,* the need for a continuing supply of mineral raw materials, then we must accept the fact that the natural environment is going to be influenced by the processes of resource extraction and use. Our problem, then, is to minimize the potentially adverse effects of resource development and to remedy them when they occur despite our efforts to avoid them. To ignore this problem is to run the risk of immersing ourselves in aesthetically displeasing surroundings; of losing those as-yet-untouched parts of the earth's surface, with their real but hard-to-quantify values; and of fouling our environment to such an extent that it literally becomes toxic to organic life. As we move to minimize the adverse influences of man's living systems; to enhance the total environment wherever and whenever possible; and to preserve some untouched areas for aesthetic, recreational, and scientific purposes, we must keep in mind that these efforts may add to the costs of the nonrenewable resources that are involved. We must be prepared to accept the added costs, knowing that they represent the purchase of values that we are sharing with all mankind and passing on to the world citizens of the future. If we put our minds to the task imaginatively, perhaps we can find ways to achieve and meet these challenges without added costs—by converting liabilities and costs into assets and profits.

Because the Arctic is practically unmodified by the various parts of modern man's living systems that eventually will influence it, it provides a unique test of our abilities to meet these challenges. In the Arctic, man and his machines are about to encounter the proverbial "blank slate." The problems of minimizing the adverse impact of man's activities are raising the cost of these activities, but certainly such costs are not as high as those involved in the tremendous task of reversing the degradational processes already in effect in our air, lakes, rivers, and communities in the lower latitudes. Meeting this challenge to safeguard the Arctic natural environment includes an added dimension because it necessarily involves several sovereign nations, each of which approaches the Arctic with a different background, different national needs, and different attitudes about resource development.

The third challenge that I am concerned with is the driving need to acquire the resource and environmental data necessary to meet the other challenges; to organize and generalize those data; and to communicate the findings effectively, not only to fellow scientists, but to all groups of people who have an interest in the Arctic. We all recognize that future actions which are firmly based on sound knowledge are going to meet challenges much more efficiently and economically than would actions based on assumptions and ignorance.

In the Arctic, the task of acquiring field data and baseline information is made difficult by the natural environment. Yet, if we are to meet the resource-development and environmental-protection challenges effectively, we must know the systems involved. When the time comes to consider the environmental impact of, for example, another transportation system like the proposed Alaska pipeline, we must know well in advance the distribution of fish and wildlife and their migration patterns, the distribution of permafrost and the engineering properties of soil and rock materials, and the nature of other aspects of the ecosystem. Acquiring the necessary data will take accelerated research into these questions, just as the quest for resources of minerals and fuels in the Arctic will require accelerated research and support at all levels.

RESPONSE LEVELS

The challenges I have posed must be met at three different levels of application and involvement. This symposium contains elements of all three levels, and I urge you to examine the role that you, as an individual, can and should play at each level. The first challenge-response level is international and the second is national; the third is hard to label, but I shall call it "individual."

It is clear that problems which are international in character require solutions which are also international, whether the problems relate to resource exploitation, protection of the natural environment, or the development of a body of knowledge. The decisions and actions of the United States, and of any other nation, in regard to resources affect every other nation directly or indirectly; and they affect future generations as well as the present generation. In a very real way, all of us, regardless of nationality, are the stewards of the earth; our responsibilities at the international level are emerging, even though they are not yet fully articulated.

The international picture of nonrenewable-resource development has been, and is, a combination of the demands of differing economic and governmental systems. In the most general way, the economic systems have functioned more or less efficiently to bring the least expensive sources of raw materials into production first, and to bring the derived materials into the marketplace in a timely fashion. This process has been affected to greater or lesser degrees at various times and in various places by the demands of national security and sovereignty. No nation is self-sufficient regarding mineral raw materials, and the continuation and improvement of worldwide standards of living depend upon the ability of nations to exist with one another—to bargain and to trade. Peace throughout the whole world would make the development and continuation of a mutually beneficial trading system easier, and would end the needless expenditure of nonrenewable and human resources that results from conflict. But we are approaching the time when peace will not be possible unless regional and global environmental deterioration and damage can be avoided.

What are the effective international approaches to the resource, environmental, and research challenges? It seems to me that they can be grouped into two main categories. One is cooperative research and investigation, and the other is international agreement based on sound understanding of the resource and environmental problems and their solutions. Neither approach has been pursued nearly as assiduously or as far as it should be, but we have some examples to point the way.

There have been joint expeditions to the Arctic, such as those in 1957–1960 and 1967–1968 by EGIG (Expédition Glaciologique Internationale au Groenland) and the Swedish-Finnish-Swiss Expedition to Nordaustlandet in 1957–1958. International commissions, such as that on periglacial geomorphology of the International Geographical Union, offer another way of coordinating Arctic research on an international basis. Perhaps the greatest accomplishments will come from internationally coordinated, and in part cooperative, studies of the International Biological Program, the International Geophysical Year, the International Polar Years, the International Hydrological Decade, and the International Decade of Oceanographic Exploration. No international institutes, except for the joint Canadian-United States Arctic Institute of North America, are actively studying the Arctic. This lack of cooperation is somewhat mitigated by the fact that many of the national institutes include scientists of different nationalities on their staffs; this situation at least provides an informal international approach to the acquisition and dissemination of scientific knowledge. The personal contact of one scientist with another now sustains the international response to the challenge of obtaining the knowledge necessary for rational and balanced activity in the Arctic.

International agreements and studies concerned with the natural environment have been relatively few, although those relating to fisheries resources, whale harvesting, and polar bears certainly have as a primary aim the conservation of these natural resources. The Nuclear Test Ban Treaty, with its prohibition of atmospheric testing, stands as an example of how international agreement can prevent further degradation of our natural environment. The Antarctic Treaty of 1961 illustrates how the influences of scientists on their governments can be combined with the cooperation of those separate governments to formulate a truly international approach to the problems of a region. The final successful proposal of that treaty grew out of the scientific cooperation and communication that took place in Antarctica during the IGY. The apparent absence of exploitable nonrenewable mineral resources perhaps made this treaty relatively easy to accomplish; but, even so, it stands as one example of the renunciation of national territorial claims in favor of joint cooperation, international study, and dedication of a region to scientific purposes. An even more far-reaching international accord now may be in sight with the United Nations' efforts regarding the seabed and related questions. The General Assembly adopted resolutions in December 1970 constituting a declaration of principles governing the seabed and ocean floor beyond national jurisdiction, and calling for a conference on the Law of the Sea in 1973. These efforts have profound implications for the Arctic, where the broad outer shelf areas may contain undiscovered accumulations of oil and gas.

Barring the extremely unlikely possibility of early agreement on a comprehensive treaty dealing with the Arctic, international Arctic policy for the near future will be the sum of all the national policies of the adjacent nations and other concerned sovereign powers. International cooperation and understanding in the "emerging Arctic" can be advanced if each concerned power develops and clearly states its policy in regard to the development of nonrenewable mineral resources, indigenous human populations, protection of the natural environment, and scientific inquiry and exchange of information. For the time being, however, the main policy initiative must come from national and state governments.

The second challenge-response level, which is more in my own area of responsibility, is the national level. In candor, I must say that the United States does not at this time have a formally articulated Arctic policy, but we do have a well-developed national response mechanism that has been, is, and will be meeting the challenges of the Arctic. Many parts of this response mechanism are in the U.S. Department of the Interior, and that department's leadership role in Arctic activities is becoming increasingly apparent. I shall describe some of our activities as an example of national-level response to the resource, environmental, and research challenges.

The activities of the Department of the Interior in the Arctic, specifically in Alaska, are broadly resource-oriented. Thus, the work of the Geological Survey is designed to establish the geologic framework of the state and to provide data needed to inventory mineral resources. In addition to these studies, the Survey is also deeply concerned with engineering-geology problems in Alaska. Responsibilities of the Bureau of Mines are to gather data on mineral production, to promote safe and healthful working conditions in the mineral industry, and to investigate mining systems that are best suited to Alaska's natural environment. The EROS (Earth Resources Observation Systems) program is a relatively new one which will utilize remote sensors of all types from aircraft and satellites to generate information that, together with ground-gathered geologic data, will aid in the evaluation of mineral resources and the geologic environment.

Three Interior bureaus are oriented toward human resources, as well as toward the natural environment. The Bureau of Indian Affairs has the responsibility for federal government liaison with the Eskimos, Aleuts, and Indians, who are in transition from their original subsistence cultures to a modern industrialized society. The Bureau of Outdoor Recreation is concerned with the utilization of the natural environment by man with due regard for enhancement of man's outdoor activities and for protection of the environment necessary so that those activities can be enjoyed. The National Park Service oversees and protects one of our greatest national parks at Mount McKinley, as well as the Katmai, Glacier Bay, and Sitka National Monuments. Its responsibilities have both natural-environmental and human-experience dimensions.

The Bureau of Sports Fisheries and Wildlife shares with State of Alaska counterpart bureaus the study, protection, and enforcement functions associated with the naturally occurring biome. The Bureau also administers wildlife refuges, including some of the major waterfowl nesting areas of North America as well as the Arctic National Wildlife Refuge.

Also, as landlord for much of the public domain in Alaska, the Interior Department, through the Bureau of Land Management, is responsible for the classification and management of large tracts of land in the interior of the state; and, together with the Geological Survey, it is responsible for administering federal mineral-leasing laws and regulations in the state, both on land and offshore.

The deep involvement of the Interior bureaus and offices in the problems of development of nonrenewable resources and protection of the natural environment in the Arctic demonstrates the leadership role of the Department in Arctic affairs. As the main steward for the public lands, as the protector of fish and wildlife resources, and as the scientist synthesizing the geologic and ecologic framework of Alaska, it brings together and integrates almost all of the elements in the total resource inventory—a procedure that is necessary before judgments about resource utilization can be made.

I hasten to mention the other federal agencies that play important roles in the Arctic part of the United States, and to point out our successful collaborations with them. The Office of Naval Research, with its magnificent Barrow Arctic Research Laboratory; the Office of Naval Petroleum Reserves; and the Corps of Engineers Cold Regions Research and Engineering Laboratory have a long history of mutually successful cooperation with the Geological Survey in particular. The U.S. Coast Guard is a valued collaborator with the Survey in oceanographic studies, as is the Coast and Geodetic Survey. The Bureau of Commercial Fisheries was recently transferred from Interior, and close collaborative ties remain. The Federal Water Quality Administration and the National Air Pollution Control Administration have had, or now are developing, in their roles as EPA (Environmental Protection Agency) divisions, close relations with the Geological Survey and the Bureau of Land Management as a result of their mutual concern with protection of the natural environment. The Forest Service, which is the steward for forest and recreational lands in Subarctic Alaska, collaborates with the BLM.

The mechanisms thus exist at the national and state level in the United States to meet the challenges of resource development, environmental protection, and knowledge acquisition. Similar agencies and mechanisms exist in the other countries concerned with the Arctic. Here and elsewhere, more interbureau coordination is desirable, but what is most important now is to formulate and formalize an Arctic policy that will clearly spell out how the U.S.

intends to approach the problems of Arctic development and protection. The Department of Interior, in its leadership role in the Arctic, intends to work toward that end and to encourage in every way the articulation of Arctic policy by all other concerned nations.

I put the label "individual" on the third challenge-response level. I should like to expand on that with a brief analysis of the roles that you, as geologists and as individuals, have played and will play in meeting the three challenges. In doing this, I shall be talking indirectly about the geological organizations of which you are a part, for, as is probably true for most scientific fields, the actions and contributions of an organization are absolutely equated with the professional background, experience, dedication, and ambition of its people.

The petroleum accumulations that are now known to exist in the North American Arctic were discovered as a result of the efforts of government geologists and geophysicists and intense and perceptive follow-up by private industry. These discoveries are a tribute to the men who had the ability and devotion necessary to carry out the early studies and to make their implications clear to agencies and/or industries, who then filled in the details and assumed the responsibility for exploration. The contributions of geologists and geophysicists in meeting the challenge to provide energy source material are far from ended. The continuing and future work onshore and on the shelf areas of Alaska alone may result in the discovery of petroleum resources well in excess of those already known to exist.

Up to now, the Arctic quest for nonrenewable resources other than petroleum has yielded less-than-spectacular results, although the extraction of gold in Siberia, Canada, and Alaska has been of great importance. Iron, copper, lead, zinc, nickel, tungsten, platinum, tin, uranium, and other metals have been found, and some are being mined, in the Arctic and Subarctic, particularly in Siberia; deposits of phosphate rock, coal, and oil shale are known but have not yet become economical to produce. These developments have been spotty and, with the possible exception of iron and nickel production in Sweden and Siberia, they have contributed only a small proportion of the world's requirements. The search for the mineral commodities in the Arctic surely will continue, aided by improved remote-sensing devices and transportation means.

It is desirable to reemphasize the role of the individual geologist in conceptualizing the framework in which exploration for mineral resources must take place. Too often we forget that the efficient path to the discovery of a new oil pool, gas field, or mining district involves the systematic and painstaking acquisition of geological and geophysical data and the integration of those data into a framework which guides and cues the geologist who is intent on discovery of mineral raw materials. The technical papers published herein provide the perfect opportunity for comparison, testing, and resynthesizing the broad geological and geophysical framework of the Arctic.

The role of the geologist and geophysicist in the protection of the natural Arctic environment is becoming increasingly important as more and more engineering-geologic decisions have to be made in connection with structures of all kinds in the Arctic environment. The studies and recommendations of the engineering geologist have two major complementary impacts: they maximize the secureness and soundness of engineering structures and they minimize adverse impacts on the natural environment. The efforts of the engineering geologist necessarily involve communication with people from other disciplines—and this matter of communication leads me into an area of extreme personal concern, an area that each of you must examine carefully.

I maintain that the traditional role which the geologist plays in our society is totally inadequate to the problems and pressures of our time. We must find more mineral resources and we must make better use of our knowledge to help protect our natural environment, but we cannot do these things effectively if we insist on staying in the field, labs, and offices all the time. If we are to be effective on behalf of our organizations, our nations, and all mankind, we must—as individuals—make an effort to communicate and to apply geology to the service of man in coping with all the problems he faces. Not only can we serve, but we can and should lead. Such involvement will require an individual commitment from each of us, but we must make it if we are going to be part of the solutions to the critical challenges. We each have a responsibility, as individuals and as essential parts of organizations, to further man's goals at the national and international levels. No one is more aware of the irrationality of artificial boundaries than is a geologist, and no one is better equipped to pursue the implications of his knowledge through to its every connection with our governmental, economic, and living systems.

REMINDERS

I should like to reiterate the problems and solutions with which we are faced. First, we have the Arctic—practically untouched by the governmental, economic, and living systems of modern man—one of the last places on the earth where we shall have the opportunity to start from scratch in the exploitation of mineral resources and, at the same time, protect the natural environment through the knowledge gained from our successes and failures elsewhere. Here is the place where we can apply our knowledge and carefully develop methods of exploration, extraction, and transportation that are compatible with the environment and will not degrade it unnecessarily.

Next are the growing needs of the world's peoples for nonrenewable resources. We are learning that we cannot burden our natural environment indefinitely with our waste and the other scars of our living systems without injuring man's health, mind, and spirit. We are learning that resource development and use are inextricably linked with our environment, by economics and by the way we live and support ourselves. Moreover, we are learning that there are real costs involved in both development of our resources and in environmental protection and/or restoration: a lessened cost for the former may mean an increased cost for the latter.

We also see that wise stewardship of the earth—whether it is at an international, national, local, or individual level—requires systematic research, communication, and application of knowledge. The Department of the Interior intends to continue its leadership in United States Arctic affairs and to encourage planning for a comprehensive Arctic policy that would state the political, scientific, economic, defense, and other interests of the United States in the north. That policy also would establish our dedication to mutually beneficial cooperation with our Arctic neighbors and other nations in exploration, exploitation, and scientific studies, as well as in free exchange of technical, scientific, and economic data regarding the Arctic.

Last of all, let me remind each of you of your personal responsibility in helping to lay the groundwork for the far-reaching decisions that are going to be made about the Arctic. Your dedication to scientific research, to the dissemination of your findings, and to their application is essential for wise national and international responses to the three challenges that I have discussed today.

Regional Arctic Geology of Canada

Tectonics of Northern Franklin Mountains and Colville Hills, District of Mackenzie, Canada[1]

DONALD G. COOK[2] and JAMES D. AITKEN[3]

Calgary, Alberta, Canada

Abstract The northern Franklin Mountains and the Colville Hills, District of Mackenzie, are a series of ridges of divergent trends separated by broad, mostly drift-covered valleys. Some ridges are supported by thrust plates, and others by asymmetric anticlines. These structures, which represent shortening of the sedimentary cover, record tangential compression. Despite a variety of structural trends, there is no evidence for more than one phase of compression.

The structural province is characterized by enigmatic thrust reversals. Typically, one end of a range is underlain by a southwest-dipping fault and the other by a northeast-dipping fault. The abrupt transition takes place via a transverse fault which separates the opposing blocks, and which seems to require longitudinal shortening of the range in addition to the more obvious shortening perpendicular to it. Reversals along the trend of a particular range are inadequately explained, but the close geometric relation between reversals and transverse faults suggests an interrelated origin dependent on longitudinal shortening in conjunction with lateral shortening.

Most of the northern Franklin Mountains appear to be floored by a *décollement* zone in shale and evaporite beds of the Cambrian Saline River Formation. Structures above the zone probably are accentuated by tectonic thickening of the Saline River Formation. The *décollement* is assumed to extend beneath the Colville Hills about 175–200 mi (280–320 km) northeast of the Mackenzie Mountain front. In the McConnell Range on the south and the Mackenzie Mountains on the southwest, the *décollement* zone must be at a lower stratigraphic level, because beds older than the Saline River Formation are exposed in structures.

INTRODUCTION

The Franklin Mountains and the Colville Hills form the outermost limit of the Mackenzie fold belt and extend into the Interior Plains (Fig. 1). Although only the northern part is discussed here, the Franklin Mountains curve southward and flank most of the Mackenzie arc. This study was part of Operation

[1] Manuscript received, October 15, 1971.

Operation Norman coordinated the efforts of more than 15 scientists including stratigraphers, paleontologists, Quaternary geologists, and structural geologists. Co-workers who have contributed directly to the information presented here are R. W. Macqueen, Cambrian to Silurian stratigraphy; W. S. MacKenzie, Devonian stratigraphy; and C. J. Yorath, Cretaceous stratigraphy.

[2] Geological Survey of Canada.

[3] University of Calgary, Alberta.

Norman, a larger, helicopter-supported reconnaissance project of the Geological Survey of Canada which included the plains areas west, north, and east of the Franklin Mountains and the Colville Hills, and much of the northern Mackenzie Mountains on the southwest (Fig. 1). Field work was begun in 1968 and was completed in 1970. From this rather large area of study, the northern Franklin Mountains and the Colville Hills have been selected for discussion because they display unusual structural relations which, in the writers' experience, are not normally found in deformed belts. Deformation nonetheless appears to have been related to that which produced the Mackenzie Mountains; thus, the conclusions drawn should hold implications regarding tectonism in the Mackenzie Mountains. The Franklin Mountains and the Colville Hills are made up of isolated structural ridges separated by broad, mostly drift-filled valleys. The ridges are formed either by thrust plates or by anticlines that are aligned along a variety of structural trends (Fig. 2). Examples and illustrations are all from the better-exposed Franklin Mountains, but the similarities between the Franklins and the Colville Hills suggest that the conclusions drawn regarding the origin of one probably apply to the other as well.

STRATIGRAPHY

The stratigraphy of the northern Franklin Mountains and the Colville Hills is illustrated schematically in Figure 3, and the distribution of gross stratigraphic units is shown in Figure 4. Tertiary continental conglomerates, sandstones, coals, and ash beds, more than 1,500 ft (450 m) in total thickness (Yorath, 1970, p. 244), are present in the Mackenzie valley south of the area shown in Figure 4. The strata are flat-lying over most of the area of exposure, but locally they are tilted and faulted.

Cretaceous sandstones and shales are more than 7,800 ft (2,400 m) thick in the Mackenzie River valley (Yorath, 1970, p. 243) but, where present in the Franklin Mountains, they form only a thin veneer. They are underlain by

FIG. 1—Location map showing report area, outline of Operation Norman, and regional physiographic provinces.

a major unconformity which truncates successively older rocks eastward (Figs. 3, 4).

More than 3,500 ft (1,100 m) of Upper Devonian shales and sandstones of the Canol and Imperial Formations (MacKenzie, 1970, p. 225) is present in the Mackenzie valley, but these strata are absent over most of the area occupied by the northern Franklin Mountains (Fig. 4).

The Middle Devonian Ramparts Formation (limestone), Hare Indian Formation (shale), and Hume Formation (limestone), and the Middle and Lower Devonian Bear Rock Formation (limestone, dolomite, solution breccia, gypsum) together are about 1,500 ft (450 m) thick in the Franklin Mountains; however, owing to pre-Cretaceous erosion, only 800 ft (250 m) or less of these strata remains in the Colville Hills. The Ramparts Formation is, at least in part, a lateral facies equivalent of the Hare Indian Formation; it is noteworthy because the only oil production in Canada's Northwest Territories to date is from this formation at Norman Wells.

Devonian rocks unconformably overlie the dolomites of the Ronning Group, which comprises four mappable units ranging in age from Late Cambrian to Silurian. The uppermost unit, the Mount Kindle Formation, is underlain by an unconformity. Because of pre–Mount Kindle and pre-Devonian erosion, the thickness of the group ranges from 500 to more than 2,600 ft (150–800 m; Macqueen, 1970, p. 226), but it is commonly in the order of 2,000 ft (600 m). The Ronning Group, which was deformed as a single competent structural-stratigraphic unit, forms the backbone of most ranges (Fig. 4).

The Late Cambrian Saline River Formation —composed of salt, gypsum, and shale—underlies the Ronning Group and is the oldest formation exposed in the northern Franklin Mountains. It is tectonically the most important in the entire sequence because deformation which formed the Franklins appears to have occurred above a *décollement* at this level. Thus, these evaporites would be expected to be thickest in the cores of anticlines or beneath thrusts. This assumption is supported by the fact that the Saline River Formation is nearly

3,000 ft (900 m) thick in a dry hole (Imperial No. 1 Vermilion Ridge) on the flank of the Norman Range (Fig. 4), whereas the normal thickness of from 200 to 400 ft (60–120 m) is present in other wells and at outcrops.

The zone of *décollement,* however, must occur at deeper levels to the south and southwest, because Lower and Middle Cambrian and Proterozoic strata are exposed in folded and thrust-faulted structures in the southern Franklin and Mackenzie Mountains.

STRUCTURE

Although few publications are available on this area, considerable geologic exploration has been carried out by oil-company personnel. It is known, from reports on file with the Depart-

ment of Indian Affairs and Northern Development, and from personal conversations, that these ranges commonly are interpreted as being a result of high-angle block faulting which presumably involved the basement. They have been considered also to be due entirely to gravity-driven "salt tectonics." Other writers interpreted them to be thrust and fold structures, and Ziegler (1969) showed thrust faults underlying most Franklin Mountain ranges. As early as 1954, Hume described thrust faults and folds and referred to obvious compressive stresses.

The writers believe that deformation was by horizontal compression with resultant shortening, and that structures in the northern Franklin Mountains and the Colville Hills developed

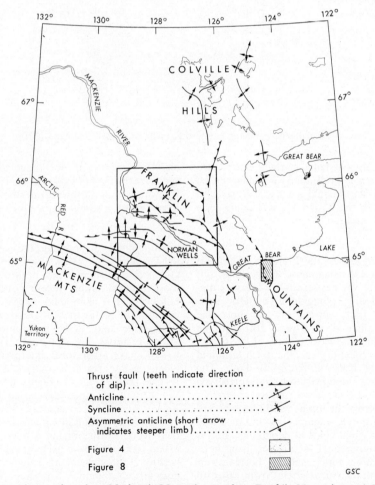

Thrust fault (teeth indicate direction
  of dip)..............................
Anticline...............................
Syncline................................
Asymmetric anticline (short arrow
  indicates steeper limb)................

Figure 4

Figure 8

GSC

FIG. 2—Structural map of northern Mackenzie Mountains, northern Franklin Mountains, and Colville Hills. Areas of Figures 4 and 8 are shown.

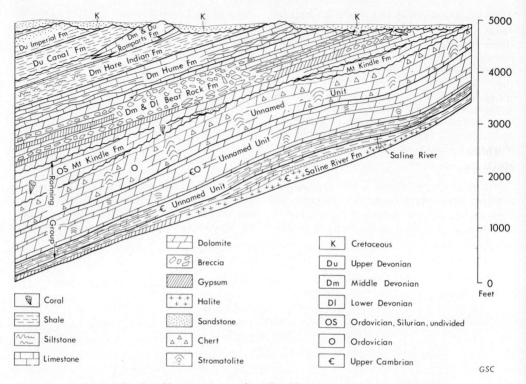

Fig. 3—Stratigraphic summary, northern Franklin Mountains and Colville Hills.

above a detachment zone in the Upper Cambrian Saline River Formation. Salt flow almost certainly has accentuated some structures, but is secondary to the horizontal shortening indicated by folds and faults.

Folds

The western end of the Franklin Mountains is dominated by asymmetric folds (Fig. 4). East Mountain, the best-exposed of these structures, is a doubly plunging asymmetric anticline. Figure 5A, a vertical mosaic, shows the structure in plan view. Figure 5B, a profile view down the eastward plunge of the structure, shows vertical beds on the north limb and gently dipping beds on the south limb. The beds shown are the uppermost strata preserved in the fold, and there is no rupture or stretching of beds across the top as would be expected if this were a purely diapiric structure or a fold draped over a tilted block at depth. This fold is clearly a compressional feature requiring horizontal translation with resultant shortening of the exposed strata. Surprisingly, from range to range the sense of asymmetry is inconsistent, and folds change from northward-facing (Den-

nis, 1967, p. 44) in one range to southward-facing in the next (Fig. 4). In the Imperial Hills, a reversal from northward- to southward-facing is evident in a single major anticline.

Faults

Although folds dominate the western end of the Franklin Mountains, elsewhere most ranges are formed by homoclinal upthrown plates. In most places the fault trace is covered by overburden, and it cannot be determined whether the fault is of thrust or normal displacement. Where the fault trace is exposed, however, thrust relations are apparent (Fig. 6). The writers have, therefore, interpreted all fault blocks in the area to be underlain by thrust or reverse faults (Fig. 4). Figure 6A illustrates a thrust fault of moderate dip in the Norman Range. Figure 6B, in contrast, shows a steeply dipping reverse fault along which the Devonian Bear Rock Formation, in a ridge northeast of Moon Lake, has been peeled back to a vertical position by the advancing hanging wall of Ronning Group dolomite. The exact nature of the peeled footwall is obscure, but horizontal shortening of the Bear Rock Formation is evident. A component of wrench movement on thrust faults cannot be ruled out, but there is no evidence for interpreting any range as having been caused by normal—that is, extension—faulting.

The exposed thrusts are important because they document deformation by horizontal translation of strata down to and including the Saline River Formation.

Thrust Reversals

Thrust faults are similar to folds in one respect; the inconsistent asymmetry and sense of relative transport of folds are paralleled by inconsistent dips and sense of relative transport of thrusts (Fig. 4). Surprisingly, at several places (Fig. 4), faults with opposing senses of transport occur nearly on strike with each other in the same range. These reversals in the sense of relative transport are the most intriguing aspect of the structures in the Franklin Mountains. Perhaps the best-exposed example of such reversal occurs at the northwest end of the Norman Range (Fig. 7). The main Norman Range plate (right side of Fig. 7) dips south-

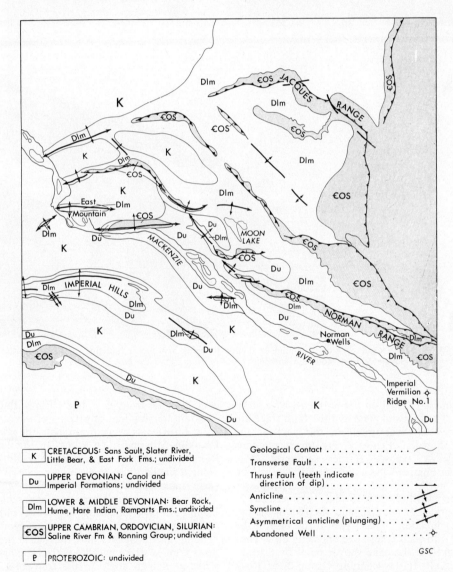

	CRETACEOUS: Sans Sault, Slater River, Little Bear, & East Fork Fms.; undivided
K	

	UPPER DEVONIAN: Canol and Imperial Formations; undivided
Du	

	LOWER & MIDDLE DEVONIAN: Bear Rock, Hume, Hare Indian, Ramparts Fms.; undivided
Dlm	

	UPPER CAMBRIAN, ORDOVICIAN, SILURIAN: Saline River Fm & Ronning Group; undivided
€OS	

	PROTEROZOIC: undivided
P	

Geological Contact . . . . ⌒
Transverse Fault . . . . ▬
Thrust Fault (teeth indicate direction of dip) . . . .
Anticline . . . .
Syncline . . . .
Asymmetrical anticline (plunging) . . . . .
Abandoned Well . . . . ◇

GSC

Fig. 4—Geologic sketch map of most of northern Franklin Mountains. See Figure 2 for location.

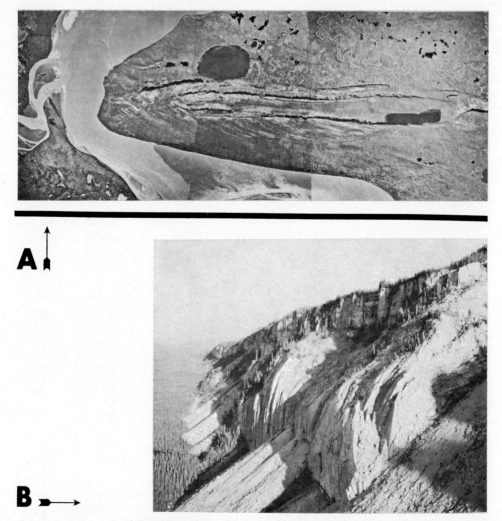

FIG. 5—**A.** Vertical mosaic of East Mountain—a doubly plunging asymmetric anticline. **B.** View eastward down plunge of East Mountain anticline. View is from right edge area of Figure 5A.

west and is fronted on the northeast by a steep scarp. The footwall plate and the fault trace are obscured by overburden in the part of the range shown in Figure 7, but thrust relations are clearly exposed farther southeast (Fig. 6A). In Figure 7, the hanging-wall plate can be traced northwestward to a point where it passes into an anticline that abruptly plunges out in the footwall of another plate dipping in the opposite direction. Thus, two thrust plates on strike with each other have opposing dips. They are linked at the change-over point by a transverse fault. If the Ronning Group–Bear Rock Formation contact is used as a marker, it is evi-

dent that the transverse fault brings about an apparent longitudinal shortening of the range.

Such reversals occur throughout the northern Franklin Mountains (Fig. 4). In the Jacques Ranges on the north, three reversals occur along a single range. In each case a small transverse fault appears to separate the opposing blocks, and each fault causes an apparent overlapping of the opposing segments, implying longitudinal shortening of the range. Moreover, bedding in the vicinity of a transverse fault deflects from a strike parallel with the range to a strike at a high angle to the transverse fault, and thus appears to have been deformed by

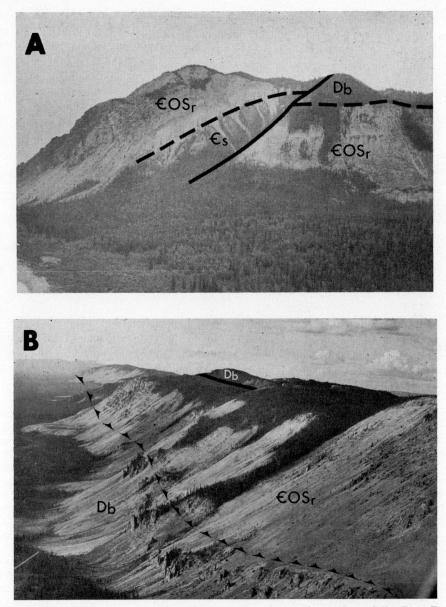

FIG. 6—**A.** Thrust fault, southeast end of Norman Range; view northwest. Єs = Saline River Formation; ЄOSr = Ronning Group; Db = Bear Rock Formation. **B.** Thrust fault with vertically dipping Bear Rock Formation in footwall. Ridge northeast of Moon Lake; view northwest. ЄOSr = Ronning Group; Db = Bear Rock Formation.

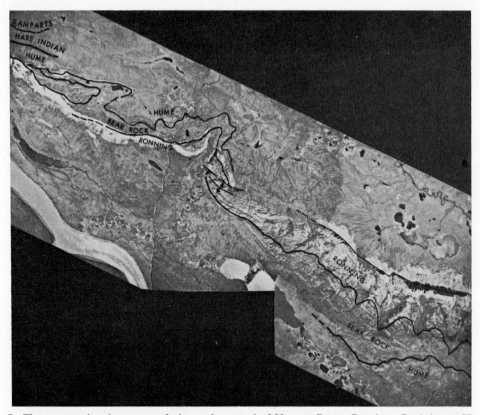

Fig. 7—Thrust reversal and transverse fault, northwest end of Norman Range. Ronning—Cambrian to Silurian Ronning Group; Bear Rock, Hume, Hare Indian, and Ramparts—Devonian formations from oldest to youngest.

drag on the fault. The sense of translation implied is invariably that which would shorten the range longitudinally. Other interpretations are possible, but, in the St. Charles Range (Figs. 2, 8), unambiguous transverse faults are well exposed. These faults are not related to transport reversals, but each unequivocally results in longitudinal shortening of the range. The close spatial relations between most transverse faults and thrust reversals imply relations in time as well. This implication leads to the interesting conclusion that deformation has achieved simultaneous shortening along more or less orthogonal axes, one perpendicular to the range and the other parallel with the range. This conclusion is surprising in view of the fact that the Franklin Mountains form the outer limit of the Mackenzie arc, where extension parallel with the arc might be expected.

Diverse Structural Trends

In addition to other complexities in the northern Franklin Mountains, there are three sharply differentiated structural trends— northwest-southeast, east-west, and north-south (Fig. 4). In the Colville Hills the east-west trend is not represented, but an additional northeast-southwest structural trend is evident (Fig. 2). There is no evidence that any one trend is superimposed on any other. Instead, entire ranges appear to kink from one trend to another and back again, and each ridge appears to have originated with its present sinuous geometry. Apparently, the various trends developed during a single deformational event, but they are not readily accommodated in any familiar dynamic or kinematic model. It might be argued that deformation has in part been localized along pre–Saline River structures of other than Laramide trend, but this argument contradicts the writers' conclusion that pre–Saline River strata are not involved in the deformation. Nevertheless, the trend and locus of the structures may have been partly controlled by pre–Saline River paleotopographic ridges, although such features have not been observed. In the Mackenzie Mountains, however, substantial topographic relief at the sub–Saline River unconformity affects the thickness of the Saline River Formation. If paleotopographic relief and variation in the thickness of salt and gypsum are present also in the northern Franklin Mountains and the Colville Hills, they would be expected to affect, if not to control, the location and trend of splays from the regional *décollement*.

It is apparent, however, that such pre–Upper Cambrian features can explain neither the reversals in sense of relative transport nor the apparent orthogonal axes of shortening. Solutions to these problems may be forthcoming as more is learned about the entire Mackenzie arc. Substantial right-lateral movement has been deduced by Gabrielse *et al.* (in press) in the southern Mackenzies, but the significance or extent of such movements with respect to Franklin Mountain deformation is not yet known. The geometry of the Saline River basin

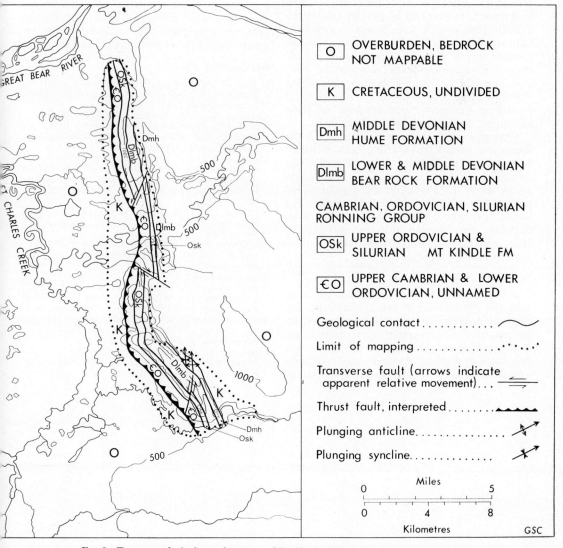

FIG. 8—Transverse faults in southern part of St. Charles Range. See Figure 2 for location.

is poorly understood, yet it may have greatly influenced localization and orientation of Franklin Mountain structures.

Décollement

Because Saline River beds are the oldest exposed in the northern Franklin Mountains and the Colville Hills and, moreover, appear to be thickened in the cores of structures, the concept of a *décollement* zone at Saline River Formation level is attractive. Nonetheless, older strata are deformed in the Franklins to the south and in the Mackenzies to the southwest, and future subsurface and geophysical studies may show that older rocks are involved in the northern Franklin Mountains and/or the Colville Hills as well. It is, however, extremely unlikely that crystalline basement was affected, because gravity maps by Hornal *et al.* (1970) show little correspondence between the Bouguer anomaly and the visible structures of the Franklin Mountains and the Colville Hills. If crystalline basement were involved in these structures, the gravity map should show it.

Examples presented here and much of the discussion pertain to the northern Franklin Mountains. The Colville Hills (Fig. 2) also contain thrust faults and asymmetric anticlines which, as in the Franklins, are compressional structures requiring horizontal shortening. The detachment zone in the Saline River Formation therefore must extend beneath the Colville Hills, about 200–250 mi (320–400 km) from the Mackenzie Mountain front.

Summary

Wherever structural relations can be determined in the northern Franklin Mountains and the Colville Hills, the ranges are formed by anticlines, mostly asymmetric, or by thrust faults. Both types of structure require that the ranges originated as a result of compression and horizontal shortening of the sedimentary strata.

Wrench movement on faults cannot be ruled out, but normal or extension faulting has not been significant in forming these structures. Deformation appears to have affected only strata lying above a *décollement* zone in Upper Cambrian shales and evaporites of the Saline River Formation; concomitant structural thickening of the Saline River is apparent in the cores of structures. Some structures may have been localized by variations in evaporite thickness caused by pre–Upper Cambrian topographic relief, but older rocks apparently were not actively involved in the Laramide deformation. Abrupt reversals in the sense of relative transport appear to be dependent on simultaneous shortening along orthogonal axes—one axis approximately perpendicular to, and the other approximately parallel with, the mountain trends.

References Cited

Dennis, J. G., compiler, 1967, International tectonic dictionary—English terminology: Am. Assoc. Petroleum Geologists Mem. 7, 196 p.

Gabrielse, H., J. A. Roddick, and S. L. Blusson, in press, Flat River, Glacier Lake, Wrigley Lake map-areas, District of Mackenzie and Yukon Territory: Canada Geol. Survey Mem. 366.

Hornal, R. W., *et al.*, 1970, Preliminary results of gravity surveys over the Mackenzie basin and Beaufort Sea: Canada Dept. Energy, Mines and Resources Earth Physics Branch Gravity Map Ser., no. 117–119.

Hume, G. S., 1954, Lower Mackenzie River area, Northwest Territories and Yukon: Canada Geol. Survey Mem. 273.

MacKenzie, W. S., 1970, Devonian stratigraphy, District of Mackenzie: Canada Geol. Survey Paper 70-1A, p. 224–225.

Macqueen, R. W., 1970, Lower Paleozoic stratigraphy and sedimentology, eastern Mackenzie Mountains, northern Franklin Mountains: Canada Geol. Survey Paper 70-1A, p. 225–230.

Yorath, C. J., 1970, Cretaceous and Tertiary stratigraphy, District of Mackenzie: Canada Geol. Survey Paper 70-1A, p. 243–245.

Ziegler, P. A., 1969, The development of sedimentary basins in western and Arctic Canada: Calgary, Alberta Soc. Petroleum Geologists.

Tectonic Styles of Northern Yukon Territory and Northwestern District of Mackenzie, Canada[1]

D. K. NORRIS[2]

Calgary, Alberta, Canada

Abstract A diversity of tectonic styles is displayed in northern Yukon Territory and northwestern District of Mackenzie. Some tectonic elements of the region, such as the Barn and White uplifts, are basically fault-bounded, ovate domes with cores of Paleozoic and possibly older carbonate and clastic rocks; the domes are separated by structural depressions largely filled with Mesozoic clastic sequences. Other structural elements are elongate and trend parallel or subparallel with one another. Because some elements were tectonically deformed more than once, stacking of styles may be present, as in the Romanzof uplift, where open folds in Carboniferous and Permian carbonate and clastic units lie with profound unconformity on acutely folded, faulted, and cleaved rocks assumed to be no younger than Silurian. Each deformed body served as a platform for the next younger sedimentary succession and possibly acquired cumulative structural features characteristic of the syles of all younger deformations.

The belt of Cretaceous, south-dipping thrust faults on the south flank of Brooks Range in Alaska is comparable in style to that along the eastern margin of the Canadian cordillera at the latitude of the 49th Parallel. The belt continues southeastward into Canada, but the number of faults and the net displacement diminish toward the Barn uplift. Southeast of the Barn uplift, steep faults, some with demonstrable strike slip, become major components of the structural style. The latter faults, active at least locally into the mid-Tertiary, also served to transport differentially the northern Yukon tectonic complex toward the Beaufort shelf and the Canada basin. Beyond this complex, in northwestern District of Mackenzie, is Kugaluk homocline, a gently northwest-dipping layered succession of Tertiary strata flanked on the southeast by Campbell uplift.

Campbell uplift is the northeast continuation of Aklavik arch, a composite structural high comprising individual northeast-trending uplifts arranged *en échelon* toward the right. The arch complex extends from the northern Yukon to the Beaufort Sea and possibly is continuous with the Minto arch in the Arctic Archipelago. Carbonate accumulations comparable to those seen in the White uplift and its vicinity, or those penetrated by the drill in the northern Eagle basin, may be present beneath suitable caprocks on the flanks of the complex. Such accumulations would greatly enhance the economic prospects of the Mackenzie delta region and the Beaufort shelf.

INTRODUCTION

The rocks of northern Yukon Territory and northwestern District of Mackenzie display a diversity of tectonic elements (Fig. 1). The style includes the following: simple, gently dipping, layered successions (such as Kugaluk homocline, east of the Mackenzie delta); uplifts and depressions cut by steeply dipping faults (*e.g.*, White and Rat uplifts and Rapid depression); thrust and fold belts comparable in style to the eastern cordillera at about the 49th Parallel and present on the south flank of Brooks Range; acutely folded and reverse-faulted, mildly metamorphosed sedimentary rocks intruded by porphyritic granites (as in Romanzof and Barn uplifts); and composite arches comprising elongate uplifts arranged *en échelon* (exemplified by Aklavik arch, as redefined).

Consequent upon a most complicated orogenic and epeirogenic history, some regions have undergone more than one period of compression and uplift, followed by denudation, depression and deposition of additional sedimentary load, and further compression. Each eroded, deformed segment of the crust served as a platform or basement for the next younger sedimentary succession and possibly acquired cumulative features characteristic of the styles of all younger deformations. In general, the youngest styles are the simplest because they have been derived by the least number of distinct orogenic episodes, whereas progressively older styles are the result of superposition of successive deformations.

STRATIGRAPHIC FRAMEWORK AND TECTONIC HISTORY

Northern Yukon Territory and northwestern District of Mackenzie are underlain mainly by sedimentary rocks. These rocks are mildly me-

[1] Manuscript received, October 15, 1971.

[2] Geological Survey of Canada.

The writer is deeply grateful to Amoco Canada Petroleum Company Limited and to Ulster and Scurry Oil Companies for permission to release his interpretation of the stratigraphic succession penetrated in the Inuvik D-54 borehole. He is also indebted to M. D. Mangus, consulting geologist, for helpful discussions relating to the Carboniferous and Permian successions in British and Barn Mountains, and to many of his colleagues in the Geological Survey, especially E. W. Bamber, J. A. Jeletsky, and A. W. Norris, for considerable paleontologic and stratigraphic information leading to a clarification of the tectonic history of the region. A. W. Norris and H. P. Trettin critically read the manuscript and provided many helpful comments.

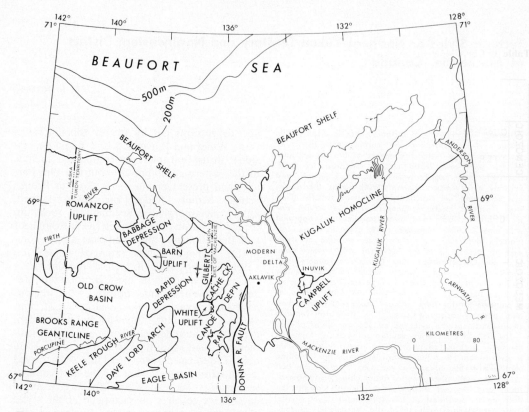

FIG. 1—Index map showing principal tectonic and physiographic elements in northern Yukon Territory and
northwestern District of Mackenzie.

tamorphosed in some regions, locally intruded by mafic igneous dikes or by porphyritic granites, and, in the extreme western part of the area, overlain by volcanic agglomerates and thin, discontinuous basic lavas. The crystalline igneous rocks of the Precambrian basement are not known to crop out in the region.

The stratigraphic succession and structural history of the Inuvik–Campbell Lake area (Table 1) are revealed in outcrop on Campbell uplift, in the Caribou Hills, and in the subsurface in the Inuvik D-54 borehole. The oldest known rocks in the area are interbedded gray to pale red, silty dolomites, dated by paleomagnetism (D. K. Norris and Black, 1964, p. 50) as late Precambrian; gray and green shale; and light gray quartzite. The succession is possibly slightly older than the Purcell system of the eastern cordillera. Folding or tilting along northeast structural trends marked the early stages of formation of the Campbell uplift. The Proterozoic rocks are overlain unconformably

by essentially flat-lying white quartzites and gray shales of Cambrian(?) age, possibly equivalent to the Old Fort Island Formation.

FACIES

	LIMESTONE
	DOLOMITE
	SHALE, MUDSTONE, SILTSTONE
	ARENITE
	CONGLOMERATE
	PYROCLASTICS & ASSOCIATED EXTRUSIONS
	BASIC IGNEOUS INTRUSIONS
G	ACIDIC IGNEOUS INTRUSIONS

NON-MARINE . . . . ||
THICKNESS(THOUSANDS OF FEET) 2.5

CONTACTS

	ESTABLISHED	UNCERTAIN	UNKNOWN
CONFORMABLE			
UNCONFORMABLE (UNDIFFERENTIATED)			
DISCONFORMABLE			
NONCONFORMABLE OR ANGULAR UNCONFORMABLE			

SYMBOLS

DIFFERENTIAL UPLIFT . . . . ↓↑
FOLDING . . . . ~
STRIKE-SLIP FAULTING . . . .
REVERSE FAULTING . . . .

Table 1. Correlation of Representative Lithostratigraphic Units Identified in Selected Tectonic Elements, Northern Yukon Territory and Northwestern District of Mackenzie[1]

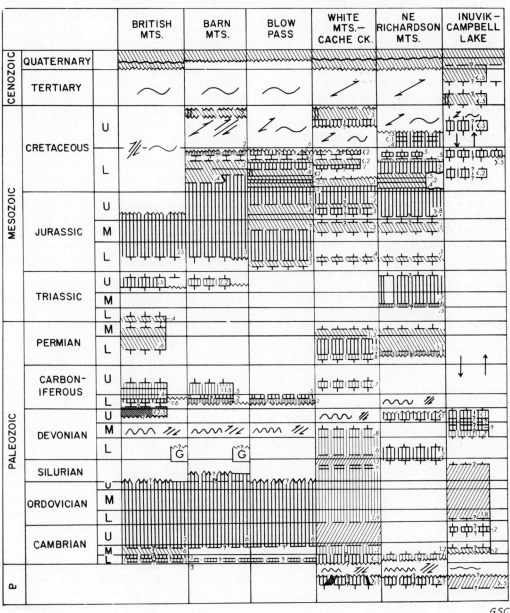

GSC

[1] Operation Porcupine and other sources are acknowledged in text.

The Cambrian(?) strata are overlain by gray shales (Road River Formation?) and gray to black, finely crystalline to cryptocrystalline dolomite, which is at least in part equivalent to the Vunta Formation. Recent biostratigraphic studies by A. W. Norris (1968a, p. 769, and personal commun., 1971) indicate a hiatus between these dolomites, which are known to be as young as Middle Silurian, and the finely crystalline to cryptocrystalline limestones of the late Early and possibly early Middle Devonian Ogilve Formation. Dark gray, silty shales of the Imperial Formation mark the top of the Devonian System.

The Campbell uplift was active again sometime between the Late Devonian and the Early Cretaceous, because the whole of this middle and early Paleozoic and late Proterozoic succession was uplifted, tilted, and eroded at least once prior to deposition of the Lower Cretaceous Series. Some of this activity undoubtedly was linked to the major orogenies which took place west of Mackenzie delta during the Devonian and Mississippian Periods.

With the sinking of Campbell uplift in Albian time, porous sandstones of the Lower Cretaceous "Silty zone" were overstepped by black shales of the "Bentonitic zone" on the northwest flank of Kugaluk homocline. This overstepping is evident near the mouth of Kugaluk River (Yorath and Balkwill, 1969; 1970, p. 3). There, soft, rusty-weathering shales of the "Bentonitic zone" lie unconformably on the Upper Devonian Imperial Formation. The "Silty zone" is absent but is presumed to exist downdip on the northwest. A similar pinching out of the porous sandstones of the "Silty zone" is inferred on the southeast flank of Campbell uplift. The hydrocarbon potential of such stratigraphic traps should not be overlooked.

In the mid-Cretaceous, the region again was tilted and was loaded with clastic sediments, folded, and possibly faulted prior to deposition of the largely nonmarine sequences of the Reindeer and Beaufort Formations. An angular unconformity identifying this latest tectonic activity is evident on the right bank[3] of an unnamed creek flowing into Campbell Lake from the southeast, about 13 km above the mouth of the creek. There, dark gray shales below the unconformity and near water level were dated by McGregor (1971) as Jurassic or younger; they are assumed by the writer to be the Albian "Bentonitic zone." The overlying, unconsoli-

[3] Right and left banks are as one faces downstream.

dated silts and sands are assigned to the undifferentiated Tertiary Reindeer and Beaufort Formations.

In the northeast Richardson Mountains, the sedimentary succession ranges in age through the Phanerozoic and probably into the Proterozoic. Disconnected exposures, especially of the older rocks, allow the piecing together of some of the stratigraphic and tectonic history of the region. The oldest beds, presumed to be late Proterozoic in age, comprise a faulted succession of foliated argillites, limestones, dolomites, and conglomerates exposed 10 km south of Rat Pass. The next-younger rocks, exposed 13 km north of the pass, are limestones of late Early Cambrian age (Norford, 1963) which are structurally conformable with younger strata but are presumed to lie with pronounced unconformity on Proterozoic rocks at depth. Early Devonian graptolitic shales have been recognized just south of Rat Pass by geologists of Shell Canada Limited (Norford, 1970); this shale facies is recognized as a lateral equivalent of part of the great carbonate accumulation seen in White uplift, 35 km to the northwest.

Northeast-trending folds and faults in shales and siltstones of the Upper Devonian Imperial Formation identify a latest Devonian or Mississippian orogeny which affected the region. The angular unconformity between the Imperial Formation and unnamed sandstones and conglomerates of Early or Middle Permian age on the left bank of Sheep Creek, 3 km above its mouth, attests to this age assignment. In Aklavik Range, Permian clastic rocks are overlain by a structurally conformable succession of shale, sandstone, and conglomerate representing parts of the Mesozoic and Cenozoic Systems; the succession, which is punctuated with disconformities, represents mainly nearshore and shoreline facies. Of prime importance among these unconformities is that which represents mid-Valanginian uplift of the "Aklavik arch" (Jeletzky, 1961, p. 538) and which is recognized by the erosional gap in the "lower sandstone division."

The whole of the stratigraphic assemblage of the northeast Richardson Mountains was buckled and cut by north- and northeast-trending, near-vertical faults, some with right-lateral strike-slip displacement, that were active in the Late Cretaceous and very probably in the Tertiary.

White and Cache Creek uplifts also expose rocks of Phanerozoic and probably late Proterozoic ages. These rocks were deformed by the same late Precambrian, mid-Paleozoic, Late Cretaceous, and Tertiary orogenies which affected the rocks of the northeast Richardson Mountains. Notable differences in the succession are the presence of highly sheared, mafic igneous dikes in probably Proterozoic rocks on the north flank of White uplift; thick limestone and dolomite accumulations which represent much of early and middle Paleozoic time; mid-Pennsylvanian dolomitic limestones which demonstrate the presence of Lisburne-equivalent rocks; a thick clastic-carbonate succession of Early and Middle Permian age, in part equivalent to the principal reservoir rocks at Prudhoe Bay; the apparent absence of Triassic rocks; and the presence of a wedge of Late Cretaceous (Chamney, 1971a) syntectonic clastic rocks (Moose Channel Formation) which thickens seaward on Beaufort shelf at the mouth of Fish River.

The stratigraphic assemblages in and around Barn and Romanzof uplifts (Barn and British Mountains, respectively) are represented by the three columns at the left on Table 1. The Blow Pass succession portrays the rocks found at the surface just east and southeast of Barn uplift; it includes gray, finely crystalline, oolitic limestones in fault contact with olive gray, slaty argillites of the Neruokpuk where exposed on the northwest flank of a small, dome-shaped structure at the headwaters of Blow River. If these limestones are correlative with limestones near the base of the exposed Neruokpuk in Romanzof uplift, and if they underlie the slaty argillites in normal stratigraphic succession, then a major, near-vertical, pre-Mississippian fault must be present in the dome. The fault trends northeast parallel with Dave Lord and Cache Creek uplifts; relative upward displacement of its northwest side has resulted in a stratigraphic separation greater than 1,800 m—the exposed thickness of the argillites.

The dating of the Neruokpuk in Barn Mountains is based on the recovery of Ordovician and Silurian graptolites from an acutely folded and faulted assemblage of dark gray to black shales, black and green chert, and red and green shales (Martin, 1959, p. 2414; Norford, 1964, p. 137; A. W. Norris, 1971, personal commun.). In this area, the Neruokpuk is evidently laterally and temporally equivalent, at least in part, with the Road River Formation. Apparently, this early and middle Paleozoic graptolite sequence was very widespread in northern Yukon Territory.

Light gray and yellowish gray, porphyritic granites that intrude the Neruokpuk in Barn and Romanzof uplifts have radiometric ages of 370 and 355 m.y., respectively, as determined in the laboratories of the Geological Survey of Canada (Wanless *et al.*, 1965, p. 22–23). The granites appear to have originated during the Middle or Late Devonian Epoch. Because the granites are foliated and hydrothermally altered, however, it is entirely possible that they may be somewhat older, perhaps genetically and temporally equivalent to granites in northeast Brooks Range dated as Early Silurian (430 m.y.; Brosgé, 1970, p. 2473).

The Neruokpuk Formation in Romanzof and Barn uplifts and at Blow Pass was acutely faulted, folded, uplifted, and peneplaned prior to the Mississippian Period. Detritus shed from this uplift was most probably a source of the Upper Devonian Imperial Formation (Martin, 1959, p. 2442). Overlying the Neruokpuk with profound unconformity are rocks ranging in age from Jurassic to Mississippian and possibly Late Devonian. In Romanzof uplift, on both sides of the International Boundary, is a thick succession of volcanic agglomerates, composed in part of boulders and cobbles of amygdaloidal basalt but also containing light gray, recrystallized limestone phenoclasts. The age of these agglomerates is uncertain, but they are believed to be younger than the Middle or Late Devonian orogeny because they appear to lie with angular unconformity on deformed Neruokpuk rocks. Gray, undated, finely crystalline limestones occur as erosional remnants on top of the agglomerates in British Mountains and possibly belong to the Carboniferous Lisburne Group.

The Carboniferous succession in British and Barn Mountains has been discussed at length by Mamet and Mason (1970) and by Bamber and Waterhouse (1971). These authors recognized the black, calcareous shales of the Kyak Formation and the more resistant gray, skeletal, cherty limestones of the Alapah and Wahoo of the Lisburne Group. Collectively, the Kyak, Alapah, and Wahoo strata, along with the quartz sandstones of the Permian and Triassic Sadlerochit Formation, form a northeast-tapering wedge. The transgressive siltstones and limestones of the Upper Triassic Shublik Formation overstep the Carboniferous and younger formations of the wedge and lie with angular unconformity on deformed Neruokpuk rocks on the northeast flank of British Mountains (Fig. 2) and, locally, on the north flank of Barn Mountains. The Jurassic shales of the

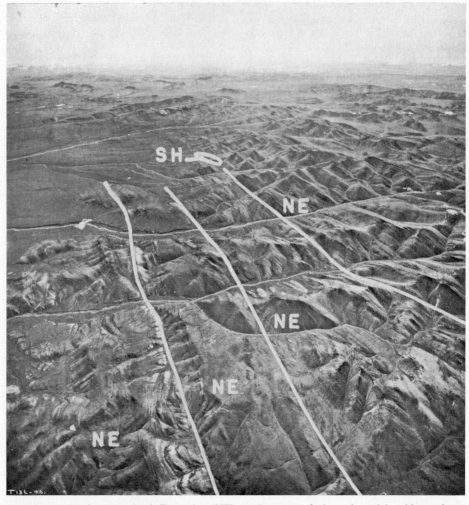

Fig. 2—Southwest-dipping Neruokpuk Formation (NE) cut by reverse faults and overlain with angular unconformity by gently inclined Triassic Shublik Formation (SH). NAPL oblique photo T13L-42.

Kingak Formation in turn overstep the Shublik to lie unconformably on the Neruokpuk north-west of Babbage River.

On the flanks of Barn Mountains and on the domelike structures just east and southeast of there, a coarse chert and quartzite pebble conglomerate intervenes between the deformed Neruokpuk and nonmarine Kyak strata. This formation is the Mississippian Kekiktuk, which is greatly varied in thickness but locally is as much as 75 m thick; it lies with marked angular unconformity on the Neruokpuk.

The Jurassic and Lower Cretaceous sandstone and shale succession in the region of Blow Pass continues westward to Barn and British Mountains, but there is a notable de-crease in content of coarser clastic material in the lower part. The unnamed Middle and Upper Jurassic sandstones of Blow Pass are not recognized westward from Barn Mountains. The Lower Cretaceous "lower sandstone division," however, persists as a prominent marker, and the shales and siltstones normally overlying it between Barn Mountains and Mackenzie delta are replaced by sandstones. Younger strata in the region make up a thick succession of upturned shales, lithic sandstones, and chert, quartzite, and lithic pebble and cobble conglomerates (identified only as conglomerates in Table 1). Dated as Albian (Chamney, 1971b), they record tectonism and erosion of Jurassic and older rocks of Romanzof uplift. These syntectonic deposits were deformed as this last great episode of tectonism spread northeastward across northern Yukon Territory and northwestern District of Mackenzie. Sediments shed onto Beaufort shelf as a result of this tectonism are recognized as the Moose Channel Formation along their southwestern limit on the Arctic coastal plain. The dying phases of this orogeny are recorded in the vertical beds of conglomerate and coal of the Moose Channel Formation near the northwest extremity of Mackenzie delta.

STRUCTURAL STYLES

Two contrasting styles characterize the rocks of British Mountains. The older style is repre-

sented by an acutely folded succession of mildly metamorphosed strata and intrusions which are cut and repeated by high-angle reverse faults; the younger style is represented by a belt of late Paleozoic and younger, unmetamorphosed, layered strata which are repeated by a family of overlapping, low-angle (thrust) faults with associated folds.

In the core of British Mountains along the canyons of Firth River, flexural-slip cylindrical folds can be seen in bedded sedimentary rocks. Axial surfaces are vertical or dip steeply to the southwest or northeast, and the folds are cut by high-angle reverse faults; whole outcrops mimic, on a mesoscopic scale, the grand style of the Neruokpuk assemblage. On the northeast

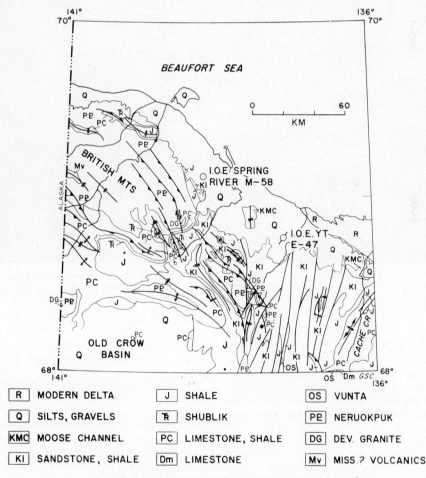

R	MODERN DELTA	J	SHALE	OS	VUNTA
Q	SILTS, GRAVELS	Ŧ	SHUBLIK	PE	NERUOKPUK
KMC	MOOSE CHANNEL	PC	LIMESTONE, SHALE	DG	DEV. GRANITE
KI	SANDSTONE, SHALE	Dm	LIMESTONE	Mv	MISS.? VOLCANICS

OIL OR GAS WELL (DRILLING, ABANDONED)....○ ⌀

FIG. 3—Simplified geologic map of parts of northern Yukon Territory and northwestern District of Mackenzie (NTS 117). Quaternary geology is after Rampton (1969).

Fig. 4—Neruokpuk Formation (NE) intruded by Sedgwick Granite (G) at southeast extremity of British Mountains and overlain with angular unconformity by folded and faulted Kekiktuk-Kyak Formations (KK), Lisburne Group (LL), Kingak-Shublik Formations (KI), and "lower sandstone division" (KS). NAPL oblique photo T15L-52.

flank of British Mountains (Figs. 2, 3), one of the southwest-dipping reverse faults has caused repetition of Neruokpuk units; the Neruokpuk is overlain with marked angular unconformity by gently inclined strata of the Shublik Formation. The Neruokpuk, which was deformed, eroded, and beveled prior to deposition of the Kyak, and further eroded before the Late Triassic, served as the basement for younger Phanerozoic rocks. The unconformity separating the Neruokpuk from the Kyak and younger rocks is one of the most profound in the Canadian cordillera; it corresponds to the uncon-

formity at the base of the Sverdrup basin in the Arctic Archipelago (Thorsteinsson and Tozer, 1960, p. 3).

On the southeast plunge of British Mountains (Fig. 4), the stacking of the younger style on top of the older can be seen clearly. There, the upturned and foliated Neruokpuk, intruded by porphyritic granites of the Sedgwick stock, is overlain with angular unconformity by conglomeratic sandstone of the Kekiktuk, regressive marine shales of the Kyak, and resistant carbonate strata of the Lisburne Group. These late Paleozoic rocks, together with the overlying regressive Kingak shales and the ridge-forming "lower sandstone division," were buckled and thrust-faulted by a Cretaceous orogeny. They display a style which contrasts with that of their Neruokpuk basement.

Although the Neruokpuk was deformed additionally during this orogeny, it does not appear to have been involved in the thrusting, because the Kyak shales commonly are present at the base of many of the plates in the imbricate structure of the thrust belt in northeastern Brooks Range (Lathram, 1965). The Kyak was doubtless a major detachment zone comparable in its control of the style of the deformation to the Kootenay Formation of the eastern cordill-

era or to the Chattanooga Shale of the western Appalachians.

The imbricate thrust belt on the southwest flank of British Mountains continues southeastward from Alaska, but the number of faults and the stratigraphic separations diminish. The belt turns southward on the west flank of Barn Mountains, giving way to a region dominated by elongate structural highs and depressions cut by near-vertical faults between the mountains and Sitidgi Lake east of Mackenzie delta. Two repetitions of the Kyak and Lisburne strata are exposed clearly on the west flank of Barn uplift (Fig. 5); in association with the thrust faults on the north flank (Fig. 3), these repetitions

Fig. 5—Mississippian Lisburne Group (LL) repeated by thrust faulting on west flank of Barn uplift. NAPL oblique photo T13L-105.

Fig. 6—Northeast-trending Cache Creek uplift exposing Middle Pennsylvanian dolomitic limestones (PL) in its core and Lower and Middle Permian shales (PS), sandstones, and limestones on its flank. Ridge-forming sandstone which outlines uplift in lower right corner of photo is Lower and Middle Jurassic Bug Creek Formation (BC). NAPL oblique photo T3-23R.

mark the southeastward termination of the thrust belt. It should be noted that the sense of motion required for these faults as they turn southward is right-lateral, which is mechanically congruent with that determined for some of the major north- and northeast-trending transcurrent faults on the east.

From Barn Mountains eastward to Campbell uplift, the style comprises a series of domes and depressions commonly elongated and arranged righthand *en échelon* (Fig. 1). One of the most prominent of these structural highs is Cache Creek uplift (Fig. 6), an open structure which plunges gently northeast beneath Mackenzie delta, exposing Lower and Middle Permian clastic and carbonate rocks on its flanks and massive Middle Pennsylvanian limestones in its core. Domes like this, as well as the juxtaposed structural depressions, are commonly cut by north- and northeast-trending faults such as the one whose relatively depressed southeast side is identified in Cache Creek uplift (Fig. 3). Another such fault truncates Gilbert anticline (Fig. 7), a prominent, more closely appressed structure in the Rapid depression. There, ridge-forming clastic units of the Aptian "upper sandstone division" have been displaced laterally to the right into line with the Valanginian "lower sandstone division."

The best-known and one of the most pronounced strike-slip faults, the Donna River fault (Jeletzky, 1960, p. 25), cuts longitudinally through Aklavik Range (Fig. 8) as it trends north and northeast to Mackenzie delta. This fault is traceable southward along the east flank of Richardson Mountains for more than 100 km. The orientation of minor structures such as thrusts and drag folds led Jeletzky (1961, p. 548) to conclude that the principal displacement on the fault was right-lateral but that the actual amount of horizontal movement

was impossible to determine with any degree of certainty without additional field study. Intrusions of gypsum can be seen along the trace of the fault on lower Willow (Donna) River, as well as at the edge of the delta (Kent and Russell, 1961). Fragments of altered basic intrusives contained in the gypsum suggest derivation from late Proterozoic(?) rocks like those seen on the north flank of White uplift and comparable with those reported from the late Precambrian (Thorsteinsson and Tozer, 1962, p. 38, 39) on Victoria Island. The fault, therefore, may cut the sedimentary veneer, at least locally, as deep as the Proterozoic.

Gravity surveys over the lower Mackenzie

Fig. 7—South-plunging Gilbert anticline exposing Upper Jurassic and Lower Cretaceous shales and sandstones; right- and left-lateral strike-slip faults cause northward truncation of anticline. NAPL oblique photo T6-17L.

Fig. 8—South-trending Aklavik Range cut longitudinally by Donna River fault. NAPL oblique photo T3-15L.

basin (Hornal *et al.,* 1970) provide some understanding of the structural and stratigraphic
framework beneath Mackenzie delta. Of special
interest is the continuity of Dave Lord–Cache
Creek, Rat, and Campbell uplifts and structures
such as the Donna River fault. As indicated,
Cache Creek uplift trends northeast and
plunges beneath the delta. Because saddles similar to that observed between Dave Lord and
Cache Creek uplifts appear to be part of the
structural habit, it is assumed that Cache Creek
uplift in fact plunges northeast into another
saddle and that the next culmination along
trend is identified by the relatively positive 30-
mgal Bouguer anomaly (Hornal *et al.,* 1970, p.
9) surrounding the location of the Tununuk H-
10 borehole (Fig. 9). Similarly, Campbell
uplift is identified in the gravity field by the
positive 10-mgal Bouguer contour near the
south end of Sitidgi Lake, and its northeast
trend is clearly evident from adjacent gravity
contours. Rat uplift cannot be identified as easily, nor can the continuation of the Donna
River fault, although the latter may be continuous with structures interpreted to exist at depth
beneath Liverpool Bay, more than 200 km to
the northeast (discussed in a succeeding para-
graph). Of prime importance is the fact that
the gravity contours trend northeast parallel
with the long direction of the individual *en
échelon* structural highs identified on both sides
of the delta. There is no suggestion that these

en échelon uplifts form one structurally continuous high from Porcupine River east-northeast to Liverpool Bay.

Campbell uplift is the most prominent structural feature flanking Mackenzie delta on the northeast. Late Proterozoic dolomites are exposed at its crest, and Paleozoic, Mesozoic, and Tertiary clastic beds dip gently northwest and southeast at less than 5° on its flanks (Figs. 9, 10). Several steeply dipping faults, possibly with some strike-slip displacement, are clearly exposed in the core of the uplift; still others probably exist but are masked by glacial deposits. The stratigraphic separation of the faults postulated for the northwest flank of the uplift, however, would have to be compensatory, be-

cause such faults do not appear to modify significantly the gentle but progressive northwest dip of the succession, as projected downdip, to the levels at which they are encountered in the D-27 borehole (Chamney, 1971c, Fig. 6). Of special interest is the possibility that the rocks directly above the Paleozoic sequence in the Inuvik well may be Albian and, hence, that the Lower Cretaceous "Silty zone" encountered in the Reindeer well (Chamney, 1971c) has been overstepped. Its featheredge has been interpreted to occur in the vicinity of the Gulf Reindeer wells in the structure section (Fig. 10).

Near the mouth of Kugaluk River in the southwestern Stanton map area, Yorath and Balkwill (1969; 1970, p. 3) have observed that

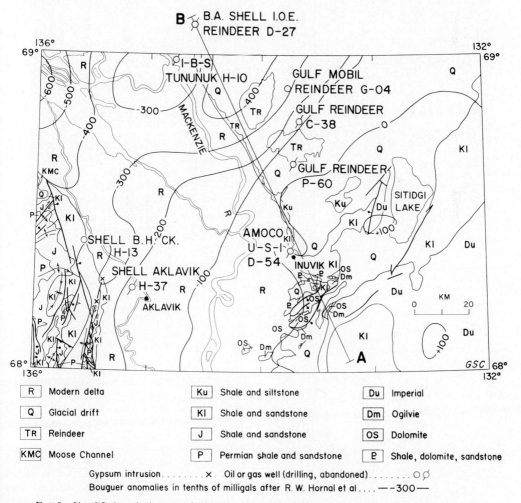

FIG. 9—Simplified geologic map of Aklavik area (NTS 107B), northwestern District of Mackenzie.

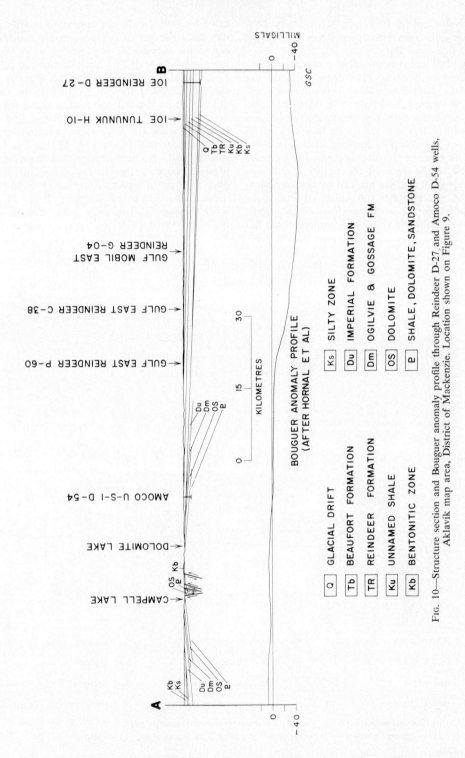

Fig. 10—Structure section and Bouguer anomaly profile through Reindeer D-27 and Amoco D-54 wells, Aklavik map area, District of Mackenzie. Location shown on Figure 9.

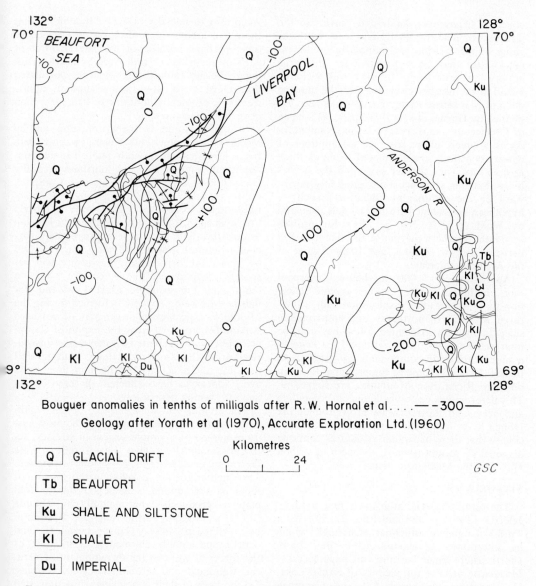

Bouguer anomalies in tenths of milligals after R. W. Hornal et al. . . . .— –300 —

Geology after Yorath et al (1970), Accurate Exploration Ltd. (1960)

Kilometres

0   24

Q	GLACIAL DRIFT
Tb	BEAUFORT
Ku	SHALE AND SILTSTONE
Kl	SHALE
Du	IMPERIAL

GSC

FIG. 11—Simplified geologic map of Stanton area (NTS 107A) with faults and folds present beneath Liverpool Bay superposed.

the Albian "Bentonitic zone" lies unconform- ably on the Upper Devonian Imperial Forma- tion and that the "Silty zone" is absent because of overstepping on a paleotopographic, north- trending high which they termed "Kugaluk arch." The writer prefers to interpret this over- stepping as occurring on the northeast exten- sion of Campbell uplift, in which case the featheredge of the "Silty zone" would trend northeast rather than north, and would occur at

relatively shallow drilling depths beneath the gently northwest-dipping panel of Tertiary shales and coarser clastic units of Kugaluk ho- mocline.

Kugaluk homocline is clearly expressed in the outcrop distribution of these youngest Phanerozoic rocks in the eastern Aklavik (Fig. 9) and adjacent Stanton (Fig. 11) map areas. The Tertiary sedimentary rocks form a thin, southeast-tapering wedge which dips beneath a cover of Quaternary sands and gravels in the direction of Beaufort shelf. The seaward thickening of this marine and nonmarine sedimentary wedge may be responsible for the large gravity low over Kugmallit Bay and Richards Island at the northern extremity of the modern delta of Mackenzie River. The low has been explained by Hornal *et al.* (1970, p. 9) as a basin of Cretaceous and Tertiary clastic sedimentary deposits which, under specified assumptions of density contrasts, are calculated to be as thick as 6,400 m. They further suggested the probability that this sequence thins gradually northward on the continental (Beaufort) shelf—a hypothesis consistent with the models prepared by Wold *et al.* (1970, p. 854) for profiles across the southern margin of the Beaufort Sea between Barrow, Alaska, and Banks Island of the Arctic Archipelago.

Approximately 1,000 m below Liverpool Bay, continuous-profile, marine seismic reflection surveys (Accurate Exploration Ltd., 1960) reveal a system of northeast- and east-trending steep faults with associated folds that may be interpreted to link in a righthand *en échelon* manner. Strike-slip components consistent with those inferred on some of the principal faults in northern Richardson Mountains are suggested. This deformation underlies Kugaluk homocline and occurs on the northeast projection of the Donna River fault. There is, therefore, the possibility that these or similar structures continue diagonally southwestward beneath Caribou Hills and the Mackenzie delta.

Aklavik Arch

The term "Aklavik arch" was first used by Jeletzky (1961, p. 538 and Figs. 22, 24) for a "mid-Valanginian anticlinal structure" which he interpreted to extend from Bell basin (northeastern Eagle basin of this paper) across Mackenzie delta to the vicinity of Sitidgi Lake. He therefore considered Rat and Campbell uplifts as one physically continuous structural high. Jeletzky applied the name "Dave Lord Creek arch" (Dave Lord arch of this paper) to one of the late Middle Devonian "broad anticlinal arches" (Martin, 1959, p. 2442 and Fig. 12b), recognized by Martin and identified by Knipping (1960, p. 1 and Fig. 5) as "Dave Lord Ridge . . . the general location of the late Paleozoic orogenic belt." The term "ancestral Aklavik arch" subsequently was introduced by Jeletzky (1963, p. 66) for a regional arch which he interpreted to be the predecessor of the "Dave Lord Creek" and "Aklavik" arches.

According to Jeletzky (1963), "It could be that these two arches . . . only arose in Cretaceous time, perhaps because of the lateral offset of parts of ancestral Aklavik Arch by north-trending strike-slip faults." He therefore postulated that Dave Lord, Rat, and Campbell uplifts were one physically continuous structural high prior to Cretaceous time.

Structural studies by the writer, supported by recent stratigraphic and biostratigraphic data from several sources, both published and unpublished, suggest that the northeast-trending Dave Lord–Cache Creek, Rat, and Campbell uplifts may be one integrated *system* of structural highs. Collectively, they may be termed "Aklavik arch." They are arranged *en échelon* toward the right, they have approximately parallel structural grains, and they are separated by structural depressions; however, they responded individually to the tectonic forces in the region. For example, Dave Lord and Rat uplifts were being actively deformed during the Middle or Late Devonian orogeny of northern Yukon Territory, whereas the region of Campbell uplift was receiving sediments, possibly derived from that orogeny. Tilting, faulting, and buckling in Cretaceous and Tertiary time, however, appear to have affected all three uplifts and intervening depressions.

The arching and some faulting of this region east of Barn Mountains appear to be most easily explained by a simple system of stresses, active spasmodically at least since Middle or Late Devonian time, but with consistent orientation. The righthand *en échelon* arrangement of these parallel uplifts is analogous to the fold patterns produced experimentally by Tokuda (1927, p. 60) and further analyzed by Campbell (1958, p. 449). Their experiments and conclusions notably clarified understanding of the forces at work in the development of natural, righthand and lefthand *en échelon* folds. On the basis of their conclusions, it is suggested that Dave Lord–Cache Creek, Rat, and Campbell uplifts and *associated* steeply dipping faults with right-lateral displacements could be the products of similarly oriented compressive stresses active at different times and places along the arch but oriented more or less consistently in a northeast direction. Mobilization and transport of Proterozoic(?) salt to the cores of the uplifts would facilitate force folding and account for the extension(?) faulting suggested, for example, in White and Campbell uplifts. The principal *en échelon* structures of northern Yukon Territory and northwestern

District of Mackenzie thus may be the products of the same or similar stress systems, but some (*e.g.*, Dave Lord–Cache Creek and Rat uplifts) are not necessarily one and the same feature cut and offset by a major strike-slip fault.

Aklavik arch is postulated as a persistent, composite structural feature comprising a system of uplifts, depressions, and faults in a specific geometric pattern. It appears to have persisted as a northeast-trending curvilinear feature at least since the mid-Paleozoic; it is possibly traceable in Canada from the Alaska border to the Beaufort Sea. It may also be the structural link between Minto arch (Thorsteinsson and Tozer, 1960, p. 6), in central Victoria Island of the Arctic Archipelago, and the Yukon-Porcupine lineation (Tailleur, 1969, Fig. 2) in Alaska. The nature of the Aklavik complex would have allowed seaways to exist at times in the (*en échelon*) structural depressions. At other times, more than one of the uplifts was sufficiently depressed to prevent great stretches of the arch from serving as barriers to sedimentation. There is, therefore, no reason to anticipate major differences in facies or faunas on the north and south solely because of the Aklavik arch. Thick Paleozoic carbonate accumulations appear to have developed on the flanks or crests of the arch complex as suggested, for example, in the core of Cache Creek uplift (Middle Pennsylvanian and Early Permian), Dave Lord arch (Pennsylvanian), and Campbell uplift (Ordovician-Silurian and Middle Devonian). A. W. Norris (1968b, Fig. 5) reported limestones and dolomites ranging in age from Silurian to Middle Devonian in the Peel Plateau No. 1 Eagle Plains well, on the southwest projection of Rat uplift. Lateral equivalents of some of these carbonate units may be seen, for example, in erosional remnants of Early Devonian graptolitic shales reported on the northwest flank of Dave Lord arch by D. K. Norris (1970, p. 231) and near the crest of Rat uplift by geologists of Shell Canada Ltd. (Norford, 1970). The possible presence of other carbonate accumulations, and their lateral transitional facies to shale, beneath suitable caprocks along and adjacent to Aklavik arch greatly enhances the prospects for hydrocarbons in the region.

This ancient, gently sinuous, composite feature, apparently more than 1,400 km long, may provide a major link between the structure and stratigraphy of the northern mainland and the Arctic Archipelago. The Franklinian miogeo-

syncline and the Sverdrup basin lie north of the arch complex and head seaward to Canada basin (Thorsteinsson and Tozer, 1960, Fig. 2). It appears rather unlikely, therefore, that these basins have been continuous with the Richardson trough and other tectonic elements south and east of Aklavik arch, at least since the Middle or Late Devonian orogeny. The fact that the Aklavik arch is so nearly linear suggests, moreover, that it is extremely unlikely that the arch complex once curved back on itself in the form of a giant "U"; such a supposition would be required, however, if the North Slope of Alaska and adjoining parts of Canada are assumed to have been in contact with the western margin of the archipelago at one time. Geological and geophysical data suggest that the Canada basin may be a true oceanic feature (*e.g.*, see Churkin, 1969, p. 553, and Berry and Barr, 1971, p. 360), and the possibility that Aklavik arch was never significantly bent through rotation about a vertical axis suggests that the basin has been in existence at least since the mid-Paleozoic.

Selected References

Accurate Exploration Ltd., 1960, Marine seismograph survey in the Liverpool Bay area of Northwest Territories: report for Hunt Oil Company, January 1971, Open File, Nov. 1, 1969.

Bamber, E. W., and J. B. Waterhouse, 1971, Carboniferous and Permian stratigraphy and paleontology, northern Yukon Territory: Bull. Canadian Petroleum Geology, v. 19, no. 1.

—— et al., 1963, Geology, northern Yukon Territory and northwestern District of Mackenzie: Canada Geol. Survey Prelim. Ser. Map 10-1963, scale 1: 1,000,000, text.

Berry, M. J., and K. G. Barr, 1971, A seismic refraction profile across the polar continental shelf of the Queen Elizabeth Islands: Canadian Jour. Earth Sci., v. 8, no. 3, p. 347–360.

Brosgé, W. P., 1970, Paleozoic of northern and central Alaska (abs.): Am. Assoc. Petroleum Geologists Bull., v. 54, no. 12, p. 2473.

Campbell, J. D., 1958, En echelon folding: Econ. Geology, v. 53, p. 448–472, discussions.

Chamney, T. P., 1970, Biostratigraphic subdivision of the first Mackenzie River Delta exploratory borehole: Canada Geol. Survey Rept. Activities, Paper 70-1, pt. B, p. 80–83.

—— 1971a, Micropaleontology report on fossils collected by D. K. Norris at Locality C-7637: Canada Geol. Survey Internal Rept. No. gen. 4-TPC-1971.

—— 1971b, Micropaleontology report on fossils collected by E. W. Mountjoy at Locality C-9082: Canada Geol. Survey Internal Rept. No. gen. 12-TPC-1971.

—— 1971c, Tertiary and Cretaceous biostratigraphic divisions in Reindeer D-27 borehole, Mackenzie Delta: Canada Geol. Survey Paper 70–30.

Churkin, M., Jr., 1969, Paleozoic tectonic history of the Arctic Basin north of Alaska: Science, v. 165, no. 3893, p. 549–555.

Gabrielse, H., 1967, Tectonic evolution of the northern Canadian Cordillera: Canadian Jour. Earth Sci., v. 4, no. 2, p. 271–298.

Hornal, R. W., et al., 1970, Preliminary results of gravity surveys over Mackenzie Basin and Beaufort Sea: Canada Dept. Energy, Mines and Resources Earth Physics Br., Gravity Maps 117, 118, 119.

Jeletzky, J. A., 1960, Uppermost Jurassic and Cretaceous rocks, east flank of Richardson Mountains between Stony Creek and lower Donna River, Northwest Territories: Canada Geol. Survey Paper 59–14, 31 p.

———— 1961, Eastern slope, Richardson Mountains— Cretaceous and Tertiary structural history and regional significance, in Geology of the Arctic: Univ. Toronto Press, v. 1, p. 532–583.

———— 1963, Pre-Cretaceous Richardson Mountains trough—its place in the tectonic framework of Arctic Canada and its bearing on some geosynclinal concepts: Royal Soc. Canada Trans., v. 56, ser. 3, sec. 3, p. 55–84.

Kent, P. E., and W. A. C. Russell, 1961, Evaporite structures in the northern Richardson Mountains, in Geology of the Arctic: Univ. Toronto Press, v. 1, p. 584–595.

Knipping, H. D., 1960, Late Paleozoic orogeny—north Yukon: Presented at AAPG-ASPG regional meeting, May 25–28, 1960, Banff, Alberta, Canada; also in Frontiers of exploration in Canada, 10 p.

Lathram, E. H., 1965, Preliminary geologic map of northern Alaska: U.S. Geol. Survey Open-File Rept.

Mamet, B. L., and D. Mason, 1970, Lisburne Group, lithostratigraphy and foraminiferal zonation, British Mountains, northern Yukon Territory: Bull. Canadian Petroleum Geology, v. 18, no. 4, p. 556–565.

Martin, L. J., 1959, Stratigraphy and depositional tectonics of north Yukon–lower Mackenzie River area, Canada: Am. Assoc. Petroleum Geologists Bull., v. 43, no. 10, p. 2399–2455.

McGregor, D. C., 1971, Micropaleontology report on fossils collected by A. W. Norris and D. K. Norris at Locality C-5624: Canada Geol. Survey Internal Rept. No. Fl-7-DCM-1971.

Miller, D. J., et al., 1959, Geology of possible petroleum provinces in Alaska: U.S. Geol. Survey Bull. 1094, 131 p.

Mountjoy, E. W., 1967a, Upper Cretaceous and Tertiary stratigraphy, northern Yukon Territory and northwestern District of Mackenzie: Canada Geol. Survey Paper 66–16, 70 p.

———— 1967b, Triassic stratigraphy of northern Yukon Territory: Canada Geol. Survey Paper 66–19, 44 p.

Norford, B. S., 1963, Paleontology report on fossils collected by R. M. Procter at Localities 54066-72: Canada Geol. Survey Internal Rept. No. C11-BSN-1963.

———— 1964, Reconnaissance of the Ordovician and Silurian rocks of northern Yukon Territory: Canada Geol. Survey Paper 63–39, 139 p.

———— 1970, Paleontology report on fossils collected by Shell Canada Ltd. at Locality C-6854: Canada Geol. Survey Internal Rept. No. D–6–BSN–1970.

Norris, A. W., 1967, Description of Devonian sections in northern Yukon Territory and northwestern District of Mackenzie: Canada Geol. Survey Paper 66–39, 298 p.

———— 1968a, Devonian of northern Yukon Territory and adjacent District of Mackenzie, in D. H. Oswald, ed., International symposium on the Devonian System: Calgary, Alberta Soc. Petroleum Geologists, v. 1, p. 753–780.

———— 1968b, Reconnaissance Devonian stratigraphy of northern Yukon Territory and northwestern District of Mackenzie: Canada Geol. Survey Paper 67–53, 287 p.

Norris, D. K., 1963, Operation Porcupine: Canada Geol. Survey Paper 63-1, Summ. Research—Field, 1962, p. 17–19.

———— 1970, Structural and stratigraphic studies, Blow River area, Yukon Territory and western District of Mackenzie: Canada Geol. Survey Paper 70–1, pt. A, p. 230–235.

———— 1971, Tectonic styles of Arctic plateau and coastal plain of Yukon Territory, western District of Mackenzie (abs.): Oilweek, Feb. 15, p. 18.

———— and R. F. Black, 1964, Palaeomagnetic age of the pre-Ordovician rocks near Inuvik, Northwest Territories: Canada Geol. Survey Paper 64–2, p. 47–51.

Ostenso, N. A., 1962, Geophysical investigations of the Arctic Ocean basin: Univ. Wisconsin Research Rept. 62–4.

Rampton, V., 1969, Herschel Island–Aklavik, surficial geology: Canada Geol. Survey Open File Rept., September 22, 9 ms. maps.

Tailleur, I., 1969, Speculations on North Slope geology, Part 1: Oil and Gas Jour., Sept. 22, p. 215–226.

Thorsteinsson, R., and E. T. Tozer, 1960, Summary account of structural history of the Canadian Arctic Archipelago since Precambrian time: Canada Geol. Survey Paper 60-7, 25 p.

———— and ———— 1962, Banks, Victoria, and Stefansson Islands, Arctic Archipelago: Canada Geol. Survey Mem. 330, 85 p., Map 1135A.

Tokuda, S., 1927, On the echelon structure of the Japanese Archipelagoes: Japanese Jour. Geology and Geography, v. 5, p. 41–76, 1926–1927.

Wanless, R. K., et al., 1965, Age determination and geological studies, Part 1—isotopic ages, Report 5: Canada Geol. Survey Paper 64–17, 126 p.

Wold, J., et al., 1970, Structure of the Beaufort Sea continental margin: Geophysics, v. 35, no. 5, p. 849–861.

Yorath, C. J., and H. R. Balkwill, 1969, Crossley Lakes: Canada Geol. Survey Map 8-1969, with marginal notes.

———— and ———— 1970, Stanton map-area, Northwest Territories (107D): Canada Geol. Survey Paper 69–9, 7 p., Map 15–1969.

Ziegler, P. A., 1969, The development of sedimentary basins in western and Arctic Canada: Alberta Soc. Petroleum Geologists Guidebook.

Geology of Beaufort-Mackenzie Basin and Eastern Part of Northern Interior Plains[1]

CHRISTOPHER J. YORATH[2]

Calgary, Alberta, Canada

Abstract The eastern part of the northern Interior Plains is underlain by rocks of Cenozoic, Mesozoic, and Paleozoic age. The region is bounded on the east by the Coppermine arch, composed of lower Paleozoic and Precambrian rocks. The plains region is a northwest-dipping homocline, interrupted in its western part by the Kugaluk arch, a north-trending pre-Cretaceous uplift.

Mesozoic rocks of the Interior Plains consist of Cretaceous sandstones, mudstones, and shales with a composite thickness of about 3,000 ft (900 m) along Anderson and Horton Rivers. The Lower Cretaceous units are correlated with similar rocks on Banks Island. On the mainland, these strata are disconformably overlain by varicolored clastic units of Late Cretaceous and early Tertiary age.

Westward, in the region of the Mackenzie delta, the Tertiary Reindeer Formation consists of a northward-thickening sequence of poorly consolidated to unconsolidated cherty gravels, crossbedded sands, and coal and ash beds. Its maximum outcrop thickness is about 4,000 ft (1,250 m). In the nearby B.A.-Shell-I.O.E. Reindeer D-27 well, the Reindeer Formation is 3,970 ft (1,210 m) thick and underlies 790 ft (250 m) of Quaternary and recent sediments. Microfaunal studies show that the Reindeer Formation overlies 2,200 ft (670 m) of Late Cretaceous clastic rocks which, in part, may be equivalent to the Moose Channel Formation, which crops out on the west side of the delta adjacent to the Richardson Mountains. These Upper Cretaceous rocks in the Reindeer well lie unconformably on 5,690 ft (1,750 m) of Lower Cretaceous sandstones and mudstones which can be correlated with similar units in the eastern Richardson Mountains.

Offshore seismic profiles obtained during the 1969 Articquest survey indicate the presence of a thick sequence of sedimentary rocks, the lower part of which has been deformed into broad domal structures. These lower rocks are unconformably overlain by nearly flatlying younger rocks. This unconformity may be the same as that separating the Lower and Upper Cretaceous rocks in the Reindeer well. Analyses of the profiles indicate that these younger rocks may have been intruded by diapiric structures.

Introduction

Beginning in 1968 the Geological Survey of Canada initiated a project under the leadership of J. D. Aitken (Aitken *et al.*, 1969), "Operation Norman," designed to map 145,000 sq mi (375,000 sq km) of the Interior Plains and mountains of the Northwest Territories (see

D. G. Cook, this volume). During the course of this project, significant hydrocarbon reservoirs were discovered at Prudhoe Bay on the North Slope of Alaska and at Atkinson Point on the Tuktoyaktuk Peninsula. Partly as an outgrowth of "Operation Norman," and in response to increased petroleum exploration, the Geological Survey initiated the Beaufort-Mackenzie program, which is a multidisciplinary venture with the object of determining the geologic history of the Mackenzie delta–Beaufort Sea basin. This paper is a brief summary of what is now known of the geology of a part of Canada's north coast and adjacent offshore area. The Canadian government's Hudson 70 program in the Beaufort Sea may yield additional information on the geology of the Beaufort Sea basin.

Important contributions to knowledge of the geology in the area as developed in this paper have come from H. R. Balkwill, T. P. Chamney, D. K. Norris, and J. A. Jeletzky of the Geological Survey, and R. W. Hornal and others of the Earth Physics Branch. Appreciation is expressed to representatives of Kenting Ltd. of Calgary for permission to publish my interpretation of their seismic data.

Surface Geology

The surface geology of the northern Interior Plains and Mackenzie delta is represented by strata of Paleozoic, Mesozoic, and Cenozoic age which are bounded on the east by Proterozoic rocks of the Coppermine arch (Fig. 1). A generalized cross section from the Coppermine arch to the Richardson Mountains is illustrated by Figure 2.

The Coppermine arch is underlain by deformed carbonate and clastic rocks that have a thickness of more than 7,000 ft (2,100 m). The northern expression of these rocks is probably in the Shaler Group of Banks Island (Thorsteinsson and Tozer, 1962; Yorath *et al.*, 1969; Balkwill and Yorath, 1971). The rocks have been intruded by diabase sills and dikes which, on the basis of K-Ar whole-rock analysis, are probably late Proterozoic in age (Wanless *et al.*, 1965). The north-trending dia-

[1] Manuscript received, September 20, 1971.

[2] Geological Survey of Canada.

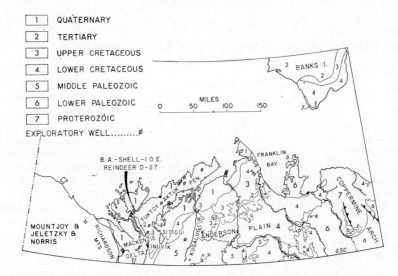

FIG. 1—Generalized geology of northernmost Interior Plains and Mackenzie delta.

base intrusions and the unconformities within the Phanerozoic rocks which flank the arch suggest that this feature had a long history of periodic tectonic activity extending at least into Cretaceous time, because rocks of that system are preserved in normal-fault basins on the west side of the arch.

Paleozoic rocks on the west side of the arch have a gentle, uniform westerly dip except for a few minor broad folds; a thin cover of Cretaceous and Tertiary strata overlies the Paleozoic rocks. The Phanerozoic sequences are bounded by disconformities of wide regional extent. The Paleozoic rocks are carbonate and clastic units of (1) the Old Fort Island, Mt. Cap, and Saline River Formations, and the Ronning Group, of Cambrian to Early Silurian age, and (2) the Bear Rock, Hume, Hare Indian, Canol, and Imperial Formations of Early to Late Devonian age. The locally angular sub-Cretaceous unconformity truncates progressively older Paleozoic units from west to east.

The Cretaceous sandstones and shales, more than 3,000 ft (900 m) thick, display normal onlap and offlap relations typical of coastal-plain sedimentation. The Lower and Upper Cretaceous rocks are separated by a regional disconformity which reflects epeirogenic movements approximately coincident with orogenic displacements in the Richardson Mountains during early Late Cretaceous time.

On the flanks of the Coppermine arch, the lowest Cretaceous rocks are Aptian to early Al-

bian sandstones and coals of nonmarine origin; they are, at least in part, equivalent to the Isachsen Formation of Banks Island. Overlying the sandstones on the Anderson Plain, and perhaps in part replacing them, are Albian mudstones and claystones which are correlative with the Christopher Formation of the northern islands (Thorsteinsson and Tozer, 1962; Yorath *et al.*, 1969). These Lower Cretaceous rocks are unconformably overlain by Upper Cretaceous variegated, bituminous shales; jarosite and earthy hematite beds; and ferruginous shales containing abundant silica shards and radiolarians. The jarosite and hematite beds are related to rapid surface oxidation which locally results in burning exposures called "bocannes" (Crickmay, 1967), from which the Smoking Hills on the west side of Franklin Bay derived their name.

Small, tight, randomly oriented folds are locally impressed upon the Upper Cretaceous sequence. These structures are probably disharmonic above extremely ductile bentonitic shales within the Lower Cretaceous rocks.

Disconformably overlying the Cretaceous units are the nonmarine sands, sandstones, and sandy shales of the Tertiary and Pleistocene Beaufort Formation, which is as thick as 400 ft (120 m) or more on Banks Island (Thorsteinsson and Tozer, 1962).

The gentle west and northwest-dipping homocline of Cretaceous and Paleozoic rocks is interrupted on the west by the pre-Cretaceous

Kugaluk arch, which, on the basis of gravity data, appears to extend northeastward through the Campbell uplift to the mouth of Kugaluk River and beyond. This arch apparently partially separated sedimentation in the Mackenzie delta region from that on the Anderson Plain to the east, and Cretaceous seas did not overstep the arch until late Early Cretaceous time. D. K. Norris (this volume) points out that the Kugaluk arch may be an extension of the Aklavik arch (Jeletzky, 1962); if so, it was active periodically from Middle Devonian to possibly Late Cretaceous time.

Between Kugaluk River and the Richardson Mountains, there are few outcrops. Devonian and Cretaceous strata are present near Sitidgi Lake, and, in the vicinity of Campbell Lake near Inuvik, deformed Precambrian(?), lower Paleozoic, and middle Paleozoic carbonate and clastic rocks occur as an inlier surrounded by Quaternary deposits. The structural grain within the Campbell uplift—a part of the Aklavik arch—coincides with that of the Keele Range of the western Yukon, and also is recognized within the Richardson Mountains (D. K. Norris, personal commun.).

On the east side of the Mackenzie delta, in the Caribou Hills, a poorly consolidated to unconsolidated succession of Tertiary sand, gravel, mudstone, and low-grade coal thickens from zero near the Campbell uplift to more

than 4,200 ft (1,300 m) where it crops out in the north. This succession, named the "Reindeer Formation" by Mountjoy (1967), is discussed in the section on the Reindeer well.

GRAVITY ANOMALIES

Figure 3 illustrates the regional Bouguer anomaly of the area as mapped and interpreted by Hornal et al. (1970). The most obvious feature is the strong "bull's-eye" anomaly of more than 115 mgal (eastern part of map area) adjacent to the west flank of the Coppermine arch. This anomaly has been interpreted as representing a plug of basic rocks, perhaps related to the igneous intrusions of the arch. No reflection of this feature is evident at the surface, and in the structure section (Fig. 2) the relation of the feature to the surrounding rocks is not shown. Another smaller positive anomaly is located near Cape Bathurst. Two large negative anomalies are present. One, occurring beneath the Anderson Plain, indicates a thick accumulation of Phanerozoic rocks. The other lies over the Mackenzie delta and reflects basinal accumulation of sediments perhaps greater than 21,000 ft (6,400 m) in thickness. What may prove to be a very important feature is shown by the well-defined gradient which extends across the Tuktoyaktuk Peninsula and separates the Kugaluk arch from the strongly negative elliptical anomaly over the Mackenzie delta. This feature

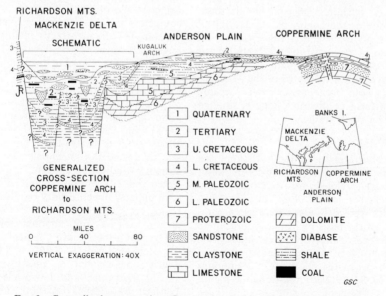

FIG. 2—Generalized cross section, Coppermine arch to Richardson Mountains.

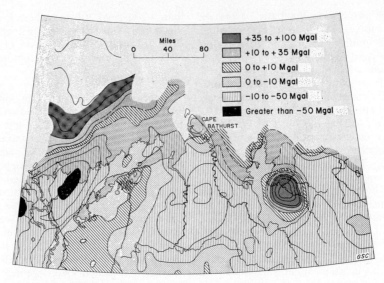

FIG. 3—Regional Bouguer anomaly map—northernmost Interior Plains and Mackenzie delta.
After Hornal *et al.* (1970).

is interpreted as a fault, possibly an extension of the Donna River fault (D. K. Norris, this volume), and may represent the main fault zone bounding the eastern side of the Mackenzie delta basin. The Kugaluk arch (Aklavik arch) is represented by the low, linear positive anomaly extending northeasterly from Campbell uplift beyond the mouth of Kugaluk River.

The steep gradient leading to a strong positive anomaly offshore reflects the northern structural edge of the continent. As Hornal *et al.* (1970) have indicated, if this gradient reflects the rise of the crust-mantle boundary at the edge of the continental plate, it would appear that the shelf on the north of the Mackenzie delta has been built outward over oceanic crust. The present continental slope is situated seaward of this steep gradient.

REINDEER WELL

Figure 4 illustrates the general lithology and time-stratigraphy of the B.A.-Shell-I.O.E. Reindeer D-27 well drilled on Richards Island in the Mackenzie delta (Fig. 1). Biostratigraphic zones were delineated by T. P. Chamney (1971) on the basis of Foraminifera; these zones enabled correlations to be established between the subsurface and surface exposures of equivalent rocks in the Richardson Mountains (Jeletzky, 1958; 1960). Additional evidence for Upper Cretaceous correlations has been provided by Mountjoy (1967) and Young (1971).

Figure 4 shows 5,640 ft (1,720 m) of Lower Cretaceous concretionary shales, glauconitic sandstones, siltstones, and mudstones which are equivalent to Jeletzky's informal units of the Richardson Mountains. This succession is unconformably overlain by 2,200 ft (670 m) of Upper Cretaceous rocks assigned to the Moose Channel Formation. Another unit, possibly equivalent to Jeletzky's Upper Cretaceous shale division, may be incorrectly included within the lower part of the Moose Channel Formation. If so, then the associated hiatus would have begun somewhat later during the Late Cretaceous. It is believed that the Moose Channel Formation represents the first part of the major orogenic pulse of the Richardson Mountains; Young (1971) has shown the unit there to consist of about 2,800 ft (850 m) of fluvial conglomeratic sandstone and mudstone with paleocurrent structures indicating a western source. It is believed that the Moose Channel Formation lies with angular unconformity on older Cretaceous rocks, but contact relations have not been fully documented (Young, personal commun.).

Overlying the Moose Channel Formation in the Reindeer well is 3,960 ft (1,200 m) of poorly consolidated to unconsolidated sand, gravel, mudstone, and low-grade coal of the Tertiary Reindeer Formation. The formation here appears very similar to rocks exposed in the Caribou Hills, where the Reindeer contains such deltaic facies as basal progradational mudstones, bar-finger sandstones, and interdistributary fine-grained sedimentary units containing plant debris and coal. Also present there are such deltaic features as trough and planar cross-bedding and scour-and-fill structures. The Reindeer Formation in the Reindeer well is overlain by 800 ft (245 m) of Quaternary deltaic sedimentary beds.

STRUCTURE OF MACKENZIE DELTA BASIN

Figure 2 shows the Mackenzie delta basin schematically as a graben structure. Until further work is done, the nature of the west boundary of the basin will remain unknown. The presence of the fault shown bounding the east side of the basin is based upon the geometry of

the steep gravity gradient extending northeastward across the Tuktoyaktuk Peninsula. This fault is parallel with the trend of the Kugaluk (Aklavik) arch, which may represent the northeastward extension of western Yukon structural grain.

The horst structure in the center of the basin is interpreted as separating the main basin into two subbasins, as indicated by gravity data (Fig. 3). Other interpretations for this separation are certainly possible, and the horst is shown mainly to indicate the presence of complexities within the main basin. The time of movement of structures within the basin was varied. Many of the data supporting a complex tectonic history are confidential; all that can be said now is that all systems were involved in deformation at different times and at different places.

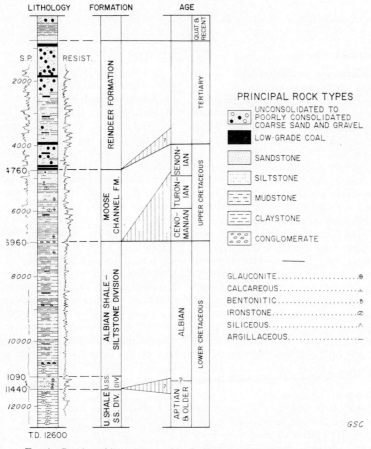

FIG. 4—Stratigraphic summary of B. A.-Shell-I.O.E. Reindeer D-27 well.

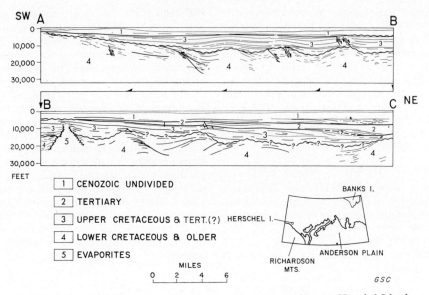

FIG. 5—Reflection depth section of "Arcticquest" seismic profile near Herschel Island.

SEISMIC PROFILE OFFSHORE

Figure 5 illustrates a marine seismic profile obtained by the Arcticquest participation survey under the direction of Kenquest Exploration of Calgary. The line runs northeastward from near Herschel Island out into the Beaufort Sea, across the subsea extension of the Mackenzie delta.

A broad, regional unconformity is believed to separate Lower Cretaceous from Upper Cretaceous and Tertiary rocks. The unconformity has been traced onto land where it is probably angular on a tributary of the Babbage River of the North Yukon. In the profile, folds and faults are truncated by the unconformity. An interpreted diapir cuts the unconformity and penetrates Upper Cretaceous strata. Anhydrite and gypsum are known to occur at a few localities along the Richardson Mountain front adjacent to the Mackenzie delta (Jeletzky, 1960). At least one of these occurrences appears to be associated with faulting, as are a number of the diapiric structures of the Sverdrup basin of the Arctic Archipelago (Thorsteinsson and Tozer, 1970). Several small faults and a deltaic sequence are shown in the upper part of the profile section. These faults and the position of the deltaic sequence are thought to indicate movement during Tertiary time that may have been coincident with other interpreted Tertiary movements elsewhere in the subsurface.

SUMMARY

The northern Interior Plains display simple, west-dipping, unconformity-bounded sequences of Paleozoic and Mesozoic rocks. Within the Mackenzie delta and Beaufort Sea basin, thick accumulations of Cretaceous and Tertiary sedimentary strata are present. The Lower Cretaceous succession is related to that in the Richardson Mountains; it accumulated within a shallow-trough environment. During early to mid–Late Cretaceous time, widespread uplift occurred within the Richardson Mountain trough and the Interior Plains. This uplifting was followed by large-scale block-fault movements within the Mackenzie delta basin, making possible the accumulation of the thick Late Cretaceous and Tertiary Moose Channel and Reindeer Formations. Diapirism and faulting occurred, probably during middle to late Tertiary time; they may have caused deltaic deposition to be terminated in the east and may have caused the westward shift of the depositional axis of the delta to its present position against the Richardson Mountains.

REFERENCES

Aitken, J. D., et al., 1969, Operation Norman, District of Mackenzie, in Report of activities, April to October, 1968: Canada Geol. Survey Paper 69–1, pt. A.

Balkwill, H. R., and C. J. Yorath, 1971, Brock River map-area (97D), District of Mackenzie: Canada Geol. Survey Paper 70–32 and Map 13–1970.

Chamney, T. P., 1971, Tertiary and Cretaceous biostratigraphic divisions in the Reindeer D-27 bore-hole, Mackenzie River delta: Canada Geol. Survey Paper 70–30.

Crickmay, C. H., 1967, A note on the term bocanne: Am. Jour. Sci., v. 265, no. 7, p. 626–627.

Hornal, R. W., *et al.,* 1970, Preliminary results of gravity surveys over the Mackenzie basin and Beaufort Sea: Earth Physics Br. Gravity Map Ser., Map No. 119.

Jeletzky, J. A., 1958, Uppermost Jurassic and Cretaceous rocks of the Aklavik Range, northeastern Richardson Mountains, Northwest Territories: Canada Geol. Survey Paper 58–2.

—— 1960, Uppermost Jurassic and Cretaceous rocks, east flank of Richardson Mountains between Stony Creek and lower Donna River, Northwest Territories: Canada Geol. Survey Paper 59–14.

—— 1962, Pre-Cretaceous Richardson Mountains trough—its place in the tectonic framework of arctic Canada and its bearing on some geosynclinal concepts: Royal Soc. Canada Trans., 3d ser., v. 56, sec. 3.

Mountjoy, E. W., 1967, Upper Cretaceous and Tertiary stratigraphy, northern Yukon Territory and northwestern District of Mackenzie: Canada Geol. Survey Paper 66–16.

Thorsteinsson, R., and E. T. Tozer, 1962, Banks, Victoria and Stefansson Islands, Arctic Archipelago: Canada Geol. Survey Mem. 330.

—— and —— 1970, Geology of the Arctic Archipelago, *in* Geology and economic minerals of Canada: Canada Geol. Survey Econ. Geology Rept. No. 1, p. 548–590.

Wanless, R. K., *et al.,* 1965, Age determinations and geological studies, Part 1—Isotopic ages, Report 5: Canada Geol. Survey Paper 64–17.

Yorath, C. J., *et al.,* 1969, Geology of the eastern part of the Northern Interior and Arctic coastal plains, Northwest Territories: Canada Geol. Survey Paper 68–27.

Young, F. G., 1971, Mesozoic stratigraphic studies, northern Yukon Territory and northwestern District of Mackenzie, *in* Report of activities, April to October, 1970: Canada Geol. Survey Paper 71–1, pt. A.

Offshore Areas of Canadian Arctic Islands—Geology Based on Geophysical Data[1]

S. A. BOURNE[2] and A. E. PALLISTER[3]

Calgary, Alberta, Canada

Abstract Surface geologic exposures in the Arctic Islands are excellent. However, the sparse subsurface information from boreholes is limited to only a few of the islands.

Geology of the inter-island areas is speculative. Preliminary interpretations based on erosion and isostatic readjustments after the melting of the continental ice sheet may have to be revised after a review of geophysical data which now are becoming available. Block faulting with associated horst and graben development has become a conservative structural interpretation, whereas consideration of rift and drift hypotheses has gained popularity.

Recently obtained reconnaissance data indicate the possibility that an entirely different geologic section exists offshore. This conclusion is based on regional geophysical data obtained by government and industry. Magnetic and gravity surveys have covered much of the Arctic Archipelago. Seismic profiles in marine areas of the southern Arctic Islands indicate a wide range of large structures; refraction probes are useful in defining the velocity, and thus the possible geologic age, of these sedimentary units.

INTRODUCTION

The Canadian Arctic Islands have allured the venturous for more than 300 years, and even in our own time we have seen men in quest of a northwest passage.

Continental borderlands have assumed major importance in the search for oil throughout the world since the development of a concept that the offshore geologic section is more than just an extension of the onshore section. In many places, continental shelves contain completely different, very thick sedimentary sections. Integration of the large volume of data compiled by the Canadian government with newly-acquired data from industry stimulates renewed interest in the offshore and inter-island areas of the Arctic Archipelago.

The Canadian Arctic Islands are on the north flank of the North American craton. Major extensions of the Precambrian basement are known as the Minto arch in the southwest and the Boothia uplift in the south (Fig. 1). Ha-

chured areas on Figure 1 indicate Paleozoic strata composing the stable shelf and trough of the Franklinian geosyncline. The thickest part of this early depositional sequence along the north edge of the Paleozoic outcrop has been compressed and faulted by late Paleozoic deformation. Rocks in most of the exposed area of the Franklinian geosyncline (Kerr, 1967a) are of the miogeosynclinal suite. Eugeosynclinal strata are exposed in northern Ellesmere Island (Trettin, 1967).

The central portion of the Arctic Islands has been called the "Sverdrup basin." This depositional basin is about 700 mi (1,100 km) long and 250 mi (400 km) wide; it contains Mesozoic and Cenozoic sedimentary sequences.

In the Paleozoic Franklinian geosyncline, a sequence of about 40,000 ft (12,000 m) of carbonate rock, shale, and some sandstone is present. An additional 40,000 ft of shales and sandstones is present in the Mesozoic Sverdrup basin.

Excellent geologic exposures facilitated airphotographic mapping of the islands, and the required field mapping was obtained during the short summer seasons. Aeromagnetic, gravity, and seismic surveys of the onshore areas followed, and, although logistics are difficult, good results generally were obtained.

Ice cover has delayed mapping of the offshore areas of the Arctic Archipelago. The southern half of the area is accessible by ship for up to 3 months of the year, whereas perennial ice conditions have virtually blocked access to offshore portions of the Sverdrup basin. Gravity surveys are possible across ice-covered areas, but dependable electronic-positioning systems are required.

Several hypotheses have been advanced to help predict the offshore geology of the Arctic Archipelago.

1. *Erosional drainage systems.* Many of the inter-island areas display a pattern of channels reminiscent of dendritic drainage (Fortier and Morley, 1956). Later modification of this system by valley glaciers produced the present U-

[1] Manuscript received, September 20, 1971.

[2] Pallister and Associates, Ltd; present affiliation: Phoenix Ventures Ltd.

[3] Kenting Ltd.

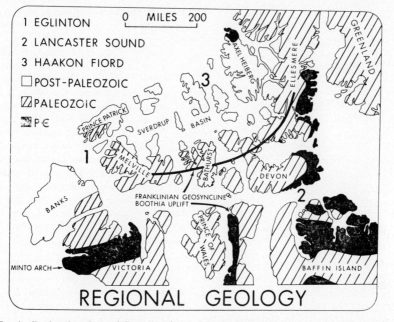

FIG. 1—Regional geology of Canadian Arctic Islands. Patterns indicate outcropping rocks.

shaped transverse profiles of most of the channels.

2. *Postglacial rebound of the islands.* Raised beaches are found throughout the Arctic Islands, and, if considered in conjunction with the rise in sea level since Pleistocene time (Craig and Fyles, 1960), this rebound could be a factor in explaining the presence of escarpments along many of the islands.

3. *Epeirogenic movements.* Movements involving subsidence and drowning of the region have been used to explain the presence of steep submarine valleys and submerged watersheds (Pelletier, 1966).

4. *Structural deformation.* The linearity and steepness of many of the sea cliffs and their abrupt submarine continuation seem to suggest fault-line scarps.

5. *Rift and drift.* Recent discussions involving the separation of Greeland from the Arctic Islands (Kerr, 1967b, c) and the opening of the Canadian basin (Tailleur and Brosgé, 1970) allow even further speculation regarding the structure of the islands.

THREE EXAMPLES FROM OFFSHORE

Three offshore sites have been selected for study (Fig. 1), and a multidisciplinary approach has been followed even where limited data are available. The sites are:

1. Eglinton Island, where a possible graben has been suggested;

2. Lancaster Sound, south of the linear coast of Devon Island, which initiated the speculation that a half-graben exists offshore;

3. Haakon Fiord, along the east coast of Ellef Ringnes Island, which is an area where piercement structures are common.

Eglinton Island

On Eglinton Island, the outcropping Cretaceous rocks dip gently southwestward (Fig. 2). Linear coastlines and channels separate Eglinton Island from adjacent Paleozoic rocks. On Melville Island, Paleozoic carbonate rocks and sandstones have been folded to form the east-west-trending Parry Islands fold belt. West of Eglinton Island, on Prince Patrick Island, there are more Paleozoic outcrops; however, the trend of the Prince Patrick uplift is north-south.

Tozer and Thorsteinsson (1964) stated: "The strike of the Mesozoic rocks on Eglinton Island is unrelated to that of Mesozoic beds on surrounding islands and it seems probable that the island is an isolated fault block, regionally depressed by faulting in Crozier Channel and Kellett Strait. Eglinton Island thus seems to constitute a small graben."

The presence of this Mesozoic sequence between Paleozoic exposures allows speculation that, even where no islands are present, the off-

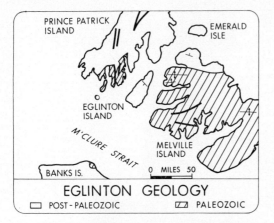

FIG. 2—Geology of Eglinton and neighboring islands. Ages of outcropping rocks are indicated.

shore could represent submerged Mesozoic grabens. Linear coastlines on the north side of M'Clure Strait and the north coast of Banks Island could be indicative of a graben within M'Clure Strait.

Figure 3 is part of an interpretation of the early reconnaissance program covering the Arctic Islands; only about 500 mi (800 km) of the aeromagnetic survey (Gregory et al., 1961) was within the area of interest.

In general, where Paleozoic rocks crop out, the depth to magnetic basement is 20,000 ft (6,100 m) or less. An additional 5,000 ft (1,500 m) of section is present in the zone extending from Prince Patrick Island to Banks Is-

land. In the Sverdrup basin, on the north, depth to basement is approximately 30,000 ft (9,100 m).

Gravity data have been obtained onshore north of M'Clure Strait. The negative Bouguer feature (Fig. 4) on Eglinton Island reaches a value of −17.5 mgal. On Melville Island, some of the gravity highs in the east-west trend have values as high as 19 mgal. The negative feature on Eglinton could represent a 7,000-ft (2,100 m) thickening of the low-density section which is above the Paleozoic carbonate rocks.

An integrated evaluation of geology with reconnaissance aeromagnetic and gravity data provides fairly good evidence that Eglinton Island is, in fact, a graben. However, its relation to water-covered areas in the Arctic Islands remains to be proved.

Lancaster Sound

Linear shorelines bordering Lancaster Sound (Fig. 5) are apparent. Glacial ice is present in this area, and fiords are cut into Devon Island.

The Paleozoic formations on Devon dip generally westward into what has been called the "Jones-Lancaster basin." Dips along the south shore of the sound are generally north and west.

Detailed contouring of all available bathymetric data (Fig. 6) has provided yet another tool to offshore explorationists. This oversimplified map indicates how abruptly the water depth increases to 1,500 ft (450 m) along the north side of the sound. On Devon Island there is little or no beach, and topographic relief is in the order of 2,500 ft (760 m). Soundings of more

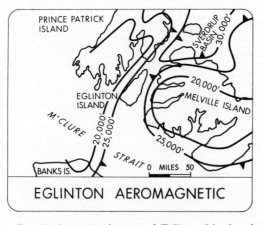

FIG. 3—Aeromagnetic map of Eglinton Island and vicinity. Contour values are depth to basement (thickness of sedimentary rocks).

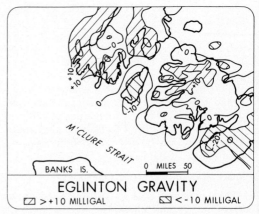

FIG. 4—Onshore gravity data, Eglinton Island and vicinity.

than 2,600 ft (800 m) were noted south of the east-west sill located at the mouth of Admiralty Inlet (northern Baffin Island). Such sills are indicative of glacial activity.

The contour interval of the original work is 100 ft (30 m). Principles applied to the interpretation of surface maps have been used in interpreting the bathymetric data. Steep submarine scarps are used as indications of faulting. Lineaments on the floor of the sound provide information useful in plotting other structural axes, such as anticlines and synclines. Collectively, the bathymetric data indicate Lancaster Sound to be a complex graben.

A sea-magnetometer program conducted in this area (Barrett, 1966) has provided another clue to the meaning of Lancaster Sound. Barrett proposed the presence of a half-graben having its major displacement along the south coast of Devon Island (Fig. 5). An aeromagnetic profile across this same area (Gregory *et al.*, 1961) displays an abrupt change between Devon Island and the offshore, and a slightly less marked change onto Baffin Island.

Refraction seismic methods have proved valuable for use across ice-covered areas such as the Sverdrup basin. The recently perfected sonobuoy technique, in conjunction with marine programs, helps to define seismic velocities (Fig. 7). For the sonobuoy refraction probe, an air-gun energy source (300 cu. in.) was used, and distances were determined from water-break arrival times.

A preliminary interpretation has identified the 22,000-ft/sec (6,700 m/sec) layer as the

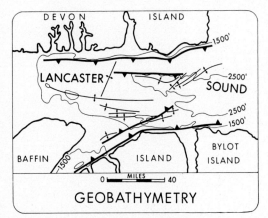

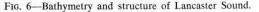

GEOBATHYMETRY

Fig. 6—Bathymetry and structure of Lancaster Sound.

top of the Paleozoic carbonate rocks; such an interpretation is in agreement with other work in the Arctic Islands (Hobson and Overton, 1967). A 4,800-ft (1,460 m) section of relatively low-velocity strata has been interpreted to be present at the site of this particular probe (Fig. 7).

Figure 8 is an example of single-trace reconnaissance seismic data. Because stacking and common-depth-point techniques were not used, the water-bottom multiple remained strong. However, in areas of marked structure it is possible to correlate true reflections through the noise. The upper marker is easily correlated at the south end of this section to the point where it intercepts the first water-bottom impulse. From this point, the multiples can be used to extend the correlation. In this case, the first and second reverberations were correlated, and segments of the true reflector were identified by working backward.

North dip on the reflector is consistent with the half-graben suggested by the sea-magnetometer data. The profile approaches the coast of Devon Island, as indicated by the abrupt shoaling, but the geologic section appears to continue to dip northward.

Figures 9 and 10 form a continuous profile of the area farther south in Lancaster Sound. A major block fault is noted on the south (Fig. 9), whereas continued north dip and a slight anticlinal flexure are evident farther north (Fig. 10).

One other point of interest regarding the seismic data is the change in noise level in the water zone. This change was caused by the variation in ice conditions—from heavy ice in the south to open water in the north.

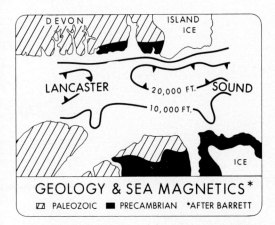

GEOLOGY & SEA MAGNETICS*

☒ PALEOZOIC   ■ PRECAMBRIAN   *AFTER BARRETT

Fig. 5—Geology and sea magnetics (after Barrett, 1966) of Lancaster Sound area. Ages of outcropping rocks are indicated. Contour values are depth to basement.

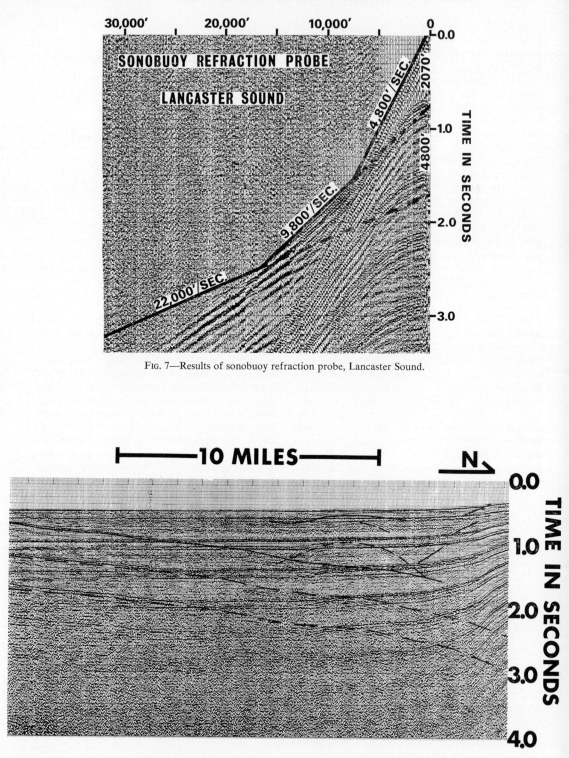

FIG. 7—Results of sonobuoy refraction probe, Lancaster Sound.

FIG. 8—Single-trace reflection seismic data, north part of Lancaster Sound.

├──────10 MILES──────┤   N↘

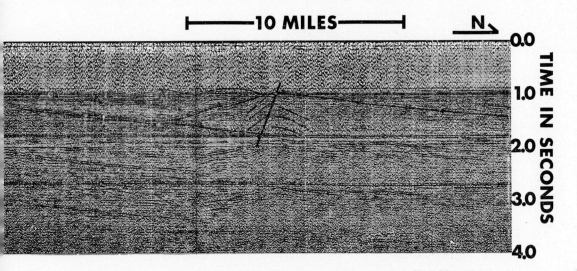

TIME IN SECONDS

Fig. 9—Single-trace reflection seismic data, Lancaster Sound; south of profile in Figure 8.

The bathymetric, sea-magnetometer, and seismic data provide strong evidence that geologic conditions are different in Lancaster Sound than onshore. The possibility of a graben is the most likely; however, rifting cannot be ruled out.

Haakon Fiord

Approximately 70 piercement features are known in the Sverdrup basin, and several other domes are present in the Paleozoic Franklinian geosyncline.

Ellef Ringnes and Amund Ringnes Islands contain five large piercements (Fig. 11). The exposed cores of these structures are composed of gypsum and anhydrite. Salt has not been found in any of these domes. Permian and Pennsylvanian evaporites are likely the mother beds; however, thick Ordovician-Silurian salt was found in the Bathurst Island well 200 mi (320 km) to the south. The Dumbbells domes, in the southwest corner of the study area, have a combined surface area of more than 50 sq mi (130 sq km; Gould and de Mille, 1964).

├──────10 MILES──────┤   N↘

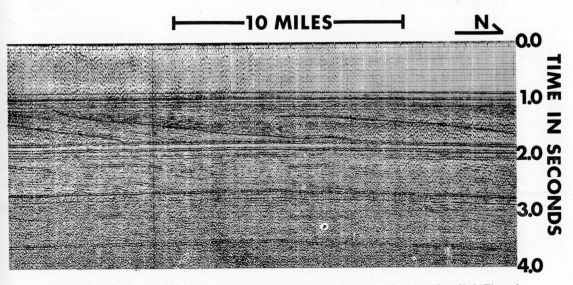

TIME IN SECONDS

Fig. 10—Single-trace reflection seismic data, Lancaster Sound; northward continuation of profile in Figure 9.

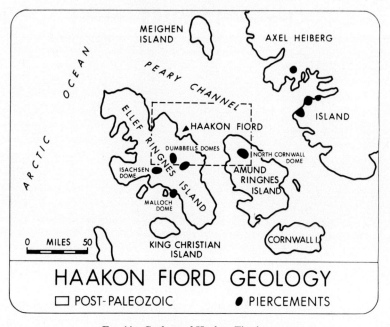

FIG. 11—Geology of Haakon Fiord area.

Geobathymetric interpretation of this area indicates an anomalous shoal offshore from Haakon Fiord along the east side of Ellef Ringnes Island (Fig. 12). The interpretation by Horn (1963) provides an interesting contour option by connecting the fiord to the closed deep. This interpretation has the effect of deflecting the glacially modified stream valley around the south side of the bathymetric shoal.

Figure 13 shows areas of high magnetic intensity that are associated with known domes. Four areas of high intensity are present offshore, one of which is a very pronounced feature coincident with the geobathymetric anomaly offshore from Haakon Fiord. Because of a gap in the magnetic coverage, the rather broad feature contoured in the southern part of the area near Amund Ringnes Island is speculative.

The magnetic character of the diapirs in the Arctic was noted early (Gregory et al., 1961). Igneous rocks, present as inclusions in the caprock or as ring dikes, have been identified as the cause of this unusual response.

A negative Bouguer gravity anomaly over the Dumbbells domes (Fig. 14) indicates the presence of low-density piercement material. Although only gypsum and anhydrite are present at the surface of the domes, it may be assumed from the gravity results that salt forms the core (Blackadar, 1963).

The three negative features present offshore are all coincident with aeromagnetic anomalies. The absence of a gravity feature near Amund Ringnes overlying the fourth aeromagnetic "high" can be attributed to a lack of data in that area; there are only about 30 stations in all of the offshore area shown on the map.

There appears to be no apparent difference in the nature of piercements offshore as compared with the onshore. The general northeast-southwest alignment of the piercements must

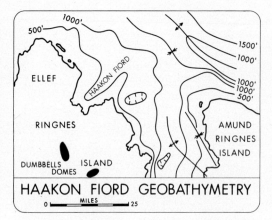

FIG. 12—Geobathymetry of Haakon Fiord area.

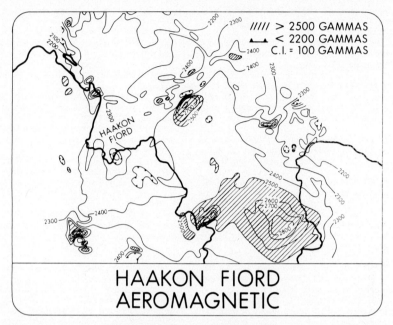

//// > 2500 GAMMAS
⌐◣ < 2200 GAMMAS
C.I. = 100 GAMMAS

HAAKON FIORD
AEROMAGNETIC

FIG. 13—Aeromagnetic map of Haakon Fiord area. Contours are from Geological Survey of Canada (Canada Geol. Survey, 1965a, b, c).

have broad structural significance, because, on the basis of aeromagnetic data, this trend extends southwest to the Sabine Peninsula.

CONCLUSIONS

Eglinton Island appears to be a graben; this conclusion is substantiated both by gravity and magnetic data and by surface mapping.

Lancaster Sound is not a simple erosional channel. Seismic data support the magnetic and geobathymetric interpretations, which indicate block faulting and graben development (Buckley, 1963).

Haakon Fiord is an area of piercement structures; the offshore area shows geologic continuity with the piercement environment seen onshore.

In Arctic exploration, use of the conceptual model of multiple working hypotheses and the multidisciplinary technique, as illustrated in these three examples, will certainly reap definitive results.

The offshore area of the Arctic Islands has petroleum potential, as is shown by the preliminary work and by the recent significant gas discoveries.

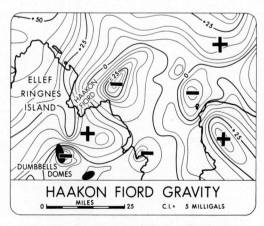

HAAKON FIORD GRAVITY

0 |————— MILES —————| 25   C.I. = 5 MILLIGALS

FIG. 14—Gravity map of Haakon Fiord area.

REFERENCES

Barrett, D. L., 1966, Lancaster shipborne magnetometer survey: Canadian Jour. Earth Sci., v. 3, no. 2, p. 223–235.
Blackadar, R. G., 1963, Dumbbells dome, in Y. O. Fortier, et al., Geology of the north-central part of the Arctic Archipelago . . . : Canada Geol. Survey Mem. 320.
Buckley, D. E., 1963, Bottom sediments of Lancaster Sound, District of Franklin: Univ. Western Ontario, London, M.S. thesis.

Canada Geological Survey, 1965a, Polar Continental Shelf project, District of Franklin: Geophys. Paper 1718, Sheet 69 F/NE, scale 1:126, 720.

—— 1965b, Polar Continental Shelf project, District of Franklin: Geophys. Paper 1719, Sheets 69 E/NE and 69 E/NW, scale 1:126,720.

—— 1965c, Polar Continental Shelf project, District of Franklin: Geophys. Paper 1721, Sheet 69 G/NW and part of 69 G/NE and 79 H/NE, scale 1:126,720.

Craig, B. G., and J. G. Fyles, 1960, Pleistocene geology of Arctic Canada: Canada Geol. Survey Paper 60-10.

Fortier, Y. O., and L. W. Morley, 1956, Geological unity of the Arctic Islands: Royal Soc. Canada Trans., Ser. 3, v. 50, Canadian Comm. Oceanography, p. 3-12.

—— et al., 1963, Geology of the north-central part of the Arctic Archipelago, Northwest Territories (Operation Franklin): Canada Geol. Survey Mem. 320.

Gould, D. B., and G. de Mille, 1964, Piercement structures in the Arctic Islands: Bull. Canadian Petroleum Geology, v. 12, p. 719-753.

—— and —— 1968, Piercement structures in Canadian Arctic Islands, in J. Braunstein and G. D. O'Brien, eds., Diapirism and diapirs: Am. Assoc. Petroleum Geologists Mem. 8, p. 183-214.

Gregory, A. F., M. E. Bower, and L. W. Morley, 1961, Geological interpretation of aerial magnetic and radiometric profiles, Arctic Archipelago, Northwest Territories: Canada Geol. Survey Bull. 73.

Hobson, G. D., and A. Overton, 1967, A seismic section of the Sverdrup basin, Canadian Arctic Islands, in A. W. Musgrave, ed., Seismic reflection prospecting: Soc. Exploration Geophysicists, p. 550-562.

Horn, D. R., 1963, Marine geology, Peary Channel, District of Franklin, Polar Continental Shelf project: Canada Geol. Survey Paper 63-11.

Kerr, J. W., 1967a, The Franklinian miogeosyncline and adjacent central stable region, Arctic Canada, in International symposium on the Devonian System: Calgary, Alberta Soc. Petroleum Geologists, v. 1, p. 677-692.

—— 1967b, Nares submarine rift valley and the relative rotation of North Greenland: Bull. Canadian Petroleum Geology, v. 15, no. 4, p. 483-520.

—— 1967c, A submerged continental remnant beneath the Labrador Sea: Earth and Planetary Sci. Letters, v. 2, no 4, p. 283-289.

Pelletier, B. R., 1966, Development of submarine physiography in the Canadian Arctic and its relation to crustal movements, in G. D. Garland, ed., Continental drift: Royal Soc. Canada Spec. Pub. No. 9, p. 77-101.

Tailleur, I. L., and W. P. Brosgé, 1970, Tectonic history of northern Alaska, in Proceedings of the Geological Seminar on the North Slope of Alaska: Los Angeles, Pacific Sec. Am. Assoc. Petroleum Geologists.

Thorsteinsson, R., and E. T. Tozer, 1960, Summary account of structural history of Canadian Arctic Archipelago since Precambrian time: Canada Geol. Survey Paper 60-7.

Tozer, E. T., and R. Thorsteinsson, 1964, Western Queen Elizabeth Islands, Arctic Archipelago: Canada Geol. Survey Mem. 332.

Trettin, H. P., 1967, The Franklinian eugeosyncline, in International symposium on the Devonian System: Calgary, Alberta Soc. Petroleum Geologists, v. 1, p. 693-701.

Early Paleozoic Evolution of Northern Parts of Canadian Arctic Archipelago[1]

H. P. TRETTIN[2]

Calgary, Alberta, Canada

Abstract A geosyncline occupied northern parts of the Arctic Islands in late Proterozoic time. It received sediments from the continent and deepened in a northerly direction. A northwestern belt, which included northernmost Ellesmere Island and the present shelf off Ellesmere and Axel Heiberg Islands, underwent orogeny in latest Proterozoic or Cambrian time. The orogen behaved as an intermittently rising geanticline and remained a site of volcanism, plutonism, and metamorphism from Cambrian to Devonian time.

Sediments derived from the geanticline accumulated in a clastic basin on its southeast side. The basin was flanked on the southeast by a subsiding carbonate shelf, in turn grading southward to a stable carbonate platform.

Three phases of sedimentation are recognized in the clastic basin in northeastern Ellesmere Island: (1) Middle to Upper Cambrian(?) post-tectonic deltaic deposition; (2) Early to Middle Ordovician deep-water deposition of starved-basin type (radiolarian chert, graptolitic shale, etc.); and (3) late Middle Ordovician to Middle Silurian deep-water deposition of flysch type (graywacke, shale, etc.).

The trough must have formed by subsidence of the continental crust rather than by sea-floor spreading, because the deep-water strata lie on shallow-water strata and not on volcanic rocks. The trough, which was separated from subaerial parts of the geanticline by a shelf on which carbonate, clastic, and volcanic materials were deposited, expanded until about mid-Silurian time, then migrated southeast, ahead of the southeast-migrating geanticline. The southeast flank of the trough, characterized by graptolitic shales and limestones, has been traced from northwestern Greenland to northwestern Melville Island. There, starved-basin conditions persisted from Early Ordovician to Early Devonian time.

A north-trending belt in the central islands, extending from the stable platform to the geanticline, was elevated in the Early Devonian. The uplift, which was basement controlled, reflects Precambrian basement trends unrelated to the early Paleozoic basin configuration.

An orogeny of the entire northern regions, locally accompanied by intrusion of quartz diorite, occurred in Middle Devonian to Mississippian time. Deformation and uplift proceeded from northwest to southeast.

INTRODUCTION

During the late Proterozoic and early Paleozoic, the Arctic Islands were the site of a mobile belt that may have extended from northern

[1] Manuscript received, September 20, 1971. Published by permission of the Director, Geological Survey of Canada.

[2] Geological Survey of Canada.

The writer is indebted for fossil identification to B. S. Norford, R. Thorsteinsson, A. J. Boucot, J. G. Johnson, J. W. Kerr, and A. R. Ormiston.

Greenland to Siberia (Churkin, 1969). This belt, extending from the craton on the southeast to the core gneisses of the orogen on the northwest, is exposed in cross section in eastern Ellesmere Island. The history of the southern part of the belt has been known for some time (Christie, 1967; Kerr, 1967a, b c; 1968; Thorsteinsson *in* Douglas, 1970, p. 552–568), but the history of the northern part, which is highly deformed and generally poor in fossils, has become apparent in outline only during the last few years. The purpose of this paper is to present a brief synthesis of the results of this recent work, both published and unpublished.

MAJOR SEQUENCES OF ARCTIC ISLANDS

The rocks (and unconsolidated sediments) of the Arctic Islands can be assigned to five major sequences that are separated by major unconformities (Douglas, 1970, Chaps. IV, X, XII). The sequences, in descending order, are:

1. Upper Tertiary and Quaternary unconsolidated sediments;

2. Upper Mississippian to lower Tertiary sedimentary and volcanic rocks deposited in the Sverdrup basin;

3. Sedimentary, metamorphic, and igneous rocks collectively ranging in age from late Proterozoic to Late Devonian and formed in two major tectonic provinces: (a) a mobile belt composed of the Franklinian geosyncline and the Pearya geanticline, and (b) the Arctic platform (Douglas, 1970, p. 3), a division of the Central Stable region of North America (The record of the geosyncline begins in the late Proterozoic rocks, that of the platform in late Early Cambrian strata, and that of the geanticline in approximately Middle Cambrian rocks.);

4. Upper Proterozoic sedimentary and volcanic successions of the Canadian shield; and

5. Lower Proterozoic and Archean crystalline terranes of the Canadian shield formed in the Churchill and Bear provinces.

RECORD OF MOBILE BELT

Late Proterozoic–Early Cambrian

The late Proterozoic and Early Cambrian record of the mobile belt is limited to southeastern Ellesmere Island and is insufficient for a regional interpretation that includes northern Axel Heiberg and Ellesmere Islands. In southeastern Ellesmere Island, more than 10,000 ft (3,050 m) of clastic and carbonate sediment was deposited in paralic and shelf environments (Kerr, 1967c). The clastic strata of the Ellesmere Group (lowermost Cambrian) increase in thickness and decrease in grain size in a northwesterly direction; these factors indicate that the sediments were derived from the craton on the southeast and were deposited in a basin, the axis of which lay to the northwest. It is unknown, however, whether that basin was a one-sided geosyncline (comparable to the present Atlantic margin) or a two-sided geosyncline bordered on the northwest by a geanticline, as was the case from Middle Cambrian time onward. If the geanticline already existed, it had no influence on sedimentation in southeastern Ellesmere Island.

Middle Cambrian–Late Devonian

The Middle Cambrian to Late Devonian record also is incomplete, but it is sufficient to outline the internal organization of the mobile belt. This organization is complex in the northern regions; it becomes intelligible only if (1) a clear distinction is made between regional subdivisions based on tectonics, deposition, and paleophysiography (see Fig. 7), and (2) the substantial shift, in the course of time, of the boundaries between these various subdivisions is considered.

Tectonic Divisions

Franklinian geosyncline—The Franklinian geosyncline was a site of pronounced, almost continuous subsidence from late Proterozoic to Late Devonian time. It was bordered on the northwest by the Pearya geanticline and on the southeast by the Arctic platform (Douglas, 1970, p. 3). The northwestern limit of the geosyncline is here defined as the limit of deposition during any given time interval. Two different criteria have been used to delineate the southeastern limit: the edge of folding and the so-called "hinge," a line north (or northwest) of which the section thickens in a marked and progressive manner. The hinge is the preferable criterion, but it has been delineated only in southeastern Ellesmere Island (Kerr, 1967a, b).

The most important tectonic element within the geosyncline is the Hazen trough—an elongate, nonvolcanic submarine basin which existed approximately from Early Ordovician to early Middle Devonian time. This feature, previously referred to informally as the "axial trough of the geosyncline" (Trettin, 1967,

1970), is named for the Hazen Plateau, where it is best exposed (Trettin, 1971b). The trough can be traced from northern Greenland to northwestern Melville Island. It not only represents a tectonic and paleophysiographic feature, but it also is a sedimentary subprovince (Fig. 7).

Pearya geanticline—The Pearya geanticline was an intermittently rising belt that provided most of the terrigenous sediments to the Franklinian geosyncline (Trettin, 1971b). The geanticline probably was located in the present offshore region during most of early Paleozoic time, but, during some time intervals, it extended into northern Axel Heiberg and Ellesmere Islands. In the record of the northernmost regions, these time intervals are marked not only by unconformities, but also by granitic intrusions and metamorphism, indicating that the uplifts were related to magmatic activity at depth.

The name "Pearya" is adapted from Schuchert (1923; Fig. 1), who correctly inferred that the source of the clastic sediments of the Franklinian geosyncline was on the north, mainly in the present offshore region, but also included the metamorphic complex of northernmost Ellesmere Island. Because the metamorphic complex was then considered Archean owing to lithologic similarities with the Canadian shield, Schuchert regarded Pearya as an outlier of the shield that was tectonically active in Paleozoic time. It is now known, however, that the metamorphic complex is mainly (or entirely) early Paleozoic, and Pearya therefore is interpreted as an orogenic belt (or geanticline) that rose out of the Franklinian geosyncline in Cambrian or late Proterozoic time.

The term "geanticline" is chosen because it is the antonym of geosyncline and because it emphasizes similarities with the Coast and Omineca geanticlines of the western cordillera (Wheeler, 1967). The term was first applied to this region by Ziegler (1969, p. 12–14), who showed the narrow, elongate "Innuitian geanticline" on the present continental shelf in his paleotectonic maps for the Late Silurian to Middle Devonian. Ziegler's concept is here retained, but the name "Pearya" is preferred because of its priority.

Sedimentary provinces—Two major sedimentary provinces are recognized—a northerly clastic province and a southerly carbonate province. The clastic province is characterized mainly by clastic sediments derived from the Pearya geanticline, but it also contains carbon-

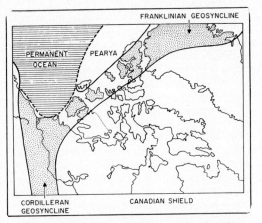

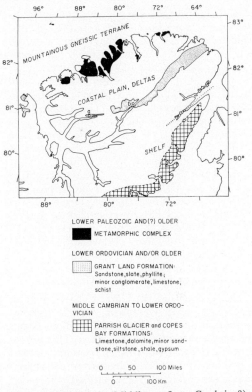

FIG. 1—Geologic framework of Arctic Canada according to Schuchert. Redrafted from part of Schuchert's (1923) Figure 3.

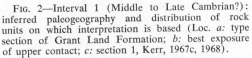

FIG. 2—Interval 1 (Middle to Late Cambrian?): inferred paleogeography and distribution of rock units on which interpretation is based (Loc. *a:* type section of Grant Land Formation; *b:* best exposure of upper contact; *c:* section 1, Kerr, 1967c, 1968).

ate, volcanic, and chert beds. The carbonate province is characterized mainly by carbonate rocks, but it also contains evaporites and clastic strata. The clastic sediments were derived from basement uplifts, from the craton, and, to a minor extent, from the Pearya geanticline.

These two sedimentary provinces do not correspond to the tectonic divisions outlined. For example, from Middle Cambrian to Middle Devonian time, the clastic province occupied the northern parts of the Franklinian geosyncline, and the carbonate province occupied the southern parts of the geosyncline plus the entire Arctic platform. In Middle and Late Devonian time, the clastic province occupied the entire geosyncline and extended into adjacent parts of the Arctic platform; the record of the carbonate province during this interval is not preserved.

PATTERNS OF SEDIMENTARY AND TECTONIC DEVELOPMENT

In describing the highly complex history of the northern regions, it is convenient to distinguish the predominant and subordinate patterns of development. The predominant pattern is evident in the entire area through most of the interval considered; subordinate interfering patterns of a different nature are more restricted in extent, both laterally and vertically.

The predominant pattern reflects intermittent uplifts and repeated advances and retreats of the Pearya geanticline, as well as the subsidence, initial expansion, and subsequent southeastward shift of the Hazen trough. These vertical and lateral movements resulted in south-

westerly to westerly depositional and structural trends which are approximately parallel with the present continental margin, and probably are related to its development.

The interfering patterns, which represent basement uplifts and local rifting, are related to divergent trends in the Precambrian crystalline basement.

Predominant Pattern

The development of the predominant pattern is reflected mainly in the record of the clastic province. Four intervals are distinguished that differed significantly in sedimentation and related tectonism.

Interval 1: Middle to Late Cambrian(?)

Clastic Province

The clastic province was limited to the interior of northern Ellesmere Island and northernmost Axel Heiberg Island, and sedimentation was predominantly deltaic (Fig. 2). The record of this depositional interval is represented by the Grant Land Formation (Trettin, 1971b), which consists of more than 3,600 ft (1,100 m) of slightly metamorphosed, originally quartzose and feldspathic sandstones; red-, green-, and gray-weathering siltstones and shales; and lesser amounts of pebble conglomerate and carbonate rocks. The Grant Land Formation is not fossiliferous, and the tentative assignment of interval 1 to the Middle and Late Cambrian is based on (1) the occurrence of clastic impurities similar to the sediments of the Grant Land Formation in Middle Cambrian and younger strata of the carbonate province (Parrish Glacier Formation and lower 1,050 ft [325 m] of Copes Bay Formation at loc. *c*, Fig. 2; Kerr, 1967c, p. 48; 1968, p. 65), and (2) the occurrence of Lower Ordovician graptolites in the strata of interval 2.

Inferences About Pearya Geanticline

The sediments of the Grant Land Formation probably were derived from gneissic terranes located on the north coast of Ellesmere Island and in the present offshore region. This provenance is inferred from facies relations, detrital mineralogy, and a few paleocurrent determinations. The source terrane probably included parts of the metamorphic complex of northern Ellesmere Island, but not necessarily all of it, because later phases of metamorphism are known to have occurred. The sedimentology of the Grant Land Formation is the earliest indirect indication of the existence of the Pearya geanticline. The earliest direct evidence from the metamorphic belt itself includes a K-Ar age determination of 465 ± 19 m.y. (Wanless, 1969) and an unconformity northwest of M'Clintock Inlet. The unconformity is underlain by metamorphic rocks and overlain by upper Middle Ordovician strata (Christie, 1957, p. 14; Trettin, 1969b, p. 16, 20).

Interval 2: Early to Early Middle Ordovician

Clastic Province

Hazen trough—The central and southeastern parts of the clastic province subsided and formed the Hazen trough (Fig. 3), characterized by graptolitic shale, radiolarian(?) chert, redeposited carbonate sediments, and minor amounts of breccia—all slaty and collectively assigned to the Hazen Formation (Trettin, 1971b). The carbonate rocks—which are thinly bedded to laminated, partly graded, and commonly impure—probably originated on adja-

cent shelves and were carried into the trough by turbid flows (Davies, 1968; Wilson, 1969). Sedimentation of solid matter was about 2.5 to 4 times as slow in the trough as it was in the geosynclinal parts of the carbonate province, and the accumulation rate for the entire interval (taking into account Early and early Middle Ordovician compaction) was about 1 cm/10^3 yr ± 50% (Trettin, 1971b).

The fact that the Hazen Formation lies on deltaic rather than volcanic beds shows that the Hazen trough formed by subsidence and not by sea-floor spreading. The subsidence must have been caused by crustal thinning, but the mechanism is not understood. A possible explanation would be a slight amount of crustal extension accompanied by basic intrusion at depth. It is interesting to note that the position of the axis of the Hazen trough during the Ordovician to early Middle Silurian interval coincides approximately with the so-called Alert anomaly, a geomagnetic and electric feature (Fig. 4). The anomaly is thought by some to be caused by a conductor in the lower crust (Praus *et al.*, 1971) that is considered as an ancient geosynclinal or orogenic feature (Niblett and Whitham, 1970).

A model explaining the stratigraphic succession in the central part of the trough (loc. *b*, Fig. 3) is shown in Figure 5. Initially, perhaps, a narrow and shallow furrow developed in which the carbonate and chert-shale facies did not separate. The trough then may have deepened and widened, causing the carbonate sediments to be deposited on the flanks, whereas the chert-shale facies predominated at the bottom.

Northwestern margin of trough—The record of the northwestern part of the clastic province is uncertain because the units tentatively correlated with the Hazen Formation are not fossiliferous. They include parts of the Rens Fiord complex (area A in Fig. 3; Trettin, 1969a); map-unit 2 of the M'Clintock Inlet area (area B; Trettin, 1969b); and the Mount Disraeli Group (Blackadar, 1954; Trettin, 1971c). Apparently, carbonate rocks, volcanic beds, chert, and shale are represented, and it is probable that shelf conditions existed, at least during the intervals of carbonate sedimentation.

Inferences About Pearya Geanticline

The Pearya geanticline, already reduced in relief near the end of interval 1 when the supply of sand ceased, probably formed a low-lying landmass or archipelago in the present off-

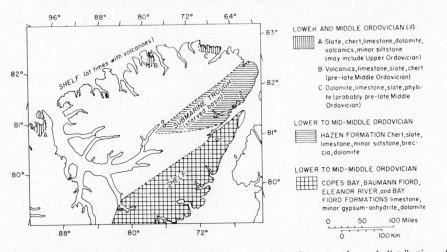

FIG. 3—Interval 2 (Early to early Middle Ordovician): inferred paleogeography and distribution of rock units on which interpretation is based (Loc. *a:* reference section for lower part of Hazen Formation; *b:* type section; *c:* section 1, Kerr, 1967c, 1968).

shore region and supplied only fine-grained sediments to the geosyncline.

Interval 3: Late Middle Ordovician– Early Middle Devonian

Clastic Province

Northwestern margin of Hazen trough—The record of this belt is limited, but available evidence suggests that coastal-plain and shelf environments existed in which clastic and carbonate sediments and, at times, volcanic materials were deposited.

The clastic strata, which range from boulder conglomerate to shale and include many redbeds, represent nonmarine to shallow-marine, predominantly deltaic environments. Typical stratigraphic units are members "A" and "D" of the Cape Discovery Formation, the Taconite River Formation, and map-units 9a and 9c—all exposed in the M'Clintock Inlet area (Trettin, 1969b).

The carbonate beds are limestones and dolomites representing supratidal to outer-shelf environments. Typical units are members "B" and "C" of the Cape Discovery Formation, the Ayles Formation, and the Marvin Formation. Outcrops of the "B" and "C" members and of the Ayles Formation are restricted to M'Clintock Inlet (Trettin, 1969b), but exposures of the Marvin Formation occur in several parts of northern Ellesmere Island (Trettin, 1971b, c). Facies relations and the numerous mixed units indicate that carbonate and clastic deposition commonly were simultaneous.

Volcanic deposition seems to have been limited to the late Middle and early Late Ordovician (Cape Discovery and M'Clintock Formations; Trettin, 1969b) and to an interval in the Late Silurian (Lands Lokk Formation, member "B" [Trettin, 1969a], and unnamed rocks at Phillips Inlet [Trettin, 1971c]).

Hazen trough—The northwestern and southeastern flanks of the Hazen trough contain graptolitic shales, siltstones, and limestones, whereas thick, flyschlike deposits are present at the bottom of the trough.

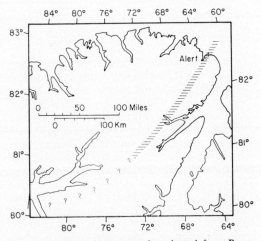

FIG. 4—Trend of Alert anomaly; adapted from Praus, de Laurier, and Law (1971, Fig. 1).

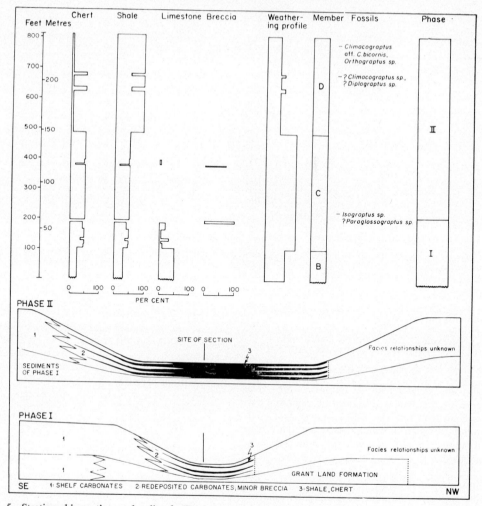

FIG. 5—Stratigraphic section at locality *b* (Fig. 3) and model explaining early development of Hazen trough (not to scale).

Graptolitic facies. Strata of the southeastern flank of the Hazen trough, widely exposed in the Arctic Islands and also in adjacent Greenland (Norford, 1970; 1972), are assigned to the Cape Phillips Formation (Thorsteinsson, 1958; Kerr, 1967a, b). Units of the northwestern flank are exposed only at M'Clintock Inlet, where they have been assigned to member "C" of the Zebra Cliffs Formation (Trettin, 1969b). Deposition in a slope environment is inferred (1) from the occurrence of the graptolitic shales between shelf-type carbonate strata and basin-type flysch—both laterally and, in transgressive successions, vertically—and (2) from the local occurrence of shelf-derived carbonate

boulders and associated slump structures in the Cape Phillips Formation (Trettin, 1971a). The sediments probably were derived from both shelves and deposited on the slopes by turbid flows or from "nepheloid" suspensions (Stanley, 1969, p. 7), which also deposited fine-grained sediments in the basin.

Flysch facies. The flysch facies (for discussion of terminology, see Hsü, 1970), previously assigned in part to the Cape Rawson Group, is now assigned entirely to the Imina Formation (Christie, 1957; Trettin, 1970; 1971b). It is characterized by extensive, alternate beds of calcareous graywacke, calcareous siltstone, and calcareous shale with minor amounts of conglomerate and breccia. Massive bedding and parallel lamination, both graded and non-graded; ripple marks; convolute lamination; and erosional sole markings such as flute casts, longitudinal furrows and ridges, groove marks, *etc.*—all are characteristic primary structures. The indigenous faunas consist of rare trace fossils and graptolites. Shallow-marine faunas occur only in transported carbonate breccias near the margin of the trough. These breccias obvi-

ously were derived from shelf edges above the depositional basin; they thus confirm that the flysch is a deep-water facies.

More than 2,200 determinations of directional structures (Fig. 6; Trettin, 1971a, Fig. 2) indicate that turbid flows entered the Hazen trough from the northwest and were deflected to the southwest at the bottom of the trough. Analogy with modern settings (*e.g.,* southern California; von Rad, 1968) suggests that the

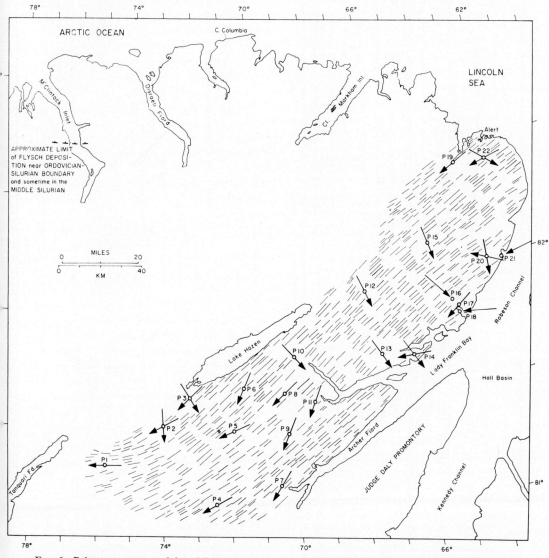

FIG. 6—Paleocurrent map of late Middle Ordovician to Middle Silurian flysch on Hazen Plateau. Lines indicate structural trend of tightly folded flysch; arrows, vector means of paleocurrent determinations; two arrows characterize bimodal distributions (see Trettin, 1970, Fig. 9).

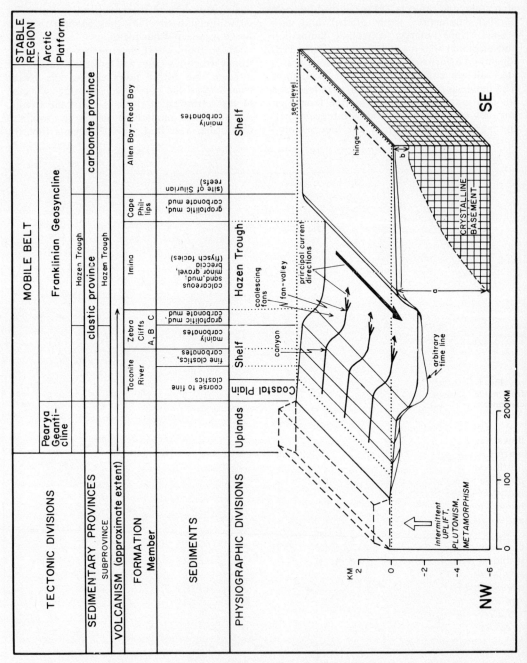

Fig. 7—Conceptual model of mobile belt during Late Ordovician. Northwestern edge of model corresponds to present edge of continental shelf. Assumed crustal shortening of geosynclinal strata is one third (arbitrary). Width of northwestern shelf and coastal plain and depth of trough are uncertain. Upper Ordovician formations occur in vertical order in a transgressive succession; transformation into facies equivalents is based on Walther's law (see Trettin, 1970, Fig. 10). Approximate depth to basement at locality *b* is from Christie (1967) and, at locality *a*, from Kerr (sec. 1, 1967c, 1968). Basement is not exposed at locality *a*, and depth shown is a minimum.

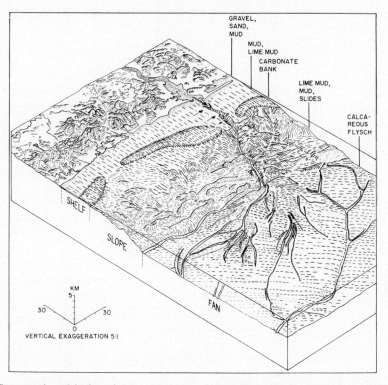

GRAVEL,
SAND,
MUD

MUD,
LIME MUD

CARBONATE
BANK

LIME MUD,
MUD,
SLIDES

CALCA-
REOUS
FLYSCH

SHELF

SLOPE

FAN

KM
5
30   30
0
VERTICAL EXAGGERATION 5:1

FIG. 8—Conceptual model of northwest side of Hazen trough during Late Ordovician. Basic physiography is from model of Astoria fan by Nelson *et al.* (1970); carbonate banks and shelf currents were superimposed, and canyonhead was slightly enlarged, as parts of original canyon have been filled since Pleistocene.

flows were channeled into the trough by submarine canyons which extended across the northwestern slope and shelf (Figs. 7, 8). It is probable that these canyons traversed belts of both carbonate and clastic deposition. Thus, the homogeneous mixing of terrigenous silicates and marine-derived carbonate particles which is characteristic of all sediments of the flysch facies would be explained (Trettin, 1970). The turbid flows probably constructed coalescing fans at the base of the northwestern slope and covered the bottom of the trough with flat-lying strata.

Lateral movements of Hazen trough and related reef formation—Figure 9 shows that the Hazen trough expanded till about mid-Silurian time and then shifted to the southeast. The southeastward expansion was accomplished by progressive downwarping of the northwestern rim of the carbonate province where reefs became established in late Early Silurian (late Llandoverian) time (Norford, 1970, 1972; Kerr, 1967a, Fig. 4). The reefs, which responded to the downwarping by upward

growth, were drowned near the end of the Llandoverian after having attained a relief of about 700 ft (210 m; Norford, 1972). The amount of relief of the reefs serves as a minimum estimate for the depth of the trough.

Inferences About Pearya Geanticline

That the geanticline briefly spread into northern Ellesmere Island in about mid-Ordovician time is inferred from an unconformity northwest of M'Clintock Inlet (IV on Fig. 9). The unconformity is underlain locally by unfossiliferous strata that are considered tentatively to be Lower to lower Middle Ordovician; it is overlain by upper Middle Ordovician strata (Trettin, 1969b, Fig. 14). The orogenic activity was initiated and terminated by volcanism (Trettin, 1969b, Fig. 14); also, it may have been accompanied by granitic intrusion at depth, because the volcanic rocks are siliceous to intermediate in composition.

It can be inferred that the geanticline remained in the offshore region throughout the subsequent interval because all known clastic

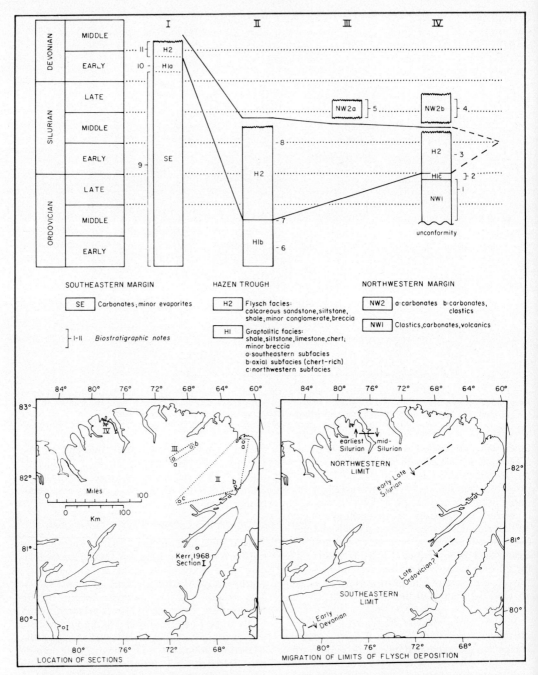

Fig. 9—Age relations of major facies of Hazen trough; note that vertical scale is an arbitrary time scale and not a scale of thickness. Biostratigraphic notes supporting age assignments:

(1) A trimerellid brachiopod in member "A" of Cape Discovery Formation and *Gonioceras* sp. in member "B" indicate that lower part of facies NW1 is late Middle Ordovician (Wildernessian). Upper part of facies NW1, represented by members "A" and "B" of Zebra Cliffs Formation, contains a rich and varied fauna of Late Ordovician (Richmondian) age. It includes *Columnana* n. sp. aff. *C. halysitoides* Troedsson, *Plasmopora lambei* Schuchert, *Calapoecia canadensis* Billings, *Halysites* sp. aff. *H. feildeni* Etheridge, *Troedssonites conspiratus*

units can be traced to the present north coast of Ellesmere Island (Trettin, 1969b, Figs. 2, 5; Trettin, 1970, Fig. 1).

Clastic deposition in the coast and shelf region was nearly continuous, but was interrupted by two brief intervals during which deposition of clean carbonate sediment prevailed. The first interval, in early Late Ordovician time, is represented by the Ayles Formation, and the second interval, in latest Middle to early Late Silurian time, is represented by the lower part of the Marvin Formation. During these intervals the geanticline may have been low in relief or submerged. At least three phases of uplift would be required to account for the clastic sediments below, between, and above the two units.

The terrigenous sediments of this interval can be assigned to three suites of source rocks exposed on the north coast of Ellesmere Island: a metamorphic suite, of supposed Cambrian or earlier age, and chert and volcanic suites, both

of supposed Early to early Middle Ordovician ages. The proportion of the first suite increases upward in the stratigraphic section of the M'Clintock Inlet area (Trettin, 1969b, Fig. 14), indicating that progressively deeper levels were denuded in the Pearya geanticline as a result of the repeated uplifts.

Interval 4: Middle to Late Devonian

Clastic Province

The Hazen trough seems to have been filled in northern Ellesmere Island by about mid-Devonian time, and sedimentation in the clastic province returned to the nonmarine to shallow-marine, predominantly deltaic type prevalent during interval 1. At the same time, the clastic province shifted to the south and southeast in response to two changes—the final advance of the Pearya geanticline and the disappearance of the Hazen trough, which had acted as a sediment trap (Fig. 10). The deposits in the east-

---

←—⫶⫶⫶

(Troedsson), *Sibiriolites, sibiricus* Sokolov, *Palaeofavosites* sp., *Rhynchotrema* sp., *Rostricellula* sp., *Austinella* sp., *etc.* (Trettin, 1969b).

 (2) *Climacograptus latus* Elles and Wood of latest Ordovician age has been found at several levels in facies H1c, which is represented by member "C" of Zebra Cliffs Formation (Trettin, 1969b).

 (3) *Monograptus* aff. *M. priodon* (Bronn) of late Early to Middle Silurian (late Llandoverian to Wenlockian) age occurs in middle part of facies H2, which is represented by Imina Formation (Trettin, 1969b).

 (4) *Atrypella* fauna of latest Middle to early Late Silurian (latest Wenlockian to early Ludlovian) age occurs in middle part of facies NW2b, represented by Marvin Formation. Underlying 90–120 m (300–400 ft) of strata and overlying 80 m (270 ft)—*i.e.*, map-units 9A and 9C, respectively, of Trettin (1969b)—have not yielded diagnostic fossils.

 (5) Fossils of *Atrypella* fauna have been collected from same formation at localities III-a and III-b (Christie, 1964, p. 28; Trettin, 1971b).

 (6) *Tetragraptus* sp. of late Early Ordovician (Arenigian) age is oldest fossil found in facies H1b, represented by Hazen Formation. It occurred several hundred feet above base of unit at locality II-a; thus, basal strata of that unit could be older than Arenigian (Trettin, 1971b).

 (7) *Climacograptus* aff. *C. bicornis* (Hall), probably of late Middle Ordovician (Wildernessian to Barneveldian) age, was found 6 m (20 ft) below base of facies H2 at locality II-b (Trettin, 1971b). Contact between units H1b and H2 is conformable.

 (8) *Monograptus* aff. *M. priodon* (Bronn) of late Llandoverian to Wenlockian age occurs in upper part of facies H2, represented by Imina Formation, at locality II-c. Age of youngest strata of unit in region II is uncertain (Trettin, 1971b).

 (9) Evidence for Early Ordovician to Early Devonian age range of carbonate sequence at southeastern margin of Hazen trough is given by Kerr (1967a, b; 1968).

 (10) *Monograptus* cf. *M. yukonensis* Jackson and Lenz of late Early Devonian age occurs about 15 m (50 ft) above base of facies H1a, represented by Cape Phillips Formation, which at that locality is only about 60 m (200 ft) thick (Trettin, unpub. data, 1970; identified by B. S. Norford and R. Thorsteinsson).

 (11) *Warburgella* sp. and *Schizophoria* sp. of probably Early Devonian age occur in transported breccias both in upper and lower parts of facies H2 (Trettin, unpub. data, 1970; identified by A. R. Ormiston, A. J. Boucot, and J. G. Johnson).

 Locality I in this figure corresponds to section I in Trettin (1971b). Facies boundaries in vicinity of that locality are highly diachronous, and facies H1a and H2 are younger at locality I than anywhere else in region. Note that *Monograptus* cf. *M. bohemicus* (Barrande) locally occurs in facies H2, indicating extension of that unit downward at least into early Late Silurian (early Ludlovian), whereas *Cyrtograptus* sp. and *Monograptus* aff. *M. priodon* (Bronn) locally occur in lower part of facies H1a, indicating extension of that unit downward into late Early or early Middle Silurian (late Llandoverian to Wenlockian; Trettin, 1971a).

ern parts of the archipelago have been assigned to the Bird Fiord and Okse Bay Formations (McLaren, 1963), which together range in age from late Middle to Late Devonian (Givetian to Famennian; see also Kerr, 1967c; Thorsteinsson *in* Douglas, 1970, p. 562–566). These units were folded in approximately Early Mississippian time, and the deformation seems to have occurred above a *décollement* (*i.e.*, without basement involvement), at least in the Parry Islands (Workum, 1965; Temple, 1965).

Inferences About Pearya Geanticline

The Pearya geanticline expanded into northern Axel Heiberg and Ellesmere Islands, where uplift, granitic intrusion, and metamorphism occurred.

Episodes of uplift—A general uplift of the northern regions in mid-Paleozoic time is inferred from an extensive unconformity underlain by strata as young as late Early or Middle Devonian (Svartevaeg Formation) and overlain by strata as old as Viséan (Kerr and Trettin, 1962). Within that broad interval of orogeny, which has been termed the "Ellesmerian orogeny" (Thorsteinsson *in* Douglas, 1970, p. 551 and Chart IV), two phases of deformation can be distinguished. A Middle to Late Devonian phase is suggested by the provenance of the clastic sediments of interval 4, which seem to have been derived, at least in part, from lower Paleozoic formations of the northern regions such as the Imina, Hazen, and Grant Land Formations (Trettin, 1971a). A Mississippian phase of deformation in the north is inferred from the Early Mississippian folding in the central and southern parts of the islands, where the folding in regions where the basement was not involved must have been caused by stress from the north.

The upraising, however, was not broad and uniform, but was concentrated in three (or more) narrow, elongate belts named the "Grant Land," "Cape Columbia," and "Rens Fiord" uplifts.

Grant Land uplift. The Grant Land uplift coincides with the southern and topographically highest part of the Grant Land Mountains. A mid-Paleozoic (Ellesmerian) uplift in this region is inferred from the fact that the base of the Sverdrup basin succession lies on the Early Ordovician or older (probably Cambrian) Grant Land Formation, whereas younger Ordovician and Silurian units are preserved both on the northwest and the southeast (Fig. 11). Parts of the mid-Paleozoic uplifted belt

must have remained tectonically positive during late Paleozoic and early Mesozoic times, because the lower part of the Sverdrup basin succession is incomplete in some areas; the entire Carboniferous to Middle Triassic succession, for example, is absent over the Tanquary structural high (Nassichuk and Christie, 1969). The Grant Land uplift was rejuvenated during the Tertiary orogeny by means of thrust faulting in the Lake Hazen fault zone and by normal faulting in the complex Porter Bay fault zone (Trettin, 1971b). The vertical uplift appears to have exceeded 3,500 ft (1,075 m) if the unconformity at the base of the Sverdrup basin succession is used as a marker. Several narrow, elongate grabens are present within the Grant Land uplift. At least one of the grabens seems to contain early Paleozoic strata younger than the Grant Land Formation; this fact suggests that the grabens date back to the mid-Paleozoic orogeny.

Cape Columbia uplift. On the coast of northernmost Ellesmere Island, the Sverdrup basin succession overlies the metamorphic Cape Columbia complex—which is definitely pre–late Middle Ordovician in age, and probably as old as Cambrian or late Proterozoic—whereas sedimentary and volcanic formations of Ordovician and Silurian ages are preserved directly to the south (Fig. 11). Thus, it appears that the northernmost part of Ellesmere Island, and probably also the adjacent present offshore region, was elevated during the mid-Paleozoic (Ellesmerian) orogeny. The uplift probably continued farther to the west and persisted there at least until Middle Pennsylvanian time, because Middle Pennsylvanian clastic sediments at M'Clintock Inlet were derived from the north (Trettin, 1969b).

Rens Fiord uplift. Sedimentary evidence (see "Interfering Patterns," below) suggests that the Rens Fiord uplift originated during the Late Silurian–Early Devonian (Caledonian *s.s.*) earth movements, and structural evidence (Fig. 12) demonstrates that it was rejuvenated both during the mid-Paleozoic (Ellesmerian) and the Tertiary (Eurekan; Tozer *in* Douglas, 1970, p. 585) movements. The mid-Paleozoic movements produced a horstlike structure, the axis of which is delineated by the Grant Land Formation and by a concentration of small quartz diorite plutons. The Grant Land Formation is flanked by Ordovician to Devonian formations which become younger away from the axis of the uplift in both northeasterly and southwesterly directions. The steeply dipping lower Pa-

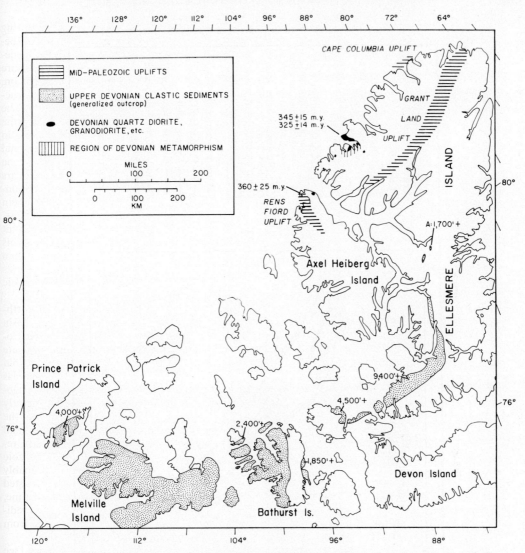

FIG. 10—Late Devonian features of Arctic Islands. Thicknesses of Upper Devonian "clastic wedge" from Douglas *et al.* (1963, Fig. 9).

leozoic formations are overlain with marked angular unconformity by moderately inclined Carboniferous and younger formations of the Sverdrup basin, which themselves are deformed into a broad arch of Tertiary age that shows complex minor folding and faulting. The feature was named the "Princess Margaret arch" by Gould and de Mille (1964), who traced it as far as the southeastern coast of Axel Heiberg Island. The northernmost part of the arch aligns approximately with the axis of the Rens Fiord uplift and appears to have been produced by weak positive movements of the Paleozoic tectonic element in Tertiary time.

Intrusion and metamorphism—Intrusions of quartz diorite and related rocks are common in northernmost Axel Heiberg Island and northwestern Ellesmere Island (Fig. 10). Most of the intrusions are small and epizonal, but some are larger and mesozonal (Trettin, 1969a; Frisch, 1967). The age of the youngest known intruded units is Early or Middle Silurian. The oldest, and probably the most reliable, K-Ar age determination—made on a small, high-level

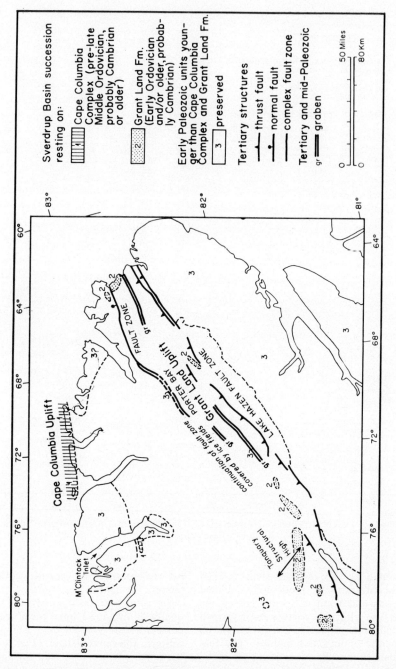

FIG. 11—Map showing Grant Land and Cape Columbia uplifts. Note that faults of Lake Hazen zone are locally covered by glaciers and therefore represented only incompletely.

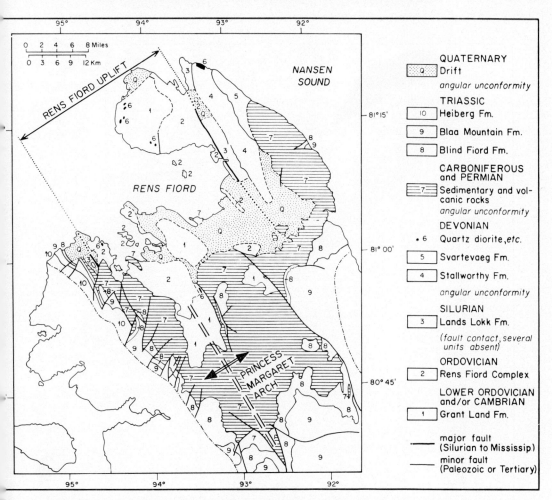

FIG. 12—Map showing Rens Fiord uplift. Simplified geology adapted from Thorsteinsson and Trettin (1972).

pluton in northern Axel Heiberg Island (360 ± 25 m.y.)—suggests emplacement in Middle to Late Devonian time. Regional metamorphism of greenschist-facies grade is associated with some of the larger intrusions in northwestern Ellesmere Island (Trettin, 1971c).

Interfering Patterns

Late Silurian–Early Devonian Basement Uplifts

Basement uplifts occurred between early Late Silurian (early Ludlovian) and late Early or early Middle Devonian times in three parts of the Arctic Islands: in southeastern Ellesmere Island (Kerr, 1967b, d; Trettin, 1971); in Boothia Peninsula and Cornwallis Island and environs (Kerr and Christie, 1965; Brown *et*

al., 1969); and in northern Axel Heiberg Island (Trettin, 1967, 1969a). The movements in the Boothia-Cornwallis belt were controlled by the northerly structural grain of the crystalline Precambrian basement, and the resultant northerly depositional and structural trends cut across the west-trending "predominant" pattern at almost right angles. (That pattern is outlined on Cornwallis Island by the contact between shelf carbonate rocks on the south and graptolitic beds on the north [Thorsteinsson and Kerr, 1968].)

The principal evidence for contemporaneous movements in northern Axel Heiberg Island consists of an angular unconformity that separates upper Middle Silurian (upper Wenlockian) strata (Lands Lokk Formation, member

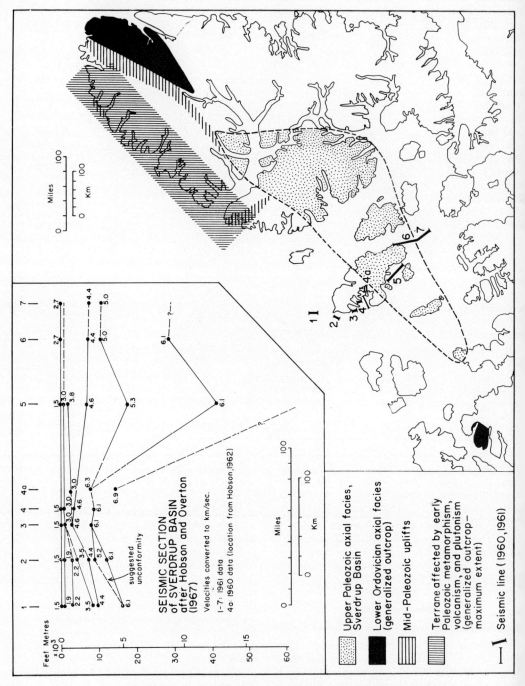

Fig. 13—Relation between Sverdrup basin and early Paleozoic mobile belt.

"A") from redbeds of probably Early Devonian age (Stallworthy Formation). The structures produced by this event cannot be distinguished from those caused by the Middle Devonian to Mississippian earth movements, but sedimentologic evidence (Trettin, 1967, 1969a) suggests that the Rens Fiord uplift was active. This complex horst trends northwest and cuts across the "predominant" pattern (outlined by the trend of the Hazen trough) in a similar manner to the Cornwallis fold belt; thus, it is suggested that this structure also was controlled by trends in the crystalline Precambrian basement. The movements, which were preceded by keratophyric volcanism, resulted in deltaic deposition in northwestern Ellesmere Island (Lands Lokk Formation).

Early or Middle Devonian Flysch Sedimentation, Volcanism, and Related Rifting— Nansen Sound Region

The Lower Devonian redbeds of northern Axel Heiberg Island (Stallworthy Formation) are overlain by about 10,400 ft (3,175 m) of volcanic-derived sandstone, siltstone, conglomerate, and breccia with lesser amounts of volcanic flows and breccias (Svartevaeg Formation; Trettin, 1967, 1969a). Most sandstones are graded and apparently are turbidites, whereas the conglomerates and breccias, in part extremely coarse and containing shelf-type carbonate rocks, are submarine-slide deposits. These sediments probably were deposited on the flanks of a trough that developed suddenly in latest Early or early Middle Devonian time. The volcanic material, which is present as keratophyre, spilite, and basalt, probably rose through extension fractures associated with the trough. The orientation of the trough has not been established, but it is speculated that the trough coincided approximately with the present Nansen Sound, a seaway separating a region with northerly to northwesterly structural trends (northern Axel Heiberg Island) from a region with predominantly northeasterly trends (northwestern Ellesmere Island).

Other anomalous features in the vicinity of Nansen Sound that are indicative of crustal extension on a minor scale are: (1) the Bourne complex of Kleybolte Peninsula, northwesternmost Ellesmere Island (Christie, 1957; Trettin, 1969a)—a thick assemblage of gabbroic intrusions of unknown age, perhaps Devonian to Carboniferous; (2) a major ultramafic dike located in a fault zone adjacent to the Bourne complex; (3) dike swarms of post-Silurian,

pre–Late Mississippian ages present between Nansen Sound and Phillips Inlet; and (4) a concentration of upper Paleozoic volcanic rocks (Thorsteinsson, in press; Thorsteinsson and Trettin, 1972).

RELATIONS WITH SVERDRUP BASIN

The Sverdrup basin, a site of subsidence and rapid sedimentation from Carboniferous to early Tertiary time (Thorsteinsson and Tozer, 1960; Thorsteinsson in Douglas, 1970, p. 569–574; Tozer in Douglas, 1970, p. 574–583), was characterized by two features: an axial depression and a sill bordering that depression on the northwest (see seismic section in Fig. 13). The deposits of the axial depression differ from those of the marginal parts because of the thicker section, the absence of unconformities, and the deeper water facies of some time intervals.

The upper Paleozoic axial facies—outlined by Thorsteinsson (in Douglas, 1970, p. 570) on the basis of the distribution of evaporites, fine-grained clastic sediments, and related diapirs—is aligned with the Lower Ordovician axial facies of the Hazen trough, represented in northern Ellesmere Island by the Hazen Formation (Trettin, 1971a) and in northwestern Melville Island by the Ibbet Bay Formation (Tozer and Thorsteinsson, 1964). This alignment suggests that the Hazen trough and the axial depression of the Sverdrup basin were controlled by the same deep-seated crustal structure. The axial depression of the Sverdrup basin, however, was laterally more restricted than the Hazen trough, and probably was shallower also.

The sill that bordered the axial depression of the Sverdrup basin on the northwest is aligned with the position of the Pearya geanticline in northern Axel Heiberg and Ellesmere Islands during the Middle and Late Devonian (compare Fig. 10), and it may be regarded as the product of differential vertical movements that succeeded the early Paleozoic orogenic activity. However, metamorphism and plutonism in this belt ceased in Carboniferous time, and uplifts became less pronounced. Middle Pennsylvanian sediments at M'Clintock Inlet (Trettin, 1969b) and some Triassic and Jurassic strata (Tozer in Douglas, 1970, p. 575) were derived from northerly and northwesterly sources, but the bulk of the clastic sediments in the Sverdrup basin seems to have come from the south and east (Tozer in Douglas, 1970; Trettin and Hills, 1966).

References Cited

Bird, J. M., and J. F. Dewey, 1970, Lithosphere plate-continental margin tectonics and the evolution of the Appalachian orogen: Geol. Soc. America Bull., v. 81, p. 1031–1060.

Blackadar, R. G., 1954, Geological reconnaissance, north coast of Ellesmere Island, Arctic Archipelago, Northwest Territories: Canada Geol. Survey Paper 53–10, 22 p.

Brown, R. L., I. W. D. Dalziel, and B. R. Rust, 1969, The structure, metamorphism, and development of the Boothia arch, Arctic Canada: Canadian Jour. Earth Sci., v. 6, p. 525–543.

Christie, R. L., 1957, Geological reconnaissance of the north coast of Ellesmere Island, District of Franklin, Northwest Territories: Canada Geol. Survey Paper 56–9, 40 p.

———— 1964, Geological reconnaissance of northeastern Ellesmere Island, District of Franklin: Canada Geol. Survey Mem. 331, 79 p.

———— 1967, Bache Peninsula, Ellesmere Island, Arctic Archipelago: Canada Geol. Survey Mem. 347, 63 p.

Churkin, M., Jr., 1969, Paleozoic tectonic history of the Arctic basin north of Alaska: Science, v. 165, p. 549–555.

Davies, D. K., 1968, Carbonate turbidites, Gulf of Mexico: Jour. Sed. Petrology, v. 38, p. 1100–1109.

Douglas, R. J. W., 1970, sci. ed., Geology and economic minerals of Canada: Canada Geol. Survey Econ. Geol. Rept. 1, 838 p.

———— et al., 1963, Geology and petroleum potentialities of northern Canada: Canada Geol. Survey Paper 63–31, 28 p.

Frisch, T. O., 1967, Metamorphism and plutonism in northernmost Ellesmere Island, Canadian Arctic Archipelago: Univ. California at Santa Barbara, PhD thesis, 236 p.

Gould, D. B., and G. de Mille, 1964, Piercement structures in the Arctic Islands: Bull. Canadian Petroleum Geology, v. 12, p. 719–753; reprinted in modified form as Piercement structures in Canadian Arctic Islands, in Diapirism and diapirs: Am. Assoc. Petroleum Geologists Mem. 8, 1968, p. 183–214.

Hobson, G. D., 1962, Seismic exploration in the Canadian Arctic Islands: Geophysics, v. 27, p. 253–273.

———— and A. Overton, 1967, A seismic section of the Sverdrup basin, Canadian Arctic Islands, in A. W. Musgrave, ed., Seismic refraction prospecting: Tulsa, Oklahoma, Soc. Exploration Geophysicists, p. 550–562.

Hsü, K. J., 1970, The meaning of the word flysch—a short historical search, in J. Lajoie, ed., Flysch sedimentology in North America: Geol. Assoc. Canada Spec. Paper 7, p. 1–11.

Kerr, J. W., 1967a, Nares submarine rift valley and the relative rotation of north Greenland: Bull. Canadian Petroleum Geology, v. 15, p. 483–520.

———— 1967b, Devonian of the Franklinian miogeosyncline and adjacent Central Stable region, Arctic Canada, in D. H. Oswald, ed., International symposium on the Devonian System, v. 1: Calgary, Alberta Soc. Petroleum Geologists, p. 677–692.

———— 1967c, Stratigraphy of central and eastern Ellesmere Island, Arctic Canada. Part I, Proterozoic and Cambrian: Canada Geol. Survey Paper 67–27, 63 p.

———— 1967d, Vendom Fiord Formation—a new redbed unit of probable early Middle Devonian (Eifelian) age, Ellesmere Island, Arctic Canada: Canada Geol. Survey Paper 67–43, 8 p.

———— 1968, Stratigraphy of central and eastern Ellesmere Island, Arctic Canada. Part II, Ordovician: Canada Geol. Survey Paper 67–27, 92 p.

———— and R. L. Christie, 1965, Tectonic history of Boothia uplift and Cornwallis fold belt, Arctic Canada: Am. Assoc. Petroleum Geologists Bull., v. 49, p. 905–926.

———— and H. P. Trettin, 1962, Mississippian rocks and the mid-Paleozoic earth movements in the Canadian Arctic Archipelago: Alberta Soc. Petroleum Geologists, v. 10, p. 247–256.

McLaren, D. J., 1963, Devonian stratigraphy, in Y. O. Fortier et al., eds., Geology of the north central part of the Arctic Archipelago, Northwest Territories (Operation Franklin): Canada Geol. Survey Mem. 320, p. 57–65.

Nassichuk, W. W., and R. L. Christie, 1969, Upper Paleozoic and Mesozoic stratigraphy in the Yelverton Pass region, Ellesmere Island, District of Franklin: Canada Geol. Survey Paper 68–31, 31 p.

Nelson, C. H., et al., 1970, Development of the Astoria canyon-fan physiography and comparison with similar systems: Marine Geology, v. 8, p. 259–291.

Niblett, E. R., and K. Whitham, 1970, Multi-disciplinary studies of geomagnetic variation anomalies in the Canadian Arctic: Jour. Geomagnetism and Geoelectricity, v. 22, p. 99–111.

Norford, B. S., 1970, Silurian stratigraphic sections at Cape Tyson, Offley Island, and Cape Schuchert, northwest Greenland (abs.): Am. Assoc. Petroleum Geologists Bull., v. 54, p. 2499.

———— 1972, Silurian stratigraphic sections at Kap Tyson, Offley Ø and Kap Schuchert, northwestern Greenland: Medd. om Grønland, v. 195, no. 2, 40 p.

Praus, O., J. M. de Laurier, and L. K. Law, 1971, The extension of the Alert anomaly through northern Ellesmere Island, Canada: Canadian Jour. Earth Sci., v. 8, no. 1, p. 50–64.

Schuchert, C., 1923, Sites and nature of the North American geosynclines: Geol. Soc. America Bull., v. 34, p. 151–229.

Stanley, D. J., 1969, Sedimentation in slope and base-of-slope environments, in The new concepts of continental margin sedimentation; application to the geological record: Am. Geol. Inst., Short Course Lecture Notes, Lect. 8, 25 p.

Temple, P. G., 1965, Geology of Bathurst Island group, District of Franklin, Northwest Territories: Princeton, New Jersey, Princeton Univ., PhD thesis, 186 p.

Thorsteinsson, R., 1958, Cornwallis and Little Cornwallis Islands, District of Franklin, Northwest Territories: Canada Geol. Survey Mem. 294, 134 p. (1959).

———— in press, Carboniferous and Permian stratigraphy of Axel Heiberg Island and western Ellesmere Island, Canadian Arctic Archipelago: Canada Geol. Survey Bull.

———— and J. W. Kerr, 1968, Cornwallis Island and adjacent smaller islands, Canadian Arctic Archipelago: Canada Geol. Survey Paper 67–64, 16 p.

———— and E. T. Tozer, 1960, Summary account of structural history of the Canadian Arctic Archipelago since Precambrian time: Canada Geol. Survey Paper 60–7, 25 p.

———— and H. P. Trettin, comps., 1972, Geology, Cape Stallworthy, District of Franklin: Canada Geol. Survey Map 1305A, scale 1:250,000.

Tozer, E. T., and R. Thorsteinsson, 1964, Western Queen Elizabeth Islands, Arctic Archipelago: Canada Geol. Survey Mem. 332, 242 p.

Trettin, H. P., 1967, Devonian of the Franklinian eugeosyncline, in D. H. Oswald, ed., International symposium on the Devonian System, v. 1: Calgary, Alberta Soc. Petroleum Geologists, p. 693–701 (1968).

———— 1969a, Pre-Mississippian geology of northern Axel Heiberg and northwestern Ellesmere Islands, Arctic Archipelago: Canada Geol. Survey Bull. 171, 82 p.

———— 1969b, Geology of Ordovician to Pennsylvanian rocks, M'Clintock Inlet, north coast of Ellesmere Island, Canadian Arctic Archipelago: Canada Geol. Survey Bull. 183, 93 p. (1970).

———— 1970, Ordovician-Silurian flysch sedimentation in the axial trough of the Franklinian geosyncline, northeastern Ellesmere Island, Arctic Canada, in J. Lajoie, ed., Flysch sedimentology in North America: Geol. Assoc. Canada Spec. Paper 7, p. 13–35.

———— 1971a, Stratigraphy and sedimentology of lower Paleozoic clastic units, Tanquary and Cañon Fiord regions, Ellesmere Island, in Report of activities, Part A: Canada Geol. Survey Paper 71–1, p. 236–241.

———— 1971b, Geology of lower Paleozoic formations, Hazen Plateau and southern Grant Land Mountains, Ellesmere Island, Arctic Archipelago: Canada Geol. Survey Bull. 203, 134 p.

———— 1971c, Reconnaissance of lower Paleozoic geology, Phillips Inlet region, north coast of Ellesmere Island, District of Franklin: Canada Geol. Survey Paper 71–12, 29 p. (1972).

———— and L. V. Hills, 1966, Lower Triassic tar sands of northwestern Melville Island, Arctic Archipelago: Canada Geol. Survey Paper 66–34, 122 p.

von Rad, U., 1968, Comparison of sedimentation in the Bavarian flysch (Cretaceous) and Recent San Diego Trough (California): Jour. Sed. Petrology, v. 38, p. 1120–1154.

Wanless, R. K., 1969, Isotopic age map of Canada: Canada Geol. Survey Map 1256A.

Wheeler, J. O., 1967, Tectonics, in Canadian upper mantle report, 1967: Canada Geol. Survey Paper 67–41, p. 3–59.

Wilson, J. L., 1969, Microfacies and sedimentary structures in "deeper water" lime mudstones, in G. M. Friedman, ed., Depositional environments in carbonate rocks: Soc. Econ. Paleontologists and Mineralogists Spec. Pub. 14, p. 4–19.

Workum, R. H., 1965, Lower Paleozoic salt, Canadian Arctic Islands: Bull. Canadian Petroleum Geology, v. 13, p. 181–191.

Ziegler, P. A., 1969, The development of sedimentary basins in western and Arctic Canada: Calgary, Alberta Soc. Petroleum Geologists, 86 p.

Geology of Sverdrup Basin—Summary[1]

BERNARD P. PLAUCHUT[2]

Pau, France

The Sverdrup basin, in the northern part of the Canadian Arctic Archipelago, contains a considerable thickness of deposits ranging in age from Carboniferous to early Tertiary (Fig. 1). These strata unconformably overlie Devonian and older rocks of the Franklinian geosyncline, which was the site of deposition of a large volume of sediments between late Precambrian and Late Devonian time.

Two major sedimentary cycles are distinguishable within the Sverdrup basin. The first includes rocks from the Carboniferous to the lowermost Cretaceous and represents sediments which were deposited within the true basin. Carboniferous and Permian rocks are distributed in several facies belts generally parallel with the basin axis; they include conglomerate, sandstone, siltstone, limestone, shale, evaporites, and volcanic rocks. Deposits of Early Mississippian age are unknown in the Sverdrup basin, but continental deposits of Late Mississippian age crop out in both the northern and axial parts. The marine transgression was initiated in general in Early Pennsylvanian time. Extensive evaporites of probably Early Pennsylvannian age have formed many diapiric structures in the region. Rocks of all three series of the Permian are present, but the very latest Permian apparently is represented by a period of nondeposition (Fig. 2).

Triassic rocks occur in two distinctive facies belts. A marginal, thin belt is mainly sandstones. In the axial belt, where shale is the predominant lithologic type, thicknesses are greater, reaching about 6,000 m (20,000 ft) on eastern Axel Heiberg Island. The youngest important limestones of the Sverdrup basin succession are of Middle Triassic age. Jurassic and lowermost Cretaceous rocks are composed of alternate sandstone, siltstone, and shale units which vary from place to place. The Hettangian and Pliensbachian Stages are not represented, and there commonly is a disconformity or a slight angular unconformity between Middle and Upper Jurassic rocks (Fig. 3).

The second major sedimentary cycle, consisting of three divisions, includes rocks ranging from Lower Cretaceous to lower Tertiary. The first division, which is of Early Cretaceous age, contains the Isachsen, Christopher, and Hassel Formations (Fig. 4). The transgressive sandstones of the Isachsen Formation are present in most of the Sverdrup basin and westward as far as Alaska. The Christopher Formation, composed mainly of monotonous shales of early to middle Albian age, is overlain by sandstones of the Hassel Formation. The succeeding division, shales of the Kanguk Formation, is of Late Cretaceous age—Senonian except on Graham Island. The third division is the Late Cretaceous and early Tertiary Eureka Sound Formation—a synorogenic deposit of sandstones, sands, conglomerates, and coal. This formation is markedly transgressive; in central parts of the basin it is conformable on the Kanguk Formation, but in marginal parts it is unconformable on rocks ranging in age from early Paleozoic to Early Cretaceous.

Three structural regions exist in the Sverdrup basin (Fig. 5): (1) a western region that extends eastward to Lougheed Island and is semicircular in form consists of a perisyncline plunging toward the center; except for radial faults, no other structural elements are present; (2) a structurally deformed eastern region is characterized by Late Cretaceous and Tertiary folding which has exposed Triassic rocks in the cores of folds; diverse faults strike northerly; and (3) an axial region between Lougheed Island and Fosheim Peninsula (Ellesmere Island) is characterized by numerous diapiric structures of varied origin.

[1] Manuscript received, September 20, 1971.

[2] Elf Oil Exploration and Production Canada Ltd.; present address, S.N.P.A., Pau, France.

My very grateful thanks go to R. G. Levy, head of ELF-RE Exploration Department in Paris, who was kind enough to authorize this publication. Gus Jutard, Elf Oil Exploration and Production Canada, provided considerable field data for this report and contributed to the synthesis. Others who have contributed in the field are Ph. Riche, M. Berthon, M. Croisile, and V. Mauguy; in the laboratory, assistance was given by M. Fischer, A. Biard, P. Biens, E. Grosdidier, S. Jardine, P. Moreau, J. P. Ragot, and L. Yapaudjan.

I am deeply indebted to D. J. McLaren, Director of the Institute of Sedimentary and Petroleum Geology in Calgary, who was kind enough to correct this report and present it before this symposium.

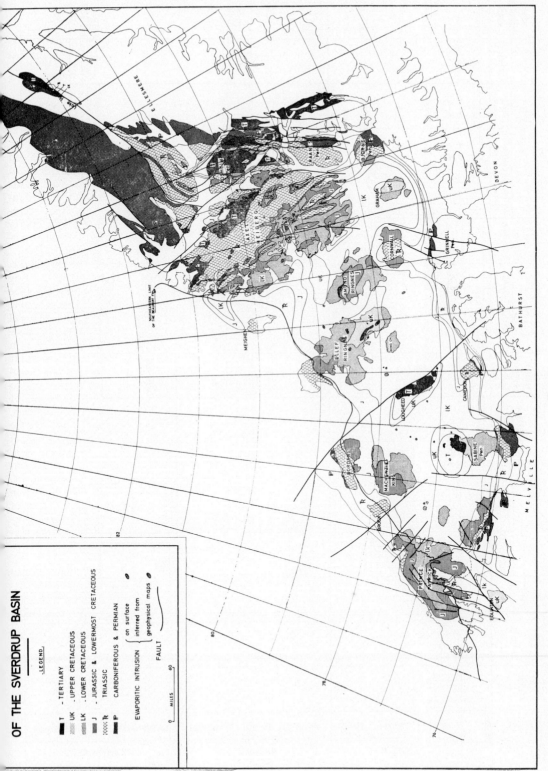

OF THE SVERDRUP BASIN

LEGEND

■ T   - TERTIARY
■ UK - UPPER CRETACEOUS
▨ LK - LOWER CRETACEOUS
▧ J   - JURASSIC & LOWERMOST CRETACEOUS
▧ Tr - TRIASSIC
▨ P   - CARBONIFEROUS & PERMIAN

EVAPORITIC INTRUSION { on surface ◖
                       inferred from
                       geophysical maps ◖

——— FAULT

0   MILES   60

Fig. 1

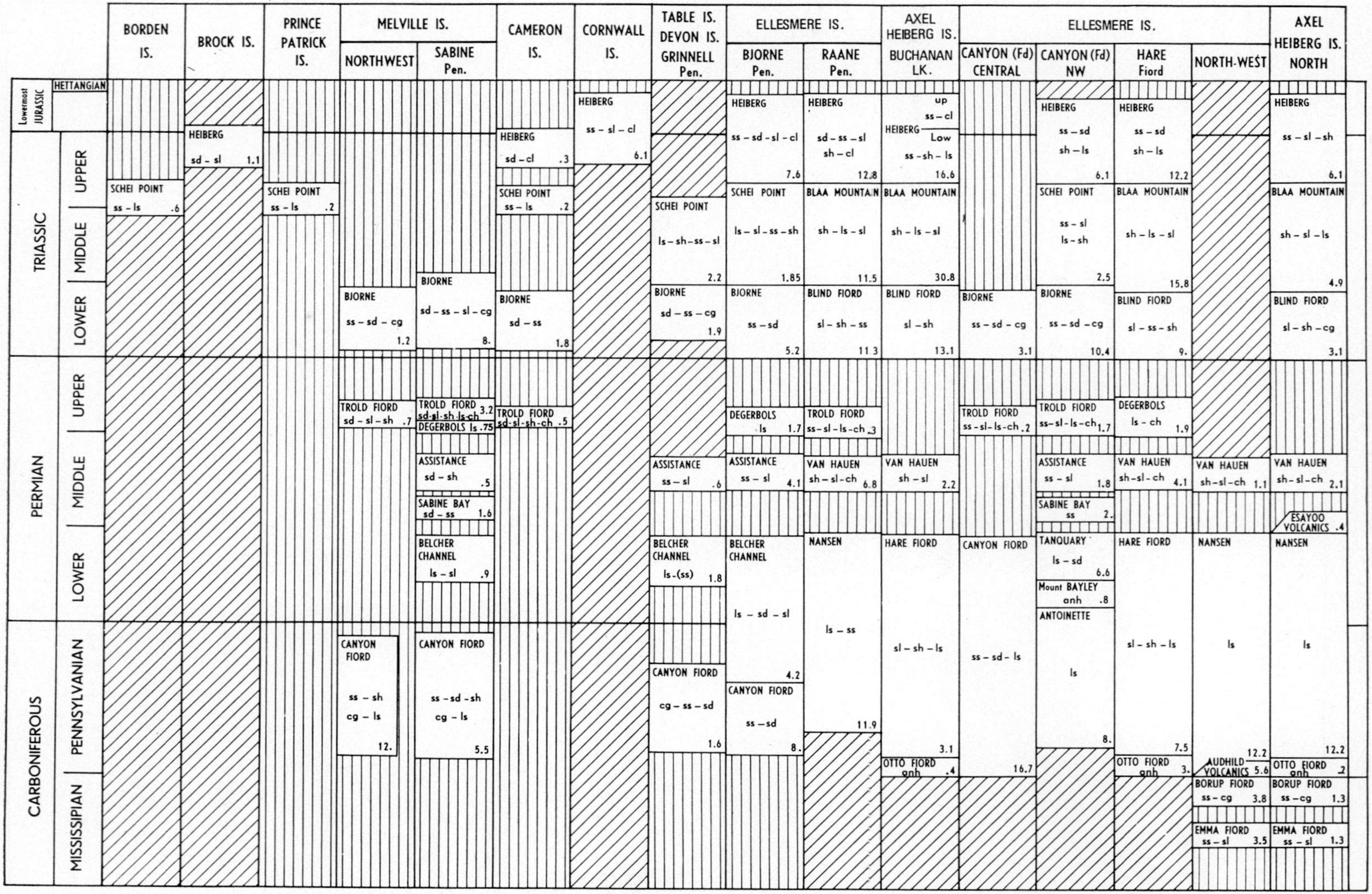

Fig. 2—Correlation chart of Carboniferous, Permian, and Triassic rocks around Sverdrup basin.

LEGEND

Up. – – Upper
Md. – – Middle } Formation
Low. – – Lower   or member

| | | | | | | | – Absence of deposits

/ / / / / – Strata non exposed

Thickness (hundreds of meters) 1.5

FACIES

cg   – – – – Conglomerate
ss   – – – – – Sandstone
sd   – – – – – – Sand
(ss) – – – Minor sandstone
sl   – – – Siltstone and silt
sh   – – – – – – – Shale
ls   – – – – – Limestone
anh   Anhydrite and evaporite
cl   – – – – – – – Coal
gl   – – – – Glauconitic
ch   – – – – – – Chert

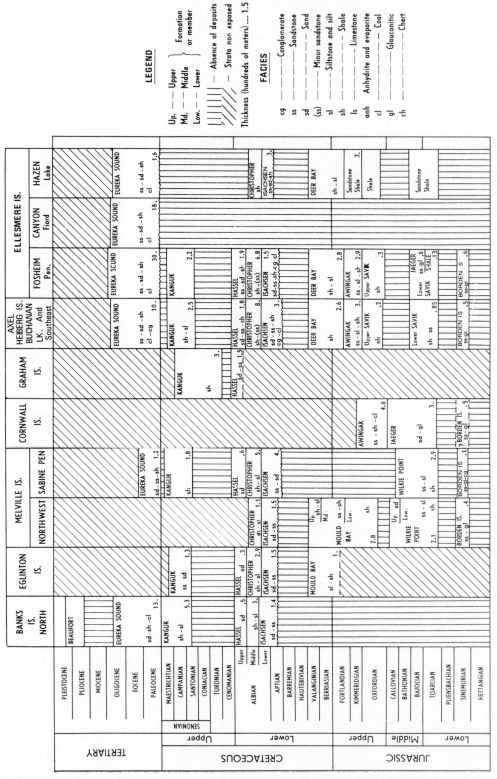

Fig. 3.—Correlation chart of Jurassic, Cretaceous, and Tertiary rocks of southern flank of Sverdrup basin.

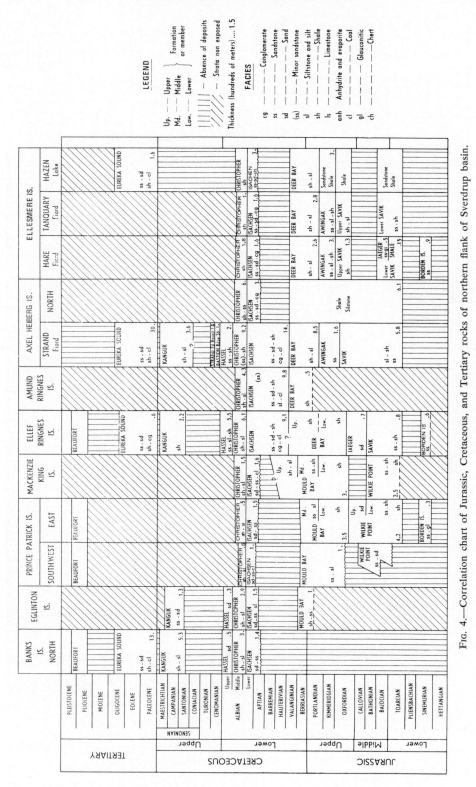

FIG. 4.—Correlation chart of Jurassic, Cretaceous, and Tertiary rocks of northern flank of Sverdrup basin.

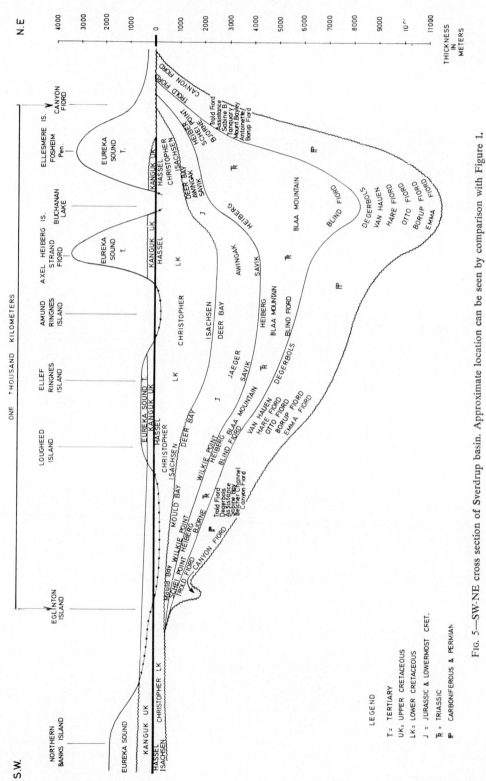

FIG. 5—SW-NE cross section of Sverdrup basin. Approximate location can be seen by comparison with Figure 1.

Facies Relations at Edge of Early Mid-Devonian Carbonate Shelf, South Nahanni River Area, N.W.T.[1]

J. P. A. NOBLE[2] and R. D. FERGUSON[3]

Fredericton, New Brunswick, and Calgary, Alberta, Canada

Abstract A broad area of shallow-shelf carbonate beds of the Nahanni Formation (Eifelian-Givetian) borders the Canadian shield in the District of Mackenzie, N.W.T. To the west, in the region of Deadman's Valley in the South Nahanni River area, the carbonate rocks grade into a basinal facies within about 3 mi (5 km).

Examination of the sediments and fauna across this transition permitted correlation between the shelf and the basin and recognition of several faunal communities. On the basis of (1) environmental deductions interpreted for these faunal communities and (2) lithosome geometry and the character of the sediments, it is concluded that the Nahanni sediments were deposited on a broad, slightly restricted, shallow shelf, and that their basinal equivalents were deposited in a marginal cratonic trough. The shelf and trough were separated by a moderately steep shelf edge, or epeiric slope. A shoal was developed near the edge of the shelf.

The boundary between the shelf and the deeper basin during deposition of the Arnica sediments (Eifelian and earlier) was much more abrupt, and was defined by the Manetoe barrier reef.

INTRODUCTION

The purpose of this paper is to examine the nature of the Middle Devonian shelf-to-basin transition from the evidence of lithofacies and biofacies changes in the Liard-Nahanni area, where carbonate rocks on the east grade generally westward into fine clastic units of the supposed Cordilleran trough (Fig. 1). An attempt will be made to relate the observed faunal associations and sediments to probable environments, to a probable depositional profile, and to possible changes in relative sea level or changes in supply of clastic sediments.

The line of cross section (Figs. 6, 7) was chosen because it passes through outcrops which include the probable zone of actual transition from shelf to basin facies (Figs. 8, 9) and are traceable in the field.

[1] Manuscript received, September 20, 1971.

[2] Associate professor, Department of Geology, University of New Brunswick.

[3] Senior Geologist, Bluemount Resources, Ltd.

Special thanks are extended to Banff Oil Ltd. and Aquitaine Company of Canada Ltd. for permission to release this paper for publication, and to D. J. McLaren of the Geological Survey of Canada for permission to include section 4 in Figure 6 of this paper.

Sincere thanks are extended to A. W. Norris and N. C. Wardlaw for valuable criticisms and suggestions.

STRATIGRAPHY

Devonian stratigraphic terminology of the Liard-Nahanni and adjacent areas is complicated by the fact that these areas are zones of abrupt facies changes at several stratigraphic levels from the Ordovician to the top of the Middle Devonian (Douglas and Norris, 1960; 1961).

Figure 1 shows the location of the study area in respect to the localities and formations listed in Figure 2, which is a chart indicating the Devonian terminology used by Douglas and Norris (1960; 1961) and its relation to faunal zones in the Liard-Nahanni area.

The detailed correlation of the formations cropping out in the Liard-Nahanni area with those of other areas, particularly in the subsurface to the east, is beyond the scope of this report. However, Pedder (1964) and Rainville (1968) have demonstrated the approximate equivalence of the Hume and Nahanni Formations, and many stratigraphers (*e.g.*, Bassett and Stout, 1967; Norris, 1963, 1965; Craig *et al.*, 1967) have correlated at least the upper parts of these formations with the Keg River Formation of north-central Alberta, the Little Buffalo Falls Formation of the Great Slave Lake area, and the Elm Point Formation of Manitoba.

Local Correlation

The Nahanni and Arnica Formations and their facies variants are related, on the basis of the evidence of their contained faunas, to the faunal zones shown in Figure 2.

The *Leiorhynchus castanea, Billingsastrea verrilli,* and *Schuchertella adoceta* zones are well known in Western Canada (McLaren, 1962; Crickmay, 1966) and are equivalent to zones 4, 3, and 2, respectively, of Crickmay (1966). The *Warrenella* sp. 1 zone of this paper lies directly below the *Schuchertella adoceta* zone and corresponds approximately to the upper part of the Arnica Formation and its facies variants—the Manetoe, "Funeral," and Landry formations. This zone is based on a species of *Warrenella* very common throughout the area and in most cases readily distinguisha-

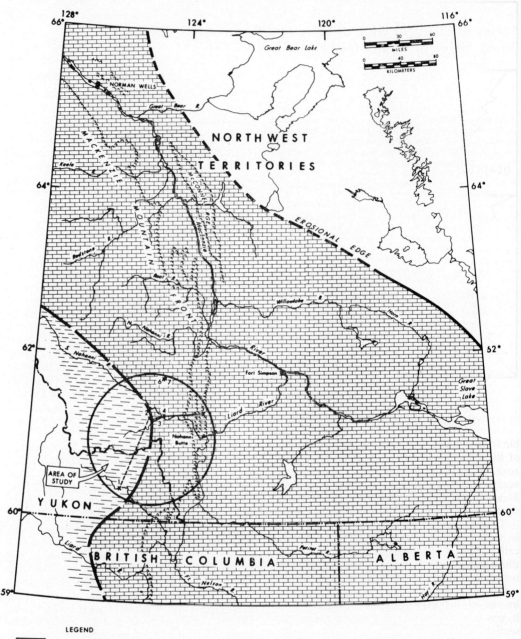

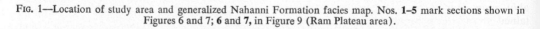

FIG. 1—Location of study area and generalized Nahanni Formation facies map. Nos. **1–5** mark sections shown in Figures 6 and 7; **6** and **7**, in Figure 9 (Ram Plateau area).

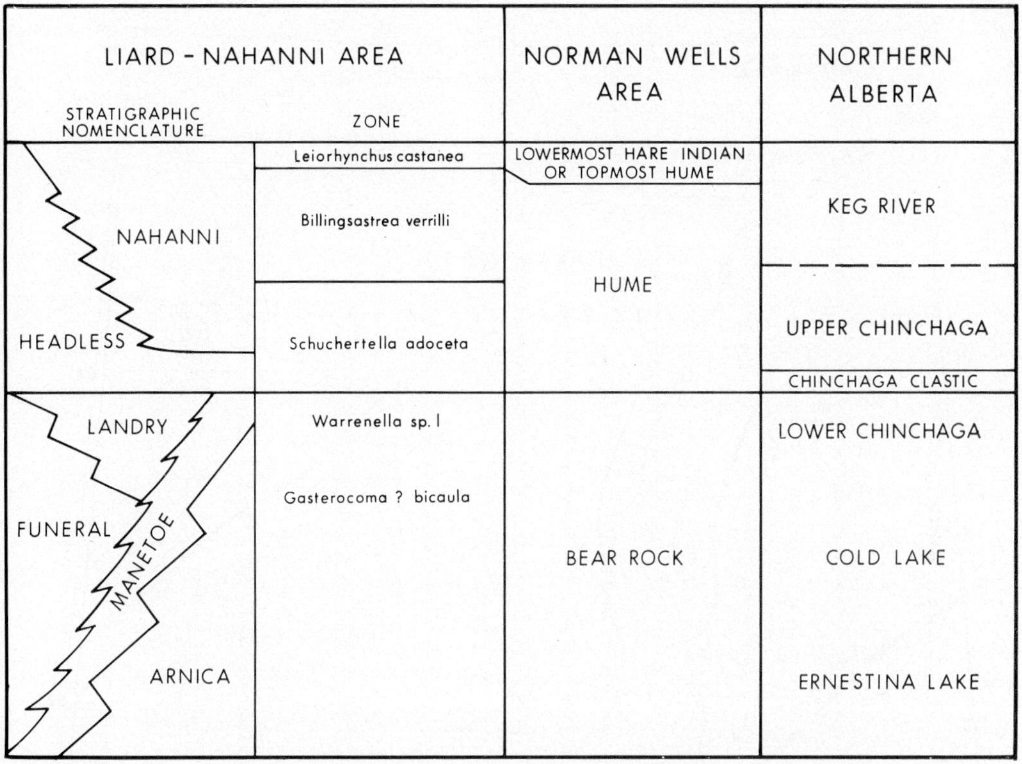

LIARD – NAHANNI AREA		NORMAN WELLS AREA	NORTHERN ALBERTA
STRATIGRAPHIC NOMENCLATURE	ZONE		
NAHANNI	Leiorhynchus castanea	LOWERMOST HARE INDIAN OR TOPMOST HUME	KEG RIVER
	Billingsastrea verrilli	HUME	
HEADLESS	Schuchertella adoceta		UPPER CHINCHAGA
			CHINCHAGA CLASTIC
LANDRY	Warrenella sp. 1		LOWER CHINCHAGA
FUNERAL · MANETOE	Gasterocoma ? bicaula	BEAR ROCK	COLD LAKE
ARNICA			ERNESTINA LAKE

FIG. 2—Zonation of Middle Devonian in Liard-Nahanni area, and correlation with Norman Wells and northern Alberta areas.

ble from younger forms of *Warrenella*. Because of its position below the *Schuchertella adoceta* zone, the *Warrenella* sp. 1 zone may be equivalent to Crickmay's (1966) *Spongonaria filicata* zone, but there is no direct faunal evidence to support such a correlation.

The lowermost zone considered in this paper is the *Gasterocoma? bicaula* zone, formerly called the "two-holed crinoid" zone because of the dominance of crinoid ossicles with dumbbell-shaped central canals.

On the basis of the above zonal scheme and by use of standard lithostratigraphic methods, it was possible to correlate most stratigraphic sections measured in the field and thus to establish the approximate contemporaneity of different facies. Section 1 (Figs. 6, 7) was correlated with the other sections on the basis of a reasonably good collection of *Warrenella* sp. 1 obtained from a thin limestone bed overlying a thin shale break directly above the dolomites of the Manetoe Formation (Fig. 7).

Epeiric Shelves

Previous writers—especially Shaw (1964), Irwin (1965), and Laporte (1969)—have discussed the concept of sedimentation within an epeiric sea, the former two from the point of view of hypothetical models and the latter by analysis of Helderberg facies in the New York area. These authors argued that the broad epicontinental shelves, characteristic of much of geologic time when continents were largely submerged, must have had depositional slopes of very low angles, probably of the order of less than 1 ft per mile (0.2 m/km). A consequence of such conditions would be broad environmental zones occupied by characteristic facies, as shown in Figure 4 (Laporte, 1969). These authors, however, did not discuss the seaward margins of such epeiric seas—that is, the transition from shallow shelf to deeper basin or geosyncline.

Other writers have attempted to interpret transitions from shallow shelf to deeper basins

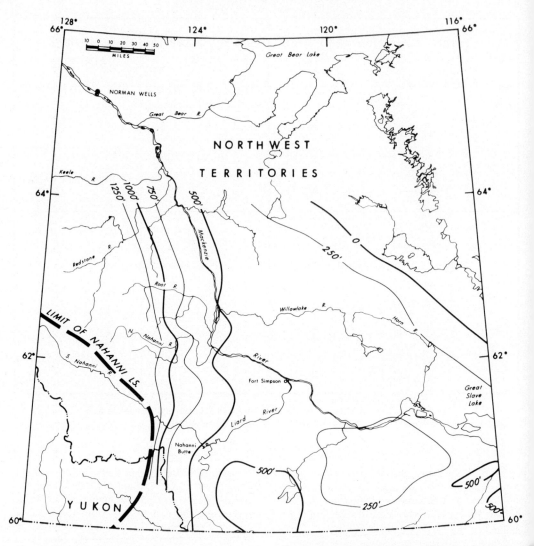

FIG. 3—Isopachs of Nahanni and Headless Formations (

on the basis of sediments, but the situations described are very different from that of the
Western Canada Middle Devonian. Thomson
and Thomasson (1969) described changes in
the Dimple Limestone (Lower Pennsylvanian)
of the Marathon region that indicate a transition in carbonate sediments from shelf through
slope into basinal facies. However, these sediments—which include many turbidites—are
the products of an active tectonic environment.
Tyrrell (1969) and McDaniel and Pray
(1969) have described and interpreted the facies changes from the Tansill Formation

(shelf) through the Capitan Formation (shelf
edge and slope) to the Lamar Limestone Member of the Bell Canyon Formation (basin) in
the Permian basin of Texas and New Mexico.
It is clear from their conclusions, and those of
others who have studied these rocks, that clastic sedimentation was negligible and the Dela-
ware basin was a "starved" basin during this interval of the Permian.

In the Liard-Nahanni area, however, an
epeiric shelf on the east is bordered on the west
by a marginal cratonic basin which received
thick clastic deposits from some extracratonic

Manetoe, Arnica, and Camsell Formations (right).

source during most of the Middle Devonian—a situation probably common in the geologic past.

The question under consideration is whether or not there existed a definite break in slope at the shelf edge coincident with, and perhaps controlling, this carbonate-shale transition during Middle Devonian time. One way of answering this question is to consider the possible models of shelf-basin transition which could occur and the pattern of deposition which would be associated with each, and then to compare the models with the facies relations of the Nahanni and Arnica Formations.

If it is assumed that the clastic sediments do represent deposition in deeper water, and that the regional paleoslope was to the west (evidence for this assumption includes regional isopachs [Fig. 3], regional lithofacies patterns [Fig. 1], and changes from dominantly benthonic to dominantly planktonic faunas), there appear to be three fairly obvious models of seafloor relief (Fig. 4).

In model I, a gently sloping, shallow shelf receives mainly carbonate sediments in its upper part and mainly clastic sediments in its lower

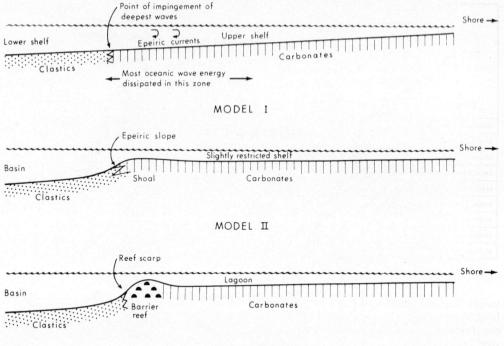

FIG. 4—Three models of shelf-basin transition. From Laporte (1969, Fig. 14).

part. This is essentially the model suggested by Laporte's Figure 14 (Laporte, 1969) for the Helderberg sediments—the subtidal, below-wave-base carbonate units of the Kalkberg Limestone grading laterally into the New Scotland mudstones without any break in depositional slope. This slope would probably be similar to that of modern shelves—*i.e.*, a fraction of a degree.

In model II, the carbonate sediments are deposited on a broad, slightly restricted, shallow shelf; the clastic sediments are deposited in a deeper basin. The two areas are separated by a moderately steep shelf edge or slope of perhaps a few degrees. A shoal may be developed at the edge of the shelf.

Model III consists of a broad, restricted shelf or lagoon bordered by a barrier reef. There is a distinct break in slope between shelf and basin, and the slope may be as steep as 30–40°.

The conditions of model I are implied by the diagrams of Shaw (1964), Irwin (1965), and Laporte (1969), though these authors do not actually discuss the shelf margin in their treatments of epeiric sedimentation. However, we believe that models II and III are more appro-priate for the Cordilleran geosyncline during the times of deposition of the Nahanni and Arnica Formations, respectively, in the Liard-Nahanni area. Other models of shelf-basin transitions in epeiric situations may apply in other areas, and at different times in the study area.

FAUNAL COMMUNITIES IN NAHANNI FORMATION

Nine principal faunal communities are observed in the Nahanni Formation in the Liard-Nahanni area. The main components for each of these communities, together with tentative environmental interpretations, are summarized in Figure 5. Not all of the communities are present in the line of cross section chosen to illustrate the shelf-basin transition (Figs. 6, 7); but they are all common in the Liard-Nahanni area, and they apparently represent a sequence of ecologic zones from the outer shelf into the basin.

Massive Stromatoporoid-Coral Community

The lithologic type associated with this community is limestone which is slightly argilla-ceous; commonly dolomitic—having irregular mottling; and, in part, siliceous. Textures are

Legend: △ MAJOR COMPONENTS · X MINOR COMPONENTS · (blank) ABSENT OR RARE

COMMUNITY	MASSIVE STROMS	BRANCHING STROMS	LAMINAR STROMS	MASSIVE TABULATE CORALS	BRANCHING TABULATE CORALS	LAMINAR TABULATE CORALS	MASSIVE RUGOSE CORALS	FASCICULATE RUGOSE CORALS	SOLITARY RUGOSE CORALS	BRACHIOPODS	CRINOIDS	GASTROPODS	PELECYPODS	TRILOBITES	OSTRACODS	BRYOZOA	CRICOCONARIDS	AMMONOIDS	INTERPRETED ENVIRONMENT
MASSIVE STROM.-CORAL				X	X		X	X	X	X	X	X							OUTER SHELF – SLIGHTLY RESTRICTED
SPINULICOSTA – ATRYPID					X				X	△	X	X		X					OUTER SHELF – SLIGHTLY RESTRICTED
LAMINAR STROM.	X		△	△		△	X		X	X	X			X	X				SHELF EDGE
SYRINGOPORA – SPINULICOSTA	X	X		△			X		X	X	X								SHELF EDGE
BRANCHING TABULATE CORAL	X	△		X	△	X	X		X	X	X				X				SHELF EDGE – SHOAL
ATRYPA – BRYOZOA					X					△	X	X				△			SHELF EDGE – SHOAL
WARRENELLA-RHYNCHONELLID									X	△	△	X	X	X	X		X		SLOPE – BASIN
EMANUELLA – PELECYPOD										△			△	X	X				SLOPE – BASIN
PELAGIC COMMUNITY										X	X				X		△	△	BASIN

Fig. 5—Composition of principal faunal communities and interpreted environments of those communities.

varied but predominantly micritic, and minor fossiliferous micrites and pelmicrites are present. Bedding ranges from thin to thick or massive, but commonly is irregular and lensoid.

This biofacies is characterized by a fauna of corals and stromatoporoids, many of which make up reefal masses on a small scale. *Amphipora* is common in some beds; the spongophyllids, *Socialophyllum, Xystriphyllum, Leptoinophyllum, Alveolites, Favosites,* and *Thamnopora,* as well as fasciculate corals of various genera, are present but not common. Gastropods, crinoids, and brachiopods are of less importance.

This community is typical of the upper part of the Nahanni Formation (Fig. 7); it reflects deposition on the outer shelf but a little behind the shelf edge.

The stromatoporoids, coral heads, reefal masses, and relatively minor percentages of fragmented shells indicate that this biofacies must have been deposited in a shallow-water environment free from the influence of terrigenous material. The limestones, however, are almost entirely micrites and pelmicrites, indicating rather low-energy conditions. They, together with the interbedded dolomites and the generally rather sparse fauna, indicate a shallow area of slightly restricted circulation, possibly behind a shoaling area at the edge of the shelf directly on the west. This biofacies may be compared with the facies of the Manlius Limestone of New York which Laporte (1969) regards as having formed in a slightly restricted environment behind crinoidal bars of the Coeymans Limestone.

Spinulicosta-Atrypid Community

The sedimentary matrix is limestone, argillaceous in part, which includes micrites, fossiliferous micrites, and some pelmicrites and biomicrites. Sparites are scarce. Thin to medium, nodular bedding is dominant.

Spinulicosta stainbrooki and atrypids are the common elements of this mixed assemblage. Other productids include *Productella.* Spiriferids may be present, especially *Emanuella,* and scattered gastropods, small solitary rugose corals, and small branching tabulate corals are present. Crinoid ossicles and trilobite fragments also are present. The fauna, however, is dominated by brachiopods, especially *Spinulicosta stainbrooki, Atrypa aperanta, Spinatrypa coriacea,* and other atrypids.

This community is closely associated with both the Massive Stromatoporoid community and the Laminar Stromatoporoid community, and is representative of a shelf-edge or possibly a slightly restricted outer-shelf environment.

This interpretation is supported by the fact that the atrypids are mostly the spinaceous types which, according to Copper (1967), are found in relatively quiet-water lagoonal environments.

Laminar Stromatoporoid Community

The lithology consists of limestones with traces of argillaceous content, slightly dolomitic

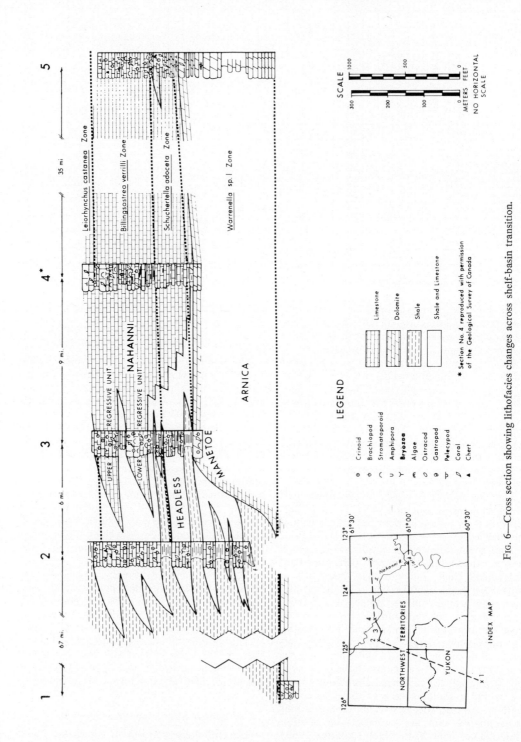

FIG. 6—Cross section showing lithofacies changes across shelf-basin transition.

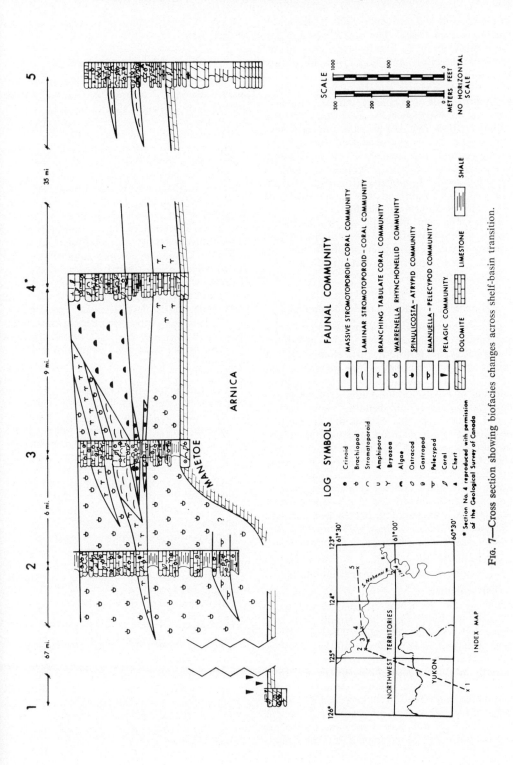

Fig. 7—Cross section showing biofacies changes across shelf-basin transition.

in places, and with irregular chert lenses and a partly silicified fauna. The limestones are predominantly micrites, but include some pelmicrites, intramicrites, and biomicrites. Bedding is thick to massive and regular.

The fauna consists mainly of small laminar stromatoporoids and small, laminar, massive tabulate corals, especially *Favosites*. Massive colonial corals and stromatoporoids and solitary rugose corals are dispersed through the biofacies, but are scarce. A few scattered brachiopods (partially fragmented) include *Spinulicosta* and *Emanuella;* fragments of trilobites, such as *Otarion* sp., and a few ostracods and crinoids occur sporadically.

The fauna and lithology of this biofacies, and its position relative to other biofacies, are consistent with a postulated subturbulent (Lecompte, 1956) shoal environment at the outer edge of the shelf.

Branching Tabulate-Coral Community

Limestones associated with this community are slightly argillaceous and partly dolomitic. Biomicrites and pelmicrites are dominant, but minor sparry calcarenites are present. This community is dominated by small branching colonies of *Favosites* and *Amphipora coenostea* concentrated in certain bedding planes. Other corals common in this community are *Xystriphyllum, Leptoinophyllum,* and various genera of tabulate corals. A few massive stromatoporoids may also be present, and these commonly are partly silicified. Scattered brachiopods, crinoids, gastropods, and ostracods are generally present, and many of the brachiopods are at least partially fragmented. Brachiopods include *Cyrtina, Carinatina dysmorphostrota, Emanuella, Schizophoria, Atrypa,* and *Biconostrophia.*

Syringopora-Spinulicosta Community

This community has many of the same elements as the Branching Tabulate-Coral community, including *Favosites,* similar brachiopods, and a similar sedimentary matrix. However, *Syringopora* is the dominant coral, *Spinulicosta* is common, and ostracods are scarce.

Both of these communities are found in a position between the Massive Stromatoporoid-Coral community and the *Warrenella*-Rhynchonellid community; they apparently represent a transitional environment somewhat similar to the subturbulent environment of Lecompte

(1956). This environment may be designated as shelf edge.

Atrypa-Bryozoa Community

The sedimentary matrix is limestone with shaly interbeds. Calcarenites and calcisiltites are much more common than in other communities; the calcarenites include biosparites, as well as biomicrites and intramicrites.

This community is dominated by brachiopods, especially atrypids and *Schizophoria,* but is characterized also by abundant bryozoans, a few very small favositids, gastropods, and some forms of *Emanuella. Spinatrypa, Productella, Schuchertella, Camerotoechia,* and *Spinulicosta* also occur sporadically. This community is not as well developed in any of the sections shown in Figure 7 as it is in sections somewhat farther north, where it is a typical development of the Headless Formation. Closely associated with this community are some beds with abundant gastropods and a few atrypids. These gastropods (pleurotomarids), which were most likely vagrant browsers on vegetable matter, indicate an environment with algal growth and of limited depth.

The *Atrypa*-Bryozoa community is well developed throughout the Liard-Nahanni area in a broad zone approximately at the boundary of the carbonate and shale provinces. Despite its association with a marked terrigenous component, it apparently is not really a basinal community. The associated calcarenties indicate a relatively high-energy environment, and the association of cemented suspension feeders and pedunculate suspension feeders and vagrant browsers (probably on algae) indicates a relatively shallow-water environment.

Furthermore, sedimentary structures which have been observed (*e.g.,* ripple bedding and mudcracks) in the sedimentary matrix associated with this community tend to confirm the foregoing interpretation of a fairly shallow-water environment, possibly shelf edge or upper slope.

Warrenella-Rhynchonellid Community

The sedimentary matrix is generally argillaceous limestone with some shaly interbeds; in a few places, the matrix is dolomitic. Micrites and biomicrites are common, and minor calcisiltites and scarce calcarenites are present. Bedding is thin to medium, very commonly nodular, and locally platy.

Brachiopods are abundant, especially *Warrenella*, *Atrypa*, *Hadrorhynchia*, *Schuchertella*, *Spinulicosta*, *Spinatrypa*, *Productella*, *Emanuella*, and other spiriferids. Crinoids are common—abundant throughout some beds—and trilobites (especially the pygidia), solitary rugose corals, pelecypods, and gastropods are scattered throughout. Cricoconarids occur in traces, and ostracods are common in some beds.

This community is very common in sections 2 and 3 (Fig. 7) and in other parts of the Liard-Nahanni area, where it appears to be confined to a rather narrow belt approximately at the boundary of the carbonate and shale provinces. Stromatoporoids and colonial rugose corals are notably absent, and the brachiopod fauna dominated by *Warrenella* and *Atrypa*, which is so abundant in the *Atrypa*-Bryozoa community, is much less fragmented and disarticulated. It appears, therefore, to be a lower energy, deeper water community of the slope.

Emanuella-Pelecypod Community

The sedimentary matrix is shale, very calcareous and commonly platy, closely interbedded with shaly limestone. The fauna includes numerous *Emanuella*, commonly in lensoid brachiopod coquinas, and scattered pelecypods, especially *Paracyclas* and *Paleoneilo*. *Paleoneilo* was probably a burrowing deposit-feeder, as were all the nuculoid bivalves, and *Paracyclas* probably was infaunal also. Trilobite fragments (*e.g.*, *Dechenella*), ostracods, and indeterminate brachiopod fragments, including spiriferids, are found in this community.

The *Emanuella*-Pelecypod community probably represents a virtually *in situ* fossil community with few transported elements. The environment was clearly one with a soft mud substrate and relatively low energy, indicating perhaps a basinal or lower-slope environment.

Pelagic Community

The lithologic type is mainly calcareous shale; platy bedding is common, and a few limestone interbeds are present. The limestones are varied, including micrites, fossiliferous micrites, calcisiltites, and scarce calcarenites. Pyrite is common.

The fauna, which is largely pelagic, includes *Tentaculites*, *Styliolina*, *Novakia*, *Agoniatites*, *Anarcestes*, other goniatites, crinoids, orthoconic nautiloids, and a few brachiopods and ostracods.

Some of the shales contain abundant *Lingula*, which normally is regarded as a littoral shallow-water genus (Ziegler, 1965; Bretsky, 1968; Paine, 1970) with an affinity for conditions of somewhat less than normal salinity. Paine's studies off the California coast have indicated, however, that some—though not most —modern lingulids are very abundant on a muddy substrate in deeper water, below wave base. Also, Bulman (1964) cited examples from the lower Paleozoic of the Welsh geosyncline where abundant, very small forms of *Lingula* are associated with graptolites and other pelagic elements of a deep-water facies. He suggested that these tiny inarticulate brachiopods may actually represent the pelagic larval stages of the nearshore benthonic adult *Lingula*, and quoted J. Wichstead (personal commun.) as having observed such larvae in modern tropical oceans where the *Lingula* larvae are much larger than those found near shore.

The populations found in the "Funeral" shales of the Liard-Nahanni area could well fit the larvae hypothesis, because almost all are very small forms. Therefore, on the basis of (1) this hypothesis regarding the *Lingula* forms present and (2) an associated fauna dominated by pelagic organisms, it is concluded that the *Lingula* associations and the entire pelagic community represent relatively deep-water or basinal environments.

NAHANNI FORMATION SHELF-BASIN TRANSITION

The pure, resistant carbonate rocks of the Nahanni Formation grade laterally into shale and limestone with a relatively high shale content in a distance of less than 1 mi (1.6 km). The lithologic changes and the principal faunal changes which accompany this transition are shown in Figures 6 and 7. The photograph in Figure 8 was taken in the vicinity of section 3 (Figs. 1, 6, 7); it clearly documents the physical outcrop expression of these changes as distinct wedge-shaped lithosomes intertonguing with their shaly time-equivalents. There is no question that sedimentation of the basinal shales and the carbonate units was contemporaneous, and the transition appears to be moderately abrupt.

Of the three suggested models (Fig. 4) for the shelf-basin transition, model III can be ruled out because there is no evidence that a barrier reef formed part of the Nahanni complex at the edge of the shelf. Model II, with a definite shelf edge and a moderate slope, ap-

Fig. 8—Photograph of Nahanni carbonate-shale transition, Meilleur Creek–South Nahanni River area.

pears to represent more accurately the actual situation—as evidenced by the faunal communities and their interpreted environments (Fig. 6)—than does model I. The communities and associated lithologies suggest broad ecologic zones of a slightly restricted environment behind the shelf edge, several narrow zones at the shelf edge and slope (some indicating a higher energy shoal environment), and an abrupt change to the deeper water pelagic environment of the basin.

Furthermore, the relatively abrupt transition between carbonate rock and shale would be difficult to explain if the clastic sediments were deposited from suspension onto an almost flat sea floor dominated by carbonate beds. Also, any change in relative sea level or change in supply of clastic sediments would be reflected in a lateral shift of lithofacies and communities —the extent of which should be controlled largely by the slope of the sea floor. Thus, on a very gentle slope, widespread shifts of lithofacies and communities should occur, whereas the relatively short wedge-shaped intertongues of different facies and communities observed in the vicinity of section 3 (Figs. 6, 7) could be expected to form in response to changes of sea level on a moderately steep slope of perhaps a few degrees.

The Nahanni carbonate-shale transition, therefore, is interpreted to represent the approximate margin of a shelf separated by a definite slope from a deeper basin, as schematized in model II (Fig. 4).

The term "epeiric slope" is suggested for this structure because of the analogy with the continental slope at the edges of the continents. Although small in dimension, the epeiric slope appears to represent a tectonic hinge line which separates basin and shelf areas and which is modified from time to time by renewed structural movement and by sedimentation.

Arnica Shelf-Basin Transition

It is evident that the carbonate-shale transition of the Arnica-"Funeral" strata is even more abrupt than the Nahanni carbonate-shale transition. The transition is shown to occur between sections 2 and 3 (Fig. 6), but the abruptness of the transition can best be demonstrated farther north in the Ram Plateau area (Fig. 1). There, the carbonate beds grade abruptly into "Funeral" shale in a distance of a few tens of feet (Fig. 9). Little or no intertonguing has been observed in these outcrops; the carbonate units at this boundary are the coarsely crystalline dolomites of the Manetoe facies. At several localities, faint relics of stromatoporoids and corals and well-developed algal laminites can be observed in the Manetoe facies, and it appears that the epeiric slope of the carbonate shelf of these older rocks was probably reefal and had a steep dip into the basin of as much as 30–40°. The relations are shown schematically in model III of Figure 4.

Further evidence in support of a reefal edge to the Arnica-Manetoe shelf is the character of the lithology and fauna shelfward of this edge. The lithology is invariably dolomitic, and the beds are barren or have a very poorly developed fauna—as is characteristic of restricted, hypersaline lagoonal conditions. It appears, therefore, that the boundary between the shelf and the deeper basin during deposition of the Arnica Formation was quite abrupt, and was defined by a barrier reef. Later, however, as the basin filled with terrigenous sediments, the relief between the shelf and basin decreased, and

FIG. 9—Photograph of Arnica-Manetoe carbonate-shale transition, Ram Plateau area.
See Figure 1 for location.

true reefal development in this area diminished. With the removal of the restriction caused by the barrier reef, almost normal saline conditions were restored to this part of the shelf, and the various faunal communities described in the Nahanni and Headless Formations were able to flourish.

CONCLUSIONS

A broad shallow area of carbonate and evaporite deposition, at least 350 mi (550 km) across, bordered the Canadian shield in early Middle Devonian time. As confirmed by the correlation of specific faunal zones, this carbonate shelf passed westerly into a clastic basin, or marginal cratonic trough, which extends hundreds of miles both north and south of the study area. The trough sediments probably were derived from a source on the west.

Examination of the faunal communities and sediments associated with the boundary between these two provinces suggests a steepening of the sea floor along the seaward side of this boundary. This paleotopographic feature of the sea floor is termed an "epeiric slope" because

of the analogy with the continental slope at the edges of the continents.

The dolomitic shelf sediments of the *Warrenella* sp. 1 and *Gasterocoma? bicaula* zones were formed in a shallow, restricted lagoonal environment, probably behind a (Manetoe) barrier reef bordering the shelf and separating it from a deeper water basin. The basin was filling with a thick wedge of fine clastic sediment from the west. The steepness of the epeiric slope at this time, which may have been of the order of 30–40°, resulted in a relatively abrupt carbonate-bank edge.

In *Schuchertella adoceta*–zone time, the shales of the Headless Formation filled the basin, transgressed the epeiric slope, and covered much of the outer shelf. During *Billingsastrea verrilli*–zone time, carbonate sediments of the Nahanni Formation were deposited not only on the outer shelf, but also on the slope at the edge of the shelf. The slope deposits are recognizable now as two wedge-shaped lithosomes representing two regressive pulses separated by a minor transgressive pulse (Fig. 6). The epeiric slope at the time appears to have been of the order of a few degrees, and the transition to clastic sediments was more gradual than during deposition of the Manetoe.

A major transgression in *Leiorhynchus castanea*–zone time resulted in widespread deposition of the Middle Devonian shales over the limestones of the Nahanni Formation at the shelf edge and well onto the shelf.

REFERENCES

Bassett, H. G., and J. G. Stout, 1967, Devonian of Western Canada, *in* D. H. Oswald, ed., International symposium on the Devonian System: Calgary, Alberta Soc. Petroleum Geologists, v. 1, p. 717–752.

Bretsky, P. W., 1968, Evolution of Paleozoic marine invertebrate communities: Science, v. 159, p. 1231–1233.

Bulman, O. M. B., 1964, Lower Palaeozoic plankton: Geol. Soc. London Quart. Jour., v. 120, p. 455–476.

Copper, Paul, 1967, Adaptations and life habits of Devonian atrypid brachiopods: Palaeogeography, Palaeoclimatology, Palaeoecology, v. 3, p. 361–379.

Craig, J., *et al.*, 1967, Chinchaga and Keg River Formations of Slave River area, northern Alberta: Bull. Canadian Petroleum Geology, v. 15, no. 2, p. 125–137.

Crickmay, C. H., 1966, Devonian time in Western Canada: Calgary, E. de Mille Books, 38 p.

Douglas, R. J. W., and D. K. Norris, 1960, Virginia Falls and Sibbeston Lake map-areas, Northwest Territories: Canada Geol. Survey Paper 60–19.

—— and —— 1961, Camsell Bend and Root River map-areas, District of Mackenzie, Northwest Territories: Canada Geol. Survey Paper 61–13.

Fagerstrom, J. A., 1964, Fossil communities in paleoecology—their recognition and significance: Geol. Soc. America Bull., v. 75, p. 1197–1216.

Irwin, M. L., 1965, General theory of epeiric clear-water sedimentation: Am. Assoc. Petroleum Geologists Bull., v. 49, p. 445–459.

Johnson, J. G., and N. G. Lane, 1969, Two new Devonian crinoids from central Nevada: Jour. Paleontology, v. 43, no. 1, p. 69–73.

Laporte, L. F., 1969, Recognition of a transgressive carbonate sequence within an epeiric sea—Helderberg Group (Lower Devonian) of New York State, *in* G. M. Friedman, ed., Depositional environments in carbonate rocks: Soc. Econ. Paleontologists and Mineralogists Spec. Pub. 14, p. 98–119.

Lecompte, M., 1956, Quelques precisions sur le phenomenon recifal dans le Devonien de l'Ardenne et sur le rythme sedimentative dans lequel il s'entégre: Belgique Inst. Royal Sci. Nat. Bull., v. 32, no. 21, p. 39.

McDaniel, P. N., and L. C. Pray, 1969, Bank to basin transition in Permian (Leonardian) carbonates, Guadalupe Mountains, Texas, *in* G. M. Friedman, ed., Depositional environments in carbonate rocks (abs.): Soc. Econ. Paleontologists and Mineralogists Spec. Pub. 14, p. 79.

McLaren, D. J., 1962, Middle and early Upper Devonian rhynchonelloid brachiopods from Western Canada: Canada Geol. Survey Bull. 86.

Norris, A. W., 1963, Devonian stratigraphy of northeastern Alberta and northwestern Saskatchewan: Canada Geol. Survey Mem. 313.

—— 1965, Stratigraphy of Middle Devonian and older Palaeozoic rocks of the Great Slave Lake region, Northwest Territories: Canada Geol. Survey Mem. 322.

Paine, R. T., 1970, The sediment occupied by recent lingulid brachiopods and some palaeoecological implications: Palaeogeography, Palaeoclimatology, Palaeoecology, v. 7, no. 1, p. 21–32.

Pedder, A. E. H., 1964, Correlation of the Canadian Middle Devonian Hume and Nahanni Formations by tetracorals: Palaeontology, v. 7, pt. 3, p. 430–451.

Peterson, C. G., 1924, A brief survey of the animal communities in Danish waters: Am. Jour. Sci., ser. 5, v. 7, no. 41, p. 343–354.

Rainville, R. A., 1968, Correlation of the Hume and Nahanni Formations, Northwest Territories, Canada: Univ. Saskatchewan, unpub. B.S. thesis.

Shaw, A. B., 1964, Time in stratigraphy: New York, McGraw-Hill Book Co., 365 p.

Thomson, A. F., and M. R. Thomasson, 1969, Shallow to deep water facies development in the Dimple Limestone (Lower Pennsylvanian), Marathon region, Texas, *in* G. M. Friedman, ed., Depositional environments in carbonate rocks: Soc. Econ. Paleontologists and Mineralogists Spec. Pub. 14, p. 57–78.

Thorson, G., 1957, Bottom communities (sublittoral or shallow shelf), *in* Treatise on marine ecology and paleoecology: Geol. Soc. America Mem. 67, v. 1, p. 461–534.

Tyrrell, W. W., Jr., 1969, Criteria useful in interpreting environments of unlike but time-equivalent carbonate units (Tansill-Capitan-Lamar), Capitan reef complex, West Texas and New Mexico, *in* G. M. Friedman, ed., Depositional environments in carbonate rocks: Soc. Econ. Paleontologists and Mineralogists Spec. Pub. 14, p. 80–97.

Ziegler, A. M., 1965, Silurian marine communities and their environmental significance: Nature, v. 207, p. 270–272.

Regional Arctic Geology of the Nordic Countries

Development of the Precambrian Shield in West Greenland, Labrador, and Baffin Island[1]

D. BRIDGWATER,[2] A. ESCHER,[2] G. D. JACKSON,[3] F. C. TAYLOR,[3] and B. F. WINDLEY[4]

Copenhagen, Denmark; Ottawa, Ontario; and Leicester, England

Abstract The Precambrian rocks on either side of Davis Strait show a similar pattern of events and are interpreted as having formed part of a single shield. Nine major stages in the development of this shield are suggested: (1) formation of an extensive early crust before 3,000 m.y. ago, relicts of which are now preserved as migmatites and high-grade gneisses in the Archean block of eastern Labrador and southwest Greenland; (2) deposition of greenstone belts 2,700–3,000 m.y. ago; (3) plutonic activity in the period 2,500–2,900 m.y. ago, affecting both the greenstone belts and the major parts of the basement on which the greenstones lie; (4) intrusion of numerous basic dike swarms in the general period 2,000–2,600 m.y. ago; (5) deposition of early Proterozoic (Aphebian) geosynclinal rocks on the consolidated Archean basement; (6) alteration of these rocks by orogenesis which occurred approximately 1,650–1,850 m.y. ago (the Hudsonian orogeny in Canada and the Ketilidian and Nagssugtoqidian orogenies in Greenland); (7) post-orogenic magmatism—particularly marked in areas affected by Hudsonian metamorphism—which extended from South Greenland through Labrador (This magmatism produced chiefly anorthosites, adamellitic granites, monzonites, and norites, which probably were emplaced between 1,400 and 1,700 m.y. ago, although the areas in which they occur commonly remained thermally active to 1,200 m.y. ago or later.); (8) graben faulting, deposition of molasse sediments, and widespread intrusion of basic dikes, in South Greenland and in parts of Baffin Island, accompanying and following emplacement of the post-orogenic rocks (Most of these dikes are tholeiitic; however, alkalic and peralkalic intrusions took place locally 1,100–1,300 m.y. ago.); (9) metamorphism and tectonic alteration of the Archean and Proterozoic rocks in the southern part of the Canadian shield by the Grenville orogeny about 900–1,100 m.y. ago. The only effect of the Grenville orogeny in South Greenland was a weak updating of older rocks in areas close to major faults, so that they yield K-Ar ages of about 900–1,000 m.y.

Introduction

Early workers in western Greenland and along the eastern coast of Baffin Island and Labrador regarded these areas as essentially similar. Recent regional mapping by the Geological

[1] Manuscript received, September 20, 1971. (*Note:* Manuscript was submitted to Editor in March; thus, late developments during interim period are not included.)

[2] Geological Survey of Greenland.

[3] Geological Survey of Canada.

[4] Leicester University.

B. F. Windley acknowledges the receipt of a grant from the National Environment Research Council, London. Permission from the Geological Surveys of Greenland and Canada, and from Leicester University, to publish this paper is gratefully acknowledged.

Surveys of Canada and Greenland has substantiated these suggestions. In this paper, we wish to present some of the main features of the areas as a unit and show how the crust in this region developed over a major part of geologic time. We hope that this paper will stimulate interest in this area outside the relatively narrow field of Precambrian regional geology and will serve as a background for a variety of studies —ranging from attempts to find out when and how much movement has taken place between Canada and Greenland to studies of the nature of the sea floor between the two areas.

In order to understand better the mutual problems encountered by geologists working in Greenland and Canada, field visits were arranged between staff members of the Geological Survey of Canada and the Geological Survey of Greenland. This type of cooperation is essential in order to unravel the complex geology encountered in these regions, and we thank Directors K. Ellitsgaard-Rasmussen and Y. O. Fortier for their help in supporting and stimulating this work. It is hoped that additional field visits can be arranged in future years, because on-the-ground discussions are a far more effective form of cooperation than are library investigations.

The development of the shield areas under discussion can be readily divided into nine stages, starting in the Archean and extending into the late Proterozoic (Hadrynian). These stages involve deposition of sediments and lavas, folding, metamorphism, and plutonism— either singly or together. The major geologic divisions correspond approximately to the subdivisions made by use of K-Ar determinations; Figure 1 shows K-Ar age provinces of the two shield areas replaced into their supposed pre-drift position on the basis of the 500-fm submarine-contour fit suggested by Bullard *et al.* (1965). The similarity of geologic phenomena observed on either side of Davis Strait and the broad continuation of the age provinces shown in Figure 1 allow the assumption that the Precambrian areas of Greenland, Labrador, and Baffin Island once formed part of a single shield. The major divisions in Greenland and

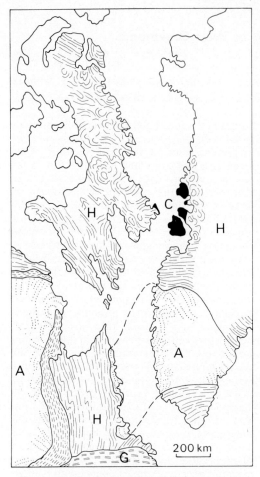

Fig. 1—Sketch map showing main K-Ar age provinces in Labrador, Baffin Island, and West Greenland replaced in their supposed predrift position. **A** = Archean rocks essentially unmodified by event younger than 2,500 m.y. ago. **C** = Cretaceous and younger sedimentary and volcanic rocks. **H** = areas giving K-Ar ages between 1,200 and 2,000 m.y.; position of Labrador trough is indicated by dashed lines. **G** = areas giving K-Ar ages between 900 and 1,200 m.y. Black = Mesozoic and Tertiary platform cover rocks.

Canada are shown in Table 1. Although there is general agreement about the timing of events on either side of the Davis Strait, the subdivision of Precambrian time used by the two Surveys differs slightly because different principals have been used.

Archean Rocks of Labrador and West Greenland

The first four stages recognized in the development of the Labrador and Greenland shield occurred before 2,400 m.y. ago; thus, they are grouped together as Archean. Archean rocks unaffected by later regional metamorphic events extend from near Frederikshåb north to Søndre Strømfjord in Greenland, and from just north of Makkovik to near Nachvak Bay in Labrador. This Archean area is only 65 mi (100 km) wide in Labrador, whereas in Greenland it extends under the Inland Ice for 250 mi (400 km) and crops out again along the east coast. Although no indisputable Archean isotopic ages have been obtained from Baffin Island rocks, two Rb-Sr isochrons of 2,341 and 2,607 m.y. on basement gneisses are significantly older than K-Ar ages from the same region; they support the conclusions, drawn from field work, that reworked Archean gneisses probably crop out in much of northwestern and central Baffin Island. Similarly, most of the rocks found north of Søndre Strømfjord in West Greenland can be shown to be Archean gneisses reworked during later metamorphic events so that they now give K-Ar ages between 1,650 and 2,000 m.y. (Ramberg, 1949; Pulvertaft, 1968).

Stage 1. Early Archean Basement

The Archean rocks of Greenland consist of two tectono-metamorphic groups—high-grade gneisses and low- or medium-grade schist belts. The former represent the first stage of shield development and involve rocks which have undergone granulite-facies or high-grade amphibolite-facies metamorphism, although many subsequently have been downgraded to amphibolite facies during a later orogenic event. Sporadic K-Ar age determinations from West Greenland have given ages older than 3,000 m.y. (Lambert and Simons, 1969; Larsen, 1971), and, although no reliance can be placed on any single determination, both the available isotopic evidence and the geologic interpretation suggest that the majority of the Archean rocks in western Greenland were formed before 3,100 m.y. ago and many of them were reworked during Kenoran plutonic activity. Petrologically, many of the Archean rocks of eastern Labrador resemble the early rocks of western Greenland and may be of the same age; however, no ages over 2,720 m.y. have been reported.

The Archean basement rocks group naturally into (1) ancient supracrustal rocks, (2) quartzo-feldspathic gneisses, and (3) anorthosites.

Ancient supracrustal rocks—The ancient supracrustal rocks, which are a common minor constituent of the Archean basement, occur as

Table 1. Subdivisions of Precambrian Used by Geological Survey of Canada and Geological Survey of Greenland

		EASTERN CANADA		WEST GREENLAND			
AGE m.y.	Time divn. GSC	**Events and Rock Units** Magmatic volcanic and sedimentary	Tectonic metamorphic	**Events and Rock Units** Tectonic metamorphic	Magmatic volcanic and sedimentary	Time divn. GGU	AGE m.y.
500	EON / HADRYNIAN ERA	Lamprophyre dikes (Makkovik); Franklin diabase dikes (Baffin Island)	Southeast tension faults		Kimberlite dikes (K/Ar age)	PRECAMBRIAN V	500
1000	PROTEROZOIC / HELIKIAN	Syn-tectonic intrusions GRENVILLE OROGENY; Uluksen sedimentary rocks; Eqalulik sedimentary and volcanic rocks (Northern Baffin Island and Bylot Island); Seal Group Mugford Group; Croteau Group Ramah Group; (sediments and volcanic rocks); Small syenite intrusions; Diabase dikes; Adamellite plutons; Anorthosite plutons; Diabase dikes	Southeast faults; East-west faults; Regional argon loss (?)	Movement on east-west faults in South Greenland; Loss of radiogenic argon in many areas suggesting slight regional metamorphism	GARDAR PROVINCE — Peralkaline intrusions; Major syenite and associated granite intrusions; Major diabase and alkali gabbro dike swarms (S. Greenland); Carbonatites; Sandstones and lavas; Widespread north-south diabase dike swarms; Rapakivi granites of Kap Farvel area, Calc-alkaline intrusions Julianehåb area	PRECAMBRIAN IV	1000
1500		Syn-orogenic porphyritic granitic intrusions HUDSONIAN OROGENY		Main phase of the KETILIDIAN OROGENY in South Greenland	Syn-tectonic granites intermediate and basic intrusions		1500
2000	APHEBIAN	Diabase dikes (?); Deposition of Kaniapiskau Supergroup, Aillik, Mary River, Hoare Bay and Piling Groups. Sedimentary and volcanic rocks, and associated basic and ultrabasic rocks and anorthosite sills		NAGSSUGTOQIDIAN — Deformation in West Greenland north of 66°N, Faulting in Archean craton	Deposition of the Vallen and Sortis Groups; Major dike swarms including syntectonic dikes in the border zone of the Nagssugtoqidian mobile belt	PRECAMBRIAN III	2000
2500	ARCHEAN	Major east-west and north-south diabase dike swarms; KENORAN OROGENY		MAJOR OROGENESIS affecting much of West Greenland	Deposition of Tartoq Group	PRECAMBRIAN II	2500
3000		Sedimentary and volcanic rocks and intrusion of small ultrabasic plutons		Widespread granulite facies metamorphism	Late tectonic anorthosites and granites; Intrusion of granites; Intrusion of calcic chrome-bearing anorthosites; Early sediments, lavas and ultrabasic intrusions	PRECAMBRIAN I	3000
3500					Major dike swarm; Early granitic crust		3500

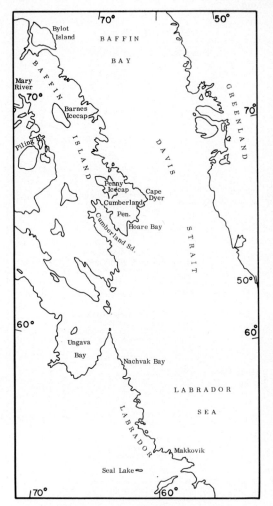

FIG. 2—Locality map of Eastern Canada.

layers of amphibolitic and metasedimentary rocks which have been metamorphosed and deformed along with the surrounding gneisses, but in which evidence of their origin has been preserved. Individual rock sequences rarely exceed 1–2 km (3,300–6,600 ft) in thickness and are generally measurable in hundreds, or even tens, of meters across the strike. They commonly persist for tens of kilometers or more along strike, and some provide good structural marker horizons. The larger units locally may contain relict structures such as pillows, agglomeratic zones, or crossbedding within the siliceous layers; these structures can be used to demonstrate the origin of the rocks. In general, the best indication of the provenance of these

rocks is the abrupt alternation of layers of markedly different composition; this condition resembles the alternation of beds in more recent, unmetamorphosed supracrustal sequences. Individual sequences are widely separated and impersistent on a regional scale, and correlation between areas is unreliable. A common pattern in widely separated sequences suggests that deposition may have taken place in similar environments.

Four main rock types are common: (1) amphibolite or pyroxene amphibolite with a general basaltic composition; (2) ultramafic pods and semiconcordant layers, commonly interstratified with the amphibolite; (3) aluminous biotite schists with sillimanite, cordierite, garnet (and, locally, graphite), thin calc-silicate bands, and iron-rich quartzites; and (4) homogeneous granitic or granodioritic gneisses with enough lithologic variation within the layers to suggest a supracrustal origin such as acidic volcanism or recrystallization of metagraywacke.

Quartzo-feldspathic gneisses—These rocks form the major rock type in the Archean block. They vary considerably in general appearance, ranging from layers of homogeneous granite or tonalitic gneiss to migmatite and agmatite. In granulite-facies areas the quartzo-feldspathic gneisses are brown and consist essentially of quartz, plagioclase, and hypersthene. In some areas, biotite and potassium feldspar are major rock-forming components, whereas in others the gneisses appear almost devoid of potassium-bearing minerals. In amphibolite-facies areas the gneisses are white or gray biotite-hornblende-quartz-plagioclase rocks with a similar variation in potassium feldspar. Three origins have been suggested for the quartzo-feldspathic rocks. They may have formed an older, mainly granitic basement on which the supracrustal rocks described above were deposited. This relation has been demonstrated in the Godthåbs Fjord region of West Greenland (McGregor, 1968, 1969), where basic dikes intrude the quartzo-feldspathic gneisses but are absent in the cover rocks. The quartzo-feldspathic rocks may represent recrystallized units of granitic or granodioritic composition—for example, acidic volcanic rocks or rocks with a variable component derived from volcanic rocks or graywackes, as advocated by Kalsbeek (1970). The third possible origin is as semiconcordant granitic or tonalitic intrusions emplaced along structural boundaries such as older unconformities. In Greenland, each of these origins is locally demonstrable; however, the proportion

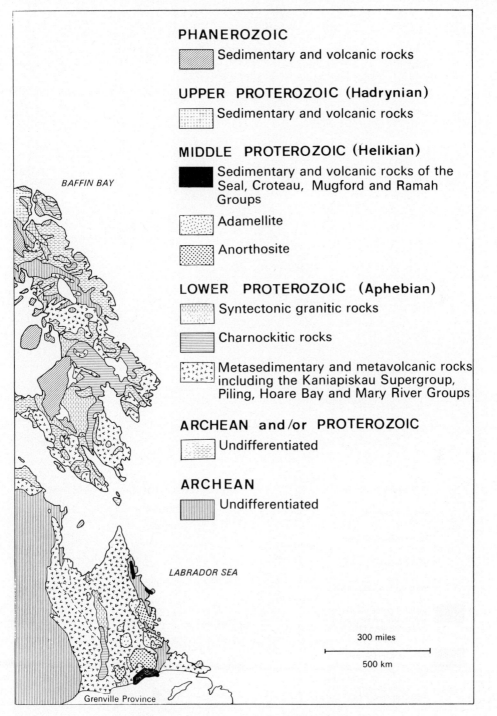

PHANEROZOIC
Sedimentary and volcanic rocks

UPPER PROTEROZOIC (Hadrynian)
Sedimentary and volcanic rocks

MIDDLE PROTEROZOIC (Helikian)
Sedimentary and volcanic rocks of the Seal, Croteau, Mugford and Ramah Groups

Adamellite

Anorthosite

LOWER PROTEROZOIC (Aphebian)
Syntectonic granitic rocks

Charnockitic rocks

Metasedimentary and metavolcanic rocks including the Kaniapiskau Supergroup, Piling, Hoare Bay and Mary River Groups

ARCHEAN and/or PROTEROZOIC
Undifferentiated

ARCHEAN
Undifferentiated

BAFFIN BAY

LABRADOR SEA

300 miles

500 km

Grenville Province

FIG. 3—Geologic sketch map of Eastern Canada.

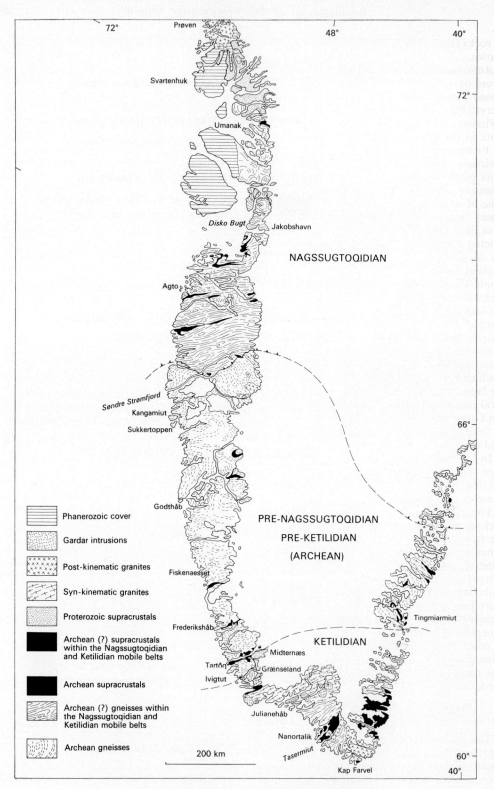

FIG. 4—Geologic sketch map of West Greenland.

The following labels appear on the map:

72° 48° 40°

Prøven

Svartenhuk

Umanak

72°

Disko Bugt   Jakobshavn

NAGSSUGTOQIDIAN

Agto

Søndre Strømfjord
Kangamiut

Sukkertoppen

66°

Godthåb

PRE-NAGSSUGTOQIDIAN

PRE-KETILIDIAN

(ARCHEAN)

Fiskenaesset

Tingmiarmiut

Frederikshåb

KETILIDIAN

Tartôq   Midternæs

Ivigtut   Grænseland

Julianehåb

Nanortalik

Tasermiut   60°

Kap Farvel   40°

Legend:

- Phanerozoic cover
- Gardar intrusions
- Post-kinematic granites
- Syn-kinematic granites
- Proterozoic supracrustals
- Archean (?) supracrustals within the Nagssugtoqidian and Ketilidian mobile belts
- Archean supracrustals
- Archean (?) gneisses within the Nagssugtoqidian and Ketilidian mobile belts
- Archean gneisses

200 km

of rocks representing each type of origin is not known.

Anorthosites—The anorthosites occur in layers or as fragments in gneisses which have passed through several periods of metamorphic recrystallization and tectonic reworking (Windley, 1969). Some persist as mappable units in the areas of Archean rocks reworked by Proterozoic metamorphism (*e.g.*, the Ivigtut gneisses). Many of these anorthositic rock units probably belong to the upper parts of an extensive lopolith, the chromite-layered root zone of which is well preserved as the Fisken-aesset meta-igneous complex in southwest Greenland (Windley *et al.*, in press). Restricted metasomatism of Mg- and Al-rich layers of the complex has given rise to many unusual mineral assemblages—for example, sapphirine–kornerupine–red corundum-bearing rocks (Herd *et al.*, 1969).

General—The early Archean rocks show complex structural patterns. Multiple folding is ubiquitous, and detailed mapping of distinctive units—the anorthosites, for example—commonly shows that some layers are themselves isoclinal folds and that these folds acted as single layers during later folding. No overall structural trend is apparent in the Archean of western Greenland, but the dominant pattern is that of "eye folds" caused by the imposition of one fold direction upon another.

In Labrador the Archean rocks show a dominant north-south structure possibly caused by the imposition of a later structure on older complex fold patterns.

The metamorphic history of the Archean rocks is equally complex. Major areas of granulite-facies rocks are surrounded by transitional zones in which older fabrics and high-grade mineral assemblages have been partially destroyed and their place has been taken by amphibolite-facies minerals. This retrograde metamorphism commonly accompanies intense deformation; thus, the amphibolite-facies areas generally show only a simple fabric. However, in other areas, gneisses with amphibolite-facies mineralogy are interlayered with granulite-facies rocks or are present as relicts within granulite-facies hosts.

Stage 2. Archean Volcanism and Sedimentation

The second stage in shield development is represented in Greenland by well-preserved Archean basic volcanic and sedimentary rocks forming belts a few kilometers wide and up to 100 km (65 mi) long. These belts are gener-ally conformable with the structures in the surrounding gneisses; only in a few places are unconformable relations with the basement rocks preserved. The general structure of the greenstone belts is very similar to the much larger greenstone belts of the Canadian shield (Goodwin, 1968). No comparable units have been recognized from the Archean of Labrador. Belts of similar rock units preserved within the areas affected by Hudsonian metamorphism and deformation in Baffin Island, and in the more northerly parts of West Greenland, may also represent Archean strata. Unpublished preliminary Rb-Sr work done recently by B. J. Fryer at Massachusetts Institute of Technology suggests a minimum age of about 1,950 m.y. for part of the Mary River Group of northern Baffin Island. The Greenland rocks have metamorphic ages of about 2,500 m.y., so the period of deposition probably preceded the Kenoran orogeny and was perhaps 2,700–3,000 m.y. ago.

In Greenland the best-known rocks are the Tartoq Group (Higgins, 1968), southeast of Frederikshåb. The group consists predominantly of basic volcanic rocks (including pillow lavas); metasedimentary rocks—including calcareous schists, conglomerates, and pale siliceous schists of possibly volcanic origin—compose 10–15 percent. Farther north at Isua, at the head of Godthåbs Fjord, the Cryolite Company of Copenhagen has discovered a 40-km-long (25 mi) belt of greenschist-facies supracrustal rocks (Keto, 1970). The succession contains a siliceous lower unit, a central meta-taconite iron formation with magnetite as the dominant iron mineral, and, at the top, a basic volcanic unit including pyroclastic material. This succession forms an arcuate belt as wide as 5 km (3 mi) surrounding a domelike structure in the older Archean gneisses.

Presumably Archean supracrustal rocks are also preserved as major units within the areas affected by Proterozoic orogenesis. Thick marbles are known from the basement rocks underlying the Proterozoic strata of the Umanak district (Henderson and Pulvertaft, 1967).

Stage 3. Late Archean (Kenoran) Orogeny

Between 2,500 and 2,800 m.y. ago, most of the Archean rocks of Labrador, Greenland, and presumably Baffin Island were affected by a major period of metamorphism and plutonic activity known in Canada as the Kenoran orogeny. In Greenland this orogeny affected both the greenstone belts and many of the basement rocks. Most of the retrogressive metamorphism at the margins of major areas of granulite is attributed to this orogeny. The unconformities between the greenstone belts and the underlying gneisses commonly acted as zones of weakness during this orogeny; the result was metamorphic and structural convergence in the boundary zones. A transitional zone between the basement and cover rocks is injected by innumerable granite veins and sheets. The thinner belts of greenstones became completely concordant with the surrounding gneisses and developed moderately high-grade mineral assemblages (sillimanite-cordierite in pelitic bands). In the Frederikshåb area of southwestern Greenland, at least two major phases of folding occurred postdating the deposition of the supracrustal rocks described under stage 2. In other areas the Kenoran orogeny is characterized by large amounts of injected granitic and granodioritic material. Locally—*e.g.*, south of Søndre Strømfjord, West Greenland—porphyritic hypersthene granites, quartz syenites, and anorthositic plutons were emplaced (Escher *et al.*, 1970). These rocks resemble petrographically the anorthosite-adamellite suites intruded in much larger amounts in the Proterozoic.

In Labrador the Kenoran orogeny is characterized by development of the dominantly north-trending structures, by amphibolite metamorphism, and by acidic plutonic activity including extensive migmatization. It is not known at present whether granulites, many of which are downgraded to amphibolite facies, are the result of an earlier orogeny or an early phase of the Kenoran. Small ultramafic plutons probably were emplaced during this mountain building.

The age and nature of the orogeny represented by the probably Archean rocks of Baffin Island have not been determined.

Stage 4. Late Archean–Early Proterozoic Dike Swarms and Faults

The end of the Archean was marked by the intrusion of several generations of late tectonic to post-tectonic diabase dikes. Great swarms of east- and north-trending dikes occur in both Labrador and Greenland. These dikes, remarkably fresh except near later tectonic zones, yield K-Ar ages of 2,000 to 2,600 m.y. In Greenland, between Sukkertoppen and Søndre Strømfjord, at least 350 dikes more than 30 m (100 ft) thick, composing the Kangâmiut dike swarm, intruded the consolidated basement. Comparable numbers of dikes of approximately the same age also are present on the east coast of Greenland. Toward the north the dikes and the sur-

rounding country rock became strongly reoriented tectonically with the formation of a new regional fabric in an ENE-NE direction (Fig. 5). Recent field observations (Escher, Escher, and Watterson, in press) suggest that this reorientation was due mainly to overthrusting and shearing from northwest to southeast. This deformation defines the Nagssugtoqidian earth movements (Ramberg, 1949), which, until recently, were regarded as broadly equivalent in time to the Hudsonian orogeny of Baffin Island. However, current work suggests that the injection of the dikes and their subsequent reorientation may be closely related—and both may have taken place in Archean time. Field evidence from the area north of Søndre Strømfjord suggests that the Kangâmiut dolerites were intruded locally after, or contemporaneous with, first movements along the east-northeast shear directions. Farther south within the Archean block in the Sukkertoppen area, one group of dikes shows petrological and textural peculiarities attributed to intrusion under synkinematic conditions (Windley, 1970).

In the center of the Archean block of West Greenland, dikes are scarcer and their chronologies are not known. At least three generations of late Archean–early Proterozoic dikes are present (Chadwick, 1969).

On Baffin Island, dikes that are correlated with this period of intrusion are commonly deformed and metamorphosed, and, in some places at least, have a predominantly northeasterly trend.

The Archean block was affected by considerable faulting, which can be described under two headings: faults developed during the final stages of Archean metamorphism and younger post-orogenic faults. In Labrador and the southern part of the Greenland Archean block, faults of both types are most common in a north-south to NNE-SSW direction. On Baffin Island and in the northern part of the Greenland Archean block, the main fault direction is more ENE-WSW to east-west, although southeasterly trends are also common on Baffin Island. In Greenland the emplacement of many of the late Archean diabase dikes was approximately contemporaneous with major movements along the faults.

THE PROTEROZOIC

Stage 5. Early Proterozoic (Aphebian) Volcanism and Sedimentation

After the consolidation of the Archean basement, early Proterozoic (Aphebian) units were deposited as a cover on the older rocks between

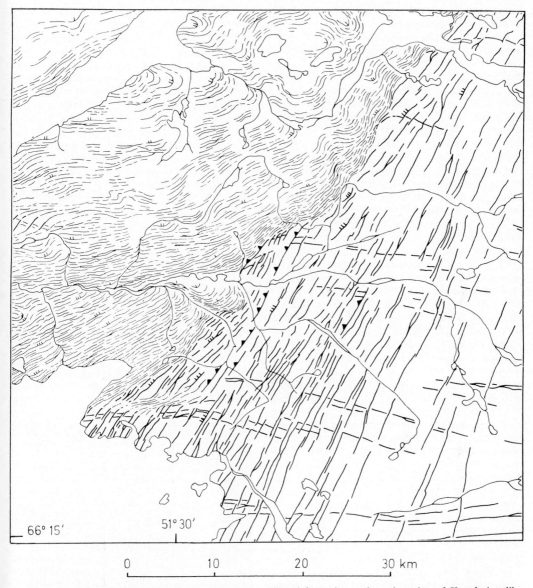

Fig. 5—Sketch map showing effects of Nagssugtoqidian deformation and reorientation of Kangâmiut dike swarm south of Søndre Strømfjord, West Greenland. In unreworked areas at southeast, two dominant directions of diabase dikes are seen. Northwestward, members of the same swarms become progressively deformed and reoriented in a general NE-SW direction.

2,500 and 1,900 m.y. ago. These sedimentary and volcanic rocks subsequently were involved in an orogeny known as the Hudsonian in Canada and the Ketilidian in South Greenland; this orogeny occurred between 2,000 and 1,600 m.y. ago.

In Labrador the unconformity between the Archean and the Proterozoic is well preserved along the western margin of the Labrador trough, a 960-km (600 mi) belt extending south of Ungava Bay. The stratigraphy of the Kaniapiskau Supergroup is known in considerable detail from numerous government and industry surveys. Recent summaries of the regional development were given by Baragar (1967), Dimroth (1970), and Dimroth et al. (1970). There is considerable variation both along the axis of the trough and across the trough from east to west, and only the broadest outlines can be given here.

The Kaniapiskau Supergroup is divided into two parts. The lower, miogeosynclinal Knob Lake Group consists of arkose, calcareous sandstone, quartzite, shale, graywacke, dolomite, chert, and ironstone. There are local volcanic units present in some areas. Stromatolitic limestones and algal structures are locally abundant. This predominantly sedimentary succession forms the western part of the supergroup where it overlaps the Archean basement. The eastern part of the supergroup is formed by the eugeosynclinal Doublet Group, which forms a belt 60–120 km (40–80 mi) east of the western margin of the trough and consists mainly of mafic volcanic rocks including pyroclastic units, pillow lavas, massive basalts, and intercalated minor shale units. The strata of the Knob Lake and Doublet Groups were intruded by massive mafic and ultramafic sills derived from tholeiitic magmas. These sills are particularly abundant in the eastern part of the Labrador trough, where the mafic rocks total more than 6,500 m (20,000 ft) in thickness.

East of the Labrador trough the effects of Hudsonian metamorphism and plutonism are progressively more intense, and recognition of stratigraphic units is impracticable. Major units of biotite and muscovite schist, quartzite, calcsilicate rock, amphibolite, and meta-andesite have been mapped and interpreted as Aphebian strata involved in Hudsonian metamorphism (Taylor, 1969, 1970). In the Makkovik Bay area of the coast of Labrador, metasedimentary and metavolcanic rocks of the Aillik Group are interpreted as metamorphosed Aphebian strata deposited unconformably on the Archean Hopedale gneisses (Gandhi *et al.*, 1969; Stevenson, 1970). The supracrustal rocks include quartzites, tuffs, conglomerates, and metamorphosed basic and acidic lavas.

In South Greenland the unconformity between Archean and Proterozoic rocks is well preserved in the Midternaes-Graenseland area north of Ivigtut (Higgins, 1970; Bondesen, 1970; Higgins and Bondesen, 1966), where virtually unmetamorphosed sedimentary rocks lie on peneplaned Archean Ivigtut gneisses. Two major units are recognized in the Midternaes-Graenseland area—the Vallen Group, below, and the Sortis Group. The Vallen Group consists of conglomerate, shale, quartzite, arkose, dolomite, graywacke, graphitic pelite, chert, and dolomitic quartzite. Deposition started in a series of isolated basins which gradually became linked by a transgressive sea. Basal conglomerate and orthoquartzite are commonly overlain by dolomitic shale, calcareous sandstone, or dolomite. The deposition of the calcareous sediments commonly was accompanied by a deep weathering and carbonitization of the basal deposits and the top 5–10 m (16–32 ft) of the underlying Archean gneiss. Higher in the succession, several graywacke sequences show features which suggest deposition in a tectonically active environment. The upper part of the Vallen Group also contains dolomite interlayered with graphitic pelite, chert, and dolomitic quartzite. Locally, rocks in this part are highly fossiliferous with both stromatolitic algal structures and microfossils. The best known of these fossils, *Vallenia* (Bondesen *et al.*, 1967), which measures about 1 mm in diameter and is clearly visible to the naked eye, is a major rock-forming component in one dolomite zone (Fig. 6). Thin coal layers suggest that life was abundant in the Proterozoic seas from which these units were deposited.

The Sortis Group, which crops out along the eastern margin of the Proterozoic supracrustal belt up against the Inland Ice, is dominated by tholeiitic volcanic rocks including pillow lavas and pyroclastic units interlayered with some graywackes and pelites; thick intrusive sills are common. A total thickness of 4,000 m (12,000

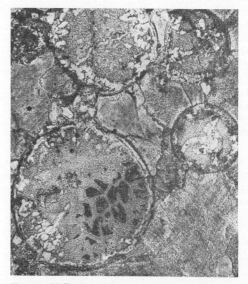

FIG. 6—*Vallenia erlingii*, a macrofossil from pre-1,900-m.y. Proterozoic Vallen Group, southwest Greenland. GGU sample 31380, ×20, collected by A. K. Higgins. (Note double-walled structure and carbonaceous material within fossil.)

ft) is recorded for the Sortis Group. Chemically, the basaltic rocks of the Sortis Group show close resemblances to the basaltic rocks of the Labrador trough.

Farther south in Greenland, effects of the Ketilidian orogeny are more pronounced, and no strict correlations are possible. The general development and many of the individual units in the Proterozoic of the Midternaes-Graenseland area show close sedimentologic similarities to the Proterozoic of the Labrador trough. However, strict correlation is neither possible nor desirable; the main conclusion to be drawn from the comparison is that the depositional environment during the early Proterozoic in the two areas appears to have been remarkably similar. Both areas show many features in common with early Proterozoic sedimentation in other parts of the North Atlantic shield—for example, the Karelian successions described by Kharitonov (1965).

South of the Midternaes-Graenseland area, in the region affected by Ketilidian orogenesis, isolated sedimentary and volcanic units have been identified in the granites. These units have been interpreted variously as lower Proterozoic rocks broadly equivalent in time to the Graenseland succession, reworked relics of Archean supracrustal sequences, and synorogenic deposits laid down during the evolution of the Ketilidian mobile belt. The high-grade pelitic and psammitic gneisses of the Nanortalik area (Escher, 1966; Dawes, 1970) show marked similarities with the high-grade paragneisses of northern Labrador (Taylor, 1969). Isolated patches of acidic volcanic flows and tuffs in the Julianehåb district and conglomerates with tuffaceous fragments found as outliers near the southern tip of Greenland show close resemblances to some rocks in the Aillik Group of the Makkovik area.

Farther north along the coast of Greenland, in the area north of Disko Bugt, extensive sequences of Proterozoic (Aphebian) supracrustal rocks were deposited on the Archean basement. A particularly extensive sequence was described from the Umanak area (Henderson and Pulvertaft, 1967), where a thickness of more than 5 km (16,400 ft) of quartzite and metagraywacke is preserved. Volcanic rocks are not present in this main area of Proterozoic cover rocks, but they have been recorded from a small area northeast of Disko Bugt (Escher and Burri, 1967).

Metasedimentary rocks of probably Aphebian age underlie much of Baffin Island (Black-

adar, 1967; Jackson, 1966, 1969, 1971). Although some of these rocks, such as the Mary River Group, may be Archean, preliminary field work suggests that most are Aphebian strata that represent a variety of depositional environments. Metamorphosed pelite, graywacke, siltstone, and sandstone predominate, and quartzite and a few carbonaceous or graphite-rich beds, probably of sedimentary origin, are also present. Ophiolite-like sequences composed of mafic and ultramafic sills and dikes and closely associated with basalt flows, various facies of iron formation, and siliceous sulfide zones compose part of the Mary River Group of northern Baffin Island (Jackson, 1966, 1969), the Piling Group of central Baffin Island, and the Hoare Bay Group of Cumberland Peninsula (Jackson, 1971). Exceptionally high-grade iron deposits, acidic metavolcanic rocks, and anorthosite sills up to 330 m (1,100 ft) thick are present in the Mary River Group (Gross, 1966; Jackson, 1966, 1969). Marble composes a persistent unit present in the lower part of the Piling Group south of the Barnes Ice Cap, and is also present in the Hoare Bay Group on Cumberland Peninsula (Jackson, 1969, 1971). A thick, sandy flysch sequence makes up the upper part of the Piling Group.

Paragneisses and migmatites derived in part from Aphebian strata dominate much of the terrane in Baffin Island. Biotite, hornblende, quartz, and feldspars predominate, but, depending in part on metamorphic grade, some rocks also contain hypersthene, clinopyroxene, garnet, andalusite, staurolite, kyanite, cordierite, sillimanite, sapphirine, vesuvianite, and/or spinel. These gneisses are difficult to differentiate from what in many places are believed to be reworked Archean rocks.

Stage 6. Late Aphebian (Hudsonian and Ketilidian) Orogenies

A large part of Labrador, virtually all of Baffin Island, and much of western and southern Greenland were involved in metamorphism, tectonism, and plutonism toward the end of early Proterozoic (Aphebian) time. K-Ar ages from the areas involved in this thermal event range from approximately 2,000 m.y. to 1,400–1,500 m.y. In the Proterozoic fold belts of both South Greenland and Labrador, there is a marked discrepancy between the sequence of formation of the different rock types as deduced from field work and the order as suggested by K-Ar determinations on individual rocks. In the Ketilidian fold belt the main metamorphic event is regarded as having taken place around 1,800–2,000 m.y. ago. The spread of K-Ar ages is ascribed partly to the regional effects of the numerous late intrusions and partly to a widespread argon loss representing high heat flow in the area for a considerable time after the end of the main geologic events recorded from field work. In Labrador the prevalence of K-Ar ages in the range 1,650–1,200 m.y. has resulted in the erection of the Elsonian as an independent orogenic term (Stockwell, 1964). In Baffin Island and in western Greenland north of Søndre Strømfjord, K-Ar determinations generally give ages older than 1,650 m.y.; these ages are believed to be a record of the time of the uplift at the end of the Hudsonian orogeny in these areas.

The fold belt that trends approximately east-northeast through southern Greenland and the belt that trends approximately north-south through Labrador show grossly similar features. Each belt may be divided into three descriptive units.

1. A marginal zone is present in which the lower Proterozoic supracrustal successions show a progressive increase in metamorphism from low greenschist facies (Baragar, 1967) to amphibolite facies with sillimanite-almandine-orthoclase in Labrador (Dimroth, 1970; Dimroth *et al.*, 1970) and sillimanite-andalusite-staurolite-almandine assemblages in South Greenland. Both areas can be broadly compared to the medium-pressure/medium-temperature type of metamorphism recorded by Barrow (1893, 1912) from the Dalradian of Scotland. Structures range from imbricate thrusts and *décollement* features in brittle rocks near the margins of the fold belt to more complex, refolded folds in possibly more ductile rocks in the higher grade zones away from the margin of the fold belt.

2. A zone of granitic gneisses, granites, and granodiorites includes scattered relicts of amphibolite-facies supracrustal rocks. In South Greenland this zone of granites and granitic gneisses includes a mappable unit—the Julianehåb Granite—approximately 100 km (60 mi) wide trending east-northeast for about 250 km (150 mi) under the Inland Ice and reappearing on the southeast coast. The Julianehåb Granite is a complex body of rock, much of which is thought to represent Archean gneisses and granites partially reworked during the Ketilidian orogeny. The area contains considerable basic and intermediate rocks including gabbroic and hornblende-gabbroic plugs, dioritic sheets, dikes and plugs, a variety of quartz-poor adamellites, and quartz-poor granites. As a group these rocks are characterized by euhedral, commonly poikilitic hornblende; they have been grouped together as the "appinitic suite" in reports and maps published by the Geological Survey of Greenland. Many generations of appinitic rocks are present within the Julianehåb Granite (Allaart, 1967), and it now seems probable that both Archean and Proterozoic members are present in the same area. In Labrador the zone of granites and granitic gneisses forms an approximately north-south belt 160 km (100 mi) wide. In contrast to the Julianehåb Granite, most of the gneisses appear to have been derived from metasedimentary units, and migmatite is abundant. Although this rock is considered to be the result of Hudsonian plutonism, the possibility that some is derived from Archean gneisses cannot be excluded.

3. A zone of high-grade migmatites and supracrustal rocks is characterized by either granulite-facies or cordierite-sillimanite amphibolite-facies assemblages. Granulite-facies paragneisses form a major component of the metamorphic rocks along the eastern margin of the Hudsonian mobile belt in Labrador. They show a marked fabric with a steep dip and north-northwest trend. Mylonite zones are common parallel with the general structure; they include units of garnet-quartz-feldspar gneiss in which the quartz has a distinctive fabric. In Greenland the high-grade rocks occupy the southernmost tip of the island. The area is characterized by flat-lying structures locally refolded during several periods of deformation and disrupted by the intrusion of late orogenic to post-orogenic igneous complexes. The flat-lying rocks generally contain cordierite-sillimanite-biotite assemblages. Granulite-facies rocks are locally developed near the mouth of Tasermiut Fjord (Dawes, 1970; Escher, 1966) and in the contact zones around younger intrusions (Bridgwater and Watterson, 1967). Changes in metamorphic facies are commonly very abrupt, suggesting that there were high thermal gradients in the area. Migmatization occurred in several stages, and large numbers of pegmatites were injected into the high-grade gneiss complex.

The lower Proterozoic (Aphebian) supracrustal rocks in northwestern Greenland and the underlying Archean basement were affected by at least two periods of deformation during Hudsonian orogenesis. In the area between Svartenhuk and Jakobshavn, the gneisses are folded into a pattern of domes analogous to the mantled gneiss domes of the Karelides (Eskola, 1949). This deformation and the accompanying amphibolite-facies metamorphism obliterated the unconformity between the Archean basement and the Proterozoic cover rocks. To the south between Jakobshavn and Søndre Strømfjord, the gneisses show a steeply dipping, predominantly east-northeast trend initiated during the same intense deformation which reoriented the Kangâmiut dike swarm (stage 4). The prevalence of Hudsonian K-Ar ages from this area suggests, however, that the region south of Jakobshavn was affected by a regional thermal event contemporaneous with the formation of the dome structures on the north. A weak refolding of the east-northeast-trending structures in the area between Jakobshavn and Søndre Strømfjord formed northwest-oriented open structures (Bondesen, 1970a). Many of the gneisses in the east-northeast-trending belt contain granulite-facies mineral assemblages which are regarded as having formed originally during Archean time; however, they have survived the later Proterozoic metamorphism, possibly owing to a regional lack of water.

The effects of the Hudsonian orogeny have almost obliterated the unconformity between the Archean basement and the lower Proterozoic strata on Baffin Island. The lower Proterozoic strata in many places have been migmatized and deformed jointly with what are believed to be remobilized Archean gneisses and granitic rocks. The unconformity is recognizable in the Cape Dyer region below the Hoare Bay Group and in central Baffin Island where the Piling Group (Jackson, 1969) is associated with mantled gneiss domes.

Steep dips prevail throughout most of Baffin Island, although broad domelike features and large areas containing subhorizontal foliation occupy much of the fiord region of northeastern Baffin Island (Eade, 1953; Jackson, 1969; Kranck, 1955). Trends are mainly east-west and northeast in northern Baffin Island and southeast in Cumberland Peninsula and in southern Baffin Island. A relatively mild fold episode produced open structures about southeast-trending axes in the Piling Group of central Baffin Island; this fold trend may have been superimposed on the dominant east-northeast trend. The southeast trend is much more marked northwestward in the Mary River Group, although the east-northeast trend still predominates. A slight east-northeast trend is present in addition to the dominant southeast

trend in the Hoare Bay Group on Cumberland Peninsula.

A small-scale crinkling of the bedding within the Piling Group of central Baffin Island may represent a third phase of deformation.

Most of the lower Proterozoic strata on Baffin Island are in the amphibolite facies. Granulite-facies rocks crop out on Bylot Island in a belt that trends northeasterly across Baffin Island just north of the Barnes Ice Cap (Jackson, 1969; Reinhardt and Jackson, in press); they also crop out throughout much of the southern half of Baffin Island. The middle of the Piling Group in central Baffin Island contains fine-grained strata—recrystallized in the upper-greenschist or lower-amphibolite facies —that have undergone concentric folding. The margins of the belt are coarser grained, more highly metamorphosed, migmatized, and flow-folded.

A group of medium- to coarse-grained, predominantly pink granite to granodiorite bodies was emplaced in Baffin Island, Labrador, and southern and western Greenland during the Hudsonian orogeny. These bodies tend to be concordant; they are commonly foliated and are only slightly migmatitic. Most of them are also porphyritic, and some of the granites seem to grade into the huge charnockite mass in central Baffin Island. The granites yield Hudsonian ages of about 1,700–1,800 m.y.

Another suite of distinctive, presumably syntectonic granites on Baffin Island (Riley, 1960; Weeks, 1928) and north of Disko Island is distinct from the other group. They are massive, coarse-grained, porphyritic, brown-weathering rocks which contain hypersthene; they could be called charnockites. The feldspar phenocrysts are commonly ovate. The Prøven granites of Greenland, north of Disko Island, occupy an area of at least 10,000 sq km (3,900 sq mi) and yield an 1,850-m.y. K-Ar date. The largest body in Baffin Island covers at least 60,000 sq km (23,000 sq mi). In places this mass grades into the above-described granites, which have a similar texture but lack hypersthene. In the vicinity of Cumberland Sound, this charnockite appears to be locally metamorphosed; it is intruded by younger gray granites and white pegmatites.

Stage 7. Post-Tectonic Plutonism

The end of the Ketilidian and Hudsonian orogenies was marked by a major period of late tectonic to post-tectonic magmatism which is well represented in both Labrador and southern

Greenland. In Labrador, huge layered plutons of anorthosite intruded all older rocks. Remnants of both Archean and Proterozoic rocks occur as roof pendants in the anorthosites. These major bodies of cumulate labradorite rock are associated with other derivatives from basic magmas such as gabbros, olivine gabbros, troctolites, and leucogabbros—including the well-layered intrusions of Kiglapait (Morse, 1969) and Michikamau (Emslie, 1970). The anorthosites and their accompanying gabbroic suite are spatially, and possibly genetically, related to slightly younger adamellites, quartz syenites, and granodiorites (Kranck, 1961; Wheeler, 1960) which are characterized in the field by coarse grain size, brown color, and rubbly-weathered surfaces. They contain iron-rich mafic minerals including fayalitic olivine and eulitic orthopyroxene (Wheeler, 1965); they may contain large potassium feldspar ovoids, some of which have oligoclase rims. Late granites and quartz syenites having brown, rubbly-weathered surfaces and containing both the large potassium feldspar ovoids and the distinctive iron-rich mafic minerals occur in southernmost Greenland (Bridgwater, 1963; Allaart *et al.*, 1969). The rock bodies of both areas have many characteristics in common with the rapakivi granites of Finland. In South Greenland, no major bodies of anorthosite are present; basic rocks are represented by norites closely associated with individual granite bodies. Many of the rapakivi-like granites of South Greenland were emplaced as mushroom-shaped intrusions with flat-lying, sheetlike tops; they were intruded as concordant bodies for tens of kilometers along subhorizontal zones of structural weakness in the gneisses.

A second group of post-tectonic plutons occurs in the Makkovik district of Labrador (Gandhi *et al.*, 1969; Stevenson, 1970), where biotite granites, quartz monzonites, and granodiorites intrude the metamorphosed Aillik Group. These plutons were accompanied by a widespread suite of minor intrusions including net-veined diorites and amphibolite dikes with a primary foliation. As a group, the Makkovik rocks show marked resemblances to the appinitic suite of the Julianehåb area, the youngest members of which were emplaced at approximately the same time.

The age of the anorthosite-suite plutons in Labrador is about 1,400 m.y. (Emslie, 1964; Beall *et al.*, 1963). The adamellite rocks are slightly younger, having K-Ar ages ranging from 1,145 to 1,340 m.y. The Makkovik plutons give older K-Ar ages and are more closely associated with the period of tectonism dated at about 1,580 m.y. on the basis of K-Ar methods (Stevenson, 1970). In South Greenland the main period of post-orogenic magmatism appears to have occurred at some time between 1,650 m.y. and 1,800 m.y. ago.

Stage 8. Mid-Proterozoic (Helikian) Sedimentation, Magmatism, and Faulting

The intrusion of the large post-orogenic plutons was followed in South Greenland by the emplacement of widespread swarms of mafic dikes. Dikes of the earliest of these swarms have a general north-northwest to north trend and are mildly tholeiitic. Where they are unaffected by younger thermal events, these bodies yield K-Ar ages of around 1,400–1,500 m.y. A comparable event in Canada is limited to scarce, chiefly north-trending, post-anorthosite and post-granite groups of dikes. South of 63°N lat. the Greenland shield was affected by severe east-west faulting, commonly with lateral displacements of several kilometers and vertical movements of a kilometer or more. These fault zones, some of which represent reactivation of older late Archean structures, were particularly active in the period 1,400–900 m.y. ago. Locally, the same zones appear to have been active in recent times, perhaps reflecting continental adjustments to transform faults on the ocean floor between Greenland and Canada. East-west hinge-type faults, postdating the anorthosites and the granite suite, occur in Labrador around Nain. Their age is uncertain, but it is thought that they were active from the middle or latest Proterozoic; thus, they are approximately contemporaneous with the main east-west faults in South Greenland. On Baffin Island, numerous southeast-trending lineaments, commonly occupied by dikes of the same age or younger, are associated with graben structures (Fahrig *et al.*, 1971).

The east-west fault zones in South Greenland formed grabens which controlled the deposition, approximately 1,300–1,400 m.y. ago, of molasse-type continental sandstones and fanglomerate, which were accompanied by basaltic and trachytic flows (Gardar continental series). Rocks of this type and age are not known with certainty in Eastern Canada, unless they are represented by the partly marine sedimentary rocks of the Seal Lake and Croteau Groups in southern Labrador (Brummer and Mann, 1961; Fahrig, 1959) or by scarce patches of arkosic sandstone in north-central Labrador

(Wheeler, 1964). On the coast of Labrador, two groups—the Ramah and Mugford—lie unconformably on the Archean. The Ramah Group is of predominantly sedimentary character (orthoquartzite, carbonate rock, and argillaceous arenite), whereas the Mugford Group contains many basaltic flow rocks as well as slaty units. Both groups have been deformed, but the Ramah in particular shows north-trending open folds (Fig. 7). Metamorphic grade is lower- to upper-greenschist facies. These rocks, which are probably shelf-type deposits for the most part, may be the Labrador expression of the Gardar sedimentation and volcanism, although they were deposited on an Archean basement rather than on Proterozoic rocks. However, because of deformation of these groups, this tentative correlation may be incorrect, and at present the position of these rocks in the overall history is uncertain. Unreliable isotopic age data suggest that these groups are 950–1,200 m.y. old, but they may be much older—perhaps Aphebian, as suggested by Christie (1952).

Marine and continental strata crop out in northern Baffin and Bylot Islands (Equalulik and Uluksan Groups). Sandstones, shales, and stromatolitic carbonate rocks, plus a few gypsiferous beds, are associated with basaltic flows; they are of middle (Helikian) or late (early Hadrynian) Proterozoic age (Blackadar, 1970; Fahrig et al., 1971; Jackson, 1969). These rocks may be the same age as similar strata on northwestern Greenland and southeastern Ellesmere Island, and may be slightly younger than the Gardar sedimentary and volcanic rocks. The northern Baffin Island strata were deposited in graben structures that may have been active during the time of deposition. The rocks have been slightly folded into broad, open folds along southeast-trending axes parallel with the grabens; they have been intruded by latest Proterozoic southeast-trending diabase dikes which yield K-Ar whole-rock dates of 450–850 m.y. Thus, mild deformation probably has affected much, if not most, of Baffin Island, and has continued, perhaps intermittently, up to the present time (Jackson, 1966, 1969, 1971).

The east-west graben structures in South Greenland controlled the emplacement of a

FIG. 7—Folded Ramah Group lying unconformably on Archean gneisses, Saglek Fiord, Labrador.

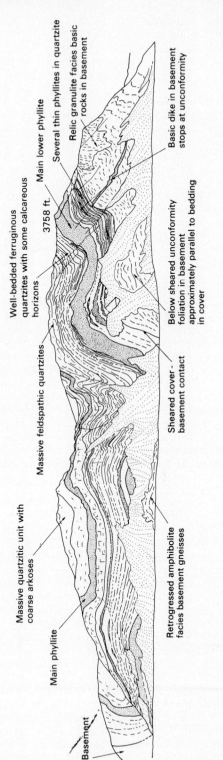

major magmatic suite in the general period 1,300–1,000 m.y. ago (Upton, in press). The rocks in this province include carbonatites; both oversaturated and undersaturated syenites; peralkalic agpaitic intrusions such as the Ilimaussaq intrusion (Ferguson, 1964), which is rich in sodalite, zirconium, and rare-earth minerals; and the almost unique cryolite deposit of Ivigtut. The same area was intruded by large swarms of dikes ranging from early, roughly east-west-trending tholeiitic dolerites to a large variety of alkalic basalts, trachydolerites, and trachytes in an ENE-WSW swarm. The latter dikes intrude the early Gardar plutons but are themselves intruded by the latest Gardar plutons. Many of the dikes contain large masses of anorthosite similar to the anorthosites of the Nain district of Labrador (Bridgwater and Harry, 1968). The alkalic and peralkalic rocks have no equivalent in Eastern Canada unless the small metasomatic bodies in the Seal Lake area rich in zirconium and rare-earth minerals (Evans and Dujardin, 1962) and the small syenitic intrusions on northern Baffin Island are considered. East-west dikes cut the anorthosites and associated granites around Nain and the intrusive rocks at Makkovik. There, they have been affected slightly by the northernmost metamorphism associated with the Grenville orogeny, so they must have been emplaced at approximately the same time as the Gardar dike swarms of South Greenland. On Baffin Island, southeast-trending diabase dikes may belong to the same period of intrusion; however, most of these diabase dikes are approximately 675 m.y. old.

Stage 9. Grenville Orogeny

The last major event to affect the Archean and Proterozoic rocks of Labrador was the Grenville orogeny, which occurred about 900 m.y. ago in the southernmost part of the area described in this paper. This orogeny produced ENE- to east-trending structures that transect the older, mainly northerly structures of the Labrador Peninsula. The extension of the Grenville front passes south of Greenland, but K-Ar ages of 900–1,000 m.y. from rocks collected close to the major east-west faults in South Greenland suggest that there may have been some reactivation of older structures at this time.

A large swarm of post-orogenic, southeast-trending, tholeiitic diabase dikes extends throughout most of Baffin Island and is about 675 m.y. old (Fahrig *et al.*, 1971). These dikes

have been related to tension faulting at or previous to that time. Equivalents in Greenland and Labrador have not been positively identified, although carbonatitic lamprophyres at Makkovik (Gandhi *et al.*, 1969) and kimberlites distributed sporadically along the West Greenland coast that gave K-Ar ages of around 580 m.y. might represent more widespread magmatism at this time.

Implications Regarding Drift

Although it is not the purpose of this paper to probe the evolution of the sea-covered regions between Canada and Greenland, this study permits a few comments pertinent to the subject.

Two main hypotheses have been advanced for the origin of the present waterway between Greenland and Canada: (1) it formed by the foundering of intervening lands, and (2) it formed by the drifting of Greenland away from the rest of North America, with movement beginning in Tertiary or possibly Cretaceous time. Figure 1 shows Greenland restored to its pre-drift position as determined by Bullard *et al.* (1965). Kerr (1967), after reviewing available geological and geophysical evidence, has concluded that: (1) Greenland could not have separated by strike-slip movement along a fault in Nares Strait; (2) Nares Strait contains a submarine rift valley; (3) Baffin Bay is probably underlain by submerged continental crust; and (4) a remnant of continental crust may be preserved in the Mid-Labrador sea-ridge structure.

Contrary to Kerr's suggestions, however, more recent work indicates that, in Baffin Island and Greenland, the gneissic trends generally do not parallel the long north-northwest-trending coasts. These coasts *are* parallel with marked northwest-trending faults and graben structures in Baffin Island which may have been active intermittently from mid-Proterozoic time to the present, and along which the 675-m.y.-old Franklin dikes were emplaced. Possibly, therefore, a seaway began to open between Greenland and Baffin Island in middle or late Proterozoic time—either by foundering, drifting, or a combination of the two. If so, Paleozoic strata may be present between Greenland and Canada, as suggested by Fahrig *et al.* (1971).

Summary

The shield on either side of Davis Strait is composed of two major groups of rock: Archean and Proterozoic. Similar features are recorded from rocks of comparable ages from Canada and Greenland. The similarity of the events recorded and the grouping of the rocks on either side of Davis Strait suggest that these two areas once formed a single shield. The initial separation of the two areas could have occurred a considerable time ago, however, and the sea-covered areas may have had an entirely different history from that of the land areas during Phanerozoic time.

REFERENCES CITED

Allaart, J. H., 1967, Basic and intermediate igneous activity and its relationships to the evolution of the Julianehaab granite, South Greenland: Grønlands Geol. Undersøgelse Bull. 69, 136 p.; also Medd. om Grønland, v. 174, no. 1.

—— D. Bridgwater, and N. Henriksen, 1969, Pre-Quaternary geology of southwestern Greenland and its bearing on North Atlantic correlation problems, in Marshall Kay, ed., North Atlantic—geology and continental drift: Am. Assoc. Petroleum Geologists Mem. 12, p. 859–882.

Baragar, W. R. A., 1967, Wakuach Lake map-area, Quebec-Labrador: Canada Geol. Survey Mem. 344, 174 p.

Barrow, G., 1893, On an intrusion of muscovite-biotite gneiss in the southeastern highlands of Scotland and its accompanying metamorphism: Geol. Soc. London Quart. Jour., v. 49, p. 330–354.

—— 1912, On the geology of lower Deeside and the southern highland border: Geol. Assoc. London Proc., v. 23, p. 268–284.

Beall, G. H., et al., 1963, Comparison of K-Ar and whole rock Rb-Sr dating in New Quebec and Labrador: Am. Jour. Sci., v. 261, p. 571–580.

Blackadar, R. G., 1967, Geological reconnaissance, southern Baffin Island, District of Franklin: Canada Geol. Survey Paper 66–47, 32 p.

—— 1970, Precambrian geology, northwestern Baffin Island, District of Franklin: Canada Geol. Survey Bull. 191, 89 p.

Bondesen, E., 1970a, Field work in the Agto-Nordre Strømfjord region: Grønlands Geol. Undersøgelse Rapp. 28, p. 17–19.

—— 1970b, The stratigraphy and deformation of the Precambrian rocks of the Graenseland area, Southwest Greenland: Grønlands Geol. Undersøgelse Bull. 86; also Medd. om Grønland, v. 185, no. 1.

—— K. R. Pedersen, and O. Jørgensen, 1967, Precambrian organisms and isotopic composition of organic remains in the Ketilidian of Southwest Greenland: Grønlands Geol. Undersøgelse Bull. 67, 67 p.; also Medd. om Grønland, v. 164, no. 4.

Bridgwater, D., 1963, A review of the Sydprøven granite and other "New Granites" of South Greenland: Dansk Geol. Foren. Medd., v. 15, p. 167–182.

—— and J. W. Watterson, 1967, Igneous intrusions and associated rocks of the mangerite-charnockite suite: Nature, v. 213, p. 897.

—— and W. T. Harry, 1968, Anorthosite xenoliths and plagioclase megacrysts in Precambrian intrusions of South Greenland: Grønlands Geol.

Undersøgelse Bull. 77, 243 p.; also Medd. om Grønland, v. 185.

Brummer, J. J., and E. L. Mann, 1961, Geology of the Seal Lake area, Labrador: Geol. Soc. America Bull., v. 72, p. 1361–1382.

Bullard, E., J. E. Everett, and A. G. Smith, 1965, The fit of the continents around the Atlantic: Royal Soc. London Philos. Trans., ser. A, v. 258, p. 41–52.

Chadwick, B., 1969, Patterns of fracture and dike intrusion near Frederikshåb, Southwest Greenland: Tectonophysics, v. 8, p. 247–264.

Christie, A. M., 1952, Geology of the northern coast of Labrador, from Grenfell Sound to Port Manvers, Newfoundland: Canada Geol. Survey Paper 52–22, 16 p.

Dawes, P. R., 1970. The plutonic history of the Tasiussaq area, South Greenland, with special reference to a high-grade gneiss complex: Grønlands Geol. Undersøgelse Bull. 88, 125 p; also Medd. om Grønland, v. 189, no. 3.

Dimroth, E., 1970, Evolution of the Labrador geosyncline: Geol. Soc. America Bull., v. 81, p. 2717–2742.

—— et al, 1970, The filling of the Circum-Ungava geosyncline: Canada Geol. Survey Paper 70–40, p. 45–142.

Eade, K. E., 1953, Petrology of the gneisses of the Clyde area in northeastern Baffin Island: Montreal, McGill Univ., PhD thesis, 175 p.

Emslie, R. F., 1964, Potassium-argon age of the Michikamau anorthosite intrusion, Labrador: Nature, v. 202, no. 1928, p. 172–173.

—— 1970, The geology of the Michikamau intrusion, Labrador: Canada Geol. Survey Paper 68–57, 83 p.

Escher, A., 1966, The deformation and granitisation of Ketilidian rocks in the Nanortalik area, S. Greenland: Grønlands Geol. Undersøgelse Bull. 59, 102 p.; also Medd. om Grønland, v. 172, no. 9.

—— and M. Burri, 1967, Stratigraphy and structural development of the Precambrian rocks in the area north-east of Disko Bugt, West Greenland: Grønlands Geol. Undersøgelse Rapp. 13, 27 p.

—— J. Escher, and J. Watterson, 1970, The Nagssugtoqidian boundary and the deformation of the Kangâmiut dyke swarm in the Søndre Strømfjord area: Grønlands Geol. Undersøgelse Rapp. 28, p. 21–23.

—— and —— in press, The mechanism of the reorientation of the Kangâmiut dyke swarm, West Greenland.

Eskola, P. E., 1949, The problem of mantled gneiss domes: Geol. Soc. London Quart. Jour., v. 104, p. 461–476.

Evans, E. I., and R. A. Dujardin, 1962, A unique beryllium deposit in the vicinity of Ten Mile Lake, Seal Lake area, Labrador: Geol. Assoc. Canada Proc., v. 12, p. 45–51.

Fahrig, W. F., 1959, Snegamook Lake, Newfoundland: Canada Geol. Survey Map 1079A.

—— E. Irving, and G. D. Jackson, 1971, Paleomagnetism of the Franklin diabases: Canadian Jour. Earth Sci., v. 8, p. 455–467.

Ferguson, J., 1964, Geology of the Ilimaussaq alkaline intrusion, South Greenland: description of map and structure: Grønlands Geol. Undersøgelse Bull. 39, 82 p.; also Medd. om Grønland, v. 172, no. 4.

Gandhi, S. S., R. L. Grasty, and R. A. F. Grieve, 1969, The geology and geochronology of the Makkovik Bay area, Labrador: Canadian Jour. Earth Sci., v. 6, p. 1019–1035.

Goodwin, A. M., 1968, Evolution of the Canadian shield: Geol. Assoc. Canada Proc., v. 19, p. 1–14.

Gross, G. A., 1966, The origin of high grade iron deposits on Baffin Island, N.W.T.: Canadian Mining Jour., v. 87, p. 111–114.

Henderson, G., and T. C. R. Pulvertaft, 1967, The stratigraphy and structure of the Precambrian rocks of the Umanak area, West Greenland: Dansk Geol. Foren. Medd., v. 17, p. 1–20.

Herd, R. K., B. F. Windley, and M. Ghisler, 1969, The mode of occurrence and petrogenesis of the sapphirine-bearing and associated rocks of West Greenland: Grønlands Geol. Undersøgelse Rapp. 24, 44 p.

Higgins, A. K., 1968, The Tartoq Group on Nunaqaqortoq and in the Iterdlak area, South-West Greenland: Grønlands Geol. Undersøgelse Rapp. 17, 17 p.

———— 1970, The stratigraphy and structure of the Ketilidian rocks of Midternaes, South-West Greenland: Grønlands Geol. Undersøgelse Bull. 87, 96 p.; *also* Medd. om Grønland, v. 189, no. 2.

———— and E. Bondesen, 1966, Supracrustals of pre-Ketilidian age (the Tartoq Group) and their relationships with Ketilidian supracrustals in the Ivigtut region, South-West Greenland: Grønlands Geol. Undersøgelse Rapp. 8, 21 p.

Jackson, G. D., 1966, Geology and mineral possibilities of the Mary River region, northern Baffin Island: Canadian Mining Jour., v. 87, p. 57–61.

———— 1969, Reconnaissance of north central Baffin Island: Canada Geol. Survey Paper 69–1, pt. A, p. 171–176.

———— 1971, Operation Penny Highlands, south central Baffin Island: Canada Geol. Survey Paper 71–1, pt. A, p. 138–140.

Kalsbeek, F., 1970, The petrography and origin of gneisses, amphibolites and migmatites in the Qasigialik area, South-West Greenland: Grønlands Geol. Undersøgelse Bull. 83, 70 p.; *also* Medd. om Grønland, v. 175, no. 4.

Kerr, J. W., 1967, A submerged continental remnant beneath the Labrador Sea: Earth and Planetary Sci. Letters, v. 2, p. 283–289.

Keto, L., 1970, Isua, a major iron ore discovery in Greenland: Copenhagen, Kryolitselskabet Øresund A/S, unpub. rept.

Kharitonov, L. Ya., 1965, Type sections, stratigraphy and problems relating to structure and magmatism of Karelides: Internat. Geol. Rev., v. 7, no. 7, p. 592–613 (translated from Sovetskaya Geologiya, 1963, no. 4, p. 25–53).

Kranck, E. H., 1955, The bedrock geology of Clyde area in northeastern Baffin Island: Acta Geog., v. 14, p. 226–248.

———— 1961, The tectonic position of the anorthosites of eastern Canada: Finlande Comm. Geol. Bull. 196, p. 299–320.

Lambert, R. St. J., and J. G. Simons, 1969, New K/Ar age determinations from southern West Greenland: Grønlands Geol. Undersøgelse Rapp. 19, p. 68–71.

Larsen, O., 1971, Reconnaissance K-Ar dating of samples from West Greenland between Søndre

Strømfjord and Frederikshaab Isblink: Grønlands Geol. Undersøgelse Rapp. 35.

McGregor, V. R., 1968, Field evidence of very old Precambrian rocks in the Godthaab area, West Greenland: Grønlands Geol. Undersøgelse Rapp. 15, p. 31–35.

———— 1969, Early Precambrian geology of the Godthaab area: Grønlands Geol. Undersøgelse Rapp. 19, p. 28–30.

Morse, S. A., 1969, The Kiglapait layered intrusion, Labrador: Geol. Soc. America Mem. 112, 204 p.

Pulvertaft, T. C. R., 1968, The Precambrian stratigraphy of western Greenland: 23d Internat. Geol. Cong., Czechoslovakia Rept., Sec. 4, p. 89–107.

Ramberg, H., 1949, On the petrogenesis of the gneiss complexes between Sukkertoppen and Christianshaab, West-Greenland: Dansk Geol. Foren. Medd., v. 12, p. 27–34.

Reinhardt, E. W., and G. D. Jackson, in press, Use of a field data collecting form on Operation Bylot, 1968: Canadian Centre for Geoscience Data.

Riley, G. C., 1960, Petrology of the gneisses of Cumberland Sound, Baffin Island, Northwest Territories: Canada Geol. Survey Bull. 61, 68 p.

Stevenson, I. M., 1970, Rigolet and Groswater Bay map-areas, Newfoundland (Labrador): Canada Geol. Survey Paper 69–48, 24 p.

Stockwell, C. H., 1964, Age determinations and geological studies. Part II, Geological studies: Canada Geol. Survey Paper 64–17, p. 1–21.

Taylor, F. C., 1969, Reconnaissance geology of a part of the Precambrian shield, northeastern Quebec and northern Labrador: Canada Geol. Survey Paper 68–43, 13 p.

———— 1970, Reconnaissance geology of a part of the Precambrian shield, northeastern Quebec and northern Labrador, Part II: Canada Geol. Survey Paper 70–24, 10 p.

Upton, B. G. J., in press, The alkaline province of South West Greenland, *in* Sørensen, ed., The alkali rocks: London and New York, Interscience.

Weeks, L. J., 1928, Cumberland Sound area, Baffin Island: Canada Geol. Survey Summ. Rept. 1927, Pt. C, p. 83–95.

Wheeler, E. P., II, 1960, Anorthosite-adamellite complex of Nain, Labrador: Geol. Soc. America Bull., v. 71, p. 1755–1762.

———— 1964, Unmetamorphosed sandstone in northern Labrador: Geol. Soc. America Bull., v. 75, p. 569–570.

———— 1965, Fayalitic olivine in northern Newfoundland-Labrador: Canadian Mineralogist, v. 8, p. 339–346.

Windley, B. F., 1969, Anorthosites of southern West Greenland: Am. Assoc. Petroleum Geologists Mem. 12, p. 899–915.

———— 1970, Primary quartz ferro-dolerite/garnet amphibolite dykes in the Sukkertoppen region of West Greenland, *in* G. Newall and N. Rast, eds., Mechanism of igneous intrusion: Liverpool Geol. Soc., p. 79–92.

———— R. K. Herd, and A. Bowden, in press, The Fiskenaesset complex, West Greenland: Grønlands Geol. Undersøgelse Bull.

Pre-Quaternary History of North Greenland[1]

PETER R. DAWES[2] and N. J. SOPER[3]

Copenhagen, Denmark, and Sheffield, United Kingdom

Abstract In North Greenland, the crystalline basement is unconformably overlain by a late Precambrian to early Paleozoic sedimentary sequence. The Inuiteq Sø Formation, containing conspicuous basic intrusions, is at least 1,000 m.y. old; the youngest dated strata are Middle to Late Silurian. A southern platform sequence of unmetamorphosed homoclinal strata passes northward into the east-west-trending North Greenland fold belt, in which mainly Cambrian to Silurian rocks are exposed. In western North Greenland, the upper part of the platform section is a reef complex showing facies changes between reef carbonate rocks and offreef argillaceous rocks.

In eastern Peary Land, folded lower Paleozoic beds underlie a cover of less severely deformed Pennsylvanian, Permian, Triassic, and Cretaceous-Tertiary strata which show the effects of Tertiary deformation. In northern Peary Land, the folded metasedimentary units have been transported northward over the Kap Washington Group of bedded lavas and tuffs along the Kap Cannon thrust. These volcanic rocks have given a minimum K-Ar age of 35 m.y.

In Peary Land, where the widest section of the fold belt is exposed, five tectonic-metamorphic zones are recognized; the deformational and metamorphic effects increase northward. The metasedimentary rocks have been subjected to a complex late Phanerozoic–Paleozoic tectonic and metamorphic history. Paleozoic orogenesis (Late Silurian to Late Devonian) involved polyphase deformation which produced three essentially coaxial fold phases. Rocks affected by these three phases of folding are overturned northward toward the highest grade rocks, which in northern Peary Land contain amphibolite-facies assemblages. Cretaceous K-Ar ages of the metamorphic rocks suggest a subsequent thermal event of regional importance. Tertiary orogenesis is indicated by evidence of folding, thrusting, and regional faulting, and of mylonitization and low-grade metamorphism associated with the Kap Cannon thrust.

INTRODUCTION

North Greenland, as used in this paper, refers to the region north of a line from Melville Bugt (75°00′N) in the west to central Kronprins Christian Land in the east. About 125,000 sq km (48,000 sq mi) of this area is ice free. This region is one of the remote areas of the world; the ice-bound coasts, isolated position, and severe climate make logistics particularly difficult.

The pioneer geologic work was undertaken by Lauge Koch (1920, 1925, 1929a, b, 1933), who distinguished the main structural elements of North Greenland. His reconnaissance, carried out under the most trying conditions, set the stage for the study of selected areas. A historical review of Koch's and later investigations, as well as reference to all relevant papers published on the bedrock geology of North Greenland, is contained in a recent paper (Dawes, 1971); this paper also gives the main results of the field work carried out by the Geological Survey of Greenland and others since 1965.

The present paper outlines the pre-Quaternary history of North Greenland and gives new structural, stratigraphic, and metamorphic details from the North Greenland fold belt.

The localities of North Greenland place names mentioned in the text are given in Figures 1, 6, and 8.

GEOLOGIC FRAMEWORK OF NORTH GREENLAND

The general geology of North Greenland is given in Figure 2, the structural-stratigraphic units in Figure 3, and regional stratigraphy in Figure 4.

The Greenland crystalline shield is bounded on the north by an orogenic belt (the North Greenland fold belt) in which mainly lower Paleozoic rocks are exposed. This belt, being part of the Innuitian orogenic system of Arctic Canada, shows the effects of both late Phanerozoic and Paleozoic diastrophism. Sedimentation on the edge of the continental shield began in late Precambrian time and continued, interrupted by periods of uplift, into the early Paleozoic. In the extreme north, the North Greenland geosyncline became a belt of fairly rapid subsidence and the site of thick lower Paleozoic sedimentation.

The crystalline basement is exposed only south of the North Greenland fold belt, where small areas crop out adjacent to the Inland Ice. The surface of the basement dips gently to the north under a stable platform block of upper Precambrian and lower Paleozoic rocks. This platform, which extends from the west to the

[1] Manuscript received, September 20, 1971.

[2] Geological Survey of Greenland.

[3] Department of Geology, University of Sheffield.

The first author wishes to thank K. Ellitsgaard-Rasmussen, Director of the Geological Survey of Greenland, for permission to contribute to this paper. Both authors thank Major John D. C. Peacock for the support given in northern Peary Land during the British Joint Services Expedition in 1969.

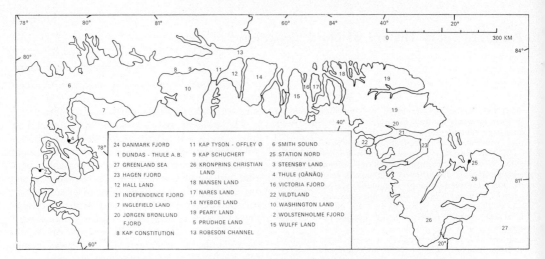

Fig. 1—Toponymic map of North Greenland. Additional localities are given in Figures 6 and 8.

24 DANMARK FJORD	11 KAP TYSON - OFFLEY Ø	6 SMITH SOUND
1 DUNDAS - THULE A.B.	9 KAP SCHUCHERT	25 STATION NORD
27 GREENLAND SEA	26 KRONPRINS CHRISTIAN LAND	3 STEENSBY LAND
23 HAGEN FJORD		4 THULE (QÂNÂQ)
12 HALL LAND	18 NANSEN LAND	16 VICTORIA FJORD
21 INDEPENDENCE FJORD	17 NARES LAND	22 VILDTLAND
7 INGLEFIELD LAND	14 NYEBOE LAND	10 WASHINGTON LAND
20 JORGEN BRONLUND FJORD	19 PEARY LAND	2 WOLSTENHOLME FJORD
8 KAP CONSTITUTION	5 PRUDHOE LAND	15 WULFF LAND
	13 ROBESON CHANNEL	

east coast, borders the folded zone of lower Paleozoic rocks on the south. Dips of the platform rocks are gentle northward, except in the Thule area, where rocks of the Thule Group overlying the basement have been affected by faulting, and in the Hagen Fjord–Danmark Fjord area, where dips change to easterly—toward the Caledonian fold belt of East Greenland.

The folded rocks form a linear belt striking parallel with the north coast. The exposed part of the fold belt has an asymmetric tectonic pattern, the main direction of overturning being north, toward the Arctic Ocean. The unfolded platform strata of the south form a hinterland, and not a foreland, to the fold belt. The fold belt shows a long and complex structural and metamorphic history. Both metamorphic and deformational effects increase northward. Unmetamorphosed and undeformed platform strata at the south grade through partially and simply folded, slightly metamorphosed strata to complexly folded schistose rocks on the north coast. The Paleozoic diastrophism took place during Late Silurian to Late Devonian time.

Magnetic data (King et al., 1966) suggest that the folded geosynclinal strata continue northward under the Arctic Ocean and occupy large areas offshore. Magnetic profiles also indicate thick deposits in the fold belt in Peary Land, where the basement is probably at a depth greater than that extrapolated from the gentle northerly dip of the exposed basement surface in the south.

In eastern Peary Land, scattered outliers of upper Paleozoic and Mesozoic-Tertiary units bear witness to a major Carboniferous transgression across the eroded lower Paleozoic land surface. This sedimentary cover was affected by Tertiary deformation. Northerly movement along the south-dipping Kap Cannon thrust in northern Peary Land has transported the fold-belt metasedimentary rocks over a suite of lavas and tuffs of probably Tertiary age (Kap Washington Group). Regional east-west-trending faults of presumably Tertiary age are prevalent in the fold belt, and two such faults —the Kap Bridgman and the Harder Fjord faults—border the uplifted block, which forms the present-day mountains of northern Peary Land.

CRYSTALLINE BASEMENT

The main exposures of crystalline basement are in western North Greenland (Fig. 2). Smaller outcrops occur at the head of Victoria Fjord, but the reported exposures at the head of Danmark Fjord (Koch, 1925) have yet to be confirmed.

The basement contains a variety of gneisses and schists with associated mafic and ultramafic rocks, as well as supracrustal igneous and sedimentary strata. Granites and granodiorites are present. The major structural trend in western North Greenland is easterly to northeasterly, although in places the trend is northwesterly. In Inglefield Land, large-scale conspicuous northeast-trending folds have refolded older isoclines. The basement shows evidence of a long plutonic history, and early crystalline rocks are

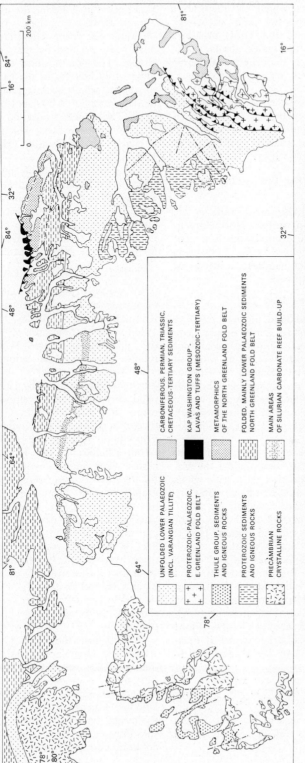
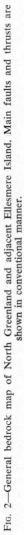

Fig. 2—General bedrock map of North Greenland and adjacent Ellesmere Island. Main faults and thrusts are shown in conventional manner.

cut by mafic intrusives which are themselves migmatized, metamorphosed, and deformed. The crystalline rocks of the Thule area are mainly of the amphibolite facies; similar rocks in Inglefield Land are associated with large tracts of granulite-facies terrane.

The complex in western North Greenland is a continuation of the Nagssugtoqidian orogenic complex of West Greenland. A K-Ar date of 1,740 ± 30 m.y. on biotite gneiss (Larsen and Møller, 1968) indicates a Hudsonian age for at least part of the plutonic activity.

LATE PRECAMBRIAN (PRE-EOCAMBRIAN[4]) HISTORY

A zircon date of 1,090 m.y. (Jaffe et al., 1959) from a gneiss in western North Greenland may reflect a late event in the basement history. However, sometime before 1,000 m.y. ago, the crystalline block had been uplifted and had been extensively eroded.

Eastern Part

In eastern North Greenland, more than 900 m (3,000 ft) of flat-lying to gently dipping late Precambrian sandstones and quartzites are cut by a network of basic intrusives. From southern Peary Land, these strata (Inuiteq Sø Formation) can be traced into Kronprins Christian Land (Norsemandal Sandstone). Apart from a contact with possible basement in the Danmark Fjord area, the base of the succession is not exposed.

The isotopic age of dolerites from the Inuiteq Sø Formation shows that they predate the Varangian tillite and proves that the clastic rocks are at least 1,000 m.y. old. Significant dates are a K-Ar age of 982 ± 19 m.y. and an Ar^{40}/Ar^{39} spectrum-analysis age of 988 ± 20 m.y. from the same rock (Henriksen and Jepsen, 1970).

The South Peary Land–Vildtland basin and the Hagen Fjord–Danmark Fjord basin were initiated in late Precambrian time and prevailed during the Paleozoic. In the former basin, the Inuiteq Sø Formation and overlying strata thin westward toward the structural high in the Victoria Fjord area (Victoria Fjord arch), where late Precambrian strata, if present, are relatively thin. In the Hagen Fjord–

[4] In this paper, events previously assigned to the Eocambrian (Troelsen, 1949, 1950a) are considered part of the Paleozoic history (Fig. 4). This assignment also is in contrast to the practice of Haller (1970), who regards the tillite-bearing Hagen Fjord beds of Peary Land as part of the post-Carolinidian Precambrian cycle.

Danmark Fjord basin, the Precambrian strata are probably more than 1,000 m (3,300 ft) thick; in Kronprins Christian Land the rocks have been affected by the Carolinidian disturbances. The northwestern trunk of the Carolinidian fold belt forms the eastern boundary of this basin, which in Paleozoic time was the site of deposition of 4,000 m (13,000 ft) of sediment. These rocks transgress westward over the late Precambrian beds, which in the west form a gentle structural high (Hagen Fjord arch; Fränkl, 1956).

The Carolinidian folds indicated by Haller (1961b, 1970; Haller and Kulp, 1962) in the Independence Fjord region have not been confirmed by recent field work (Jepsen, 1971b), and it is probable that the proposed westward projection of the Carolinidian fold belt across the platform of North Greenland is incorrect.

Western Part

In western North Greenland, the Thule Group, *sensu stricto,* is at least 2,300 m (7,550 ft) thick (Kurtz and Wales, 1951; Davies et al., 1963). The restricted use of "Thule Group" for the type region around Wolstenholme Fjord follows the practice adopted by Christie (1967) and Kerr (1967a), but varies from the usage of Haller (1961b, 1970), who has applied the name to all pre-Carolinidian sediments in North and East Greenland. Haller's redefinition, based on Koch's (1929a) Thule Formation, bypasses the original use of Thule Group (Troelsen, 1949, 1950a) and introduces a strict time control—which seems inadvisable for the description of such widely spaced stratigraphic sections when the age of the strata in the type region, and elsewhere, is not accurately known. No unequivocal evidence exists that all the Thule Group in the type region is part of the pre-Carolinidian cycle; on the contrary, overlying the basement in Inglefield Land is an unfossiliferous succession which is part of Koch's Thule Formation and which now is considered to be of Paleozoic age. Thus, Paleozoic elements might also occur farther south in the type region.

Nevertheless, the Thule Group s.s. in western North Greenland unconformably overlies the crystalline basement. The Wolstenholme Formation, composed of quartzite, sandstone, and conglomerate, grades upward into the Dundas Formation, which is mainly black shales penetrated by diabase sills. The Narssârssuk Formation is composed of cyclic-bedded dolomite and arenaceous rocks with some lime-

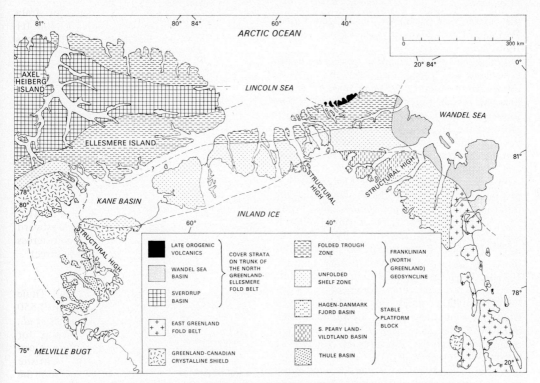

FIG. 3—Map showing major structural-stratigraphic units of northern part of Greenland and adjacent Arctic Canada.

stone and gypsum in the middle section (Kurtz and Wales, 1951; Davies *et al.*, 1963).

The flat-lying or gently inclined strata are preserved in downfaulted areas of the basement. Some steeper dips are due to faulting. The sediments in Steensby Land and Prudhoe Land were deposited in a distinct basin (Thule basin) which Koch (1929a) regarded as being a positive structure in Precambrian time. Apart from fucoidal markings, the Thule Group *s.s.* has proved unfossiliferous; the top of the group is not seen and the age of the rocks is unknown. It could be all, or in part, late Precambrian or Paleozoic. If the mafic sills in the Dundas Formation are of comparable age to the intrusives of the Inuiteq Sø Formation, then at least the lower part of the Thule Group *s.s.* is Precambrian.[5]

[5] Field work by one of the writers (PRD) in the summer of 1971 demonstrated that the Thule Group *s.s.* reaches a composite thickness of at least 3,500 m (11,500 ft) and that the section in northernmost Prudhoe Land can be correlated with the lowest part of the Inglefield Land succession. Subsequent isotopic age determinations on basic intrusive material collected from the Thule Group *s.s.* and Inglefield Land successions

EARLY PALEOZOIC SEDIMENTATION

During the early Paleozoic, the North Greenland geosyncline was present on the northern flank of the Precambrian platform block. This roughly east-west-trending belt, which is the site of a mixed suite of Cambro-Silurian deposits, probably became unstable at the end of the late Precambrian. The sediments change in facies northward from predominantly carbonate units of the platform and shelf area to the more clastic deposits of the trough.

Stable Platform and Shelf

Eastern part—Tillite deposits in southern Peary Land, where they are as thick as 100 m (330 ft; Troelsen, 1956), and in eastern Kronprins Christian Land (Fränkl, 1954) indicate a glacial period following erosion of the late Precambrian strata. No tillite has been found in

prove that the Rensselaer Bay Sandstone, directly overlying the crystalline basement in Inglefield Land, and at least the Wolstenholme and Dundas Formations of the Thule Group *s.s.* are of Precambrian age.

the undeformed strata of the Hagen Fjord–Danmark Fjord basin or west of the Victoria Fjord arch.

Following the glaciation, eastern North Greenland was transgressed from the north by the Eocambrian and Cambrian seas, the coastlines of which ran roughly east-west across southern Peary Land and continued southeasterly into the Hagen Fjord–Danmark Fjord basin. Unconformities in the Eocambrian and younger succession indicate periods of uplift and erosion.

In southern Peary Land, the Morænesø Formation (117 m or 380 ft thick), containing the tillite and dolomite with *Collenia* and Cryptozoon reefs described by Troelsen (1949), is separated from the overlying Lower Cambrian(?) Portfjeld Formation (206 m or 680 ft thick) by an erosional unconformity (Jepsen, 1971b). In places, both the tillite and dolomite have been removed. The Morænesø and Portfjeld Formations pinch out south of Jørgen Brønlund Fjord, leaving the Lower Cambrian Buen Formation (425 m or 1,400 ft thick) unconformable on the Precambrian Inuiteq Sø Formation (Jepsen, 1971a).

A 700-m (2,300 ft) section of sandstones and dolomites in the Danmark Fjord area (Adams and Cowie, 1953) is comparable to the Eocambrian and Lower Cambrian succession in southern Peary Land.

In southern Peary Land the Buen Formation, composed of cyclic sandstone, shale, and graywacke sequences, has yielded olenellid trilobites. This formation grades upward into a 600+-m (2,000 ft) Cambro-Ordovician section dominated by carbonate rocks. Similarly, above the Lower Cambrian Kap Holbæk Sandstone (135 m or 440 ft thick) in the Danmark Fjord area is a 3,000+-m (10,000 ft) sequence of Cambro-Ordovician carbonate rocks.

Western part—West of the Victoria Fjord arch, more than 3,000 m (10,000 ft) of lower Paleozoic rocks form a homoclinal platform with a persistent gentle northerly dip. The base of this succession is seen in Inglefield Land and southern Wulff Land.

In Inglefield Land, a thin basal sequence is composed of the Rensselaer Bay Sandstone (190 m or 620 ft thick) overlain by the Cape Leiper Dolomite (40 m or 130 ft thick) and the Cape Ingersoll Dolomite (10 m or 33 ft thick). This sequence—the Algonkian Thule Formation of Koch (1929a) and the Eocambrian of Troelsen (1950a)—now is considered to be of Early Cambrian age on the basis of

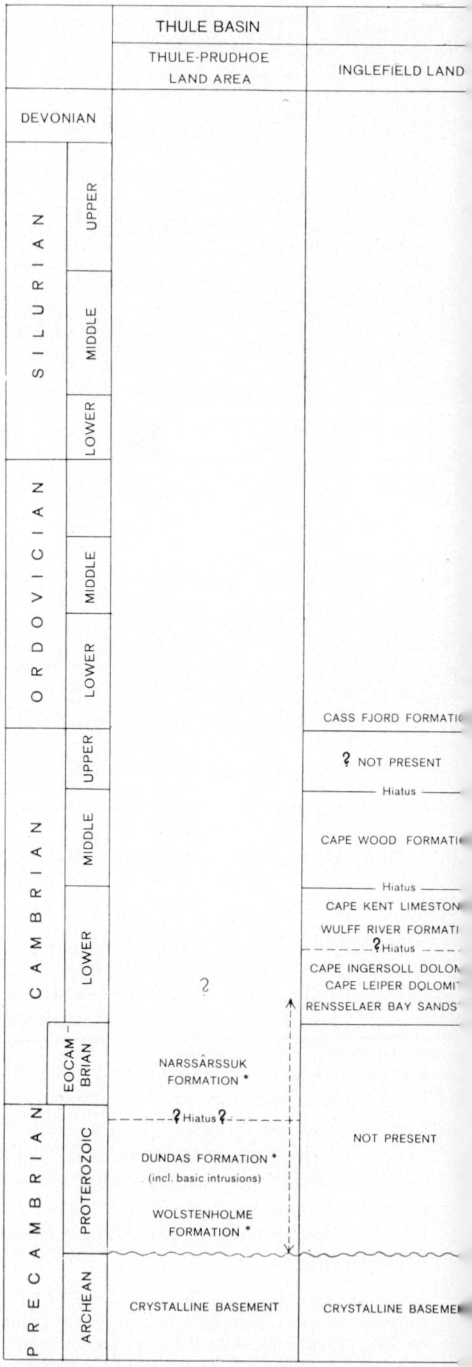

			THULE BASIN	
			THULE-PRUDHOE LAND AREA	INGLEFIELD LAND
DEVONIAN				
SILURIAN	UPPER			
	MIDDLE			
	LOWER			
ORDOVICIAN	UPPER			
	MIDDLE			
	LOWER			CASS FJORD FORMATIO...
CAMBRIAN	UPPER			? NOT PRESENT
				——— Hiatus ———
	MIDDLE			CAPE WOOD FORMATI...
				——— Hiatus ———
	LOWER			CAPE KENT LIMESTON...
				WULFF RIVER FORMATI...
			?	- - - - ?Hiatus - - - -
				CAPE INGERSOLL DOLO...
				CAPE LEIPER DOLOMIT...
				RENSSELAER BAY SANDS...
EOCAMBRIAN			NARSSÅRSSUK FORMATION *	
PRECAMBRIAN	PROTEROZOIC		- - - - ?Hiatus?- - - -	NOT PRESENT
			DUNDAS FORMATION * (incl. basic intrusions)	
			WOLSTENHOLME FORMATION *	
	ARCHEAN		CRYSTALLINE BASEMENT	CRYSTALLINE BASEME...

FIG. 4—Chart giving Precambrian–lower Paleo...graphic evidence or on isotopic age dates. Age...Dolomite, and Cape Ingersoll Dolomite, ages of w...known extent of certain sections; broken vertical...

...RTH GREENLAND GEOSYNCLINE				HAGAN-DANMARK FJORD BASIN
...SHINGTON LAND	HALL-NYEBOE-WULFF LAND AREA	NORTH AND EAST PEARY LAND	CENTRAL AND SOUTH PEARY LAND	KRONPRINS CHRISTIAN LAND-DANMARK FJORD
	∧ ?	∧ ?	∧ ?	∧
...LLACEOUS ...STONE ...E PIO-STROMAL AND BIOHERMAL LIMESTONES	CAPE RAWSON GROUP CAPE TYSON BIOHERMAL LIMESTONES AND SHALES	SANDSTONE. ARKOSE. SHALE. WITH SOME CARBONATE	SANDSTONE. CALCAREOUS SANDSTONE. SHALE *	PROFILFJELDET SHALES
				——Hiatus——
				DRØMMEBJERG LIMESTONE
CAPE SCHUCHERT FORMATION	OFFLEY ISLAND BIOSTROMAL LIMESTONE			CENTRUM LIMESTONE
——? Hiatus—————	?			?
CAPE CALHOUN FORMATION				
——Hiatus——	DOLOMITE. LIMESTONE. CARBONATE BRECCIA AND CONGLOMERATE. SHALE	LIMESTONE. CARBONATE BRECCIAS. GRAPTOLITIC SHALE	BØRGLUM RIVER LIMESTONE	
...GONIOCERAS BAY FORMATION				CENTRUM LIMESTONE
——Hiatus—— WEBSTER FORMATION ...NATAMI FORMATION ...E WEBER FORMATION ...AARD BAY LIMESTONE ...ULSEN CLIFF SHALE ...PE CLAY FORMATION ...S FJORD FORMATION			WANDEL VALLEY LIMESTONE	?
? PRESENT	∧ ?	∧		
...E WOOD FORMATION	LIMESTONE. DOLOMITE. SHALE	CARBONATES. SANDSTONE *	?	?
—— Hiatus —— (probably present) (probably present)			——Hiatus—— BRØNLUND FJORD DOLOMITE —— Hiatus ——	DANMARKS FJORD DOLOMITE * —— Hiatus ——
INGERSOLL DOLOMITE ...PE LEIPER DOLOMITE (probably present)	SANDSTONE. QUARTZITE, QUARTZITIC CONGLOMERATE	SCHLEY FJORD SHALE	BUEN FORMATION PORTFJELD FORMATION * —— Hiatus —— MORÆNESØ FORMATION * ——Hiatus——	KAP HOLBÆK SANDSTONE * —— Hiatus —— FYNS SØ DOLOMITE * CAMPANULADAL SANDSTONES AND LIMESTONES * ——Hiatus——
? NOT PRESENT	?	?	INUITEQ SØ FORMATION * (incl. basic intrusions)	NORSEMANDAL SANDSTONE * (incl. basic intrusions)
NOT EXPOSED	CRYSTALLINE BASEMENT	NOT EXPOSED	? NOT EXPOSED	? CRYSTALLINE BASEMENT

...tigraphy of various parts of North Greenland. Ages of rock units marked by an asterisk are based on strati-
...r rock units are based on faunal evidence from Greenland, except for Rensselaer Bay Sandstone, Cape Leiper
...based on faunal and stratigraphic evidence from Ellesmere Island. Solid vertical "arrowed" lines indicate
...ed" lines indicate possible age extent. Adapted from Dawes (1971).

correlation with strata in Ellesmere Island (Christie, 1967; Kerr, 1967b). The Cambrian part of the overlying 450-m (1,500 ft) succession is of predominantly arenaceous character, although it includes some limestone beds, whereas the Ordovician Cass Fjord Formation is composed of limestone and conglomerate.

A similar succession is present between Washington Land and Wulff Land. In Washington Land the oldest strata exposed are (1) the yellow dolomites which were referred by Koch (1929b) to the Thule Formation and which now have yielded Middle Cambrian trilobites, and (2) a succession of carbonate and some clastic rocks which have yielded a tentatively Upper Cambrian fauna (J. C. Sproule and Associates, personal commun.). In Wulff Land a section of pink and gray sandstones and quartzites above the basement is of Precambrian and/or Early Cambrian age; these rocks grade upward into Cambrian clastic beds and light-weathering dolomites.

The Ordovician section is characterized by a predominance of carbonate rocks, but includes some shale and conglomerate beds. Formations recognized in Washington Land are shown in Figure 4 (after Koch, 1929a, b; Troelsen, 1950a). In the Nyeboe Land area, the Ordovician section—composed of well-bedded gray to yellow dolomites together with some massive and brecciated, hard, gray dolomites—grades into Silurian biohermal and biostromal carbonate rocks and a complex intertonguing system of argillaceous reefal and offreef rocks, the main features of which have been described (Dawes, 1971). This reef complex, which developed at the northern, seaward edge of the Cambro-Ordovician platform unit, involves the Cape Schuchert, Offley Island, and Cape Tyson Formations of Koch (1929a), together with underlying Ordovician strata.

A main bioherm is the Kap Tyson reef, extending from Hall Land into Wulff Land (Fig. 2). At Kap Tyson (Fig. 5) the bioherm forms the upper part of a major carbonate accumulation. The richly fossiliferous reef limestones are flanked by offreef argillaceous limestones and graptolitic shales, and these rocks form an extensive forereef area north of the main bioherm. Farther north, the rocks pass laterally into the clastic rocks of the folded geosynclinal trough. Lateral facies changes are abrupt in many places, and intertonguing of reefal and offreef deposits is common. Patch reefs are present also.

A second reef belt parallel with the Kap Ty-son reef occurs in Washington Land, where biohermal developments are common, and, at Kap Constitution, reef knolls form bold coastal cliffs flanked by argillaceous and graptolitic shales (Dawes, 1971, Pl. 2). Other intricate facies changes within this reef occur at Kap Schuchert (Norford, 1967).

The Greenland reef complex is part of the extensive lower Paleozoic reef development of Arctic Canada (Kerr, 1967a). In Greenland, the thick biohermal and biostromal section, with flanking offreef argillaceous and arenaceous beds as potential caprocks, makes the region attractive for oil and gas exploration. Many of the limestones are vuggy and fetid, and porosity in them is generally good. Bituminous shales also are present in the area. Thus, if the reefs now exposed at the surface have substantial subsurface development, prospects for hydrocarbon accumulation are exceedingly promising.

After the initial field work and the recognition of the reef complex (Allaart, 1965; Dawes, 1966), it became clear that the system of Silurian formations recognized by Koch (1929a) needed critical revision. Koch's Silurian formations are in part facies equivalents, and they cannot all be regarded as rock units of different age separated by erosional unconformities. Consequently, the Offley Island Formation has been extended to include the rocks of Koch's Cape Tyson Formation (Dawes, 1971).

Unstable Trough

Cambrian to Silurian faunas have been collected from mixed suites of rocks in both the eastern and western parts of the fold belt. A few outcrops of possibly late Precambrian strata exist.

Stratigraphy, Western Part

A sandstone, quartzite, and conglomerate section with some carbonate elements in northern Wulff Land is correlatable with the Cambrian and possibly late Precambrian section overlying the basement in southern Wulff Land. A 350-m (1,150 ft) limestone-dolomite-shale succession in northern Nyeboe Land has yielded a Middle Cambrian trilobite fauna (Poulsen, 1969); this succession passes into Ordovician carbonate rocks typified by intraformational conglomerates but including some shales and slates. The Silurian is a turbidite sequence of sandstones and shales with some chert, platy limestone, and graptolitic shale beds. Conglomerates containing well-rounded

FIG. 5—Kap Tyson reef in western face of Kap Tyson, viewed from east from summit of Offley Ø. Lower part of bluff is composed of biostromal limestones (Koch's [1929a] Offley Island Formation) which correlate with flat-lying banded limestones making up Offley Ø. Upper part is a thick bioherm reef which shows variable depositional dips and constitutes Koch's Cape Tyson Formation. These biohermal limestones grade into platy limestones on both sides of bioherm core, and a well-developed forereef facies of argillaceous rocks is present at north. Whole section (±730 m or 2,400 ft from sea ice to summit of bluff) forms part of revised Offley Island Formation (Dawes, 1971). Photograph taken July 29, 1965.

pebbles of chert, quartzite, and minor granite occur in Nyeboe Land and eastward. This arenaceous and argillaceous succession is referred to the Cape Rawson Group (Feilden and De Rance, 1878; Christie, 1964). The unfossiliferous sandstone and graywacke succession with interbedded shales and slates present eastward in Nansen Land (Ellitsgaard-Rasmussen, 1955) is a possible equivalent.

The rocks of the Cape Rawson Group in Greenland are sparsely fossiliferous. In northern Hall Land and to the south in correlatable argillaceous limestones, graptolites—including *Monograptus priodon*, *M. vomerinus*, *M. spiralis* Geinitz, *Cyrtograptus* cf. *multiramis*, *Stomatograptus* sp., *Retiolites* sp., and *Climacograptus* sp. (identified by V. Poulsen)—prove that the clastic section in Hall Land is of Silurian age (in part late Llandoverian–Wenlockian). In Nyeboe Land, graptolites of *Monograptus dubius* and *M. bohemicus* types (identified by W. B. N. Berry) indicate a Ludlovian age—possibly late Ludlovian—for part of the section. Whether the clastic rocks in Peary Land extend into the Devonian (as does the Cape Rawson Group on Ellesmere Island) is not yet known. Categorical statements that Devonian rocks exist in western North Greenland (Kerr, 1967a) are assumptions.

Stratigraphy, Northern Peary Land

Field work in 1969 in northern Peary Land has led to a change in the earlier structural in-terpretation of the fold belt (Fränkl, 1955; Haller, 1961a; Haller and Kulp, 1962), which, in turn, has led to a revision and simplification of the stratigraphy (Soper and Dawes, 1970; Dawes and Soper, 1970). Table 1 summarizes the stratigraphic succession adopted here for that part of Peary Land indicated in Figure 6 and the relation of the constituent formations to the lithostratigraphic units recognized by Fränkl (1955).

Paradisfjeld Group—The lowest stratigraphic group recognized crops out on Paradisfjeld (Fig. 6). It consists mainly of calcareous rocks and comprises three of Fränkl's lithostratigraphic divisions which he regarded to be separated by thrusts. Although the structure is complex, a single stratigraphic sequence is mappable throughout Paradisfjeld (Fig. 7), where four formations of unknown thickness make up the group.

1a. Graphitic and calcareous phyllites with subsidiary dark gray limestones and calcareous siltstones; base not seen. All rock types consist of varied proportions of detrital quartz and feldspar, and recrystallized carbonate, sericite, and graphite.

1b. Dark gray limestone, typically rubbly in appearance and containing much quartz-carbonate veining. Bedding is rarely visible, being obliterated by a penetrative schistosity. Subsidiary rusty-weathering quartz-sericite-phyllite and thin bands of yellow limestone are present.

1c. Thin green calc-phyllite composed of quartz, carbonate, chlorite, and muscovite; markedly banded with varied proportions of detrital quartz to carbonate and phyllosilicate minerals.

1d. Yellow limestone; originally finely laminated,

Table 1. Revised Stratigraphy of Polkorridoren Area, Northern
Peary Land, North Greenland Fold Belt

Group	Formation	Fränkl (1955)
3. SYDGLETSCHER	3e Calc-sandstone (Sydgletscher sandstone)	Sydgletscher Sandstones
	3d Calcareous and graphitic slates (Upper Sydgletscher shales) 3c Black quartzite (Sydgletscher quartzite)	Lower and Upper Nysne Gletscher Graphitic Slates
	3b Calcareous and graphitic slates (Lower Sydgletscher shales)	Brown Series
	3a Purple and green mudstones (Nysne Gletscher mudstones)	Frigg Fjord Mudstones
2. POLKORRIDOREN	2b Arkosic psammite (Polkorridoren psammite) 2a Rusty, green quartz-phyllite	Polkorridoren Series, Grønnemark Sandstones and Shales
1. PARADISFJELD	1d Yellow limestone 1c Green calcareous phyllite 1b Dark gray limestone 1a Graphitic and calcareous phyllites	Malcantone Gletscher Marbles and Slates, Paradisfjeld Marbles and Phyllites, Nordgletscher Marbles

now with lithologic banding highly deformed by minor folds. Main assemblage: sericite-carbonate-phlogopite-quartz. The formation grades upward in the southern part of Paradisfjeld into more graphitic calc-phyllite with thin quartzite ribs.

Polkorridoren Group—This chiefly arkosic group overlies the Paradisfjeld Group. It forms the hills bordering Polkorridoren and occupies large tracts of the Roosevelt Fjeld, forming, for example, Mary Peary Tinde, Birgit Koch Tinde, and Helvetia Tinde (see Fig. 8). The group almost certainly reappears in a higher metamorphic state in the north, forming a belt of meta-arkosic rocks across the southern end of Sands Fjord and extending well eastward and westward—as parts of the Nunatak Quartzitic Slates and the Sands Fjord Quartzphyllites of Fränkl (1955). This group probably also reappears in the south in an east-west belt north of Harder Fjord fault—as the Grønnemark Sandstones and Shales of Fränkl. These correlations follow from the structural interpretations adopted here (Fig. 7). Two formations are recognized:

2a. Rusty- or green-weathering quartz-phyllite containing quartz, feldspar carbonate, muscovite, and chlorite.

2b. Polkorridoren psammite, of unknown, but undoubtedly great, thickness. The formation is composed of major graded units several tens of meters thick, each of which is composed of several subunits which grade from pebbly arkose through arkosic sandstone to ripple-drift siltstone with argillaceous layers at the top. Quartz and feldspar are in roughly equal proportions, both potassium feldspar and sodic plagioclase generally being present. Intraformational conglomerates composed of mudstone fragments in an arkosic matrix are common. Load-cast and current structures of various types are present, and the formation is very similar to the Silurian Cape Rawson Group of the western part of the fold belt. At the south, the Grønnemark Sandstone, which is mineralogically similar but is finer grained and shows less spectacular grading, is a probable lateral equivalent.

Sydgletscher Group—This group, composed of five formations, crops out on either side of Sydgletscher, from where it has been traced far to the west and east.

3a. Nysne Gletscher mudstones; purple, green, and gray, poorly cleaved mudstones, forming the low ground around the Nysne and Sydgletscher snouts. Fränkl correlated these strata with similarly colored mudstones around the head of Frigg Fjord. Although this correlation may well be correct, the Harder Fjord fault intervenes, and a local, informal name is therefore introduced. The Nysne Gletscher mudstones almost certainly overlie the Polkorridoren psammite, although the contact relation has not been observed.

3b. Lower Sydgletscher shales. Interbedded dark calcareous and graphitic cleaved shales; banded dark gray limestones; thin, brown-weathering calcareous siltstones with ripple-drift bedding. Thin beds of quartz grit are present toward the top. The formation thins southward; about 250 m (800 ft) is exposed.

3c. Sydgletscher quartzite, consisting of about 100 m (330 ft) of black cleaved shale with two conspicuous bands of fine-grained black quartzite, each about 30 m (100 ft) thick; the bands thin southward. The quartzite consists of partly recrystallized, silt-grade detrital quartz with little feldspar and a small admixture of pelitic material, now recrystallized to sericite. The quartzites are markedly jointed and contain numerous quartz veins.

3d. Upper Sydgletscher shales, about 300 m (1,000 ft) thick and similar in lithology to the Lower Sydgletscher shales; the shales become more arenaceous upward.

3e. Sydgletscher sandstone; about 300 m is exposed,

but the top is not seen. Buff-weathering, well-bedded calcareous sandstone composed of detrital quartz, perthite, and plagioclase with recrystallized carbonate and sericite. The lower part has yielded unidentifiable graptolite fragments.

TECTONIC-METAMORPHIC ZONES OF FOLD BELT

Northern Peary Land

In northern Peary Land, five roughly east-west-trending zones that show a northerly increase of deformation and metamorphic effects are recognizable (Fig. 8). These zones are described as follows.

1. Weakly deformed lower Paleozoic strata pass southward into the dominantly carbonate platform deposits. The strata are flat-lying or gently inclined to the north, but in places toward zone 2, broad warps several kilometers in wavelength are developed.

2. The southern margin of the folded zone is abrupt but involves no dislocation. The overall structure is characterized by large north-facing fold pairs which are monoclinal in the south but, northward, develop overturned common limbs. These folds appear to be superimposed on earlier upright or south-facing folds. These two phases of essentially coaxial folding may be correlated with phases D_1 and D_2 recognized farther north.

The strata of this zone are unmetamorphosed; they have yielded Cambrian trilobite, Ordovician graptolite, and Silurian trilobite-coral-brachiopod faunas. They are of a wide variety of types but in general contain more clastic material than the shelf deposits of equivalent age to the south; calcareous sandstones and grits predominate.

3. The Harder Fjord fault delimits this zone on the south. North of the fault, the more ductile rocks show a slaty cleavage. The cleavage is inclined at moderate angles to the south

congruent with the axial planes of F_2 folds, and is designated "S_2." Major east-west-trending F_1 folds determine the general disposition of the stratigraphic units. F_2 open structures refold F_1 folds almost coaxially, and S_2 cleav-

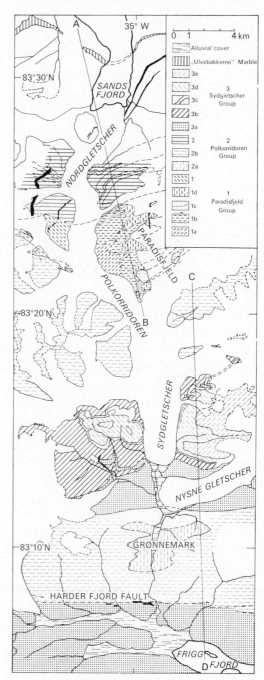

Fig. 6—Geologic sketch map of Polkorridoren area between Sands Fjord and Frigg Fjord, showing lines of cross section in Figure 7. Location of this area in northern Peary Land is indicated by inset rectangle in Figure 8. Unlettered pattern marked 1 and 2 in legend represents undifferentiated rocks of Paradisfjeld and Polkorridoren Groups, respectively. Unpatterned land area around Sands Fjord makes up Sortevæg Marbles and Phyllites, Nunatak Quartzitic Slates, and Sands Fjord Quartzphyllites of Fränkl (1955)—rocks which are almost certainly high-grade equivalents of rock groups recognized to south. Basic dikes are shown as black, ice cover is left white, and faults are shown by conventional symbol.

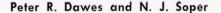

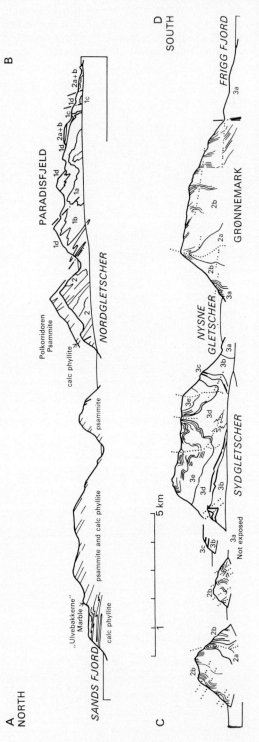

age is clearly superimposed on the variably oriented F_1 limbs. F_1 hinges range from more open in the south to isoclinal in the north. Massive rocks are uncleaved, but most rock types have been weakly recrystallized, as evidenced by the growth of sericite and carbonate.

4. The slates of zone 3 pass northward across the strike into chlorite-phyllites of zone 4. The chlorite isograd is not delimited precisely, as pelitic lithologies are of limited development. In the southern part, F_1 hinges can be recognized by the manner in which the S_2 cleavage is superimposed incongruently across fold limbs. In the northern part of Paradisfjeld, the F_2 folds become isoclinal, and S_2 cleavage is subparallel with the axial planes of both F_1 and F_2 folds. A third phase of deformation becomes important in the north; small- to medium-scale upright folds, F_3, are approximately coaxial with the earlier phases, and a congruent crenulation cleavage (S_3) is present.

5. In this zone, biotite is present and the metasedimentary rocks are completely recrystallized. S_2 is a thoroughly penetrative schistosity and the dominant fabric of all rock types; bedding is generally transposed along the S_2 planes. This composite, gently southerly inclined, planar fabric characterizes the whole of the higher grade area bordering the Arctic Ocean. F_3 fold structures are widely developed, and they become more important northward. S_3 cleavage is inclined at moderate to high angles southward. Minor F_1-F_2 interference patterns still are recognizable (Fig. 9), but superimposed F_3 minor folds and a southerly inclined S_3 schistosity are locally developed. The metamorphic grade continues to increase northward, and the highest grade rocks occur between Kap Morris Jesup and Benedict Fjord. The local northern boundary of the metamorphic belt is tectonic. The metasedimentary units have been transported northward on the Kap Cannon thrust over unmetamorphosed, mainly acidic volcanic rocks of the Kap Washington Group. These movements involved mylonitization and diaphthoresis of the overlying metasedimentary rocks.

FIG. 7—Geologic cross section of Roosevelt Fjelde from Sands Fjord to Frigg Fjord. Lines of section are shown in Figure 6. Faults are shown in conventional manner, and basic dikes are represented by near-vertical, heavy, dashed lines. F_1 and F_2 axial-plane traces are indicated in southern part of section by dotted lines (for F_2 folds, dots are in pairs). In northern part, F_2 folds become isoclinal and axial-plane traces of F_1 and F_2 essentially coincide.

In Nansen Land, west of the area shown in Figure 8, zone 5 is not reached. The sandstones and shales, which have been recrystallized, contain chlorite and muscovite. The fold style is characterized by a conspicuous northerly overturning (Ellitsgaard-Rasmussen, 1955), due presumably to D_2.

Western Part

In the western part of the fold belt, zones comparable to the three southern tectonic zones of Peary Land are exposed. In the Hall Land–Wulff Land area, zone 1 is composed of the forereef argillaceous facies (calcareous shales, platy limestones, graptolitic shales, mudstones) of the Silurian reef complex, which, farther north, grades into the clastic units of the Cape Rawson Group. These rocks are flat-lying to gently dipping in juxtaposition with the Kap Tyson bioherm; on the north the rocks form a gently folded area characterized by broad, open flexures. Zone 2 is marked by north-facing monoclines which, to the north, pass into northerly-overturned asymmetric folds with a coarse fracture cleavage. In northern Nyeboe Land, Wulff Land, and Nares Land, isoclinal folds with a well-developed, southerly-inclined slaty cleavage correspond to zone 3 folds of Peary Land. This slaty cleavage (S_2) postdates earlier fold structures. The strata are mainly unmetamorphosed, and recrystallization has occurred only along the north coast. There, secondary mica is present and quartz-carbonate veining is common.

STRUCTURAL INTERPRETATION

Fränkl (1955), following a reconnaissance across the Roosevelt Fjeld, indicated several east-west-trending thrusts between Kap Morris Jesup and Frigg Fjord, and accounted for the structure in terms of intense superficial thrusting with northerly-directed nappes of possibly alpine dimensions. Haller (1961a; Haller and Kulp, 1962) described the fold belt in terms of "long extended thrust-systems." Field work by the present authors has not confirmed these reports, and the structure has been interpreted without recourse to overthrust and nappe tectonics (Soper and Dawes, 1970). At one of Fränkl's thrusts on Paradisfjeld, extremely complex deformation in the calc-phyllites was interpreted by him as a disturbed zone beneath a major slice of allochthonous Polkorridoren rocks. The structure of such zones, however, may be resolved into nearly coaxial interference patterns between minor folds of two or

even three deformation phases. Furthermore, stratigraphic continuity between the Paradisfjeld and Polkorridoren Groups is evident on Paradisfjeld (Fig. 7), and the Paradisfjeld rocks represent a tectonic inlier rather than a fenster.

The major dislocations in the fold belt are high-angle faults and thrust faults, the majority of which are subparallel with lithostratigraphic units. Some of these faults are related to folding; others are clearly younger. The Kap Cannon thrust—the only major thrust so far recognized by the authors in northern Peary Land—postdates the northerly overturning and is of Tertiary age.

METAMORPHISM IN FOLD BELT

The northerly increase in metamorphic intensity in the widest part of the fold belt is illustrated in Figure 8, in which two metamorphic boundaries are shown. The boundary between zone 4 and subzone 5a marks the first occurrence of biotite, and that between subzones 5a and 5b marks the southern limit of amphibolite-facies assemblages.

The northward increase in grade is accompanied by an intensification of S_2 and a progressive destruction of sedimentary fabric. Thus, in zone 3 virtually undeformed clastic grains of quartz and feldspar are present, mixed carbonate is recrystallized, and secondary sericite is developed. In zone 4 quartz shows undulose extinction, feldspars have deformed twin lamellae, and intergranular boundaries are generally sutured. Muscovite and chlorite are unstrained and commonly oriented with basal planes paralleling S_2. In the northern part of zone 4, polygonization of quartz and feldspar is apparent, and strongly polygonized fabrics become characteristic of zone 5. This process clearly postdates S_2, because unstrained micas aligned in the S_2 direction are involved in the polygonization.

Between Kap Morris Jesup and Sands Fjord, garnet of unknown, but probably almandine, composition is conspicuous; it has overgrown the S_2 fabric. In the highest grade area to the west, garnet is accompanied locally by staurolite, andalusite, and cordierite, and these phases show evidence of syntectonic (presumably "syn-S_2") growth. In subzone 5b calc-silicate bands contain clinozoisite or amphibole with calcic andesine, whereas metadolerites develop epidote, amphibole, and intermediate plagioclase.

On the basis of present evidence, the thermal

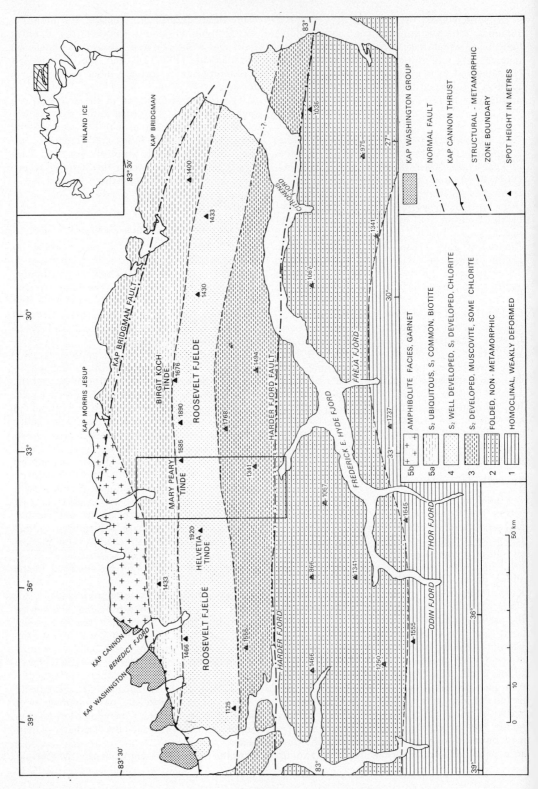

maximum appears to have occurred synchronous with, or to have outlasted, D_2 deformation. A facies series of Abukuma type was developed under a geothermal gradient probably greater than 40°C/km. Metamorphic conditions during D_1 deformation are not known. During the development of D_3 structures, the grade appears to have been lower, but there still was a northward increase. In zone 4, chlorite and muscovite, originally parallel with S_2, were deformed by microfolds and subsequently polygonized; the resultant limited growth of new muscovite and chlorite parallels S_3. In subzone 5b, garnet was replaced by chlorite; many rock types in this subzone are conspicuously rich in chlorite—for example, the schists south of Kap Morris Jesup. Well-polygonized quartz, muscovite, chlorite, and biotite associated with F_3 microfolds in this area suggest that chlorite and mica were in mutual equilibrium during and after D_3 deformation.

Greenschist retrogression is associated with the Kap Cannon thrust; there, the metamorphic and tectonic effects appear to die out southward in a short distance. Highly deformed metasedimentary rocks in juxtaposition to the thrust have undergone some recrystallization, as shown by the development of unstrained grains of sericite and chlorite. Less-deformed amphibolites show the destruction of a hornblende-epidote-plagioclase-ilmenite assemblage and the development of actinolitic amphibole, chlorite, sericite, carbonate, and leucoxene. This retrogression—and thus the thrusting—postdates the metamorphic maximum (D_2) and, almost certainly, D_3.

Upper Paleozoic and Mesozoic-Tertiary Cover

Outliers of Carboniferous, Permian, Triassic, and Cretaceous-Tertiary strata are present in eastern North Greenland bordering the Wandel Sea and in eastern Kronprins Christian Land overlying the folded rocks of the North and East Greenland fold belts (Fig. 2). The areal extent of these isolated outliers and their probable extension onto the continental slope of the

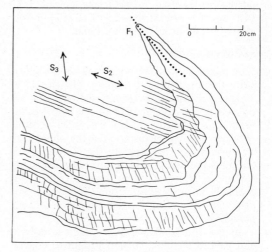

FIG. 9—A refolded F_1 isocline in limestones of subzone 5a (see Fig. 8) from area south of Kap Morris Jesup. S_2 southerly-dipping cleavage congruent with axial plane of F_2 is truncated by S_3, which is more steeply inclined and is superimposed incongruently across F_2 fold limb.

Wandel and Greenland Seas suggest a significant basin of deposition—referred to here as the "Wandel Sea basin."

The composite section totals more than 2,500 m (8,200 ft). Early Carboniferous continental sandstones and shales, with coal beds, form the base of the succession in Kronprins Christian Land (Nathorst, 1911) and grade into a marine section of Late Carboniferous and Early Permian age (Grönwall, 1916; Dunbar et al., 1962). In eastern Peary Land, the oldest strata are *Triticites*-bearing beds of Pennsylvanian age which grade into a Permian-Triassic section more than 1,000 m (3,300 ft) thick. The Lower Permian is mainly a carbonate facies; the Upper Permian is clastic. The Lower Triassic sandstones and shales contain a fish fauna of late Scythian age, and the Middle Triassic part contains ammonites of Anisian age (Kummel, 1953). No Jurassic rocks have been recognized in the Wandel Sea basin, but plant-bearing beds in Peary Land (Troelsen, 1950b) and sandstones in northern Kronprins Christian Land (Nielsen, 1941) are of Cretaceous and/or Tertiary age.

Breaks in the succession indicate the fluctuating position of the sea following the major Carboniferous transgression. The strata are flat-lying to gently dipping, but Tertiary faulting and folding have resulted in some steeply dipping sections. Although the main flexures trend

←‒‒‒‒

FIG. 8—Map showing structural-metamorphic zones in northern Peary Land, illustrating northerly increase in metamorphic and deformational effects across North Greenland fold belt. Boundaries were plotted on basis of a limited number of rock samples and must be regarded as preliminary. Inset rectangle marks area shown in Figure 6. Spot heights are approximate.

northwest, Nielsen (1941) recognized folds with north-northeast axes in the Carboniferous strata in Kronprins Christian Land.

MAGMATIC ACTIVITY

A mixed suite of igneous rocks is associated with the crystalline basement (Koch, 1920, 1933). Subsequent magmatic activity was significant in the development of the late Precambrian crust. Basaltic dikes and sills, together with more acidic intrusives, cut the oldest clastic cover rocks and predate the Varangian tillite, thus providing a minimum radiometric age for those strata. Certain basaltic layers are probably of extrusive origin, indicating volcanic activity during the late Precambrian sedimentation.

In the Independence Fjord region, dolerite and gabbro in thick, subconcordant to concordant sheets are cut by basic dikes. These intrusives correspond to the "Thulean intrusives" of Haller (1970), and the two undeformed generations possibly correspond to the pre- and post-Carolinidian intrusives of East Greenland.

The basic sills in the Thule Group s.s. and the dikes in the Victoria Fjord arch that cut the basement but not the overlying sedimentary cover are probably also of late Precambrian age.

In eastern Peary Land, basic intrusives cut the folded Ordovician-Silurian strata but predate the Pennsylvanian cover. In northern Peary Land, minor intrusions were involved in the Paleozoic deformation and metamorphism. Later swarms of basic dikes (northwest- and northeast-trending dolerites and east-west-trending lamprophyres) are possibly all of Late Cretaceous to early Tertiary age (K-Ar dates of 66.0 ± 6.6 m.y. and 72.9 ± 9.0 m.y. [Henriksen and Jepsen, 1970; Dawes, 1971]). These dikes, which transect the Paleozoic folds in tectonic zones 1 to 3, are unmetamorphosed. To the north, although the dikes are still discordant to the fabric of the metamorphic rocks, they locally show evidence of metamorphism and deformation, suggesting a late Phanerozoic tectonic-thermal event.

The effusion of the Kap Washington Group is considered to be of Cretaceous-Tertiary age (Dawes and Soper, 1971). At the type locality the group is composed of essentially rhyolitic extrusives, both lavas and reworked tuffs, characterized petrographically by partially unmixed anorthoclase. The volcanic pile—at least 1,500 m (4,900 ft) thick—dips gently southward, but local flexures are present. Tuffs are locally

cleaved, indicating tectonism of Tertiary age, presumably associated with the Kap Cannon thrust.

AGE OF OROGENESIS

In the northern part of the North Greenland fold belt, where deformation and metamorphism have been greatest, no unconformable sedimentary cover has been observed. In eastern Peary Land, unmetamorphosed Pennsylvanian strata lie unconformably on gently folded, unmetamorphosed lower Paleozoic strata (Fig. 2). There is thus no precise stratigraphic evidence of the main orogenic deformation and metamorphism described. However, the thermal maximum and the D_2 deformation clearly predate the Late Cretaceous basic dikes and the Tertiary Kap Cannon thrust, along which retrogression occurred. It is difficult to differentiate the D_3 tectonic event from this earlier orogenic activity, because the F_3 folds are essentially coaxial with F_2 folds and developed under a similar northerly-increasing temperature regime. D_3 deformation is thus unlikely to be associated with the Kap Cannon thrust, which strikes east-northeast and is oblique to both the structural trend of the fold belt and the metamorphic boundaries (Fig. 8). On the basis of a comparison with the Canadian part of the Franklinian geosyncline, where no major Mesozoic diastrophism occurred, it is concluded that the main orogenic activity in North Greenland took place in Late Silurian to Late Devonian time (Dawes, 1971).

K-Ar age determinations on metamorphic rocks from subzones 5a and 5b have failed to date this Paleozoic diastrophism. Four dated samples show a range of Cretaceous-Tertiary ages (84.2 m.y. on biotite; 75.9 m.y. on biotite; 47.1 m.y. on total rock; 42.3 m.y. on muscovite —Dawes and Soper, 1971). The 84.2-m.y. age is from a staurolite-garnet-cordierite-andalusite-biotite-muscovite schist; theoretically, the date could refer to the crystallization of the mineral assemblage. Such mineral phases, however, appear to have been stable during and after D_2 deformation. The age thus might relate to later metamorphism, which is evident in the Kap Morris Jesup area and which appears to be associated in time with D_3 deformation. However, since D_2 and D_3 are regarded as Paleozoic, a subsequent thermal "event" of late Phanerozoic age (Cretaceous and/or Tertiary) must be involved. The spread of K-Ar ages may reflect partial argon loss connected with this "event," which may be associated with the weak metamorphism of the Late Cretaceous basic dikes and retrogression along the Kap Cannon thrust. Tertiary folds affect the Kap Washington Group and the strata of the Wandel Sea basin, and thrusts and other faults of similar age are of regional importance.

REGIONAL TECTONIC CONSIDERATIONS

The North Greenland fold belt was an unstable zone of the earth's crust throughout Phanerozoic time, being the site of complex Paleozoic–late Phanerozoic orogeny. The belt borders the Arctic Ocean and lies at the junction of oceanic and continental structures.

The earlier structural interpretation of intense superficial overthrust tectonism with northerly-directed nappe structures (Fränkl, 1955; 1956) is refuted: the stratigraphy and structure can be explained in terms of repeated, more or less coaxial, folding. Fränkl, although recognizing the possibility of southerly movement at depth (1956), attributed the remarkable north-facing character of the fold belt to a "push from the south" (1955). Relative movement of higher crustal rocks over lower rocks no doubt took place, but it is difficult to envisage how powerful tangential stress could have been transmitted through the undeformed platform strata of the hinterland; nor is there evidence of a root zone from which northerly-directed nappes could have been derived. It seems necessary to invoke significant movements of crustal material at depth beneath the fold belt, perhaps influenced by mantle creep. Southerly movements could be the result of the underthrusting of oceanic material against the continental block of Greenland. If so, the existence of a Paleozoic Arctic ocean, floored by oceanic crust, is indicated.

The northerly overturning, so conspicuous in North Greenland, apparently is absent west of the Robeson Channel where, in northeastern Ellesmere Island, the folds that are coaxial with the Greenland structures are south-facing (Christie, 1964; Kerr, 1967a). Whatever the true nature of the Nares Strait linear feature, it forms the junction between geometrically different tectonic patterns, and it must have been an active lineament when this divergence in structure developed. Kerr (1967a) stressed that the fold geometry in eastern Ellesmere Island is a consequence of "SE overriding" conditions during both the Paleozoic and Tertiary deformations. He attributed the northerly overturning in Greenland to Tertiary deformation and considered the divergence in tectonic pattern to

be a consequence of the developing late Phanerozoic Nares Strait lineament. In fact, the northerly overturning in Greenland developed in the Paleozoic. Thus, if Paleozoic deformation in eastern Ellesmere Island truly resulted in south-facing structures, as stressed by Kerr (1967a), then the Nares Strait most probably represents the site of a megafracture which was initiated much earlier than hitherto realized.

REFERENCES CITED

Adams, P. J., and J. W. Cowie, 1953, A geological reconnaissance of the region around the inner part of Danmarks Fjord, northeast Greenland: Medd. om Grønland, v. 111, no. 7, 24 p.

Allaart, J. H., 1965, The lower Paleozoic sediments of Hall Land, North Greenland: Grønlands Geol. Undersøgelse, unpub. rept., 11 p.

Christie, R. L., 1964, Geological reconnaissance of northeastern Ellesmere Island, District of Franklin: Canada Geol. Survey Mem. 331, 79 p.

———— 1967, Bache Peninsula, Ellesmere Island, Arctic Archipelago: Canada Geol. Survey Mem. 347, 63 p.

Davies, W. E., D. B. Krinsley, and A. H. Nicol, 1963, Geology of the North Star Bugt area, Northwest Greenland: Medd. om Grønland, v. 162, no. 12, 68 p.

Dawes, P. R., 1966, Lower Palaeozoic geology of the western part of the North Greenland fold belt: Grønlands Geol. Undersøgelse Rapp. 11, p. 11–15.

———— 1971, The North Greenland fold belt and environs: Dansk. Geol. Foren. Medd., v. 20, p. 197–239.

———— and N. J. Soper, 1970, Geological investigations in northern Peary Land: Grønlands Geol. Undersøgelse Rapp. 28, p. 9–15.

———— 1971, Significance of K/Ar age determinations from northern Peary Land: Grønlands Geol. Undersøgelse Rapp. 34, p. 65–68.

Dunbar, C. O., et al., 1962, Faunas and correlation of the late Paleozoic rocks of Northeast Greenland. Pt. 1, General discussion and summary: Medd. om Grønland, v. 167, no. 4, 16 p.

Ellitsgaard-Rasmussen, K., 1955, Features of the geology of the folding range of Peary Land North Greenland: Medd. om Grønland, v. 127, no. 1, 56 p.

Feilden, H. W., and C. E. De Rance, 1878, Geology of the coasts of the Arctic lands visited by the late British expedition under Captain Sir George Nares, R. N., K. C. B., F. R. S.: Geol. Soc. London Quart. Jour., v. 34, p. 556–567.

Fränkl, E., 1954, Vorläufige Mitteilung über die Geologie von Kronprins Christians Land (NE-Grönland, zwischen 80°–81°N und 19°–23°W): Medd. om Grønland, v. 116, no. 2, 85 p.

———— 1955, Rapport über die Durchquerung von Nord Peary Land (Nordgrönland) im Sommer 1953: Medd. om Grønland, v. 103, no. 8, 61 p.

———— 1956, Some general remarks on the Caledonian mountain chain of East Greenland: Medd. om Grønland, v. 103, no. 11, 43 p.

Grönwall, K. A., 1916, The marine Carboniferous of north-east Greenland and its brachiopod fauna: Medd. om Grønland, v. 43, no. 20, p. 509–618.

Haller, J., 1961a, Account of Caledonian orogeny in Greenland, in G. O. Raasch, ed., Geology of the Arctic: Univ. Toronto Press, v. 1, p. 170–187.

—— 1961b, The Carolinides: an orogenic belt of late Precambrian age in Northeast Greenland, *in* G. O. Raasch, ed., Geology of the Arctic: Univ. Toronto Press, v. 1, p. 155–159.

—— 1970, Tectonic map of East Greenland *and* An account of tectonism, plutonism, and volcanism in East Greenland: Medd. om Grønland, v. 171, no. 5, 286 p., map scale 1:500,000.

—— and J. L. Kulp, 1962, Absolute age determinations in East Greenland: Medd. om Grønland, v. 171, no. 1, 77 p.

Henriksen, N., and H. F. Jepson, 1970, K/Ar age determinations on dolerites from southern Peary Land: Grønlands Geol. Undersøgelse Rapp. 28, p. 55–58.

Jaffe, H. W., *et al.,* 1959, Lead-alpha age determinations of accessory minerals of igneous rocks (1953–1957): U.S. Geol. Survey Bull. 1097-B, p. 65–148.

Jepson, H. F., 1971a, Notes on the Precambrian to Lower Cambrian stratigraphy of the south-eastern part of Heilprin Land, Independence Fjord, North Greenland: Grønlands Geol. Undersøgelse Rapp. 35, p. 9–13.

—— 1971b, The Precambrian, Eocambrian and Early Palaeozoic stratigraphy of the Jørgen Brønlund Fjord area, Peary Land, North Greenland: Medd. om Grønland, v. 192, no. 2, 42 p.

Kerr, J. Wm., 1967a, Nares submarine rift valley and the relative rotation of North Greenland: Bull. Canadian Petroleum Geology, v. 15, p. 483–520.

—— 1967b, Stratigraphy of central and eastern Ellesmere Island, Arctic Canada. Pt. 1, Proterozoic and Cambrian: Canada Geol. Survey Paper 67-27, 63 p.

King, E. R., I. Zietz, and L. R. Alldredge, 1966, Magnetic data on the structure of the central Arctic region: Geol. Soc. America Bull., v. 77, p. 619–646.

Koch, L., 1920, Stratigraphy of northwest Greenland: Dansk Geol. Foren. Medd., v. 5, no. 17, 78 p.

—— 1925, The geology of North Greenland: Am. Jour. Sci., 5th ser., v. 9, p. 271–285.

—— 1929a, Stratigraphy of Greenland: Medd. om Grønland, v. 73, 2 afd., no. 2, p. 205–320.

—— 1929b, The geology of the south coast of

Washington Land: Medd. om Grønland, v. 73, 1 afd., no. 1, 39 p.

—— 1933, The geology of Inglefield Land: Medd. om Grønland, v. 73, 1 afd., no. 2, 38 p.

Kummel, B., 1953, Middle Triassic ammonites from Peary Land: Medd. om Grønland, v. 127, no. 1, 21 p.

Kurtz, V. E., and D. B. Wales, 1951, Geology of the Thule area, Greenland: Oklahoma Acad. Sci. Proc., v. 31 (1950), p. 83–92.

Larsen, O., and J. Møller, 1968, K/Ar age determinations from western Greenland. I. Reconnaissance programme: Grønlands Geol. Undersøgelse Rapp. 15, p. 82–86.

Nathorst, A. G., 1911, Contributions to the Carboniferous flora of north-eastern Greenland: Medd. om Grønland, v. 43, no. 12, p. 337–346.

Nielsen, E., 1941, Remarks on the map and the geology of Kronprins Christians Land: Medd om Grønland, v. 126, no. 2, 35 p.

Norford, B. S., 1967, Biostratigraphic studies, northeast Ellesmere Island and adjacent Greenland, *in* Report of activities, Pt. A: May to October, 1966: Canada Geol. Survey Paper 67-1, 12 p.

Poulsen, V., 1969, An Atlantic Middle Cambrian fauna from North Greenland: Lethaia, v. 2, p. 1–14.

Soper, N. J., and P. R. Dawes, 1970, A section through the north Peary Land fold belt: Geol. Soc. London Proc., no. 1662, p. 60–61.

Troelsen, J. C., 1949, Contributions to the geology of the area round Jørgen Brønlunds Fjord, Peary Land, North Greenland: Medd. om Grønland, v. 149, no. 2, 29 p.

—— 1950a, Contributions to the geology of northwest Greenland, Ellesmere Island and Axel Heiberg Island: Medd. on Grønland, v. 149, no. 7, 86 p.

—— 1950b, Geology, *in* A preliminary account of the Danish Pearyland Expedition, 1948–9: Arctic, v. 3, p. 6–8.

—— 1956, The Cambrian of North Greenland and Ellesmere Island: 20th Internat. Geol. Cong. (Mexico), pt. 3, v. 1, p. 71–90.

Mesozoic Geology of Svalbard[1]

W. B. HARLAND[2]
Cambridge, England

Abstract Mesozoic rocks are known from most of the major islands of Svalbard, namely, Spitsbergen, Nordaustlandet, Barentsøya, Edgeøya, Kong Karls Land, Hopen, and Bjørnøya.

Sedimentary rocks range in age from Triassic (early Scythian) through Early Cretaceous (Albian) and comprise three lithostratigraphic units: Sassendalen Group (Griesbachian to Anisian), Kapp Toscana Formation (Ladinian to Toarcian), and Adventdalen Group (Bathonian to middle Albian). The facies are mostly drab shale, siltstone, and sandstone (generally marine shales and continental sandstones), which contrast markedly with the underlying Permian cherty carbonate rocks, and not so obviously with the resistant overlying Tertiary coal measures. The marine strata are characterized by the presence of ammonites, bivalves, and saurians; the continental strata contain plant beds and thin coal seams, some bivalves, and vertebrates. The succession and the facies are very similar to those of Arctic Canada. The most conspicuous rocks in the older part of the sequence are the cliff-forming mafic igneous sills and flows of latest Jurassic and/or Early Cretaceous age.

The Mesozoic tectonic activity followed a relatively stable late Paleozoic history, producing a marked change of facies but conformable strata. The maximum known thickness of Mesozoic strata is about 3 km (10,000 ft). The first distinguishable disturbance (warping and faulting) accompanied basic igneous activity but caused little change in sedimentary facies. The principal unconformity represents a hiatus which lasted from late Albian to early Paleocene(?) time. There is local overstep of Tertiary rocks onto the lowermost Triassic, but generally only the uppermost Albian members are missing. These minor disturbances may be related to (1) movements that culminated in the West Spitsbergen orogeny in early to mid-Tertiary time and (2) the mainly Tertiary Arctic Ocean spreading. Svalbard probably was moved from subtropical to temperate latitudes in Mesozoic time, and Arctic latitudes were not reached until later.

Petroleum prospects in the Arctic are enhanced by the presence of Mesozoic rocks which provide source and reservoir rocks and caprocks.

Introduction

Svalbard is the Norwegian-administered archipelago between 74° and 81°N lat. and 10° and 35°W long. The name "Spitsbergen" at one time referred to the entire archipelago, but later was restricted to the main archipelago comprising Vestspitsbergen, Nordaustlandet, Edgeøya, Barentsøya, and small adjacent islands; the outly-

ing islands of Bjørnøya, Hopen, Kong Karls Land, and Kvitøya were excluded. In 1969 it was officially announced that the name "Vestspitsbergen" for the largest island would be discontinued and that this island would be renamed "Spitsbergen"—which term would no longer apply in its former sense to the group of adjacent islands; these islands would no longer have a collective name (Hoel, 1942; Helle, 1970). Current official Norwegian terminology, without translation, is used for Svalbard place names throughout this paper.

Svalbard is the archipelago marking the northwest corner of the Barents shelf of Europe; it separates the Barents Sea from the ocean basins of the Norwegian and Greenland Seas on the west, and from the Nansen basin of the Arctic Ocean on the north. Mesozoic rocks crop out on all the principal islands of the archipelago (excluding Kvitøya and Prins Karls Forland)— namely, Spitsbergen, Nordaustlandet, Wilhelmøya, Barentsøya, Edgeøya, Kong Karls Land (Svenskøya and Kongsøya), Hopen, and Bjørnøya (Fig. 2).

A. E. Nordenskiöld (1866*; translated 1867), in the first comprehensive "Sketch of the Geology of Spitsbergen," distinguished seven groups of strata: (1) crystalline rocks (metamorphosed Hecla Hoek); (2) Hecla Hoek formation (including late Precambrian, Cambrian, and Ordovician strata—i.e., today's Hecla Hoek plus Old Red Sandstone); (3) Mountain limestone (including some Precambrian but mainly Carboniferous and Permian strata); (4) Triassic formation (Swedish expeditions, especially 1861–1864, made rich fossil collections); (5) Jurassic formation (Jurassic and Lower Cretaceous strata); (6) Miocene formation (Paleocene); (7) the "Recent" strata. In addition, "hyperite" (mostly dolerite and basalt) beds were recorded in all strata up to and including the "Jurassic formation." "During these periods [Mesozoic] powerful eruptions of hyperite took place; so that thick deposits of volcanic ashes, transformed into hy-

[1] Manuscript received, November 21, 1971.

[2] Reader in Tectonic Geology, University of Cambridge.

Assistance with the bibliography was given by Kay Herod and Joan Hawkes and, with the figures, by Ailsa Reynolds.

* Reference names and dates in text marked with an asterisk will be found in Buchan et al. (1965) or Parker (1967).

perite, interstratify the sedimentary layers" (Nordenskiöld, 1866*). Nordenskiöld's account is substantially correct for Spitsbergen. Nathorst (1910*) summarized the predominantly Swedish work that followed and provided a general account of the geology of all of Svalbard; his account, in some respects, has hardly been replaced to this day.

Summary accounts including mainly Norwegian work done during the inter-war years were given by Frebold (1935,* 1951*) and Orvin (1940*).

In recent years, substantial exploration of Mesozoic rocks has been undertaken by a series of expeditions: Norsk Polarinstitutt (Nagy, 1965, 1968; Norsk Polarinstitutt Årbok, 1960–1968); American, French, and Belgian petroleum companies (Årbok, 1961–1966; 1962–1968; 1968, p. 128; Nagy, 1965, p. 707–708; 1968; King, 1961–1964); Leningrad (Nagy, 1965, p. 707–708; 1968; Årbok, 1962–1968); and Norsk-Cambridge Svalbard Exploration (Harland, 1970; Howells, 1967; Wallis and Harland, 1968). Because of the confidential nature of much of the information acquired during the search for oil, this paper has been written strictly from the published work. Indeed, its main function is to provide a survey of Mesozoic literature.

Only recently has the Mesozoic stratigraphy of Svalbard been expressed according to a systematic rock-stratigraphic terminology (The Kapp Toscana Formation was incorrectly included in the Sassendalen Group by Harland [1969, p. 834].)—e.g., by Buchan et al., 1965; Parker, 1967; and Nagy, 1970—and this work, as yet, has been done only for the main island of Spitsbergen. Names used for other areas are still informal. Nevertheless, with few exceptions, it appears that sequences throughout Svalbard may correspond closely to the Spitsbergen sequence; consequently, the scheme for Spitsbergen may serve for all of Svalbard.

Figure 1 shows the Mesozoic rocks in their tectonic context; they form, together with the late Paleozoic strata, a single sedimentary complex of platform strata overlying a basement of Devonian and Caledonian tectonized rocks. Unconformably overlying the Mesozoic rocks are Tertiary strata. Figure 2 shows the outcrops of Mesozoic rocks, and Figure 5 shows the Mesozoic igneous outcrops.

ROCK SEQUENCE

With few exceptions the Mesozoic sequence (of around 2,000 ± 1,000 m [6,100 ± 300 ft]

where known) throughout Svalbard consists of terrigenous marine and continental sedimentary units of drab color—mostly shales, siltstones, and sandstones. Limestones are scarce; carbonate and ironstone concretions are common.

This facies contrasts markedly with the clean carbonate rocks of the underlying Permian, which, in the Kapp Starostin Formation facies, is distinguished by abundant chert. Thus, the relatively soft, brown, muddy-weathering Mesozoic strata lie conformably on a cliff or platform of resistant light-colored Permian rock.

The overlying Tertiary sedimentary strata are generally sandstones distinguishable by their coarseness and resistance; a slight unconformity is present at the base.

The most distinctive Mesozoic rocks, however, are the dolerites and basalts which appear to be of earliest Cretaceous age, and which occur in Cretaceous rocks as sills and lavas and in all earlier rocks as sills and scattered dikes. These sills stand up as black craggy cliffs and are generally concordant; thus, where they are thin, they may be mistaken for resistant strata.

Spitsbergen

A large part of south-central and eastern Spitsbergen is occupied by the outcrop of the NNW-SSE asymmetric brachysyncline, the western margin of which is steep and overthrust and the rest of which has gentle dips and a few folds. Tertiary strata fill its elliptical core in central Spitsbergen.

Flat-lying Triassic strata of Dickson Land were first investigated during a series of Swedish expeditions between 1861 and 1873, which were reported by Blomstrand (1864*), Lindström (1865*), Nordenskiöld (1866,* 1867,* 1875*), Hulke (1873*), Dames (1895*), Öberg (1877*), Mojsisovics (1886*), and Noetling (1905*). The other classic Triassic area—Sabine Land—with a similar sequence of flat-lying rocks, was first explored on Conway's expedition through Sassendalen (Gregory, 1921*). West-coast outcrops provided (in Grønfjorden) the earliest Mesozoic (Jurassic) record (1837); they were explored by Nathorst in 1882 and 1898 (Lündgren, 1883,* 1887*; Nathorst, 1910*) and were at first difficult to interpret. Areas to the east were first visited by the Russo-Swedish expeditions of 1899–1902 (Yakowlew, 1903*; Wittenberg, 1910*).

Norwegian exploration began with the Prince of Monaco's expedition in 1907 (Wit-

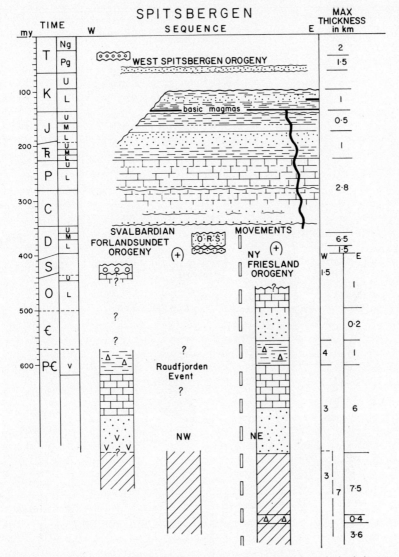

FIG. 1—Diagrammatic stratigraphic sequence in Spitsbergen to show Mesozoic rocks in their tectonic context.

tenberg, 1912*); from 1908 until 1920, there was an almost annual succession of Swedish expeditions, largely to collect Triassic fossils from central Spitsbergen (*e.g.,* Nathorst, 1910*; Wiman, 1910a,* b,* 1914,* 1916b*; Gothan, 1910*; Stolley, 1911).

In 1914, Hoel and Orvin (1937*) measured the now-standard Festningen section where the western vertical limb of the syncline is traversed by accessible cliffs south of Isfjorden. This section and later Norwegian material were described by Frebold (1929,* 1930, 1931*),

Sokolov and Bodylevsky (1931*), and Frebold and Stoll (1937*).

After World War I, Mesozoic exploration was more widely based but perhaps less systematic, as reported by Tyrrell (1933*), Spath (1934,* 1951*), Gripp (1929*), Wiman (1928,* 1933*), Säve Söderbergh (1936*), Frebold (1936,* 1939*), and Rozycki (1959*).

After World War II, apart from the regular official Norsk Polarinstitutt expeditions (*e.g.,* Nagy, 1970; and Flood *et al.,* 1970), systematic Mesozoic studies recommenced about 1959

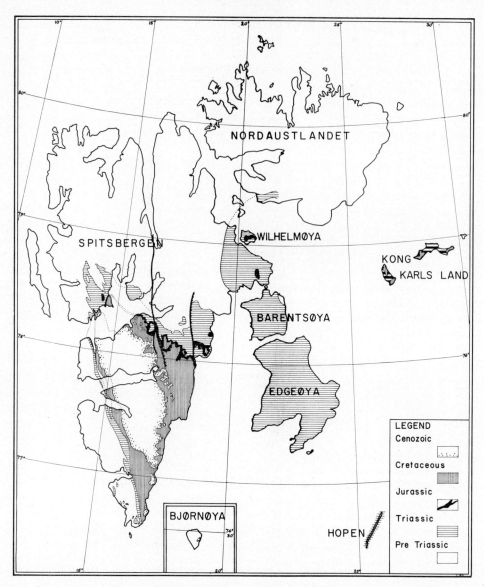

FIG. 2—Map of Mesozoic sedimentary outcrops in Svalbard (with names of principal islands).

and coincided with the search for oil. Cambridge expeditions also measured sections systematically to record detailed rock successions (Buchan *et al.,* 1965; Parker, 1967). Leningrad expeditions conducted widespread research, and many of the results have been published.

Stratigraphic terminology was dominated by fossil zones, or *niveaux,* but a rock-stratigraphic scheme which accords with current practice is used herein (Fig. 3); it is from Buchan *et al.* (1965), Parker (1967), and Nagy

(1970). The sequence of strata, plotted according to thickness and age, is summarized in Figure 4.

Bjørnøya

Nathorst's 1898 expedition visited Bjørnøya; the whole succession was described by Andersson (1900*) and Nathorst (1910*), and a rich Triassic fauna was described by Böhm (1899,* 1903*). Norwegian surveys resulted in a memoir written by Horn and Orvin (1928*) in

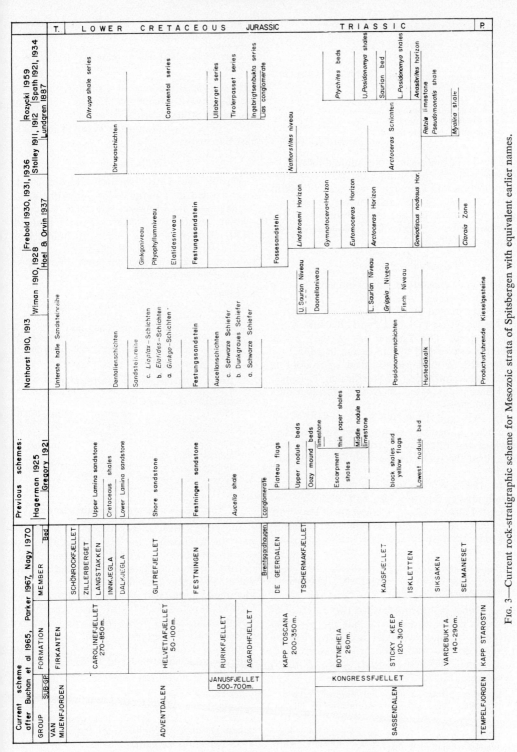

Fig. 3.—Current rock-stratigraphic scheme for Mesozoic strata of Spitsbergen with equivalent earlier names.

which the following sequence is given:

3. *"Myophoria* sandstone,"
20 m (66 ft), with rich
fauna
2. Dark fissile shales with
ironstone concretions, 44
m (145 ft)
1. Dark shale with sandstones
and bituminous limestone
concretions, 140 m (475
ft)
} (= Kapp Toscana Fm.)

(= Sassendalen Group)

The *Myophoria* sandstone undoubtedly correlates with the lower part of the Kapp Toscana Formation; although it was said by Böhm
to be Karnian, Tozer and Parker (1968) argued for a Ladinian age. A labyrinthodont was
discovered by a Cambridge biological expedition in 1948 (Lowry, 1949*).

Edgeøya and Barentsøya

The first expedition to investigate Triassic
rocks in Svalbard was a visit to Tjuvfjorden
and Negerpynten in 1859 by Lamont (1960*).
Nordenskiöld visited Kvalpyntfjellet and Kapp
Lee in 1864. The Triassic age of these rocks
was first established by Lindström in 1865.

In 1910, Wittenberg published an account of
the Triassic formation of Storfjorden, Edgeøya,
and Barentsøya based on Arc of Meridian Survey collections.

In 1919 and 1920, the Scottish Spitsbergen
Syndicate Expedition to Storfjorden visited Barentsøya and Edgeøya (Tyrrell, 1933*). Tyrrell
described the rocks on the west side of Barentsøya.

In 1927, Watkins led an expedition from
Cambridge to Edgeøya with N. L. Falcon as geologist. Falcon's 1928* account for a long time
provided the only available published information. His three stratigraphic divisions still stand
thus:

3. Upper Sandstone Group (= de Geerdalen Member)
2. Purple Shale Group (= Tschermakfjellet Member)
1. Bituminous Shale Group (= Sassendalen Group)

King (1964, p. 1331) recorded two outcrops of
Permian rocks on Edgeøya, but the principal
advance is due to Soviet work by Klubov
(1965a, b, c), who published measured sections and detailed faunal lists (Klubov,
1965a):

5. Sandstone formation
(with thin coals) 130–
300 m (430–980 ft)
4. Passage Bed formation
165 m (540 ft)
3. Argillite formation 39–70
m (130–230 ft)

Part Jurassic?; upper
140 m (460 ft) Norian

365 m (1,200 ft) "Kar-
nian" (probably Ladi-
nian)

2. Brown bituminous argillites with septarian
nodules
1. Gray argillites with thin
limestones

58 m (190 ft) Ladinian
56 m (184 ft) Anisian

54 m (177 ft) Olenekian
(u. Scythian)

Klubov (1965b) described a similar succession
for Barentsøya, except that 120 m (390 ft) of
Olenekian strata overlies 70 m (230 ft) of Induan rocks which lie on the Permian in northeast Barentsøya.

Wilhelmøya

During the 1901 Swedish expedition, de
Geer landed at Tumlingodden on Wilhelmøya
to examine the Triassic sequence, which is
overlain there by Jurassic strata (Frebold,
1930). It was visited by others, including Holland (1961*) in 1951. Buchan *et al.* (1965)
published a section, and Klubov (1965c) gave
a measured section thus:

6. Siltstones .... Kimeridgian
(with dolerite sill of 22
m [72 ft])
and Callovian ....
.... 19.5 m (64 ft)
5. Argillites .... Bajocian and Callovian ..
..........5.5 m (18 ft)
4. Argillites with phos-
phatic conglomerates Pleinsbachian and Toarcian
.........15.0 m (49 ft)
3. Sandstones and argil-
lites .... Rhaetian .. 80 m (262 ft)
Norian ... 175 m (574 ft)
15 m (49 ft)
33 m (108 ft)
2. Argillites with sand-
stones .... Karnian ... 195 m (640 ft)
1. Argillite with limestone
nodules .... Karnian ... 85 m (280 ft)

Nordaustlandet and Hinlopenstretet

In 1898, a Russian expedition, as a preliminary reconnaissance for the determination of
the Arc of Meridian, visited many areas; fossiliferous rocks were discovered on Nordaustlandet by V. Carlheim-Gyllensköld, and were later
identified by de Geer (1923*) as Triassic. An
Oxford expedition in 1949 discovered additional outcrops of Triassic shale with associated
dolerite sills (Thompson, 1953*). Tozer reported on Kulling's 1932 Swedish Expedition
collection and identified middle Anisian ammonites (Tozer and Parker, 1968).

Kong Karls Land

After reports by Schroeter (1880), the published geologic accounts stem from Nathorst's
1898 expedition (Nathorst, 1901, 1910*)—for
example, Andersson and Hesselman (1898),

Pompeckj (1899*), Lindström (1900), Gothan (1907, 1910,* 1911), and Stolley (1912). Abstracts were published by Blüthgen (1936) and Frebold (1935,* 1951*).

The succession on the two largest islands—Kongsøya and Svenskøya—is not much more than 300 m (980 ft) thick; it is summarized from Nathorst (1901):

8. Two or more basalt flows cap the hilltops; the flows are separated by plant-bearing beds.

7. Sandstones with plant beds	(cf. *Elatides* and *Ginkgo schichten*—Hauterivian and Barremian)
6. Shales with belemnite knolls	(Valanginian with a rich fauna including *Aucella* and *Acroteuthis*)
5. Gray marly limestone	(lower Volgian with *Aucella mosquensis*)
4. Gray and black marly limestone	(lower Kimeridgian and upper Oxfordian with *Cardioceras*)
3. Shales with nodules	(upper Callovian with *Quenstedtoceras;* middle Callovian with *Cadoceras*)
2. Brown ferruginous sandstones	(Bathonian with *Pseudo-monotis*)
1. Thick pale sands with plant beds and clay bands	(Bajocian? and older to Rhaetian?).

Hopen

This island is an elongate ridge surrounded by shallow seas that restrict access. Very little geologic information has been published (*e.g.,* Bodylevsky, 1926; Høeg, 1926, 1929*; Werenskiöld, 1926; Hoel and Orvin, 1937*; Thorén, 1969). The results of investigations in 1969 and 1970 by FINA and Norsk Polarinstitutt parties should provide the first reliable information.

The strata, which are relatively flat lying, are largely sandstones that have been correlated with Kapp Toscana–type sandstones of Negerpynten by Nathorst (on the basis of inspection by small boat) and, presumably, with Cretaceous sandstones such as the Festningen sandstone or the Carolinefjellet Formation by Orvin (1940*), who showed the island as Cretaceous on his map (scale 1:1,000,000). A Cretaceous age based on mollusks was given by Høeg (1926), but Flood *et al.* (1970) may imply a Triassic age.[3]

[3] At the meeting in San Francisco on February 2, 1971, H. J. Schweitzer asked for an opinion on the age of Hopen. The writer regretted that he was not permitted to say more, but referred the question to T. Gjelsvik, who gave his opinion that the rocks are Triassic in age.

EVIDENCE OF STRATIGRAPHIC AGES

Marine facies predominate among the finer grained strata: typical assemblages reported are ammonites and bivalves, marine vertebrates (mainly fish and saurians), and driftwood. Although much work is in progress, few records of microfossils have been published. The environments seem to have been suited to pelagic (and planktonic) rather than benthonic assemblages. Continental facies are typically coarse sandstones with abundant plant beds or coals, some bivalves, and scattered evidence of vertebrates. The continental facies in places may alternate with, or grade into, deltaic facies.

Radiometric data from dolerites are not sufficiently consistent for precise time correlation (Gayer *et al.*, 1966*), which has been dependent almost entirely on the study of molluscan faunas, mainly ammonites.

The following evidence for the successive Mesozoic ages of rocks is summarized from Parker (1967), Tozer and Parker (1968), and Nagy (1970).

Lower Triassic (Scythian)

1. Griesbachian—There is no evidence of the *Concavum* chronozone, but *Otoceras boreale* identifies the *Boreale* chronozone of the upper part of the lower Griesbachian. *Claraia stachei* probably identifies the upper Griesbachian.

2. Dienerian—The upper part of the Vardebukta Formation contains *Pseudomonotis multiformis* of the *Sverdrupi* chronozone, to which probably belong the *Retzia* beds of Akseløya.

3. Smithian—Both chronozones (*Romunderi* and *Tardus*) may appear, possibly with *Euflemingites* in the lower chronozone and *Arctoprionites*, *Xenoceltites*, and other ammonites in the upper chronozone. *Arctoceras blomstrandi* occurs throughout.

4. Spathian—Only the upper chronozone (*Subrobustus*) is identified, *e.g.*, by *Svalbardiceras spitsbergense*, *Keyserlingites subrobustus*, and *Posidonia aranea* at the top of the Sticky Keep Formation.

Middle Triassic

5. Anisian—At least three of the four chronozones are represented:

a. *Caurus* (lower Anisian), by *Grambergia* and possibly *Koptoceras;*
b. *Varium* (middle Anisian), by *Anagymnotoceras;*
c. *Deleeni* is not evident;

d. *Chischa* (top Anisian) is well represented by *Gymnotoceras, Parapopanoceras,* and *Daonella lindstroemi.*

6. Ladinian—Of the five chronozones, the lower two (lower Ladinian) are characterized by *Daonella degeeri* at the top of the Botneheia Formation, which, together with the zone beneath, constitutes the *Daonella* zone or *"niveau." Nathorstites* appears to range throughout the Ladinian. *Daxatina canadensis* of the *Myophoria* sandstone of Bjørnøya confirms the topmost Ladinian zone (*Sutherlandi*) and is not Karnian.

Upper Triassic

7. Karnian—Ammonite-bearing marine facies characteristic of the pre-Karnian Triassic give way in the de Geerdalen Member of the Kapp Toscana Formation to sandstone facies with freshwater mollusks, plant beds, and coals; the only chronozone that can be determined on the basis of marine faunas is the upper one (*Nanseni*) of the lower Karnian, recognized by the presence of *Sirenites* (from Wilhelmøya) and *Halobia zitteli.*

8. Norian—No marine faunas confirm Norian rocks.

9. Rhaetian—The sequence of continental plant-bearing sandstones of the Kapp Toscana Formation that yields ancestral forms of Liassic ammonites at the top could represent at least parts of the last three Triassic stages and the earliest Jurassic stages. Plants of approximately this Triassic-Jurassic age are traditionally labeled "Rhaetian" without precise evidence.

Lower Jurassic

10. Hettangian.
11. Sinemurian.
12. Pliensbachian—The Hettangian, Sinemurian, and Pliensbachian Stages are not evident, but they may well be represented by the continental Rhaeto-Liassic plant-bearing Kapp Toscana sandstones.
13. Toarcian—Middle and upper Toarcian ammonites were recorded from the Lias conglomerate (Frebold, 1929,[*] 1930[*]), which, as the Brentskardhaugen Bed, constitutes the top of the Kapp Toscana Formation and consists of reworked Kapp Toscana material, including phosphatic nodules with the ammonite *Harpoceras.*

Middle Jurassic

14. Bajocian—No recognizably Bajocian fossils have been recorded.
15. Bathonian—The upper part of this stage and/or the base of the next one may be represented by *Kepplerites* in the lowest Agardhfjellet Formation.
16. Callovian—Lower Callovian, see above. Upper Callovian faunas appear to be widespread (*Cadoceras, Longaeviceras,* and *Quenstedtoceras*), suggesting an extensive marine transgression.

Upper Jurassic

17. Oxfordian—Lower Oxfordian with *Cardioceras* (*Cordatum* chronozone) and upper Oxfordian with *Amoeboceras* (*Bimammatum* chronozone) are well known.
18. Kimeridgian—Kimeridgian age is marked by the *Amoeboceras-Rasenia* fauna (*Mutabilis* chronozone).
19. Tithonian—*Dorsoplanites* is found extensively within 20 m (66 ft) of the top of the Agardhfjellet Formation (*Dorsoplanus* chronozone); the rest of the formation has not yielded diagnostic fossils. It would appear that the upper Tithonian is not represented, and the time gap may correspond to the locally evident unconformity that probably also represents part or all of the Berriasian.

Lower Cretaceous

20. Berriasian—The Berriasian ammonite *Subcraspedites* is not now thought to occur.
21. Valanginian—The Valanginian ammonites *Polyptychites, Dichotomites,* and *Thorsteinsonoceras?* occur near the base of the Rurikfjellet Formation.
22. Hauterivian—*Simbirskites* and *Speetoniceras* from the top of the Rurikfjellet Formation extend its age to late Hauterivian.
23. Barremian—The Helvetiafjellet continental sandstones contain plant beds for which an Aptian age has been suggested, but a Barremian age is also supportable by interpolation between marine faunas.
24. Aptian—The Dalkjegla Member, lowest member of the Carolinefjellet Formation, is composed of marine beds containing *Ditrupa.* The only Aptian ammonite recorded is *Tropaeum arcticum,* of late Aptian age, in the lower shale of the overlying Innkjegla Member.

25. Albian—Five distinct ammonite faunas have recently been established (Nagy, 1970), three lower Albian and two middle Albian: (1) *Freboldiceras* fauna (*F. remotum*, *Arcthoplites birkenmajeri*, and *Leymeriella germanica*), typical of the middle Innkjegla Member; (2) *Arcthoplites* fauna (*A. jachromensis* and *Brewericeras* cf. *hulense*), from the upper Innkjegla Member; (3) *Otohoplites* fauna (*O. guersoni*, *O. glyphus*, etc.), mostly in the lower part of the Zillerberget Member; (4) *Hoplites* fauna (*H. svalbardensis*, *Grycia sablei*, *G. whittingtoni*), from the lower part of the Zillerberget Member; and (5) *Dimorphoplites*, *Euhoplites*, and *Gastroplites* fauna, which represents the upper part of the middle Albian and occurs in the upper Carolinefjellet Formation.

No upper Albian fossils are known from Svalbard, nor are any Upper Cretaceous rocks known. Biostratigraphic evidence for the age of the overlying Firkanten Formation (Paleocene-Eocene according to Ravn, 1922) was more precisely given by Vonderbank (1970), largely on the basis of foraminiferal evidence from newly-measured sections. The lowest strata, Vonderbank's "Adventfjordenschichten," he concluded to be Dano-Montian. The stratigraphic gap thus corresponds almost exactly to the Late Cretaceous.

TECTONIC AND MAGMATIC SEQUENCE

Late Paleozoic, Mesozoic, and also Paleocene tectonic history was relatively uneventful compared with the preceding Caledonian orogeny and the minor Tertiary orogeny that followed. Mesozoic sedimentation in a platform environment is thus part of a mid-Phanerozoic chapter of gentle subsidence almost unaffected by late Paleozoic diastrophism. Nevertheless, the pattern of mid-Phanerozoic movements not only reflects basement control by the Caledonian structures, but also anticipates the impending, thermally generated movement of lithosphere plates concerned with the opening of the adjacent ocean basins.

Pre-Mesozoic Events

Throughout Svalbard, the vast and complex Hecla Hoek succession (late Precambrian and early Paleozoic) in the North Atlantic geosyncline was tectonized during a major orogenic phase of approximately Silurian age (Ny Friesland orogeny) and a phase of minor folding

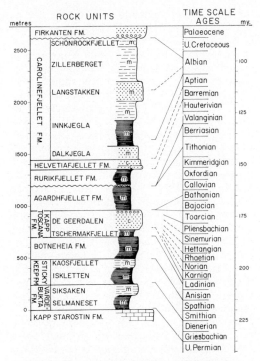

FIG. 4—Mesozoic rock sequence and time scale for Spitsbergen.

and transcurrent faulting of Late Devonian age (Svalbardian movements). In southernmost Spitsbergen the Mesozoic succession lies directly on the Hecla Hoek (latest Precambrian–Cambrian).

Mesozoic Subsidence and Sedimentation

Figure 4 is a plot of thickness against time. It shows an average rate of net sedimentation for approximately 2.5 km (8,200 ft) of Mesozoic sediment during the period 225–100 m.y. ago as 0.02 mm/year. This rate is typical for a relatively stable platform. Variations show a slowing of subsidence in Triassic time that led to continental conditions. Jurassic subsidence averaged only 0.005 mm/year, whereas the rate increased in Cretaceous time to a maximum of 0.1 mm/year in Albian time.

Mid-Mesozoic Folding and Faulting

Movement occurred along two earlier fault zones marking the Agardhfjellet-Rurikfjellet unconformity, which is hardly evident elsewhere.

Mesozoic Magmatism

The most conspicuous Mesozoic rocks are

the cliff-forming tholeiitic dolerite sills and basalt lava flows, studies of which have resulted in a considerable literature. The early work stemming from Nathorst's 1898 expedition included evidence from the conspicuous lava flows of Kong Karls Land. (Nathorst [1901, 1910*], Backlund [1907a, b, 1920], and Hamberg [1899] described the petrography of the lavas of Kongsøya, and Goldschmidt [1911] described nepheline-bearing lavas from northwest Spitsbergen.) In the inter-war years, a systematic petrologic study and review of the intrusive dolerites were undertaken by Tyrrell and Sandford (1933*; summarized by Orvin, 1940*), and later work was done by Birkenmajer and Morawski (1960), Burov (1964), Burov and Livshitz (1965*), and Firsov and Livshitz (1967). Gayer et al. (1966*) discussed the rather inconclusive isotopic age determinations, and Parker (1966*) gave the first conclusive stratigraphic evidence of the age of the intrusions. Spall (1968) and Krumsiek et al. (1968) reported on paleomagnetic investigations.

Berriasian(?) sills—All the rocks of Mesozoic or possibly Mesozoic age are mafic. Most are intrusive sills commonly cutting Triassic and older strata. Intrusions may have spanned a long period, but all the evidence is consistent with a late Volgian to Berriasian or early Valanginian age. For example, structural evidence in east Spitsbergen, where an intrusion cuts the Agardhfjellet Formation and the Rurikfjellet Formation terminates the intrusion, shows that the unconformity between these formations could represent the time span of all observed intrusions. At Marmierfjellet, in central Spitsbergen, the Rurikfjellet Formation cuts a sill in the Botneheia Formation (Parker, 1966*).

Barremian(?) volcanism—The age of the capping lavas in Kong Karls Land is post-Hauterivian, possibly Barremian or later. Supporting evidence for a Barremian age is found in the "Tuff conglomerate" in the Glitrefjellet Member of the Helvetiafjellet Formation.

Genesis of magmas—The magmatic events of Early Cretaceous time reflect some thermal change in the upper mantle. The magmatic events occurred during a time of renewed continental drift in the Arctic, but they preceded the generation of the neighboring oceans. It is possible that they relate to the opening of the Canada basin (possibly as a result of the drifting away of Alaska). Thus, the presence of similar volcanic and intrusive rocks in the Canadian Arctic may be significant (Blackadar, 1964), so that a thermal zone extended approx-

imately east-west along northern Canada and the Barents shelf.

Other plateau lavas—At least two ages of possibly widespread basic Mesozoic magmatism are well established. Moreover, Late Cretaceous magmatism is known from both the Canadian Arctic Islands and the USSR Pechora basin. Several other known magmatic events are dated only as post-Devonian or post-Carboniferous. Throughout much of north Spitsbergen, lavas cap table mountains, especially in Dickson Land and to the west and east of Woodfjorden, and also at Bivrastfonna near Lomfjorden (Fig. 5). These lavas could all be Tertiary plateau lavas, but some might correspond to the Barremian or a later Cretaceous phase. On Wilhelmøya the "sill" in Kimeridgian rocks described by Klubov (1965c) was thought by de Geer (1923*) to be an Early Cretaceous lava, and de Geer thus argued that the Bivrastfonna lava was Early Cretaceous. However, the lavas are olivine-bearing; therefore, they relate more closely to the Quaternary volcanic rocks of Bockfjorden and contrast with the typically tholeiitic rocks known to be Mesozoic. A Cenozoic age is suggested.

Ages of lavas on Franz Josef Land may not be so well controlled, but the lavas could fit the two Early Cretaceous ages, *i.e.*, approximately Berriasian and Barremian.

Late and Post-Mesozoic Diastrophism

Late Cretaceous diastrophism—Post-Albian, pre-Paleocene strata are not recorded in Svalbard. This hiatus included a time of warping or differential uplift to the northwest (Orvin, 1940*). Thus, the youngest units in the succession are found in the southeast (*e.g.*, see Nagy, 1970). Northwest of the Mesozoic outcrop, Paleocene beds lie on Permian rocks at Ny Ålesund and on different members of the Carolinefjellet Formation farther south. The differential movement is also indicated by the varied thicknesses of the youngest Cretaceous (Carolinefjellet) formation, which increases from 180 m (590 ft) in thickness at Festningsodden to 270 m (890 ft) at Carolinefjellet, and, by degrees, to 850 m (2,800 ft) at Tromsøbreen in Sørkapp Land (Nagy, 1970). This thickening suggests an acceleration of subsidence prior to the Late Cretaceous uplift. It is not known how much more sediment was deposited above the preserved Carolinefjellet Formation; nor is the pattern of movement within the Late Cretaceous interval of approximately 30 m.y. known.

Post-Paleocene orogeny—The West Spits-

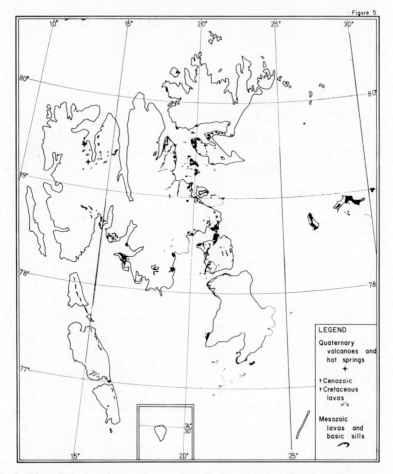

FIG. 5—Map of Mesozoic igneous outcrops on a background of pre-Cretaceous land outcrops.

bergen orogeny overfolded and overthrust (toward the east) all rocks along the central and southwest coast of Spitsbergen. At the same time, minor folding and faulting occurred throughout Svalbard, but the intensity decreased eastward.

PALEOGEOLOGY

Reconstruction of Lithosphere Plates

In another contribution to this symposium (see Contents), I have attempted a sequence of reconstructions for the Barents shelf and related plates. Without further qualification here, I have adopted Figure 5 of that paper—the reassembly for the plates in the present Arctic region 350–100 m.y. ago—as a base map for plotting the principal Mesozoic outcrops (Fig. 6). This distribution is suggested for earlier Mesozoic time—but by Cretaceous time, and certainly by Late Cretaceous time, the Canadian basin of the Arctic Ocean had begun to open, if, indeed, it was not already in existence.

Stratigraphic Relations

Reassembly of areas of Mesozoic sedimentation in such a way leads to a distribution of facies and ages of rocks that appears to make a simple and coherent pattern (except that I have not made detailed comparisons with Alaska, whose restored position in Figure 5 of my other paper is adopted with minimal evidence). Neighboring areas of the Barents shelf, whose relative position is not thought to have changed since Paleozoic time, are mentioned first in order to extend the picture given here.

Barents Sea floor—Little direct knowledge is

FIG. 6—Possible reconstructions of lithosphere plates for Mesozoic time to show areas of Mesozoic outcrops which include shallow-marine facies. Oceanic marginal facies are restricted to areas of southern Alaska and north part of Verkhoyansk belt.

available of Mesozoic rocks from the sea floor around Svalbard. However, the Russian tectonic map of the Arctic (Atlasov *et al.*, 1964) shows submarine outcrops with some interpreted sedimentary ages and inferred igneous rocks.

Franz Josef Land—The following sequence, which suggests relatively uniform Mesozoic conditions extending eastward from Kong Karls Land, was recorded by Dibner (1957). Few fundamentally new data have been added since Nathorst's (1910*) account.

Early Cretaceous	Volcanic
Late Jurassic	"Middle Formation"—Marine
M. Jurassic	
Early Jurassic(?)	"Lower Formation"—Continental,
and/or	with flora similar to Rhaetian of
Late Triassic(?)	Kapp Toscana Fm. Dibner suggested a sedimentary source to the WSW (possibly even a Svalbard source).

Novaya Zemlya—No Mesozoic rocks *in situ* are known to have been recorded from these islands. However, several well-preserved ammonites have been found in gravels in the middle part of the west coast, and these have been

figured by Sokolov (1913) and Salfeld and Frebold (1924); listed by Bodylevsky (1936); and discussed by Frebold (1930, 1951*). According to Arkell (1956*), the ammonites range in age from earliest Callovian through middle and late Callovian, late Oxfordian (no Kimeridgian or Volgian), late Volgian, and Berriasian or Valanginian.

Northwestern Europe—Richly fossiliferous successions are known from Russia, *e.g.*, east of Timan in the basin of the Pechora River. The succession in this region includes rocks representative of nearly all Mesozoic ages, including Late Cretaceous sedimentary and igneous rocks.

Scandinavian Arctic—Jurassic and Cretaceous strata 500 m (1,640 ft) thick crop out at Andøy in Vesterålen. According to Ørvig (1960), they range in age from Oxfordian (with coal) to Kimeridgian to Portlandian (with *Aucella*), then to Valanginian (all sandy) and Hauterivian(?) (shales); no Berriasian rocks are present.

Greenland—Coastal areas of central East Greenland, well known from the expeditions of Lauge Koch, expose a very complete sequence of Mesozoic strata which differs in many details from that of Svalbard; for example, the redbeds of Triassic age (Kap Biot Formation) have no analogue in Svalbard. Too little is known of Peary Land to make a fair comparison, but Triassic strata (Scythian and Anisian) have long been known to show some similarities with the Svalbard sequence (Kummel, 1953*).

Canadian Arctic—The Sverdrup basin has yielded rich data concerning widespread and relatively complete successions (*e.g.,* see Tozer in Fortier *et al.,* 1963,* p. 74–95). There are close similarities in the Triassic sequence of Sverdrup basin and the marginal facies of Axel Heiberg Island, for example. Similar rocks of Jurassic age are present in both areas. As in Svalbard, Cretaceous volcanic rocks and intrusives are present in the Sverdrup basin. However, whereas Upper Cretaceous rocks are totally absent in Svalbard, they are present in the center of the Sverdrup basin, where they include volcanic units.

Paleocurrents and Source Areas

Triassic—No detailed sedimentologic investigations have been published. The fence diagram in Buchan *et al.* (1965) shows a thicker sequence in the center west than in the center east or the southwest. Overall facies variations are very minor.

Jurassic and Cretaceous—Paleogeographic interpretations were given by Frebold (1930, 1931*). From published information it is difficult to reconstruct the sedimentary pattern, but Birkenmajer (1966*) attempted to assess current directions in southeast Spitsbergen. He concluded, on the basis of brief observations of sedimentary structures of the Carolinefjellet Formation at Festningen and Adventfjorden, that tidal ebb and flow was approximately north-south, which fitted a hypothesis of a land source in north Spitsbergen. Nagy (1970), on the basis of more extensive observations, proposed a northeasterly and easterly source for Albian sediments.

Paleolatitudes and Climate

Buchan *et al.* (1965, p. 62, 63) commented that the paleolatitude of Svalbard may have been between 55° and 60°N. This latitude may be higher than would, in itself, promise the richest petroleum source rocks of Triassic age. However, Triassic bituminous facies are well known. Older facies (*e.g.,* Permian) suggest much lower latitudes. The Cretaceous rocks are not likely to have been formed within the Arctic Circle, judging by the presence of *Iguanodon* footprints near the top of the Mesozoic sequence at Festningen (Heintz, 1963). It is possible, especially if a progressively northward motion took place, that the suggested Triassic paleolatitudes may be too high.

References*

Andersson, G., and H. Hesselman, 1898, Verzeichnis der in König Karls Land während der schwedischen Polarexpedition 1898 gefundenen Phanerogamen: Stockholm, Kgl. Öfversigt Vetens.-Akad. Förh., no. 8.

Atlasov, I. P., and V. D. Dibner, eds., 1964, Tectonic map of the Arctic and Subarctic (scale 1:5,000,000), *in* M. V. Muratov, ed., Skladchatye oblasti Evrazii (Materialy soveshchaniya po problemam tektoniki v Moskve): Moscow, Akad. Nauk SSSR Doklady, v. 156, no. 6, p. 1341–1342 (Transl. 1970 by E. R. Hope, Defense Research Board of Canada, under the title "A new tectonic chart of the Arctic").

Backlund, H., 1907a, Les diabases du Spitsberg oriental, missions scientifiques pour la mésure d'un arc de méridièn au Spitsberg, 1899–1901, russe et suedois. Mission Russe: Uppsala Univ. Geol. Inst. Bull., v. 2, no. 9, B., p. 1–29, 4 pls.

———— 1907b, Über einige diabase aus arktischen Gebiet: Mineralog. und Petrograph. Mitt., new ser., v. 26, p. 357–390.

———— 1920, On the eastern part of the Arctic basalt plateau: Acad. Aboensis Acta, Math. et Phys., v. 1, p. 1–53.

Birkenmajer, K., and T. Morawski, 1960, Dolerite intrusions of Wedel-Jarlsberg Land, Vestspitsbergen: Studia Geol. Polonica, p. 103–123.

Blackadar, R. G., 1964, Basic intrusions of the Queen Elizabeth Islands, District of Franklin: Canada Geol. Survey Bull. 97.

Blüthgen, J., 1936, Die Fauna und Stratigraphie des Oberjura und der Unterkreide von König Karl Land: Grimmen, 75 p.

Bodylevsky, V. I., 1926, Fossil shells, *in* T. Iversen, ed., Hopen (Hope Island), Svalbard; Results of a reconnaissance in the summer of 1924: Oslo, Skr. om Svalbard og Ishavet, no. 10, p. 34.

————1936, On the Jurassic and Lower Cretaceous fossils from the collection of A. Petrenko from Novaya Zemlya: Inst. Geologii Arktiki Trans., v. 49.

Buchan, S. H., *et al.,* 1965, The Triassic stratigraphy of Svalbard: Norsk Polarinst. Skr., no. 135, 94 p.

Burov, Yu. P., 1964, Intrusive dolerites of the Spitsbergen Archipelago: Conference on Geology of Spitsbergen, Leningrad, 1964; Summ. Contr., p. 26–28 (in Russian).

Dibner, V. D., 1957, The geological structure of Franz Josef Land, *in* F. G. Markov and D. V. Nalivkin, eds., Geologiia Sovetskoi Arktiki: Nauchno-Issled. Inst. Geologii Arktiki Trudy, v. 81, p. 11-20 (in Russian).

Firsov, Z. V., and Yu. Ya. Livshitz, 1967, Potassium-argon dating of the dolerites in the Sassenfjorden region (West Spitsbergen), *in* V. N. Sokolov, ed.,

* References in Buchan *et al.* (1965) and Parker (1967), marked in text with an asterisk, are not repeated here.

Materials on the stratigraphy of Spitsbergen: Leningrad, Inst. Geologii Arctiki, p. 178-184 (in Russian).

Flood, B., J. Nagy, and Th. S. Winsnes, 1970, Stratigrafiske undersøkelser av den Triasiske Lagrekke pa Edgeøya, Barentsøya (og Hopen), Svalbard: Norsk Geol. Tidsskr.; Norsk Polarinst. Medd., no. 100 (1971, in Engl.).

Frebold, H., 1930, Die mesozoische Entwicklung des Barentssee-schelfes: Geol. Rundschau, v. 21.

Goldschmidt, V. M., 1911, Petrographische Untersuchung einiger Eruptivgesteine von Nordwestspitzbergen: Skr. Kristiania Vidensk.-Selskab Inst. Mat.-Naturvid. Kl., v. 1, no. 9, p. 1–17.

Gothan, W., 1907, Die Fossilen hölzer von König Karls Land: Kgl. Svenska Vetens.-Akad. Handl., v. 42, no. 10, p. 1–41.

——— 1911, Das geologische Alter der Holzreste von König Karls Land: Zeitsch Deutsch. Geol. Gesell., v. 63, p. 163–166.

Hamberg, A., 1899, Über die Basalte des König Karl Landes: Geol. Fören. Stockholm Förh., v. 21, no. 5, p. 509–532.

Harland, W. B., 1969, Contribution of Spitsbergen to understanding of tectonic evolution of North Atlantic region, in Marshall Kay, ed., North Atlantic—geology and continental drift: Am. Assoc. Petroleum Geologists Mem. 12, p. 817-851.

——— 1970, Norsk-Cambridge Svalbard Expedition, 1969: Polar Rec., v. 15, no. 96, p. 331–332.

Heintz, N., 1963, Dinosaur-footprints and polar wandering: Norsk Polarinst. Årb. 1962, p. 35–43.

Helle, S. G., 1970, Change of name in Svalbard: Norsk Polarinst. Årb. 1968, p. 79–80.

Høeg, O. A., 1926, Fossil plants, in T. Iversen, ed., Hopen (Hope Island), Svalbard; Results of a reconnaissance in the summer of 1924: Oslo, Skr. om Svalbard og Ishavet, no. 10, p. 32–33.

Hoel, A., ed., 1942, The place-names of Svalbard: Skr. om Svalbard og Ishavet, no. 80, p. 1–539, map.

Howells, K., 1967, Cambridge Spitsbergen Expedition, 1966: Polar Rec., v. 13, no. 85, p. 458–459.

King, R. E., 1961-1964, Petroleum exploration and production in Europe: Am. Assoc. Petroleum Geologists Bull., vs. 45-47, no. 7; v. 48, no. 8.

Klubov, B. A., 1965a, A geological sketch of Edgeøya, in V. N. Sokolov, ed., Materiali po geologii Shpitsbergena: Leningrad, Inst. Geologii Arktiki, p. 71–82 (transl. 1970).

——— 1965b, The main features of the geological structure of Barentsøya, in V. N. Sokolov, ed., Materiali po geologii Shpitsbergena: Leningrad, Inst. Geologii Arktiki, p. 83–92 (transl. 1970).

——— 1965c, Triassic and Jurassic deposits of Wilhelmøya, in V. N. Sokolov, ed., Materiali po geologii Shpitsbergena: Leningrad, Inst. Geologii Arktiki, p. 174–184 (transl. 1970).

Krumsiek, K., J. Nagel, and A. E. M. Nairn, 1968, Record of palaeomagnetic measurements on some igneous rocks from the Isfjorden region, Spitsbergen: Norsk Polarinst. Årb. 1966, p. 76–83.

Lindström, G., 1900, On Theocyathus nathorsti n. sp., a Neocomian coral from King Charles Land: Kgl. Svenska Öfversigt Vetens.-Akad., Förh. Årg. 57, p. 5–12.

Nagy, Jeno, 1965, Oil exploration in Spitsbergen: Polar Rec., v. 12, no. 81, p. 703–708.

——— 1968, Oil exploration in Spitsbergen, 1967: Polar Rec., v. 14, no. 89, p. 197.

——— 1970, Ammonite faunas and stratigraphy of Lower Cretaceous (Albian) rocks in southern Spitsbergen: Skr. Norsk Polarinst, no. 152, p. 1–58.

Nathorst, A. G., 1901, Bidrag til König Karls Lands geologi: Geol. Fören. Stockholm Förh., v. 23, p. 341–377.

Nordenskiöld, A. E., 1875, Utkast till Isfjordens och Bellsunds geologi: Geol. Fören. Stockholm Förh., v. 2, 1874–1875, p. 243–260, 301–322, 356–373.

Norsk Polarinstitutt Årbok, 1960–1968: Oslo, pub. 1962–1970.

Ørvig, Tor, 1960, The Jurassic and Cretaceous of Andøya in Northern Norway, in O. Holtedahl, ed., Geology of Norway: Norges Geol. Undersokelse Skr., no. 208, p. 344–350.

Parker, J. R., 1967, The Jurassic and Cretaceous sequence in Spitsbergen: Geol. Mag., v. 104, no. 5, p. 487–505.

Ravn, J. P. J., 1922, On the Mollusca of the Tertiary of Spitsbergen: Oslo, Result. Norske Spitsbergen Eksped., v. 1, no. 2, 28 p.

Salfeld, H., and H. Frebold, 1924, Jura- und Kreidefossilien von Nowaja Semlja. Report, Scientific Research Norwegian Expedition to Novaja Zemlya 1921: Vidensk. i Kristiania.

Schroeter, C., 1880, Fossile Holzer aus der arctischen zone. I. Fossiles Holz von Konig-Karl-Land (früher Giles-Land), in O. Heer, ed., Flora fossilis arctica: Zurich, Die Fossile Flora der Polarländer, v. 6, pt. I, 38 p.

Sokolov, D., 1913, Sur les fossiles des blocs erratiques de Novaja Zemlja: Travaux du Musée Géol. près l'Acad. Imp. d. Sc. de St.-Pétersbourg, v. 7.

Spall, H., 1968, Anomalous paleomagnetic poles from late Mesozoic dolerites from Spitsbergen: Earth and Planetary Sci. Letters, v. 4, no. 1, p. 73–78.

Stolley, E., 1911, Zur Kenntnis der arktischen Trias: Neues Jahrb. Mineralogie, Geologie u. Paläontologie Abh., v. 1, p. 114–126.

——— 1912, Uber die Kriedeformation und ihre Fossilien auf Spitzbergen: Kgl. Svenska Vetensk.-Akad. Handl., v. 47, no. 11, 29 p.

Thorén, R., 1969, Picture atlas of the Arctic: Amsterdam, London, New York, Elsevier Publishing Co., 449 p., 589 pls.

Tozer, E. T., and J. R. Parker, 1968, Notes on the Triassic biostratigraphy of Svalbard: Geol. Mag., v. 105, no. 6, p. 526–542.

Vonderbank, K., 1970, Geologie und Fauna der Tertiären Ablagerungen Zentral-Spitsbergens: Norsk Polarinst. Skr., no. 153, 119 p. (Engl. abs.).

Wallis, R. H., and W. B. Harland, 1968, Cambridge Spitsbergen Expedition, 1967: Polar Rec., v. 14, no. 88, p. 43–45.

Werenskiöld, W., 1926, Physical geography and geology; coal deposits, in T. Iversen, ed., Hopen (Hope Island), Svalbard: Results of a reconnaissance in the summer of 1924: Oslo, Skr. om Svalbard og Ishavet, no. 10, p. 25–29.

Mesozoic Geology of East Greenland—Summary[1]

TOVE BIRKELUND[2]

Copenhagen, Denmark

Mesozoic deposits crop out in East Greenland mainly between lat. 70°25′ and 76°20′N. The sediments were deposited in fault-bounded basins having a north-northeast trend. The faulting began during the late Paleozoic, but block faulting persisted through the Mesozoic and into Tertiary (tensional faulting) time. In the Mesozoic, tectonic activity occurred particularly during the Late Jurassic. During much of the Mesozoic, the area formed the margin of the northern Atlantic sea of that time.

The composite thickness of the Mesozoic sequence is 6,000–7,000 m. The sequence is dominated by clastic material deposited in shallow water.

The lowermost Triassic (lower Scythian) is marine; in certain areas it is separated from the Upper Permian by only a minor disconformity. Thick arkose and conglomerate beds of fluvial origin overlie the marine Scythian. The Middle(?) Triassic and the lower part of the Upper Triassic consist of evaporites, dolomite with stromatolites, and redbeds of littoral and sublittoral origin. During the Rhaetic–early Liassic, nonmarine sandstones and shales containing a rich flora were deposited. Except for the Scythian, the Triassic facies are very similar to facies of the same agees in northern Europe.

All Jurassic stages (Pliensbachian and younger) are known. The succession consists mainly of coarse clastic sandstone of shallow-water to very shallow-water deposition, and the *"Skolithos"* ichnofacies and the *"Cruziana"* ichnofacies are dominant. Siltstone and sandstone containing more prolific marine faunas are intercalated.

The Cretaceous stages present are the Berriasian, Valanginian, Aptian, Albian, Cenomanian, Turonian, Santonian, and Campanian. As in the Jurassic, clastic sediments are predominant; impure limestone is widely distributed only in rocks of Valanginian age.

The Scythian and Middle and Late Jurassic ammonite faunas are especially abundant. These faunas are most significant to the knowledge of northern faunal provinces and boreal biostratigraphy.

[1] Manuscript received, September 20, 1971.

[2] University Institute for Historic Geology and Paleontology.

Tertiary of Greenland—A Volcanic and Plutonic Record of Continental Break-up[1]

C. KENT BROOKS[2]

Copenhagen, Denmark

Abstract This review of the chiefly magmatic Tertiary rocks in the central parts of East and West Greenland shows that the most abundant magmas were tholeiitic, and the most primitive magmas probably formed the picrites of West Greenland. The voluminous quartz tholeiites are very similar in composition to those of other plateau-basalt areas. Present in smaller amounts are alkalic basalt and nephelinitic types. The predominant salic magma was a nordmarkite, which differentiated to foyaite and peralkalic granite. Stratigraphic and radiometric evidence shows that magmatic activity was limited to the Paleocene and Eocene, and indicates that the lava was extruded at roughly the same rate as were postglacial Icelandic lavas. Tectonism was characterized by uplift of continental blocks and subsidence of adjoining areas. The abundant tholeiitic volcanism was associated with early rifting in the Paleocene, whereas the production of alkalic rock types probably occurred after the area had migrated away from the most active zone.

INTRODUCTION

Large areas of Tertiary rocks in the central parts of both the east and west coasts are conspicuous on the geologic map of Greenland. These rocks are predominantly volcanic and, in fact, count among the world's most voluminous occurrences of continental volcanic rocks. Thus, a study of the Greenland Tertiary is largely concerned with the origin of magmas, their development, and the associated tectonic controls.

These Tertiary rocks form an important part of the North Atlantic or Brito-Arctic province (cogent reasons for avoiding the term "Thulean province" have been given by Wenk [1961], who discussed the classic paper by Holmes [1918]). Many subsequent workers have stressed the importance of interrelations within the province. Thus, Wager (1947, p. 29) stated: "Simultaneous extrusion of lavas in such widely separated regions (*i.e.,* as Britain and Greenland) can scarcely be regarded as coincidence, but rather as the result of some major

[1] Manuscript received, September 20, 1971.

[2] Institute of Petrology, University of Copenhagen.

The author is indebted to Asger Ken Pedersen for the use of unpublished information and to the late L. R. Wager and to W. A. Deer for initiating and stimulating his interest in this subject. T. C. R. Pulvertaft and S. Watt have given valuable criticism.

process within the earth . . ." More recently, Haller (1970, p. 174) stressed that the Tertiary of East Greenland cannot be considered in regional terms alone. He also drew attention to the crosscutting nature of the Tertiary province with respect to older structures—a clear tectonic indication, with which petrologists would agree, that the activity responsible for these rocks is subcrustal in origin, *i.e.,* located in the mantle.

Views regarding this province have tended to be polarized between the rival theories of crustal subsidence and continental separation with which the names of de Geer (1912) and Wegener (1924), respectively, are mainly associated. During recent years, however, evidence has increased in favor of continental separation, which is visualized in terms of the process of ocean-floor spreading (Hess, 1962) and plate tectonics (*e.g.,* see Isacks *et al.,* 1968).

The purpose of this paper is to give a summary of the more important features of the Greenland Tertiary (excluding those of purely regional interest) and to indicate relations with other areas in the North Atlantic region in the light of recent information obtained from exploration of the intervening ocean floor.

DISTRIBUTION

Knowledge of the extent of various major rock types in the Greenland Tertiary is now fairly complete; it is only in details—as, for example, the occurrence of different types of basalt—that there are considerable gaps. No attempt will be made to consider the various areas in detail, as a publication in preparation by the Geological Survey of Greenland will contain contributions by experts in more specific areas. Detailed information can also be obtained from the works cited herein.

East Greenland

Volcanic, plutonic, and sedimentary rocks are present in East Greenland (Fig. 1), but sediments are of inconsiderable extent and thickness. *Basalts* with a present outcrop area of roughly 60,000 sq km (23,000 sq mi—although basaltic

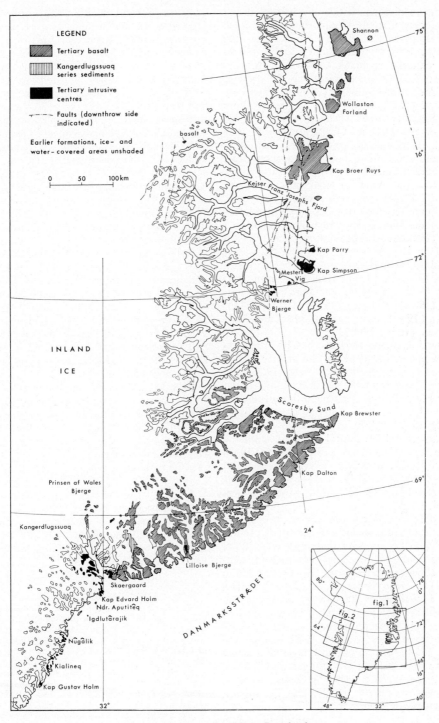

LEGEND

Tertiary basalt

Kangerdlugssuaq
series sediments

Tertiary intrusive
centres

Faults (downthrow side
indicated)

Earlier formations, ice- and
water-covered areas unshaded

0   50   100km

Shannon
Ø

75°

16°

Wollaston
Forland

basalt

Kap Broer Ruys

Kejser Franz Josephs Fjord

Kap Parry

72°

Mesters
Vig

Kap Simpson

Werner
Bjerge

INLAND

ICE

Scoresby Sund

Kap Brewster

Kap Dalton

Prinsen af Wales
Bjerge

69°

24°

Kangerdlugssuaq

Lilloise Bjerge

Skaergaard

Kap Edvard Holm
Ndr. Aputitêq

Igdlutârajik

Nûgâlik

Kialineq

Kap Gustav Holm

32°

DANMARKSSTRÆDET

80°

78°

fig.1

fig.2

0°

64°

72°

48°

16°

32°

60°

66°

FIG. 1—Tertiary rocks of East Greenland.

xenoliths in plutons outside the present basalt area indicate that the basalts once were much more extensive) extend from Kangerdlugssuaq (68°N lat.) to Scoresby Sund (70°N). Additional scattered remnants of a once probably continuous cover are found along the coast as far north as Shannon Ø (75°N). These are typical plateau basalts, closely similar to those in comparable areas such as the Columbia River or the Deccan. Characteristically, they have a monotonous appearance, are either aphyric or contain plagioclase phenocrysts, and, where undisturbed by later events, are nearly horizontal and show no signs of central-type eruption. Pyroclastic rocks are not common, but they are recorded from the upper and lower parts of the succession, which is as thick as 7 km (23,000 ft). Abrupt thinning occurs toward the Inland Ice. Basalts of this type are widely believed to have been erupted from tensional fissures (Tyrrell, 1937). They have been studied by Holmes (1918), Backlund and Malmquist (1932), Wager (1934, 1935, 1947), Rittman (1940), Krokström (1944), and Fawcett et al. (1966, 1968).

Apart from these tholeiitic basalts, other extrusives occur. Included are the *greatly undersaturated basalts* described by Katz (1952) and Haller (1956) from the nunataks inland from Kejser Franz Josephs Fjord and those found as pebbles in the Kap Dalton conglomerates (Wager, 1935). *Mafic, somewhat alkalic extrusives* are found in central volcano remnants inland from Kangerdlugssuaq (Wager, 1947; Anwar, 1955), *trachytic tuffs* are present on Keglin Ø (Wager, 1934, p. 35), and *rhyolites* are present in the Kialineq area (Brown, (1968).

Plutonic complexes are many, ranging in composition from mafic and ultramafic (commonly with pronounced layering) to syenitic, foyaitic, and granitic. They are present, generally along the coast, from Kap Gustav Holm (67°N) to Kap Broer Ruys (73½°N). Detailed investigations have been made on the Kap Edvard Holm layered gabbros (Elsdon, 1970), the Kangerdlugssuaq quartz syenite–foyaite series (Kempe et al., 1970; Kempe and Deer, 1970), the Kaergaard layered gabbros (Wager and Deer, 1939; Wager and Brown, 1968), the Werner Bjerge syenites, granites, and foyaites (Bearth, 1959), and the subvolcanic stocks of syenite, peralkalic granite, etc., in the Mesters Vig area (Kapp, 1960). Preliminary field descriptions are available for the Kap Parry and Kap Simpson syenites and

granites (Schaub, 1938; 1942) and the gabbros, granites, and syenites of the Kialineq area (Brown, 1968). Relatively unknown are the intrusive rocks of Kap Gustav Holm (gabbro, syenite), Nûgâlik (gabbro, microgranite), Igdlutârijik (gabbro), Nordre Aputitêq (gabbro), Lilloise (syenites, nepheline syenites), and Kap Broer Ruys(?), as well as many minor intrusions such as the Bagnaesset and Kap Deichman syenites and Kangerdlugssuaq.[3]

Swarms of *dikes* and *sills* are found in many areas—e.g., the coast-parallel dike swarm described by Wager (1934, 1947), dike swarms associated with major intrusive centers, and the extensive sill complexes in the strata north of Scoresby Sund. A detailed study of basaltic and lamprophyric dikes in the Skaergaard area was published by Vincent (1953).

Both subbasaltic and intrabasaltic *sedimentary rocks* are known—of marine, estuarine, and limnic deposition. The basalts lie on sedimentary rocks at several places in northeast Greenland (Haller, 1970, p. 229–231) and in the Kangerdlugssuaq area (Wager, 1934), where they contain basalt pebbles indicating that volcanism had already started in neighboring areas. Intrabasaltic sedimentary beds are fairly common; they consist mainly of thin sandstones and zones containing silicified tree trunks. Better developed sequences are at Kap Dalton and Kap Brewster (Wager, 1935; Hassan, 1953), where they are near the top of the plateau-basalt sequence and contain rich marine fossil assemblages.

West Greenland

In contrast to the east coast, subbasaltic sedimentary rocks in West Greenland are thicker and more extensive, intrusions are much less common, and the older lavas are submarine and picritic. A map of the area is shown in Figure 2.

[3] *Note added in proof:* Recent expeditions (Brooks, 1972, *Polar Record*, v. 16, p. 261) have resulted in the discovery of two new major plutons in East Greenland. These are located at Gardiners Plateau at the head of Kangerdlugssuaq and at Borgtinderne, 30 km northeast of Lilloise Bjerge. The former is a ring complex containing melilite-bearing rocks, pyroxenites, and other ultramafic alkalic types, whereas the latter contains syenites and nepheline syenites. Lilloise Bjerge consists mainly of ultramafic and mafic plutonic rocks with only subordinate syenites (*cf.* text descriptions). A further alkalic complex appears to exist on Batbjerg at the head of Kangerdlugssuaq. The discovery of these intrusives reveals an interesting pattern of increasing alkalinity inward from the continental margin.

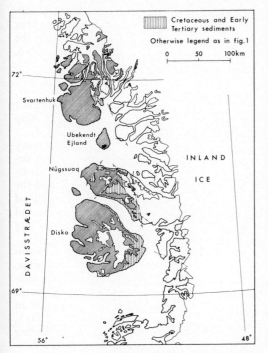

Cretaceous and Early
Tertiary sediments

Otherwise legend as in fig.1

0   50   100km

72°

Svartenhuk

Ubekendt
Ejland

INLAND

Nûgssuaq

ICE

Disko

DAVISSTRÆDET

69°

56°   48°

FIG. 2—Cretaceous and early Tertiary rocks of West
Greenland.

In the Nûgssuaq and Svartenhuk Peninsulas
and on Disko, *sedimentary deposits* lie on the
deeply eroded Precambrian basement. They
reach more than 1,000 m (3,300 ft) in thickness but pinch out toward the Inland Ice—as
do the overlying volcanic rocks. Thus, data
from both the west and east coasts support the
view that the two areas are not related. The
sediments are limnic in the southern part of the
area, whereas marine beds are found in the
more northwesterly occurrences. Both sedimentary types contain rich fossil assemblages.
A detailed review of the Cretaceous-Tertiary
stratigraphy and tectonics was written by Rosenkrantz and Pulvertaft (1969), and a review
of the marine deposits was published by Rosenkrantz (1970). Significant intrabasaltic sedimentary zones are also present in West Greenland.

The onset of volcanism in West Greenland is
recorded by tuff layers in the Danian rocks,
which are overlain by approximately 500 m
(1,640 ft) of basalt breccias and pillow lavas.
These breccias are of submarine origin; cross-
bedding indicates that their source was located
on the west (*i.e.,* in the present Davis Strait).
Petrologically, the breccias are very rich in oli-

vine, and, together with the directly overlying
subaerial basalts, they make up the *picrite unit*
which is at least 5 km (16,400 ft) thick in the
central part of the area. Olivine content decreases upward and the lavas grade into *tholeiites* similar to those of the east coast; minor *trachytes* and *rhyolites* are present in the upper
part of the succession. Descriptions of these
volcanic rocks can be found in Noe-Nygaard
(1942), Munck and Noe-Nygaard (1957),
Drever (1958), Clarke (1968, 1970), and Rosenkrantz and Pulvertaft (1969). Recent detailed research by Pedersen (1970) on Disko
has revealed many additional features besides
the well-known *iron-bearing lavas* in this area
(Pauly, 1969). Many of the lavas must have
been fed from fissures, and clear examples of
feeder dikes have been found by Drever
(1958); however, central-type eruptions are
also known from Ubekendt Ejland and Disko.
The total thickness of lavas is believed to be of
the order of 10 km (33,000 ft).

The only pluton in West Greenland is the
relatively minor Sarqâta qâqâ *gabbro-grano-
phyre intrusion* on Ubekendt Ejland (Drever
and Game, 1948; Drever, 1958; Thompson and
Patrick, 1968), although *dikes* and *sills* abound.
The dikes and sills include picritic (Drescher
and Kruger, 1927; Drever, 1956) and tholeiitic
(Munck, 1945) types, and are very similar to
the lavas. Drever and Game (1948) and
Drever (1958) recorded an interesting assemblage of dike rocks, including alkalic (nepheline
basalt, monchiquite) and granitic types, on
Ubekendt Ejland.

MAGMA TYPES

The occurrence of numerous different magmatic rocks in a province such as this may be
traced to two main factors: different types of
magma arriving at the surface and differentiation of these magmas near or at the surface.
Effects of low-pressure differentiation, commonly tending to accentuate original small differences in magma batches, have been traced
by investigations of differentiated intrusives.
The generation and development of magmas at
high pressure in the earth's mantle have in recent years been considerably clarified by experimental studies. It is clearly desirable to attempt
to determine the causes of the diversity of rock
types in the study area: to what extent are they
due to a corresponding diversity of primary
magmas, and to what extent are they due to
fractionation of a small number of primary
magmas in high-level plutons?

Basaltic Magmas

Because the earth's mantle is believed to be ultramafic in composition, magmas formed by partial melting are generally basaltic. Basaltic rocks may be conveniently classified by use of the scheme of Yoder and Tilley (1962); the divisions supposedly are based on genetic importance. However, magmatic evolution is a highly subtle process, as demonstrated, for example, by Coombs (1963).

Most of the volcanic rocks under discussion fall into Yoder and Tilley's quartz-tholeiite class, as do other extensive plateau basalts such as the Columbia River and Deccan basalts and the sill complexes of Tasmania and Karroo (Coombs, 1963, p. 234). Table 1 gives an average of twelve recent analyses of basalts from the area south of Scoresby Sund, together with

an average of similar lavas from the upper part of the West Greenland succession. Fawcett et al. (1968) considered that the quartz-normative character of these rocks may be caused by late-stage alteration processes acting on a composition originally of olivine tholeiitic character (Yoder and Tilley, 1962; Coombs, 1963). This late-stage alteration is also suggested by the difference in oxidation state commonly found between dike rocks and lavas. For example, the $Fe_2O_3 / FeO + Fe_2O_3$ ratio for column 1 in Table 1 is 0.29, whereas that ratio for the Skaergaard chilled margin (olivine normative) is 0.13. Reduction of the amount of Fe_2O_3 in the former analysis to 1.5 percent, as was done by Coombs (1963), and adjustment of the FeO content accordingly give a value of 0.11, and the rock becomes olivine normative. The oxida-

Table 1. Average Analyses of Important Tertiary Magmatic Rock Types from Greenland

(recalculated water-free)

Samples:	1	2	3	4	5	6	7	8	9	10	11	12
SiO_2	48.4	48.5	49.3	48.0	45.7	53.1	45.1	39.1	63.8	54.7	72.3	71.2
Al_2O_3	13.6	13.7	14.5	13.2	10.5	14.5	13.3	6.6	17.9	23.4	12.3	13.0
Fe_2O_3	4.0	1.5	4.4	3.0	3.9	1.6	4.2	7.3	1.5	1.7	2.0	2.0
FeO	9.9	12.2	8.1	8.2	7.7	7.8	7.1	8.4	1.7	0.9	1.2	3.4
MgO	6.5	6.5	5.9	11.5	19.1	10.0	7.7	13.9	0.6	0.2	0.7	0.2
CaO	11.1	11.1	12.0	11.9	10.0	9.0	13.6	14.8	1.2	1.4	1.1	2.1
Na_2O	2.5	2.5	2.6	2.1	1.4	1.9	3.0	2.1	6.7	9.4	4.9	4.2
K_2O	0.4	0.5	0.4	0.3	0.1	0.6	2.0	1.2	5.5	7.7	4.7	3.2
MnO	0.2	0.2	0.2	0.2	0.2	0.2	0.1	0.3	0.1	0.1	0.1	0.1
TiO_2	2.9	2.9	2.3	1.5	1.2	1.2	3.1	5.4	0.8	0.3	0.3	0.6
P_2O_5	0.3	0.3	0.3	0.2	0.1	0.1	0.7	1.1	0.2	0.1	0.2	0.1

CIPW Norms

	1	2	3	4	5	6	7	8	9	10	11	12
Quartz	1.2	—	1.8	—	—	4.2	—	—	1.0	—	23.9	28.7
Orthoclase	2.6	2.6	2.3	1.5	0.8	3.3	11.4	—	32.1	43.3	28.0	18.6
Albite	20.4	20.4	21.5	16.9	11.6	15.6	6.3	—	56.6	8.8	36.9	35.4
Anorthite	24.1	24.4	26.1	25.5	21.3	28.9	16.7	4.6	2.3	—	—	7.1
Nepheline	—	—	—	—	—	—	9.9	9.6	—	36.4	—	—
Acmite	—	—	—	—	—	—	—	—	—	2.3	4.3	—
Diopside	22.7	23.1	24.9	24.8	20.5	11.2	35.2	44.3	2.1	2.2	3.4	2.4
Hypersthene	14.9	14.7	9.8	9.2	8.5	30.1	—	—	1.2	—	1.4	2.9
Olivine	—	4.4	—	12.0	26.3	—	4.5	9.9	—	—	—	—
Magnetite	5.8	2.2	6.2	4.2	5.5	2.3	5.9	10.2	2.1	1.3	0.8	2.8
Ilmenite	5.5	5.5	4.4	2.9	2.2	2.2	5.8	9.9	1.5	0.5	0.5	1.1
Apatite	0.7	0.7	0.6	0.4	0.3	0.3	1.7	2.5	0.4	0.2	0.5	0.1

　　1. 13 unpublished analyses from the Scoresby Sund area collected by S. Watt (Greenland Geological Survey) and Oxford University 1965 Expedition.
　　2. Analysis 1, with Fe_2O_3 reduced to 1.5% (Coombs, 1963).
　　3. 14 feldspar-phyric lavas, Svartenhuk (Clarke, 1970, Table 1, col. 7).
　　4. 10 Svartenhuk olivine tholeiites (Clarke, 1970, Table 1, col. 6).
　　5. 7 Svartenhuk olivine-rich tholeiites (Clarke, 1970, Table 1, col. 4).
　　7. Disko bronzite-pigeonite lavas (Pedersen, 1970).
　　7. 12 alkali basalts, largely dikes, from NE Greenland (Bearth, 1959; Kapp, 1960; Tyrrell, 1932; Backlund and Malmquist, 1932).
　　8. Average of a melilitite and a nephelinite from nunatak region, NE Greenland (Haller, 1956, p. 128); includes 5.4% lc and 1.1% ln.
　　9. 9 quartz-syenites: Werner Bjerge (Bearth, 1959), Mesters Vig area (Kapp, 1960), and Kangerdlugssuaq intrusion (Kempe et al., 1970).
　　10. 5 foyaites: Werner Bjerge (Bearth, 1959; including a tinguaite) and Kangerdlugssuaq (Kempe et al., 1970); includes 1.6% wo.
　　11. 3 alkali granites: Werner Bjerge (Bearth, 1970), Pictet Bjerge, Mesters Vig (Kapp, 1960).
　　12. 3 Skaergaard granophyres (Wager and Brown, 1968, nos. 4489, 5259, and 3058).

tion state of a magma is important not only in classification, but also in the potent control it has on subsequent differentiation trends (Osborne, 1959). The special trend exhibited by Skaergaard magma has been attributed to its oxidation state (Wager and Brown, 1968, p. 240–244).

In addition to the quartz tholeiites already mentioned, normal olivine tholeiites and also olivine-rich lavas are abundant in West Greenland. Averages for all these types are represented in Table 1. Clarke (1970) discussed the origin of these lavas and concluded that the picritic-magma type is a relatively unmodified magma from the mantle whose composition is consistent with partial melting of a garnet lherzolite at 30 kilobars, whereas the olivine-poor and olivine-free magmas were probably modified at lower pressures. These various types of tholeiitic rock are also characteristically low in the group of elements commonly called "incompatible elements."

Pedersen (1970), working on Disko, identified lavas transitional between tholeiites and alkalic basalts which he believes to be caused by the fractionation of eclogite at depth. He also noted unusual lavas with a high content of normative orthopyroxenes which can be interpreted to be partial melts from a hydrated mantle.

Alkalic basaltic magmas were also available in East Greenland. Nepheline-normative basaltic dike rocks have been analyzed by Tyrrell (1932), Bearth (1959), and Kapp (1960), and analyses taken from these sources have been used to give a rough idea of the composition of the alkalic basalt magma. The highly undersaturated lavas with normative larnite and leucite from the nunatak region (Katz, 1952; Haller, 1956) have been mentioned.

In summary, a wide spectrum of magma types was present during the period of volcanicity of this region. In East Greenland the bulk of the lavas was of a common quartz-tholeiite type, which probably was derived directly from an olivine-normative type. In West Greenland, magmas were also tholeiitic but of several distinct types. Also present in both areas were alkalic magmas with increasing degrees of undersaturation; these magmas probably were derived from different depths of partial melting.

Granitic and Syenitic Magmas

Many of the East Greenland plutons are evidence that syenitic magmas were available there at a late stage in the evolution of the province.

This magma was presumably slightly oversaturated, the commonest syenite being a quartz-bearing type (Table 1). No evidence exists as to the origin of this magma, but it probably developed from alkalic basalt magmas by low-pressure fractionation in the same way that the syenitic magmas of the Precambrian Gardar province of South Greenland (e.g., see Upton, 1960) developed. The transition through intermediate types is recorded there in closely associated intrusives. Another parallel with the Gardar province is seen in the association of oversaturated (granitic) and undersaturated (foyaitic) rocks with this predominant nordmarkitic type. The work of Kempe et al. (1970) clearly traces the evolution of the undersaturated type from the nordmarkite; it is also likely that the granitic type, which tends to be peralkalic, developed from this magma. Whether the two contrasting trends are due to small differences in the original magma or to differences in such variables as pressure and temperature is at present unknown. This problem was discussed by Upton (1960, p. 135) in connection with the Gardar rocks. Average analyses of foyaites and granites associated with the quartz syenites are given in Table 1.

A type of granite is distinguishable which differs from that mentioned in that it is not peralkalic and generally occurs in close association with the tholeiitic gabbro plutons. Examples are the granophyres of Skaergaard and Sarqâta qâqâ. Considerable controversy still exists as to whether such granitic rocks are differentiates of the basaltic magmas or are products of partial melting of country rocks. The scope of the present paper does not permit a discussion of this interesting problem, and the reader is referred to existing literature (e.g., Brown, 1963; Dunham and Thompson, 1967). Two distinct types of granitic rock also are present in Iceland (Sigurdsson, 1970). The differentiation trend of East Greenland tholeiites is indicated by Vincent's (1950) study of the glassy residuum in a basalt from Kap Daussy.

Time Relations

In Nûgssuaq the volcanism started with the tuff layers in the Danian, but the major activity occurred in the Paleocene and possibly the Eocene (Rosenkrantz and Pulvertaft, 1969). K-Ar ages of 54–58 m.y. have been obtained on West Greenland rocks (Clarke, 1968). In East Greenland, although paleontologic evidence is inconclusive, it appears to indicate that activity began near the beginning of Tertiary time and continued into Eocene time. This date is confirmed by K-Ar determinations, which indicate an age of 55–60 m.y. for the upper lavas (Beckinsale et al., 1970).

The East Greenland coastal dike swarm, which is younger than both the lavas and the gabbroic intrusions, does not cut the syenitic rocks. Apart from certain late dikes, these coastal dikes are the latest manifestations of magmatic activity; K-Ar ages of about 50 m.y. have been obtained on hornblendes from these dikes by Beckinsale et al. (1970).

The length of the magmatic episode appears to have been extremely limited, being of the order of 10 m.y., and the time of accumulation of the great thicknesses of plateau basalt was probably only a few million years—a figure consistent with that given for the rate of extrusion of postglacial lavas in Iceland by Sigurdsson (1967, p. 38).

Low ages given by minerals weakly retentive to argon (Beckinsale et al., 1970) indicate that the volcanic pile remained hot for a long period; indeed, hot springs now occur in several places. Wager (1934, p. 31) drew attention to thermal metamorphism in the lowermost basalts.

TECTONIC ACTIVITY

The most impressive Tertiary tectonism in Greenland is the coastal flexure with its accompanying dike swarm described by Wager and Deer (1938) and Wager (1947). This structure dies away northward and is replaced by a system of coast-parallel faults with a net downthrow on the east. These faults were observed just south of Scoresby Sund by Fawcett et al. (1966) and also were described from regions to the north where faulting was initiated in the late Paleozoic and continued into the Tertiary under the influence of tensional stress (Haller, 1969; 1970, p. 238). Apart from the impressive regional uplift which occurred after the basalt extrusion in association with this flexuring, and which affected most of the East Greenland coast, uplift initiated at the end of the Mesozoic in the northern part of the area caused a widespread change from marine to terrestrial conditions (Haller, 1970, p. 190). Tertiary uplift was particularly intense in the Kangerdlugssuaq region, where a dome rising about 6.5 km (21,000 ft) above present sea level was formed. The highest mountains within the Arctic Circle—the Watkins Bjerge—are in the eroded remnant of this dome.

The tectonic activity of West Greenland at this time is characterized by coast-parallel faults downthrown on the seaward side and by evidence of epeirogenic uplift (Rosenkrantz and Pulvertaft, 1969).

RELATIONS WITH OTHER NORTH ATLANTIC AREAS

The importance of viewing Greenland in relation to widespread late Mesozoic and Cenozoic magmatic activity in other parts of the North Atlantic area has already been stressed.

Late Jurassic and Early Cretaceous tholeiitic basalts are found in Svalbard (Hamberg, 1899; Tyrrell and Sandford, 1933; Parker, 1967), where they are dated radiometrically at 149 m.y. (Gayer et al., 1966), and in Franz Joseph Land (Koettlitz, 1898; Frebold, 1935). Similar basaltic rocks of this age have been reported from northeastern Canada (Blackadar, 1964), and clay zones in the British Cretaceous have recently been recognized as ash layers (Hallam and Sellwood, 1968). In southwest Greenland, doleritic dike swarms with accompanying lamprophyres dated at 138–162 m.y. were noted by Watt (1969). These igneous intrusions and related events occurred at a time when the Atlantic had opened farther to the south but probably was not yet in existence in these latitudes (Dietz and Holden, 1970).

The beginning of active rifting in the North Atlantic area appears to be recorded by intense magmatic activity in the Paleocene of Baffin, Greenland, the Faeroes, and Britain. Radiometric dates from all these areas (Bekinsale et al., 1970) confirm that this activity began about 60 m.y. ago. This date is in close agreement with studies of magnetic anomalies of the intervening ocean (Vogt et al., 1969) and with extrapolations based on the present spreading rates and separation (Vine, 1966). The latter method is applied with caution in view of the evidence that spreading has not been uniform (Vogt et al., 1969a). In southern Scandinavia, volcanic activity in the Skagerrak (Sharma, 1970) and in Skåne (Norin, 1934) is well dated by the presence of ash layers in the Eocene of Denmark (Bøggild, 1918). Clarke (1968) has discussed the relation of the West Greenland and Baffin lavas in the Davis Strait region to the formation of Baffin Bay. Continued rifting along the line of the midocean ridge can be traced through the Pliocene and Pleistocene to recent times in Iceland, Jan Mayen, and Spitsbergen (where post-Pleistocene volcanoes have been described by Hoel and Holtedahl, 1911).

The reason for the localization of intense magmatic activity along the northwesterly-trending belt from Britain through the Faeroes and Iceland to Greenland and Baffin has been attributed by Wilson (1965) to a "hot spot" or thermal center in the mantle, although the nature of such a hot spot is obscure. The aseismic "thread ridges," or "nemataths" (Carey, 1958, p. 195–196), of Walvis Bay and the Rio Grande—which meet near Tristan da Cunha in the South Atlantic and are closely related to basaltic volcanism in Southwest Africa and Brazil —and the aseismic Laccadive-Chagos ridge leading to the Deccan basalts are believed to represent analogous cases of crustal plates being transported over mantle hot spots (Dietz and Holden, 1970).

It has become fashionable to compare the midocean-ridge volcanism and tectonism with that of continental rift systems; indeed, many points of similarity between Greenland and the African rift emerge (Haller, 1970). A recent discussion of magmatic rock types and their relation to tectonism in the African rift by Harris (1969) may be advantageously applied to the North Atlantic region. In Africa and the Red Sea, the most active areas of rifting produce tholeiitic lavas with a low content of potassium and similar elements, whereas the more alkalic and undersaturated lavas are found in less active areas. In Greenland, the earlier phases of volcanicity involving voluminous tholeiites probably accompanied the initial rifting of the continent. These tholeiites are similar to those found along the midocean ridges at present, in that they tend to have a low potassium and other incompatible-element content. (Schilling [1969] claimed that continental tholeiites are clearly distinguished from oceanic ones by their patterns of rare-earth abundance. The only data available for Greenland—namely, Haskin's [1968] analysis of the Skaergaard chilled margin—appear to confirm Schilling's conclusion.) Many examples can be given of closely similar tholeiites (*e.g.*, in Tasmania, Antarctica, South Africa, South America, eastern North America, and India) which are widely regarded as having been erupted in connection with continental break-up. During later stages, as the areas moved farther from the active rift zone, magmas became more alkalic. Harris (1969) explained the genesis of the different magmas in terms of the geothermal environment: tholeiites form with shallow melting and rapid eruption under the influence of convective uprise from the mantle (which also gives rise to continental upwarp); alkalic basalts and nephelinites form at much greater depths in regions of low thermal gradient where they equilibrate with large amounts of mantle to become enriched in K, H_2O, CO_2, P, Sr, Nb, U, *etc.* On oceanic islands, a characteristic distribution about the midocean ridge of lavas with different degrees of silica saturation was observed by McBirney and Gass (1967), who explained this distribution on the basis of the geothermal environment. Chemical differences which appear to exist between the Greenland-Iceland-Faeroes belt and other parts of the midocean-ridge system (Noe-Nygaard, 1966) would be consistent with an unusual temperature regime in this region.

CONCLUSIONS

Although much information exists on the Tertiary formations of Greenland, there is still considerable scope for detailed research. In terms of size, variety, and good exposure, the area is outstanding, and close investigation probably will yield considerable valuable data. Furthermore, the Greenland Tertiary is pertinent to the question of the origin of the Atlantic Ocean.

Apart from a closer investigation of the areas which still have been only superficially examined, several lines of research appear to be worth further attention.

1. Relations between magmatism and tectonics and comparisons with other regions of continental break-up. The epeirogenic rise of East Greenland appears similar to the well-known upwarp of the African shield in association with rifting there (Cloos, 1939) and, possibly, to certain features of oceanic rises also (Menard, 1965; Vogt *et al.*, 1969a). Gibson (1966) has pointed out parallels between the East Greenland flexure and similar structures in the Deccan, Lebombo, Red Sea, and Snake River basalts—all of which are related to midocean-ridge systems. The fact that Iceland is the largest island on the ridge is further evidence that it overlies an abnormally hot region which has given rise to greater uplift and volcanism than elsewhere on the ridge.

2. Types of magmatism and comparisons with other areas, both in the North Atlantic province and elsewhere. A significant difference between East Greenland and the eastern Atlantic is the greater abundance of salic alkalic rocks in the former. The greater abundance of these rocks may be related to their proximity to the continental margin, and comparison of East Greenland with Rockall—which lies in a sym-

metrical position with respect to the Mid-Atlantic Ridge, as pointed out by Vine (1966)—may be preferable.

3. Offshore investigations. Although the adjoining ocean floor is now fairly well known (e.g., Vogt et al., 1969b, 1970), the precise relation to the continental magmatic rocks of Greenland and the younger magmatic rocks of Iceland is only sketchily understood. In particular, the seaward extension of the East Greenland flexure has never been traced.

REFERENCES CITED

Anwar, Y. M., 1955, Geological investigations in East Greenland. Part V, Petrography of the Prinsen of Wales Bjerge lavas: Medd. om Grønland, v. 135, no. 1, 31 p.

Backlund, H. G., and D. Malmquist, 1932, Zur Geologie und Petrographie der nordöstgrönländischen Basaltformation. Teil I, Die basische Reihe: Medd. om Grønland, v. 87, no. 5, 61 p.

Bearth, P., 1959, On the alkali massif of the Werner Bjerge in East Greenland: Medd. om Grønland, v. 153, no. 4, 63 p.

Beckinsale, R. D., C. K. Brooks, and D. C. Rex, 1970, K-Ar ages for the Tertiary of East Greenland: Dansk Geol. Foren. Medd., v. 20, p. 27–37.

Blackadar, R. G., 1964, Basic intrusions of the Queen Elizabeth Islands, District of Franklin: Canada Geol. Survey Bull. 97, 36 p.

Brown, G. M., 1963, Melting relations of Tertiary granitic rocks in Skye and Rhum: Mineralog. Mag., v. 33, p. 533–562.

Brown, P., 1968, Igneous rocks of the Kialineq area, East Greenland: Geol. Soc. London Proc., no. 1649, p. 106.

Bøggild, O. B., 1918, Den vulkanske Aske i Moleret: Danmarks Geol. Undersøgelse Række 2, no. 37, 159 p.

Carey, S. W., 1958, A tectonic approach to continental drift, in S. W. Carey, conv., Continental drift—a symposium: Hobart, Univ. of Tasmania, 375 p.

Clarke, D. B., 1968, Tertiary basalts of the Baffin Bay area: Univ. Edinburgh, PhD thesis.

—— 1970, Tertiary basalts of Baffin Bay—possible primary magma from the mantle: Contr. Mineralogy and Petrology, v. 25, p. 203–224.

Cloos, H., 1939, Hebung-Spaltung-Vulkanismus, Elemente einer geometrischen Analyse irdischer Grossformen: Geol. Rundschau, v. 30, p. 405–527.

Coombs, D. S., 1963, Trends and affinities of basaltic magmas and pyroxenes as illustrated on the diopside-olivine-silica diagrams: Mineralog. Soc. America Spec. Paper No. 1, p. 227–250.

de Geer, G., 1912, Kontinentale Niveauänderungen im Norden Europas: Stockholm, 11th Internat. Geol. Cong. (1910), Compte Rendu, pt. 1, p. 849–860.

Dietz, R. S., and J. C. Holden, 1970, Reconstruction of Pangaea—breakup and dispersion of continents, Permian to present: Jour. Geophys. Research, v. 75, p. 4939–4956.

Drescher, F. K., and H. K. E. Kruger, 1927, Der peridotit von Kaersut (Grönland) und sein Gangefolge als Beispiel einer Sekretions differentiation: Neues Jahrb. Mineralogie Monatsh., v. 57A, p. 569–616.

Drever, H. I., 1956, The geology of Ubekendt Ejland. Part II, The picritic sheets and dykes of the east coast: Medd. om Grønland, v. 137, no. 4, 39 p.

—— 1958, Geological results of four expeditions to Ubekendt Ejland, West Greenland: Arctic, v. 11, p. 199–210.

—— and P. M. Game, 1948, The geology of Ubekendt Ejland. Part I, A preliminary review: Medd. om Grønland, v. 134, no. 8, 35 p.

Dunham, A. C., and R. N. Thompson, 1967, The origin of granitic magmas—Skye and Rhum: Geol. Soc. Australia Jour., v. 14, p. 339–343.

Elsdon, R., 1970, The Kap Edvard Holm complex, East Greenland: Geol. Soc. London Proc., no. 1663, p. 158–160.

Fawcett, J. J., J. C. Rucklidge, and C. K. Brooks, 1966, Geological expedition to the Tertiary basalt region of Scoresby Sund, East Greenland: Nature, v. 212, p. 603–604.

—— —— and E. Gasparrini, 1968, Chemistry of some Tertiary basalts from East Greenland: Canadian Mineralogist, v. 9, p. 572.

Frebold, H., 1935, Geologie von Spitzbergen der Bäreninsel, des König Karl und Franz-Joseph-Landes, in Geologie der Erde: Berlin, Borntraeger, 195 p.

Gayer, R. A., et al., 1966, Radiometric age determinations on rocks from Spitzbergen: Norsk Polarinst. Skr., no. 137, 39 p.

Gibson, I. L., 1966, Crustal flexures and flood basalts: Tectonophysics, v. 3, p. 447–456.

Hallam, A., and B. W. Sellwood, 1968, Origin of Fuller's Earth in the Mesozoic of S. England: Nature, v. 220, p. 1193–1195.

Haller, J., 1956, Geologie der Nunatakker—Region von Zentral—Ostgrönland zwischen 70°30′ und 74°10′ N. Br: Medd. om Grønland, v. 154, no. 1, 172 p.

—— 1969, Tectonics and neotectonics in East Greenland—review bearing on the drift concept, in Marshall Kay, ed., North Atlantic—Geology and continental drift: Am. Assoc. Petroleum Geologists Mem. 12, p. 852–858.

—— 1970, Tectonic map of East Greenland: Medd. om Grønland, v. 171, no. 5, 286 p., scale 1:500,000.

Hamberg, A., 1899, Uber die basalte des König Karl-Landes: Geol. Fören. Stockholm Förh., v. 21, p. 509–532.

Harris, P. G., 1969, Basalt type and African rift valley tectonism: Tectonophysics, v. 8, no. 4–6, p. 427–442.

Haskin, L. A., and M. A. Haskin, 1968, Rare-earth elements in the Skaergaard intrusion: Geochim. et Cosmochim. Acta, v. 32, p. 433–447.

Hassan, M. Y., 1953, Tertiary faunas from Kap Brewster, East Greenland: Medd. om Grønland, v. 111, no. 5, 42 p.

Hess, H. H., 1962, History of ocean basins, in A. E. J. Engel et al., eds., Petrologic studies: Geol. Soc. America, A. F. Buddington vol., p. 599–620.

Hoel, A., and O. Holtedahl, 1911, Les nappes de lave, des volcans et les source thermal dans les environs de Baie Wood au Spitsberg: Vidensk.-Selsk. Skr. I. Mat.-Nat. Kl., no. 8, 37 p.

Holmes, A., 1918, The basaltic rocks of the Arctic region: Mineralog. Mag., v. 18, p. 180–223.

Isacks, B., J. Oliver, and R. Sykes, 1968. Seismology and the new global tectonics: Jour. Geophys. Research, v. 73, p. 5855–5900.

Kapp, H., 1960, Zur Petrologie der Subvulkane szwischen Mesters Vig und Antarctic Havn (Ost-Grönland): Medd. om Grønland, v. 153, no. 2, 203 p.

Katz, H. R., 1952, Ein Querschnitt durch die Nunatakzone Ostgrönlands (ca. 74° n. Br): Medd. om Grønland, v. 144, no. 8, 65 p.

Kempe, D. C. R., and W. A. Deer, 1970, Geological investigations in East Greenland. Part IX, The mineralogy of the Kangerdlugssuaq intrusion, East Greenland: Medd. om Grønland, v. 190, no. 3, 95 p.

———— ———— and L. R. Wager, 1970, Geological investigations in East Greenland. Part VIII, The petrology of the Kangerdlugssuaq alkaline intrusion, East Greenland: Medd. om Grønland, v. 190, no. 2, 49 p.

Koettlitz, R., 1898, Observations on the geology of Franz Joseph Land: Geol. Soc. London Quart. Jour., v. 54, p. 620–652.

Krokström, T., 1944, Petrological studies on some basaltic rocks from East Greenland: Medd. om Grønland, v. 103, no. 6, 75 p.

McBirney, A. R., and I. G. Gass, 1967, Relations of oceanic volcanic rocks to mid-ocean rises and heat flow: Earth and Planetary Sci. Letters, v. 2, p. 265–276.

Menard, H. W., 1965, Sea floor relief and mantle convection, in Physics and chemistry of the earth, v. 6: New York, Pergamon Press, p. 315–364.

Munck, S., 1945, On the geology and petrography of the West Greenland basalt province. Part V, Two major doleritic intrusions of the Nugssuaq peninsula: Medd. om Grønland, v. 137, no. 5, 61 p.

———— and A. Noe-Nygaard, 1957, Age determination of the various stages of the Tertiary volcanism in the West Greenland basalt province: Mexico, 20th Internat. Geol. Cong. Rept., Sec. 1, p. 247–256.

Noe-Nygaard, A., 1942, On the geology and petrography of the West Greenland basalt province. Part III, The plateau basalts of Svartenhuk peninsula: Medd. om Grønland, v. 137, no. 3, 78 p.

———— 1966, Chemical composition of tholeiitic basalts from the Wyville-Thompson ridge belt: Nature, v. 212, p. 272–273.

Norin, R., 1934, Zur Geologie der südschwedischen Basalte: Lunds Geol.-Mineralog. Inst. Medd., no. 57, 174 p.

Osborne, E. F., 1959, Role of oxygen pressure in the crystallization and differentiation of basaltic magma: Am. Jour. Sci., v. 257, p. 609–647.

Parker, J. R., 1967, The Jurassic and Cretaceous sequence in Spitsbergen: Geol. Mag., v. 104, p. 487–505.

Pauly, H., 1969, White cast iron with cohenite, schreibersite and sulphides from Tertiary basalts on Disko, Greenland: Dansk Geol. Foren. Medd., v. 19, p. 8–26.

Pedersen, A. K., 1970, En petrologisk undersøgelse af tertiære vulkaniske bjergarter fra det nordlige Disko: Unpub. Gold Medal thesis (reviewed in Festskrift Københavns Universitet, 1970, p. 379–383).

Rittman, A., 1940, Studien an Eruptivegesteinen aus Ost-Grönland: Medd. om Grønland, v. 115, no. 1, 156 p.

Rosenkrantz, A., 1970, Marine Upper Cretaceous and lowermost Tertiary deposits in West Greenland: Dansk Geol. Foren. Medd., v. 19, p. 406–453.

———— and T. C. R. Pulvertaft, 1969, Cretaceous-Tertiary stratigraphy and tectonics in northern West Greenland, in Marshall Kay, ed., North Atlantic—geology and continental drift: Am. Assoc. Petroleum Geologists Mem. 12, p. 882–898.

Schaub, H. P., 1938, Zur Vulkantektonik der Inseln Traill und Geographical Society (Nordostgrönland): Medd. om Grønland, v. 114, no. 1, 44 p.

———— 1942, Zur Geologie der Traill Insel (Nordost-Grönland): Eclogae Geol. Halvetiae, v. 35, 54 p.

Schilling, J.-G., 1969, Red Sea floor origin—rare earth evidence: Science, v. 165, p. 1357–1360.

Sharma, P. V., 1970, Geophysical evidence for a buried volcanic mount in the Skagerrak: Dansk Geol. Foren. Medd., v. 19, p. 368–377.

Sigurdsson, H., 1967, The Icelandic basalt plateau and the question of sial, in Iceland and mid-ocean ridges: Reykjavík, Soc. Sci. Islandica, v. 38, p. 32–46.

———— 1970, Origin of some Icelandic pitchstones—discussion of a paper by I. L. Gibson: Lithos, v. 3, p. 369–371.

Thompson, R. N., and D. J. Patrick, 1968, Folding and slumping in a layered gabbro: Liverpool, Geol. Jour., v. 6, p. 139–145.

Tyrrell, G. W., 1932, The petrography of some Kainzoic igneous rocks, and of the Cape Parry alkaline complex, East Greenland: Geol. Mag., v. 69, p. 520–527.

———— 1937, Flood basalts and fissure eruption: Bull. Volcanol., Ser. 2, v. 1, p. 89–111.

———— and K. S. Sandford, 1933, Geology and petrology of the dolerites of Spitsbergen: Royal Soc. Edinburgh Proc., v. 53, pt. 3, no. 21, p. 284–321.

Upton, B. G. J., 1960, The alkaline igneous complex of Kungnat Fjeld, South Greenland: Medd. om Grønland, v. 123, no. 4, 145 p.

Vincent, E. A., 1950, The chemical composition and physical properties of the residual glass of the Kap Daussy tholeiite dike, East Greenland: Mineralog. Mag., v. 29, p. 46–62.

———— 1953, Hornblende-lamprophyre dykes of basaltic parentage from the Skærgaard area, East Greenland: Geol. Soc. London Quart. Jour., v. 109, p. 21–50.

Vine, F. J., 1966, Spreading of the ocean floor—new evidence: Science, v. 154, p. 1405–1415.

Vogt, P. R., N. A. Ostenso, and G. L. Johnson, 1970, Magnetic and bathymetric data bearing on seafloor spreading north of Iceland: Jour. Geophys. Research, v. 75, p. 903–920.

———— E. D. Schneider, and G. L. Johnson, 1969a, The crust and upper mantle beneath the sea, in The earth's crust and upper mantle: Am. Geophys. Union Geophys. Mon. Ser., v. 13, p. 556–617.

———— et al., 1969b, Morphology, magnetic anomalies and evolution of the Northeast Atlantic and Labrador Sea. Part III, Evolution (abs.): Am. Geophys. Union Trans., v. 50, p. 184.

Wager, L. R., 1934, Geological investigations in East Greenland. Part I, General geology from Angmagssalik to Kap Dalton: Medd. om Grønland, v. 105, no. 2, 46 p.

———— 1935, Geological investigations in East Greenland. Part II, Geology of Kap Dalton: Medd. om Grønland, v. 105, no. 3, 32 p.

———— 1947, Geological investigations in East Greenland. Part IV, The stratigraphy and tectonics of Knud Rasmussens Land and the Kangerdlugssuaq region: Medd. om Grønland, v. 134, no. 5, 64 p.

———— and G. M. Brown, 1968, Layered igneous

rocks: Edinburgh and London, Oliver and Boyd, 588 p.

———— and W. A. Deer, 1938, A dyke swarm and crustal flexure in East Greenland: Geol. Mag., v. 75, p. 39–46.

———— and ———— 1939, Geological investigations in East Greenland. Part III, The petrology of the Skaergaard intrusion, Kangerdlugssuaq, East Greenland: Medd. om Grønland, v. 105, no. 4, 352 p.

Watt, W. S., 1969, The coast-parallel dike swarm of southwest Greenland in relation to opening of the Labrador Sea: Canadian Jour. Earth Sci., v. 6, p. 1320–1321.

Wegener, A., 1924, The origin of continents and oceans: London, Methuen, 212 p. (transl. of 3d German ed.)

Wenk, E., 1961, Tertiary of Greenland, in G. O. Raasch, ed., Geology of the Arctic: Toronto, Univ. Toronto Press, v. 1, p. 278–284.

Wilson, J. T., 1965, Submarine fracture zones, aseismic ridges, and the International Council of Scientific Unions Line—proposed western margin of the East Pacific Ridge: Nature, v. 207, p. 907–911.

Yoder, H. S., and C. E. Tilley, 1962, Origin of basalt magmas—an experimental study of natural and synthetic rock systems: Jour. Petrology, v. 3, p. 342–532.

Marine Geology of Atlantic Ocean North of the Arctic Circle[1]

G. L. JOHNSON[2] and P. R. VOGT[2]

Washington, D.C. 20390

Abstract Magnetic and paleontologic data indicate that the Norwegian-Greenland sea opened about 60 m.y. ago with the initiation of sea-floor spreading along the axis of a midoceanic ridge. Within the Norwegian basin, evidence points toward an extinct ridge axis which shifted westward during the mid-Tertiary. Complex Iceland-style sea-floor spreading may have existed on the largely emergent Iceland plateau until about 10 m.y. ago, when Kolbeinsey Ridge became active.

Introduction

This review paper is an attempt to summarize the known marine geology and geophysics of the northernmost Atlantic (Figs. 1, 2). For recent geologic investigations, the reader is referred to the following: for the Labrador Sea—Johnson et al. (1969), Manchester (1964); for the Norwegian-Greenland sea—Johnson and Heezen (1967a), Johnson et al. (1971a); for magnetics of the Labrador Sea—Godby et al. (1966), Avery and Vogt (in press); for magnetics of the Norwegian-Greenland sea—Avery et al. (1968), Ostenso (1968), and Vogt et al. 1970).

A brief review of the sea-floor spreading processes is in order as an explanation for the succeeding text. A more thorough discussion was given by Vogt et al. (1969). The growth of the midoceanic ridge by tensional faulting, intrusion, and volcanism was first deduced from morphologic comparisons (Heezen et al., 1959). Dietz (1961) and Hess (1962) went one step further in proposing the broad hypothesis that all oceanic crust is generated at the axis of the midoceanic ridge and is probably destroyed along fold-mountain belts such as the Himalayas and along oceanic trenches. Vine and Matthews (1963) noted that magnetic-field reversals revealed by subaerial lavas should be applicable to lavas extruded beneath the sea. Vine (1966) and Pitman and Heirtzler (1966) also observed that symmetrical anomalous magnetic profiles were obtained across midoceanic ridges; thus, if the sea-floor axial-accretion hypothesis is assumed to be correct, the mantle derivatives, as they are injected into the axial crust and are cooled, must acquire a magnetization dependent on the ambient strength and direction of the geomagnetic field.

The broad, conspicuous, positive axial anomaly long known to exist over the midoceanic-ridge axis (Heezen et al., 1953) is caused, therefore, by normally polarized intrusives injected since the last field reversal (Brunhes magnetic polarity epoch, about 0.7 m.y. ago; Figs. 3A, B). A pattern of flank anomalies thus has been generated by a time sequence of polarity reversals and a spreading-rate history. Therefore, the linear magnetic anomalies in the Norwegian-Greenland sea (Fig. 3; Avery et al., 1968) are dependent upon (1) the rate of ocean-floor movement and (2) the chronologic history of geomagnetic polarity reversals.

In harmony with this theory, Morgan (1968) proposed that the earth's surface can be considered to be composed of several rigid crustal blocks. He assumed that each plate is bounded by a midocean ridge (where new material is created), trenches or young fold mountains (where surface is destroyed), and transform faults. According to this model, the aseismic areas move as rigid plates with negligible internal deformation. On a spherical surface (the earth), the motion of one plate as it slides over the mantle relative to another block is a rotation defined by a pole of rotation and an angular velocity. The positions of the poles of rotation and the angular velocity may change over time scales of 10–20 m.y. (Vogt et al., 1969). The plates as defined by Morgan (1968) are shown in Figure 4 for the Arctic regions, and the poles of rotation are shown in Figure 5. As is readily apparent, a wide scatter in the data exists; neither the pole of Le Pichon (1968) or that of Horsfield and Maton (1970) fits the additional data from the Norwegian-Greenland sea. The pole for the opening of the Labrador Sea appears to be near 55°N, 175°W, in the Bering Sea. Fracture zones of the Reykjanes Ridge in sea floor that is 15–45 m.y. old indicate a probable pole position seaward of eastern Greenland. It was hoped that the pole described by these fracture zones would be close to one for the older fracture zones in the

[1] Manuscript received, September 20, 1971.
[2] U.S. Naval Oceanographic Office.

161

Fig. 1—Physiographic sketch chart of eastern Arctic basin, Norwegian-Greenland sea, Labrador Sea, Baffin Bay, and northernmost Atlantic. Sketched by Barbara Grosvenor.

Norwegian-Greenland sea—*i.e.*, Greenland, Hovgaard, and old Jan Mayen. The Norwegian-Greenland sea fracture zones, however, show such scatter that no indication of the location of a pole of rotation is possible.

MIDOCEANIC RIDGE

The midoceanic ridge (Fig. 2) is a broad, rugged arch which strikes northward from 30°W long. It passes through the Norwegian-Greenland sea to enter the Arctic basin. Throughout the history of the ocean floor, the midoceanic ridge has been the dominant and controlling feature.

Kolbeinsey Ridge

The branch of the midoceanic ridge between Iceland and Jan Mayen was named "Kolbeinsey Ridge" after the island by that name just north of Iceland (Sigurdsson and Brown, 1970). Kolbeinsey Ridge does not have a well-developed axial valley such as that found farther south in the Atlantic (Heezen *et al.*, 1959); rather, it resembles Reykjanes Ridge (Johnson *et al.*, 1971a). However, profiles do show an irregular depression along the axial province of the ridge. Relief is characterized by amplitudes of 50–200 fm and wavelengths of 1–5 mi (1.8–8 km). Figure 3 illustrates magnetic profiles across the ridge (Vogt *et al.*, 1970). There are possible correlations to 10 m.y. B.P. on the east side of profile B (Fig. 3), and additional data presented by Young *et al.* (1971) clearly show that anomaly 5 is also on the western flanks of the ridge. It can, therefore, be safely assumed that Kolbeinsey Ridge is at least 10 m.y. old.

Mohns Ridge

Mohns Ridge (Fig. 3, profile R) resembles in topographic form a typical part of the Mid-Atlantic Ridge. A deep axial rift is present. The crestal zone averages 40 mi (60 km) in width and lies from 500 to 100 fm shallower than the rift valley, whose bottom generally is found at depths greater than 1,600 fm. Profile R illustrates the large axial magnetic anomaly over the crest of Mohns Ridge, the lack of sediment along the crestal zone (indicating youth), and the more deeply buried flank provinces.

Avery *et al.* (1968), from a study of the magnetic anomalies, deduced that Norway and Greenland began to separate about 60–70 m.y. ago, approximately along what are now the

edges of their continental shelves. Evidence for this date is seen in Figure 6B, constructed from the aeromagnetic data. Anomaly 23 is probably present on profile D, illustrating the 60–70-m.y. opening date for the Norwegian Sea. Because the Norwegian basin involves the same plate boundary, the events there must have been similar to those deduced from the Reykjanes Ridge area. Correlations with a model derived from the sequence of reversals recorded on the midoceanic ridge in the South Atlantic (Heirtzler *et al.*, 1968; Fig. 6) suggest that the average spreading rate on Reykjanes Ridge between 60 and 42 m.y. ago was 1.13 cm/yr. Spreading rates probably declined steadily throughout this period, from 1.9 cm/yr to about 0.7 cm/yr by 30 m.y. ago, after which they increased again to 1.13 cm/yr. This spreading history is largely deduced from the detailed magnetic surveys between Reykjanes Ridge and Rockall Bank (Avery *et al.*, 1968).

Knipovitch Ridge

The junction of the Greenland fracture zone and the sharp northward turn of the midoceanic ridge has been only sparsely sounded. However, we believe that the contours in Figure 2 are generally accurate. The ridge is characterized by a long linear depression, 2 or 3 mi (3–5 km) wide at the 1,800-fm isobath, with well-developed structural benches on its landward wall. The earthquake epicenters tend to lie in or very near the deep. The thick sedimentary fill of the depression appears to descend in fault steps. Thus, a recent origin for the depression is suggested.

FRACTURE ZONES

Wilson (1965) proposed that oceanic fracture zones along which the midoceanic ridge has been offset are not strike-slip faults postdating the sea floor, but that both the ridge segments and fracture zones represent a single, continuously rejuvenated zone of weakness. Pure ridge segments are line sources where mantle derivatives rise to accrete to the edges of the crust and thence move away at right angles to the ridge axis parallel with fracture zones. A full review of this process was presented by Vogt *et al.* (1970). Fracture zones are as common on the sea floor in the Norwegian-Greenland sea as they are along the 40,000-mi (64,000 km) length of the midoceanic ridge (Fig. 1).

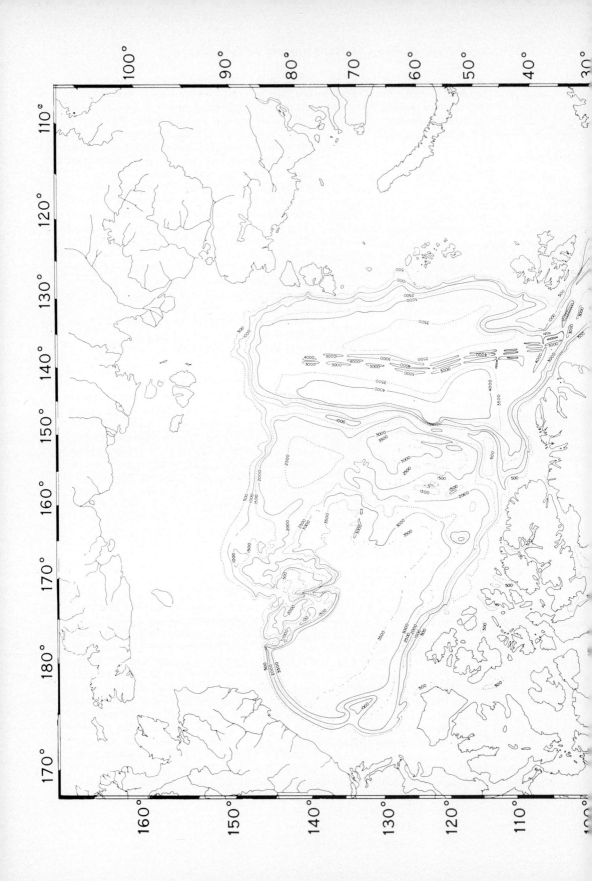

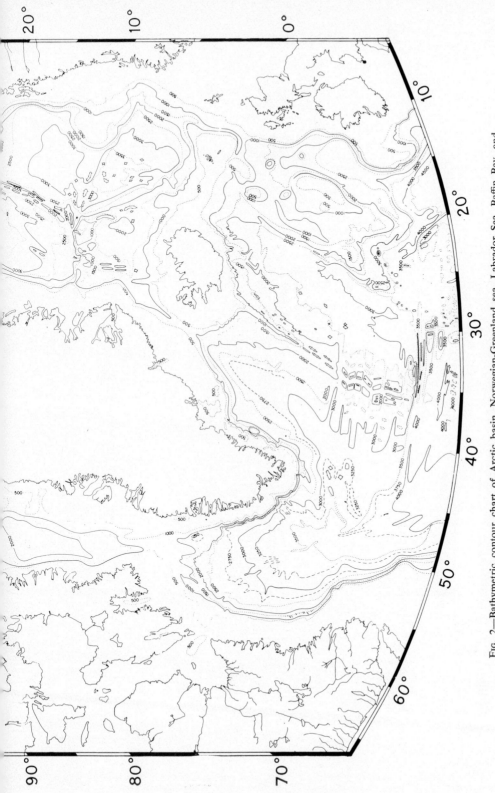

FIG. 2.—Bathymetric contour chart of Arctic basin, Norwegian-Greenland sea, Labrador Sea, Baffin Bay, and northernmost Atlantic. Based on studies by senior author.

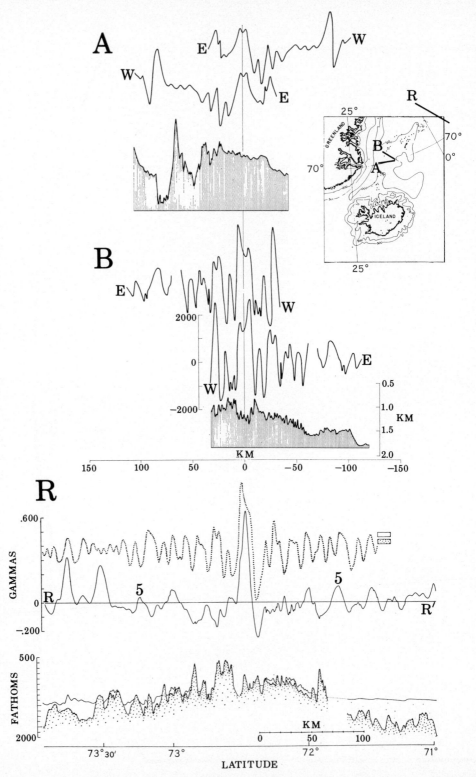

FIG. 3—**A.** Shipborne residual magnetic and bathymetric profiles obtained by USCGS *Spar* across Kolbeinsey
Ridge (*see* Fig. 1). A 1.0 cm/yr spreading model for these profiles is presented in Vogt *et al.* (1970). **B.** Residual
magnetic, bathymetric, and seismic reflection (dotted line) profiles across Mohns Ridge. Data obtained by USNS
Keathley. Note large central magnetic anomaly centered over crest of Mohns Ridge and fairly symmetrical pattern
of magnetic anomalies on either side. Magnetic anomaly 5 has been dated at approximately 9.5 m.y. (Heirtzler
et al., 1968). One second of travel time on seismic record is equal to approximately 1 km.

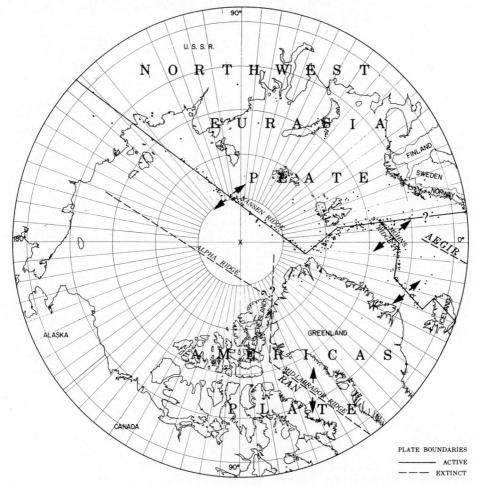

Fig. 4—Tectonic-plate boundaries of Arctic. Dashed lines denote boundaries of possible extinct plates. Earthquake epicenters 1961-1968, courtesy of ESSA, Rockville, Maryland. From Vogt *et al.* (1970).

ORIGIN

Demenitskaya and Dibner (1966) proposed that the Labrador Sea and Bay of Biscay may have at one time formed an early Atlantic. Johnson and Heezen (1967a, b) subsequently favored this concept and suggested that the Iberian Peninsula was joined to the Grand Banks in Jurassic time and a proto-ocean extended from the Bay of Biscay through the Labrador Sea, thence, via transform faults, shifted in direction through Baffin Bay. Possibly the Wegener fault connects the old Labrador rift to the Alpha Ridge, which has been tentatively identified as a fossil center of sea-floor spreading in the Arctic (Hall, 1970; Vogt and Ostenso, 1970).

This hypothesis would indicate opening of the western Arctic basin in early Mesozoic time. The hypothesis, however, is not in agreement with Hamilton (1970), who suggested that the Canadian basin was created by post-Triassic rotation of Alaska. This rotation is perpendicular to the assumed direction of spreading of the Alpha Ridge. Dietz and Holden (1970) suggested that the Canadian basin may be a relic of the ancient Pacific and possibly may be as old as Paleozoic. Pitman (1970) suggested that activity along the Nansen Ridge in the Eurasian Arctic began about 81 m.y. ago. The Nansen Ridge is symmetrically located between Lomonosov Ridge (Fig. 2) and the Barents continental shelf; therefore, Lomo-

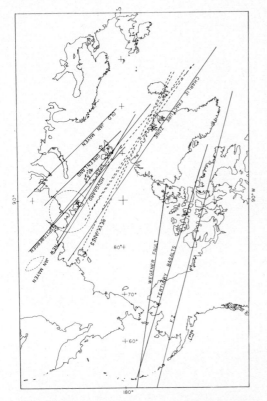

FIG. 5—Great circles drawn perpendicular to fracture zones in manner described by Morgan (1968). Le Pichon's (1968) pole is a large circle near Lena delta; Hornsfield and Maton's (1970) pole is elliptical area in Siberia. "Charlie" refers to Charlie fracture zone (Johnson and Heezen, 1967a); Davis Strait lineament is from an approximate line connecting Disko Island and Labrador Tertiary basalts; Labrador Sea fracture zones are from Johnson et al. (1971). Dashed lines are constructed from fracture zones along flanks of Reykjanes Ridge in sea floor 15–45 m.y. old (Avery et al., 1969; Johnson et al., 1971).

nosov Ridge would seem to be a sliver that split off from the Barents continental shelf (Wilson, 1963).

Recent detailed magnetic surveys at the junction of the Labrador Sea and the North Atlantic show fairly conclusively that there was slow sea-floor spreading (about 0.6 cm/yr) between Greenland and Labrador from 60 to perhaps 30 m.y. ago (Avery et al., 1969; Vogt et al., 1970). Marine Jurassic dredge hauls from the Labrador Sea (Bartlett, 1969) indicate that initial rifting may have occurred as early as the Jurassic (Johnson et al., 1969) for the Labrador Sea, and that a width of only several hundred kilometers of sea floor had formed prior to 60 m.y. ago.

Avery et al. (1968) determined that Norway and Greenland began to separate about 60–70 m.y. ago approximately along the present edges of their continental shelves (Vogt et al., 1970). Supporting evidence for this date is the presence of upper Paleocene planktonic and benthic foraminifers on the Voring Plateau (Saito et al., 1967), which indicates a marine seaway was already in existence about 60 m.y. ago. Isotopic dates from East Greenland and Britain, as summarized by Ostenso (1968), also support the continuity of Greenland and the European plate prior to the formation of the Atlantic Ocean basin about 180 m.y. ago.

The median location of Mohns Ridge between Greenland and Norway suggests spreading has always proceeded from a single axis in the northern Norwegian Sea. In the southern Norwegian Sea, the history of the sea floor is more complex. The present midoceanic ridge is located asymmetrically between the Jan Mayen Ridge and Greenland. Johnson and Heezen (1967a) first proposed that the Jan Mayen Ridge was split off from the Greenland shelf during a recent relocation of the rift axis and that the partially buried chain of seamounts in the Norwegian basin (Fig. 1) delineates the extinct rift axis. Vogt et al. (1970) interpreted the magnetic data of Avery et al. (1968) in terms of a spreading axis that became extinct about 30 m.y. ago. For convenience, it is suggested that this extinct axis be named "Aegir Ridge," after the Icelandic god of the deep sea, and that the Labrador relic ridge be named "Ran," after his wife (Fig. 4).

Figure 6 shows a close similarity between magnetic profiles across the possible extinct rift in the central Norwegian Sea and the Labrador Sea, and suggests that both ridges—Ran and Aegir—became extinct at the same time. The central "quiet" zones of both areas are believed to represent the dying phase of the central rifts; however, the model profile, which was prepared on the basis of abrupt stoppage, implies that the low amplitudes of the magnetic anomalies are probably related also to the increased frequency of polarity reversals after 42 m.y. ago (Heirtzler et al., 1968). Spreading probably ended about 30 m.y. ago in both the Labrador and Norwegian Seas. The central quiet zone is very similar to that reported by Malahoff and Handschumacher (1971) for a relic spreading center in the Pacific south of the Murray fracture zone. Activity along this axis commenced about 38 m.y. ago, and this axis, like its northern Atlantic counterparts, became

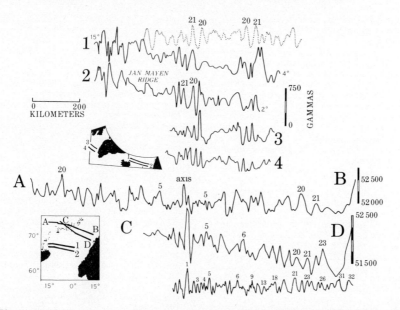

Fig. 6—*Upper:* Residual magnetic profiles across Norwegian and Labrador basins illustrating general similarity. Two upper profiles cross Norwegian basin (from Avery *et al.*, 1968); two lower profiles cross Labrador basin (from Godby *et al.*, 1966). Dotted line is model calculated for 0.63 cm/yr. Anomaly 20 is dated at about 49 m.y. Probable spreading rates in Norwegian and Labrador basins were 1.1 and 0.5 cm/yr, respectively (Avery *et al.*, 1969). *Lower:* Aeromagnetic profiles across Norwegian basin. Profiles *AB* and *CD* cross Mohns Ridge and show excellent agreement with a model presented by Vogt *et al.* (1970). Profiles constructed from aeromagnetic data of Avery *et al.* (1968). Anomaly 5 is dated as 9.5 m.y.; anomaly 6, 21 m.y.; anomaly 20, 49 m.y.; anomaly 21, 53 m.y.; and anomaly 23, 58 m.y. Note conspicuous positive axial anomaly.

extinct about 27 m.y. ago.

When spreading ended in the central Norwegian Sea along Aegir Ridge, the axis of the midoceanic ridge shifted westward to form Kolbeinsey Ridge. Kolbeinsey Ridge is at least 10 m.y. old, and possibly 20 m.y. (Young *et al.*, 1971). At the time of activation, it apparently split the Jan Mayen Ridge off from the Greenland continental shelf. The continental nature of the Jan Mayen Ridge is supported by seismic reflection data (Johnson and Heezen, 1967a) and by the absence of any marked magnetic anomalies (Fig. 6, profiles 1 and 2).

Another hypothesis is that the entire Iceland Plateau is oceanic in nature, having been created approximately between 30 m.y. and 10 m.y. ago. The volcanic island of Jan Mayen, which probably was constructed in mid-Tertiary to early Pleistocene time, thus may represent an emerged portion of a middle to late Tertiary Iceland. The flat-topped, previously subaerial Jan Mayen Ridge would be the highest remnant of a northern extension of Iceland that has foundered with time. This hypothesis is attractive because the Iceland style of sea-floor spreading would have occurred during the

period of known slow spreading on Reykjanes Ridge. Thus, it suggests that complex Iceland-style sea-floor spreading in part required slow spreading rates. Still another possibility is that an early basin, comprising what is now Voring Plateau and Jan Mayen Ridge, was bisected by the extinct rift. Later, a new rift (Kolbeinsey Ridge) split the western edge of the old basin, which was still attached to Greenland.

SUMMARY

Based on studies of the Reykjanes Ridge to the south by Avery *et al.* (1969) and Vogt *et al.* (1970), and on Figure 3, the chronology of plate movements in the Norwegian-Greenland sea and the Arctic basin is as follows.

1. Prior to 60 m.y. ago, the Labrador Sea–Bay of Biscay rift was active. Alpha Ridge in the Arctic basin was possibly a spreading center.

2. During the period 60–42 m.y. ago, the Norwegian-Greenland sea began to split apart at a rate of 1.13 cm/yr. Nansen Ridge possibly was already a spreading axis. Ran Ridge was still active at a rate of 0.6 cm/yr. Alpha Ridge possibly was a spreading center until the end of this period.

3. During the period 42–30 m.y. ago, the Labrador Sea rift slowly became extinct and Greenland became attached to the Americas plate; spreading values in

the Norwegian-Greenland sea area decreased to about 0.7 cm/yr. The Nansen Ridge continued to spread at an even slower rate.

4. From 30 m.y. ago to the present, spreading rates increased to 1.13 cm/yr; the increase may have occurred relatively abruptly about 10 m.y. ago. The spreading axis shifted westward in the southern Norwegian basin. Within the Norwegian basin, evidence points toward an extinct midoceanic ridge which shifted its axis to the Iceland plateau during the mid-Tertiary. Complex Iceland-style sea-floor spreading may have occurred on a largely emergent Iceland plateau, and may have shifted westward to the present Kolbeinsey Ridge about 10 m.y. ago.

REFERENCES

Avery, O. E., and P. R. Vogt, in press, Detailed magnetic surveys in the northeast Atlantic and Labrador Sea: Jour. Geophys. Research.

——— G. D. Burton, and J. R. Heirtzler, 1968, An aeromagnetic survey of the Norwegian Sea: Jour. Geophys. Research, v. 73, p. 4583–4600.

——— P. R. Vogt, and R. H. Higgs, 1969, Morphology, magnetic anomalies and evolution of the northeast Atlantic and Labrador Sea. Part II. Magnetic anomalies: Am. Geophys. Union Trans. (now EOS), v. 50, p. 184.

Bartlett, G. A., 1969, Biostratigraphy and paleoecology of the Canadian Atlantic continental margin: Geol. Soc. America Abs., p. 7.

Demenitskaya, R. M., and V. D. Dibner, 1966, Morphological structure and the earth's crust of the North Atlantic region, in W. H. Poole, ed., Continental margins and island arcs: Canada Geol. Survey Paper 66–14, p. 62–79.

Dietz, R. S., 1961, Continent and ocean basin evolution by spreading of the sea floor: Nature, v. 190, p. 354–357.

——— and J. C. Holden, 1970, Reconstruction of Pangaea: breakup and dispersion of continents, Permian to present: Jour. Geophys. Research, v. 75, p. 4939–4956.

Godby, E. A., et al., 1966, Aeromagnetic reconnaissance of the Labrador Sea: Jour. Geophys. Research, v. 71, no. 2, p. 511–517.

Hall, J. K., 1970, Arctic Ocean geophysical studies, the Alpha Cordillera and Mendeleyev Ridge: New York, Columbia University, PhD thesis.

Hamilton, W., 1970, The Uralides and the motions of the Russian and Siberian platforms: Geol. Soc. America, v. 81, p. 2553–2576.

Heezen, B. C., M. Ewing, and E. T. Miller, 1953, Trans-Atlantic profile of total magnetic intensity and topography, Dakar to Barbados: Deep-Sea Research, v. 1, p. 25–33.

——— M. Tharp, and M. Ewing, 1959, The floors of the oceans: Geol. Soc. America Spec. Paper 65, 122 p.

Heirtzler, J. R., et al., 1968, Marine magnetic anomalies, geomagnetic field reversals, and motions of the ocean floor and continents: Jour. Geophys. Research, v. 73, p. 2119–2136.

Hess, H. H., 1962, History of the ocean basins, in Petrologic studies: Geol. Soc. America Buddington vol., p. 599–629.

Horsfield, W. T., and P. I. Maton, 1970, Transform faulting along the De Geer line: Nature, v. 226, p. 256–257.

Johnson, G. L., and B. C. Heezen, 1967a, The morphology and evolution of the Norwegian-Greenland sea: Deep-Sea Research, v. 14, p. 755–771.

——— and ——— 1967b, The Arctic Mid-Oceanic Ridge: Nature, v. 215, p. 724–725.

——— A. W. Closuit, and J. A. Pew, 1969, Geologic and geophysical investigations in the northern Labrador Sea: Arctic, v. 22, p. 56–68.

——— J. Freitag, and J. Pew, 1971a, Structure of the Norwegian Basin: Norsk Polarinst. Årbok, 1969.

——— P. R. Vogt, and E. D. Schneider, 1971b, The morphology and structure of the northeast Atlantic and Labrador Sea: Deut. Hydro. Zeit., v. 2, no. 24, p. 50–73.

Le Pichon, X., 1968, Sea-floor spreading and continental drift: Jour. Geophys. Research, v. 73, p. 3661–3698.

Malahoff, A., and D. Handschumacher, 1971, Magnetic anomalies south of the Murray fracture zone: new evidence for a secondary sea-floor spreading center and strike slip movement: Jour. Geophys. Research, v. 76, p. 6265–6275.

Manchester, K. S., 1964, Geophysical investigations between Canada and Greenland: Halifax, Dalhousie Univ., M.S. thesis.

Morgan, W. J., 1968, Rises, trenches, great faults and crustal blocks: Jour. Geophys. Research, v. 73, p. 1959–1982.

Ostenso, N. A., 1968, Geophysical studies in the Greenland Sea: Geol. Soc. America Bull., v. 79, p. 107–132.

Pitman, W. C., III, 1970, Sea floor spreading in the North Atlantic and its implications regarding the closing of the Tethys: Geol. Soc. America Abs., v. 2, no. 7, p. 752–753.

——— and J. R. Heirtzler, 1966, Magnetic anomalies over the Pacific-Antarctic Ridge: Science, v. 154, p. 1164–1171.

Saito, T., L. H. Burckle, and D. R. Horn, 1967, Palaeocene core from the Norwegian Basin: Nature, v. 216, p. 357–359.

Sigurdsson, H., and G. M. Brown, 1970, An unusual enstatite-forsterite basalt from Kolbeinsey Island, north of Iceland: Jour. Petrology, v. 11, p. 205–220.

Vine, F. J., 1966, Spreading of the ocean floor: new evidence: Science, v. 154, p. 1405–1415.

——— and D. H. Matthews, 1963, Magnetic anomalies over oceanic ridges: Nature, v. 199, p. 147–149.

Vogt, P. R., N. A. Ostenso, and G. L. Johnson, 1970, Magnetic and bathymetric data bearing on sea-floor spreading north of Iceland: Jour. Geophys. Research, v. 75, p. 903–920.

——— and N. A. Ostenso, 1970, Magnetic and gravity profiles across the Alpha Cordillera and their relation to the Arctic sea-floor spreading: Jour. Geophys. Research, v. 75, p. 4925–4937.

——— E. D. Schneider, and G. L. Johnson, 1969, The crust and upper mantle beneath the sea, in The earth's crust and upper mantle: Washington, D.C., Am. Geophys. Union, p. 556–617.

——— et al., 1969, Discontinuities in sea-floor spreading: Tectonophysics, v. 8, p. 285–317.

Wilson, J. T., 1963, Continental drift: Scientific American, v. 208, p. 86–100.

——— 1965, A new class of faults and their bearing on continental drift: Nature, v. 207, p. 343–347.

Young, P., et al., 1971, Sea-floor spreading north of Iceland: Am. Geophys. Union Trans., v. 52, p. 236.

Geology of Iceland[1]

THORLEIFUR EINARSSON[2]

Reykjavík, Iceland

Abstract Volcanic rocks which have piled up more or less continuously since the middle Tertiary virtually compose the Iceland landmass. The rocks can be divided into four major formations: Tertiary Plateau Basalt formation; lower Pleistocene Grey Basalt formation; upper Pleistocene Palagonite formation; and Weichselian till, Holocene sediments, and volcanic rocks. Basaltic lava flows make up the largest percent of the Tertiary Plateau Basalt formation. The Pleistocene formations contain a greater variety of rock facies and notably more subglacial hyaloclastic sediments, fluvial and marine sediments, and tillites. The rocks contain records of sudden climatic changes— e.g., about 3 m.y. ago (at the beginning of the Pleistocene). Holocene volcanism in Iceland has produced mostly basaltic lavas, but also intermediate and acidic rocks. Volcanic fissures and faults charaterize the Neovolcanic zone, which is believed to be related to the position of Iceland on the Mid-Atlantic Ridge.

INTRODUCTION

Iceland is almost wholly volcanic rocks which have been piled up more or less continuously since the middle Tertiary. The rock series can be divided into four major formations: (1) the Tertiary *Plateau Basalt formation,* (2) the lower Pleistocene *Grey Basalt formation,* (3) the upper Pleistocene *Palagonite formation* (younger than 0.7 m.y.), and (4) the *Weichselian till,* together with late-glacial and postglacial sediments and lava flows which in many areas cover the other three formations.

TERTIARY

The Tertiary Plateau Basalt formation (TPB) is the oldest geologic formation of Iceland. It is of middle and late Tertiary age; the oldest rocks dated (K-Ar) give an age of approximately 16 m.y. (Moorbath *et al.,* 1968). The Icelandic TPB forms the middle part of the extensive Brito-Arctic volcanic area, and only in Iceland and Jan Mayen does volcanic activity still persist. The TPB occurs in two main areas: (1) in east Iceland and (2) in west, northwest, and north Iceland (Fig. 1). These two areas are separated by a broad zone with Quaternary rocks at the surface—the Neo-

[1] Manuscript received, September 20, 1971.

[2] Division of Geosciences, Science Institute, University of Iceland.

volcanic zone, which the TPB seems to underlie as a "continuous layer." The TPB is mainly built up of lava flows. Basaltic flows constitute 80 percent of the thickness; 8 percent of the lava flows are rhyolitic, and 3 percent are andesitic. The proportions are very similar to those of the Pleistocene and Holocene rocks. The rest of the formation is made of volcanic tuffs, breccias, and sediments. The visible thickness of the TPB is approximately 10,000 m. Minor intrusions are common in the TPB as dikes, mainly feeder dikes, but in some areas there are also smaller batholiths and bosses of gabbro and granophyre which are mainly concentrated in areas of "central volcanoes" (Walker, 1964). Structurally, the TPB has been slightly folded and faulted (Fig. 2). Paleobotanical studies of sedimentary interbeds indicate a mixed forest of conifers and warmth-loving deciduous trees, *i.e.,* a warm-temperate climate (Friedrich, 1966). During the Pliocene the climate grew cooler, and many of the trees suited to warmer climates disappeared. Also at this time the first tillites were formed (Jónsson, 1955; Schwarzbach and Pflug, 1957; Einarsson *et al.,* 1967).

PLEISTOCENE

Rocks of Pleistocene age are mainly exposed in the Neovolcanic zone, but are found also on Snæfellsnes (west Iceland) and Skagi (north Iceland; Fig. 1). They differ in many ways from the TPB, mainly by their greater variety of rock facies. During the interglacial stages the volcanic activity was mainly effusive, as in Tertiary and postglacial times. Characteristic of much of the basalt is a doleritic texture (gray basalts). During times of glaciation, when the country was covered with ice sheets, volcanic products were piled up over the eruption centers as tuff ridges (pillow lavas and breccias), which were capped by subaerial lavas to form table mountains if the volcanoes were built up through the ice sheets (Kjartansson, 1960; Sigvaldason, 1968; Jones, 1970). In the Pleistocene formations, sediments (fluvial and marine, and tillites) are more common and much thicker than in the TPB, commonly constitut-

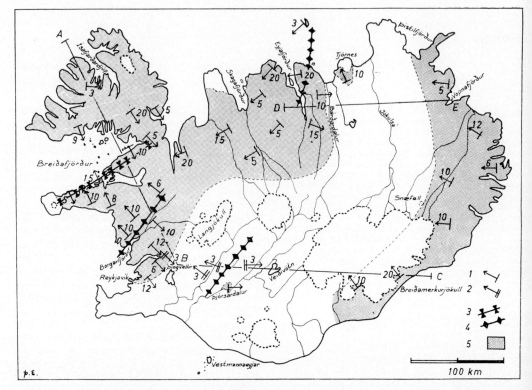

Fig. 1—A map showing extent, dips, and fold axes in Tertiary Plateau Basalt formation of Iceland. Shaded areas represent Tertiary; unshaded, Quaternary. Symbols: (1) dips of Tertiary basalts (TBF), (2) dips of older Quaternary basalts (GBF), (3) syncline axis, (4) anticline axis, (5) Tertiary Plateau Basalt formation (TPB). From Th. Einarsson (1968).

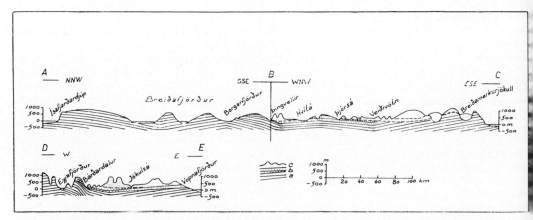

Fig. 2—Diagrammatic cross sections of Iceland (locations shown on Fig. 1). Symbols: (a) Tertiary basalts (TBF), (b) older Quaternary rock series (GBF), and (c) younger Quaternary rock series (PGF). Dip near true scale. From Th. Einarsson (1968).

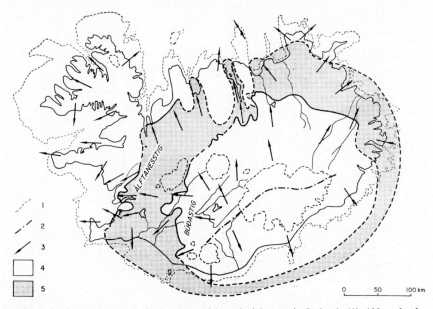

Fig. 3—Glacial striae and retreat of inland ice of last glacial stage in Iceland. (1) 100-m depth contour of shelf, (2) ice divide during late glacial, (3) glacial striae, (4) Alftanes readvance (older Dryas), (5) Búdi readvance (younger Dryas). From Th. Einarsson (1968).

ing more than half the pile. Stratigraphic studies indicate approximately 12 periods of glaciation during the Pleistocene. According to paleomagnetic studies, the sequence can be divided into two formations: (1) the *Grey Basalt formation* (GBF), which comprises rocks 3–0.7 m.y. old, and (2) the *Palagonite formation* (PGF), which is composed of rocks formed in the last 0.7 m.y., *i.e.,* the present normal geomagnetic epoch (Brunhes). At the beginning of the Pleistocene, approximately 3 m.y. ago, a sudden climatic deterioration took place that affected both the marine fauna and the flora. The change in the marine fauna is to some extent obscured by the arrival of boreal Pacific mollusks, but rocks dating from late during the formation of the GBF contain only species of the "present" fauna. The flora, however, was completely changed early during formation of the GBF; the conifers and the temperate deciduous forests vanished, and the flora became similar to the present one (Einarsson *et al.,* 1967).

LATE GLACIAL AND HOLOCENE

At the maximum height of the last glaciation, Iceland was almost completely covered by glaciers. During the retreat some readvances occurred, the latest being the Alftanes stage (12,500–12,000 years B.P.) and the Búdi stage (11,000–10,000 years B.P.; Fig. 3). By 8,000 years B.P. the glaciers were probably smaller than the present ones. Owing to isostatic and eustatic sea-level adjustments, the greater part of the lowlands was flooded by the sea as the glaciers retreated. The highest shorelines are approximately 100 m above present sea level in south Iceland and 40–50 m elsewhere. They are of Alleröd age (12,000–11,000 years B.P.). The isostatic readjustment was very rapid, and by 9,000 years B.P. the shore was everywhere lower than today. During approximately the last 3,000 years the country has been submerged to a depth of 5–10 m. Until the arrival of man in the late 9th century A.D., there were no significant changes in the flora except for ecologic changes induced by climatic changes. A very sudden climatic deterioration took place 2,500 years B.P.; glaciers descended from high mountains (Thorarinsson, 1964) and the birch forest declined rapidly (Einarsson, 1963, 1968). Probably many of the present ice caps began to form at this time also. Very soon after the beginning of the settlement of Iceland, a remarkable floristic change took place. The birch forest was suddenly cleared, whereupon very

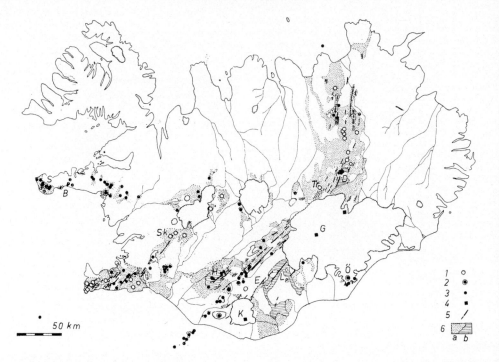

Fig. 4—Postglacial volcanism in Iceland. Symbols: (1) shield volcanoes, (2) stratovolcanoes, (3) single craters and short fissures, (4) active subglacial volcanoes, (5) volcanic fissures, (6a) lava flows older than 900 A.D., and (6b) historic lava flows, *i.e.*, younger than 900 A.D. From Th. Einarsson (1968).

rapid soil erosion began. The postglacial volcanism has continued mainly in the Neovolcanic zone and on Snæfellsnes (Fig. 4). On the average there has been one eruption every fifth year. The volcanicity has been variable, and nearly all kinds of volcanoes have been active, although fissure eruptions have been most common. Postglacial lava flows cover 10,000 sq km (10 percent) of the country, and the overall volume amounts to 400 cu km. Petrologically, the Holocene volcanic products are mostly basaltic—90 percent—but 10 percent are andesitic and rhyolitic (Thorarinsson, 1967).

Iceland is situated at the junction of two oceanic ridges, the Wywille-Thompson Ridge and the northern part of the Mid-Atlantic Ridge—the Reykjanes Ridge, which is believed to continue through Iceland in the Neovolcanic zone. This zone is characterized by volcanic fissures and faults (Fig. 4). In recent years the Neovolcanic zone has been thoroughly studied with respect to ocean-floor spreading, *etc.* (*cf.* Björnsson, 1967; Sigurgeirsson, 1970).

SELECTED REFERENCES

Björnsson, S., 1967, ed., Iceland and the mid-ocean ridges: Soc. Sci. Islandica, v. 38, 209 p. (different papers on the geology of Iceland by many authors).

Einarsson, Th., 1963, Pollen-analytical studies on the vegetation and climate history of Iceland in late and postglacial times, *in* Löve, North-Atlantic biota and their history: Oxford, p. 355–365.

———— 1968, Jarðfræði—saga bergs og lands: Reykjavík, 335 p. (outlines of the physical and historical geology of Iceland, in Icelandic).

———— D. M. Hopkins, and R. R. Doell, 1967, The stratigraphy of Tjörnes, northern Iceland and the history of the Bering land bridge, *in* The Bering land bridge: Stanford, Stanford Univ. Press, p. 312–324.

Friedrich, W., 1966, Geologie von Brjánslækur unte bes. Berücksichtigung der fossilen Flora: Sonderveröff. d. Geol. Inst. Köln, 10, 110 p. Cologne.

Jones, J. G., 1970, Intraglacial volcanoes of the Laugarvatn region, Southwest Iceland II: Jour. Geology v. 78, no. 2, p. 127–140.

Jónsson, J., 1955, Tillite in the Basalt Formation i Eastern Iceland. The Hoffellssandur, Part II: Geog Annaler, v. 37, p. 170–175.

Kjartansson, G., 1960, The Móberg formation, *in* O the geology and geophysics of Iceland: Copenhagen 21st Internat. Geol. Cong. Proc., p. 21–28.

Moorbath, S., H. Sigurdsson, and R. Goodwin, 1968, K-Ar ages of the oldest exposed rocks in Iceland: Earth and Planetary Sci. Letters, v. 4, p. 40–60.

Schwarzbach, M., and H. D. Pflug, 1957, Das klima des jüngeren Tertiärs in Island: Neues Jahrb. Geologie u. Paläontologie Abh., v. 104, no. 3, p. 279–298.

Sigurgeirsson, Th., 1970, A survey of geophysical research related to crustal and upper mantle structure in Iceland: Jour. Geomagnetism and Geoelectricity, v. 22, no. 1–2, p. 213–221.

Sigvaldason, G. E., 1968, Structure and products of subaquatic volcanoes in Iceland: Contr. Mineralogy and Petrology, v. 18, p. 1–16.

Thorarinsson, S., 1964, On the age of the terminal moraines of Brúarjökull and Hálsajökull: Jökull, v. 14, p. 65–75.

——— 1967, Hekla and Katla. The share of acid and intermediate lava and tephra in the volcanic products through the geological history of Iceland. *in* S. Björnsson, ed., Iceland and the mid-ocean ridges: Soc. Sci. Islandica, v. 38, p. 190–197.

Walker, G. P. L., 1964, Geological investigations in E. Iceland: Bull. Volcanol., v. 29, p. 375–406.

Regional Arctic Geology of the USSR

Work of Soviet Geologists in the Arctic[1]

V. V. MENNER[2]

Moscow, USSR

I should like to thank the organizers of the Second International Symposium on Arctic Geology for inviting our group to San Francisco. Also, I should like to give all those present here heartiest greetings from their Soviet colleagues who work in the Soviet Arctic regions, and their wishes for your successes in the future.

Ten years ago most of the work in the Soviet Arctic was done only by NIIGA geologists (Institute of Arctic Geology); now the situation is quite different. Research on the geology of the Soviet Arctic takes place in several different organizations. Many geologists and geophysicists attending this symposium tell us that the same decentralization has taken place in other countries.

In the 1930s and 1940s the largest part of work in the Arctic was mapping, especially of "blanks" in Soviet Arctic areas. Now that general maps have been compiled, the work is quite different. Although no data on the achievements in our country in tectonics are to be given at this symposium, an example of this work is the tectonic map of the Arctic belt by Yu. M. Puscharovsky, G. B. Udintzev, et al.[3] I am glad to be able to present this map as a gift to the Pacific Section of The American Association of Petroleum Geologists with the hope that it might facilitate the coordination of our work.

We have large groups of researchers who work in the Arctic only. An important contribution in this respect was the creation of new institutes in Siberia by both the Academy of Sciences and the Ministry of Geology like those in Novosibirsk, in Magadan, and on Kamchatka. Much work has been done by prospecting and exploration organizations in the Arctic region where large ore deposits and extensive oil and gas fields have been discovered in the north of Western Siberia. The character of research has also changed because large amounts of accumulated material have resulted in many interesting ideas in all branches of the geologic sciences.

In stratigraphy, one of the most interesting generalizations is a paleontologic basis for the subdivision and correlation of the upper Precambrian. Data for this correlation have been obtained from the Urals, Timan, Turukhansk, and Yenisey regions and, especially, from the north of Central Siberia. This material has provided a basis for a subdivision of Riphean deposits dating from 1.6 billion years to 0.5 billion years.

Data from Siberia and its northern territories have made possible an objective characterization of the Cambrian-Precambrian boundary, and research in Scandinavia, Svalbard, and other parts of the world has demonstrated the global nature of a stratigraphic scheme of the upper Precambrian.

During this symposium we shall hear a paper by B. S. Sokolov on the uppermost strata of the Precambrian Vendian deposits and their fauna. Vendian deposits of the USSR are analogous to Ediacaran beds in Australia.

Interesting results have been obtained also on the lithology and paleogeography of younger deposits. Unfortunately, a series of paleogeographic maps of the Soviet Union that will form a large atlas with maps for each stage is not yet printed,[4] but I. S. Gramberg will present the geologic history of one region—the northern part of Central Siberia—and will tell about the prospects for gas and petroleum there.

Many interesting studies have been done in paleobiogeography. The Paleozoic faunas of Siberia have been described by the pupils of B. S. Sokolov, O. I. Bogush, and V. N. Dubatilov, as well as by other geologists. The Mesozoic fauna was described by the students of V. N. Sachs. At this symposium, Sachs will present maps showing faunas of the Jurassic and Lower Cretaceous of the Arctic region.

We have had great difficulty in reconstruct-

[1] Introductory remarks at Second International Symposium on Arctic Geology in San Francisco, California, February 1, 1971. Manuscript received, April 30, 1972.

[2] Geological Institute, USSR Academy of Sciences.

[3] Editor's Note: This map is now out of print.

[4] A Lithologic-Paleogeographic Atlas of the U.S.S.R. (A. P. Vinogradov, editor-in-chief, 4 vols.) was published by the USSR Academy of Sciences in 1967–69. It is available from Telberg Book Corp., Box 545, Sag Harbor, N.Y. 11963.

ing the Tertiary history of Siberia. Now, however, extensive exploration in the petroliferous basin of Western Siberia has yielded ample information in this respect, and the paper of S. F. Biske, which will be read by D. M. Hopkins, gives the first review of the composition of all Tertiary deposits of the Far East and Alaska.

All these data suggested a new interpretation of zonal schemes and their units in Arctic regions, which I shall present in a separate paper.

The research work has opened ways for wide tectonic and stratigraphic summarizations like those made for the Far East by L. I. Krasny and for the Koryak region by B. Kh. Egiaza-rov. They supply all the latest information on the structure of the northern part of the Pacific belt.

Owing to the trend of this symposium, we have also chosen a paper by V. N. Semenovich, I. S. Gramberg, and I. I. Nesterov on the prospects for oil and gas finds in the Soviet Arctic.

I hope that all the papers read by Soviet participants of this symposium will give you a general idea on the geologic research taking place in Soviet Arctic regions and will enable us to coordinate our efforts in the exploration of the Arctic zone.

Main Features of Geologic Structure and History of North-Central Siberia[1]

V. A. VINOGRADOV, I. S. GRAMBERG, Yu. E. POGREBITSKY, M. I. RABKIN,
M. G. RAVICH, V. N. SOKOLOV, and D. S. SOROKOV[2]

Leningrad, USSR

Abstract The post-Archean history of north-central Siberia is essentially the history of the reconstruction of the North Asiatic craton and its associated mobile belts.

The formation of the craton dates back to the early Proterozoic (1,900 m.y.). The craton was bordered on the east by the Olenek fold system and on the west by the geosynclinal belts which were developed as a result of Baykalian, Caledonian, and Hercynian movements. The oldest Archean rocks (charnockite rocks) are exposed on the Anabar shield; the youngest rocks of the craton are the Taymyr-Kara gneisses.

During the Proterozoic, a sedimentary cover was deposited across the craton; this sedimentary platform is broken into plates by troughs containing eugeosynclinal strata (presumably of the Grenville series). The overlying rocks are composed of unmetamorphosed terrigenous and marine carbonate deposits of Riphean age.

Within the craton the Cambrian-Devonian rocks represent a platform regime. Troughs within the platform are filled with black shale and terrigenous-carbonate marine formations, including gypsiferous sequences. Mottled terrigenous and gypsiferous strata of a lagoonal facies and marine limestones and sandstones were deposited in the pericratonic trough in Severnaya Zemlya.

The Carboniferous-Triassic was marked by intensive movements of the Pacific orogenic cycle, which also affected extensive areas beyond the geosynclinal belts. These movements rejuvenated the craton structures and those of the Caledonian and Hercynian systems bordering it. The linear zones of arcogenesis and the associated parageosynclinal trough formed the Taymyr-Severnaya Zemlya fold system on the periphery of the craton.

The Tungusska synclinorium and the Anabar anticlinorium developed in the center of the craton. In the eastern part of the region the active area joined the Verkhoyansk-Chukotsk geosyncline. The Tungusska synclinorium, the Taymyr trough, and the Verkhoyansk geosyncline formed a single system of troughs filled with continental coal-bearing, paralic coal-bearing, and marine terrigenous sediments, respectively. Plateau basalts also occur in the epicratonic troughs, and granitic magmatism is evident in the zones of arcogenesis.

The Jurassic-Paleogene was characterized by the return of a platform regime to areas that were formerly active. The age of the basal layer of cover ranges from Liassic in the west to Cenomanian in the east, and there is an eastward reduction in folding. Terrigenous Meso-Cenozoic marine and paralic formations fill isometric and linear troughs and swells.

Two sedimentary basins representing the Kara and Laptev Sea shelves were formed on the platform base-ment during the Neogene-Quaternary. Although the structural framework of these basins differs, their formation is thought to be connected with the development of the Arctic Ocean basin.

INTRODUCTION

North-central Siberia is a vast territory lying between the Arctic Ocean and the Arctic Circle and stretching from the western side of the Kara Sea and the Ob tundra to the New Siberian Islands and the Verkhoyansk Range. Structural features include the northern part of the West Siberian plate and the Siberian platform, the Taymyr–Severnaya Zemlya fold system, the northern Verkhoyansk fold system, and two neotectonic sedimentary basins—the Kara and Laptev Sea shelves.

A paleotectonic analysis shows that the structural history of all seven geostructures mentioned is the result of the transformation of the old North Asiatic craton and associated mobile belts.

The history of the craton is subdivided into three main segments: during the first (Archean), a crystalline basement was formed; during the second (Proterozoic), the craton was developed; and during the third (Phanerozoic), the present epicratonic geostructures were formed.

ARCHEAN GEOLOGY AND STRUCTURAL HISTORY

The crystalline basement of the North Asiatic craton is exemplified by the geology of the Anabar shield, where some deep-seated Archean rocks of north-central Siberia crop out. The other region which sheds light on the Archean history is the northern side of Taymyr, where crystalline rocks appear to belong to the upper Archean.

The Anabar shield, situated in the north of the Siberian platform, occupies a central part of the Anabar anticlise. Intensively disturbed metamorphic rocks composing the shield are overlain in the periphery by undisturbed Riphean sandstones containing glauconite that yields an age of 1,550 m.y.

The larger part of the territory is underlain

[1] Manuscript received, April 30, 1972.
[2] Research Institute of the Geology of the Arctic.

by granulite-facies rocks, and a lesser part is underlain by amphibolite-facies rocks. Also within the shield are magmatic and ultrametamorphic formations of various ages.

Granulite Facies

The granulite facies is subdivided into three series (in ascending order): Daldyn, Upper Anabar, and Khapchan.

In the Daldyn Series, which originally was composed mainly of volcanic rocks, pyroxene plagiogneisses and pyroxene-plagioclase schists predominate. In the lower part of the series, marker zones are garnet and other high-alumina gneisses, magnetite schists, and sapphirine rocks; in the upper half, quartzite beds and lenses predominate.

The Upper Anabar Series was also a primarily volcanic sequence with subordinate sedimentary deposits. It consists mainly of hypersthene gneisses, but also contains pyroxene-plagioclase schists and scarce bands of high-alumina gneisses and calciphyres.

The Khapchan Series originally was a carbonate-terrigenous sequence with an admixture of volcanic material. It now is characterized by an alternation of pyroxene, garnet-hypersthene, and graphite-biotite-garnet gneisses with marble and calciphyre bands.

Total thickness of the three granulite-facies series, although difficult to estimate, is about 15 km.

Amphibolite Facies

An amphibolite facies composing the Upper Lamuika complex is exposed mainly in the western part of the shield. These rocks are thought to be remetamorphosed Daldyn and Upper Anabar Series rocks. In places there are relict rocks and minerals of the granulite facies. Diaphthoresis took place under two temperature ranges of the amphibolite subfacies (600–660° and 480–550°C).

Different processes of metamorphism are closely associated with tectonic movements, which were most active in the Anabar shield during three stages of development.

During late Archean time the original sedimentary-volcanic sequence was folded into large, gentle, northwest-striking folds. Folding was accompanied by the formation of metamorphic rocks represented at different levels by two subfacies of pyroxene granulites: (1) a very high-pressure subfacies and (2) a high-pressure subfacies. The first subfacies is characterized by pyrope-almandine garnet of low ferruginous content ($f = 45$–50%)[3] and by cor-

dierite ($f = 10$–15%) in garnet-cordierite-aluminohypersthene-sillimanite-quartz paragneisses. Thermodynamic parameters of the subfacies are estimated as 800–$900°C$ temperature and about 10 kbar pressure. The second subfacies is marked by garnet of higher ferruginous content and by cordierite in similar associations.

Small, conformable peridotite and pyroxenite bodies formed at the beginning of this stage. Later, the ultrametamorphic products under granulite-facies conditions—enderbite and charnockite—were formed.

The second stage of development occurred at the beginning of the early Proterozoic. During that time, intensive plicate dislocations (folding) took place along the uplifts; the result was refolding of a gneiss sequence which was complicated by deep, narrow, steep isoclinal folds striking mainly northwest. Plicate movements in some zones were accompanied by intensive faulting. The creation of biotite-hornblende granitoids and younger, widespread alaskite granites with extensive migmatite and pegmatite fields also took place during the second stage.

During the third stage of development (to the middle Proterozoic), faulting resulted in the block structure of the shield. Between separate blocks, especially in the western part of the shield, multiple metamorphic processes in rather wide, northwest or almost meridional fracture zones caused the formation of polymetamorphic rocks (the Upper Lamuika complex). The close of the third stage was marked by the formation of anorthosite related to a zone of multiple metamorphism and, in the shield, by invasion of the anorthosite by the youngest shield granitoids. The granitoids are represented by biotite granite veins and large bodies of two-mica granites with which muscovite pegmatites are associated. The K-Ar age of mica in the granitoids is 1,900–2,080 m.y. Older intrusive and metamorphic formations as determined on the basis of geologic data have the same radiogenic age. It is possible that the active tectonic movements of the third stage affected the K-Ar ratio in all the rocks.

On the northern Taymyr coast, Archean rocks compose blocks exposed in the core of a late Paleozoic–early Mesozoic arch called the "Kara arch." The rocks are represented by various plagiogneisses and schists. In the lower

---

[3] $$f = \frac{FeO + Fe_2O_3}{FeO + Fe_2O_3 + MgO}.$$

part of the section there are enstatite-paragasite gneisses; in the middle, garnet-biotite, diopside hornblende, fibrolite-cordierite, and graphite plagiogneisses; and, in the upper part, fine-grained garnet-biotite and garnet-hornblende plagiogneisses and schists.

The whole complex is a regionally metamorphosed, protogeosynclinal, terrigenous sequence containing mafic extrusive and intrusive deposits. The metamorphism occurred at great depths; in general, it corresponds to high-temperature mineral equilibrium of the amphibolite facies.

Proterozoic Geology and Structural History

The Proterozoic structural history is divided into two stages: early-middle Proterozoic, or pre-Riphean, and Riphean. During the first stage the basement of the North Asiatic craton was formed. The second stage, which marked the beginning of deposition of a sedimentary cover, is considered to be an intermediate structural stage. Despite the differences in metamorphic grade and rock dislocation, rocks of the intermediate stage are closely related to the structural history and structural features of the basement.

Early-Middle Proterozoic

Early and middle Proterozoic sedimentary deposits are present between the Lena and Olenek Rivers, in the Taymyr northern coast, and in the Severnaya Zemlya Islands.

Between the Lena and Olenek Rivers, outcrops of Proterozoic rocks are present in the center of the so-called Olenek uplift. Over a small area, phyllites (Zekit Series) are exposed below the Riphean platform cover and are folded into linear northwest-trending folds and invaded by granites and granite-gneisses. The K-Ar age of these granites is 1,950–2,080 m.y. Poor outcrops do not permit an estimate of the thickness of the lower Proterozoic rocks present beneath the platform cover in this region.

In the southern Anabar shield, a complex dike unit of gabbro-diabase rocks accompanied by garnet-syenite porphyry is of middle Proterozoic age (1,500–1,600 m.y.).

On the northern Taymyr coast, Proterozoic rocks crop out in the core and on the sides of the late Paleozoic–early Mesozoic (Kara) arch. Two major areas of structural facies are distinguished there.

A stratigraphic section of the western area (to the Lena River) is composed of epidote-chlorite slates and metamorphosed polymictic and tuffaceous sandstones about 1,500–2,000 m thick; these are overlain by a sequence of metamorphosed sandstones and shales with subordinate mafic and silicic extrusives. The thickness of the latter sequence does not exceed 2,000 m. Among relatively mildly metamorphosed rocks there are gneisses and amphibolites. The origin of the rocks of the western area is associated with a superimposed magmatic process and accompanying contact metamorphism due to Carboniferous-Triassic tectogenesis. Marked longitudinal and transverse dislocations of the rocks also are due to this process of activization. Paleotectonically, Proterozoic strata of the western structural facies were widely distributed until the end of the cycle. The area as a whole belonged to a platformlike structure.

The eastern area is characterized by an increased thickness of deposits and an abundance of extrusive rocks. At the base of the stratigraphic section is a series of mafic lavas and tuffs that have been metamorphosed into a sequence of greenschists up to 3,000 m thick. Overlying the greenschists is a sequence of quartzites and phyllites formed from flysch deposits up to 3,500 m in thickness. The lower porphyritic and upper flysch formations are disconformably overlain by a sequence of spilites, quartzites, and silicic extrusives which, together, may be considered as a porphyry ranging in thickness from 1,500 to 2,500 m. Rocks of the eastern structural facies show deformation of two types: primary (Precambrian) and superimposed (Carboniferous-Triassic) tectogenesis. The area was invaded by granites of a comagmatic porphyry. Radiogenic age determinations correspond to the time of the superimposed tectogenesis (270–220 m.y.). Metamorphic rocks and granites, however, were found in Riphean conglomerates lying directly on eroded rocks of the comagmatic porphyry. Tectonically, the eastern structural facies is interpreted to represent a eugeosyncline. Opinions differ regarding the age of folding in the eugeosyncline because of different viewpoints about the age of the overlying conglomerates. Geologists who consider the overlying conglomerates to be basal conglomerates, Riphean in age (1,500–1,600 m.y.), assign the Proterozoic folded formation of Taymyr to the Karelides. Others date the conglomerates as late Riphean (1,000 m.y.), and thus correlate the Proterozoic folded formations of Taymyr with the Grenvillides.

The oldest intrusive rocks in Taymyr are early Proterozoic gabbroids altered into orthoamphibolites. Somewhat later, porphyroblastic granitoids were formed partly as a result of granitization of enclosing gneisses and partly as a result of rheomorphism. During the transition from early to middle Proterozoic, intrusions resulted in the formation of muscovitized granitoids, whereas, in the middle Proterozoic, major sills and diabase and gabbro-diabase dikes were intruded and were transformed into orthoamphibolites. The appearance of dikelike porphyritic granitoid intrusions is assigned to the middle Proterozoic–Riphean transition. Later greenschist-facies metamorphism of these intrusives resulted in albitized, chloritized, and severely altered granitoids.

Proterozoic formations of Severnaya Zemlya are assigned to the eastern structural facies of Taymyr; they strike in the same direction as the structures in eastern Taymyr.

Summary of Pre-Riphean

Data on composition, age, and environment of the Archean and lower-middle Proterozoic rocks of the Anabar shield and adjacent regions allow the following conclusions.

The craton was formed in the early Proterozoic (1,900 m.y.). The time was characterized by the development of geosynclinal belts along the periphery of the Archean folded region. Geosynclinal belts situated in the southwest and northwest (beyond North Siberia's borders) were at that time in an early stage of development. The development of fold systems composing these belts resulted from Baykalian, Caledonian, and Hercynian movements. The Archean folded region bordered by these fold systems underwent uplift, structural transformation, and denudation. As a result, this region was transformed into a northwest-striking shield composed of granulite- and amphibolite-facies rocks. The shield became the basement for the North Asiatic craton.

During middle Proterozoic time, the Archean shield and the early Proterozoic fold system on its eastern margin subsided.

As a result of subsidence, the shield was broken into blocks separated by geosynclinal troughs. The major trough crossed Taymyr, linking these developing geosynclinal belts in the southwest and northwest peripheries of the craton. The craton again became a single structure after folding of the troughs. As was mentioned, the time of this folding corresponds to the stage of tectogenesis of 1,500–1,600 m.y. ago or that of 1,000 m.y. ago.

Riphean

The Riphean (570–1,600 m.y.) in north-central Siberia also includes the formation of the Vendian strata, which have an age of 570–650 m.y. Riphean and Vendian deposits are widespread over the general region. They compose arches and uplifts within the Central Siberian highland, the Igarka-Turukhansk region, the northern Taymyr foothills, and the Severnaya Zemlya Islands. The most extensive areas of Riphean rocks are at the periphery of the Anabar shield and on the southern side of the Kara arch. Riphean stratigraphic sections of different regions are in general similar. For example, almost everywhere at the base there is a terrigenous (sandstone) formation with terrigenous-carbonate (variegated) rocks above, and the section is capped by a carbonate formation. Carbonate deposits yield stromatolites, oncolites, and kathagraphia.[4] The thickness of the deposits, which varies gradually from place to place, reaches a maximum of 500 m in the Turukhansk-Igarka region and in Taymyr. The oldest radiogenic age is 1,500 ± 50 m.y. It was determined by the K-Ar method on glauconite from the lower part of the Anabar anticlise section. On the west and east sides of the anticlise, gabbro-diabase dikes and sills with an age ranging from 800 to 1,100 m.y. were recently reported; this age is consistent with other geologic evidence.

Tectonically, the Riphean may be called a "homogenization" stage of the North Asiatic craton. At the beginning of the Riphean, structures of the preceding stages formed part of a single sedimentary basin bordered by geosynclinal beds of the future Baykalides, Caledonides, and Hercynides. Within the Riphean sedimentary basin, there was generally moderate subsidence and a persistent similarity of formations. However, there were also zones of greater mobility. These zones represent relict troughs in areas of former geosynclines. The troughs are characterized by the presence of a rather thick sedimentary sequence (more than 5,000 m) and of deformation along the geostructure. As was mentioned, the age of sediments filling relict troughs is disputable. There may be deposits representing the entire Riphean, but it is more probable that a section of subplatform deposits corresponds only to the late Riphean and Vendian. The tectonic environment of the Riphean sedimentary basin of north-central Siberia is correlative with the younger (mobile) platform.

Phanerozoic Geology and Structural History

In the territory studied, Phanerozoic geologic history can be subdivided distinctly into geotec-

---

[4] Carbonate structures of probably organic origin.

tonic stages or cycles: Cambro-Devonian, Carboniferous-Triassic, Jurassic-Paleogene, and incomplete Neogene-Quaternary (or neotectonic). Field work shows that within the North Asiatic craton each cycle (excluding the neotectonic) begins and ends with peneplanation. The formation of the peneplain surfaces began in different places at different times. Direct evidence of peneplains is obscured only in limited areas where relict basins of continuous sedimentation are situated.

After a short time, corresponding to a time of regional peneplanation, transformation of the craton occurred and a new system of epicratonic structures was formed. A composite vertical section of Phanerozoic formations separated by peneplain surfaces is represented by a column consisting of sedimentary megarhythms disconformably overlying each other. Megarhythms reflect cyclic development of the region in the Phanerozoic. The territory studied has four such megarhythms (megacycles). Beyond the craton boundary, paleopeneplains cross time boundaries and thus are of no regional significance.

Cambro-Devonian

Lower and middle Paleozoic rocks are widespread over the territory of north-central Siberia and form a part of the Siberian platform cover. They occur in the Taymyr–Severnaya Zemlya fold system, crop out at the base of the Verkhoyansk complex, and compose linear folds in the New Siberian Islands. They belong to a single sedimentary basin which is characterized by a persistent facies zonation and ubiquitous platform environment.

Along the northwest limit with the Caledonides geosynclinal belt, a wide zone of littoral facies is present. Tectonically, that zone was part of the Severnaya Zemlya pericratonic trough. There, marine arenaceous-argillaceous Cambrian deposits (up to 3,000 m) form the base of the stratigraphic section. Overlying the Cambrian strata with local angular unconformity are Ordovician sandstones, dolomites, marlstones, and mixed variegated carbonate-terrigenous units containing gypsum (about 2,500 m). The Silurian marine limestone sequence (up to 1,000 m) lies on the erosional surface of the Ordovician strata. The section is capped by a variegated carbonate-terrigenous gypsiferous Devonian sequence (about 1,500 m). The upper units of the Devonian are represented by red continental sandstones of "Old Red" type. South of the Severnaya Zemlya trough, there is a zone of deep-water, silty basinal facies; farther south this facies is replaced by a zone of open-

marine shallow-water strata. Both facies were deposited in the Taymyr trough, and the sediment entered the Yenisey trough through a bay. A stratigraphic section of these two facies begins at the base with Cambrian rocks of chemical carbonate and biogenic origin; they formed in a shallow-water environment. Presence of a complete section has been proved paleontologically. A minimum thickness (600–800 m) of these facies is observed in the Taymyr trough and a maximum (> 3,000 m) in the Yenisey trough.

A subdivision into facies zones begins with the Ordovician. Within the abyssal basin, Cambrian deposits are conformably overlain by Ordovician and Early Silurian graptolite shales. Above, there are conformable pteropod carbonate-shaly deposits of Ludlovian and Middle Devonian ages. The section is capped by Domanik shales of Late Devonian age. Pteropod and Domanik facies are replaced in eastern Taymyr by a dolomite sequence. The total thickness of black shale is about 3,500 m. The open-marine shallow-water zone is characterized by the accumulations of biogenic and, in lesser quantities, chemical calcareous and dolomite-calcareous deposits. The total thickness of these deposits for the Ordovician-Devonian interval is about 4,000 m in the Taymyr trough and about 1,500 m in the Yenisey trough.

Farther south, the open-marine shallow-water facies was gradually replaced by a wide zone of littoral facies bordering the Central Siberian landmass. A transition to littoral facies is observed in the Yenisey and Taymyr troughs and the north Verkhoyansk area. The Central Siberian zone of littoral facies is characterized by the development of variegated gypsiferous marlstones and chemical and organic carbonate deposits. The thickness of the sequence ranges from 0 to 1,000 m. Tectonically, the Central Siberian zone of littoral facies belongs to the central stable region of the craton.

Near the end of the cycle, gentle structures were formed within the sedimentary basin, but their reconstruction is difficult because superposed deformation of a subsequent cycle was more intensive. Part of the broken folds mapped in Severnaya Zemlya appear to be due to the later cycle.

Fissured intrusions of trap rock in regional fault zones are related to the development of the Patom-Vilyuy aulacogene (in particular, the Vilyuy-Markha, Muna-Olenek, and Molodo-Udzha complexes). They, as well as the fissured intrusions, developed on the Anabar-Olenek anticlise flank.

The general structural-stratigraphic scheme

of a Cambro-Devonian sedimentary basin in north-central Siberia is not consistent with the lower and middle Paleozoic of the New Siberian Islands, where marine carbonate and terrigenous rocks are either platform strata of the Hyperborean craton or they are early miogeosynclinal strata of the Novosibirsk-Chukotsk fold system.

Carboniferous-Triassic

The Carboniferous-Triassic was marked by intensive movements of the Pacific orogenic cycle in the adjacent geosynclinal belt on the east. The Verkhoyansk and Novosibirsk-Chukotsk geosynclines, which were boundary structures, formed a part of the Pacific belt. As a result of the Pacific tectogenesis, a part of the North Asiatic craton was broken into a group of genetically related positive and negative structures. They were directly linked with the Verkhoyansk geosyncline and, with it, composed a system of communicating troughs. The system included a trough in southern Taymyr, the Tungusska synclise, and a trough situated on the western coast of the Laptev Sea.

Opinion differs regarding the structure of the Taymyr trough. Some workers believe that the Taymyr trough and the Yenisey Bay area had cellular structure; two major depressions (West Taymyr and East Taymyr depressions) were separated by the diagonal Tareya swell. The zone of swells of the Yenisey area formed the western border of the Tungusska synclise and joined *en échelon* with the Tareya swell west of the Pyasina River. Thus, the Tungusska synclise was directly connected with the East Taymyr depression. The latter branched also into a trough situated on the coast of the present Laptev Sea. On the basis of geophysical data, its northern end was situated approximately at the latitude of the October Revolution Island (part of Severnaya Zemya).

In the opinion of others, the Taymyr trough was, in late Paleozoic time, a single entity. The area of maximum downwarping was the central part of the trough. No signs of thinning of the upper Paleozoic deposits toward the Tareya swell have been observed by workers. Thus, it appears that the Tareya swell was not present in late Paleozoic time.

Parts of the North Asiatic craton, separated by troughs, have undergone uplifting. The following structures formed contemporaneously with the troughs: the Kara arch, the Yenisey area uplifts (swell zone), the Anabar anticlise, and the Laptev projection. The troughs have gentle sides at the boundary with the Anabar

anticlise and steep, flexurelike sides that show evidence of linear stretching at the northern and western boundaries of the area of downwarping.

Sedimentary formations filling troughs have many similar features and represent a continuous lateral series from the Tungusska Series to the Taymyr complex and to the Verkhoyansk complex. Type sections of the continuous series have the following main features.

The Tungusska Series is represented in the lower part of the section mainly by continental coal-bearing deposits of the Middle and Upper Carboniferous and of the Lower Permian and, in part, the Upper Permian (up to 1,000 m). It is overlain by a sequence of tuffs and plateau basalts of Permo-Triassic age (about 3,000 m). The Tungusska Series is underlain by Lower Carboniferous marine terrigenous-carbonate deposits about 300 m in thickness.

The Taymyr complex in the western part of the trough is characterized by the presence of marine flyschlike deposits of the Middle and Upper Carboniferous. Also present are flyschlike deposits of Sakmarian and Artinskian ages (Permian) that are conformably overlain by paralic deposits. The paralic strata are overlain by Permo-Triassic trap rocks. The thickness of marine deposits is about 1,500 m, and that of coal-bearing beds is as great as 2,500–3,000 m; the thickness of the trap rocks is about 1,000 m.

The Taymyr complex in the central and eastern parts of the trough differs from that in the western part in two ways: coal-bearing deposits are less extensive, and a marine sandstone sequence is present at the base of the Upper Permian. Thickness of the terrigenous rocks is as much as 8,000 m. The thickness of the trap sequence there reaches 3,000 m. It is overlain by Middle-Upper Triassic molassic strata in central Taymyr and by a coal-bearing paralic sequence of Triassic age in the east of the peninsula. The Taymyr complex within the trough is underlain by marine carbonate and carbonate-shaly deposits of the Lower Carboniferous.

Magmatic formations are represented by upper Paleozoic domelike bodies of subalkalic granitoids that intrude Upper Silurian deposits and by widespread Triassic sills and trap-rock dikes. The youngest, possibly Jurassic, rocks are minor intrusions of subalkalic and alkalic granitoid rocks, syenites, nepheline syenites, and scarce monzonites which intrude Triassic terrigenous deposits.

In the Verkhoyansk complex, Viséan deposits form the lower part and Lower Cretaceous deposits form the upper part. A stratigraphic section consists of four mesorhythms (cycles), each of which begins with fine-grained marine and terrigenous deposits and ends with coarse-grained nearshore-marine deposits. The following dates were determined for the close of the cycles: the end of the Bashkirian, the end of the Permian, the end of the Triassic, and the end of the Early Cretaceous. In contrast to the sections in intracratonic troughs, trap rocks and coal-bearing formations are absent in the interval from the Carboniferous to the Triassic.

The genetic unity and continuous transitions from one complex into another is emphasized by marine deposition. The invasion routes of the first Early Carboniferous transgressions were of the "Pacific" type. Transgression was from east to west along the flexurelike flanges and trenches whose positions were controlled by deep-seated faults. The most extensive transgressions correspond to the Late Carboniferous and to the Kazanian Age of the Permian. The first covered the whole Taymyr trough and penetrated deeply into the Laptev branch (it may have passed around Severnaya Zemlya and penetrated into the Novaya Zemlya trough). Further evidence of this transgression is found in paralic units on the western side of the Tungusska syneclise. The second extensive trangression advanced to the East Taymyr depression area, and did not extend beyond the Tareya swell on the west. The sea moved toward the Tungusska syneclise and reached the Gorbiyachin River area. In the Triassic, during a period of trough closing, transgressions of Induan, Anisian, and Norian ages did not advance farther than the Khatanga region. Lithologic evidence suggests short-term transgression in the form of narrow bays into the Fadyukuda graben-syncline and the depression in the Dudypta River area.

Longitudinal and transverse dislocations (folds) of beds are connected with the development of positive and negative geostructures. Although they are found in all the geostructures, these dislocations reached the highest intensity within the Kara arch and in the Taymyr–Severnaya Zemlya fold system, which is subdivided into two zones. The southern zone (Byrranga Mountains) is represented by linear and broken folds formed as a result of inversion of the Taymyr trough—the intracratonic branch of the Verkhoyansk geosyncline. The nothern, or the Taymyr–Severnaya Zemlya arc, resulted from arcogenesis during the span from the Dzhungarian to the Triassic, inclusive. In the arcogenesis zone, a part of the ancient platform was broken into narrow, elongate blocks which were overthurst from northwest to southeast. In general, they are common in cross sections of the arch. Structures in the basement and in the sedimentary cover were deformed by the movements along a new structural framework. Structural reworking was accompanied by intensive granite magmatism.

Weak dislocations of Carboniferous-Triassic age were more marked along the western fringe of the Tungusska syneclise and in some areas of the Verkhoyansk geosyncline. Rather mild folding affected the sides of the Anabar anticlise and, presumably, the center of the Tungusska syneclise.

Except within the Verkhoyansk geosynclinal trough and the adjacent Lena-Anabar region, structures became consolidated in Jurassic time and formed the basement for a young platform. In the Lena part of the Verkhoyansk geosynclinal zone and in the Lena-Anabar region, disturbances of the Carboniferous-Triassic cycle formed structures of the first generation which continued to develop after peneplanation and terminated at the end of the Early Cretaceous.

During Carboniferous-Triassic time, magmatic activity was very intensive; it resulted in the formation of a trap-rock sequence in the extensive territory of Siberia and in Taymyr. The sequence includes basalt lavas, which commonly form thick sheets; various tuffs; and intrusive rocks which compose thick sills, dikes, and stocklike bodies. Intrusive trap rocks are represented mainly by dolerites and gabbro dolerites; in differentiated intrusions, however, a range of other rocks is present. The youngest trap rocks are almost ultramafic alkalic rocks, whereas the youngest differentiated intrusive rocks are plagiogranites.

At the same time, in the junction zone of the Anabar anticlise, the Tungusska syneclise, and the Khatanga trough, a rather intricate multiphase complex of extrusive, veined, and intrusive rocks of ultramafic and alkalic composition was formed. It is known in the literature as the Maymecha-Kotuy complex. Alkalic-ultramafic volcanism and trap-rock volcanism took place contemporaneously for a long time. Two types of kimberlite volcanism also occurred contemporaneously; the beginning of kimberlite volcanism is assigned to the Early Permian and the final stage is considered to be Cretaceous. Both explosive and hypabyssal kimberlites are distinguished. The former comprises chimney deposits and is represented by kimberlite breccias; the latter forms dikes and veins and is made up of massive rocks. Kimberlite bodies are confined to junction areas of various structures and to nodes of intersection zones of ancient deep-seated faults in the northeastern Siberian platform.

Jurassic-Paleogene

The Jurassic-Paleogene of north-central Siberia was a time of regeneration of the platform environment. The platform environment was regenerated over the entire area of the North Asiatic craton. The craton earlier was affected by late Paleozoic–early Mesozoic tectonic activity, and platform conditions extended eastward to boundary systems of the Pacific geosynclinal belt.

In the western part of the territory, during the Jurassic-Paleogene, the largest platform geostructure formed—the West Siberian plate. Eastward, along the northern margin of the Siberian platform, the Lena-Yenisey trough system was formed (Yenisey-Khatanga, Lena-Anabar, and Verkhoyansk area troughs). The two sedimentary basins have different structural histories and sedimentary environments and differ in basement structure and thickness of platform cover.

Stratigraphic sections in both basins are characterized by alternation of predominantly fine-grained terrigenous marine and paralic coal-bearing formations. Sedimentary units are lithified at the base of the section, but they are poorly lithified to nonlithified in the upper parts of the complex. In the western part of the Yenisey-Khatanga trough, which is continuous with the West Siberian plate, the thickness of these deposits reaches 7 km. In the eastern part of the trough, which is a transitional zone confined to the eastern boundary of the craton, the thickness of Jurassic-Cretaceous deposits decreases to 2 km. In the Lena-Anabar region and in the northern part of the area west of the Verkhoyansk geosyncline (Verkhoyansk trough), the thickness is as much as 3 km in the western or platform part and as much as 5 km in the eastern or folded part.

The inner structure of the sedimentary basins is characterized by the combination of numerous troughs, swells, and depressions. Areas of uplift fringing sedimentary basins correspond to zones of intense movements of the previous cycle. Their central parts were permanent source areas of Jurassic-Paleogene sediments.

At the end of the Cretaceous or the beginning of the Paleogene, the last magmatic cycle of the Siberian platform occurred. The local magmatism is represented by andesite lavas and rather peculiar pyroclastic rocks confined to the Popigay depression.

Neotectonic Cycle

In the neotectonic cycle during Neogene-Quaternary time, two separate sedimentary basins formed on the platform—the Kara and Laptev Sea shelves. The initial stage of the basins is assigned to the Neogene, whereas the formation of their present boundaries is related to late Pleistocene and Holocene movements. Neotectonic uplifts fringing the present Kara and Laptev Sea shelves coincide in their main features with uplifts of a preceding cycle. Thus, the neotectonic basins were superimposed on the older Meso-Cenozoic basins. Geophysical investigations, however, show unconformities in areal relations of minor structures between neotectonic and Meso-Cenozoic complexes. The most pronounced structural unconformity is manifested within the Kara shelf.

Stratigraphic sections of both basins are extremely similar, excluding the coastal zones. The sections are usually represented by fine-grained terrigenous marine, glacial-marine, and deltaic deposits. Their thickness ranges from 0 to 300 m. Tectonically, the Kara and Laptev sedimentary basins of Neogene-Quaternary time can be related to the development of such a geostructure as the Arctic Ocean basin. Thus, the Kara basin is considered as a separate but collateral structure. The Laptev basin represents a direct continuation, along strike, of the Amundsen and Nansen basins. The earth's crust in both basins is as thin as 25–30 m.

Summary

Studies of the geology and structural history of north-central Siberia show that emplacement of the earth's crust in this vast region was cyclic and evolutionary at the same time. Despite the repetition of events (craton separation–craton consolidation), geologic phenomena and formations display progressive change in time and also in cycle duration. Only peneplains are invariant and uniform and correspond to the state of tectonic equilibrium of the region. The disturbance of the periodicity is by the displacement within Central Siberia of tectonic processes originating in different segments of the earth, *i.e.*, the Atlantic and the Pacific.

Main Features of Geologic Structure of Eastern USSR and Contiguous Territories[1]

L. I. KRASNY[2]

Leningrad, USSR

Abstract Three geochrons are distinguished: (1) Protogey (before 1,600 m.y.), (2) Mesogey (1,600–600 m.y.), and (3) Neogey (younger than 600–550 m.y.).

Within the Aldan and Sino-Korean shields, the oldest volcanic regions and primary uplifts (e.g., Yendyr') are present. After consolidation of the early Archean mobile regions in the protogeosynclines, the Stanovoy fold system formed. Later, around 1,900–1,800 m.y. ago, a gigantic collapse (*Einbruch*) took place. During the last 300 m.y. of the Protogey geochron, large basins developed.

During the 1,000 m.y. that composed the Mesogey geochron, a calm, catastable regime predominated. At the beginning and at the end of the Mesogey, volcanic activity was intense (El'gete volcanism).

Five stages of the Neogey geochron are distinguished: (1) early Paleozoic, during which broad geosynclines, filled mainly with terrigenous and carbonate sediments, and late Baykalian structures associated with broad granitoid magmatism formed; (2) middle Paleozoic, during which thick eugeosynclinal and miogeosynclinal sequences subsided; (3) late Paleozoic, during which subsidence continued and the Mongolo-Okhotsk, Sikhote-Alin, and Nippon (Japan) systems were rebuilt; (4) Mesozoic—especially significant in the eastern USSR—during which various types of mobile regions and systems developed (Verkhoyansk and Chukotsk geosynclinal systems, Mongolo-Okhotsk system, Selengino-Yablonovyy and Stanovoy regions of mountain uplift and block faulting and formation of the Jurassic-Cretaceous rift basin; the Chugoku, Eastern Sikhote–Alin, Okhotsk-Chukotsk, and Nunivak [Alaska] volcanic belts; and the Simanto orthogeosynclinal belt); (5) Cenozoic, during which intense mountain building was accompanied by evolution of intermontane basins on continents and formation of systems of island arcs in a transitional region of continent-ocean (Kuril-Kamchatka and Aleutian systems). During this time, an accelerated rate of tectonic processes apparently existed.

INTRODUCTION

The eastern USSR belongs to the northwest part of the Pacific mobile belt. It includes the large territory from the Lena River to the Kuril Islands and from Chukotsk Peninsula to the south Primor'ye. This region is characterized by a great variety of structural forms, among which are the margins of the Siberian platform, with a foredeep and a pericratonic sag; the projection of the China platform and the hypothetical Hyperborean platform; and other large mobile regions formed on various basements at various times. Also present in the region are excellent examples of volcanic and metamorphic belts and an active geosyncline, which includes the Kuril-Kamchatka island-arc system, where regions of recent volcanism and deep basins and trenches are found. Study of the development of Mesozoic and Cenozoic faults, as well as the stabilized structures, leads to a better interpretation of the geologic history. The nature of the juncture of the continents and oceans is pertinent to solving the theoretical problems of the origin and evolution of the earth's crust and upper mantle. It appears that an understanding of the northwestern part of the Pacific mobile belt can form the basis for the solution of scientific and practical problems. Recent conclusions regarding the geologic structure of the northwestern Pacific mobile belt are based on the following: (1) the geologic structure of eastern USSR as represented on a recent geologic map cannot be understood without geophysical data (Considerable generalization of geophysical data has been done by B. A. Andreyev, R. M. Demenitskaya, I. P. Kosminskaya, A. A. Nikolayevsky, and I. K. Tuyesovors from the Institute of Physics of the Earth, Sakhalin, and the northeastern complex of Institutions of the Academy of Sciences of the USSR, Scientific Research Institute of Geophysics, Scientific Research Institute of the Geology of the Arctic, VSEGEI of the Ministry of Geology of the USSR, the Shterenberg State Astronomical Institute, and the Ministry of High Education of the USSR.); and (2) the main peculiarities of the earth's crust of the northeast of the Asiatic continent and adjacent regions of the Pacific Ocean and the Arctic basin can be understood only as understanding is gained concerning the contiguous territories of Japan, Korea, Northeast China, and Alaska.

The geological-geophysical regional study of the eastern USSR and contiguous regions helps to explain the variety in the geologic history and abyssal structure and the attendant block faulting of different ages. This variety is clearly shown in the peculiar distribution of gravity

[1] Manuscript received, April 30, 1972.

[2] Research Institute of the Geology of the Arctic.

and geomagnetic fields and regions of high seismicity. A synthesis of the joint efforts of scientific bodies doing geological and abyssal studies of the eastern USSR has made possible the outlining of three regions: the continental region, with a crustal thickness of more than 35 km; the oceanic region, with a crustal thickness of less than 15–20 km; and the perioceanic region between them, with various thicknesses of crust from 15 to 33 km. Boundaries of these regions extend in a northeast direction.

Over the great distance from East China to Chukotsk, the boundary between continental and transitional regions coincides with the East Asian volcanic belt. The boundary between transitional and oceanic regions follows the steep slope of deep-water trenches. The large regions outlined along the eastern USSR, which are characterized by a more or less homogeneous type of crust and thickness, are subdivided into important regional structures, or geoblocks (Fig. 1). These geoblocks, which have lengths

of a few thousand kilometers, have specific crustal peculiarities. Magmatism and metamorphism, as well as definite lineations of formations with accompanying metallogenic zonation, are evident. These geoblocks have enclosed some geosynclinal fold systems of similar, but not identical, evolution.

In the continental parts of northeastern Asia, the following blocks are distinguished: Aldan-Stanovoy, Kolyma, and Amur. In the transitional zone, the blocks are the Nippon, Okhotsk, and Bering. Paleozoic processes of the Sikhote-Alin and Nippon geosynclinal regions show a marked similarity; probably, during this era, an independent Nippon-Sikhote-Alin geoblock was present which did not include Hokkaido.

Geoblocks of Eastern USSR

The *Aldan-Stanovoy geoblock* is bounded by zones of deep fractures expressed by linear maximum Δt of more than 100 gammas. Up-

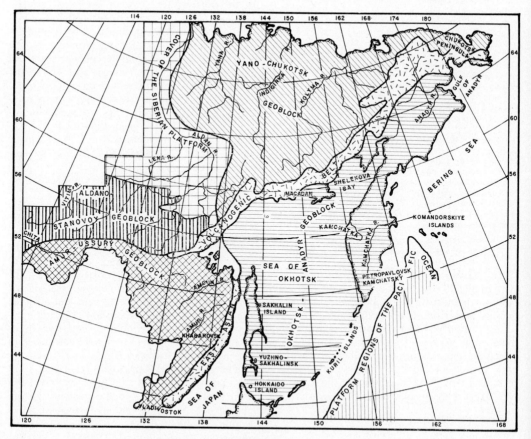

Figure 1

lift of this structure was continuous and great. As a result of this uplift, large areas of metamorphic rocks characteristic of the deep zones of the earth's crust crop out at the surface. Among these old complexes, cup-shaped and loaf-shaped folded structures have simple cores but complicated peripheral areas. These structures have a neutral geomagnetic field. In this field, a sigmoidal system of maximum Δt and minimum Δt for brachyanticlinoriums and brachysynclinoriums, respectively, is distinguished. Abundant, and commonly specific, ultramafic alkalic magmatism is peculiar to the juncture of the abyssal fractures of the Aldan-Stanovoy geoblock.

Mesozoic faulting and uplift encompassed the whole Aldan-Stanovoy geoblock. These movements were independent and not connected with those of adjacent geosynclinal regions. Maximum contrast and amplitude of movements are evidenced for the period of Jurassic to Early Cretaceous time; however, the movements are traceable from Triassic to Paleogene time, and a gradual rejuvenation of movements from west to east is apparent. North of China, in the upper parts of the Vitim and Olekma Rivers, granitoid intrusions are Triassic; in the Prishilka region and in the upper Primor'ye, they are Early-Middle Jurassic; in the Stanovoy and Dzhugdzhur Mountains, they are Cretaceous and probably Paleogene. Deep-seated movements inducing tectonic activity of the Aldan-Stanovoy geoblock were accompanied by a sudden revival of magmatic activity, which produced the Aldan volcanic-intrusive complex and the Udsk intrusive complexes. The composition of the former ranges from alkalic andesites to scarce alkalic rocks of the potassium series, and that of the latter includes granodiorite and related rocks of other compositions.

Mesozoic activity was not confined to magmatic revival. In the Early-Middle Jurassic, along the north margin of the Stanovoy region, a rift belt was initiated. Within this belt, erosion and redeposition resulted in (1) filling of the Chul'man, Tonin, and other basins by late Mesozoic and younger deposits containing coal and argillite and (2) isolation of the basins.

The *Kolyma geoblock* differs from the Aldan-Stanovoy block because of the Paleozoic and Mesozoic subsidence of the former. Its boundaries are zones of subsidence on the margins of the Siberian platform. The zones of subsidence are the Sette Daban pericratonic trough and the Pre-Verkhoyansk marginal trough on

the southeast and west, respectively, and the Okhotsk-Chukotsk volcanic belt on the east of the platform.

Generally, the rocks of the Mesozoic fold zone of this geoblock are characterized by lower Δt values; however, the Kolyma, Omolon, and Okhotsk massifs are characterized by an increased Δt field, which shows their tectonic peculiarity.

The thickness of the crust within the geoblock is 35–40 km. In regions of active neotectonic movements (Chersky and Verkhoyansk Ranges), the thickness of the crust increases to 45–47 km. Within this geoblock, small blocks of crystalline basement have subsided somewhat, and almost everywhere they underlie younger sedimentary beds.

Some similar features of the eastern part of the Siberian platform and the Verkhoyansk-Kolyma folded region are apparent. In the platform and in the geosynclinal regions, Paleozoic (pre-Carboniferous) formations are mainly carbonaceous, and late Paleozoic and Mesozoic formations are terrigenous. In zones of subsidence at the margins of the platform (Sette Daban pericratonic and Pre-Verkhoyansk troughs) and in the geosynclinal regions (in formations of the geosynclinal stage of crustal evolution), dikes, sills, and laccoliths of mainly diabasic (trap) composition are present.

Along with these peculiarities of the basement of the Verkhoyansk-Kolyma folded region, there is a special structural form called a "planorium" (Adycha area, *etc.*), which consists of undulate uplifts over a large area. Of significance is the migration of geosynclinal sags, in time and space, from the axial parts of the planorium and mega-anticlinorium to the edge of the Kolyma massif in Late Permian, Early Triassic, and Jurassic times and to the edge of the Siberian platform in the Jurassic.

The rejuvenation of sags from south to north is marked in the Chukotsk geosynclinal region, where probably the youngest of the geosynclinal sags are of Early Cretaceous age. The appearance of the middle Paleozoic and probably younger siliceous-volcanic formations at the edge of the Omolon massif and in the Chukotsk region permits correlation with contemporaneous geosynclines of Alaska.

The very complex *Amur geoblock* has a crustal thickness of about 30–35 km and generally is characterized by a subdued magnetic Δt field. The large Mongolo-Okhotsk deep-seated fault forms its north boundary. The south part of the geoblock occupies the vast area of

Northeast China to the Selyache River. It was supposed not long ago that the East Sikhote–Alin volcanic belt, which is recorded by a clear gravitational gradient, was the east boundary of the geoblock. This boundary now can be observed in a belt eroded in recent geologic time. However, if the geoblocks are considered in a historic sense, it appears that their main features may unite with other geoblocks. It is now clear that, from the Early Carboniferous to the Late Permian, and probably in the Mesozoic, the Sikhote-Alin geosynclinal regions were united with the Nippon region.

The Amur geoblock is situated on broken, submerged folded blocks which were permeable to magmatic intrusions. These intrusions occurred during the latter parts of all stages of evolution of the folded regions. They caused disintegration of the blocks and promoted the formation of narrow fault-bounded geosynclines along deep-seated fracture systems. In these narrow geosynclinal zones, some of which are framed by reef structures, the accumulation of siliceous-terrigenous volcanic units took place. Despite the distinctions of the Kolyma and Amur geoblocks, they have certain similarities. During geosynclinal lithogenesis and magmatism of the post-inversion stage, there were similar conditions of faulting and granitoid magmatism and metallogenesis as the two blocks consolidated. This process embraced vast areas of East Asia (Korea, China). Analysis of the dynamics of the evolution of geoblocks reveals an essential distinction in pre-inversion and post-inversion types of evolution: the latter was more "universal."

Geoblocks of Northeastern Transitional Zone

On the east and northeast, the Nippon, Okhotsk, and Bering geoblocks are in the region of rebuilding of the crust at the juncture of the continent and the ocean. Here, there is a complex of continental, transitional, and oceanic crusts. Fault boundaries of the geoblocks are evident, and the presence of zones of deep faulting is confirmed by bands of continuous volcanism on the west (rhyolite-andesite boundary) and on the east (andesite boundary). These zones are also outlined by gravity measurements. Within the geoblocks studied, low Δt values and somewhat increased gamma anomalies predominate.

Data from deep seismic sounding (DSS) show that these differences are related to the structure of the crust. For example, within the Okhotsk geoblock, the thickness of the crust is about 20–25 km over much of the central part. In the northern part it is 15 km, and in the area of the south Okhotsk deep basin the thickness is about 42 km. Within the Kuril island arc is a system of linear blocks of thick (up to 35 km) and thin (15 km or less) crust. The boundaries of some zones with thick and thin crust are expressed by "gravitational gradient" anomalies and also by linear Δt maximums.

Geoblocks of transitional zones are characterized by broad development of siliceous-volcanic and marine diatomic units, ultramafic magmatism, recent volcanism, and high seismicity. Of special interest are deep-focus earthquakes which are situated within a linear uplifted zone west-northwest of Japan and the Kuril-Kamchatka abyssal basin. Within geoblocks there are mobile regions of intense folding (e.g., Sakhalin, the southwestern part of the Honn-Nippon region, and the west Kamchatka–Koryak region) and recent geosynclinal activity (e.g., Kuril–east Kamchatka).

Conclusions

From the examples given, it is evident that division of the crust into blocks represents the main working hypothesis of modern geotectonics, and this method should be taken into account during tectonic zonation of large complex regions. Two zones are present simultaneously: extended linear zones and belts which may restrict systems of geoblocks (e.g., East Asian volcanic belt and intergeoblock zones (e.g., Amur-Okhotsk folded system between Aldan-Stanovoy and Amur geoblocks).

In their recent studies, geophysicists A. A. Borisov, E. V. Artiushkov, especially Yu. Ya. Vashchilov, A. G. Gaynanov, and P. A. Stroyev showed data and computations which prove the existence of geoblocks. The last-mentioned authors have shown block structure of offshore areas on the margins of Northeast Asia, where they proved the formation of the Nippon, Okhotsk, and Bering geoblocks (recent papers by Krasny and Krasny and Andreyev). The presence of heterogeneities with near-vertical lateral limitations in beds of the crust and upper mantle was revealed by these authors' investigations of gravimetric data. The data show that the subhorizontal surfaces in the crust and upper mantle consist of alternate layers of very dense and less dense materials. Most workers consider that the boundaries of the geoblocks were related to existing faults. Such an assumption is supported by the polygonal shapes of the geoblocks in plan view.

SUMMARY

In summing up the results of this brief survey of geologic structures of Northeast Asia, it is necessary to deal with some general problems. The interest of geologists and geophysicists in the margins of the continent, the Pacific Ocean, and the transitional zone between makes it necessary to understand the deep interrelation of magmatic movements (in a broad sense) in the large oceans and on vast margins of large continents on near and far boundaries of the Pacific Ocean. It is time for geologists and geophysicists to work out the hypothesis of mantle currents under the Asian continent that generate magmatic formations from an initial primordial substance. In this framework, the problem of interrelation of the Mesozoic-Cenozoic basaltic magmatism of the Pacific Ocean and the age of granitoid magmatism of the margins of the Asiatic and American continents should be studied.

Oil and Gas Possibilities in the Soviet Arctic[1]

V. N. SEMENOVICH,[2] I. S. GRAMBERG,[3] and I. I. NESTEROV[4]

Moscow, Leningrad, and Novosibirsk, USSR

Abstract The Soviet Arctic, including the continental shelf, occupies about one third of the area of the entire Soviet Union. Within this area, major platform structures with thick sedimentary sections are developed. These structures are the West Siberian and Pechora plates and the Siberian, Barents-Kara, and Hyperborean platforms. All the known oil and gas areas and the most prospective territories and shelves are related to these platforms. Areas favorable for petroleum exploration make up 60–70 percent or more of this area.

The largest prospective area is the West Siberian oil and gas area. In the Arctic part of the West Siberian province, a unique gas field was discovered (Urengoy, 4.1×10^{12} cu m). Productive and prospective units are known to range through the Jurassic to the Upper Cretaceous (another field is Medvezh'ye, 1.6×10^{12} cu m). Prospective structures for oil and gas extend from the land into the southern part of the Kara shelf.

In the Timan-Pechora oil and gas area, several oil and gas fields have been discovered. Productive and prospective strata are the middle-upper Paleozoic and possibly the Mesozoic. Structures favorable for oil and gas accumulation continue into the southern areas of the Barents shelf.

The high petroleum possibilities for the northern part of the Siberian platform and the bordering Mesozoic troughs are confirmed by the discovery of gas fields in the western part of the Yenisey-Khatanga basin and oil fields in the eastern part of the basin. In addition, a large bitumen field (similar to Athabaska) is located on the southern border of the Lena-Anabar syneclise, and abundant oil and bitumen shows occur through the whole section from the upper Precambrian to the Lower Cretaceous.

The Mesozoic-Cenozoic troughs and depressions of the Verkhoyansk-Kolyma, Koryak-Kamchatka, and Chukotsk areas in the northeastern part of the USSR are prospective for oil and gas.

The high estimate of the oil and gas possibilities for the offshore shelves is based on the favorable geological and geophysical facts from the Soviet Arctic islands and shelf. The most prospective are structures within the Barents-Kara platform; the West Siberian trough; the Chukotsk–East Siberian, southern Chukotsk, and southern Laptev basins; and the Wrangel Rise.

INTRODUCTION

The European part of the Soviet Arctic is the part which has been studied more and which has been economically developed. The main

[1] Manuscript received, April 30, 1972.

[2] Ministry of Geology of the USSR, Moscow.

[3] Research Institute of the Geology of the Arctic, Leningrad.

[4] Institute of Geology and Geophysics, Siberian Branch, Novosibirsk.

structural feature for oil and gas prospects in the European sector of the Soviet Arctic is the Russian platform, within which the Timan-Pechora oil- and gas-bearing region has been discovered.

The economic development of North Siberia is just beginning. Oil and gas prospects are associated there with the northern margins of the West Siberian plate and the Siberian platform. These structures are separated from the adjacent regions by the Northern Ural, Pay-Khoy, Novaya Zemlya, Taymyr, and northern Verkhoyansk fold systems. In the northern part of West Siberia, several oil and gas areas already have been discovered.

The importance of the Yenisey-Khatanga oil and gas area north of the Siberian platform is now evident also.

The least investigated is the northeastern territory of the USSR. In contrast to Northern Europe and North Siberia, where platform structures are dominant, the northeastern territory of the USSR is substantially an area of Mesozoic-Cenozoic fold systems. Oil and gas prospects of the northeast USSR are principally in the fold systems of the basins and troughs that are filled with Mesozoic sediments.

Oil and gas prospects of the Arctic shelf of the USSR are evaluated on the basis of general geologic considerations. However, there is no doubt that several of the oil- and gas-bearing structures of the Arctic mainland extend onto the shelf. Therefore, it is believed that the oil and gas possibilities of the offshore in such seas as the Pechora and the Kara Seas are very great. The existence of areas of steady downwarping and the great thicknesses of the sedimentary cover within other seas of the Soviet Arctic suggest their oil and gas potential.

Oil and gas prospects of the European sector of the Arctic are associated with the Timan-Pechora oil and gas region (Krems et al., 1968; Karta Perspectiv Neftegazonosnosti SSSR, 1969). Tectonic features of this region are a result of its position on the northeastern margin of the Russian platform at the junction with the Ural fold system. The largest structural elements here are the following: Timan ridge, Pechora basin, Malaya Zemlya arch, Denisovka trough, Kolva megaswell, Khoreyver basin, Upper Kolva swell, Bolshaya Zemlya basin, and Korotaikha basin. This area is composed of Paleozoic, Mesozoic, and Cenozoic deposits up to 8,000 m thick. The basement is composed of highly dislocated, metamorphic Riphean schists.

The main gas- and oil-bearing complexes are the terrigenous deposits of the Middle Devonian and the lower Frasnian substage of the Upper Devonian, the Lower Carboniferous, and the Lower and Upper Permian—and also carbonate rocks of the Devonian, Carboniferous, and Permian. New oil- and gas-bearing zones are being sought in Mesozoic deposits, where many oil and gas shows have been recorded.

The following rocks are regional seals: the argillaceous rocks of the lower Frasnian, argillaceous and argillaceous-carbonate rocks of the Upper and Middle Carboniferous salt-bearing sequence of the Kungurian Stage, and the argillaceous members of the Upper Permian section.

In the Timan-Pechora region, several oil, gas, and oil-gas fields have been discovered. Tectonically, they are associated with the northeastern slope of the southern Timan-Pechora basin, the Kolva megaswell, and the Pechora tectonic ridge. The different genetic types are structural, stratigraphic, lithologic, massive, and combined (see glossary in Introduction). Most of these deposits are associated with brachyanticlines, but some are related to folds and pinchouts.

The northern margins of the two major platform structures, the West Siberian plate and the Siberian platform, extend into North Siberia. Oil and gas propsects there are associated mainly with these structures.

The West Siberian Epihercynian plate is one of the largest oil- and gas-bearing provinces in the world; its northern part is considerably richer than the southern part (Gurari et al., 1963; Chochia et al., 1968). The deformed Paleozoic rocks serve as a basement for the marginal parts of the plate; the central areas are occupied by Precambrian basement. Mainly carbonate Paleozoic rocks with thicknesses of 6–7 km compose the intermediate structural stage. In the buried Hercynian zone, this stage is represented by parageosynclinal formations of Triassic age. The upper structural stage is represented by a thick (up to 7 km) sequence of sandy argillaceous rocks of Jurassic, Cretaceous, and, in the basin deep, possibly Triassic age.

In the upper stage of the northern part of the West Siberian plate, several major structures are distinguished: Shchuchinskiy arch; Baydaratsky megatrough; Murma and Gydanskiy megaswells; Yamal, Nenetskiy, and Tazovskiy arches; and others. These major uplifts and troughs are complicated by structures of a higher order.

The Mesozoic-Cenozoic cover consists of alternate permeable and nonpermeable sequences, and the distribution and relation of these sequences, along with tectonic and other factors, control the distribution of oil and condensate. Two main oil and gas complexes are distinguished: the Lower-Middle Jurassic, which is covered by the Upper Jurassic–Valanginian regional caprock, and the Barremian-Cenomanian. The oil and gas fields in these complexes are very large and are controlled by brachyanticlinal folds in the contact zone between Cenomanian sandstones and the Turonian-Cenomanian argillaceous sequence. Several of the fields associated with the Barremian-Cenomanian sedimentary complex—such as the Urengoy (4.1×10^{12} cu m), Zapolyarnoye (1.6×10^{12} cu m), Medvezh'ye (1.6×10^{12} cu m), and Yamburg (1.5×10^{12} cu m) fields—may be classified as unique because of their reserves (Rudkevich et al., 1970).

Oil and gas prospects of the northern Siberian platform are associated with Mesozoic basins, the Tungusska syneclise, and slopes of the Anabar syneclise (Vasil'yev et al., 1968; Gramberg et al., 1969). Mesozoic troughs trending along the northern side of the platform merge into the West Siberian plate at the Yenisey River, and at the Lena River they pass into the Pre-Verkhoyansk trough. The Yenisey-Khatanga and Lena-Anabar troughs are divided by the Anabar swell. The basement of the troughs, like that of other Siberian-platform structures, is composed of Archean-Proterozoic metamorphic and igneous rocks.

At the base of the sedimentary section of the basins are upper Proterozoic–middle Paleozoic carbonate and terrigenous-carbonate rocks with thicknesses up to 4–5 km. These rocks occur at depths of about 5–7 km; only at the basin margins do they occur as shallow as 1.5–2 km below sea level. Upper Paleozoic, Triassic, Jurassic, and Cretaceous deposits are composed of alternate argillaceous and arenaceous rocks. The thicknesses of the upper Paleozoic and Triassic are as much as 2.5–3.0 km. These deposits occur at depths of approximately 5–7

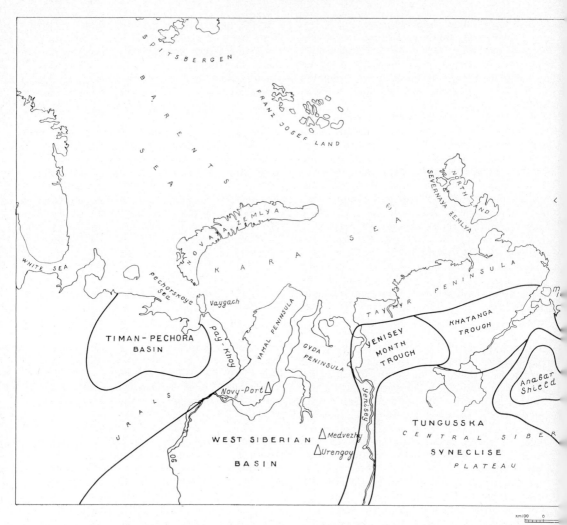

Fig. 1—Index m

km in the western part of the Yenisey-Khatanga basin; in the eastern part of that basin, in
the Lena-Anabar basin, and in the northern
part of the Pre-Verkhoyansk trough, their
depth is not more than 2.5–3.0 km. Thus, the
thickness of Jurassic-Cretaceous deposits decreases from west to east. The inner structure
of the basins is complicated by several large
uplifts and synclines.

Oil and gas prospects in the western part of
the Yenisey-Khatanga trough, which is known
as the Ust'-Yenisey basin, are associated mainly
with the Jurassic-Cretaceous sedimentary complex. In the Jurassic-Cretaceous complex,

Lower-Middle Jurassic, Upper Jurassic–lower
Valanginian, middle Valanginian–Albian, and
Upper Cretaceous prospective rocks are distinguished; each sequence includes a regional reservoir and a seal composed of argillaceous
rocks. Gas fields are found in all four sequences. Seven gas and condensate fields are
known, the largest of which are the Messoyakha and Pelyata fields.

In the eastern part of the Yenisey-Khatanga
trough (Khatanga basin), oil and gas shows are
recorded throughout the sedimentary section,
but they are most abundant in upper Paleozoic
rocks.

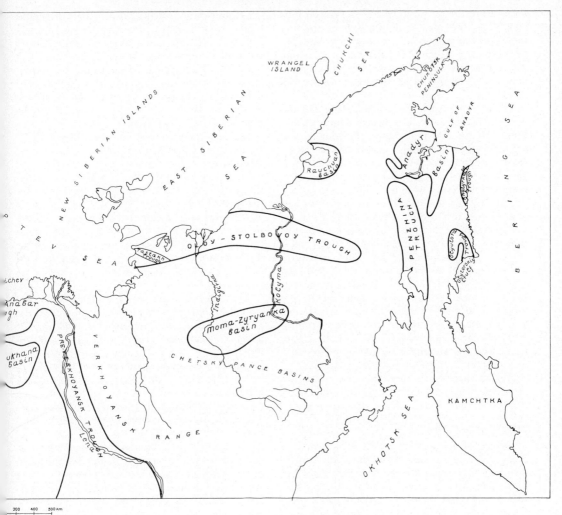

Soviet Arctic.

Oil fields discovered in Permian and Triassic deposits of the trough are small. They are related to anticlinal structures, complicated in some places by diapiric tectonism. It is believed that more favorable tectonic conditions may have existed near the trough axis; if so, large oil and gas fields may be discovered there (Kalinko, 1958).

Within the Lena-Anabar trough and in the northern part of the Pre-Verkhoyansk trough, regional oil- and gas-bearing deposits are of Permian age. The Olenek bitumen field (similar to Athabaska), the largest in North Siberia, is associated with the Permian rocks. The best reservoir-rock properties are recorded in Permian deposits on the platform side of the Lena-Anabar trough. The reservoir-rock properties become poorer toward the north.

Argillaceous members that may serve as cap-rocks for oil and gas accumulations are known both in Permian strata and in overlying Triassic deposits. Potential oil and gas areas are local anticlinal uplifts, which were discovered in the course of the geologic survey of the central parts of the troughs and of the platform flanks.

In the northern part of the Tungusska syne-clise, the thickness of the platform cover is about 5–6 km; the upper part of the section, up to 2 km thick, is composed of Triassic tuffs and lavas. The greater, lower part of the section is represented by terrigenous-carbonate upper Proterozoic–middle Paleozoic rocks and upper Paleozoic coal measures. In the sedimentary cover, several large swell-like uplifts can be traced.

The most prospective sequences are the upper Riphean–Lower Cambrian, Upper Cambrian, Upper Silurian, Lower Devonian, and Upper Devonian. These sequences, in structures bordering the syneclise, have more favorable reservoir-rock properties and higher bitumen content (Sorokov *et al.*, 1969).

The Anabar anticlise is prospective for gas and oil only in those structures where the basement crystalline rocks are submerged under terrigenous-carbonate Riphean–lower Paleozoic rocks at a depth of 2–2.5 km. Such structures are monoclines of the southern and southeastern slopes of the Anabar shield and the Sukhana trough. Within these, some swells are known. The most prospective units are terrigenous-carbonate deposits of the upper Proterozoic and carbonate rocks of the Middle-Upper Cambrian that are characterized by good reservoir properties and high bitumen content.

Abrupt changes in reservoir-rock properties along the strike suggest that stratigraphic traps may be present along with the structural traps.

NORTHEAST USSR

In the northeast of the USSR, two structural areas differing in time of folding are usually distinguished. These are the Verkhoyansk-Chukotsk area, where folding occurred during Mesozoic time, and the Koryak-Kamchatka area, where folding occurred during the Meso-Cenozoic. Among the fold systems of the Verkhoyansk-Chukotsk and Koryak-Kamchatka areas, several troughs and basins are considered prospective or possibly prospective for oil and gas. This prediction is based on general geologic considerations and, in some cases, direct oil and gas indications. Because of their structural position, these troughs and basins are isolated; some are limited in size, and some are structurally complex. However, several large structures of this type are favorable for oil and gas (Brod *et al.*, 1963).

Within the Verkhoyansk-Chukotsk area of Mesozoic folding, the Moma-Zyryanka and Rauchuan basins, and also the Oloy-Stolbovoy, Tastakh, and Mechigmen troughs, are prospective for oil and gas. The largest of these areas are the Moma-Zyryanka basin and the Oloy-Stolbovoy trough, filled with terrigenous Upper Jurassic and Lower Cretaceous rocks.

The Moma-Zyryanka basin is restricted to the southwestern edge of the Kolyma median massif. In the modern structure of the Moma-Zyryanka basin, the Moma and Indigirka-Zyryanka Early Jurassic troughs are distinguished, as well as the complex Il'in-Tasskiy anticlinorium which separates them.

Oil and gas prospects for the Indigirka-Zyryanka trough are very promising. Lower Cretaceous and Upper Jurassic strata are potential oil and gas reservoirs. Other possible accumulations are in arenaceous strata of the Upper Jurassic Batystakh Series with thicknesses up to 70–120 m; argillaceous silty sediments of the upper part of the Lower Cretaceous may serve as a regional caprock. Direct oil and gas indications are not very numerous, but general conditions for oil and gas occurrence are highly favorable.

The greater part of the Oloy-Stolbovoy trough is covered by Cenozoic sediments of the Kolyma and Primor'ye lowlands, and thus is poorly investigated. The southeastern end of the trough is known as the Oloy basin. The trough is a complex structure with a heterogeneous basement. Under the greater part of the basin, the basement is composed of dislocated rocks of Carboniferous to Middle Jurassic age. The trough is filled with Upper Jurassic and Lower Cretaceous strata that are overlain extensively by Upper Cretaceous and Paleogene volcanic rocks. Some units in this section have good reservoir properties. Argillaceous units are of middle Early Cretaceous age, and volcanic rocks are Late Cretaceous. Paleogene strata may serve as regional caprocks. The zones with oil and gas potential are the Upper Jurassic and the lower part of the Lower Cretaceous. The areas of greatest potential are the southeastern part of the trough and its northwestern extension, where the thickness of the sedimentary section is greater and the oil and gas indications are more evident.

Within the Mesozoic-Cenozoic Koryak-Kamchatka fold system, six troughs are distinguished that are interesting with respect to oil and gas potential. These are the Anadyr', Khatyrka, Penzhina, Olyutorskiy, Parapol', and Al'-katvaam troughs (Egiazarov *et al.*, 1965), most of which are rather small. The troughs are filled mainly with Upper Cretaceous, Paleogene, and Neogene terrigenous rocks from 3 to 9 km thick. In the structural pattern of the troughs, uplifts and basins are distinguished, complicated by local anticlines. Some reservoirs with sufficient interstitial porosity are present, but fracture porosity is generally required in addition in the highly compacted rocks. Oil and gas shows are most widely distributed in the Khatyrka trough.

The best investigated is the Anadyr' basin, where oil and gas exploration has recently been conducted (Agapitov et al., 1970). Because of the structural position and type of sediments, the basin may be classified as intermontane. The sediments are mainly terrigenous Cretaceous, Paleogene, and Neogene deposits with thicknesses up to 4,000 m. Within the basinal area, several large uplifts and troughs are present. Of these, the Predrarytkin trough is considered to have the most potential for oil and gas exploration. Considerable geological-geophysical investigation has been carried out in the Anadyr' basin, including the drilling of six shallow coreholes and two deep boreholes. During drilling, hydrocarbon gas "kicks" were recorded, and a gas flow came from Miocene rocks in one of the deep holes. Apart from the Neogene strata, the Paleogene and Albian–Upper Cretaceous arenaceous-argillaceous strata also may have potential for oil and gas in this basin.

The Penzhina trough is filled with a thick sequence (about 7,000 m) of Late Jurassic, Cretaceous, and Cenozoic deposits, mainly terrigenous. The central part of the trough is complicated by several large uplifts and basins. The most prospective structures for oil and gas are the Kondyrev graben; the Mayorskaya, Chernaya Rechka, and Orlovskaya basins; and the Mid-Anadyr' graben. Fracture porosity, alone and in combination with interstitial porosity, is the main type in the oil reservoirs. The upper part of the Cretaceous deposits contains favorable reservoir-rock types. Cretaceous and Paleogene deposits are considered to have potential for oil and gas.

Undoubtedly, the Khatyrka trough is prospective for oil and gas. Its onshore extent is very large, and, together with its offshore extension, the area of the trough is about 15,000 sq km. The trough is filled with terrigenous deposits of Late Cretaceous, Paleogene, and Neogene age that have a total thickness of 13–15 km. Local structures are present within the trough. Numerous bitumen indications are recorded throughout the section. Oil and gas prospects are mainly associated with Paleogene and Miocene deposits.

The Olyutorskiy, Parapol'skiy, and Al'-katvaam troughs are structurally complex, and only limited data are available regarding their oil and gas possibilities.

POLAR (ARCTIC) BASIN SHELF

Most of the major prospective structures of the continental part of the northern USSR, including those with established economic oil and gas accumulations, extend onto the shelf of the Polar basin. Numerous oil and gas indications also have been recorded in the Arctic Islands. Geological-geophysical investigations of the offshore shelf suggest favorable oil and gas prospects (Demenitskaya and Levin, 1970).

The Arctic shelf of Eurasia is the most extensive shelf in the world, both in width and in length. The greatest width, more than 1,500 km, is in the Barents Sea; it is about 800 km in the East Siberian Sea, and, at the narrowest point off the coast of Severnaya Zemlya, it is 100–150 km. The total length of the Soviet Arctic shelf is over 5,500 km, and its area is 4,400,000 sq km.

Within the Soviet Arctic, the Barents, Kara, Laptev, East Siberian and Chukotsk shelves are distinguished.

The Barents shelf is situated in the western sector of the Soviet Arctic between Novaya Zemlya on the east and Spitsbergen on the west. Its area is 1,400,000 sq km, and its average depth is 230 m. Structurally, the greatest part of the shelf belongs to the Barents plate of the Barents-Kara Epicaledonian platform, and its southeastern part belongs to the Pechora plate of the Russian platform (Atlasov et al., 1967). The Pechora plate, which is situated in the southeastern part of the Barents Sea, is a direct continuation of the mainland structure. Its folded basement is composed of Baykalian-age rocks, and the sedimentary mantle is composed of carbonate and terrigenous-carbonate Paleozoic, Mesozoic, and Cenozoic deposits with a total thickness of more than 6 km.

On the basis of geological and geophysical data, it appears that the oil and gas units distinguished on the mainland can be traced offshore at the same depths. Thus, the northern part of the Pechora plate, the offshore area, is prospective for oil and gas. This Pechora offshore area is an extension of the Timan-Pechora oil and gas region. The submarine extensions of the Malaya Zemlya arch, Kolva megaswell, Upper Kolva swell, Denisovka trough, and Khareyver basin, and the intrashelf Southern Barents basin, are considered to be the most prospective structures for oil and gas within the shelf part of the Pechora plate. The Barents plate is situated in the central and northern parts of the Barents shelf. It also includes Franz Josef Land and several islands of the Spitsbergen archipelago.

The folded basement of the Barents plate is composed largely of pre-Baykalian complexes and Caledonian structures along the southern and southeastern margins. The lower part of the sedimentary mantle of the plate is composed of Silurian to Permian carbonate deposits with a total thickness of 2.5–3 km or more; the upper part is composed of a terrigenous and terrigenous-volcanic sequence of Triassic, Jurassic, Cretaceous, and Cenozoic deposits with a total thickness up to 2–2.5 km.

Numerous shows of oil are seen in the terrigenous Mesozoic and Paleogene deposits of Spitsbergen, and bitumens are also recorded in the Upper Triassic and Lower Jurassic deposits of Franz Josef Land. The shows indicate potential for oil and gas production in the sedimentary cover of the Barents plate (Gramberg et al., 1967). The thickness of the sedimentary cover and the presence of major platform structures indicate that the part of the Barents plate underlain by pre-Baykalian basement is highly prospective for oil and gas.

The structures within the Barents plate which are considered to be most prospective for oil and gas are the Gruma Zemlya and Olga troughs and the Medvezh'ye trench. Within these structures, the potential oil and gas zones should be present at depths of 2.1 km in the troughs and up to 2.5–3 km in the trench.

The Kara Sea shelf includes the central sector of the Soviet Arctic between Vaygach Island, Novaya Zemlya, and Franz Josef Land, in the west, and Severnaya Zemlya in the east. Its area is 883,000 sq km and the water depth is generally 10–100 m, although it is as much as 300–600 m in the trenches.

Structurally, the southern part of the Kara Sea shelf is part of the West Siberian Epihercynian plate, and the northern part belongs to the Kara plate of the Barents-Kara Epicaledonian platform.

The basement of the West Siberian plate over most of the shelf is composed of lower and middle Proterozoic fold systems—Archean on the east and Hercynian along the margins (Pay-Khoy, Novaya Zemlya, and Taymyr).

The portion of the West Siberian plate within the Kara shelf is a direct continuation of the West Siberian oil and gas province. The structures of the Yamal-Gydanskiy and South Yamal oil and gas provinces, which include the major Novyy Port and Arctic oil and gas fields, are known to extend into this region. Productive and potential oil and gas units of Jurassic and Cretaceous age occur on the shelf at depths up to 5 km. Thus, the oil and gas possibilities of the West Siberian shelf are very high. The most prospective oil and gas structures are the submarine continuations of the Murma and Gydanskiy swells and the Yamal arch, the intrashelf West Kara uplift, the Sverdrup trough, and the West Kara basin.

The Kara plate is the eastern part of the Barents-Kara platform. It is bounded on the south by the Novaya Zemlya Hercynides, on the west and east by the early Proterozoic Barents megaswell and Severnaya Zemlya structures, respectively, and on the north by the continental slope.

The basement of the Kara plate is composed of rocks of the Caledonides. The lower part of the sedimentary cover of the plate is composed of terrigenous-carbonate Devonian deposits and possibly Lower Carboniferous deposits; total thickness of these rocks is more than 1,700 m. The upper part of the cover is composed of terrigenous Triassic and Jurassic deposits and terrigenous-volcanic Lower Cretaceous strata with a total thickness of more than 2 km.

In the clastic-carbonate Devonian deposits on Pioneer (Pioner), Komsomolets, and October Revolution (Oktyabr'skoy Revolyutsii) Islands, an increased bitumen content is recorded and inclusions of hard and semifluid bitumens are common. Sandstones with good porosity and permeability are present also. Tar-sand occurrences are widespread in clastic Triassic and Jurassic deposits in Franz Josef Land (Gramberg et al., 1967). The presence of the thick Devonian to Cretaceous sedimentary cover and of major platform structures within the Kara plate, together with bitumen occurrences on the islands, gives the Kara plate high potential for petroleum. The most potential structures for oil and gas are the Uyedineniye and Shmidta troughs. The Ushakova uplift and the Central Kara megaswell are less prospective. The depths of Devonian deposits with oil and gas potential range from 2 km on the uplifts to 2.5–3 km in the troughs.

The Laptev shelf is situated in the central sector of the Soviet Arctic, between the Taymyr peninsula on the west and the New Siberian Islands on the east. Its area is 650,000 sq km, and the water depths are 50–100 m and, on the continental slope, 200–1,000 m.

The greater part of the shelf is structurally a part of the Laptev block of the Siberian platform. However, the southern margin belongs to the Verkhoyansk-Kolyma fold system, and the eastern margin is part of the New Siberian–Chukotsk fold system; both of these fold systems are Mesozoic (Atlasov et al., 1967).

The basement of the Laptev block is composed of the lower Proterozoic folded rocks. The sedimentary cover is composed mainly of (1) carbonate deposits of the upper Proterozoic and lower and middle Paleozoic with a total thickness of at least 4–5 km and (2) terrigenous Upper Cretaceous and Cenozoic strata with a total thickness of 0.5–1 km. Along the southern margin of the block, terrigenous Permian and Triassic units have thicknesses up to 2–3 km; Jurassic and Lower Cretaceous strata have a thickness of at least 3 km.

The structures of the Verkhoyansk-Kolyma and New Siberian–Chukotsk fold systems within the shelf are almost completely covered by unconsolidated deposits, and are exposed only on the islands. These mainly unconsolidated deposits are chiefly terrigenous Upper Cretaceous and Cenozoic units with a thickness of about 0.5 km on the uplifts and up to 3 km in the troughs and grabens. The geologic-tectonic, geophysical, and geographical data indicate that most of the Laptev shelf is unfavorable for major hydrocarbon occurrences because of intense disjunctive tectonism (folding and faulting). However, opinions regarding the petroleum potential of the South Laptev trough and the northern part of the Oloy-Stolbovoy trough are more optimistic.

The South Laptev intrashelf trough of the Laptev block is similar to the Lena-Anabar trough in its stratigraphic section, thickness, lithology, and geologic history. By analogy with the Anabar trough, the Permian and Triassic deposits that occur at a depth of 3–4 km may be considered as the most prospective strata in this basin.

The Oloy-Stolbovoy trough is typical of the superimposed troughs of the Mesozoic fold system. Its northern part, located in the East Siberian Sea, contains terrigenous Upper Jurassic and Lower Cretaceous strata which may have potential for oil and gas. The thickness of these deposits is 2–3 km. They are exposed on Stolbovoy Island, but in the offshore they occur at a depth of 0.5–1 km.

The East Siberian and Chukotsk shelves are situated in the eastern sector of the Arctic between the longitudes of Boyshoy Lyakhovskoy

Island and Kotel'nyy Island in the west and Point Barrow, Alaska, in the east. The border between these seas follows the longitudes of Wrangel Island. The sea areas are 900,000 and 500,000 sq km, respectively, and average water depths are 58 m and 88 m.

Structurally, the western part of the East Siberian shelf and the southern part of the Chukchi Sea belong to the New Siberian Mesozoic fold system, and the remaining parts belong to the South Hyperborean block (Atlasov et al., 1967).

SOUTH HYPERBOREAN PLATFORM

The South Hyperborean platform includes the northeast Laptev Sea and the northern East Siberian and Chukchi Seas. The North Slope of Alaska also is thought to be a part of the South Hyperborean platform. Thus, the Chukchi Sea, East Siberian Sea, and Laptev Sea areas are a western extension of the Alaskan North Slope province. The folded basement of the South Hyperborean block is formed by metamorphic rocks of pre-Riphean age which are exposed on the Shatsky massif (Chukotsk dome). The sedimentary cover of the platform is composed of clastic and clastic-carbonate deposits of late Proterozoic and early Paleozoic age. Thickness is as much as 3 km in the lower part, which consists of clastic deposits of middle and late(?) Paleozoic, Triassic, Jurassic, and Early Cretaceous ages. Thicknesses are 3–5 km in the middle part, which consists of terrigenous Late Cretaceous and Cenozoic deposits. The upper part has thicknesses of 0.5–3 km.

There have been no oil and gas occurrences recorded within the South Hyperborean block in the Soviet Arctic. However, in the Arctic plains of northern Alaska, which also forms part of the Hyperborean platform, oil and gas fields have been discovered in Triassic, Jurassic, and Cretaceous rocks (Bogdanov et al., 1969). Thus, a similar potential for oil and gas occurrence is suggested for the platform cover of the South Hyperborean block and for part of the Chukotsk–East Siberian trough and other basins. The depth range for prospective Triassic strata is 2–3 km on the uplifts and 4–5 km in the troughs; the depth of the Jurassic and Cretaceous rocks is 2–3 and 3–4 km, respectively. Greater potential for oil and gas occurrence within the South Hyperborean block possibly lies in Upper Cretaceous and Paleogene terrigenous rocks, which are 2–3 km thick (and thicker in the troughs). Terrigenous deposits of middle and late Paleozoic age are present on the structural swells of the Wrangel uplift.

NEW SIBERIAN–CHUKOTSK FOLD SYSTEM

The New Siberian–Chukotsk fold system of Mesozoic age is exposed only in the islands; in the shelf, the Mesozoic folds are overlain by a terrigenous and terrigenous-volcanic sheet of unconsolidated deposits of Late Cretaceous and Cenozoic age. The thickness of this sheet ranges from 0 to 6 km.

The continuations of the Rauchuan basin and the Oloy-Stolbovoy troughs of the continent have been traced into the structure of the adjacent shelf. Furthermore, the intrashelf uplifts (DeLong and Ayon), the East Siberian basin, and the South Chukotsk trough are also recognized there.

Oil and gas shows within rocks of the Mesozoic fold belt of the East Siberian and Chukchi shelves are recorded only on Kotel'nyy Island (New Siberian Islands) and Wrangel Island (Gramberg et al., 1969). On Kotel'nyy Island, oil shows are known throughout the Paleozoic and Triassic section, but they are most intensive (bitumen content, 0.5–1.2 percent) in a Devonian carbonate unit. On Wrangel Island, bitumen occurrences are recorded only in Lower Carboniferous limestones.

On the basis of all these data, as well as the degree of deformation of the strata, the East Siberian and Rauchuan basins (the northern parts) are designated as potential oil and gas areas of the East Siberian Sea shelf within the Mesozoic fold system, and the South Chukotsk trough is designated as a potential oil and gas area within the Chukchi Sea shelf.

The East Siberian basin includes the greatest part of the East Siberian Sea shelf, New Siberian Islands, Zemlya Bunge, Faddeyevskiy Island, and the eastern part of Kotel'nyy Island. It is filled with terrigenous deposits of Late Cretaceous and Cenozoic age with a total thickness up to 4–6 km. The inner structure of the basin is complicated by several major, but gentle, troughs and uplifts. Upper Cretaceous and Paleogene rocks lying at depths of 1–5 km are considered to have oil and gas potential.

The northern part of the Rauchuan basin includes the Chaun Bay, Ayon Island, and a part of the East Siberian Sea shelf. It is filled with terrigenous deposits of Late Jurassic, Cretaceous, and Cenozoic ages with a total thickness up to 3–4 km. The Upper Jurassic and Lower Cretaceous units, according to their formational features, belong to the marine molasse deposits, and the basin is an intermontane type. Although the inner structure of the basin has not been studied, the maximum downwarping apparently is restricted to the shelf part. The Lower Cretaceous rocks, at depths of not more than 2 km, may also be oil and gas bearing.

The South Chukotsk trough is situated in the southern part of the Chukchi Sea. It is composed of terrigenous Upper Cretaceous and Cenozoic deposits with a total thickness of 2–4 km. Several local uplifts and basins are present within the trough. Oil and gas potential in this basin is assigned to Upper Cretaceous and Paleogene strata occurring no deeper than 2–3 km.

SUMMARY

This analysis of the geologic structure of the Soviet Arctic territory and offshore suggests that extensive structures (plates, platforms, fold areas) are developed within this area. The geologic history of the structures is characterized by steady subsidence and accumulation of thick sedimentary sequences with subsequent geotectonic modification which produced structures favorable for accumulation and preservation of large oil and gas deposits. The economic accumulations of oil and gas in some of these structures (Pechora and West Siberian plates) are confirmed. It is possible that the magnitude of the oil and gas potential in other major structures will be determined in the near future.

REFERENCES

Agapitov, D. I., *et al.*, 1970, Rezultatiy geologorazvedochnykh rabot na neft i gaz v Anadyrskoy vpadine i zadachi dalneyshikh issledovaniy: Geologiya Nefti i Gaza, no. 8, p. 22–25.

Atlasov, I. P., *et al.*, 1967, Tektonicheskaya karta Arktiki i Subarktiki (Tectonic map of the Arctic and Subarctic): 22d Internat. Geol. Cong., New Delhi, Comm. Geol. Map World, Sci. Commun., Vesoul, France, Imprimerie Marcel Bon; also published in Moscow, Izd. "Nauka," p. 154–165.

Bogdanov, N. A., and A. A. Geodokyan, 1969, Alaskinskaya nauchnaya konferentsiya na temu "Chelovek, neft i priroda": Akad. Nauk SSSR Vestnik, no. 12, p. 106–107.

Brod, I. O., *et al.*, 1963, Izvestnyye i vozmozhnyye neftegasonosnyye basseyny Dalnego Vostoka, Severo-Vostoka SSSR i sopredelnykh territory Yakutska i Alyaski, *in* "Problemy Sibirskoy nefti": Novosibirsk, Akad. Nauk SSSR Sibirskoye Otdeleniye, p. 151–163.

Chochia, N. D., *et al.*, 1968, Geologicheskoye stroyeniye i prognoz neftegazonosnosti Severa Zapadnoy Sibiri: Vses. Neft. Nauchno-Issled. Geol.-Razved. Inst. Trudy, no. 263; Leningrad, Izd. "Nedra," 240 p.

Demenitskaya, P. M., and L. E. Levin, 1970, Tektonika i neftgazonosnost' okrainnykh i vnutrennikh morey SSSR: Leningrad, Izd. "Nedra," p. 252–272.

Egiazarov, B. Kh., 1969, Geologicheskoye stroyeniye Alyaski i Aleutskikh ostrovov, *in* Suranitelnaya kharakteristika s sopredelnymi regionami Severo-Vostoka Azii: Leningrad, Izd. "Nedra," 264 p.

――― *et al.*, 1965, Geologiya i poleznyye iskopayemyye Koryakskogo nagorya: Inst. Geologii Arktiki Trudy, v. 148; Leningrad, Izd. "Nedra," 342 p.

――― *et al.*, 1967, Perspektivy neftegazonosnosti tsentral'nogo sektora Sovetskoy Arktiki: Nauchno-Issled. Inst. Geologii Arktiki, Uchenyye Zapiski, Regional'naya Geologiya, no. 2, p, 27–40.

Gramberg, I. S., D. S. Sorokov, and D. V. Lazurkin, 1969, Zadachi i napravleniya regionalnykh geologogeofizicheskikh rabot na neft i gaz v arkticheskoy chasti Vostochoy Sibiri na 1971–1980: Geologiya Nefti i Gaza, no. 2, p. 27–31.

Gurari, F. G., *et al.*, 1963, Geologiya i neftegazonosnosti Zapadno-Sibirskoy nizmennosti novoy neftyanoy bazy SSSR: Novosibirsk, Akad. Nauk SSSR Sibirskoye Otdeleniye, 200 p.

Kalinko, M. K., 1959, Istoriya geologicheskogo razvitiya i perspektivy neftegazonosnosti Khatangskoy vpadiny: Inst. Geologii Arktiki Trudy, v. 104, 360 p.

Karta Perspektiv Neftegazonosnosti SSSR, 1969, Po sostoyaniyu na 1 yanvarya 1967: Moscow, scale 1: 5,000,000. Glavn. upr. geodezii i kartografii pri Sovete Ministrov SSSR.

Krems, A. Ya., D. G. Begun, and M. Sh. Modelevsky, 1968, Neftyanyye mestorozhdeniya Timano-Pechorskoy neftegazonosnoy oblasti: Geologiya Nefti i Gaza, v. 2, pt. 1., Izd. "Nedra," p. 228–251.

Rudkevich, M. Ya., N. Kh. Kulakhmetov, and E. M. Maksimov, 1970, Perspektivy neftenosnosti nizhnemelovykh i yurskikh otlozheny Severa Tumenskoy oblasti: Geologiya Nefti i Gaza, no. 8, p. 1–9.

Sorokov, D. S., *et al.*, 1969, Geologiya i prognoz neftegazonosnosti Severo-Zapadnoy Sibirskoy platformy: Inst. Geologii Arktiki Trudy, v. 160; Leningrad, Izd. "Nedra," 264 p.

Vasil'yev, V. G., *et al.*, 1968, Perspektivy neftegazonosnosti Vostochno-Sibirskoy platformy: Moscow, Izd. "Nedra," 131 p.

Vendian of Northern Eurasia[1]

B. S. SOKOLOV[2]

Novosibirsk, USSR

Abstract Recent studies allow refinement of the principal Vendian stratigraphic standard of the Russian platform. The Vendian, which was established 20 years ago as the youngest sedimentary complex of the upper Precambrian of the Russian platform, is significant in correlation of upper Precambrian rocks on a wide scale. Peculiar geologic features of the Vendian, its structural and stratigraphic position, and its stratigraphic boundaries and subdivisions are in many respects comparable with upper Precambrian rocks of other regions and continents. The Vendian is also significant in determination of the position of a main glacial formation, in recording the earliest appearance of an Ediacaran-type fauna and in the relation of this fauna with a paleontologic succession of the oldest Precambrian, and in isotopic-age characteristics. All these features are of more universal importance than are facies characteristics of the formations composing the Vendian (and its equivalents); thus, the Vendian of the Russian platform has rapidly become a most significant time-stratigraphic standard.

Although the Vendian is represented by terrigenous deposits on the Russian platform and by carbonate and carbonate-terrigenous deposits on the Siberian platform, it undoubtedly represents an important, separate stage in the geologic history of the earth. At the transition from the Vendian to the Cambrian, an important biologic change took place which resulted in the appearance of skeletal-building properties of organic parts of animals. The significance of such a succession is worldwide. It is concluded that the Vendian represents the beginning of the Phanerozoic—not the close of the Cryptozoic—and is more closely related to the Paleozoic, though formally it is not included in that era.

INTRODUCTION

The Vendian was established as the youngest sedimentary complex of the upper Precambrian of the Russian platform in the USSR 20 years ago (Sokolov, 1952). It directly underlies the oldest fossiliferous Early Cambrian deposits, the well-known "Baltic blue clays." The paleontologic content of the latter (sabelliditids; hyolithids; sedentary annelids; scarce, inarticulate problematic *Mobergella; Gdowia;* and others) and the isotopic age (554 m.y.) of glauconitic sandstones which form the base of the "blue clays" leave no doubt that the basal stratigraphic unit of the Lower Cambrian is represented on the Russian platform by pre-trilobite strata (sub-*Holmia* beds) deposited before the Baltic Stage (Sokolov, 1965). The time range of the unit does not exceed that of the Tommotian Stage of the Siberian platform (Rosanov, 1966).

The Vendian and Early Cambrian of the Russian platform (Fig. 1) belong to the same stage of geologic development, though there was a short hiatus (Mens and Pirrus, 1969–1970) in some places—in particular, the western margin of the basin—between deposition of the Vendian Kotlin clays (also called "Laminarites clays") and the Baltic Series. As a whole, however, the Vendian-Baltic succession appears to be essentially complete over the entire Baltic-Moscow syneclise and in Volhyno-Podolia. It is characterized by the general correlation of upper Valday strata with beds bearing the ribbonlike algae *Vendotaenia* and the especially persistent *Sabellidites cambriensis* Yan. These beds are typically developed in the suburbs of Leningrad and in the Volhyn and Dniester areas, and are reported from the base of the Early Cambrian (Baltic) transgressive sequence over the entire Russian platform.

Thus, the Precambrian position of the Vendian is certain, and the boundary between the Vendian and the Baltic Series on the Russian platform is fundamental to delimiting the Precambrian-Cambrian boundary. The section is represented by epicontinental marine terrigenous deposits yielding a rich flora of microphytoplankton and brown algae and a relatively poor fauna of nonskeletal organisms (Vendian) and the first skeletal Cambrian organisms (Baltic Series). The northwestern Black Sea area and the most stable zones of the Baltic-Moscow syneclise are of utmost interest for the study of Vendian-Cambrian boundary deposits, because the time gap there was apparently insignificant.

The lower boundary of the Vendian is not as definite. It has been established on historic-geologic principles. In contrast to the more ancient late Proterozoic deposits (Riphean) which occupy only part of the narrow aulacogenes of the miogeosynclinal areas on the margin of the Russian platform (Sokolov, 1964; I-

[1] Manuscript received, April 30, 1972.

[2] Institute of Geology and Geophysics, Siberian Branch, USSR Academy of Sciences.

golkina *et al.*, 1970), the Vendian, especially its upper subdivision, is widely distributed in this most ancient sedimentary cover and testifies to the beginning of a new stage in structural evolution of the platform. This most important geologic peculiarity of the Vendian has made it an especially popular topic for study and has led to the extension of the Vendian concept beyond the Russian platform, and even beyond the borders of the USSR. However, it is quite evident that the succession of stages (both tectonic and organic stages of evolution) is not marked by definite chronologic limits. Stage succession is everywhere a gradational process taking place at different times in different areas. Therefore, the search for a stratigraphic division between the Vendian and the Riphean must be based on more critical methods of stratigraphic correlation—*i.e.*, paleontology, isotopic dating, paleoclimatology, *etc.*

The Vendian, as is true of any large stratigraphic subdivision, has no single stratotype, but the Baltic-Moscow syneclise and the Volhyno-Podolian depression on the Russian platform may be considered type areas for its main subdivisions. Hundreds of different investigations have dealt with the Vendian of these regions. The most recent studies (Aksenov and Volkova, 1969; Bessonova and Chumakov, 1968; Bukatchuk, 1969; Zayka-Novatsky *et al.*, 1969; Kirsanov, 1968, 1970; Makhnach and Veretennikov, 1970; Solontsov and Aksenov, 1970; and many others) and the latest observations allow refinement of the principal Vendian stratigraphic standard of the Russian platform (Table 1).

Only a few of the numerous regional stratigraphic subdivisions recognized in the Vendian of the Russian platform are given to illustrate the extent of these series.

Some workers assign to the lower Vendian only the Volhyn Formation, which includes Vilchany and Pachel'ma tillites and variegated volcanic-sedimentary rocks, but others consider as Vendian the typically aulacogenic Pachel'ma Series. The age of the latter, based on dating of glauconite, is 630–765 m.y. (Keller and Semikhatov, 1967). This age is close to that of the Pugachev Series of the Transvolga area (up to 770 m.y.), from which the so-called IV (Yudomian) microphytolite assemblage is known. An equivalent microphytolite assemblage is also found in the upper Byelorussian Polessiye Series, the age of which is undoubtedly 700–720 m.y. or more (Semenenko and Tkachuk, 1970).

The arising contradiction between the isotopic and paleontologic ages of these deposits shows the need for caution in considering the Pachel'ma Series as Vendian—and especially in considering the upper dolomites of the Pugachev and Polessiye Series as Vendian, because the Yudomian microphytolite assemblage is dated as 650–675 m.y. or less in the stratotype. However, a probable explanation of the contradiction comes from new studies of the Siberian microphytolites. It was found that several Yudomian microphytolite "species" appear for the first time in the upper Riphean (*e.g.*, the Dashka Formation of Yenisey Range); to make conclusions about age, it is necessary to use a large assemblage of forms (Yakshin, 1970). The assumption that the Yudomian forms exhibit homotaxial relations already has been proposed; that they should be found on the Russian platform also has been proposed (Zhuravleva and Chumakov, 1968). Now those assumptions have been confirmed. Consequently, the tillite-bearing deposits on the Russian platform should be assigned to the lower Vendian.

Because the age of upper Pachel'ma glauconites is determined now as 670–680 m.y. (Harris and Postnikov, 1970)—*i.e.*, close to the age of the pre-Yudomian Ingili intrusion (650–680 m.y.)—the Volhyn Formation must correlate with the lower Yudomian complex (635–650 m.y.; Semikhatov *et al.*, 1970) of the Siberian platform. The data on absolute age of the Volhyn Formation are scarce, but the age of basalts of the Volhyn Formation of Pripyat' swell (640 m.y.; Harris and Postnikov, 1970) correlates well with the figures mentioned.

VOLHYN FORMATION

The oldest of the rock sequences in the Vendian appears to be the Volhyn Formation. There apparently is no evidence that the Kamenka Formation of the Dniester area (the age of its main components is as much as 1,020 m.y.; Kazakov *et al.*, 1970) should be included in the Volhyn. The rocks associated with the Dniester aulacogene undoubtedly belong to the Riphean and have equivalents in more northern regions, where their age was determined as 810 and 850–1,120 m.y. The age of rocks in the same narrow zone of the Olchedayev and Lomozov Beds (Mogilev Formation *s.s.*) is now disputable; glacial structural features indicate correlation with a tillite part of the Volhyn, but the isotopic age of the Lomozov glauconite

(800 m.y.) is at variance with the age of the tillite.

In the Dniester area, the writer considers the Yaryshev Formation, with the Yampol' sandstones at the base transgressively overlying all of the older formations down to the basement, as an equivalent of the Volhyn of the Moscow syneclise (Yartsevo Formation). This part of the section (tuff-argillites and sandstones; Bukatchuk, 1969; Zayka-Novatsky, 1969) is of utmost interest because it is associated with the oldest Vendian faunal assemblage of the Ediacaran type. Impressions of abundant and diverse medusoids (*Cyclomedusa, Bronicella, Beltanella, etc.*), problematic articulates, and true imprints of life activity of creeping organisms are found in these rocks. Microphytoplankton is poorly known, and *Vendotaenia* algae are absent. Evidence of a younger age for the Yaryshev Formation consists only of age determinations of glauconites from the Bernashev sandstone (520 m.y.), which must be checked. It is interesting to note that, from the dolomite bands of the Yartsevo Formation in the Pachel'ma trough, Z. A. Zhuravleva reported microphytolites which, in her opinion, are more characteristic of the lower Yudomian assemblage of Siberia—*i.e., Vesicularites concretus* Z. Zhur. and *Volvatella zonalis* Nar.

The interpretation that, in content and age, the Volhyn Formation closely resembles the Mogilev-Podolian Series of the Dniester area is in good agreement with considerations about the correlation of the overlying upper Vendian deposits. The Valday Series is commonly assigned to the Volhyn. At the base of the Valday, according to Sokolov (1952) and others, is the Gdov Formation of the Baltic Sea area; other workers consider the underlying Redkino strata of the Moscow syneclise to be the base of the Valday (Postnikova and Kirsanov, 1970); still others believe that the Gdov and the Redkino are contemporaneous (Kirsanov, 1970). However, the Redkino originally was recognized (Kopeliovich, 1951) as a unit commensurate in rank with the Valday Series, and considerable study has now shown the correctness of this viewpoint. Therefore, the writer believes the Redkino should be considered as a separate pre-Valday series of the lower part of the upper Vendian.

REDKINO SERIES

Over the entire Russian platform, the Redkino Series has a transgressive contact with underlying sequences, and, in many places north of the Moscow graben, which contains a 3,500-m thickness of the unique Riphean-Vendian section, it lies directly on the basement. In different parts of the platform, it appears to contain one, two, or three formations (central region, Verkhnyaya Kama trough). On the basis of the peculiar lithologic features (structure of submarine slumps, ash tuff, dark siltstones with phosphorite nodules, *etc.*) and of microphytoplankton, this series is well correlated as far as the eastern regions of the platform (*e.g.*, with the Kairovo and Kirsan Formations). In the southwest part of the platform, the section equivalent to the Redkino is a thick (up to 280 m) sequence of rocks including the transgressive Dzhurzhevka sandstone at the base, the overlying Kal'ya phosphorite-bearing argillites, and the Solkutska beds of Moldavia at the top.

The Redkino Series marks the appearance of widespread peculiar *Vendotaenia* flora (ribbonlike brown algae), remains of which are well documented in the literature as "laminarite films" or *"Laminarites" antiquissimus* Eichw. These oldest marine plants with noncalcified thalli are preserved abundantly in places (especially in the Valday Series) and are characterized by perfect preservation of plant tissue. Equally important are paleozoologic findings in the Redkino Series—*i.e.*, mass accumulations of imprints of small medusoids of *Beltanelloides sorichevae* Sok. and other forms, abundant annelid tracks, and the first occur-

---

＞＞＞→

FIG. 1—Paleogeographic scheme for USSR in Vendian time (675 ± 25 to 570 ± 10 m.y.). 1—mountains; 2—plains; 3—accumulative lowlands; 4–17—zones of preferential accumulation; 4—pebble beds; 5—sandstones; 6—claystones and aleurolites; 7—sandstones, aleurolites, and claystones; 8—carbonate-terrigenous sediments; 9—limestones; 10—dolomites; 11—limestones, sandstones, and aleurolites; 12—dolomites sandstones, and aleurolites; 13—limestones and claystones; 14—dolomites and claystones; 15—siliceous rocks; 16—effusive-sedimentary series of intermediate mafic composition; 17—same series of persilicic composition; 18—tillite-like rocks; 19—inclusions of (a) halite, (b) gypsum; 20—land and sea boundary; 21—contour area of episodic uplifts and appearance of lagoons; 22—volcanic island arcs (ophiolite belts); 23—supposed glaciers; 24—main directions of transportation; 25—areas of absence of deposits of given age; indices show superposition of deposits; 26—certain isopach lines (in km); 27—thickness (in km); 28—Paleozoic Talasso-Fergana shift.

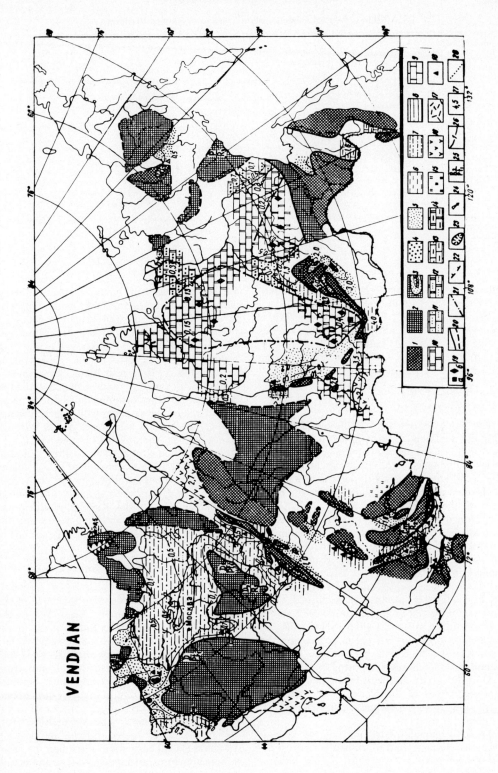

Table 1. General Correlations of Vendian of Russian Platform

Lower Cambrian:
  Baltic Series, *Sabellitides cambriensis* beds.

Vendian:

General	Western and Central Russian Platform	Southwestern Russian Platform*
3. Valday Series (thickness 100–400 m)	Kotlin Fm. *s.l.* and other formations Gdov Fm.	Vishnevka Fm. Komarovo Fm. Sokolets Fm.
2. Redkino Series (thickness 100–400 m)	Borodino Fm. Nelidovo Fm. Vyasma Fm. (=Pletenevo Fm.)	Solkutska Fm. Kal'ya Fm. Dzhurzhevka Fm. (=Ataki ss.)
1. Volhyn (Mogilev-Podolian) Series (thickness 120–400 m)	Svisloch Fm. (=Yartsevo) Vilchany Fm. (=Toropets Fm.)	Yaryshev Fm. (including Yampol' ss.) Mogilev Fm. *s.s.*

Riphean:
  Pachel'ma Series (thickness up to 700 m).

* Ukraine and Moldavia.

---

rences of trilobitomorph scars of *Vendia sokolovi* Keller (in the middle Redkino Series).

The isotopic age of glauconites from several sections of the lower part of the Redkino Series is 595–607 m.y. (Aksenov, 1967; Kirsanov, 1968b; and others), which coincides with the age of the Asha Formation of the southern Urals.

VALDAY SERIES

The Valday Series is rather closely associated with the Redkino Series (in the southwestern part of the platform, the equivalent Avdarmin Series is undivided) and covers the same area. The well-known Gdov Formation (gritstones, sandstones, claystones) is equivalent to the basal part of the main Kotlin Formation in the northwest part of the platform. There are well-layered claystones and siltstones with films of sapropelitic material. The facies boundary of the Gdov and the overlying Kotlin strata changes in age from place to place. Therefore, in the Moscow syneclise, only the complex Kotlin Formation is usually distinguished. The most complete outcrops are found in Lyubim (parastratotype of the Valday Series). P. D. Bukatchuk (1969) is correct in correlating the Gdov-Kotlin section with the Sokolets and Ferapont'yev (Komarovo) Formations of the southwestern part of the Russian platform. In the eastern part of the platform, the Shkapov Formation is approximately correlative with the named formations.

All the regional subdivisions of the Valday Series are characterized by ribbonlike brown algae (*Vendotaenia, Tyrasotaenia,* and others; Gnilovskaya, 1971) and numerous tracks of nonskeletal organisms, mainly annelids. Fragments of imprints of the *Plagiogmus* type also have been found, as well as *Dictyonema*-like structures in sandstones of the Ataki area that were discovered by I. M. Sukhov.

The youngest deposits of the Valday Series occur in the northwestern Black Sea area (the Vishnevka Formation) and in the central Moscow syneclise (the Reshman Formation); Kotlin variegated claystones with algae (*Tyrasotaenia*) and quartz sandstones of the Voronka River area near the town of Lomonosov occupy almost the same stratigraphic position. The isotopic age of glauconitic sandstones of the Valday Series at different stratigraphic levels ranges from 570 to 620 m.y. In general, the position of the Vendian on the Russian platform between the top of the Pachel'ma Series and the base of the Baltic Series fixes its age at 570 to 670 m.y.

VENDIAN OF RUSSIAN PLATFORM (AND SIBERIAN PLATFORM)

The thick, complex Vendian sequence of the Russian platform—from the Black Sea to the Barents Sea and from the Polish plain to the Urals—belongs to some of the best-known late Precambrian complexes. Peculiar geologic features of the Vendian, its structural and stratigraphic position, and its stratigraphic boundaries and subdivisions are in many respects comparable with late Precambrian rocks of other regions and continents. The Vendian has further significance in regard to fixing the position of a main glacial formation, recording the earliest appearance of an Ediacaran-type fauna and showing its relation to a paleontologic suc-

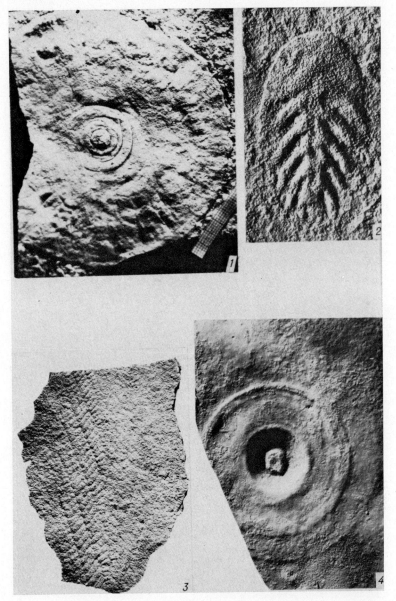

FIG. 2—Vendian fossils.

No. 1 *Cyclomedusa plana* Glaessner and Wade, 1966 (×1). Lower Vendian, Mogilev-Podolian Series, Yaryshev Formation, Bernashevka Beds; Podolia, Mogilev-Podolsk suburbs, village of Serebria. Imprint on sandstone, 95 mm diameter. Kiev University, Paleontologic Museum (coll. of V. S. Zayka-Novatsky, No. 1710, 1967).

No. 2. *Vendia sokolovi* Keller, 1969 (*in* Sokolov, 1965), holotype (×4). Upper Vendian, Redkino Series, Nelidovo Formation; north part of Russian platform, Yarensk, borehole. Arthropod imprint on argillite, 14 mm length. Geologic Institute of USSR Academy of Sciences, Moscow (coll. of B. M. Keller, No. 3593/1, 1961).

No. 3. "*Rangea*" *sibirica* Sokolov, 1972, holotype (×1). Lower Vendian, Khatyspyt Formation; Olenek uplift, Khorbusuonka River (discovered by T. N. Kopylova, 1959). Imprint on aleurite shale. Fragment length, 76 mm; width, about 36 mm; axial line slightly curved; angle between primary lateral branches (polyps?) is about 35-40°, branch width is 5-6 mm, and number of "segments" (siphonozoids?) in branches is up to 25. Institute of Geology and Geophysics, Siberian Branch of USSR Academy of Sciences.

No. 4. *Charniodiscus planus* Sokolov, 1972, holotype (×1). Lower Vendian, Mogilev-Podolian Series, Yaryshev Formation, Bronitsa Beds; Mogilev-Podolsk, Borshchov ravine (coll. of B. S. Sokolov, 1969). Disklike imprint with axial boss, diameter about 72 mm. Institute of Geology and Geophysics, Siberian Branch of USSR Academy of Sciences.

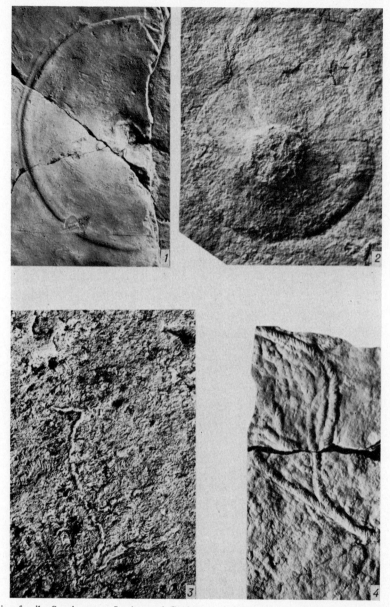

Fɪɢ. 3—Vendian fossils. Specimens at Institute of Geology and Geophysics, Siberian Branch of USSR Academy of Sciences.

No. 1. *Planomedusites grandis* Sokolov, 1972, holotype (×⅔). Lower Vendian, Mogilev-Podolian Series, Yaryshev Formation, Bronitsa Beds; Mogilev-Podolsk, Borshchov ravine (coll. of B. S. Sokolov, 1969). Disklike medusoid organism, smooth surface with peripheral ridge, diameter about 125 mm.

No. 2. *Medusinites patellaris* Sokolov, 1972, holotype (×1). Age and occurence are same. Medusoid patelloid organism with wide central disk (20 mm), from which radial furrows are faintly outlined; diameter about 65 mm.

No. 3. Traces of mud-eater life activity (×1). Age and occurrence are same.

No. 4. *Harlaniella podolica* Sokolov, 1972, holotype (×1). Upper Vendian, upper part, Valday Series, Komarovo Formation; Podolia, Dniester River at mouth of Ushiza River (coll. of B. S. Sokolov, 1969). Curving, lashlike, slightly twisted forms with distinct oblique wrinkles, similar to transverse wrinkles of *Harlania-Arthrophycus;* lash length, up to 100 mm and more, diameter 3-4 mm, wrinkle width 0.5-0.8 mm; probably belong to traces of annelid activity.

Table 2. General Correlation of Yudomian (Vendian) of Siberian Platform

Lower Cambrian:
  Tommotian Stage, Sunnagin Horizon.

Vendian (= Yudomian complex); thickness up to 360–1,100 m:

Yudoma-Maya Region	Anabar Massif	Olenek Uplift	Baykal-Patom Area
2. Upper Yudomian subcomplex	Nemakit-Daldyn Horizon	Turkut Fm.	Irkutsk Horizon
1. Lower Yudomian subcomplex	Staraya Rechka Fm.	Khatyspyt Fm. Maastakh Fm.	Moty Horizon

Riphean:
  Baykalian complex

cession of the oldest Precambrian, and determining isotopic-age characteristics. These features are of more universal importance than are facies characteristics of the formations composing the Vendian (and its equivalents), and they explain why the Vendian of the Russian platform has so rapidly acquired its role as a most significant time-stratigraphic standard.

The Vendian sequence of the Siberian platform is characterized by predominantly carbonate strata in contact with the Cambrian. However, the presence of some carbonate-terrigenous facies containing an Ediacaran fauna (Glaessner, 1963; Glaessner and Wade, 1966; and others) makes it easier to correlate Siberian sections with those of the Russian platform and of ancient Gondwana, where the Ediacaran fauna is best known.

YUDOMIAN COMPLEX OF SIBERIAN PLATFORM

The Yudomian complex of the Siberian platform is a complete stratigraphic equivalent of the Vendian. This conclusion is based on many recent regional and biostratigraphic studies (Datsenko *et al.*, 1968; Egorova and Savitsky, 1969; Kaban'kov, 1968; Khomentovsky *et al.*, 1969; Komar, 1966; Korolyuk and Sidorov, 1969; Nuzhnov, 1967; Postnikov and Postnikova, 1968; Rozanov *et al.*, 1969; Savitsky *et al.*, 1968; Semikhatov *et al.*, 1970; Titorenko, 1970; Tkachenko, 1970; Yakshin, 1970; Zharkov and Khomentovsky, 1965; Zhuravleva, 1964; and many others). Some workers (V. E. Savitsky *et al.*, 1968) think there is no need to separate the Yudomian complex from the Lower Cambrian because of the close historic-geologic similarity of the two sequences. Others (Dragunov, 1967; Musatov, 1966) prefer to consider the base of the "Siberian Vendian" to be at the 800-m.y. level and to consider the Yudomian complex as upper Vendian exclusively.

However, on the basis of study of the old sedimentary cover of the Russian platform, the Vendian stratigraphic position is taken by the Yudoma Formation and its stratigraphic equivalents of the Yudoma-Maya region. The approximate correlations are shown in Table 2.

The Yudomian complex lies with transgressive contact on pre-Yudomian deposits, including crystalline basement. Its basal beds in different parts of the platform are of different ages. A more or less noticeable break between Baykalian and Yudomian complexes, marked generally by the presence of basal sandstones, is commonly observed within troughs (*e.g.*, Zherbin Formation of Patom Highland). However, in the west, where terrigenous strata are present, sedimentation apparently was continuous (Shushkov, 1965). In general, the Yudomian complex of the Siberian platform is clearly separated from the upper Riphean but is closely associated with the Lower Cambrian— *i.e.*, it is equivalent to the Vendian. Determination of a precise lower stratigraphic boundary involves the same problems as in the Russian platform.

The base of the Yudomian complex in the stratotype area is not older than 650–680 m.y. This age was determined by dating of the underlying Ingili intrusion by three radiogenic methods. This age is in good agreement with isotopic ages of glauconite from the lower Yudomian (635–650 m.y.), from the lower Staraya Rechka Formation of Kotuykan (624–673 m.y.), and from Yudomian deposits of the Olenek uplift (675 m.y.). The younger age of the Zherbin sandstones of the Patom trough (602–620 m.y.) indicates that they may be almost correlative with the Parfenov sandstones of the Irkutsk amphitheater or basin (609 m.y.), or they may represent the base of the Irkutsk Horizon (as determined by M. A. Zharkov and

FIG. 4—Vendian fossils. Specimens at Institute of Geology and Geophysics, Siberian Branch of USSR Academy of Sciences.

No. 1. *Baikalina sessilis* Sokolov, 1972, holotype (×3). Upper Vendian, Irkutsk Horizon, Baykal area, Malyi Anai River (discovered by A. G. Pechkin, 1968). Cast of organism with sacklike body narrowing at base, probably benthonic; coating is elastic organic, slightly wrinkled; dimensions, 20–22 × 30 mm; wrinkle width, about 1 mm.

No. 2. *Pteridinium* sp. (×3). Age and occurrence are same. Fragment of small specimen, 12.5 × 6 mm; interval between furrows, about 1 mm.

No. 3 (a) *"Cylindrichnus"* sp. (b) Fragment of *Pteridinium* sp. and other problematics (×3). Age and occurrence are same.

No. 4. *?Ovatoscutum* sp. (×1). Vendian, Boxon Formation, middle part, *Boxonia gracilis* Kor. beds; East Sayan, Boxon (discovered by V. V. Zhabin, 1967). Imprint diameter, 60 mm.

No. 5. *Suvorovella aldanica* Vologdin and Maslov, 1960 (×2.5). Upper Vendian, lower part, upper Yudoma Formation; eastern Yakutia, Maya River above Ust'-Yudoma settlement (discovered by V. I. Korshunov, 1963). Calcified imprint is likely of a medusoid organism; diameter up to 50 mm (on oncolite dolomite).

No. 6. *Cyclomedusa* sp. (×1). Age and occurrence are same.

Fig. 5—Vendian fossils. Specimens at Institute of Geology and Geophysics, Siberian Branch of USSR Academy of Sciences.

No. 1. *Beltanelloides sorichevae* Sokolov, 1965 (×2). Upper Vendian, lower part, Redkino Series; north of Russian platform, Nenoxa, borehole (discovered by A. I. Soricheva, 1948–49). Imprints of accumulations of flattened spheroidal forms with peripheral concentric wrinkles (medusoids?), on argillite; diameters 10–20 mm.

No. 2. *Beltanelloides sorichevae* Sokolov (=*Beltanelliformis brunsi* Menner *in* Kirsanov, 1968; ×3). Upper Vendian, Redkino Series, Kairovo Formation; east of Russian platform, Loino, borehole (discovered by Z. P. Ivanova, 1965). Peripheral wrinkles of elastic imprints are comparatively rough; diameter 15 mm.

No. 3. *Beltanelloides sorichevae* Sokolov forma *minor,* n., holotype (×4). Upper Vendian, Redkino Series; north part of Russian platform, basin of Mezen' River, Leshukonskoye, borehole (discovered by L. S. Kossovoy, 1970). Imprint on argillite; diameter 5–7 mm.

No. 4. *Beltanelloides sorichevae* Sokolov (×1). Upper Vendian, Redkino Series; lower part of Onega River, borehole (discovered by V. N. Rostovtsev, 1970). Imprints on argillite; diameter 18–20 mm.

No. 5. *Beltanelloides sorichevae* Sokolov forma *major,* n., holotype (×1). Age and occurrence are same. Imprint on argillite; fine concentric wrinkles are typical; diameter 40–44 mm.

No. 6. *Beltanelloides sorichevae* Sokolov forma *minor,* n. (×1). Age and occurrence are same. Numerous imprints on argillite; diameter 5–7 mm.

No. 7. *Beltanelloides sorichevae* Sokolov forma *minor,* n. (×2). Upper Vendian, Redkino Series, Kairovo Formation; east part of Russian platform, Kirs, borehole (discovered by A. A. Klevtsova, 1965). Accumulation of imprints with extremely thin peripheral wrinkles; diameter 5–8 mm.

V. V. Khomentovsky). Probably, the lower-upper Vendian boundary in Siberia correlates in age with the Asha Formation of the Urals (598 m.y.) and the Redkino Series of the Russian platform (595–607 m.y.). The Nemakit-Daldyn Horizon is close in age to the Kotlin Formation (about 580 m.y.). The top of the Yudomian complex is at the base of the Sunnagin Horizon and its stratigraphic equivalents (Kessyusin, Usol'ye) in the Lower Cambrian. These rocks have been dated as 550–575 m.y.

In the stratotype section and in many other places (*e.g.,* the northern margin of the Siberian platform), the Yudomian complex is represented mainly by dolomites and limestones. These rocks contain a peculiar association of stromatolites and microphytolites (IV complex), which are important in correlation of the Vendian carbonate sections of the USSR. The following stromatolites are characteristic of the lower Yudomian complex (Semikhatov *et al.,* 1970): *Boxomia grumulosa* Kom. and *Jurusania judomica* Kom. and Semikh. Stromatolites characteristic of the upper part are *Stratifera irregularia* Kom. Some stromatolites are found in the entire complex—*e.g., Paniscollenia emergens* Kom. The microphytolites of the Yudomian complex are: *Vesicularites lobatus* Reitl., *V. bothrydioformis* (Krasnop.), *Vermiculites tortuosus* Reitl., *V. irregularis* (Reitl.), *Ambigolamellatus horridus* Z. Zhur., and others. The microphytoplanktons are abundant in the terrigenous sections of the Irkutsk amphitheater and other regions. Remains of *Vendotaenia* flora very similar to flora of the Russian platform are present in the Nemakit-Daldyn strata and in the Sukharikha and Platonovskaya Formations of the upper Vendian in the northern and northwestern parts of the Siberian platform.

The following paleozoologic occurrences are generally characteristic of the Yudomian complex: typical Ediacaran (or Charnian) *Rangea* from the lower Vendian Khatyspyt Formation of the Olenek uplift, impressions of medusoids from the Moty Horizon of the Irkutsk amphitheater, and abundant upper Vendian chitinoid sabelliditids (*Paleolina evenkiana* Sok.; Sokolov, 1967) from the Irkutsk Horizon. From the Nemakit-Daldyn strata and from the Platonovskaya and Sukharikha Formations, impressions of *Cyclomedusa,* problematic *Suvorovella aldanica* Vol. and Masl., and others are present. In the lower part of the upper Yudomian are found peculiar molds of medusoid "sacs," ovoid serial formations of the paundian (*Cylin-*drichnus sp.; Glaessner, 1966) type, and impressions of problematic organisms from the lower part of the Irkutsk Horizon of the Baykal Lake area.

In the Nemakit-Daldyn sequence, which corresponds to the upper Yudomian subcomplex, are found remnants of peculiar ancient tubular organisms with a carbonate shell (*Anabarites trisulcatus* Miss. and the *Angustiochreida* group; Valkov, 1970) and traces of rare hyolithellids. The writer considers the overlying Chabur Horizon, which contains gastropods (*"Oelandiella" korobkovi* Vost. and others), hyoliths, and tommotiids (Bengston, 1970), to be related closely to the Sunnagin Horizon, which contains archaeocyathids. Thus, the Chabur is assigned to the lowermost Cambrian. On the slopes of the Anabar massif is one of the best continental sections where the Cambrian-Precambrian boundary can be biochronologically documented within a continuous succession of normal-marine deposits.

REGIONAL CORRELATIONS

Vendian deposits of higher latitudes are rather poorly known. In Taymyr they are represented, on the basis of stratigraphic position, by the Sovinskaya Formation, which contains limestones, dolomites, carbonate-argillaceous shales, and, at the base, conglomerate-breccia (500–550 m). This formation appears to be similar to the Yudomian carbonate rocks of the Kharayuyetekh Formation (400 m) of the Kharaulakh Mountains in the lower Lena River area. The carbonate type of the section is similar to recently discovered Vendian deposits in the region of the middle Kolyma River—the Korkodon Formation (about 500 m), which yields microphytolites and stromatolites of Yudomian age (Komur and Furduy, 1969; Rabotnov *et al.,* 1970). These strata are overlain conformably by variegated deposits with an Early Cambrian fauna. All the Vendian outcrops in the northern regions of Siberia and in Northeast Russia are characterized by common features: transgressive overlap onto the Riphean and predominantly carbonate sedimentary units which are relatively thin. Undoubtedly, a stable regime of Vendian sedimentation far beyond the Siberian platform is suggested.

In the European sector of the Arctic, the Vendian is also widespread. In early works about the Russian platform, the writer assigned to the Vendian the upper part of the Scandinavian Sparagmite Formation (Sokolov, 1958), which is now called "Eocambrian *sensu stricto*"

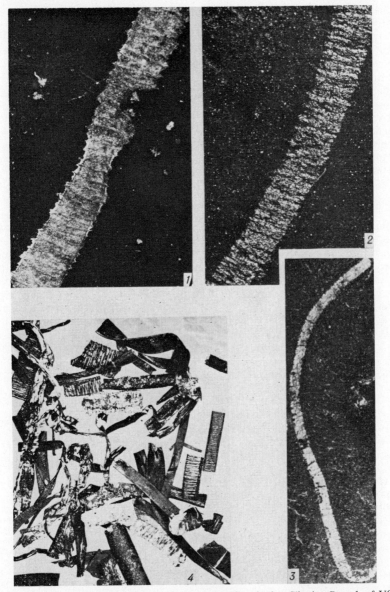

Fɪɢ. 6—Vendian fossils. Specimens at Institute of Geology and Geophysics, Siberian Branch of USSR Academy of Sciences.

No. 1. *Paleolina evenkiana* Sokolov, 1967 (×15). Upper part of upper Vendian, lower part of Platonovskaya Formation; west part of Siberian platform, Sukhaya Tungusska River (discovered by V. U. Petrakov, 1962). Fragment of semitransparent, tea-colored, cross-wrinkled tube; about 1 mm diameter (slide in glycerine).

Nos. 2, 3. *Paleolina* ex gr. *evenkiana* Sokolov, 1967 (×15, ×4). Upper Vendian, lower part of Sukharikha Formation, northwest part of Siberian platform, Norilsk suburbs, Gremiaka River, borehole (discovered by V. I. Dragunov, 1965). Imprint on black argillite. Diameter of cross-wrinkled tubes is no more than 1 mm; tube organic substance is preserved in form of thinnest graphitized membrane.

No. 4. *Sabellidites* spp. (×4). Upper Vendian–Lower Cambrian boundary deposits, base of Baltic Series, beds with *Sabellidites cambriensis* Yan., west part of Russian platform, Leningrad suburbs, Luga (discovered by L. B. Paasikivi, 1959). Accumulation of black chitinoid tubes, after dissolving clay in fluoric acid (slide in glycerine).

or "Varangian" (from Mullf Tillite to Ring-saker Sandstone); in Finnmark it corresponds to a section from lower Varangian tillite at the base (top of the Esmark–upper Riphean) to the base of the Lower Cambrian (Spjeldnaes, 1964). N. M. Chumakov (1971) proposed that the lower glacial-marine zone of the Fennosar-matian region be assigned entirely to the Lapp-landian (about 650 m.y.) and that the more complete section in Tanafjord be considered as the type section. In the regional stratigraphy of northern Norway, the Westertana Group (Størmer, 1967), with two tillite units in the lower part, corresponds to the Vendian. In the adjacent region of the Kola Peninsula and in the Ainovye Islands in the Barents Sea, the ter-rigenous Volokovaya Series (Keller and Soko-lov, 1960; Bekker et al., 1970) is no doubt up-per Vendian. It forms the upper part of the Hy-perborean sequence.

Recently, much attention has been given to evidence for Riphean and Vendian ages of cor-responding deposits in Spitsbergen. Some So-viet writers (Zabrodin, 1967; Raaben and Za-brodin, 1970; and others) have proposed as-signment of a Vendian age to the sequence be-ginning with the Draken Conglomerate at the base and extending to the Polarisbreen Group, inclusive (Ny Friesland). Such an assignment would bring the Polarisbreen tillite and the Sveanor (northeastern Spitsbergen) within the Vendian. However, it is more probable that just the Polarisbreen (up to 700–1,700 m in thick-ness) and its equivalents on Spitsbergen corre-spond to the Vendian. Such a conclusion logi-cally comes from W. B. Harland's (1968) con-cepts; it also corresponds to the later chart by A. A. Krasilshchikov (1970). Furthermore, there is no contradiction with significant data on microphytolites and stromatolites from this series (Zabrodin, 1967; Golovanov, 1969) which, in many respects, are similar to phyto-lites of the Uksa Formation of the lower Ven-dian of the Urals (665 m.y.) and with the Yu-doma Formation of Siberia.

Thus, the Arctic tillites appear at the same stratigraphic level as do the Volhyn tillites of the lower Vendian of the Russian platform and other regions of the continent, and a climate-stratigraphic factor becomes important in the worldwide characteristics of the original stage of the Vendian. A paleogeographic summary of recent concepts of the Vendian has been made only for the USSR (Keller et al., 1968), and it differs considerably from standards known in the West (Termier and Termier, 1960; and oth-ers).

The Vendian, despite being represented by terrigenous deposits on the Russian platform and by carbonate and carbonate-terrigenous de-posits on the Siberian platform, undoubtedly represents an important and a quite separate stage in the geologic history of the earth. Wide-spread environments of marine sedimentation within ancient platforms and many appear-ances of ancient nonskeletal organisms such as coelenterates, annelids, arthropods, and others are associated with this series. In the evolution of these organisms, at the transition from Ven-dian to Cambrian, an important biologic change took place which resulted in the appear-ance of skeletal-building properties of organic parts of animals. Such a Vendian–Early Cam-brian succession is worldwide in both paleobio-logic and paleogeologic senses, and is much more important than the monotonous evolution of ancient thallophytes and their structures dur-ing the Riphean, Vendian, and the entire Cam-brian. Therefore, the Vendian represents the beginning of the Phanerozoic rather than the close of the Cryptozoic, and it thus is more closely related to the Paleozoic, though for-mally it is not included in that era.

REFERENCES

Aksenov, Ye. M., 1967, O vendskom komplekse na vostoke Russkoy platformy: Akad. Nauk SSSR Izv. Ser. Geol., no. 9, p. 81–91.
——— and S. A. Volkova, 1969, Volkanogenno-osa-dochnyye gorizonty redkinskoy svity valdayskoy serii: Akad. Nauk SSSR Doklady, v. 188, no. 3, p. 635–638.
Bekker, Yu. R., N. S. Krylov, and V. Z. Negrutsa, 1970, Hyperborey Ainovykh ostrovov Barentsevogo morya: Akad. Nauk SSSR Doklady, v. 193, no. 6, p. 1349–1359.
Bengston, S., 1970, The Lower Cambrian fossil Tom-motia: Lethaia, v. 3, p. 363–392.
Bessonova, V. Ya., and N. M. Chumakov, 1968, O led-nikovykh otlozheniyakh v pozdnem dokembrii Byelo-russii: Akad. Nauk SSSR Doklady, v. 178, no. 4, p. 905–908.
Bukatchuk, P. D., 1969, Riphey, Dokembry. Kembry-skaya sistema, in A. V. Sidorenko, ed., Geologiya SSSR; Moldavskaya SSR, v. 45: Izd. "Nedra," p. 42–70.
Chumakov, N. M., 1970, O kharaktere verkhnedokem-bryskogo oledeneniya Yevrazii: Moskov Obshch. Is-pytateley Prirody Byull., Otdel. Geol., v. 45, no. 4.
——— 1971, Vendskoye oledeneniye Yevropy i Sever-noy Atlantiki (verkhny dokembry): Akad. Nauk SSSR Doklady, v. 198, no. 2, p. 419–422.
Datsenko, V. A., et al., 1968 Biostratigrafiya i fauna kembryskikh otlozheny severo-zapada Sibirskoy plat-formy: Izd. "Nedra," p. 1–213.
Dragunov, V. I., 1967, Vendskiye, nizhne-i srednekem-bryskiye eolozheniya pravoberezhya nizovyev r. Yenisey, in B. M. Keller et al., eds., Stratigrafiya dokembriya i kembriya Sredney Sibiri: Krasnoyarsk, p. 107–123.
Egorova, L. I., and V. E. Savitsky, 1969, Stratigrafiya i

biofacii kembriya Sibirskoy platformy: Moscow, Izd. "Nedra," p. 1–408.

Glaessner, M. F., 1963, Zur Kenntnis der Nama-Fossilien Südwest-Afrikas: Naturh. Mus. Wien Ann., v. 66, p. 113–120.

—— 1969, Trace fossils from the Precambrian and basal Cambrian: Lethaia, v. 2, p. 369–393.

—— and M. Wade, 1966, The late Precambrian fossils from Ediacara, South Australia: Palaeontology, v. 9, pt. 4, p. 599–628.

Gnilovskaya, M. B., 1971, Drevneyshiye vodnyye venda Russkoy platformy: Akad. Nauk SSSR Paleont. Zhur., no. 3, p. 101–107.

Golovanov, N. P., 1969, Stromatolity i stratigrafiya verkhnedokembryskikh otlozheny severa tsentralnoy chasti Sibiri i Shpitsbergena: Leningrad, p. 1–24.

Harland, W. B., 1968, On the principle of a late pre-Cambrian scale: Prague, Czechoslovakia, 23d Internat. Geol. Cong. Rept., Sec. 4, p. 253–264.

Harris, M. A., and D. V. Postnikov, 1970, Geokhronologicheskiye rubezhi pozdnego dokembriya: Akad. Nauk SSSR Kom. Opredeleniyu Absolyut. Vozrasta Geol. Formatsiy Trudy, no. 15, p. 53–71.

Igolkina, N. S., V. P. Kirikov, and T. Yu. Krivskaya, 1970, Osnovnyye etapy formirovaniya osadochnogo pokrova Russkoy platformy: Sovetskaya Geologiya, no. 11, p. 16–35.

Kaban'kov, V. Ya., 1968, Verkhnedokembryskiye otlozheniya Arktiki: Mezhdunarodnyy Geol. Kong., "Geologiya dokembriya": Moscow, Izd. "Nauka," Sov. Geologov., p. 111–115.

Kazakov, G. A., et al., 1970, Absolyutnyy vozrast dokembryskikh osadochnykh tolshch zapadnoy i yugo-zapadnoy chasti Russkoy platformy (Byelorussiya, Severo-Zapadnaya Ukraina, Moldaviya) i ikh korrelya'siya: Akad. Nauk SSSR Kom. Opredeleniyu Absolyut. Vozrasta Geol. Formatsiy Byull., v. 9, p. 95–103.

Keller, B. M., and B. S. Sokolov, 1960, Pozdny dokembry Murmanskoy oblasti: Akad. Nauk. SSSR Doklady, v. 133, no. 5, p. 1154–1157.

—— and M. A. Semikhatov, 1967, Opornyye razrezy rifeya materikov, Itogi Nauki: Moscow, Stratigrafiya Paleontologiya, Ser. Geol., no. 14, p. 5–108.

—— et al., 1968, The main features of the late Proterozoic paleogeography of the U.S.S.R.: Prague, Czechoslovakia, 23d Internat. Geol. Cong. Rept., Sec. 4, p. 189–202.

Khomentovsky, V. V., V. Yu. Shenfil, and M. S. Yakshin, 1968, Korrelyatsiya otlozheny pozdnego dokembriya vneshnego poyasa Baykalo-Patomskoy skladcnatoy oblasti: Geologiya i Geofizika, no. 1.

—— et al., 1969, Analogi Yudomskogo kompleksa v Prisayan'ye i vo vneshnem poyase Baykalo-Patomskoy skladchatoy oblasti, in B. S. Sokolov, ed., Stratigrafiya nizhnego kembriya i verkhnego dokembriya yuga Sibirskoy platformy: Moscow, Izd. "Nauka," p. 56–72.

Kirsanov, V. V., 1968a, Novyye dannyye po stratigrafii dokembryskikh otlozheny tsentralnykh rayonov Russkoy platformy: Akad. Nauk SSSR Izv. Ser. Geol., no. 4, p. 98–113.

—— 1968b, K voprosu o stratigrafii i korrelyatsii otlozheny vendskogo kompleksa na vostochnoy okraine Russkoy platformy: Akad. Nauk SSSR Izv. Ser. Geol., no. 6, p. 86–103.

—— 1970, Vendskiye otlozheniya tsentralnykh rayonov Russkoy platformy: Akad. Nauk SSSR Izv. Ser. Geol., no. 12, p. 55–65.

Komar, Vl. A., 1966, Stromatolity verkhnedokembryskikh otlozheny severa Sibirskoy platformy i ikh stratigraficheskoye zacheniye: Moscow, Izd. "Nauka," p. 1–122.

—— and R. S. Furduy, 1969, O kembryskikh i yudomskikh othlozheniyakh Prikolymskogo podnyatiya: Akad. Nauk SSSR Doklady, v. 184, no. 4, p. 915–916.

Kopeliovich, A. V., 1951, Nekotoryye voprosy stratigrafii nizhnego kembriya tsentralnykh oblastey Russkoy platformy: Akad. Nauk SSSR Doklady, v. 78, no. 5, p. 975–977.

Korolyuk, I. K., and A. D. Sidorov, 1969, Stromatolity motskoy svity Yuzhnogo Pribaykal'ya i Yugo-Vostochnogo Prisayan'ya: Akad. Nauk SSSR Doklady, v. 184, no. 3, p. 669–671.

Krasilshchikov, A. A., 1970, Skhema stratigrafii dokembriya nizhnego paleozoya arkhipelaga Shpitsbergen: Akad. Nauk SSSR Doklady, v. 194, no. 5, p. 1153–1156.

Makhnach, A. S., and N. V. Veretennikov, 1970, Vulkanogennaya formatsiya verkhnego proterozoya (venda) Byelorussii: Minsk, Izd. "Nauka i Tekhnika," p. 1–234.

Mens, K., and E. Pirrus, 1969–1970, Drevnyaya kora vyvetrivaniya lyaminaritovykh glin na severo-zapade Russkoy platformy: Akad Nauk Eston. SSR Izv., Ser. Fiz.-Mat. i Tech. Nauk, v. 18, p. 385–391; v. 19, p. 84–89.

Musatov, D. I., 1966, Nekotorye osnovnyye voprosy stratigrafii i tektonicheskoy istorii Sayano-Yeniseyskoy skladchatoy oblasti: Krasnoyarsk, p. 1–113.

Nuzhnov, S. V., 1967, Ripheyskiye otlozheniya yugo-vostoka Sibirskoy platformy: Moscow, Izd. "Nauka," p. 1–160.

Postnikov, V. G., and I. Ye. Postnikova, 1968, K stratigrafii i sopostavleniyu verkhneripheyskikh i vendskikh otlozheny yuga Sibirskoy platformy i yeye obramleniye: Akad. Nauk SSSR Izv. Ser. Geol., no. 7, p. 85–93.

Postnikova, I. Ye., and V. V. Kirsanov, 1970, Razrez verkhnego dokembriya Moskovskogo Grabena: Moskov. Obshch. Ispytately Prirody Byull., Otdel Geol., v. 45, no. 3, p. 26–33.

Raaben, M. E., and V. E. Zabrodin, 1969, K biostratigraficheskoy kharakteristike verkhnego ripheya Arktiki: Akad. Nauk SSSR Doklady, v. 184, no. 3, p. 676–679.

Rabotnov, V. T., et al., 1970, K stratigrafii verkhnego dokembriya srednego techeniya r. Kolymy: Akad. Nauk SSSR Doklady, v. 194, no. 5, p. 1157–1160.

Rozanov, A. Yu., 1966, Problema nizhney granitsy kembriya: Moscow, Itogi Nauki, Obshch. Geol. i Stratigrafiya, p. 92–111.

—— 1967, The Cambrian lower boundary problem: Geol. Mag., v. 104, no. 5, p. 415–434.

—— et al., 1969, Tommotsky yarus i problema nizhney granitsy kembriya: Moscow, Izd. "Nauka," p. 1–380.

Savitsky, V. E., et al., 1968, Problema verkhney granitsy dokembriya Sredney Sibiri. Mezhdunarodnyy Geol. Kong, "Geologiya dokembriya": Moscow, "Nauka," p. 121–123.

Semenenko, N. P., and L. G. Tkachuk, 1970, Absolyutnyy vozrast dokembriya zapadnogo obramleniya Vostochno-Yevropeyskoy platformy, in G. D. Afanas'yev, Geokhronologiya dokembriya: Moscow, Izd. "Nauka," p. 23–35.

Semikhatov, M. A., Vl. A. Komar, and S. N. Serebryakov, 1970, Yudomskiy kompleks stratotipicheskoy mestnosti: Moscow, Izd. "Nauka," p. 1–200.

Shushkov, G. I., 1965, O polozhenii i ob'eme analogov ushakovskoy svity i baykalskogo kompleksa v razreze drevnikh tolshch zapadnoy okrainy Sibirskoy platformy: Geol. i Geofiz., no. 6, p. 47–54.

Sokolov, B. S., 1952, O vozraste drevneyshego osadochnogo pokrova Russkoy platformy: Akad. Nauk SSSR Izv. Ser. Geol., no. 5, p. 21–31.

—— 1958, Le problème de la limite inférieure du Paléozoïque et les dépôts les plus anciens sur les plates-formes antésiniennes de l'Eurasie: Centre Natl. Rech. Sci. Colloques Internat., no. 76. p. 103–128.

—— 1964a, Pozdny dokembry, in A. P. Vinogradov, Istoriya geologicheskogo razvitiya Russkoy platformy i yeye obramleniya: Moscow, Izd. "Nedra," p. 15–24.

—— 1964b, The Vendian and the problem of the boundary between the Precambrian and the Paleozoic group: New Delhi, India, 23d Internat. Geol. Cong. Rept., pt. 10, p. 288–304.

—— 1965, Drevneyshiye otlozheniya rannego kembriya i sabelliditidy. Vsesoyuznyy simpozium po paleontologii dokembriya i rannego kembriya: Novosibirsk, p. 78–91.

—— 1967, Drevneyshiye pogonophory: Akad. Nauk SSSR Doklady, v. 177, no. 1, p. 202–204.

Solontsov, L. F., and Ye. M. Aksenov, 1970, O stratigrafii Yevaldayskoy serii Vostochno-Vropeyskoy platformy: Vyssh. Ucheb. Zavedeniy Izv. Geologiya i Razved., no. 6, p. 3–13.

Spjeldnaes, N., 1964, The Eocambrian glaciation in Norway: Geol. Rundschau, v. 54, p. 24–45.

Størmer, L., 1967, Some aspects of the Caledonian geosyncline and foreland west of the Baltic-Shield: Geol. Soc. London Quart. Jour., v. 123, p. 183–214.

Termier, H., and G. Termier, 1960, L'Ediacarien, premier étage paléontologique: Paris, Rev. Gén.

Sci., v. 67, p. 79–87.

Titorenko, T. N., 1970, Stratigrafiya otlozheny venda i nizhnego kembriya vostochnoy chasti Irkutskogo amfiteatra (po mikrofitolitam i vodoroslyam): Irkutsk, Izd. Irkutsk gos. un-ta, Avtoreferat, p. 1–30.

Tkachenko, V. B., ed., 1970, Opornyy razrez verkhnedokembryskikh otlozheny zapadnogo sklona Anabarskogo podnyatiya: Leningrad, Nauchno-Issled Inst. Geologii Arktiki Trudy, p. 1–144.

Val'kov, A. K., 1970, Biostratigrafiya i hiolity kembriya Severo-Vostoka Sibirskoy platformy: Yakutsk, Avtoreferat; p. 1–28.

Yakshin, M. S., 1970, Mikrofitolity verkhnego dokembriya yuzhnogo obramleniya Sibirskoy platformy i ikh stratigraficheskoye znacheniye: Novosibirsk, Avtoreferat, Akad. Nauk SSSR Sibirskoye Otdeleniye, Inst. Geologii i Geofizika, p. 1–23.

Zabrodin, V. E., 1967, Mikrofitolity ripheya Urala i Shpitsbergena: Moscow, Avtoreferat, Akad. Nauk SSSR Geol. Inst. Trudy. p. 1–18.

Zayka-Novatsky, V. S., E. A. Aseyeva, and V. A. Velikanov, 1969, Vendskiy kompleks Podillya: Akad. Nauk Ukrayin RSR Dopovīdī, no. 5, p. 391–393.

Zharkov, M. A., and V. V. Khomentovsky, 1965, Osnovnyye voprosy stratigrafii nizhnego kembriya i venda yuga Sibirskoy platformy v svyasi s solenosnostiyu: Moskov. Obshch. Ispytateley Prirody Byull., Otdel. Geol., v. 40, no. 1, p. 100–118.

Zhuravleva, Z. A., 1964, Onkolity i katagrafii ripheya i nizhnego kembriya Sibiri i ikh stratigraficheskoye znacheniye: Moscow, Izd. "Nauka," p. 1–99.

—— and N. M. Chumakov, 1968, Katagrafii, onkolity i stromatolity iz pozdnego dokembriya Vostochnoy Byelorussii: Akad. Nauk SSSR Doklady, v. 178, no. 3, p. 668–671.

Paleozoogeography of Boreal-Realm Seas in Jurassic and Neocomian[1]

V. N. SACHS, V. A. BASOV, A. A. DAGIS, A. S. DAGIS, E. F. IVANOVA,
S. V. MELEDINA, M. S. MESEZHNIKOV, T. I. NALNYAYEVA,
V. A. ZAKHAROV, and N. I. SHULGINA[2]

Novosibirsk, USSR

Abstract During the Jurassic and Early Cretaceous, Arctic seas were linked with the Atlantic and Pacific Oceans. Warm oceanic currents penetrated from the Atlantic Ocean, and a greater abundance and diffusion of the marine fauna in the Atlantic part of the Arctic resulted; this penetration was especially pronounced during the Late Jurassic. The north pole, on the basis of paleomagnetic and paleobiogeographic data, was situated north of the Bering Strait during the whole Jurassic and Neocomian.

The marine fauna was only slightly differentiated during the Hettangian, Sinemurian, and early Pliensbachian. The Tethyan and Boreal faunal provinces developed; the latter, situated around the north pole, was characterized by sparser cephalopod associations and by the appearance of endemic forms (up to families) in the benthos. During the late Pliensbachian, faunal differentiation reached the province level. The Boreal region was differentiated into the West European and Arctic provinces, which continued during the Toarcian and early Aalenian. During the Middle Jurassic (from late Aalenian), faunal variability in the Boreal region greatly increased, and the Arctic and North American provinces became differentiated within this region. The West European province appears to have extended beyond the limits of the Boreal region. During the Callovian, Oxfordian, and Kimeridgian, the Boreal region tended again to fall into two subregions: the Arctic region—which included the North Siberian, Chukchi-Canadian, and North American provinces—and the Boreal-Atlantic region—which included the West European and Greenland-Uralian provinces.

During the Volgian and early Berriasian, the Boreal fauna was still somewhat isolated from the Tethyan fauna and constituted a Boreal realm with Arctic and Boreal-Atlantic regions. The Arctic region included the North Siberian, Chukchi-Canadian (around the pole), and Boreal-Pacific provinces, and the Boreal-Atlantic region consisted of the West European, East European, and Greenland-Uralian provinces. During the late Berriasian, Valanginian, and early Hauterivian, the Arctic region extended westward and included the Trans-Uralian region.

INTRODUCTION

During the Jurassic and Neocomian, the Boreal sea basins surrounding the north pole were faunistically different from those in the Tethys, those around the periphery of the Pacific Ocean, and those in the Southern Hemisphere.

[1] Manuscript received, April 30, 1972.

[2] Institute of Geology and Geophysics, USSR Academy of Sciences.

Accordingly, two basic paleozoogeographic units can be recognized for the Mesozoic seas: (1) Boreal—for the Northern Circumpolar Zone, and (2) Tethyan—for the Pre-Equatorial Zone and the Southern Hemisphere. During Early Jurassic time, differentiation of the Boreal and Tethyan faunas permitted their geographic division at the paleozoogeographic level into the Boreal and Tethyan regions. By mid-Jurassic time, these differences had become so great that the former regions could be recognized as distinct paleozoogeographic realms which could be divided into appropriate regions and provinces.

Paleozoogeographic zonation of the Boreal realm implies that distinct boundaries exist between intercommunicating sea basins and between paleozoogeographic regions and provinces. However, zonal boundaries with respect to different faunal groups—especially benthos and free-swimming organisms—do not coincide in many respects. The peculiarities in the paleozoogeographic zonation may be defined as a function of the basin depth. Because predominant depths in the Mesozoic Boreal seas were only as great as 200 m, the following faunal zonation was constructed on the basis of such shallow sea areas.

The results of paleozoogeographic study (seas) and paleophytogeographic study (land), plus paleomagnetic investigations, show that the position of the pole in the Northern Hemisphere during the Mesozoic was somewhat farther north from the Bering Strait than it now is. The Arctic basin was under permanent influence of water currents coming from the Atlantic.

At the beginning of Jurassic time (Hettangian and early Pliensbachian), the Boreal basins differed from those in the Tethyan region in several ways: they contained relatively fewer ammonites and some endemic benthonic groups (*e.g.*, *Ochotorhynchia* among brachiopods, *Otapiria* among bivalves), and they lacked belemnites. During late Pliensbachian time, the faunal differentiation greatly increased, and Amaltheidae and *Harpax* dominated in the Boreal region. The peculiarities in geographic distribution of these fossils permit the distinguishing of three provinces within the Boreal region (Fig. 1): (1) Boreal-Atlantic (in northwestern Europe); (2) a former part of the Tethyan region as well as the Arctic (Siberia and North America); and (3) Boreal-Pacific (Southern Alaska and Western Canada).

At the end of late Pliensbachian time, belemnites penetrated northward from the waters surrounding Europe into the Arctic seas, and, during Toarcian time, they expanded throughout the Boreal region (Fig. 2). During the Toarcian the predominant groups in the Arctic were related to those characteristic of the Pliensbachian in Europe. After late Toarcian time, however, the difference between the Tethyan fauna and the West European fauna became less distinct; but, within the Boreal region proper, the differences between faunas of the Arctic province and the Boreal-Pacific province became much more distinct.

During Middle Jurassic time, especially after late Aalenian, the Boreal basins were dominated by endemic forms such as *Erycitoides*

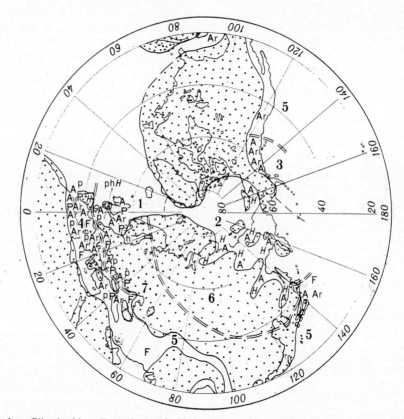

Fɪɢ. 1—Late Pliensbachian (Domerian) paleobiogeographic distribution in Northern Hemisphere. **1.** Boreal-Atlantic province; **2.** Arctic province; **3.** Boreal-Pacific province; **4.** Mediterranean province; **5.** Indo-Pacific province; **6.** Siberian paleophytogeographic region; **7.** Indo-European paleophytogeographic region.

Marine faunas: **Ammonites:** A-*Amaltheus;* P-*Pleuroceras;* Ar-Aristiceratinae; F-*Fuciniceras.* **Belemnites:** p-Passaloteuthidae; h-Hastitidae. **Pelecypods:** H-*Harpax.*
Key for all figures (though some figures do not contain all lines):
   White = Sea
   Specks = Dry land
   Thick dashed lines = Boundaries of paleobiogeographic realms
   Double dashed lines = Boundaries of paleobiogeographic regions
   Dashed lines with dots = Boundaries of paleozoogeographic subregions
   Dashed lines = Boundaries of paleozoogeographic provinces
   Dotted lines = Boundaries of paleozoogeographic subprovinces

FIG. 2—Early and middle Toarcian paleobiogeographic distribution in Northern Hemisphere. **1.** Boreal-Atlantic province; **2.** Arctic province; **3.** Mediterranean province; **4.** Indo-Pacific province; **5.** Siberian paleophyto-geographic region; **6.** Indo-European paleophytogeographic region.

Marine faunas: **Ammonites:** E-*Eleganticeras;* K-*Kedonoceras;* T-*Tiltoniceras;* Z-*Zugodactylites;* N-*Nodicoeloceras;* M-*Merkaticeras;* P-*Peronoceras;* B-*Bouleiceras.* **Belemnites:** p-Passaloteuthidae, Nannobelinae; h-Megateuthinae, Hastitidae. **Brachiopods:** *bot*-Boreiothyridae.

and *Tugurites* among the ammonites, by Pseu-dodicoelitinae and *Sachsibelus* among the belemnites, and by Retroceramidae and *Arctotis* among the bivalves. In contrast, Middle Jurassic faunas in the seas surrounding Europe were similar to those of the Tethys. Among Bajocian ammonites in the Boreal region are scarce occurrences of endemic forms such as the early Bajocian *Arkelloceras* (Fig. 3). During, but mainly after, the late Bajocian, there appeared an endemic Boreal family of ammonites—Cardioceratidae (subfamily Arctocephalitinae, including the following: *Megasphaeroceras, Eocephalites* [late Bajocian], *Boreiocephalites, Cranocephalites, Arctocephalites, Paracephalites, Arcticoceras* [Bathonian and early Callovian]). Moreover, after the late Bajocian, endemic belemnites and Cylindroteuthidae became more common in the Boreal region. Occasionally during early late Bathonian time, Tethyan

ammonites such as *Oxycerites* penetrated into the Boreal seas from Europe. Such differences between the Boreal and Tethyan faunas make reasonable their division into separate realms. Furthermore, greatly increased faunal diversity in the Boreal region differentiated that region into two provinces—the Arctic and the Boreal-Pacific.

The great advance of the sea in Europe and West Siberia during Callovian time favored expansion of the Boreal fauna, such as Cardioceratidae (subfamily Cadoceratinae) among the ammonites and Cylindroteuthidae among the belemnites, as far south as the Caucasus and Central Asia. Thus, the European seas were linked with the Boreal realm as a separate Boreal-Atlantic paleozoogeographic region comprising three provinces: West European, Polish, and East European.

During the Callovian, the Arctic zoogeographic region was dominated by *Cadoceras* and *Longaeviceras* among the ammonites, and was divisible into four provinces: Greenland, North Siberian, Chukchi-Canadian, and Boreal-Pacific. Its benthos was richer than during mid-Jurassic time, although still much poorer than that of the Boreal-Atlantic region.

During early Oxfordian time, the zoogeographic zonation of the Boreal realm remained similar to that of the Callovian. The Boreal realm, as a whole, was characterized by developing Cardioceratidae among the ammonites, Cylindroteuthidae among the belemnites, and *Buchia* among the bivalves. In the Boreal-Atlantic region, both Cardioceratidae and abundant Perisphinctidae were present, whereas they were entirely absent in the Tethyan region. Among ammonites in the Arctic region, only *Cardioceras* and *Goliathiceras* remained fairly common.

During late Oxfordian time, thermophilic faunal groups penetrated as far as the Boreal seas (corals, rudists, *etc.*). The boundaries of the zoogeographic regions and provinces inside the Boreal realm shifted northward. Poland and Donbass were apparently beyond the framework of the Boreal realm. Even in the East European province, the influence of the Tethyan faunal elements appears to have been dominant. The Greenland-Uralian province merged into the Boreal-Atlantic region.

Kimeridgian time was characterized by expansion of the Arctic faunal geographic range and by southward shifting of the boundaries of the zoogeographic regions and provinces. Perisphinctidae predominated among the ammonites of the Boreal realm, but they did not penetrate into the Circumpolar zone or into the Chukchi-Canadian province, in which Cardioceratidae alone persisted (Fig. 5). During the

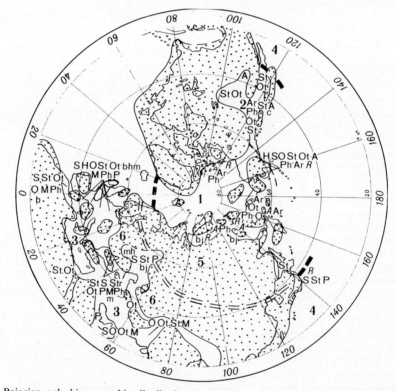

Fig. 3—Bajocian paleobiogeographic distribution in Northern Hemisphere. **1.** Arctic province; **2.** Boreal-Pacific province; **3.** Mediterranean region; **4.** Indo-Pacific region; **5.** Siberian paleophytogeographic region; **6.** Indo-European paleophytogeographic region.

Marine faunas: **Ammonites:** Ar-*Arkelloceras;* A-Arctocephalitinae; S-Sonniniidae; H-Haploceratidae; O-Oppeliidae; Ot-Otoitidae; St-Stephanoceratidae; Str-Strigoceratidae; P-Parkinsoniidae; M-Morphoceratidae; Ph-Phylloceratidae. **Belemnites:** bj-*"Mesoteuthis"* ex gr. *bajosicus;* c-Cylindroteuthidae; m-Megateuthinae; h-*Holcobelus;* b-Belemnopsidae. **Pelecypods:** A-*Arctotis;* R-Retroceramidae.

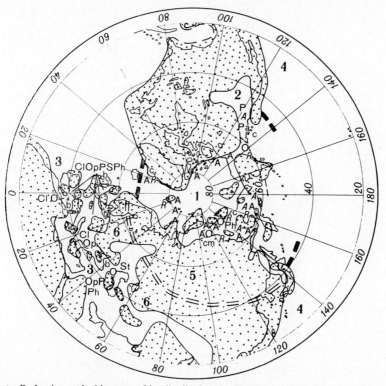

FIG. 4—Late Bathonian paleobiogeographic distribution in Northern Hemisphere. **1.** Arctic province; **2.** Boreal-Pacific province; **3.** Mediterranean region; **4.** Indo-Pacific region; **5.** Siberian paleophytogeographic region.

Marine faunas: **Ammonites:** A-*Arctocephalites;* Pa-*Paracephalites;* Ph-Phylloceratidae; Cl-Clydoniceratidae; Op-Oppeliidae; P-Perisphinctidae; S-Sphaeroceratinae; St-Stephanoceratidae. **Belemnites:** c-Cylindroteuthidae; m-Megateuthinae; b- Belemnopsidae. **Pelecypods:** *A-Arctotis; R*-Retroceramidae.

late Kimeridgian, the differentiation of the Boreal-Atlantic and Arctic faunas became still greater, as shown by restriction to the Arctic of such ammonites as *Euprionoceras* and *Hoplocardioceras* and such belemnites as *Arctoteuthis* and *Holcobeloides.* Simultaneously, some representatives of the Tethyan fauna migrated to the Boreal realm during the late Kimeridgian; for example, *Virgataxioceras* reached as far as the Urals, and *Streblites* reached the Taymyr peninsula.

Volgian time was characterized by significant separation of the faunistic assemblages from basin to basin and by development of specific assemblages within those basins. Faunal isolation of different basins greatly increased within the Boreal realm and became especially pronounced between the Boreal and Tethyan realms. In early Volgian time, however, differentiation of ammonites within the Boreal realm was mainly at the species level. Among belemnites, only the Cylindroteuthidae were re-stricted to the Arctic region during the entire Volgian.

During the Volgian, the Chukchi-Canadian province, just as in the earlier epochs, was distinguished by impoverishment of faunas and by the predominance of *Buchia.* In the Boreal-Pacific province, the expansion of Cylindroteuthidae and *Buchia* continued and reached as far south as California and Mexico and Sikhote-Alin, particularly during the late Volgian.

During mid-Volgian time (Fig. 6), the ammonite subfamily Virgatitinae was developing in the Boreal-Atlantic region and, presumably, also in the East European province. The Dorsoplanitinae forms were present among different groups in the Boreal-Arctic and Arctic regions, whereas *Taimyrosphinctes* and *Laugeites* occurred only in the Arctic region. Belemnite, bivalve, brachiopod, and foraminifer assemblages were essentially varied also (Fig. 7). It may be significant to note the difference between the faunas of the Greenland-Uralian and the North

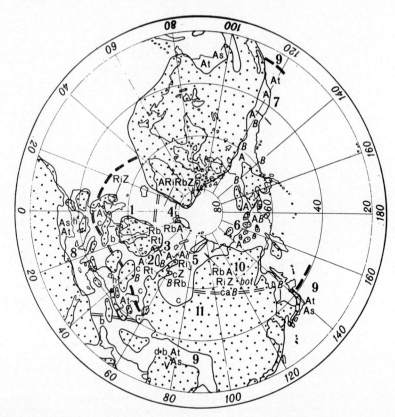

FIG. 5—Early Kimeridgian (time of *Rasenia cymodoce*) paleobiogeographic distribution in Northern Hemisphere. **1.** West European province; **2.** East European province; **3.** Pechoran province; **4.** Greenland-Uralian province; **5.** North Siberian province; **6.** Chukchi-Canadian province; **7.** Boreal-Pacific province; **8.** Mediterranean region; **9.** Indo-Pacific region; **10.** Siberian paleophytogeographic region; **11.** Indo-European region.

Marine faunas: **Ammonites:** Ri-*Rasenia* ex gr. *involuta;* Rb-*R.* ex gr. *borealis;* Rt-*R.* ex gr. *trimera;* Z-*Zonovia;* A-*Amoebites;* V-Virgatosphinctinae; At-Ataxioceratinae; As-Aspidoceratinae. **Belemnites:** c-*Cylindroteuthis* s.s., *Lagonibelus, Pachyteuthis;* a-*Arctoteuthis;* b-*Belemnopsis;* h-*Hibolites;* d-Dicoelitidae. **Pelecypods:** B-*Buchia.* **Brachiopods:** bot-Boreiothyridae.

Siberian provinces, which were separated by a West Siberian sea at least 500 m deep.

During late Volgian time, craspeditidid ammonites occurred everywhere in the Boreal realm, and the belemnite *Acroteuthis* was predominant in the Boreal-Atlantic region. *Cylindroteuthis, Lagonibelus,* and *Pachyteuthis* also lived in the Arctic region. After late middle Volgian, the Tethyan Virgatosphinctinae and Berriasellidae penetrated into the Arctic region from the Tethyan region but did not cross Western Europe, from which the seas were retreating.

After early Neocomian time, in the region of the Mesozoic fold systems, the process of drainage which had started during the Late Jurassic resulted in disturbing the links between the Arctic and Pacific basins. Craspeditidae continued to be dominant in the seas of the Boreal realm, penetrating into the West European province after early Berriasian time and into the Polish province after middle Berriasian time. The very marked influence of the Tethyan elements can be observed among the Berriasian ammonites in the Polish and East European provinces (*e.g., Riasanites, Euthymiceras, Neocomites*). The Berriasian of the Boreal-Atlantic region is characterized by domination of *Acroteuthis* among the belemnites, whereas *Cylindroteuthis, Lagonibelus,* and *Pachyteuthis* dominated in the Arctic region east of the Urals, as they had earlier. Some ammonites were typical of the Arctic region (*e.g., Craspeditidae, Hectoroceras, Praetolia, Bojarkia,* and

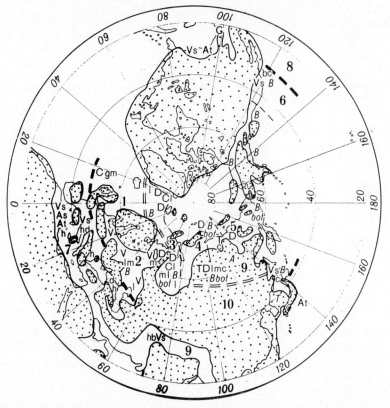

FIG. 6—Middle Volgian (time of *Virgatites virgatus*) paleobiogeographic distribution in Northern Hemisphere. **1.** West European province; **2.** East European province; **3.** Greenland-Uralian province; **4.** North Siberian province; **5.** Chukchi-Canadian province; **6.** Boreal-Pacific province; **7.** Mediterranean region; **8.** Indo-Pacific region; **9.** Siberian paleophytogeographic region; **10.** Indo-European paleophytogeographic region.

Marine faunas: **Ammonites:** V-*Virgatites;* D-*Dorsoplanites* ex gr. *maximus;* T-*Taimyrosphinctes;* G-*Crendonites* ex gr. *gorei;* Cl-*C.* ex gr. *leslie;* Vs-*Virgatosphinctinae;* At-Ataxioceratinae; As-Aspidoceratinae. **Belemnites:** l-*Lagonibelus* s.s.; c-*Cylindroteuthis;* m-*Microbelus;* b-*Belemnopsis;* h-*Hibolites;* d-*Duvalia.* **Pelecypods:** B-*Buchia;* A-*Arctotis.* **Brachiopods:** bot-Boreiothyridae.

others; Fig. 8). Some of them sporadically reached as far as the Boreal-Atlantic seas. However, the benthic faunas east and west of the Urals were essentially different (Fig. 9). In the Boreal-Pacific province, Boreal and Tethyan (Pacific) ammonites were mixed with the purely Boreal Cylindroteuthidae and *Buchia.*

In Valanginian time, the Polyptychitidae were the predominant ammonites everywhere in the Boreal realm, especially during the early Valanginian. Among belemnites, *Acroteuthis,* as well as *Lagonibelus,* dominated in the Arctic region (Fig. 10). By the end of early Valanginian time, the predominance of Polyptychitidae and *Acroteuthis* became fixed over the whole area of the Boreal realm, and the differences between the Boreal-Atlantic and Arctic regions

became trivial. In only the Boreal-Pacific province do the Boreal ammonite groups, belemnites, and *Buchia* occur together with Tethyan forms.

In early Hauterivian time, the faunal assemblages of the Boreal realm were rejuvenated. In the West European province of the Boreal-Atlantic region, the predominance was gained by immigrants from Tethyan ammonites of the Neocomitinae. In the East European province, however, the widespread forms were the Arctic Rolliinae (*Homolsomites*) and Simbirskitidae (*Pavlovites, Gorodzovia,* etc.). For the Arctic region, more advanced forms of Cylindroteuthidae (*Acroteuthis*) are characteristic. During the late early Hauterivian and late Hauterivian, the Simbirskitidae expanded over the whole Bo-

Fig. 8—Middle Berriasian paleobiogeographic distribution in Northern Hemisphere. **1.** West European province; **2.** Polish province; **3.** East European province; **4.** Greenland-Pechoran province; **5.** West Siberian province; **6.** North Siberian province; **7.** Chukchi-Canadian province; **8.** Boreal-Pacific province; **9.** Mediterranean region; **10.** Indo-Pacific region; **11.** Siberian paleophytogeographic region; **12.** Indo-European paleophytogeographic region.

Marine faunas: **Ammonites:** C-Craspeditinae; H-*Hectoroceras;* N-Neocomitinae; B-*Berriasella;* E-*Euthymiceras;* R-*Riasanites.* **Belemnites:** c-*Cylindroteuthidae;* a-*Acroteuthis* s.s.; m-*Microbelus;* b-Belemnopsidae; d-Duvaliidae. **Pelecypods:** B-*Buchia;* Bo-*Boreionectes;* T-*Trigonia.* **Brachiopods:** *bot*-Boreiothyridae.

⋙→

Fig. 7—Middle Volgian paleobiogeographic distribution in Northern Hemisphere. **1.** Boreal-Atlantic region; **2.** East Greenland subprovince; **3.** North Siberian subprovince; **4.** North Uralian province; **5.** Chukchi-Canadian subregion; **6.** Boreal-Pacific subregion.

Marine benthonic faunas: **Pelecypods:** A-*Arctotis; An-Anopaea; Bo-Boreioxytoma; C-Ctenostreon; Ex-Exogyra, Lo-Loripes; O-Opis; Pl-Plicatula; Lp-Liostrea praeanabarensis, Arctotis intermedia, Boreionectes breviauris; Isc-Isognomon cuneatum; Ii-Inoceramus impurus; Mth-Mytilus habitus; Mtt-Mytilus taimyricus; Asy-Astarte yatriyaensis, A. lyuliyaensis; Lya-Eriphyla (Lyapinella) asiatica; Lg-Liostrea gibberosa; Bnp-Boreionectes praecinctus.* **Brachiopods:** *bot*-Boreiothyridae. **Gastropods:** *Cl*-Calyptraeidae.

⋙→

Fig. 9—Middle Berriasian paleobiogeographic distribution in Northern Hemisphere. **1.** Boreal-Atlantic region; **2.** North Uralian province; **3.** North Siberian province; **4.** Chukchi-Canadian province.

Marine benthonic faunas: **Pelecypods:** A-*Arctotis; C-Ctenostreon; Ex-Exogyra; My-Myoconcha; O-Opis; S-Spondylus; T-Trigonia; La-Liostrea* aff. *anabarensis; Ll-Liostrea lyapinensis; Lu-Liostrea uralensis; Asv-Astarte veneris; Cal-Camptonectes lamellosus.* **Brachiopods:** *bot*-Boreiothyridae. **Gastropods:** Calyptraeidae (not shown),

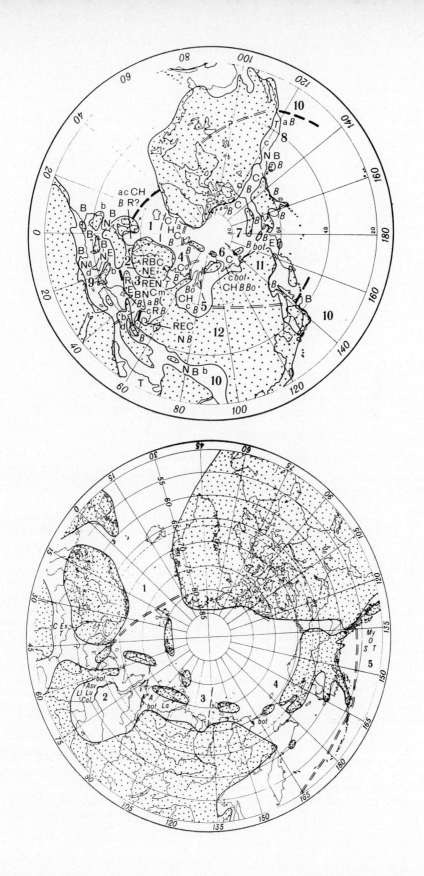

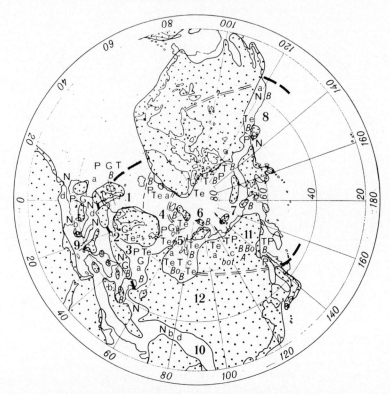

Fig. 10—Early Valanginian paleobiogeographic distribution in Northern Hemisphere. **1.** West European province; **2.** Polish province; **3.** East European province; **4.** Greenland-Pechoran province; **5.** West Siberian province; **6.** North Siberian province; **7.** Chukchi-Canadian province; **8.** Boreal-Pacific province; **9.** Mediterranean region; **10.** Indo-Pacific region; **11.** Siberian paleophytogeographic region; **12.** Indo-European paleophytogeographic region.

Marine faunas: **Ammonites:** T-Tolliinae; Te-*Temnoptychites;* G-Garniericeratinae; P-Polyptychitidae; N-Neocomitinae. **Belemnites:** c-Cylindroteuthidae; a-*Acroteuthis;* b-Belemnopsidae; d-Duvaliidae. **Pelecypods:** *B-Buchia; Bo-Boreionectes; A-Arctotis.* **Brachiopods:** *bot-*Boreiothyridae.

real realm, whereas the Ancyloceratidae expanded at the same time over the Boreal-Atlantic region. Among the belemnites, Oxyteuthidae and Cylindroteuthidae (*Acroteuthis*) appeared during the late Hauterivian and became predominant. *Buchia* became extinct in early Hauterivian time.

In Barremian time, both of the Boreal ammonite groups of the Northern Hemisphere disappeared, whereas the Ancyloceratidae expanded into the Tethyan region. Although the Boreal belemnites Oxyteuthidae and scarce *Acroteuthis* still survived, no biologic reasons are known for separating the Boreal and Tethyan faunas.

No doubt, these suggested conclusions and structural schemes will be defined more exactly after new data become available and are thoroughly analyzed. However, it is indisputable

that there was distinct latitudinal zonation during Jurassic and Neocomian times in the Northern Hemisphere—corresponding to displacement of the geographic north pole in the direction of the Bering Strait—and that marine faunas became impoverished toward high latitudes. These facts may be explained only by recognizing that the seas became colder toward the pole. Furthermore, evidence concerning the land vegetation, the composition of the marine faunas, and data on weathering processes on the land surface, as well as determination of paleotemperatures of seawater, imply that the temperature variation was not very great—within 5°C in Early and Middle Jurassic times but reaching 10°C in Late Jurassic and Neocomian times.

The extent of differentiation of marine faunas during Jurassic time was gradually increasing, though this process was not constant or undirected. Faunal differentiation may be explained both by the presence of abrupt climatic contrasts during Late Jurassic time (with arid zones appearing) and by progressive specification of the faunal assemblages. The differences in the faunal assemblages of various basins were not constant as to the rank of taxons under comparison; the same is true of the areas of individual taxons. Evidently, migration of individual faunal groups took place from one region to another.

The boundaries of the Boreal realm did not remain constant. The Boreal region (realm, since Middle Jurassic time) expanded during late Pliensbachian and early Oxfordian times. Its area was greatly reduced in Middle Jurassic time and somewhat reduced during late Oxfordian and Kimeridgian time. It is noteworthy that the analogues of the Boreal realm expressed so clearly for the Northern Hemisphere are nearly unkown for the Southern Hemisphere. Some of the elements of the Boreal fauna (*Otapiria,* Retroceramidae, *Buchia*) occur, however, in the Southern Hemisphere (New Zealand, Australia, Indonesia, and India), far from the possible pole position north of Queen Maude Land. Hence, the conclusion may be drawn that the position of the continents in the Southern Hemisphere during Jurassic time was different from that which exists today. It is implied that Gondwanaland split into several fragments which subsequently did not drift far away from each other.

In the Boreal realm, the affinity between the Jurassic and Early Cretaceous faunas of East Greenland with the faunas of the Pechora basin, the eastern slope of the Urals, and the Taymyr Peninsula indicates the existence of only a relatively narrow, shallow channel between Greenland and Eurasia. Faunal migration could have been realized through it from the Atlantic to the Arctic and back again; this channel did not obstruct the exchange of shallow-water faunal assemblages between Greenland and northern Eurasian seas.

Comparative Appraisal of Zonal Scales for Warm-Water and Arctic Areas[1]

V. V. MENNER[2]

Moscow, USSR

Abstract Much work has been done in the last decade toward setting up a worldwide stratigraphic scale based on zonal subdivisions. The outlook for resolving the remaining problems regarding such a worldwide scale is optimistic for the warm-water belt; however, the cold-water Arctic and Antarctic areas present greater difficulties. The erroneous assumption is commonly made that sections in cold-water basins can be dated on the basis of concomitance of definite species of certain genera in subtropical sections. Little is known about rates of evolution for particular groups in various regions. Disagreement exists on the necessity of working out independent zonal scales for Arctic regions. Such scales obviously have merit; however, it might be wise to use a local zonal scale for geologic maps, where a single scale is required, in conjunction with a system of indices indicating the degree of precision with which a certain division is isolated.

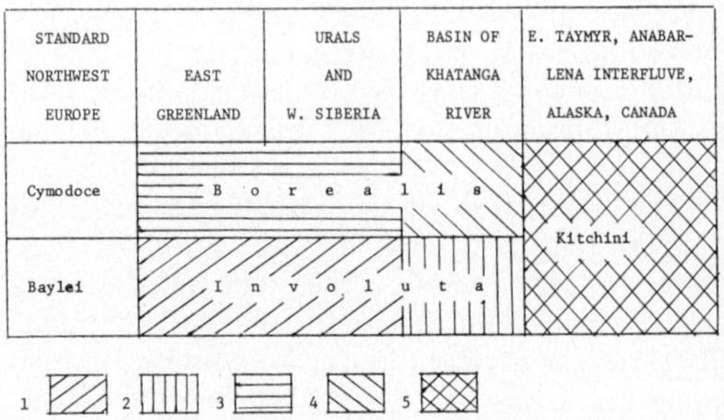

FIG. 1—Correlation of lower Kimeridgian of Arctic regions. **1.** Zone Involuta, complex with various Perisphinctidae and *Amoeboceras;* **2.** Zone Involuta, complex with *Pictonia* and *Amoeboceras.* **3.** Zone Borealis, complex with few species of *Rasenia* and *Zonovia.* **4.** Zone Borealis, complex with numerous endemic species of *Rasenia* and *Zonovia.* **5.** Zone Kitchini.

INTRODUCTION

One of the great achievements of the last decade was the establishment of worldwide zonal subdivisions for several systems in the Phanerozoic. It is possible to disagree about the number of zones in a certain stage or system and about the way in which those zones should be distinguished—by important species or by complexes of species (in the latter case, they can be easily traced in space). Nevertheless, the same sequence of zones can be distinctly traced throughout the entire warm-water area extending from 45°N to 45°S lat.—a fact which essentially solves the problem as to which principles should serve as a basis for worldwide chronostratigraphic categories of the fifth (zonal) order. There is no longer any doubt that the necessary bases for working out a worldwide stratigraphic scale are provided by the remains of graptolites for the Ordovician and Silurian; cyclymenids, goniatites, and ammonites for the middle and upper Paleozoic and the Mesozoic; *Inoceramus* for the Jurassic and Cretaceous; and planktonic foraminifers for the upper Paleozoic, upper Mesozoic, and Cenozoic.

Although the outlook is optimistic for learning more details regarding the stratigraphy of the warm-water belt, working out zonal scales for the cold-water Arctic and Antarctic areas is much more difficult. Some idea of what these

[1] Manuscript received, April 30, 1972.
[2] Geological Institute, USSR Academy of Sciences.

difficulties consist of can be gained from study of the specific features of the distribution of recent forms, and even from a general analysis of zonal schemes of the upper Paleozoic, Mesozoic, and Cenozoic.

From the well-known summary by F. L. Parker (1967) on the distribution of planktonic foraminifers in latitudinal belts of the ocean, it directly follows that modern foraminifers are mostly associated with warm waters, whereas, in cold waters—north of 55–60°N lat.—they are represented only by *Globigerina* species, which occur also in the waters of the temperate and subtropical zones. *Globigerina* tests are found in sediments of the Arctic Ocean among benthonic forms; apparently, they are brought into the eastern part of the basin by the warm waters of the Gulf Stream. Such changes in the planktonic-foraminiferal complexes, from low to high latitudes, also agree with data on the distribution of foraminiferal assemblages in the geologic past. In the peripheral part of the warm-water zone of the Paleogene—for example, as demonstrated by V. Krasheninnikov (1969) on Hokkaido, Sakhalin, and Kamchatka, as well as in the Chilean Andes— planktonic-foraminiferal complexes are developed with a marked predominance of *Globigerina* rather than *Globorotalia;* only their occurrence together in sections of subtropical areas

Table 1. Zones of Middle Carboniferous of Russian Platform, Pay-Khoy, and Northeast Asia

System	Series	Stage	Horizons	Russian platform	Pajchoi	North-East of Asia
CARBONIFEROUS	Upper	Moscow	Kasimovian	Obsoletes obsoletus	Obsoletes timanicus	Aktubites lenensis
			Mjachkovian	Fusulinella bocki (Fusulina cylindrica)	Fusulinella ex. gr. bocki	
	Middle		Podolian	Fusulinella colaniae	Fusulinella nipperensis	
			Kashirian	Aljutovella priscoidea (Hemifusulina)	Aljutovella priscoidea	Orulganites trianguliunibili-cutus
			Verejan	Aljutovella aljutovica	Profusulinella prisca	
		Bashkir	Melekessian	Profusulinella rhombiformis	Pseudostaffella gorskyi	
			Tscheremshanian	Ozawainella pararhomboidalis		
			Prikamian	Pseudostaffella antiqua grandis	Pseudostaffella antiqua	Planospirodiscus minimus
			Severokeltmian	Pseudostaffella antiqua		
			Krasnopoljanian	Eostaffella postmosquensis	Archaediscus krestovnikovi	
	Lower					

EXPLANATIONS FOR ALL TABLES

○ Zones charazterized by complexes of a stratigraphic section.

X Zones distinguished according to ammonite remains.

⋊ Zones not thoroughly distinguished according to ammonite remains.

⊓ Subdivisions established on basis of Myarian remains.

⊗ Subdivisions characterized by complex of stratotype section and by other forms.

(⊗) Subdivisions that have not been characterized thoroughly.

? Subdivisions not distinguished.

+ Zones distinguished according to Globotruncanides.

Note: Spelling of Pajchoi within the table is incorrect; should be "Pay-Khoy."

seems to resolve the question of comparing the warm-water and cold-water zones.

However, it would be erroneous to assume, as is commonly done, that it is possible to date sections in cold-water basins on the basis of concomitance of definite species of *Globigerina* and *Globorotalia* in subtropical sections. Data that would warrant a statement on a varying rate of development for warm-water and cold-water forms are unavailable. So little is known about the evolution rate of individual groups that we cannot assert that they have been identical during definite moments of geologic time

in different belts. However, if the duration of existence of separate species of a certain genus is examined, a striking picture emerges. Whereas the majority of *Globorotalia* and *Acarinina* species occurs throughout one zone—and, rarely, two or three zones—*Globigerina* species generally are found in three to five or six zones.

Approximately the same picture is observed in the Carboniferous if the zonal sequences of the Russian platform, Vaygach, and Novaya Zemlya—rich in fusulinids—are compared with foraminiferal zones observed in the se-

Table 2. Zonal Scales of Triassic

System	Series	Stage	Substage	American zonal scale (after Tozer, 1967) Ammonites	American zonal scale Bivalves	Himalayas O	Nevada B. Columbia	Alaska Spitsbergen	Greenland	Canadian Archipel.	The North East The Far East	Zonal scale of North East Asia (after Arkhipov, 1970) Bivalves	Zonal scale of North East Asia Ammonites X
T R I A S S I C	U p p e r	Norian	Rhae-tian	Choristoceras marchi		○					⊓	Megalodon loczyi Tancredia dittmari	-
			Sup.	Rhabdoceras suessi		○					X		-
					Monotis subcircularis	⊓	⊓			⊓	⊠	Monotis ochotica M. subcircularis	-
			M.	Himavatites columbianus Drepanites rutherfordi Yuvavites magnus	Monotis scutiformis Halobia affallax H. symmetrica H. dilatata H. pacalis	⊓	⊓			⊓	⊓	Monotis scutiformis typ.	-
			Inf.	Malayites dawsoni Mojsisovicsites kerri	Halobia alascana	? ○							
		Karnian	Sup.	Klamathites macrolobatus Tropites welleri Tr. dilleri	Halobia superba Halobia ornatissima	○ ○	?		○	⊓		Halobia superba	
			Inf.	Sirenites nanseni Trachyceras obesum	Halobia rugosa H. zitteli Halobia sp.	○	? ? ?		○ ○		⊠	Halobia kolumensis H. zitteli	Sirenites senticosus
	M i d d l e	Ladinian	Sup.	Paratrachyceras sutherlandi Maclearnoceras maclearni Meginoceras meginae	Daonella elegans Daonella nitanae	○ ○ ○		? ?		X X	Halobia	Stobleites gibbosus Suordachites neraensis	
			Inf.	Progonoceratites poseidon Protrachyceras subasperum	Daonella subarctica D. longobarctica D. frami D. degeeri	○ ⊓				⊓ X	Daonella subarctica	Arctoptychites kolymensis Longobardites	
		Anisian	Sup.	Gymnotoceras chischa Gymnotoceras deleeni	Daonella dubia Daonella americana	○ ○	○		○	⊓ X	?	Daonella monssoni D. dubia	Frechites humboldtensis Gymnotoceras blakei
			M.	Anagymnotoceras varium		⊗	⊗ ⊗		⊗	⊗		Hoernesia torta	Metoptychites verchojanicus
			Inf.	Lenotropites caurus		○				⊗ X ⊗			Arctohungarites laevigatus Grambergia taimyrensis
	L o w e r	Olenekian	Inf.-Smi-Sup.Spa-thian thian	Keyserlingites subrobustus Olenekites pilaticus	Posidonia aranea	○ ○		⊓		⊓ ? X ⊗ ?	Posidonia aranea	Projungarites curviseptatus Parasiberites grambergi
				Wasatchites tardus Eoflemingites romunderi	Pseudomonotis occidentalis Posidonia mimer	⊗ ⊗	⊗	⊗		⊗ ⊗ ⊓ ⊗		Anasiberites multiformis Meekoceras gracilitatus
		Indian	Sup. Dinerian	Paranorites sverdrupi Proptychites candidus Pachyproptychites strigatus	Claraia stachei	⊗ ⊗ ⊗ ⊓	⊗	⊗	?	⊗ X ○ ⊗	Claraia stachei	Potoptychites turgidus Pachyproptychites strigatus
			Inf.Czisbach. Gandian	Ophiceras commune Otoceras boreale Otoceras concavum.	Claraia clarai	○ ○		⊓	○ ? ○	⊗ ⊗ ⊗	Claraia clarai	Otoceras boreale

Table 3. Zonal Scales of Lower and Middle Jurassic

System	Series	Stage	Substage	Zonal scale of Western Europe X	S. England	The Lower Lena	Kolyma	Key Complexes of Arctic Regions Bivalvia	Ammonites X
JURASSIC	MIDDLE	Callovian	Inf.	Macrocephalites macrocephalus	X	X			Arcticoceras ishmae
		Bathonian	Sup.	Clydoniceras discus	X			Inoceramus alaskensis I. porrectus I. retrorsus	Arctocephalites ellipticus
				Oppelia aspodiodes	X				
			M.	Tulites subcontractus	X				
			Inf.	Gracilisphinctes progracilis				I. kystatymensis	Procerites procerus
				Zigzagiceras zigzag	X				
		Bajocian	Sup.	Parkinsonia parkinsoni	X			I. elongatus	Cranocephalites vulgaris Lissoceras bakeri
				Garantiana garantiana	X				
				Strenoceros subfurcatum	X				
			Inf.	Stephanoceras humphriesianum				I. lueifer	Cranocephalites x borealis Chondroceras
				Otoites sauzei	X				
				Sonninia sowerbyi	X				
		Aalenian	Sup.	Ludwigia murchisonae	X	X	X	I. subambiguus	Tugurites
				Tmetoceras scissum				I. jurensis	
			Inf.	Leioceras opalinum	X	X			Leioceras opalinum
	LOWER	Toarcian	Sup.	Lytoceras jurense	X	X	X		Pseudolioceras compactilis
				Hildoceras bifrons	X	X	X X	Pseudomytiloides quenstedtii	P. whitbiense
			Inf.	Harpoceras falcifer	X	X			
				Dactylioceras tenuicostatum	X	X			Dactylioceras athleticum
		Pliensbachian	Sup. Domerian	Pleuroceras spinatum	X	X	X	Posidonia bronni Arctotis talageis	Acanthopleuroceras viligensis
				Amaltheus margaritatus	X	X	X	Meleagrinella tiungensis	Amaltheus margaritatus
				Prodactylioceras davoei	X	X		Velopecten viligcensis	
			Inf.	Tragophylloceras ibex	X				
				Uptonia jamesoni	X		X		Uptonia jamesoni
		Sinemurian	Sup.	Echioceras raricostatum	X				
				Oxynoticeras oxynotum	X		X		Oxynoticeras oxynotum
			M.	Asteroceras obtusum	X				
				Enasteroceras turneri	X				
			Inf.	Arnioceras semicostatum	X				
				Arietites bucklandi	X		X		Arietites
		Hettangian	Sup.	Schlotheimia angulata	X		X	Monotis originalis Otapiria limaeformis	Schlotheimia Psiloceras
			Inf.	Psiloceras planorbis	X				

I. formosulus

Table 4. Zonal Scales of Upper Jurassic

System	Series	Stage	Substage	Zonal Scale of Western Europe (0)	England	Greenland	The Pechora	Lapian Urals	Khatanga	Kolyma	Zonal Scale of Arctic Regions (X)
JURASSIC	UPPER	Volgian	Upper Aquilonian	Craspedites nodiger	—	—	—		X		Chetaites chetae / Craspedites (Taimyroceras) taimyrensis
				Craspedites subditus / Kaschpurites fulgens	X	X		X	X		Craspedites subditus / Kaschpurites fulgens — Craspedites okensis
			Middle Portlandian	Titanites (Kerberites) giganteus	O	X	?	X	X	X	Laugeites groenlandicus
				Crendonites gorei (Behemoth) / Progalbanites albani	O	X	X	X	?	?	Crendonites / Dorsoplanites sachsi
				Pavlovia pallasoides	O	X		X	X		Dorsoplanites maximus / Dorsoplanites panderi
				Pavlovia rotunda	O	X	?	X	?		Pavlovia iatriensis
			Lower Vetlianian	Pectinatites pectinatus	O	⊗	?	X	X		Pectinatites pectinatus
				Virgatasphinctoides wheatleyensis	C O	X	?	X			Ilovaiskia sokolovi — Subdichotomoceras subcrassum
				Gravesia gigas / Gravesia gravesiana	C O		?	X			Subplanites klimovi
		Kimeridgian	Sup.	Aulacostephanus autissiodorensis / Aulacostephanus pseudomutabilis / Rasenia mutabilis	? O O	X	X	X X X	X X (?)	X	Streblites taymirensis / Aulacostephanus pseudomutabilis — Amoeboceras decipiens
			Inf.	Rasenia cymodoce / Pictonia baylei	C C	X		X X	X X	X	Rasenia borealia / Pictonia involuta — Amoeboceras (Amoebites kitchini)
		Oxfordian	Sup.	Ringsteadia pseudocordata / Decipia decipiens	O O			O	X		Amoeboceras alternans
			M.	Perisphinctes cautisnigrae / Perisphinctes plicatilis	O O	X	X				Amoeboceras alternoides
			Inf.	Cardioceras cordatum / Quenstedtoceras mariae	O		X		X	X	Cardioceras cordatum
		Callovian	Sup.	Quenstedtoceras lamberti / Peltoceras athleta	C O		X			X	Longaeviceras keyserlingi
			M.	Erymnoceras coronatum / Kosmoceras jasoni	C O					X	Cadoceras milaschevici
			Inf.	Sigaloceras calloviense / Proplanulites koenigi	O O	X	X		X X	X	Cadoceras elatmae
				Macrocephalites macrocephalus	O	X	X		X	X	Arcticoceras ishmae

Table 5. Zonal Scales of Lower Cretaceous[1]

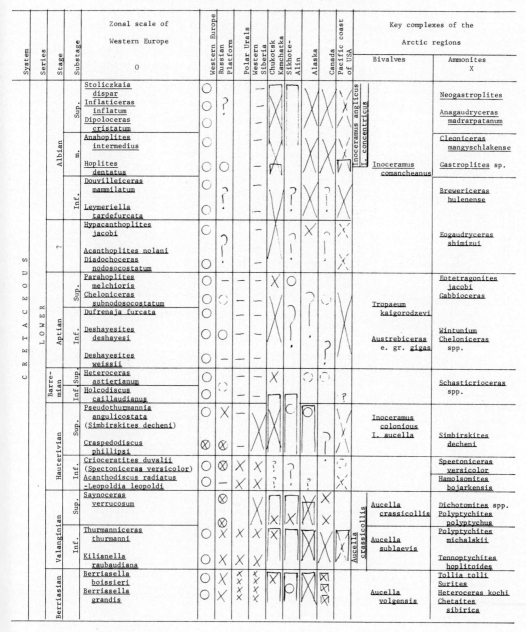

Table 6. Zonal Scales of Upper Cretaceous

System	Series	Stage	Substage	Zonal scale (Globotruncanidae) +	Zonal scale of Western Europe o	Trinidad	Alpine zone	India	South Japan	Hokkaido	Sakhalin	S-W Kamchatka Korjakskyi ridge	Mouth of the Yenisei	Zonal scale of Northeastern Asia x
CRETACEOUS (UPPER)		Danian		Globorotalia trinidadensis Eoglobigerina taurica										
		Maastricht	Sup.	Abathomphalus mayaroensis	Scaphites constrictus — Pachydiscus neubergieus / Belemnitella arkhangelskii									Inoceramus tegulatus
		Maastricht	Inf.	Globotruncanita gansseri (=Globotruncana)	Belemnella lanceolata / Acanthoscaphites tridens									Inoceramus balticus
		Campanian	Sup.	Globotruncana morozovae	Belemnitella langei / Bostrychoceros polgolocum / Belemnitella mucronata / Hoplitoplacenticeras coesfeldiense								Inoceramus schmidti	Canadoceras sachalinensis / Canadoceras kossmati
		Campanian	Inf.	Globotruncana stuartiformis	Gonioteuthis quadrata / Diplomoceras bidorsatum									Anapachidiscus naumanni
		Santonian	Sup.	Globotruncana fornicata	Marsupites testudinarius									Inoceramus patootensis
		Santonian	Inf.	Globotruncana concavata	Texanites texanus (Inoceramus cardissoides)									Inoceramus undulatoplicatus
		Coniacian	Sup.	Globotruncana primitiva	Paratexanites emscheris									Inoceramus involutus
		Coniacian	Inf.	Globotruncana coronata	Barroisiceras haberfellneri									Inoceramus multiformis I. stantoni
		Turonian	Sup.	Globotruncana lapparenti	Subprionocyclus neptuni / Collignoniceras wbolgari								Inoceramus lamarckii	Inoceramus cuvieri / Inoceramus lamarckii
		Turonian	Inf.	Helvetoglobotruncana helvetica	Mammites nodosoides / Metoicoceras whitei									Inoceramus labiatus
		Cenomanian	Sup.	Thalmanninella deeckei	Calicoceras nuviculare / Acanthoceras rhotomagense								Inoceramus nipponicus	Calicoceras naviculare / Calicoceras asiaticum
		Cenomanian	Inf.	Thalmanninella appenninica	Mantelliceras mantelli / Mantelliceras martimpreji									Mantelliceras spp. Inoceramus aff. crippsi
		Albian	Sup.	Thalmanninella ticinensis	Stoliczkia dispar									
		Albian	Sup.	Ticinella roberti	Inflaticeras inflatum									

quences of the Verkhoyansk region, where, according to O. V. Yuferev and O. I. Bogush, there are from two to four subdivisions for each subdivision in the section of the Soviet Far East. A similar situation has been revealed by M. S. Mesezhnikov (1968) from comparisons of complexes of lower Kimeridgian ammonite zones in England and on the Russian platform, in the Urals, and in the Khatanga depression. For two zones of the lower Kimeridgian of England, the northern Urals, and Western Siberia (*Pictonia baylai-involuta* and *Rasenia cymodoce*), only one zone (*Amoeboceras kitchini*) is present in Eastern Siberia and perisphinctids are absent.

In all these cases, the writer tried to adhere to the international zonal scale for warm-water basins or to work out a local zonal scale on the basis of certain species or the sequence of their appearance in the sections; such local scales are naturally less accurate and more schematic. Both methods are, undoubtedly, fully legitimate. However, they clearly demonstrate the unreliability of detailed dating with our present state of knowledge (*e.g.,* where diagnostic complexes of fossils are absent in a particular sequence). Moreover, dating might not be accurate on the basis of the zonation of a local species complex which is found together with some zonal marker forms in more southern sections, because the marker forms can exist in the north for a much longer time than in the south, where evolution is more rapid.

Therefore, the necessity to work out independent zonal scales for Arctic regions is asserted by many. These independent scales would be based on forms more commonly found in these deposits and, obviously, would be less detailed than scales for regions of warm waters. Such independent scales might be desirable. However, the need for a single scale for geologic maps makes it much more advisable to use a local zonal scale, but with a system of indices indicating the degree of precision with which a certain division is isolated. In the cases discussed, for example, $C_2{}^1{}_{2-3}$ $_{Sun}$ or $J_3{}^{Km}{}_{2-3}$ $_{Kitch}$ should be used. We cannot indicate $C_2{}^{Sun}$, but we can indicate $C_2{}^1{}_{2-3}$ $_{Sun}$, in which 1_{2-3} stands for the lower stage of C_2 and the zones 2 and 3 that are represented in Arctic sections by only one zone; or, we can indicate $J_3{}^{Km}{}_{2-3}$ $_{Kitch}$, which means that the zone of *Card. kitchini* in the Arctic section is the analogue of Kimeridgian zones 2 and 3, which are represented by only one zone in the Arctic.

I shall mention a few stratigraphic scales that show a possible subdivision of sediments accumulated under cold-water conditions in the Soviet Arctic region.

The Triassic scheme shows clearly that zonal scales in Canada and Eastern Siberia for the Lower, Middle, and a part of the Upper Triassic are nearly the same. The situation is very similar for the Upper Jurassic and Upper Cretaceous. However, Lower Jurassic and Lower Cretaceous scales have not been worked out so fully.

I wish to stress that these scales are only the first approximations to the work on detailed scales for the Arctic areas. Certainly, they are greatly idealized and are subject to discussion. They essentially indicate scales on which geologic surveys are based, but they cannot be regarded as generally accepted. They are based on data from the best-studied regions and only purport to show the extent of refinement of stratigraphic scales for Arctic regions that may be realized in the future, with respect to deposits accumulated in cold-water basins, by use of biostratigraphic material alone.

However, there is no doubt that, in addition to paleontologic and biostratigraphic methods, an important place in the refinement of stratigraphic scales for the Arctic region should be given to physical and geochemical investigations. Such studies can supply a method of checking the details of synchroneity of biostratigraphic boundaries in near and distant territories, thus establishing the exactness and reliability of the correlations.

REFERENCES

Avdeyko, G. P., 1968, Nizhnemelovyye otlozheniya severa Tikhookeanskogo kol'tsa (Lower Cretaceous deposits of northern Pacific Ocean margin): Moscow, Izd. "Nauka," p. 1–126.

Arkhipov, V. G., 1970, Zonalnaya stratigrafiya nizhne i srednetriasovykh otlozheny Verkhoyanya (Stratigraphic zonation of Lower and Middle Triassic deposits of Verkhoyansk region): Leningrad, Vses. Nauchno-Issled. Geol. Inst. Trudy, p. 1–26.

Bogush, O. I., and O. V. Yuferev, 1966, Foraminifery karbona i permi Verkhoyanya: Akad. Nauk. SSSR Sibirskoye Otdeleniye, Geol. i Geof. Inst., p. 1–208.

Koshelkina, Z. V., 1970, Sredneyurskiye otlozheniya Severo-Vostoka SSSR, smezhnykh territory i zarubezhnoy chasti boreal'noy oblasti (Middle Jurassic deposits of Far East of USSR, adjacent territories and foreign areas in boreal regions): Akad. Nauk. SSSR Sibirskoye Otdeleniye, Severo-Vostoch. Kompleks. Nauchno-Issled. Inst. Trudy, v. 37, p. 157–173.

Krasheninnikov, V. A., 1969, Geograficheskoye i stratigraficheskoye raspredeleniye planktonnykh foraminifer v otlozheniyakh paleogena tropicheskoy i subtropicheskoy oblastey (Geographic and stratigraphic distribution of Paleogene planktonic Foraminifera

in deposits of tropical and subtropical regions):
Akad. Nauk SSSR Geol. Inst. Trudy, v. 202, p. 1–
183.

Mesezhnikov, M., 1968, Zonalnoye podrazdeleniye nizhnego kimeridzha Arktiki (Zonal subdivisions of lower Kimeridgian of Arctic): Akad. Nauk SSSR Doklady Ser. Geol., v. 178, no. 4, p. 912–915.

Mikhaylov, N. P., 1966, Boreal'nyye yurskiye ammonity (Dorsoplanitinae) i zonalnoye raschleneniye volzhskogo yarusa (Boreal Jurassic ammonites [Dorsoplanitinae] and zonal division of Volgian Stage): Akad. Nauk SSSR Geol. Inst. Trudy, v. 151, p. 1–109.

Parker, F. L., 1971, Distribution of planktonic Foraminifera in recent deep-sea sediments, in B. M. Funnell and W. R. Riedel, The micropalaeontology of oceans: Cambridge, Massachusetts, Cambridge Univ. Press, p. 289–307.

Pergament, M. A., 1969, Zonalnyye podrazdeleniya mela Severo-Vostoka Azii i sopostavleniye s amerikanskoy i yevropeyskoy shkalami (Zonal subdivisions of Cretaceous of northeastern Asia and comparison with American and European scales): Akad. Nauk SSSR Izv. Ser. Geol., no. 4, p. 106–119.

Serova, M. Ya., 1969, Zonalnyye raschleneniya i korrelyatsiya paleogenovykh otlozheny Severo-Zapadnoy chasti Tikhookeanskoy provintsii. Biostratigrafii, fauny i flory kaynozoya (Zonal division and correlation of Paleogene deposits of northwest part of Pacific Ocean province—its biostratigraphy, fauna and flora in Cenozoic time): Moscow, Izd. "Nauka," p. 101–114.

Solovyeva, M. N., 1963, Stratigrafiya i fuzulininovyye zony srednekamennougol'nykh otlozheny Sredney Azii (Stratigraphy and fusulinid zonation of middle Carboniferous deposits of Soviet Central Asia): Akad. Nauk SSSR Geol. Inst., no. 76, p. 1–133.

Tuchkov, I. I., 1967, Novyye dannyye po stratigrafii sredneyurskikh otlozheny nizov'yev r. Leny (New data on stratigraphy of Middle Jurassic deposits of lower Lena River): Akad. Nauk SSSR Doklady, v. 175, no. 6, p. 1355–1358.

Correlation of Tertiary Nonmarine Deposits in Alaska and Northeastern Asia[1]

S. F. BISKE[2]
Novosibirsk, USSR

Abstract Comprehensive paleobotanic studies of the major stratigraphic sections of the Tertiary nonmarine deposits of Alaska and Asia show that correlation is possible.

In Alaska, the basal Tertiary Chickaloon Formation is correlative with the Avekova Suite of Asia. Warm-temperate plant assemblages with minor quantities of subtropical plants characterized the time of deposition of these strata. The Fultonian of Alaska correlates with the lower Ravenian Tastakh Suite of Asia. This depositional period was characterized by subtropical and tropical assemblages, but some flora represent warm-temperate trees. Both angiosperms and gymnosperms (of the latter, mainly Cupressaceae and Taxodiaceae with minor Pinaceae) are present.

The upper Kummerian Omoloy Suite is characterized by a warm-temperate flora including angiosperms (Betulaceae with minor evidence of broad-leaved trees) and gymnosperms (Pinaceae, including *Ketelleria*, *Cedrus*, and *Dacridium*, and minor Taxodiaceae). The assemblages from the lower units of the Koynatkhun Beds resemble those of the upper Angoonian Stage in northeastern Asia, and the upper strata resemble lower Seldovian units. In Alaska, the Miocene(?) Tsadaka Formation and the lower part of the Kenai Group are equivalents of the Omoloy.

Among the Seldovian suites—Marekane, Pekulney-veyem, Namtsy, and Mamontova Gora, and the upper Nera Beds—are found flora of coastal conifers (e.g., broad-leaved trees with minor subtropical components) and midland-upland conifers and birch and minor broad-leaved trees. The age of the Marekane Suite is confirmed by marine mollusks. In Alaska, the Kenai Group, except for the lower part, is considered to be equivalent to the named Seldovian suites.

In the Osinovskaya Member of the Homerian, Pinaceae and Betulaceae predominate, but scarce broad-leaved plants are represented.

Transitional beds characterize the upper Homerian and the lower Clamgulchian Stage of Alaska. In northeastern Asia, the following units are correlative with those transitional beds: Tirekhtyakh, Khapchan, Gusinka, Delyankyr, and Erman. The lower units of the Clamgulchian are similar to the Homerian, whereas middle and upper units contain boreal assemblages with a dominance of Betulaceae and Pinaceae. The age of the Erman Suite is confirmed by marine faunas. The middle Clamgulchian is correlative with the Enemten Suite and the Impoveyem Beds of northeastern Asia. The Enemten contains *Salix* assemblages with Betulaceae and Pinaceae; the Impoveyem contains different genera of Pinaceae.

The evolution of the Tertiary floras in Asia proceeded from warm-temperate Paleogene floras to subtropical Eocene floras; in middle Oligocene–late Miocene time, the dominant floras were warm-temperate ones of Turgay type, which gradually became extinct. Miocene floras were a temperate type which were ancestors of the Quaternary floras.

INTRODUCTION

The correlation presented here is based on systematic studies of stratigraphy of nonmarine Tertiary deposits which have been carried out in Alaska by J. A. Wolfe, with the participation of D. M. Hopkins, E. B. Leopold, and others (Wolfe, 1966, 1969; Wolfe *et al.*, 1966; Wahrhaftig *et al.*, 1969), and in northeastern Asia, on the type section, by the writer and his colleagues (Biske and Kulkova, 1969; Baranova *et al.*, 1968, 1970). The correlation scheme is given in Figure 1, which shows the distribution of plant assemblages in nonmarine deposits of separate suites that are correlated chiefly by palynologic data. Also, the suites are characterized by paleocarpologic evidence, and three sections (1, 6, 7) include data from leaf imprints. For two sections, an additional confirmation of age was obtained by mollusk fauna from marine beds underlying or interbedded with the nonmarine strata. The initial basis for the correlation was provided by the phytostratigraphic stages of Wolfe (1969).

BASAL TERTIARY

The Chickaloon Formation where present in Alaska forms the basal part of the Tertiary. It is correlated with the Avekova Suite of Asia on the basis of warm-temperate plant assemblages with minor quantities of subtropical plant remains.

TASTAKH-OMOLOY SUITES AND LOWER KOYNATKHUN

The lower Ravenian is referred to as the Tastakh Suite, which consists of a sequence of clays with sideritic concretions at the base, succeeded by brown coals and grading upward into heterogeneous sandstones. The Tastakh flora (mouth of Indigirka River) has some peculiar features; for example, it contains a combination of forms now belonging to genera and families of tropical, subtropical, and temperate

[1] Manuscript received, April 30, 1972.

[2] Institute of Geology and Geophysics, Siberian Branch, USSR Academy of Sciences.

lineages. This composition is similar to that of the Eocene flora of the London Clay. The similarity of the 20 pollen species of the Tastakh Suite to species of the Burrard Formation (British Columbia) has been shown, particularly by the zonal species *Pistillipolenites macgregorii* Rouse (Kulkova, 1968). This flora compares with the Alaskan Kushtaka Formation flora for the same genera and families: *Glyptostrobus*. Palmae, *Sabal, Engelhardtia, Juglans, Pterocarya, Actinidia, Magnolia, Sapindus*, Myrtaceae, *Alangium, Platanus, Sorbus, Ilex, Hamamelis, Liquidambar*, Anacardiaceae, *Ulmus*, and *Alnus*.

As shown in Figure 1, the Tastakh is characterized by the predominance of forms which must be assigned to form genera with no analogues in present vegetation. Part of these forms are from the groups *Castanea-Castanopsis, Quercus gracilis*, and *Q. graciliformis*, which are regarded by palynologists as representative of ancient evergreen plants. Among Angiospermae, subtropical and nearly subtropical plants dominate: Palmae, *Hamamelis, Sterculia, Nyssa, Aralia, Magnolia, Alangium, Ficus, Morus, Rhus, Abutilon, Growia, Hibiscus, Loranthus, Cardiospermum*, Pistaceae, Myrtaceae, *Cissus*, and *Cissites*.

Small-leaved Betulaceae are scarce. Some of the more abundant broad-leaved Betulaceae are: *Fagus, Carya, Ulmus, Juglans, Carpinus, Platanus, Castanea*, and *Acer*. Among the Gymnospermae, Cupressaceae and Taxodiaceae predominate; *Ginkgo* is present also, along with a small number of other genera: *Cedrus, Pinus, Picea, Tsuga*, and *Abies*.

The preceding data and other data based on seeds, fruits, and leaves indicate that the Tastakh flora is an almost subtropical one which records the warmest climate in the Cenozoic history of northeastern Asia. This warm period occurred at the end of the middle Eocene and the beginning of the late Eocene. During this climatic period, there was abundant moisture, and, because of the proximity to the warm sea, there apparently were no abrupt seasonal variations. The period had long polar days and nights.

The Omoloy Suite (lower Yana) and the lower units of the Koynatkhun Beds are referred to the upper Angoonian Stage in sections of northeastern Asia. The basal deposits consist of clays with brown coals which grade into sandstones at the top. Based on paleobotany, the age of the Omoloy is middle-late Oligocene.

In the Cook Inlet basin, the stratigraphic equivalents to the Tastakh, Omoloy, and the lower part of the Koynatkhun are the Tsadaka Formation and the lower units of the Kenai Group. In the Alaska Range, the Healy Creek Formation is an equivalent.

In the Omoloy flora (seeds, fruits, pollen, spores), in contrast to the older Tastakh flora, subtropical plants among the Angiospermae (*Ilex, Liquidambar, Rhus, Sterculia*, and *Nyssa*) are present in insignificant quantities. The flora consists basically of small-leaved Betulaceae with many *Fagus, Castanea, Quercus, Carya, Pterocarya, Juglans cinerea, Ulmus, Zelkowa, Celtis, Tilia*, and *Acer*. Although Angiospermae are still predominant, Gymnospermae are present in increased quantities. Distinctive features in the flora are: (1) a decrease of the role of Cupressaceae, (2) the elimination of *Ginkgo*, and (3) an increase in the amount of Pinaceae. These peculiarities are more pronounced in the late Oligocene floras of northeastern Asia than in Alaska because the Asian floras are located inside the continent at higher latitude, chiefly in the mountains. The Angoonian and the northeastern floras reveal a warm-temperate climate.

SELDOVIAN STAGE

Deposits of the Seldovian Stage in northeastern Asia are exposed in many sections in intramontane basins (Fig. 1). The section at Mamontova Gora in the Aldan region is especially rich in plant remains; at its base is the Namtsy Suite of early Miocene age, and, higher in the section, is the middle Miocene Mamontova Gora Suite.

The comparison of Seldovian flora of the Kenai Group of Alaska with flora found as leaf imprints in the Namtsy Suite at Mamontova Gora indicates the great extent of the community at the generic level. A common and widely distributed species is *Cercidiphyllum crenatum*. Several genera observed in the Kenai Seldovian —such as *Dryopteris, Populus, Salix, Carya, Juglans, Corylus, Betula, Alnus, Castanea, Ulmus, Acer, Fagus, Quercus, Vitis*, and *Prunus* —are represented by a variety of species in the Mamontova Gora flora. A great fossil complex is established according to seeds and fruits; it includes not only the flora of the Namtsy and Mamontova Gora Suites, but also *Juglans cinerea* and the genera *Potamogeton, Carex, Scirpus, Juncus, Comptonia, Juglans, Alnus, Betula, Aralia, Diervilla*, and others. The sections of the Koynatkhun Beds contain remains of fruits of *Juglans cinerea*, whereas the Pekulney-

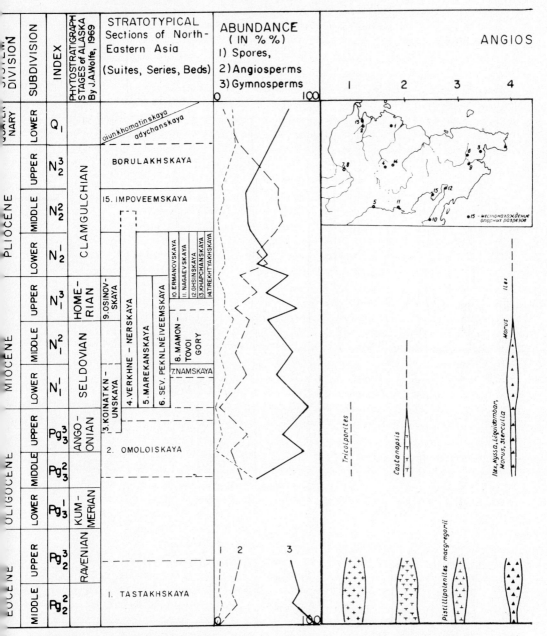

FIG. 1—Palynologic composition of Paleogene and Neogene deposits in stratotype sections of northeastern Asia, and correlation with phytostratigraphic stages of Alaska (continued on two following pages).

1. Formal genus group: *Tricolporopollenites, Triporites,* and *Tetraporites.*
2. Formal species group: *Castanea crenataiformis, Quercus conferta,* and *Q. graciliformis.*
3. *Pistillipollenites macgregorii.*
4. Subtropical and similar flora: Palmae, *Loranthus, Aralia, Nyssa, Hibiscus, Alangium, Ficus, Morus, Oleanus, Hamamelis, Sterculia,* and *Rhus.*
5. Warm-temperate, broad-leaved flora: Numerous genera of families Juglandaceae, Fagaceae, Myricaceae, Plantanaceae, Ulmaceae, Aceraceae, and Tiliaceae.
6. Temperate and temperate-warm flora: Betulaceae.
7. Salicaceae.
8. Ericaceae.
9. Grasses.
10. Podocarpaceae.
11. *Ginkgo.*
12. Cupressaceae.
13. Taxodiaceae: exotic—*Sequoia, Sciadapitys, Glyptostrobus;* warm-temperature—*Metasequoia, Taxodium.*
14. Pinaceae.
15. Ferns.
16. Mosses.

PERMAE

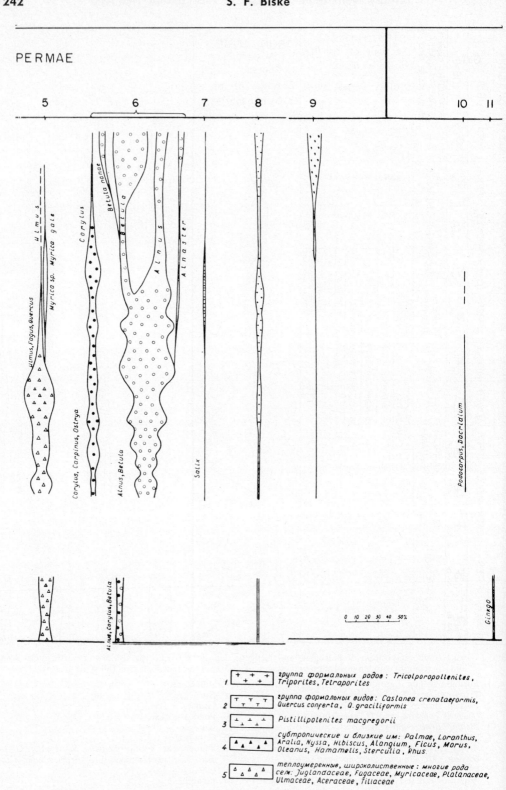

1 | + + + | группа формальных родов: Tricolporopollenites, Triporites, Tetraporites

2 | T T T | группа формальных видов: Castanea crenataeformis, Quercus conferta, Q. graciliformis

3 | ⊥ ⊥ ⊥ | Pistillipolenites macgregorii

4 | ▲ ▲ ▲ | субтропические и близкие им: Palmae, Loranthus, Aralia, Nyssa, Hibiscus, Alangium, Ficus, Morus, Oleanus, Hamamelis, Sterculia, Rhus

5 | △ △ △ | теплоумеренные, широколиственные: многие рода сем: Juglandaceae, Fagaceae, Myricaceae, Platanaceae, Ulmaceae, Aceraceae, Tiliaceae

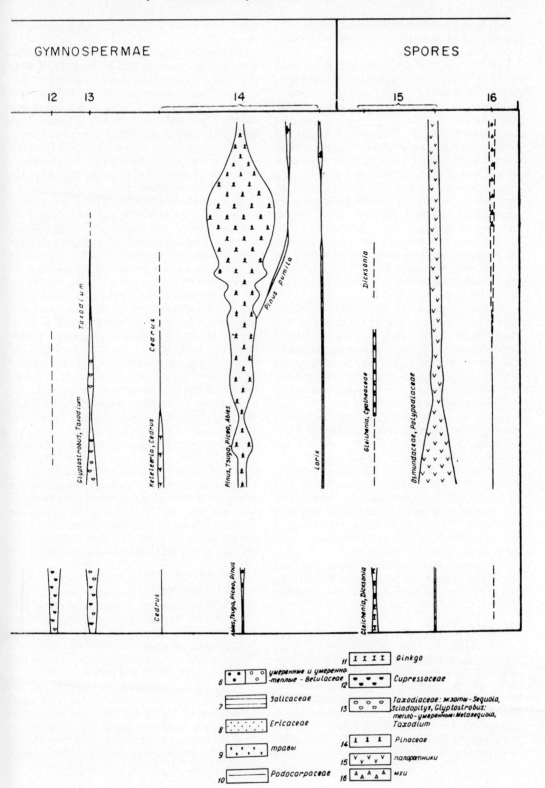

GYMNOSPERMAE

SPORES

12   13   14   15   16

Taxodium

Glyptostrobus, Taxodium

Cedrus

Keteleeria, Cedrus

Cedrus

Pinus, Tsuga, Picea, Abies

Pinus pumila

Larix

Abies, Tsuga, Picea, Pinus

Dicksonia

Gleichenia, Cyatheaceae

Gleichenia, Dicksonia

Osmundaceae, Polypodiaceae

Legend:

6 — умеренные и умеренно-теплые - Betulaceae

7 — Salicaceae

8 — Ericaceae

9 — травы

10 — Podocarpaceae

11 — Ginkgo

12 — Cupressaceae

13 — Taxodiaceae: жаты - Sequoia, Sciadopitys, Glyptostrobus: тепло- умеренные: Metasequoia, Taxodium

14 — Pinaceae

15 — папоротники

16 — мхи

veyem Beds (Anadyr' embayment) contain this species and an abundance of cones of *Metasequoia disticha* also.

Pollen floras are dominated by Betulaceae, including a constant admixture of warm-temperate broad-leaved species and of pollen of Nyssaceae, Araliaceae, and Aceraceae, which prefer warmer climates.

Gymnospermae are represented chiefly by Pinaceae (which are found also in cones) and by fewer Taxodiaceae. Generally, rich warm-temperate flora and intracontinental flora of the Turgay type were restored in the Seldovian. In composition, the flora resembles floras from the Koynatkhun, Pekulneyveyem, and upper Nera–upper Indigirka strata. In sections of the Pekulneyveyem and upper Nera, more conifers are present, indicating mountain vegetation. In contrast, the Alaskan Seldovian floras show a low development of Pinaceae and a dominance by Taxodiaceae.

The composition of the Seldovian Kenai flora is very similar to that of the shoreline Marekane Suite of the north shore of the Sea of Okhotsk; the age of the Marekane is confirmed by marine mollusks. In the Marekane, the greatest development was reached by the families Taxodiaceae and Cupressaceae (in pollen and seeds); *Gingko* remains have been found. Pinaceae are represented by a variety of genera. Among Angiospermae, representatives of Magnoliaceae, Nyssaceae, and Anacardiaceae are present.

Northeastern Seldovian floras are partly indicative of a wide development in North Asia of the mesophytic forests, and the floras belong to a general geographic region. These Seldovian floras were found by J. Wolfe on coasts of northwest America and on the northern Japanese islands.

The northeastern Siberian floras represent the north part of the mesophytic forest zone and show vertical zonation as in mountain regions.

HOMERIAN STAGE

The Homerian Stage in northeastern Asian sections is represented by the Osinovskaya Member (Anadyr' basin) and by the lower units of the Tirekhtyakh (upper Indigirka River), Khapchan Beds (Arctic coast, Yana River), and the Delyankyr Beds (intracontinental region). Lower beds of the Erman Suite and the Gusinka Beds in Kamchatka yield additional evidence of upper Miocene faunas from marine sediments underlying nonmarine deposits.

Among the vegetation remnants in the Osinovskaya Beds is *Betula anadyrensis* Dorf. Floras similar to recent birches of Japan and Korea are *Cornus aldanensis* Dorf, which is present in the Mamontova Gora Suite, and *Nyssa sibirica* Dorf, which is known in Oligocene and middle Miocene deposits of Western Siberia.

Palynologic data and stratigraphic position of the Osinovskaya Beds over the Pekulneyveyem make it possible to assign the Osinovskaya to the upper Miocene.

Flora of the northeastern Homerian, as well as flora of the Grubstake and Bear Lake Formations and of the upper part of the Kenai Group of Alaska, reveals less variable composition than that of the Seldovian. Small amounts of warm-temperate exotic elements—such as *Carya, Pterocarya, Carpinus, Ulmus*, and *Taxodium*—are present. As Figure 1 indicates, palynologic complexes still reflect the predominance of Angiospermae; however, the percentage of Gymnospermae has increased. Betulaceae (especially *Alnus*) and *Salix* became dominant among the flowering plants. The genera of the Pinaceae which are present are characteristic of the Gymnospermae; in addition, the composition of conifers shows the correlation of the American species *Pinus monticola* (cones) and of the Japanese species *Tsuga oblonga* and *Picea hondoensis* (cones) to floras of eastern regions.

Floras of various areas are characterized by peculiar features of provincial character; the floras are divided into mountain, intracontinental, and coastal. As a whole, however, the Homerian floras display clear indications of impoverishment as compared with Seldovian floras, and they are characterized as temperate.

CLAMGULCHIAN STAGE

The Clamgulchian Stage in Alaska corresponds in northeastern Asia to most of the sections of the Nagayevskaya, Gusinka, Erman, Khapchan, Delyankyr, and Impoveyem beds. Stratigraphic subdivisions mentioned above are characterized by cold-temperate floras—leaf imprints, seeds, fruits, and pollen.

Palynologic complexes of deposits of the lower Pliocene indicate approximately an equal abundance of Gymnospermae and Angiospermae. In the middle Pliocene, the Gymnospermae became more abundant than the Angiospermae for the first time during the Neogene.

The correlations between leaf and conifer plants are dependent on location. Mountain and intracontinental floras are rich in Pinaceae and show the contribution of mountain-tundra plant assemblages. Floras of the plains, and especially the coastal plains, contain more plants of the families Salicaceae and Betulaceae, plus a negligible admixture of *Ulmus;* and *Myrica,* especially *Myrica* Gale, is present everywhere in these floras.

The richest is the Erman flora, the base of which is referred to the Homerian; the middle and upper parts are impoverished and typical for the Clamgulchian. In this flora, *Alnus corrallina* Lesq., *Ribes stanfordianus* Dorf., *Populus kobayashii* Suz., *Alnus* sp., *Betula* sp., *Salix* sp., and *Fraxinus* sp. were determined according to leaf imprints. Several extinct forms (*Aracispermum* cf. *hippuriformis* Nikit.) and Neogene exotic forms (*Epipremnum crassum* C. and E. M. Reid, *Pterocarya* cf. *kireevskiana* Dorf., *Decodon gibbosus* E. M. Reid, *Aralia* spp., *Andromeda bremnea* Dorf., *etc.*) are represented in the Erman flora by seeds and fruits. This flora is similar to recent Pacific maritime floras of North America and of the southern part of the Soviet Far East. The flora has few extinct and exotic forms, but some forms resembling living ones are found. Floral composition shows a transition from the Neogene to the Quaternary. This transitional flora is characteristic of beds of the Clamgulchian of northeastern Asia.

The poorest floras were found in the middle Pliocene Impoveyem Beds (north shore, Sea of Okhotsk). The palynologic complexes (Fig. 1) are represented chiefly by Pinaceae; *Cedrus* and *Keteeleria* are absent. Among the warm-climate plants, *Tsuga* is present everywhere and a few grains of *Abies* are present; most abundant, however, is the pollen of *Picea* and *Pinus,* including the species *Pinus silvestris* L., which is now living. Among the few Angiospermae, most pollen belongs to the family Ericaceae,

(*e.g., Alnus, Corylus,* and *Betula*). *Myrica* Gale is present everywhere. The number of spores—composed of Polypodiaceae, *Lycopodium, Sphagnum,* and *Bryales*—is greater than in older units. The palynologic complexes mentioned reflect the cold-temperate vegetation typical of the Quaternary Period.

Conclusion

Because nonmarine deposits of northeastern Asia correlate with phytostratigraphic stages of Alaska in many stratigraphic subdivisions, it is possible to establish the general framework for paleogeographic development of the northern regions of the Pacific Ocean sector.

References Cited

Baranova, Yu. P., *et al.,* 1968, Kaynozoy Severo-Vostoka SSSR: Akad. Nauk SSSR Sibirskoye Otdeleniye, Inst. Geologii i Geofiziki Trudy, no. 38, p. 1–124.

——— *et al.,* 1970, Novyye dannyye o miotsenovykh otlozheniyakh Mamontovoy Gory na Aldane: Akad. Nauk SSSR Doklady, v. 193, no. 5, p. 1119–1123.

Biske, S. F., and I. A. Kulkova, 1969, O vydelenii neogena v kontinentalnoy formatsii kraynego Severo-Vostoka Azii: Akad. Nauk SSSR Sibirskoye Otdeleniye, Inst. Geologii i Geofiziki Trudy, no. 6, p. 137–141 (with Engl. Summ.).

Kulkova, I. A., 1968, Pyltsa *Pistillipolenites macgregorii* Rouse v eotsenovykh otlozheniyakh Yakutii: Akad. Nauk SSSR Doklady, v. 182, no. 6, p. 1410–1412.

——— 1970, Palynologicheskiye issledovaniya eotsenovykh otlozheny Yano-Indigirskoy nizmennosti: Novosibirsk, Akad. Nauk SSSR, unpub. doctoral dissert., p. 1–24.

Wahrhaftig, Clyde, *et al.,* 1969, The Coal Bearing Group in the Nenana coal field, Alaska: U.S. Geol. Survey Bull. 1274-D, p. 1–30.

Wolfe, J. A., 1966, Tertiary plants from the Cook Inlet region, Alaska: U.S. Geol. Survey Prof. Paper 398-B, p. 1–32.

——— 1969, Paleogene floras from the Gulf of Alaska region: U.S. Geol. Survey Open-File Rept., p. 1–111.

——— D. M. Hopkins, and E. B. Leopold, 1966, Tertiary stratigraphy and paleobotany of the Cook Inlet region, Alaska: U.S. Geol. Survey Prof. Paper 398-A, p. 1–29.

Paleogene and Neogene Stratigraphic Zones of North Pacific Area[1]

Yu. B. GLADENKOV[2]

Moscow, USSR

Abstract According to many micropaleontologists, worldwide correlation of Tertiary successions in tropical and subtropical areas can be based on planktonic foraminiferal zones (chronozones). The taxonomic assemblages of such zones correspond to *evolution stages* of foraminifers. Current studies show that many of these zones can be traced in Japan and, to a certain extent, on Sakhalin, in Kamchatka, and in North America. For the first time, the stratigraphic scales of the North Pacific area can be related rather confidently to the general world scale. The following have helped make worldwide correlations more reliable: studies of nannoplankton and mammals (hipparions and Desmostyliidae in particular) and use of isotopic-age dating, paleomagnetism, and paleoclimatology.

Unfortunately, the planktonic fauna is very sparse in the Tertiary rocks of the North Pacific region. Therefore, the establishment of regional scales there must be based mainly on benthonic faunas. A change of systematic composition of some mollusk genera (*Yoldia*, *Acila*, and genera of the families Arc'dae and Pectenidae) and the general number of species and newly-appearing species in certain stages of their development are reflections of their evolution stages. These stages can be used to subdivide the sections into several zones and to correlate them. Distinguishing such zones independent of the facies composition of the rocks and correlation of the zones with the planktonic zones are the bases for applying the international scale in the Boreal Pacific area. Seven such zones have been proposed for the Neogene of the USSR on the basis of *Yoldia* and other fossil groups; many of the zones have analogues in adjacent areas.

Establishment of the faunal succession relative to evolution is of great importance because the composition of each faunal assemblage in any particular section is related to stratigraphic facies; underestimating this factor has resulted in significant mistakes in correlation.

To make the provincial schemes more exact, it may be necessary to use data on other faunal groups, floral successions, paleoclimatology, *etc.* In order to work out regional stratigraphic scales, the establishment of *evolution stages of ancient basins*—including changes of fauna and lithology during each of these stages—and also the study of faunal assemblages of like and unlike facies of contemporaneous and successive levels are of great importance.

Local subdivisions (suites, members, beds) that are related to facies peculiarities of the sequences should be based on this framework of zones that was established according to evolution stages of the faunas. Paleoecologic and paleogeographic methods also are important in these studies.

Introduction

During the last decade, knowledge of the Tertiary stratigraphy of the Pacific area has advanced considerably, as can be seen from the correlation of regional zones which have been developed. However, many stratigraphic problems remain unsolved. First, the age datings of many stratigraphic schemes are somewhat conditional; the province correlation (based mainly on lists of faunas) has not yet been fully agreed upon. Therefore, geologists of the Soviet Union studying the Pacific area try to work out local and interregional zones and to correlate them with the international scheme. These tasks should be solved by various methods and on the basis of different faunistic groups.

New geologic data obtained during recent years serve as a basis for the solution to these problems. (1) Abundant corehole logs are available, and the scope of detailed studies has increased, making geologic knowledge more objective. (2) In biostratigraphy, geologists are using planktonic assemblages on a large scale; also, work on biostratigraphy is more versatile in that various groups of fauna are used. (3) Physical methods are applied widely in stratigraphy. (4) The study of evolution stages in analyzing the fauna is particularly significant. (5) Paleoecologic and paleogeographic studies are of great importance.

New Approach

Despite these advances, however, until recently there had been no reliable correlation of the Pacific scale with the general (European) scale. The Tertiary stages of Western Europe, based on sections in semiclosed basins and on complexes of mollusks, *etc.*, are of a regional nature. Therefore, in certain areas of the globe, including the Pacific, local stratigraphic zones have been created. The geologic literature of recent years has enabled us to develop a new approach to the solution of this correlation problem.

According to the research of micropaleontologists (O. Bandy, H. Bolli, W. Blow, V. Krasheninnikov, and others), the worldwide correlation of Tertiary successions of tropical and subtropical areas is based on planktonic foraminiferal zones (chronozones); these zones corre-

[1] Manuscript received, April 30, 1972.

[2] Geological Institute, USSR Academy of Sciences.

spond to the *evolution stages* of these foramin-ifers. The current literature shows that many of these zones can be traced in Japan (Asano and Hatai, 1967) and, to a certain extent, on Sakhalin and Kamchatka (Serova, 1969), and also in the northern part of North America (Bandy, 1968a, b; also R. Kolpack and others). Thus, it has become possible for the first time to correlate rather confidently the stratigraphic scales of the North Pacific area with the European scale (Table 1; Berggren, 1969; Krasheninnikov, 1971).

The establishment of synchronous *climatic fluctuations* in the past also is significant in cor-relation, the most convincing data being evi-dences of temperature fluctuations during the Pliocene Epoch and the Quaternary Period.

It is now definitely established that, in the northern parts of Europe, Asia, and America, relatively warm-water benthonic assemblages were present in the early Pliocene (Coralline Crag of England, Etchegoin of North America, Enemten of Kamchatka, Takikawa of Japan). They were replaced in the late Pliocene by cold-water assemblages (Red Crag of England, Ust'-Lemimten of Kamchatka, Bering of North America, Setana of Japan). These assemblages, in turn, were replaced by "cool" Pleistocene as-semblages (Anvil deposits with their analogues and overlying Pinakul-Karaginsky beds; Petrov and Khoreva, 1968). This succession of assem-blages seems to be related to significant climatic changes on a worldwide scale. In certain conti-nental deposits, determination of the Pliocene-Pleistocene boundary can be based on spore and pollen spectra (change of *Metasequoia* flora in Japan, *etc.;* Minato *et al.,* 1968; Boyar-skaya, 1969; and others, including E. Mala-yeva).

Physical methods—primarily *radiometric age determinations* for rocks—and *paleomagnetic data* are also of great importance. Radiometric age determinations in the northern USSR have been carried out on a small scale, mainly for magmatic formations.

Interesting data have been obtained on age determinations for the Neogene of Japan (Ik-ebe and Chiji, 1969), where the positions of samples analyzed were correlated with the zones of planktonic foraminifers, radiolarians, mollusks, and mammals. Comparison of age dates for Japanese deposits with available data on European sequences shows a great similarity that appears to support the suggested correla-tion based on fauna and to differ from stage interpretations given by Japanese authors (K.

Asano, T Saito, and others).

Exceptionally interesting also is a scale of ra-diometric ages that has been prepared by Amer-ican researchers.

Paleomagnetic data are also very promising. However, the practical application of this method in correlation is rather difficult because of gaps in the sections, the absence of radiomet-ric age data, and, in some places, an unde-tected magnetization of sedimentary rocks.

First attempts have been made to correlate paleomagnetic sections of the Pacific area with the world scale (Kochegura *et al.,* 1969; Pevzner, 1968). On Kamchatka and in the Koryak Highland, geologists were able to draw the upper boundary of the last zone of reverse polarity—the Matuyama (0.7 m.y.)—and to outline the boundaries of the "Jaramillo event" (0.9 m.y.; V. Kochegura, M. Pevzner, S. An-dreyev, B. Genin, and others). Unfortunately, the paleontologic characteristics of the section studied are not reliable enough. Extremely in-teresting in this respect are the data on Iceland that permit elucidation of the relations between Pliocene and Quaternary paleomagnetic zones and zones of mollusks (Tjörnes Formation; Ei-narsson *et al.,* 1967). However, two or three interpretations of these data are possible, de-pending on the age of the unconformity at the base of the Breidavik Formation.

Studies carried out in the oceans by Lin'kova (1969) and others (*e.g.,* Lisitzyn) show the possibility of determining paleomagnetic zones in bottom sediments. Attempts are being made to correlate sediment zones with assemblages of foraminifers, nannoplankton, radiolarians, and diatoms. It has been established that the re-placement of Pliocene diatoms by Pleistocene forms occurs near the "Jaramillo level"; the change in silicoflagellate complexes also takes place at this level (A. Zhuze). The appearance of the assemblage with *Globorotalia truncatu-lionoides,* which is usually considered to mark the beginning of the Pleistocene, seems to be associated with the level of the Gilsa or the Ol-duvia event (J. Hays *et al.,* 1969).

Unfortunately, the planktonic fauna is very poor in the Tertiary rocks of the North Pacific area. Therefore, the establishment of regional zones must be based mainly on benthonic fau-nas. A certain change in molluscan assemblages (*Yoldia,* Arcidae, Pectenidae, Turritellidae, *Acila*) and the general number of species and newly-appearing species at certain moments of their development (data have been published by T. Kotaka, K. Masuda, F. S. MacNeil,

Table 1. Planktonic Zones of Paleogene and Neogene

System	Series	Subseries	Stages (by Selli and others)	Radiometric by Selli m.y.	time by ky Berggren up m.y.	Stages	Zones (Tropical and subtropical regions)	Subzones	Trinidad	Europe	Syria	Pacific O	Japan	Sakhalin	Kamchatka	N.America	Assemblages (Asano, Hatai, 1967)	Stages	Radiometric time (m.y.) by Ikebe and others	Standard Stages of Japan
Neogene	Pliocene	Upper	Calabrian; Upper Villafranchian	0,6; 1,8	1,8	Calabrian	Globorotalia truncatulinoides		+	+		+	+			Globorotalia truncatulinoides				Shibikawa
		Middle	Astian; Piacenzian	3,1 3	3	Astian	Globorotalia tosaensis		+	+		+	+			Sphaeroidinella dehiscens			–0,6	
		Lower	Piacenzian			Piacenzian	Globoquadrina altispira		+	+		+	+						1,6–2	Wakimoto
			Fabianian	7	5,5	Messinian (Sarmatian)	Sphaeroidinella dehiscens		+	+		+	+	+ ?		Globorotalia inflata			–6	Kitaura
	Miocene	Upper	Messinian	11,8	9		Globorotalia miocenica (Orbulina universa)	G. tumida; G. plesiotumida; G. acostaensis – G.merotumida; Globorotalia mayeri	+	+	+	+	+		+	Sphaeroidinella seminulina G. Bulloides, G. menardii menardii; G. nepenthes	Tortonian	10	Onnagawa Nishikurosawa
			Tortonian			Tortonian	Globorotalia menardii (Orbulina universa)		+	+	+	+	+			Globorotalia menardii; Globorotalia bykovae; Globorotalia mayeri	Helvetian	13–16	Daishima
		Middle	"Helvetian"	18,8	11,7 14	"Helvetian"	Globorotalia fohsi (Candorbulina universa)	Globorotalia fohsi; Globorotalia peripheroacuta; P. glomerosa; G. bisphaerica; G. dehiscens	+	+	+	+	+	+	+ ?	Candorbulina universa; Globigerinoides bisphaericus; Globigerinatella insueta	Burdigalian	17–19	Nishinoiwa Funadawa Nishisonōgi
		Lower	Burdigalian	17,5		Burdigalian	Globigerinatella insueta		+	+	+	+	+		+	Globirerinita dissimilis; G. venezuelana	Aquitanian	22	
			"Aquitanian"	22,5		"Aquitanian"	Globigerinita dissimilis	Globirerinita stainforthi; Globigerinita dissimilis	+	+	+	+	+		+			25	Madze
Paleogene	Oligocene	Upper	Chattian	26	23	Chattian	Globigerina kugleri		+	+		+	+	+		Globorotalia opima opima; Globigerina ampliapertura; Globigerina sakitoensis				Funadsu
							Globigerina ciperoensis		+	+		+	+							Okinawa
		Lower	Rupelian	30	26	Rupelian	Globorotalia opima opima		+	+		+	+							
				36	30		Globigerina ampliapertura		+	+		+	+							
							Globigerina corpulenta		+	+		+	+							
	Eocene	Upper	Priabonian (Priabonian)	41 45	36	Bartonian	Truncarotaloides rohri	Globorotalia cerroazulensis; Globigerapsis semiinvoluta	+	+	+	+	+			Glob. linaperta				
						Dverian	Hantkenina alabamensis (Orbulinoides backmanni)		+	+	+	+	+			Hantkenina lehneri				
					41 45		Acarinina rotundimarginata (Globorotalia lehneri)		+	+	+	+	+							
		Middle	Lutetian		49	Lutetian	Acarinina bolibrooki (A. "crassaformis")	Globigerapsis kugleri; Hantkenina aragonensis	+	+	+	+	+			Porticulasphaera mexicana; Globigerinatheca barri; Acarinina bullbrooki; Globorotalia centralis; Globigerina bowerii				Takasima
		Lower	Ypresian	53,5 56		Ypresian	Globorotalia aragonensis	A. pentacamerata; G. aragonensis	+	+	+	+	+							
							Globorotalia marginodentata		+	+	+	+	+		+					
							Globorotalia subbotinae (G. wilcoxensis)		+	+	+	+	+		+					
	Paleocene	Upper	Thanetian	58		Landenian– Thanetian	Globorotalia velascoensis (Acarinina subsphaerica)	Globorotalia velascoensis; Globorotalia pseudomenardii; G. velascoensis	+	+	+	+	+		+	Globorotalia pseudomenardii				
			Montian	60		Montian	Globorotalia angulata (G. pusilla)	G. pseudomenardii; Globorotalia conicotruncata; Globorotalia angulata	+	+	+	+	+							
		Lower		61,5			Acarinina uncinata (A. inconstans)		+	+	+	+	+							
			Danian		65	Danian	Globorotalia trinidadensis (Globoconusa daubjergensis)	Globigerina (Eoglobigerina) taurica; Globigerina (trivialis)	+	+	+	+	+			Globoconusa daubjergensis; Globorotalia pseudobulloides				

Table 2. "Zones" (Horizons) and Assemblages of Mollusks

Age				Japan				
			Turritellidae (Kotaka, 1959)	Pectinidae (Masuda, 1962)	Arcidae (Noda, 1966)	Yoldia (Oyama, 1960; Uozumi, 1957)		Yoldia (Gladenkov, 1970)
Q								
Pliocene	Neogene	saishuensis	T.andenensis T. otukai T.s. etigoensis	P. naganumanus	A. amicula rotunda- A. akitaensis	Y. johanii		Y. hyperborea
			T. s.	Amus. praesignis(Fort.takanashii) Pat. tokunagai	A.suzuki-A. castellata	A.tatunocutiensis -A.amicula elongata	Y.macroschema	Y. supraoregona-Y. enemtensis
		T.	T.s. mo-	Pat.yamasakii (Amus.iitomensis) Pat. yessonensis tonbetsuensis	A. hokkaidoensis-A.amicula amicula	Y. sagittaria-P. kakimii		Y.ermanensis Y. kulluntunensis- Y.chejsliensis
Middle Miocene			T. tanaguraensis	Myagipec.matsumoriensis (Pat. kimurai)	A. tsudai-A. tozawaensis A. hataii-A. ninohensis	Y. Notabilis		Y.scapha-J. epilongissima Y.chojensis
Lower Miocene			T.s-hataii	Nanaoch. notoensis	A. kakehataensis-A.makiyamai	Y.uranoi Y.biremis		Y. pennulata
							Y.sobrina	Y.watasei-Y. longissima
							Y. watasei	
						P. owata		
						J. watasei ogasawarai		

H. Noda, S. Uozumi, L. Krishtofovich, V. Slodkevich, V. Sinelnikova, and Yu. Gladenkov) can reflect *evolution stages* of these groups and can be used both for subdivision of the sections into zones and for their correlation (Tables 2, 3; Fig. 1). The isolation of such zones and their correlation with planktonic zones give a more solid basis for applying the international scale to the North Pacific area. Seven zones of this kind have been suggested for the Neogene of the USSR on the basis of *Yoldia* and other groups; many of these zones can be determined in adjacent areas as well (Gladenkov, 1970).

The establishment of a succession in faunal assemblages related to their evolution is of great importance, because the composition of a certain assemblage in any particular section is always related to the facies. An underestimation of this factor can result in substantial stratigraphic errors. To make the provincial schemes more exact, we naturally use data on other faunal groups, flora, paleoclimatology, *etc.*

In working out regional stratigraphic zones, it is important to establish *evolution stages in*

ancient basins—including changes in lithology and fauna during these stages—and also to study faunistic complexes of different and similar facies of synchronous and nonsynchronous levels. The isolation of local subdivisions (suites, members, beds) that are related to facies peculiarities of the sections should be based on the framework of zones that were established on the basis of evolution stages of the fauna. Paleoecologic and paleogeographic methods are significant in these studies.

CONCLUSIONS

All these factors, plus the increased reliability resulting from such a complex approach to correlations, make it possible to suggest a new correlation of Neogene deposits for the North Pacific belt, in which we can outline seven zones of *Yoldia* and other mollusks which are shown in Table 3 under "Neogene Horizons by Gladenkov." Because key assemblages of old faunas are widely developed, it is possible to trace them over extensive areas. Such assemblages are the following: (X) *Papyridea harrimani,*

Table 3. Neogene of North Pacific Area (Stages and Horizons)

Age	N. Japan	Sakhalin	Kamchatka	N. America	Neogene Horizons by Gladenkov (1970)	Horizons and Age by L. Krishtofovich (1959)		Age
Q		?	Tusatuwaam ?	Anvil beds ?			Pleistocene	Q
Pliocene — Setana	A	4 horizons of Marujam.stage A	Ust-limimtewajam A	Bering beds A	VI	?		Pliocene "U."
Pliocene — Takikawa	P	3 horizons of Marujam.stage P	Enemten P	Etchegoin Jacalitos P H	V		Pleistocene	Pliocene "L."
Miocene Upper — Wakkanai	D	Takoi / Okobikai D	Erman / Etolon E	Neroly / Cierbo D	IV / IIIe	Erman / Etolon	U. / M. / L.	Upper Pliocene
Miocene Middle — Kawabata		Sertunai / ?	Kakert / Iljin / Kuluwen	Briones / Temblor	III / II	Kakert / Kamchat / Sertunai	Upper Miocene	Middle Miocene
Miocene Lower — Takinoue / Asahi		Sakhalin Upper-duj / Tshechov	Wiwentec / Utcholok	Vaqueros	I	Sakhalin	Middle Miocene	Lower Miocene
Oligocene — Poronai / Ushikari ?	X	Cholm Machigar X / Lesogor	Gakch Amanin X / Kovatshin	Blakeley X		Machigar / Kovatshin	Lower Miocene / Oligocene	Oligocene

X = Assemblage with <u>Papyridea harrimani</u>, <u>Yoldia watasei</u>, and <u>Yoldia longissima</u>.
D = Upper stratigraphic limit of Desmostilidae.
E = Echinoids with <u>Astrodapsis antisella</u>.
H = Upper stratigraphic limit of hipparions of upper Miocene.
P = Assemblage with <u>Pecten takahashii</u>, <u>Cosibensis cosibensis heteroglypta</u>, and <u>Anadara trilineata</u>.
A = Assemblage with <u>Astarte</u>.

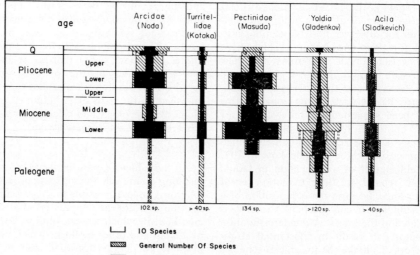

FIG. 1—Changes of quantity of various mollusk genera.

Yoldia watasei (upper Oligocene); (D,E) Demostylidae and Echinoidae with *Astradapsis antisella* (middle Miocene); (P) *Anadara trilineata trilineata, Pecten takahashii* ("lower" Pliocene); and (A) complexes with *Astarte* ("upper" Pliocene).

A precise correlation of these assemblages awaits further acceptance and application.

REFERENCES

Asano, Kiyoshi, and Kotora Hatai, 1967, Micro- and macropaleontological Tertiary correlations within Japanese islands and with planktonic foraminiferal sequences of foreign countries, *in* Tertiary correlations and climatic changes in the Pacific: Tokyo, 11th Pacific Sci. Cong. Symp., no. 25, p. 77–87.

Bandy, O. L., 1968a, Neogene polar planktonic foraminiferal invasions of temperate regions (abs.): Prague, Czechoslovakia, 23d Internat. Geol. Cong. Rept., Abs. Vol., p. 269–270.

———— 1968b, Cycles in Neogene paleoceanography and eustatic changes, *in* Tertiary sea-level fluctuations: Palaeogeography, Palaeoclimatology, Palaeoecology, v. 5, no. 1, p. 63–75.

Berggren, W. A., 1969, Cenozoic chronostratigraphy, planktonic foraminiferal zonation and the radiometric time scale: Nature, v. 224, p. 1072–1075.

Boyarskaya, T. D., 1969, The Pleistocene of eastern Siberia, based on data from the Mamontova mountain section: Assoc. Fr. Étude Quaternaire Bull., v. 6, no. 1 (18), p. 63–73 (in Fr., including Russ. summ.).

Einarsson, Th., D. Hopkins, and R. Doell, 1967, The stratigraphy of Tjörnes, Northern Ireland, and the history of the Bering land bridge, *in* The Bering land bridge: Stanford, California, Stanford Univ. Press.

Gladenkov, Yu. B., 1970, *Yoldia* in Paleogene and Neogene of North Pacific: Akad. Nauk SSSR Geol. Ser., no. 3, p. 112–123.

Hays, J. D., T. Saito, and N. D. Opdyke, *et al.,* 1969, Pliocene-Pleistocene sediments of the equatorial Pacific; their paleomagnetic, biostratigraphic, and climatic record: Geol. Soc. America, v. 80, no. 8, p. 1481–1513.

Ikebe, N., and M. Chiji, 1969, Neogene biostratigraphy and geochronology in Japan: Shizenshi-Kemkyu, Osaka Museum Nat. Hist. Occ. Papers, v. 1, no. 4.

Kochegura, V. V., N. V. Ogorodov, and N. N. Kozhemyaka, 1969, Paleomagnetic correlation of Pliocene-Pleistocene extrusives of the Kamchatka central range: Akad. Nauk. SSSR Sibirskoye Otdeleniye, Geologiya i Geofizika, no. 8, p. 81–90 (in Russ., with Engl. summ.).

Kotaka, T., 1959, The Cenozoic Turritellidae of Japan: Sendai, Japan, Tohoku Univ. Sci. Repts., v. 31, no. 2, p. 1–135.

Krasheninnikov, V. A., 1971, Stratigrafiya i foraminifery kaynozoyskikh pelagicheskikh osadkov severozapadnoy chasti Tikhogo okeana: Voprosy Mikropaleontologii, no. 14, p. 140–199.

Krishtofovich, L. V., 1961, Sopostavleniye tretichnykh otlozheny Tikhookeanskogo koltsa kaynozoyskoy skladchatosti, *in* Unifitsirovannyye stratigraficheskiye skhemy Severo-Vostoka SSSR: Moscow, Gostoptekhizdat, p. 83–91.

Lin'kova, T. I., 1969, Position of the magnetic reversal zone in deep-water bottom sediments: Akad. Nauk SSSR Sibriskoye Otdeleniye, Geologiya i Geofizika, no. 3, p. 117–121 (in Russ., with Engl. summ.).

Masuda, K., 1962, Tertiary Pectinidae of Japan: Sendai, Japan, Tohoku Univ. Sci. Repts., Ser. 2 (Geol.) Spec., v. 33, no. 2, p. 1–238.

Minato, Masao, *et al.,* 1968, Pacific geology, Pt. 1: Tokyo, Japan, Tsukiji Shokan Pub. Co., 182 p.

Node, H., 1966, The Cenozoic Arcidae of Japan: Sendai, Japan, Tohoku Univ. Sci. Repts., v. 38, no. 1, p. 1–63.

Oyama, K., A. Mizuko, and T. Sakamoto, 1960, Illustrated handbook of Japanese Paleogene mollusks: Geol. Survey Japan, p. 1–244.

Petrov, O., and I. Khoreva, 1968, Correlation of upper Neogene and Quaternary deposits of the extreme northeast of the U.S.S.R. and Alaska: Tertiary-Quaternary boundary: Prague, Czechoslovakia, 23d Internat. Geol. Cong. Sess.; also *in* Granitsa tretichnogo i chetvertichnogo periodov: Moscow, Izd. "Nauka," p. 70–74.

Pevzner, M. A., 1968, Paleomagnetic investigations of the upper Pliocene and Quaternary deposits of Kamchatka (abs.): Moskov. Obshch. Ispytateley Prirody Byull., Otdel. Geol., v. 43, no. 3, p. 139.

Saito, Tsunemasa, and L. H. Burckle, 1968, Cretaceous and Tertiary sediments from the world's oceans (abs.): Prague, Czechoslovakia, 23d Internat. Geol. Cong. Rept., Abs. Vol., p. 352–353.

Serova, M. Ya., 1969, Zonalnoye raschleneniye i korrelyatsiya paleogenovykh otlozheny severo zapadnoy chasti Tikhookeanskoy provintsii, *in* Biostratigrafiya, fauna i flora kaynozoya severo-zapadnoy chasti Tikhookeanskogo podvizhnogo poyasa: Moscow, Izd. "Nauka," p. 101–114.

Slodkevich, V. S., 1967, Tretichnyye Acila Sakhalina: Moscow, Izd. "Nauka," p. 1–78.

Uorumi, S., 1957, Studies on the molluscan fossils from Hokkaido. Part 2, Genera *Yoldia* and *Portlandia:* Hokkaido Univ. Fac. Sci. Jour., Ser. 4, v. 9, no. 4, p. 539–596.

Zhuze, A. P., 1968, Pleistocene stratigraphy of the Pacific Ocean: Akad. Nauk SSSR Kom. Izucheniyu Chetvertich Perioda Byull., no. 35, p. 3–19.

Okhotsk-Chukotsk Fold Belt and the Problem of Volcanic Arcs in Northeast Asia[1]

V. F. BELYI[2]

Magadan, USSR

Abstract The East Asian system of volcanic belts is situated between the area of Cenozoic folding in the northeast Circum-Pacific region and more ancient, mainly Mesozoic tectonic zones. The extent of the East Asian volcanic system is comparable to that of recent volcanic arcs.

The largest element of the East Asian system, the Okhotsk volcanic belt, contains structures characteristic of those of the marginal volcanic belts. The basic features of the belt were formed during the Aptian-Albian and Cenomanian-Turonian. During that time period, andesite volcanism prevailed, although granitoid magmatism was widespread and was accompanied by the formation of ignimbrite fields of large volume.

Comparative structural, petrologic, and historic-geologic analyses have revealed considerable differences between the Okhotsk-Chukotsk belt and the Kuril-Kamchatka volcanic arc.

A specific zone of intensive uplift and subaerial, mainly andesite volcanism was stabilized in the structures of the basement of the Okhotsk-Chukotsk belt. Formation of this zone was simultaneous with the deep-seated faulting which separated the Verkhoyansk-Chukotsk and the Koryak-Kamchatka geosynclinal regions in the Mesozoic. During the Late Jurassic and the first half of the Early Cretaceous, the Okhotsk-Chukotsk volcanic zone (in relation to the mentioned regions) had the same function as does the Kuril-Kamchatka volcanic arc today in relation to Kamchatka, the Okhotsk Sea, and Hokkaido, on one side, and the Kuril-Kamchatka trench on the other.

The presumably Late Jurassic–Early Cretaceous volcanic arc was a peculiar bordering structure which separated the Anadyr'-Koryak geosynclinal system (in an early stage of its development) from the Verkhoyansk-Chukotsk region of Mesozoic folding (in the epigeosynclinal stage of orogenesis). Development of the Okhotsk-Chukotsk marginal volcanic belt began in Aptian-Albian time—when a considerable volume of terrigenous sediment was accumulating in the Anadyr'-Koryak geosynclinal system, and the Verkhoyansk-Chukotsk area represented part of a continental block with a tendency to rise. The volcanic belt included not only the volcanic arc, but also extended far beyond—over Mesozoic fold structures, ancient rigid massifs, and the peripheral zone of the Anadyr'-Koryak geosynclinal system.

Gradual migration of volcanic arcs toward the Pacific did not occur in Northeast Asia. Their appearance and development in space and time bore an uneven character. The development and the nature of the mentioned structures are important tectonic aspects of the general problem of andesite volcanism.

INTRODUCTION

The East Asian system of volcanic belts is situated in the northwest sector of the Circum-Pacific between regions of Cenozoic folding and older, mostly Mesozoic tectonic zones. Its length is about 8,000 km. No similar structure exists in the continental structures of West Asia. Only the system of Quaternary and modern offshore volcanic arcs which includes the Aleutian, Kuril-Kamchatka, Japanese, and Ryukyu (Nansei) islands can be compared with this structure (Fig. 1).

The greatest element of the East Asian system of volcanic belts is the Okhotsk-Chukotsk belt, the length of which is perhaps 3,000 km. The northwestern and northern ends of this peculiar geologic structure, formed by subaerial geosynclinal-type volcanism, lie on a geosynclinal folded complex of Mesozoic and older rigid massifs. In the southeast, the Okhotsk-Chukotsk belt borders structures of the Cenozoic Anadyr'-Koryak fold system. In the middle part of Anadyr', in the basin of the lower Penzhina River, and on the Taygonos Peninsula, the superposition of volcanic strata of the Okhotsk-Chukotsk belt on chiefly marine, but minor continental, sediments lithologically identical with the coeval series which form the northwestern flank of the Penzhina depression is evident. Although angular unconformities separate the volcanic beds and the underlying strata, both sequences have identical strike.

AGES OF ROCKS

In the Chukotsk part of the volcanic belt, the lower units of the volcanic series contain fossil plants of such genera as *Arctopteris, Coniopteris, Onychiopsis, Asplenium, Cladophlebis, Nilssonia, Anomozamites, Taeniopteris, Ctenis, Heilungia, Ginkgo, Baiera, Sphenobaiera, Phoenicopsis, Podozamites, Araucarites, Pagiophyllum, Elatocladus, Cephalotaxopsis, Torreya, Pityophyllum, Sequoia, Paratoxodium,* and *Cyparissidium;* scarce imprints of leaves of dicotyledons also are present.

A similar complex of flora is also characteristic of essentially sedimentary series developed both in basins of the Chukotsk Mesozoic fold

[1] Manuscript received, April 30, 1972.

[2] Northeastern Complex, Scientific Research Institute, USSR Academy of Sciences.

system and in some areas which are adjacent to the Penzhina basin. Distinct overlap of these sedimentary rocks by volcanic strata of the Okhotsk-Chukotsk belt is apparent everywhere. In older units of the sedimentary series are marine beds containing *Aucellina* spp. According to the complex of fossil organisms and plants, the beginning of development of the Chukotsk part of the volcanic belt cannot be older than the second part of the Aptian. With less confidence, it is possible to say that the beginning of formation of the Okhotsk part may have been as late as Early Cretaceous.

The younger volcanic series, which are present along most of the length of the Okhotsk-Chukotsk belt, contain a rather monotonous assemblage of flora; together with predominant representatives of coniferous *Cephalotaxopsis*, *Torreya*, *Sequoia*, and *Thuya* are the ubiquitous *Phoenicopsis steenstrupii* Sew. and *Quereuxia angulata* (Newb.) Krysht. and abundant *Baiera*, *Sphenobaiera*, *Czekanowskia*, *Trochodendroides*, and *Menispermites*. This complex suggests a Cenomanian age for the country rocks. In some areas, Turonian volcanic deposits probably are present with the Cenomanian strata. The main part of the Okhotsk-Chukotsk belt, approximately 85 percent of it, was formed in the period ranging from Aptian to Turonian.

The youngest volcanic series, of Late Cretaceous–early Paleogene age, are present mainly in the Chukotsk part of the volcanic belt, which borders the Anadyr'-Koryak system. These series comprise ignimbrites and tuffs of acidic composition (latest Cretaceous) and flows of tholeiitic and alkalic basalts (early Paleogene?).

TECTONICS OF OKHOTSK-CHUKOTSK BELT

The tectonic pattern of the Okhotsk-Chukotsk belt is heterogeneous. Its main structural-stratigraphic elements are related to the volcanic series of the early Aptian–Turonian stage of development. Andesite basalts and andesites are predominant; however, fields of ignimbrites are extensive, both in volume and area, and basalts are present locally. For a length of about 2,000 km between the source areas of Amguyema on the northeast and Inya on the southwest, the volcanic belt exhibits longitudinal zonation. Toward the region of Cenozoic folding, outer and inner zones are apparent. The flanks east and southwest of this part of the volcanic belt have no longitudinal zonation; they lie mainly on ancient rigid massifs and appear to be the dormant regions of the volcanic belt.

There are two subzones in the inner zone, one of which I suggest be called "inherited" and the other "new-formed." The "new-formed" subzone is contiguous with the Anadyr'-Koryak system, and the inherited subzone is situated between the "new-formed" subzone and the outer zones. The "new-formed" subzone is characterized by uplifts wherein the lower series of the volcanic belt are exposed. The inherited subzone is, on the contrary, a complex volcano-tectonic depression. It reflects the position of the system of large deep fractures which apparently divided two different geosynclinal regions as long ago as the Paleozoic (based on data by Belyi, Nikolayevsky, Tilman, and Shilo). Since the Norian, this system of fractures and faults has been marked by intense volcanic activity.

The tectonic nature of the Okhotsk-Chukotsk belt is unresolved, and discussion of the various opinions would form a separate report. Therefore, perhaps a short discussion of the late Mesozoic history of the northeast part of Asia will provide an understanding of the historic-geologic position of the Okhotsk-Chukotsk belt in relation to the framework of the whole region.

REGIONAL STRUCTURE AND STRATIGRAPHY

During the Late Jurassic and Valanginian, the Anadyr'-Koryak system was in an early stage of evolution. In the inner eugeosynclinal zone (Fig. 2), a thick siliceous-volcanic and terrigenous (considerable graywacke) series accumulated. Volcanism was accompanied by emplacement of ultramafic rocks and gabbro, the locations of which mainly coincide with the zones of deep fractures that separated the eugeosynclinal zone from the outer miogeosynclinal zones.

In the outer zone of the Anadyr'-Koryak system, the terrigenous volcanomictic series accumulated. The vast northwestern zone occupied the whole area of the Talova-Mayn anticlinorium, the Penzhina depression, and the "new-formed" subzone of the volcanic belt. The Upper Jurassic and Valanginian deposits are formed mainly by volcanomictic sandstones, siltstones, and tuffites, which consist of clastic material of essentially andesitic composition. The Hauterivian deposits (800–3,000 m thick) consist mainly of green-violet and blue-green tuff breccias and tuffs of andesite-basaltic, andesitic, dacitic, and basaltic composition. On the northwest, in the Upper Jurassic and Valanginian sequences, green tuffs and tuff breccia

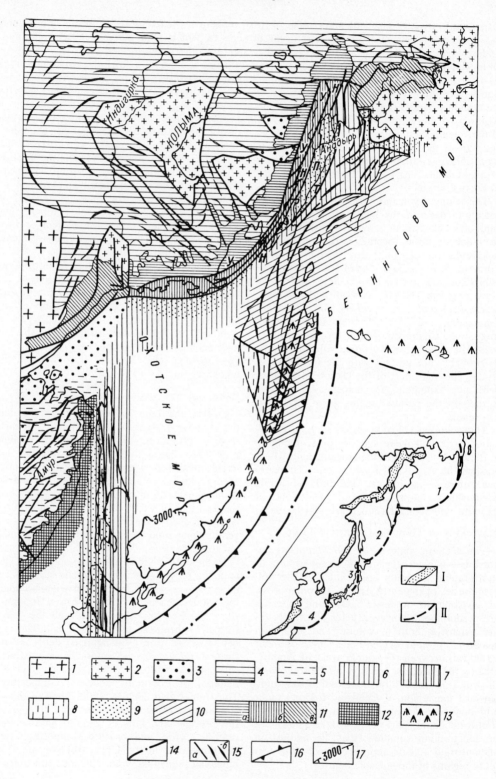

are abundant, and, in Hauterivian strata, the quantity of lavas of intermediate composition is greatly increased.

In the Verkhoyansk-Chukotsk region, folding was initiated in the Late Jurassic. It was accompanied by formation of extensive uplifts, composed of dislocated blocks of the main geosynclinal complex. Near these uplifts, different negative structures were formed—basins where marine and continental molasse deposits and sedimentary-volcanic complexes accumulated and residual and regenerated geosynclinal depressions. Hauterivian marine deposits are not widespread in these areas. Terrigenous rocks, with a total thickness of about 500–600 m, fill most of the depressions. The only direct indications concerning the origin of the zone of juncture of the Anadyr'-Koryak system and the Mesozoic Verkhoyansk-Chukotsk fold system —i.e., the site of the inherited subzone of the Okhotsk-Chukotsk belt—are found in the Taygonos Peninsula region. There, late Volgian– Valanginian subaerial volcanic formations of mafic, intermediate, and silicic composition

(3,500–4,500 m thick) fill the sutural volcano-tectonic depression (Zaborovskaya, Gelman, and others). The width of the depression is 25– 30 km and the observed length is 150 km. The overlying Hauterivian sequence (1,500–2,000 m) consists of marine volcanic-sedimentary and subaerial volcanic deposits. Late Volgian– Valanginian and Hauterivian rocks and the overlying Aptian-Albian sedimentary-volcanic and subaerial volcanic formations (3,000 m) belong to the structural complex of the Okhotsk-Chukotsk belt. The sutural structure is bordered on the northwest by structures of the Mesozoic fold system and on the southeast by the outer zone of the Anadyr'-Koryak system, which is composed of marine Late Jurassic and Valanginian deposits. Similar structures of the sutural type are present in the region of the Pyagina Peninsula. The characteristic lithology of the Late Jurassic, Valanginian, and Hauterivian section in the basins of the Penzhina and Anadyr' Rivers and in regions of the northwest Chukotsk Peninsula indicates that intensive andesite-basaltic volcanism occurred during this

---

←⫷⫷⫷⫷

FIG. 1—Location of Okhotsk-Chukotsk volcanic belt relative to other structures of East Asia. Key is as follows:
    1. Siberian platform
    2. Pre-Riphean
    3. Hercynian rigid massifs
    4. Verkhoyansk-Chukotsk region of Mesozoic folding
    5. Sikhote-Alin and Mongolo-Okhotsk regions of Mesozoic folding
Cenozoic folded region—fold systems formed during Laramide orogeny:
    6. Anadyr'-Koryak
    7. Hokkaido-Sakhalin
    8. Southwestern Kamchatka
    9. Outer zones of named systems
    10. Olyutorskiy-Kamchatka region of late Neogenic folding
    11. Okhotsk-Chukotsk volcanic belt
       (a) Outer zone
       (b) Inner zone
       (c) Flanks
    12. Sikhote-Alin volcanic belt
    13. Kuril-Kamchatka volcanic arc
    14. Axial zone of Kuril-Kamchatka trench
    15. (a) Deep faults. (b) Strike of folds
    16. Outcrop of focal zone of Kuril-Kamchatka system
    17. Outline of South Okhotsk abyssal basin on 3,000-m isobath
Alphabetical Symbols:
    y = Inherited subzone
    H = "New-formed" subzone of inner zone of Okhotsk-Chukotsk volcanic belt
    n = Penzhina depression
    T = Talovka-Mayn anticlinorium of Anadyr'-Koryak system
Inset:
    I = East Asian system of volcanic belts
    II = Offshore Quaternary and Holocene volcanic arcs
       1. Aleutian
       2. Kuril-Kamchatka
       3. Japanese
       4. Ryukyu (Nansei)

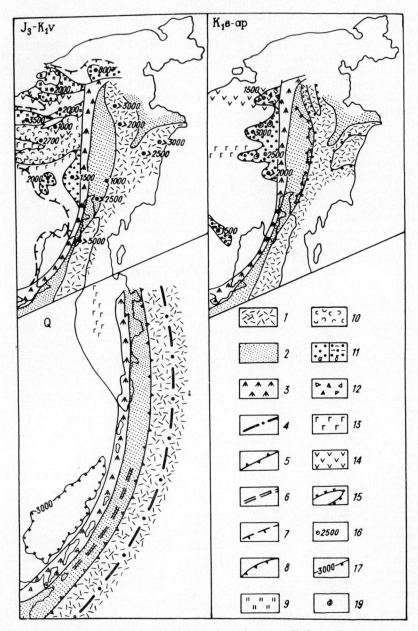

Fig. 2—Paleotectonic schemes of Koryak highland and northwestern Chukotsk Peninsula and main tectonic elements of recent Kuril-Kamchatka system.

1. Inner eugeosynclinal zones
2. Outer zones
3. Volcanic arcs
4. Axial zone of Kuril-Kamchatka trench
5. Outcrop of focal zone of Kuril-Kamchatka system
6. Axial line of submarine Vityaz Ridge
7. Diagrammatic contour of Late Jurassic–Valanginian sea in Mesozoic fold system
8. Contours of main basins and geosynclinal depressions in Early Cretaceous developmental stage of Mesozoic fold system
9. Residual and regenerated geosynclinal depressions
10. Depressions and basins with essentially volcanic-sedimentary strata and subaerial volcanic rocks

period on the site of the inherited subzone of the Okhotsk-Chukotsk belt. An analysis of the paleogeography of this time indicates that the volcanism was related to an island-arc system.

At the end of the Hauterivian and during the Barremian, folding occurred within the Anadyr'-Koryak system, accompanied by considerable subsidence and the emergence of anticlinal uplifts. During this same period, in the Mesozoic fold system, the basins were greatly reduced in area, but the intensity of subsidence still was greater than that of the Late Jurassic–Valanginian (Fig. 2). Marine deposits accumulated in some basins up to the beginning of the Aptian. Hence, the basins must have had direct paleogeographic connections with marine basins of the Anadyr'-Koryak system. During the Early Cretaceous, the intensity of volcanism diminished in the zone of juncture of the Anadyr'-Koryak system and the Verkhoyansk-Chukotsk region of Mesozoic folding.

The main structural-stratigraphic zones of the Late Jurassic–Early Cretaceous stage of the development of the Koryak highland and the northwestern Chukotsk Peninsula are identical to the modern structures of the Kuril-Kamchatka system, Kamchatka, the Okhotsk Sea, and Hokkaido. The Kuril-Kamchatka trench appears to be an analogue of the inner eugeosynclinal zone of the Anadyr'-Koryak system. The focal zone that crops out on the northwestern slope of the trench evidently can be compared with the system of deep fractures and ultramafic intrusions which are clearly evident on the border between the inner zone of the Anadyr'-Koryak system and its northwestern outer zone. The analogue of the latter in the modern structure of the Kuril-Kamchatka system is the nonvolcanic arc with the underwater Vityaz Ridge and depression. Size of the orogenic residual basins and of the regenerated geosynclinal depressions of the northwestern Chukotsk Peninsula and the thickness of sediments accumulated there are commensurate with the size and depth of warping of the South Okhotsk basin.

Thus, the Late Jurassic–Early Cretaceous (pre–late Aptian) volcano-tectonic structures in the junctural zone of the Anadyr'-Koryak system and the Mesozoic fold system can be considered analogous to the modern Kuril-Kamchatka volcanic arc. Of course, the absolute identification of all tectonic zones under consideration is not possible because of (1) their different orientation with respect to the Pacific Ocean and (2) the great difference between the Verkhoyansk-Chukotsk Mesozoic fold system and the Cenozoic fold system of the Koryak-Kamchatka region and Hokkaido.

The latest stage of development of structures of Northeast Asia evidently began at the end of the Aptian. Within the Mesozoic fold system there were no marine basins or large depressions. The Mesozoic fold system appears to be united with the more or less rising continental block. Within the Anadyr'-Koryak system, however, intensive downwarping was renewed, accompanied by accumulation of a thick terrigenous, commonly flyschoid, volcanomictic series. The Okhotsk-Chukotsk belt originated within the framework of these processes. The intense subaerial volcanism which led to the formation of the Okhotsk-Chukotsk belt spread (almost "instantly," relative to geologic time) over an enormous territory with varied tectonic structures.

In the inner zone during all of the early stage (Aptian-Turonian), a thick accumulation (up to 5,000 m) of mainly andesitic basalts was formed. The basalts were intruded by granitoids, among which quartz diorites, tonalites, and granodiorites are predominant. The granitoids are characterized by a high sodium content. Intrusions are grouped in rows, commonly situated en échelon. The strike of the rows is parallel with the trend of the belts. The emplacement of intrusions was accompanied in several places by the formation of elongate anticlinal uplifts, where Hauterivian and Valanginian deposits crop out.

During the Aptian-Albian, in most regions of

---

11. Basins filled by essentially terrigenous strata
    (a) Marine and continental
    (b) Continental coal-bearing
12. Basins with predominantly subaerial volcanic rocks of intermediate and silicic composition
13. Zones of mafic and intermediate volcanism
14. Zones of silicic and intermediate volcanism
15. Contours of main uplifts within Anadyr'-Koryak system
16. Thickness of deposits in meters
17. Outline of South Okhotsk basin on 3,000-m isobath
18. Localities with *Aucellina* spp. within basins of Mesozoic fold system

the outer zone and on the flanks of the volcanic belt, intense andesitic volcanism took place. At the end of the Albian and during the Cenomanian, intense silicic volcanism resulted in the formation of voluminous ignimbrite fields. On the flanks, together with prevailing liparitic (rhyolitic) and dacitic ignimbrites, rocks of trachytic and trachyliparitic composition are widely spread. A decrease in silicic volcanism and an increase in eruptions of andesitic basalts occurred at the end of the Cenomanian and evidently continued into the Turonian. The silicic volcanism of the outer zone and flanks of the Okhotsk-Chukotsk belt was related to the numerous epizonal granitoid intrusions. In contrast to quartz monzonite massifs of the inner zone, granodiorites and granites of the outer zone have a comparatively high content of potassium. Most of the ignimbrite intrusions are grouped around large volcano-tectonic depressions or form rows transverse to the general volcanic belt.

The development of the Koryak-Kamchatka region during Late Cretaceous and Cenozoic times is characterized by distinct diminution of geosynclinal areas and their shifting toward the Pacific Ocean. Synorogenic formations are evident everywhere along the outer parts of the Anadyr'-Koryak system and within its geanticlinal structures, dating from the beginning of the Late Cretaceous. The Senonian intensive eugeosynclinal magmatism is characteristic only of the Olyutorskiy-Kamchatka system. In the Anadyr'-Koryak system, the siliceous-volcanic sequence of Senonian age was developed only in narrow fracture zones and was subordinate to the thick, essentially flyschoid, volcanomictic series. Geosynclinal depressions of the Anadyr'-Koryak system were filled during the Laramide orogeny, and the depressions of the Olyutorskiy-Kamchatka system were filled in the late Miocene. It is significant that, during this complicated and considerably long process, the structures identical to the modern Kuril-Kamchatka volcanic arc did not appear within the Koryak highland and Kamchatka. The development of these structures, which began at the end of the Pliocene and continued into the Anthropogene (Holocene), evidently was related to the same processes that caused initiation of a new geosynclinal cycle.

CONCLUSIONS

The following should be emphasized.

1. In Northeast Asia, the volcanic-arc structure of the Kuril-Kamchatka system appeared first at the end of the Mesozoic in connection with the origin and development of the Koryak-Kamchatka geosynclinal region.

2. Apparently, at the end of the Aptian, the structure of the Okhotsk-Chukotsk marginal volcanic belt was superimposed on the volcanic arc. The origin of the Okhotsk-Chukotsk belt is related to the considerable changes in the Anadyr'-Koryak geosynclinal system and the Verkhoyansk-Chukotsk orogenic region.

3. In the process of the development of the Koryak-Kamchatka geosynclinal region, migration of the volcanic arc did not take place. Possibly, this absence of migration is the main distinguishing feature of this offshore type of volcanic arc as compared with Indonesian arcs which, according to Umbgrove (1947) and van Bemmelen (1960), migrated with the shift of geosynclinal troughs.

SELECTED REFERENCES

Baranova, Yu. P., et al., 1968, Kaynozoy Severo-Vostoka SSSR: Akad. Nauk SSSR Inst. Geol. i Geof. Trudy, no. 38.

———— et al., 1970, Novye dannye o miocenovykh otlozheniyakh Mamontovoy Gory na Aldane: Akad. Nauk SSSR Doklady, v. 193, no. 5.

Biske, S. F., and I. A. Kulkova, 1969, O videlenii neogena v kontinentalnoy formatsii Kraynego Severo-Vostoka Azii: Akad. Nauk SSSR Inst. Geol. i Geof., no. 8.

Kulkova, I. A., 1968, Pyltsa Pistillipolenites macgregorii Rouse v eocenovykh otlozheniyakh Yakutii: Akad. Nauk SSSR Doklady, v. 182, no. 6.

———— 1970, Palinologicheskiye issledovaniya eocenovykh otlozheny Yano-Indigirskoy nizmennosti: Novosibirsk, unpub. dissert.

Umbgrove, J. H. F., 1947, The pulse of the earth, 2d ed.: The Hague, Martinus Nijhoff, 358 p.

van Bemmelen, R. W., 1960, New views on east-Alpine orogenesis: Copenhagen, 21st Internat. Geol. Cong. Rept., pt. 18, p. 99–116.

Wahrhaftig, C., et al., 1969, The Coal Bearing Group in the Nenana Coal Field, Alaska: U.S. Geol. Survey Bull. 1274-D.

Wolfe, J. A., 1966, Tertiary plants from the Cook Inlet region, Alaska: U.S. Geol. Survey Prof. Paper 398-B.

———— 1969, Paleogene floras from the Gulf of Alaska region: U.S. Geol. Survey Open-File Rept.

———— D. M. Hopkins, and E. B. Leopold, 1966, Tertiary stratigraphy and paleobotany of the Cook Inlet region, Alaska: U.S. Geol. Survey Prof. Paper 398-A.

Silurian-Devonian Boundary and Correlation of Lower Devonian of Soviet and Canadian Arctic[1]

S. V. CHERKESOVA[2]

Leningrad, USSR

Abstract Most recent investigators have placed the Silurian-Devonian boundary at the base of the *Monograptus uniformis* Zone. In the Arctic there are several graptolite-bearing clastic and clastic-carbonate sequences where this boundary may be drawn, but correlation of these separate sections with more widely distributed carbonate formations is tentative. The boundary position within carbonate sequences is unclear.

The best key marker traceable throughout the Arctic consists of argillaceous limestone containing *Atrypella phoca* and *A. scheii*. This marker bed near the Silurian-Devonian boundary is important because it is easily recognizable elsewhere.

In the western Soviet Arctic, deposits containing *A. phoca* and *A. scheii* are assigned to the Greben Horizon. At its type section on Vaygach Island, the Greben Horizon lies on carbonate rocks of the Khatanzeya Horizon (Ludlow). The gray and greenish-gray weathered nodular limestone of the Greben, about 200 m thick, is characterized by a rich fauna which includes *A. phoca* and *A. scheii*. On the basis of the fauna, the Greben Horizon has been dated as Silurian—either Ludlovian or post-Ludlovian.

In the overlying Vaygach Horizon, bioclastic detrital limestone with bioherms grades upward into predominantly algal limestone. The Vaygach Horizon, which is characterized by the presence of tabulates, may correspond to the post-Ludlovian–pre-Gedinnian and Gedinnian deposits.

In the western Soviet Arctic, the genus *Atrypella* has wide vertical distribution, but *A. phoca* and *A. scheii* are characteristic only of the Greben Horizon, especially of its lower part.

Atrypella phoca and *A. scheii* are the most characteristic faunas of the Read Bay Formation (late Wenlockian to late Ludlovian or Gedinnian) and its equivalents in the Canadian Arctic Archipelago. The Read Bay Formation at its type section on Cornwallis Island corresponds to the whole Khatanzeya and Greben Horizons.

The Sutherland River Formation on Devon Island is of Late Silurian or Devonian age; it has been correlated with the Snowblind Formation, which lies on the Read Bay Formation. The Sutherland River fauna includes forms similar to those of the upper Greben and lower Vaygach Horizons. The Greben Horizon appears to correlate with the part of the Upper Silurian in southeastern Alaska which contains *Atrypella scheii* and *Camarotoechia* sp.

The Lower Devonian Salmontrout Limestone of the Porcupine basin corresponds to the rocks of the Pragian and Zlikhovian in the Soviet Arctic.

Correlation of Lower Devonian deposits of the Soviet Arctic with deposits of the Canadian Arctic Islands is complicated and tentative. The Blue Fiord Formation, considered by the writer to be upper Emsian, contains fossils typical of the upper Valnev Horizon and the lower *Favosites regularissimus* local zone in Novaya Zemlya. The Stuart Bay Formation on Bathurst Island

may correspond to the Valnev Horizon. The overlying Eids Formation contains fossils present elsewhere in both upper Emsian and Eifelian rocks.

The deposits underlying the Gedinnian and those equivalent to the upper Emsian are the most promising levels for correlation of Lower Devonian deposits in the Arctic.

Recently, most investigators have placed the Silurian-Devonian boundary at the base of the *Monograptus uniformis* Zone. Within the Arctic the boundary may be drawn more or less precisely at this level because of the presence of clastic and clastic-carbonate sequences containing graptolites. Churkin and Brabb (1968) described such sections from areas such as the Porcupine River valley, southeastern Alaska, east-central Alaska, and the Yukon basin (Churkin, 1967; Lenz, 1967). An additional section is known on Bathurst Island in the Canadian Arctic Archipelago (McLaren, 1963), where *Monograptus uniformis* Prib. was found. In the Soviet Arctic the Silurian-Devonian boundary was studied in detail by Koren (Koren and Enokyan, 1970) in Pay-Khoy near Livanov Cape, where it is also drawn at the base of the *Monograptus uniformis* Zone. Unfortunately, these are separate sections, and their correlation with more widely distributed carbonate formations is tentative. The boundary position within carbonate sequences is not yet clear.

The best key marker which can be traced over a vast area of the north European part of the USSR, islands of the Canadian Arctic Archipelago, northwestern Greenland, and southeastern Alaska consists of argillaceous limestone containing *Atrypella phoca* and *A. scheii*. Detailed study of this marker bed is important, because it is located near the Silurian-Devonian boundary and is easily recognizable in regions other than the Arctic. O. Holtedahl (1930), when studying *Lissatrypa* (= *Atrypella*) *phoca* Salt. and *A. scheii* Holt, stated that the fauna is present in northwestern Greenland and on Somerset, Cornwallis, Devon, and Ellesmere Is-

---

[1] Manuscript received, August 1, 1972.

[2] Research Institute of the Geology of the Arctic.

lands, as well as in southeastern Alaska. He also considered the fauna to be similar to that of the Urals and partly similar to the fauna of Gotland.

In the western Soviet Arctic, deposits containing *A. phoca* and *A. scheii* are assigned to the Greben Horizon, which can be traced from Severnyy Island (Novaya Zemlya) through Vaygach Island to the Subpolar Urals (Pershina, 1960; Dubatolov *et al.,* 1968) and farther south. The Greben Horizon is also known on Chernyshev Ridge (Pershina, 1962), on Chernov Rise (Chernov, 1945), in Bolshaya Zemlya Tundry, and in the Pechora Sea on Dolgiy and Zelenets Islands (Chernov, 1945).

A comprehensive, detailed study of the Greben Horizon was made at the type section on Vaygach Island, where it lies on carbonate rocks of the Khatanzeya Horizon (Ludlow) that contain *Thecia swinderniana* (Gold), *Laceripora cribrosa* Eichw., *Fardenia* cf. *attenuata* Amsd., *Conchidium novosemelicum* Nal., *Atrypella modesta* Nikif., *Delthyris elevatus* (Dalm.), *Homeospira baylei waigatschensis* Nikif., *Didymothris didyma* (Dalm.), *Schrenckia tumefacta* Abush., *Beyrichia* (*Simplicibeyrichia*) *bifaria* Abush., *Encrinurus* (*Frammia*) *rossicus* Z. Max., *Archegonaspis bimaris* Novit, and others.

The Greben Horizon consists of gray and greenish-gray weathered nodular limestone about 200 m thick. The presence of large specimens of *A. phoca* and *A. scheii* in association with a relatively abundant and variable fauna of tabulate and rugose corals, bryozoans, brachiopods, ostracods, pelecypods, trilobites, and others is the most characteristic feature of the Greben Horizon.

The most typical fauna of the Greben Horizon is as follows: among tabulates—*Squameofavosites russanovi* (Tchern.), *Fistulipora arctica* Astr., *Fistuliramus sinensis* Astr.; among brachiopods—*Fardenia* cf. *attenuata* Amsd., *Atrypella phoca* (Salt.), *F. typica, F. media, F. longa, A. scheii* (Holt.), *F. gibbera, A. insigne* Nikif., *A. camelina karpovensis* Nikif., *Howellella pseudogibbosa* Nikif., *H. pseudomagna* Nikif., *H. parvula* (Tschern. and Yakov.), *Pseudohomeospira polaris* Nikif., *Collarothyris canaliculata* (Wen.); among ostracods—*Kiaeria lindstroemi* Gleb., *Kloedenia? bacta* Abush.; among trilobites—*Hemiarges lindstromi* (Tschern. and Yakov.), *Warburgella* (*Waigatchella*) *waigatschensis* (Tschern. and Yakov.), *W.* (*W.*) *yakovlevi* Z. Max., *Warburgella* (*Podolites*) *tcherkesovae* Z. Max.; and among co-

nodonts—*Hindeodella irregularidentata* Mash., *Ligonodina elegans* Wall.-Legault, *Lonchodina antis* Mash., *L. greilingi arctica* Mash., *L. swetlana* Mash., *Neopriniodus bicurvatus* Brans. and Mehl., *Ozarkodina jaegeri* Wall., *O.* aff. *O. ortuformis* Wall., *O. squarrosa* Mash., *O. typical denckmanni* Zieg., *Plectospathodus flexuosus* Brans. and Mehl., *Spathognathodus inclinatus* Rhodes, *S. interpositus* Mash., *S. primus* Brans. and Mehl., *S. steinhornensis eosteinhornensis* Wall., *Trichonodella symmetrica zeravshanica* Moskal., *T. triquetra* Mash.

According to experts who have studied the fauna[3] from the Greben Horizon, it may be dated as Silurian, but it is difficult to say whether it is Ludlovian or post-Ludlovian. The above assemblage of conodonts reported from the Karpov beds in the upper Greben Horizon, which includes *S. steinhornensis eosteinhornensis,* possibly can be correlated with the Whitcliffe and the Ludlow "bone bed" or with the Hamra and Sundre beds from Gotland. However, according to the data of T. L. Modzalevskaya, A. F. Abushik, and T. V. Mashkova, the Greben Horizon is correlated with the Kaugatoma and Okhesaara Horizons of Estonia, which some workers (Kalio *et al.,* 1968) compare with the Downtonian of England. Fahraus (1969), however, suggests a correlation of the Kaugatoma Horizon with the uppermost Ludlovian as well. Obviously, the Greben Horizon cannot be considered to be dated with certainty. It is interesting to note that many representatives of the genus *Atrypella* are present in the Karpov beds but that *A. phoca* and *A. scheii* occur only in the lower beds.

The overlying deposits are those of the Vaygach Horizon. Their lower part (unit I) is represented by bioclastic detrital limestone with bioherms, grading upward in the section (units II–IV) into predominantly algal limestone.

The Vaygach Horizon (units I–II) is characterized by the presence of tabulates—*Favosites socialis* Sok. and Tes., *Squameofavosites favositiformis* (Holt.); by brachiopods—*Atrypella insigne* Nikif., *F. grebenensis, A. alata* Nikif.; by trilobites—*Hemiarges lindstromi* (Tschern. and Yakov.); by ostracods—*Kiaeria alata* Abush., *K. katerinne* Abush., *Hogmochilina subformosa* Abush.; and by conodonts—*Spathognatodus steinhornensis remscheidensis*

[3] Tabulates by M. A. Smirnova, rugose corals by V. A. Sytova, bryozoans by L. V. Nekhorosheva, brachiopods by O. I. Nikiforova and T. L. Modzalevskaya, ostracods by A. F. Abushik, trilobites by Z. A. Maximova, and conodonts by T. Mashkova.

Zeigler and the other conodonts that are also present in the Karpov beds. It is possible that this part of the section may correspond to the post-Ludlovian–pre-Gedinnian deposits. *S. steinhornensis remscheidensis,* which was assigned previously to the *Ictiodus woschmidti* assemblage, has been reported (Klapper, 1969) from Nevada, where it occurs beneath *I. woschmidti* and beneath *Monograptus* aff. *M. praechercynicus,* both of which belong to the *Monograptus uniformis* Zone (Berry, 1970).

The overlying deposits of the Vaygach Horizon (units III–V) correspond to the rocks of the Gedinnian. In this part of the section (unit III), the interbedded bioclastic limestones yield *Favosites socialis heterostila* Dubat., *Pachyfavosites? kozlowskii* Sok., *Holmophyllum taltiense* Nik., *Gypidula* sp., *Lenatoechia kuliki* Nikif., and *Protathyris* ex gr. *praecursor* Kozl.

In the upper part of the Vaygach Horizon, only *Thamnopora* sp. is identified. In M. A. Smirnova's opinion, this species is similar to *T. faceta* Yanet, which is characteristic of the Early Devonian. The equivalents of the Vaygach Horizon in the northeastern Vaygach Island yield *Atrypella? alata* Nikif., a new species of the genus *Gracianella,* known previously from Ludlovian and Přídolian deposits and found in Nevada in association with *S. steinhornensis remscheidensis.* In addition, *Howellella* sp. (cf. *H. laeviplicata* Kozl., *H. prima* Aleks.), *Protathyris* sp., and others are found there.

Thus, in the western sector of the Soviet Arctic, representatives of the genus *Atrypella* have wide vertical distribution (from the Khatanzeya to the Vaygach Horizons), but *A. phoca* and *A. scheii* are characteristic only of the Greben Horizon, especially of its lower part.

Atrypella phoca and *A. scheii* are the most characteristic of faunas of the Read Bay Formation and its equivalents on the Canadian Arctic Archipelago. This formation was recognized on Cornwallis Island (Thorsteinsson, 1958) and subdivided into four members—A, B, C, and D. The age of the formation is between late Wenlockian and late Ludlovian. However, according to McLaren (1963, p. 47), the position of *A. scheii* has not been precisely determined, though it is known to be absent in member D. *Catenipora* was found in outcrop 38 associated with *A. scheii* in the Read Bay Formation. Within the Soviet Arctic, representatives of the genus *Catenipora* have never been found at the level of the Greben Horizon in as-

sociation with *A. scheii.* It is clear that a refinement of specific identification of *Atrypella* is desirable.

The presence of *Catenipora* in the Read Bay Formation supports the age assignment given for the lower boundary of the formation. Hence, the Read Bay Formation in the type section on Cornwallis Island corresponds to the whole Khatanzeya and Greben Horizons of the western Soviet Arctic.

Kerr (1967) considered the age of the Read Bay Formation to be Wenlockian-Gedinnian. Berdan *et al.* (1969) considered the formation to be in part Ludlovian-Gedinnian. The Gedinnian age is proved by a finding of *Hemiarges beginer* (Bolton, 1965) on Cornwallis Island in the middle part of the formation together with Early Devonian and Late Silurian vertebrate fossils. Ormiston (1967) suggested that the Read Bay Formation is post-Ludlovian. According to Z. A. Maksimova (1970), a similar species—*Hemiarges lindstromi* (Tschern. and Yakov.)—belonging to a group of Silurian species of this genus is present in the Karpov beds, in the Greben Horizon, and in unit I of the Vaygach Horizon. *Favosites favositiformis,* which is found at the base of the Vaygach Horizon on Vaygach Island, was described by O. Holtedahl in 1914 from deposits of Ellesmere Island (Series B). On Ellesmere Island, Holtedahl described *Favosites favositiformis* in association with *Atrypella scheii.* However, in the Polar Urals the species is known from the upper Greben Horizon described by Chekhovich *et al.* (1969). *Encrinurus (Frammia) arcticus* (Haugt.) was reported from the Read Bay Formation and was later studied by Bolton (1965), who, in Z. A. Maksimova's opinion, gathered under this specific name all *Frammia* from the Canadian Arctic Archipelago. Maksimova (1970) considers that one specimen of *E. (F.) arcticus* belongs to her *E. (F.) rossicus* from the Khatanzeya Horizon. This specimen is assigned, on the basis of Bolton's data, to the lower part of the Read Bay Formation.

Correlation of the Sutherland River Formation on Devon Island with horizons of the Soviet Arctic is of interest. The formation is considered to be of Late Silurian or Early Devonian age. McLaren (1963) correlated it with the Snowblind Formation, which lies on the Read Bay Formation. Among the fauna described by Boucot *et al.* (1960) from the Sutherland River Formation are forms similar to those from the Soviet Arctic. Thus, *Protathyris* sp., with a rounded, uniformly convex shell, resembles *Protathyris* sp. from equivalents of the Vaygach Horizon in northeastern Vaygach, and a trilobite which is similar to representatives of the genus *Warburgella* is found in the upper Greben Horizon and from unit I of the Vaygach Horizon. The conodont assemblage from the Sutherland River Formation is very poor and includes only a few common forms which are assigned to the upper Greben and lower Vaygach Horizons in the section studied.

The Greben Horizon appears to be correlative with the part of the Upper Silurian in southeastern Alaska from which Kirk and Amsden (1952) reported *Atrypella scheii* and *Camarotoechia* sp.; the latter species is very similar to *Hemitoechia distincta* Nikif. from the top of the Khatanzeya Horizon.

The age comparison of Lower Devonian carbonate deposits of Alaska is complicated by insufficient knowledge of the fauna. However, these deposits are believed to reveal a close similarity to deposits of the Soviet Arctic (Churkin, 1968). The most complete section of Lower Devonian limestone is present in the Porcupine basin, where these strata lie on Lower Devonian (Siegenian) shale containing *Monograptus hercynicus*. The so-called Salmontrout Limestone (Churkin and Brabb, 1967) is correlative with the Pragian and Zlikhovian Stages. This correlation is proved by an occurrence of *Nowakia acuaria* at the base of the sequence and *Nowakia barrandei* at the top. *Tryplasma altaica* Dyb., known from contemporary deposits of the Soviet Arctic, is also present in the Salmontrout Limestone, as are representatives of the genus *Xystriphyllum.*

The latter genus is present in abundance in the upper Salmontrout Limestone, which corresponds to the *Favosites regularissimus* local zone in Novaya Zemlya (Zlikhovian; Table 1). In Novaya Zemlya, representatives of *Xystriphyllum* are present at the base of the Valnev Horizon. *X. devonicum* is found at its boundary with the *F. regularissimus* local zone.

The correlation with Lower Devonian deposits of the Canadian Arctic Islands is complicated and tentative. In the Blue Fiord Formation on Devon Island, according to Klapper (1969), *Cortezorthis* aff. *bathurstensis* John *et al., Phragmostrophia* sp., and *Polygnathus faveolatus* were found. He considered the formation to be upper Emsian. In Novaya Zemlya, representatives of *Cortezorthis* and *Phragmostrophia* are the most typical forms of the upper Valnev Horizon and the lower *Favosites regularissimus* local zone.

The Stuart Bay Formation in Bathurst Island possibly corresponds to the Valnev Horizon, but, on the basis of known fauna (brachiopods *Cortezorthis bathurstensis* and *Toquinaella kayi*), it is difficult to correlate. However, in the overlying Eids Formation, *Mimagoniatites,* which is characteristic of the upper Emsian, was found in addition to the following species: *Spiroceras thoas,* known from the *Favosites regularissimus* local zone in Novaya Zemlya; *Spiroceras karpinsyi* Zhurav., reported from the lower Eifelian of the Urals (upper Emsian of Germany); and *Folioceras segmentum* Coll., known from the Eifelian in Novaya Zemlya (*Megastrophia uralensis* local zone).

Thus, the deposits underlying the Gedinnian

Table 1.   Correlation of Lower Devonian of Russian and Canadian Arctic

	Novaya Zemlya	Alaska	Canadian Arctic Archipelago	
Stage	Southeast (after Cherkesova)	East—Porcupine River area (after Churkin, 1967)	Devon Island (after Ormiston, 1969)	Bathurst Island (after McLaren, 1963; Kerr, 1967)
Eifelian	Megastrophia uralensis local zone	Calcareous siltstone and shale	Blue Fiord Formation	Blue Fiord Formation
Zlikhovian	Favosites regularissimus local zone	Salmontrout Limestone		Eids Formation
Pragian	Valnev Horizon		Prince Alfred Formation	Stuart Bay Formation
Lochkovian	Morzhovaya Bay Horizon	Graptolite shale with M. uncinatus-M. hercynicus		Bathurst Island Formation and top of Cape Phillips Formation
Přídolian	Kamenka Bay Horizon			
	Greben Horizon	Graptolite shale	Sutherland River Formation	Cape Phillips Formation

and those equivalent to the upper Emsian are the most promising levels for a correlation of Lower Devonian deposits in the Arctic.

REFERENCES

Berdan, J. M., et al., 1969, Siluro-Devonian boundary in North America: Geol. Soc. America Bull., v. 80, no. 11, p. 2165–2174.

Berry, W. B. N., 1970, The base of the Devonian and an Early Devonian graptolite succession in central Nevada: Geol. Soc. America Bull., v. 81, no. 2, p. 513–520.

Bolton, Th. E., 1965, Trilobites from Upper Silurian rocks of the Canadian Arctic Archipelago: *Encrinurus (Frammia)* and *Hemiarges:* Canada Geol. Survey Bull. 134, p. 3–14.

Boucot, A. J., et al., 1960, A Late Silurian fauna from the Sutherland River Formation, Devon Island, Canadian Arctic Archipelago: Canada Geol. Survey Bull. 65, p. 1–40.

Cherkesova, S. V., 1970, Nizhnedevonskiye otlozheniya Sovetskoy Arktiki: Nauchno-Issled. Inst. Geologii Arktiki, Uchenyye Zapiski, Regional'naya Geologiya, no. 29, p. 5–13.

Chernov, G. A., 1945, Novyye dannyye po geologii i perspektivy neftenosnosti i uglenosnosti vostochnoy chasti Bolshezemelskoy Tundry: Sovetskaya Geologiya, no. 4, p. 3–23.

Churkin, M., 1968, Silurian and Devonian stratigraphy of Alaska and the Silurian-Devonian boundary (abs.): Leningrad, 3d Internat. Symp. of Silurian-Devonian Boundary and Stratigraphy of Lower and Middle Devonian, Abs. of Proc., p. 51.

—— and E. E. Brabb, 1965, Ordovician, Silurian, and Devonian biostratigraphy of east-central Alaska: Am. Assoc. Petroleum Geologists Bull., v. 49, no. 2, p. 172–185.

—— and —— 1967, Devonian rocks of the Yukon-Porcupine Rivers area and their tectonic relation to other Devonian sequences in Alaska, in D. H. Oswald, ed., International symposium on the Devonian System, v. 2: Calgary, Alberta Soc. Petroleum Geologists, p. 227–258.

Dubatolov, V. N., V. D. Chekhovich, and F. Ye. Yanet, 1968, Tabulyaty pogranichnykh sloyev silura i devona Altaye-Sayanskoy gornoy oblasti i Urala, in Korally pogranichnykh sloyev silura i devona Altaye-Sayanskoy gornoy oblasti i Urala: Moscow, Izd. "Nauka," p. 5–108.

Fahraus, L. E., 1969, Conodont zones in the Ludlovian of Gotland and a correlation with Great Britain: Sveriges Geol. Undersokning Arsb., ser. C, no. 639, arsb. 63, no. 2, p. 4–33.

Gryc, G., et al., 1967, Devonian of Alaska, in D. H. Oswald, ed., International symposium on the Devonian System, v. 1: Calgary, Alberta Soc. Petroleum Geologists, p. 703–717.

Harper, C. W., Jr., J. G. Johnson, and A. J. Boucot, 1967, The Pholidostrophiinae (Brachipoda; Ordovician, Silurian, Devonian): Senckenbergiana Lethaea, v. 48, no. 4, p. 403–441.

Holtedahl, O., 1914, On the fossil faunas from Per Schel's Series B in southwestern Ellesmere Land, in Second Norwegian Arctic expedition in the *Fram,* 1898–1902: Vidensk.-Selskab i Kristiania, Rept. 32, 48 p.

—— 1930, On the rock formations of Novaya Zemlya with notes on the Paleozoic stratigraphy of other Arctic lands, p. 1–184.

Jackson, D. E., and A. G. Lenz, 1969, Latest Silurian graptolites from Porcupine River, Yukon Territory: Canada Geol. Survey Bull. 182, p. 17–29.

Johnson, J. G., 1967, *Toquimeella,* a new genus of karpinskiinid brachiopod: Jour. Paleontology, v. 41, no. 4, p. 874–880.

—— and J. A. Talent, 1967, Cortezorthinae, a new subfamily of Siluro-Devonian dalmanellid brachiopods: Palaeontology, v. 10, pt. I, p. 1–170.

Kalio, D. L., et al., 1968, Morskoy daunton Pribaltiki (abs.): Leningrad, 2d Internat. Symp. of Silurian-Devonian Boundary and Stratigraphy of Lower and Middle Devonian, Abs. of Proc., p. 86.

Kerr, J. W., 1967, Devonian of the Franklinian miogeosyncline and adjacent central stable region, Arctic Canada, in D. H. Oswald, ed., International symposium on the Devonian System, v. 1: Calgary, Alberta Soc. Petroleum Geologists, p. 677–692.

Kirk, E., and T. W. Amsden, 1952, Upper Silurian brachiopods from southeastern Alaska: U.S. Geol. Survey Prof. Paper 233-C, p. 53–66.

Klapper, G., 1969, Lower Devonian conodont sequence, Royal Creek, Yukon Territory and Devon Island: Canada Jour. Paleontology, v. 43, no. 1, p. 1–27.

—— 1969, Lower Devonian conodont succession in Central Nevada: Geol. Soc. America Spec. Paper 121, p. 26–27.

Koren, T. N., and V. S. Enokyan, 1970, Siluryskiye i nizhnedevonskiye otlozheniya severo-zapadnoy chasti Yugorskogo p-ova i ostrovov Pechorskogo morya: Nauchno-Issled. Inst. Geologii Arktiki, Uchenyye Zapiski, Regional'naya Geologiya, no. 30, p. 5–25.

Lenz, A. C., 1967, Upper Silurian and Lower Devonian biostratigraphy, Royal Creek, Yukon Territory, Canada, in International symposium on the Devonian System, v. 2: Calgary, Alberta Soc. Petroleum Geologists, p. 587–599.

Maksimova, Z. A., 1970, Siluryskiye trilobity ostrova Vaygach, in Stratigrafiya i fauna siluryskikh otlozheny Vaygacha: Leningrad, Nauchno-Issled. Inst. Geologii Arktiki, p. 195–209.

McLaren, D. J., 1963, Stratigraphy of formations of possible Silurian and/or Devonian age, in Geology of the north-central part of the Arctic Archipelago, Northwest Territories (Operation Franklin): Canada Geol. Survey Mem. 320, p. 47–56.

Ormiston, A. R., 1967, Lower and Middle Devonian trilobites of the Canadian Arctic Islands: Canada Geol. Survey Bull. 153, 148 p.

Pershina, A. I., 1960, Stratigrafiya i fatsii silura i devona Pechorskogo Urala: Moscow-Leningrad, Akad. Nauk SSSR, Komi Filial, no. 10, p. 1–25.

—— 1962, Siluryskiye i devonskiye otlozheniya gryady Chernysheva: Moscow-Leningrad, Akad. Nauk SSSR, Komi Filial, 122 p.

Thorsteinsson, R., 1958, Cornwallis and Little Cornwallis Islands, District of Franklin, Northwest Territories: Canada Geol. Survey Mem. 294, 134 p.

—— 1963, Ordovician and Silurian stratigraphy, in Geology of the north-central part of the Arctic Archipelago, Northwest Territories (Operation Franklin): Canada Geol. Survey Mem. 320, p. 31–50.

Marine Upper Paleozoic Deposits of the Arctic[1]

V. I. USTRITSKY and G. E. CHERNYAK[2]

Leningrad, USSR

Abstract Correlations of upper Paleozoic rocks in the Arctic have been poorly understood because of incomplete study and because faunas in different parts of this territory belong to different paleozoogeographic regions. The Tropical paleozoogeographic region is characterized by the abundance and variety of faunas, and the Boreal region is characterized by faunal impoverishment. The areal extent of the Boreal environment was smallest in the Middle Carboniferous; it gradually spread throughout the Arctic by Late Permian time.

In the Tropical region, the Bashkirian and Moscovian Stages of the Middle Carboniferous are clearly distinguished on the basis of fusulinids and brachiopods. The writers consider the Upper Carboniferous as a single stage (Gzhelian). In the Boreal region, we assign to the Bashkirian Stage deposits containing a brachiopod complex best represented in Taymyr. This section was originally assigned to the Lower Permian. The Moscovian Stage is distinguished by a fauna differing significantly from the Bashkirian fauna. Upper Carboniferous deposits are difficult to distinguish in the Boreal region, because of their sparse atypical fauna.

The Carboniferous-Permian boundary in the Tropical region is thought to be at the base of the Asselian Stage. The boundary in the Boreal region is currently determined by the appearance of characteristic brachiopods, but the true boundary is probably at a lower level.

The writers distinguish two Lower Permian stages. The Asselian Stage corresponds to the *Schwagerina* Horizon, and the Artinskian Stage includes the Sakmarian, Artinskian, and Kungurian Stages of the Urals and the Russian platform.

The Lower-Upper Permian boundary is debatable. The writers define this boundary in the Boreal region by faunal development associated with a general sea transgression. The boundary thus drawn approximates the base of the Ufimian and the Lower-Upper Permian boundary of the Tethys.

Within the Upper Permian the writers accept the Paykhoyan and Kazanian Stages. The Paykhoyan Stage is well established in the Boreal region by typical brachiopod and pelecypod complexes. We consider the Kazanian Stage to include the Kazanian and Tatarian Stages of the Russian platform. In continuous marine sections, no faunal change that would allow distinguishing of the two stages is found.

Marine upper Paleozoic deposits are widespread within the Arctic. They are known in Novaya Zemlya, the Pechora basin, Taymyr, the Verkhoyansk region, the northeastern USSR, Spitsbergen, Greenland, the Canadian Arctic Archipelago, and Alaska. Correlations and precise ages of upper Paleozoic rocks in

[1] Manuscript received, August 1, 1972.
[2] Research Institute of the Geology of the Arctic.

the Arctic have, for long periods, remained poorly understood and debatable because of incomplete study and because faunas in different parts of this vast territory belong to different paleozoogeographic regions. The latter factor, particularly, has led most investigators to assign middle Upper Carboniferous deposits of Taymyr, the Verkhoyansk region, and the northeastern USSR to the Permian. To understand the correlation and age of upper Paleozoic rocks in this region, it is necessary to examine the zoogeographic classification of the Arctic marine basins during late Paleozoic time.

Principles of the zoogeographic division of late Paleozoic seas were studied by Ustritsky (1967, 1970). At the beginning of late Paleozoic time, the Tropical and Boreal paleozoogeographic regions were well differentiated. The Tropical region is characterized by the abundance and variety of faunas, whereas the main features of the Boreal region are distinct faunal impoverishment and the absence of several groups of organisms. No calcareous algae, echinoids, or fusulinids are present. At the beginning of late Paleozoic time, colonial corals continued to exist in the Boreal region; however, they did not form large accumulations and, since Moscovian time, they have been absent. Brachiopods also are markedly impoverished; such families as Tegulierinidae, Scacchinellidae, Richthofeniidae, and others which are typical of the Tropical region are absent. The number of endemic taxa in the Boreal region is not large. The single endemic brachiopod family is Horridoniidae. In other groups, endemism is marked only at the generic level. Most genera in the Boreal region have bipolar distribution, but they are absent or extremely rare in the Tropical region.

The extent of environmental influence of the Boreal region gradually changed during late Paleozoic time; the area was smallest in the Middle Carboniferous. Former limits are revealed by the presence of mixed Tropical-Boreal faunal complexes at Novaya Zemlya on the west and in the Chukotsk Peninsula on the east. At the beginning of Permian time, rather significant spreading of the Boreal region is indicated, especially in Novaya Zemlya and Pay-

Khoy. Eastward, the Boreal region extended into the Chukotsk Peninsula and northern Alaska. This spreading of the Boreal region is related to general worldwide cooling during Middle and Late Carboniferous time. During the Permian, the areal extent of the Boreal region continued to increase and, during the Artinskian Stage, the Boreal region encompassed all the marine basins under consideration. This spreading of the Boreal region was, for the most part, not due to climatic changes but to paleogeographic causes, for, since the beginning of the Artinskian, the Arctic marine basin appears to have been completely isolated from the Tethys seas.

During Middle and Late Carboniferous time, marine basins of the Canadian Arctic Archipelago, Spitsbergen, and Greenland, and the Pechora basin, were within the Tropical paleozoogeographic region, and abundant and varied faunas existed in these basins. Stratigraphically, fusulinids and brachiopods were the most important groups within this fauna. Novaya Zemlya was located within the transitional zone between the Tropical and Boreal regions, as is indicated by the presence there of fusulinids and brachiopods that are characteristic of the Tropical region and that are confined to the most shallow-water deposits. In all the regions mentioned above, the Bashkirian and Moscovian Stages of the Middle Carboniferous (Table 1) are clearly distinguished on the basis of fusulinids and brachiopods.

We consider the Upper Carboniferous sequence to represent a single stage. Critical analysis of attempts to divide the Carboniferous into stages was made by Miklukho-Maklay (1963) and Stepanov (1968).

In more eastern Arctic regions, the presence of Middle-Upper Carboniferous marine deposits has been denied by most investigators. First proof of the widespread presence of such deposits in Taymyr was published by Ustritsky and Chernyak (1963). Presence of rocks of this age was then established in other regions (Adrianov, 1966; Solomina et al., 1970). Attempts to distinguish generally accepted stages of the Middle and Upper Carboniferous in these regions were made by some authors (Ustritsky and Chernyak, 1965; Yeliseyeva et al., 1969).

In the Boreal region, we assign to the Bashkirian Stage deposits containing a brachiopod assemblage best represented in strata present in Taymyr (Tareya River). This stratigraphic section was first described by Einor (1939), who assigned it to the Lower Permian. Later, the section was described by the writers (Ustritsky and Chernyak, 1963). In this fossil complex are the genera Praehorridonia, Waagenoconcha, Alexenia, Tangshanella, and Choristites. Such species as Echinoconchus taimyrensis, Buxtonia tenuicostata, Dichtyoclostus byrangi, Spirifer tegulatus, S. engelhardthi, and others are widespread. These taxa are usually present in association with forms which are characteristic of the Lower Carboniferous. Together with this brachiopod complex, a rather sparse foraminiferal complex is present in many areas. Most Foraminifera of this complex range from the Viséan Stage to the Bashkirian Stage. The ammonites Stenopronorites uralensis, Verneuilites verneuili, and Bisatoceras sp. are present but are very scarce.

The Moscovian Stage fauna differs significantly from the Bashkirian fauna. Foraminifera and brachiopods typical of the Lower Carboniferous are almost completely absent from the Moscovian fauna. The genera Achunoproductus, Fimbriaria, Taimyrella, and Spiriferella occur in the brachiopod complex. Such typical species as Yakutoproductus cheraskovi, Balakhonia insinuata, and Orulgania tukulaensis are widespread. Ammonites of the genera Yakutoceras, Parayakutoceras, and Aldanites are abundant, but those of the genera Stenopronorites, Pseudoparalegoceras, and Owenoceras are scarce.

Upper Carboniferous deposits are difficult to distinguish in the Boreal region. The fauna of these deposits is very sparse and atypical. Among brachiopods, only Brachythyrina kharaylakhensis and Spiriferella turusica may be considered as characteristic; the main assemblage is composed of species which are transitional from the Moscovian Stage. Ammonites are represented by the endemic genus Eoschumardites. In practice, the Middle-Upper Carboniferous boundary is recognized conditionally on the basis of general faunal impoverishment and the disappearance of some genera which are common in the Middle Carboniferous rocks (Echinoconchus, Buxtonia, Antiquatonia, Torynifer). Foraminifera of the genus Protonodosaria occur in places in the upper half of the Upper Carboniferous deposits.

The Carboniferous-Permian boundary within the Tropical zoogeographic region is thought to be at the base of the Asselian Stage (Schwagerina Horizon). It is more difficult to establish this boundary in the Boreal region. At present, the Carboniferous-Permian boundary in the

Table 1. Stratigraphic Chart of Upper Paleozoic Deposits in the Arctic

SYSTEM	Series	Stages of Urals and Russian Platform	Proposed Stages	Canadian Arctic Archipelago	Greenland	Spitsbergen	Novaya Zemlya and Vaygach	Pechora Basin	Taymyr	Kharaulakh Range	Orulgan Range	Okhotsk Stable Region	Kolyma and Omolon Stable Region
PERMIAN	Upper	Tatarian	Kazanian	Glauconite limestone / Assistance Formation	Martiniakalk Posidonia shale, gypsum	Selander Formation / Starostin Formation	Green and violet sandstone	Pechora Series	Tuff-lava suite / Chernayarsky Horizon	Kharaulakh Formation	Delgalakh Formation	Duskan'ya Formation	Khivach Horizon / Gizhiga Horizon
		Kazanian					Sandstone and conglomerate						
		Ufimian	Paykhoyan				?		Upper Baikura Subhorizon / Baikura Hor. / Lower Baikura Subhorizon				
	Lower	Sakmara–Artin–Kungur	Artinskian	Belcher Channel Formation	Domkirhen Series	Wordiekammen Limestone — Upper	Kazakov Formation	Vorkuta Series	Sokolinaya Horizon	Verkhoyansk Formation	Delenzha Formation / Tumara Formation	Evrichan Formation / Nonkichan Formation	Omolon Horizon / Dzhigdaly Horizon
		Asselian	Asselian		Lebahia Series	Middle	Glazowa Formation	Talata Formation / Belkovskaya Formation / Gusinaya Formation	Byrrangy Formation				
					Upper Marine series	Lower	Sezym Horizon	Sezym Horizon	Upper Turuza Subhorizon (Turuza Horizon) / Lower Turuza Subhorizon	Soubol Formation	Echiy Formation	Ingychan Formation	Munugudzhak Horizon
CARBONIFEROUS	Upper	Gzhelian	Gzhelian	Canyon-Fiord Formation	Lower marine series / Blik klippen Series	Black-Craig Beds / Transitional beds	Clay limestone	Limestone			Megan Formation		Paren Horizon
		Moscovian	Moscovian			Lower Gypsiferous Series	Limestone	Limestone	Upper Makarova Subhorizon (Makarova Horizon) / Lower Makarova Subhorizon	Tiksi Formation (upper part)	Khaldan Formation / Suorgan Formation / Yupencha Formation	Yangada Formation	Burgali and Irbychan Horizons
	Middle	Bashkirian	Bashkirian				Limestone and limestone-conglomerate				Setachan Formation	?	Magar Horizon

Boreal region is determined by the appearance of such characteristic brachiopod species as *Yakutoproductus verchoyanicus* and *Anidanthus boikovi*. This level has practical convenience, but its synchronism with the base of the Asselian Stage has not been proved. Further study of this section probably will show that this boundary in the Boreal region is actually at a lower level.

We distinguish two Lower Permian stages— the Asselian and the Artinskian. We consider the Asselian to correspond to the *Schwagerina* Horizon. We understand the Artinskian Stage to include the Sakmarian, Artinskian *s.s.*, and Kungurian Stages of the Urals and the Russian platform. Because it is practically impossible to distinguish the Sakmarian and Kungurian Stages beyond the Urals and the Russian platform, outside these areas the Artinskian Stage is considered to have the same vertical extent as that defined by Karpinsky (1874).

In the Boreal region the separation of Artinskian deposits from Asselian strata causes great difficulties, because in this area all the Lower Permian strata are characterized by a rather uniform assemblage of brachiopods, of which *Yakutoproductus verchoyanicus* is the most significant. The Asselian deposits locally contain assemblages of small Foraminifera typical of the marlaceous beds, and the Artinskian deposits in places contain ammonites of the genera *Paragastrioceras, Uraloceras,* and *Neopronorites.*

The Lower-Upper Permian boundary is still debatable. In the type area for the Permian, the western foothills of the Urals, this boundary is drawn at the base of the Ufimian Stage. The Ufimian Stage is composed of continental deposits which are sparsely fossiliferous; hence, it is difficult to determine its analogues in other regions. We consider that the Lower-Upper Permian boundary in marine deposits of the Boreal paleozoogeographic region is marked by the appearance of such brachiopod genera as *Grumantia, Megousia, Svalbardoproductus, Pterospirifer,* and *Pseudosyringothyris;* by the appearance of the pelecypod genera *Procrassatella, Prooxytoma,* and *Pseudobakewellia;* and by mass development of representatives of the genus *Kolymia.* This faunal development is connected with a general sea transgression and establishment of the brief connection between the Arctic and Tethys seas. The boundary drawn in such a way coincides with, or approximates, the base of the Ufimian Stage and the Lower-Upper Permian boundary of the Tethys region (Ustritsky, 1965).

Within the Upper Permian, we accept the Paykhoyan and Kazanian Stages. The Paykhoyan Stage, as distinguished by Ustritsky ("Pai-Khoy"; 1960), is well established for marine deposits of the whole Boreal region on the basis of typical brachiopod and pelecypod assemblages. Brachiopods of the lower Paykhoyan Stage have been studied in most detail; they have been described from Greenland by Dunbar (1955) and from Spitsbergen by Gobbet (1963). In the upper Paykhoyan, *Cancrinelloides, Stepanoviella, Taeniothaerus,* and *Licharewia* appear among the brachiopods. However, other genera common to the Lower Permian—such as *Chonetina, Uraloproductus, Kochiproductus, Purdonella,* and *Attenuatella* —are absent. These changes in the brachiopod fauna provide a basis for distinguishing two substages in the Paykhoyan. Two ammonite species found in the Lower Permian, *Paragastrioceras jossae* and *Popanoceras tumarense,* are present in the lower Paykhoyan Stage. The Upper Permian genera *Spirolegoceras, Altudoceras, Eumedlicottia,* and *Cyclolobus* appear higher in the section. At the end of the Paykhoyan, ammonites apparently became extinct in all of the Arctic. Among small Foraminifera, a wide distribution of *Frondicularia* and *Nodosaria* is characteristic of the Paykhoyan Stage.

We consider the Kazanian Stage of the Arctic region to include both the Kazanian and Tatarian Stages of the Russian platform. Separation of the Kazanian and Tatarian Stages in the type section is based, not on evolution of the fauna and flora, but on an abrupt vertical change of marine Kazanian deposits into continental strata. In marine sections of Arctic deposits which extend from the base of the Kazanian Stage to the top of the Permian, no change in faunal complexes is found that would allow the distinguishing of two stages. An analogous situation exists in the Upper Permian of the Tethys (Miklukho-Maklay, 1963). A small foraminiferal complex in which the genera *Tristix, Pseudonodosaria, Lenticulina,* and some earlier species became widespread is typical for the Kazanian Stage. Among pelecypods in the Kazanian Stage, the genera *Thracia, Corbula,* and *Intomodesma* appear. Brachiopods of the Kazanian Stage are rather uniform; representatives of the genera *Cancrinelloides, Stepanoviella, Strophalosia,* and *Licharewia* are predominant. In the middle of the Kazanian Stage of the Arctic, brachiopods became extinct. In the lower Kazanian Stage of the Verkhoyansk region and the northeastern USSR, a sequence of glacial-marine deposits is characteristic (Andrianov, 1966; Mikhaylov et al., 1970). The upper half of the Kazanian Stage in the Arctic region is marked by the largest marine regression known to have occurred during all of Paleozoic time. Oceanic basins were preserved only in the Verkhoyansk geosyncline and in geosynclinal troughs fringing the Kolyma and Omolon stable regions.

References

Andrianov, V. N., 1966, Verkhnepaleozoyskiye otlozheniya Zapadnogo Verkhoyanya: Moscow, Izd. "Nauka," p. 1–130.

Einor, O. L., 1939, Brakhiopody nizhney permi Taymyra (basseyn r. Pyasiny): Akad. Nauk. I. I. Trudy, v. 135, Izd. "Glavsevmorputi," 150 p.

Gobbet, D. I., 1963, Carboniferous and Permian brachiopods of Svalbard: Norsk. Polarinst. Skr., no. 127, p. 1–201.

Karpinsky, A. P., 1874, Geologicheskiye issledovaniya v Orenburgskom kraye: Zap. S-Peterb. Mineral, obva ser. 2, ch. 9, p. 53, 65.

Mikhaylov, Yu A., et al., 1970, Verknepermskiye ledovomorskiye otlozheniya Severo-Vostoka SSSR: Akad. Nauk SSSR Doklady, v. 190, no. 5, p. 1184–1187.

Miklukho-Maklay, A. D., 1963, Verkhny paleozoy Sredney Asii: Leningrad, Leningrad. Gosudar. Univ., 329 p.

Solomina, R. V., et al., 1970, Stratigrafiya kamennougolnykh i permskikh otlozheny Severnogo Verkhoyanya: Nauchno-Issled. Inst. Geologii Arktiki Trudy, v. 154, p. 1–190.

Stepanov, D. L., 1968, Obyem i yarusnoye podrazdeleniye verkhnego karbona: Akad. Nauk SSSR Izv. Ser. Geol., no. 4, p. 17–21.

Ustritsky, V. I., 1960, O granitse nizhney i verkhney permi v Pechorskom basseyne i v Arktike: Nauchno-Issled. Inst. Geologii Arktiki Trudy, v. 114, p. 39–49.

——— 1965, O korrelyatsii verkhnepermskikh otlozheny Arktiki i Tetisa: Nauchno-Issled. Inst. Geologii Arktiki, Uchenyye Zapiski, Regional'naya Geologiya, Ser. Paleont. i Biostratigr., no. 7, p. 10–13.

——— 1967, O polozhenii Severnogo polyusa v pozdnem paleozoye na osnovanii paleontologicheskikh dannykh: Geologiya i Geofizika, no. 1, p. 52–32.

——— 1970, Zoogeografiya pozdnepaleozoyskikh morey Sibiri i Arktiki: Nauchno-Issled. Inst. Geologii Arktiki, Uchenyye Zapiski, Regional'naya Geologiya, Ser. Paleont. i Biostratigr., no. 29, p. 58–77.

——— G. E. Chernyak, 1963, Biostratigrafiya i brakhiopody verkhnego paleozoya Taymyra: Nauchno-Issled. Inst. Geologii Arktiki Trudy, v. 134, p. 1–140.

——— and ——— 1965, O yarusnom raschlenenii kamennougolnykh otlozheny severa Sibiri: Nauchno-Issled. Inst. Geologii Arktiki, Uchenyye Zapiski, Regional'naya Geologiya, Ser. Paleont. i Biostratigr., no. 10, p. 5–14.

Yeliseyeva, V. K., G. V. Kotlyar, and G. Ye. Chernyak, 1969, Stratigrafiya kamennougolnykh otlozheny Vostoka SSSR: Sovetskaya Geologiya, no. 11, p. 3–18.

Structural History of Spitsbergen and Adjoining Shelves[1]

V. N. SOKOLOV, A. A. KRASIL'SHCHIKOV, Yu. Ya. LIVSHITZ, and D. V. SEMEVSKY[2]

Leningrad, USSR

Abstract Four main periods in the geologic history of Spitsbergen are the early Precambrian geosynclinal period, the Riphean—early Paleozoic miogeosynclinal period, the Devonian postgeosynclinal (orogenic) period, and the late Paleozoic–Cenozoic platform period.

In the pre-Riphean period, intensive downwarping was followed by subaqueous flows (mostly mafic) and then by inversion of the geosynclinal troughs.

The early Riphean stage is characterized by flyschlike sedimentation. In the middle-late Riphean stage, a complete sedimentary cycle was developed, ending with pre-Paleozoic uplift and peneplanation. At the end of this stage, the slow downwarping which had compensated the general uplift of the archipelago was replaced by smaller-scale uplift and downwarp. In the early Paleozoic stage, a basin developed in Spitsbergen, and shallow-marine sedimentation took place. In the late Ordovician-Silurian stage, the Caledonian geosyncline developed into a complex fold area, the crystalline basement blocks of the Caledonides were "rejuvenated," and granite and subalkalic intrusions were emplaced.

In the Devonian postgeosynclinal period, horsts and grabens were formed. Orogenic processes were accompanied by development of superimposed basins that were filled with molassic terrigenous deposits up to 6,500 m thick. During the same period, lamprophyre dikes were emplaced.

The late Paleozoic–Cenozoic period included four stages of platform development. In the late Paleozoic stage, terrigenous and carbonate deposits about 2 km thick were formed. Quiet conditions in the Early Carboniferous were followed by intense block movements in the Bashkirian Age. At the end of the Late Carboniferous, the complex of uplifts and depressions became a single basin, and total uplift at the end of the Permian completed the stage. In the Mesozoic, mainly terrigenous sediments 3 km thick accumulated in a great basin. Total uplift in Late Cretaceous time ended this stage. Intensified block movements localized early Cenozoic basins, which were filled with coal-bearing and conglomerate formations 1.5–4 km thick. The early Cenozoic stage ended with the inversion of the sedimentary troughs, followed by faulting and overthrusting. In the late Cenozoic stage, intense differential motion was renewed along preexisting faults. Uplift was greatest in the inverted mobile zone of the Vestspitsbergen trough. At the end of the stage the center of uplift migrated eastward, and uplift decreased in the Holocene. The Holocene was characterized by volcanic activity and a possible increase in seismicity.

Spitsbergen is now characterized by platform development. The basement of the platform contains two Caledonian fold systems, which frame the Precambrian stable region. The Caledonides of Spitsbergen and Greenland are very similar, but probably were not directly connected to the British–Scandinavian–Severnaya Zemlyan Caledonides.

Main tendencies of Spitsbergen's post-Caledonian history are an increase in mobility at the western edge of the platform and steady uplift of the northern part.

Analysis of Spitsbergen's structural history allows a positive prognosis for oil and gas prospects in the southern part of the archipelago and the adjoining shelf.

The Spitsbergen archipelago is the extreme northwestern outcrop of the continental structures of Eurasia. Its key geotectonic position and the variety of geologic formations of different ages explain the great interest that scientists of many countries have shown in this remote Arctic region.

The analysis of Spitsbergen's structural history is based on a generalization of data obtained by Soviet and foreign geologists during the last 10 years. Their data open new possibilities for solving many theoretical problems concerning the Atlantic sector of the Arctic and may contribute to an evaluation of oil and gas prospects in the shelf areas.

It is possible to distinguish four main periods in the geologic history of Spitsbergen: the early Precambrian (pre-Riphean), typically a geosynclinal period; the Riphean–early Paleozoic miogeosynclinal period; the Devonian postgeosynclinal (orogenic) period; and the late Paleozoic-Cenozoic platform period (Fig. 1).

On most of the archipelago, the pre-Riphean period (up to 1,650 m.y.) was characterized by intensive downwarping followed by subaqueous flows, mainly of mafic composition. Inversion of geosynclinal troughs characterized the end of the period. Within Vestspitsbergen, the inversion was of a local nature, but the eastern edge of the archipelago had become a part of a vast consolidated area, which afterward appeared as a relatively rigid block.

The Riphean–early Paleozoic period (1,650–400 m.y.) was the period of formation of the "main geosynclinal complex" of the Spitsbergen Caledonides. The accumulation of sedimentary formations took place in three stages: early Riphean, middle-late Riphean (including Vendian), and early Paleozoic. These stages are marked by changes in composition of the enclosed formational sequences and by reworking of the structural pattern.

[1] Manuscript received, August 1, 1972.

[2] Research Institute of the Geology of the Arctic.

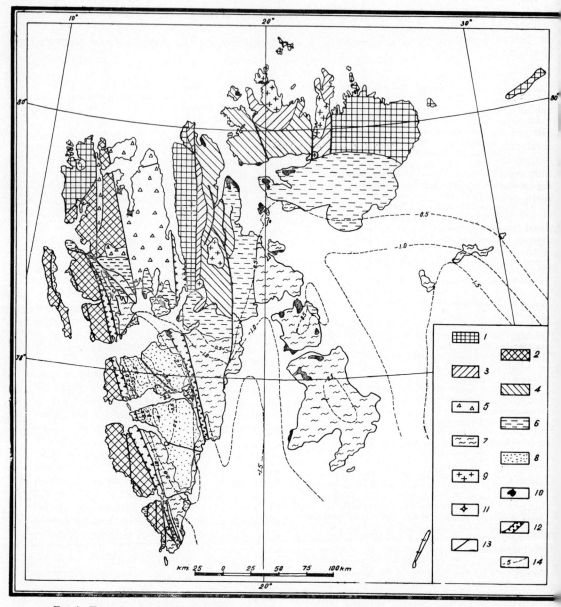

FIG. 1—Tectonic scheme of Spitsbergen archipelago: **1.** "Rejuvenated" blocks of the pre-Riphean crystalline basement—Caledonides. **2.** Riphean–early Paleozoic undissected miogeosynclinal complex of structures and formations. **3.** Early Riphean subcomplex. **4.** Middle-late Riphean and early Paleozoic subcomplexes (undissected)—postgeosynclinal superimposed depressions. **5.** Devonian orogenic complex.

Platform mantle (late Paleozoic–Cenozoic complex of structures and formations): **6.** Late Paleozoic subcomplex. **7.** Mesozoic subcomplex. **8.** Early Cenozoic subcomplex. **9.** Middle Paleozoic granites and subalkalic intrusions. **10.** Mesozoic dolerites. **11.** Holocene volcanoes. **12.** Western and eastern marginal fault zones (greatly displaced upper Paleozoic and Mesozoic rocks are embedded within these zones). **13.** Major faults outside boundary zones. **14.** Structure contours along base of platform rocks (in km).

The early Riphean Stage (1,650–1,400 m.y.) represents the transition period between two geosynclinal cycles and is characterized by an extensive sequence of flyschlike units. Northeast of the deep-seated Hinlopen fault, a clastic-volcanic formation is developed, with which a massif of porphyritic granites (including rapakivi) is associated spatially and perhaps genetically (Krasil'shchikov, 1969).

In the middle-late Riphean Stage (1,400–570 m.y.), a complete sedimentary cycle was developed, ending with pre-Paleozoic uplift and peneplanation. Three first-order paleostructures with different tectonic regimes existed at the site of the present Spitsbergen archipelago: the northeastern block of the crystalline basement of the Caledonides; the Hinlopen miogeosynclinal trough, developed on the early Riphean troughs in Ny Friesland and in the western part of Nordaustlandet; and the Vestspitsbergen geanticlinal complex, parts of which had been involved periodically in the downwarping. At the end of this stage, the slow compensating downwarping that had accompanied the general uplift of the archipelago was replaced by smaller-scale uplift and downwarp. The result was the accumulation of a regressive terrigenous formation, whose origin has been associated with Precambrian glaciation (Kulling, 1934; Harland, 1961).

The early Paleozoic stage (570–440 m.y.) began with minimal tectonic activity. The thin Lower Cambrian quartzose sandstone formation corresponds to this time. Most of the lower Paleozoic sequences in Spitsbergen are shallow-marine carbonate sedimentary beds. The development of the early Paleozoic basin in Spitsbergen ended in the Middle Ordovician (Harland, 1961).

The Late Ordovician–Silurian stage was a turning point in Spitsbergen geologic history. The most significant tectonic result of this stage was that the broad Caledonian geosyncline developed into a fold area with a complex inner structure. The general inversion and particularly the associated metamorphic processes led to a "rejuvenation" of the crystalline basement blocks of the Caledonides (Krasil'shchikov, 1965). In the final stage, the granitic and subalkalic intrusions occurred. The consolidation of the Caledonian fold structures ended between Silurian and Devonian time. The resulting structural pattern is characterized by submeridional strike of linear folds, complicated by thrust faults, overthrusts, and wrench faults.

The Devonian postgeosynclinal (orogenic) period was characterized by intensive block movements that created horsts and grabens. This motion took place along major faults which were active during the preceding tectonic stage of development in this area. The orogenic processes caused by these movements were accompanied by the development of superimposed grabenlike basins that inherited submeridional strike from the Caledonian structures. These basins were filled with a thick sequence (up to 6,500 m) of variegated terrigenous deposits of molassic character. The sequence includes conglomerates at the base, lying with angular unconformity on the eroded surface of the older rocks. Analogous formations (Old Red Sandstone) are characteristic of the whole Caledonian belt of the North Atlantic.

The largest superimposed basin is situated in the north of Vestspitsbergen. The rate of sedimentation during the postgeosynclinal period was not less than 130 m per million years. Lamprophyre dikes were emplaced during the same period. The block movements at the close of the period led to the development of the Devonian graben, which has an inner block structure with folds and faults.

Some geologists associate these dislocations (faulting and folding) with the final "Svalbardian" phase of the Caledonian tectogenesis (Harland, 1961).

The late Paleozoic–Cenozoic platform period began in the Early Carboniferous. Four stages of platform development are distinguished, coinciding with the main sedimentary cycles and separated by events of uplift and later peneplanation. These stages are the late Paleozoic, Mesozoic, early Cenozoic, and late Cenozoic.

During the late Paleozoic, a series of terrigenous and carbonate deposits about 2 km thick was formed. The basal units of the platform mantle, coal-bearing sediments of the Lower Carboniferous, were deposited in relatively quiet conditions. At the beginning of the Bashkirian, however, intense block movements had developed again, and these movements led to the accumulation of the variegated sandstones and conglomerates (up to 800 m). At the end of the Late Carboniferous, the complex of depressions and uplifts was transformed into a single basin, in which mainly carbonate sediments accumulated until Late Permian time. In the first half of the late Paleozoic stage, including the Bashkirian, the rate of sedimentation was 60 m per million years. The end of this stage was marked wholly by uplift at the end of the Permian, as is expressed by a general lack of Tatarian and Kazanian deposits in Spitsbergen.

The Mesozoic was characterized by less tectonic activity. During this time a series of mainly marine clastic sediments nearly 3 km thick accumulated. Within this series, several hiatuses of varying lengths are apparent, the greatest of which is assigned to Early-Middle Jurassic time. In the Mesozoic stage of platform development, as in the Late Permian, sedimentation took place in a great basin, the deepest part of which migrated gradually eastward. The average rate of sedimentation during the stage was 16 m per million years. This stage ended with total uplift in the Late Cretaceous. The main phase of basic magmatism of the platform was also Cretaceous.

Intensification of block movements, which started in the Late Cretaceous, localized the early Cenozoic basins. The basins became smaller, similar to aulacogenes. They are filled with coal-bearing and conglomerate formations of the orogenic type. The thickness of the basin strata exceeds 1.5 km in the Vestspitsbergen trough and 4 km in Forlandsundet (Livshitz, 1967; 1970). In Vestspitsbergen, the average rate of sedimentation during this stage increased to 72 m per million years, and in Forlandsundet it reached 250 m per million years.

The early Cenozoic stage ended with the inversion of the sedimentary troughs, followed by faulting and overthrusting—forming the modern block structure of the archipelago.

During the whole late Cenozoic stage, intense differential movements occurred repeatedly along the zones of the rejuvenated faults, and these movements finalized the modern structure of the archipelago and determined its morphologic appearance. Uplifting developed most intensely in the inverted mobil zone of the Vestspitsbergen trough, where the amplitude of the uplift is about 1,000 m. On the adjoining part of the shelf, disturbances of a wrench-fault type possibly took place in the Pleistocene. The center of the persisting uplift migrated eastward from the archipelago in the later part of the stage, and the rates of uplift, which were maximal at the end of the Pleistocene, progressively diminished in the Holocene. The Holocene was characterized by volcanic activity (Semevsky, 1965) associated with zones of rejuvenated faults in the north of Vestspitsbergen and, possibly, by a total increase of seismicity in the region (Fig. 2).

What place does Spitsbergen occupy in the general structure of the Atlantic sector of the Arctic? Despite the evident heterogeneity in the tectonic structure of Spitsbergen and that of the adjoining shelves, it is possible to state that the whole area now is characterized by platform development.

The formation of the folded basement of this young platform[3] ended during the Caledonian orogeny; its heterogeneity was predetermined by the very different development of individual parts of the Caledonian geosynclinal belt. Within the basement of the young platform, two Caledonian fold systems are distinguished —the Spitsbergen and Scandinavia–Severnaya Zemlya fold systems. They frame the Precambrian stable region, which is raised above sea level in places in the east part of Nordaustlandet and the nearby islands. Recent investigations (Krasil'shchikov *et al.*, 1964; Gayer *et al.*, 1966) affirm the "geochronologic rejuvenation" of the Barents massif during the Caledonian orogeny.

The analysis of the geologic development of the Spitsbergen Caledonides in the Precambrian and early Paleozoic shows that they are very similar in structure and sedimentary succession to the East Greenland Caledonides. Both fold systems are characterized by miogeosynclinal development throughout the period. During the same time, the British-Scandinavian Caledonides, and probably their supposed continuation under the Barents Sea, were formed on the site of an early Paleozoic narrow trough that can be clearly differentiated into eugeosynclinal and miogeosynclinal zones. The difference in development of the Greenland-Spitsbergen and the British-Scandinavian geosynclinal troughs is also confirmed by a discordance of general strikes of the fold systems. The conclusion regarding a direct union of these systems in the north of the Scandinavian peninsula (Atlasov *et al.*, 1964; Gafarov, 1966) is thus uncertain, particularly if the evidence from Bjørnøya geology is considered (*i.e.*, the horizontal occurrence of Ordovician carbonate rocks and the coal-bearing nature of Devonian strata grading into Lower Carboniferous deposits). It is more probable that the Greenland-Spitsbergen and the British–Scandinavian–Severnaya Zemlyan Caledonides were divided by a system of median masses such as the Barents massif and the "Eria" platform.

[3] This platform may be considered provisionally as a part of the young West European platform (after Yanshin, 1965) or as the western part of the Barents-Kara plate (after Atlasov *et al.*, 1964).

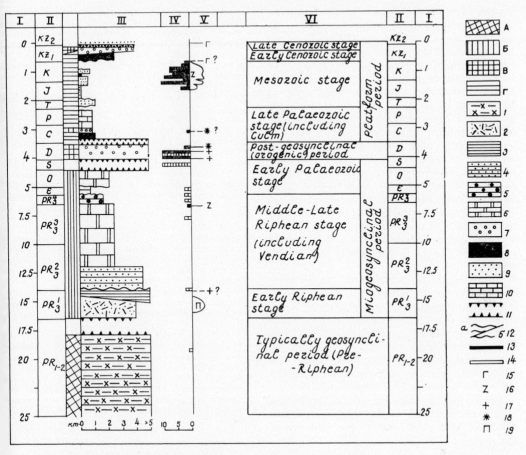

FIG. 2—Scheme of Spitsbergen geologic history.

I. Geochronologic time scale (in 100 m.y.).

II. International stratigraphic scale.

III. Types of formations. **A.** Eugeosynclinal types: **1.** Gneisses and schists. **B.** Miogeosynclinal types: **2.** Volcanic-clastic. **3.** Flysch. **4.** Terrigenous transgressive. **5.** Terrigenous regressive. **6.** Carbonate. **C.** Orogenic types (epigeosynclinal or epiplatformic): **7.** Rudaceous. **D.** Platformic types: **8.** Coal-bearing. **9.** Terrigenous. **10.** Siliceous-carbonate (gypsiferous in places). *Unconformities:* **11.** Structural. **12.** Regional stratigraphic. (a) known time interval, (b) unknown time interval. Horizontal scale = thickness of formations.

IV. Isotopic ages (including unpublished results obtained by L. W. Firsov in Laboratory of Siberian Branch of Academy of Science on samples from collections of Institute of the Geology of the Arctic). Horizontal scale = number of determinations on **13.** intrusive rocks, **14.** metamorphic rocks.

V. Magmatism. **15.** Basalts. **16.** Dolerites. **17.** Granitoids and subalkalic intrusions. **18.** Lamprophyre dikes. **19.** Porphyries of acidic and medium composition.

VI. Stages and periods of tectonic development.

The tectonic heterogeneity of the folded basement of the young platform caused considerable differences in the development of its parts, as is reflected in the different thicknesses of the platform cover and in the types of folds and faults. During the whole post-Caledonian platform history, two main tendencies of development are demonstrated. First is the greater mobility of the western platform edge in comparison to the remaining part, and second is the steady slow uplift of the northern part of the platform that resulted in the formation of the archipelago system (Spitsbergen, Franz Josef Land). The latter may be considered to be the result of marginal uplifts of the young platform.

The tendency for increased mobility in the western part of the platform was probably in-

herited from the Caledonian geosyncline. The
intensification of the tectonic movements in the
last stage was caused by the rift zones of the
Mid-Atlantic Ridge occurring near the Spitsbergen archipelago (Ivanov *et al.*, 1968). The
lateral influence of these zones effected the
powerful thrusting along the west coast of
Spitsbergen which has caused many geologists
to speak of Alpine folding in this area (Orvin,
1940; Harland, 1961, *etc.*).

Continuing uplift of the northern platform
edge may be explained as the result of isostatic
compensation for the formation of the Arctic
basins in the western part. Such basinal development could result from downwarping of
great marginal blocks of the continental crust
in the vicinity of recent abyssal trenches in the
Barents shelf periphery, or it could be caused
by crustal changes in the central part of this
shelf.

The influence of "riftogenesis" on Spitsbergen structure is demonstrated by faults intrud-
ing into the archipelago transverse to the Knipovich and Gakkel midoceanic ridges. These
faults are expressed morphologically as fjords.
The west-east faults are aseismic and are expressed mainly by small-scale strike faults. The
north-south faults in northern Vestspitsbergen
are seismic and have large displacements.

The further development of the Spitsbergen
area is characterized by the continued rejuvenation of fault zones and by the tendency of
the archipelago to sink.

This analysis of the structural history of
Spitsbergen allows us to give a positive prognosis for oil and gas prospects in the southern half
of the archipelago and in adjoining parts of
the Barents shelf. The most promising prospects
are land areas situated within the Vestspitsbergen grabenlike trough with a thick sedimentary
cover (over 5,000 m). The sedimentary strata
are late Paleozoic to Cenomanian terrigenous
and carbonate deposits. Less promising are the
areas of Edgeøya and Barents, where the thickness of the sedimentary sequence diminishes
considerably. The recent data available for
Kong Karls Land, Hopen, and Franz Josef
Land show a great increase in thickness of platform rocks in an eastern and southeastern direction; thus, the prospects for oil and gas in the
central part of the Barents shelf are good.

SELECTED REFERENCES

Atlasov, I. P., *et al.*, 1964, Novaya tektonicheskaya
    karta Arktiki: Akad. Nauk SSSR Doklady, v. 156,
    no. 6, p. 1341–1342.

Firsov, L. V., and Yu. Ya. Livshitz, 1967, Kaly-argo-
    novaya datirovka doleritov rayona Sassen-f'orda (za-
    padnyy Shpitsbergen), *in* Materialy po stratigrafii
    Shpitsbergena: Leningrad, Nauchno-Issled. Inst.
    Geologii Arktiki, p. 178–184.
Gafarov, R. A., 1966, Voprosy tektoniki fundamenta
    severa Vostochno-Yevropeyskoy platformy: Geotek-
    tonika, no. 4, p. 81–91.
Gayer, R. A., *et al.*, 1966, Radiometric age determina-
    tions on rocks from Spitsbergen: Norsk Polarinst.
    Skr., no. 137, 39 p.
Harland, W. B., 1961, An outline structural history of
    Spitsbergen, *in* Geology of the Arctic, v. 1: Toronto,
    Univ. Toronto Press, p. 68–132.
Ivanov, S. S., A. M. Karasik, and V. N. Sokolov, 1968,
    O svyazi struktury Shpitsbergena so sredinno-oceani-
    cheskim riftogenezom: Nauchno-Issled. Inst. Geolo-
    gii Arktiki, Uchenyye Zapiski, Regional'naya Geolo-
    giya, no. 12, p. 224–227.
Klitin, K. A., 1960, O tektonike Shpitsbergena: Akad.
    Nauk SSSR Izv. Ser. Geol., no. 10, p. 62–69.
Krasil'shchikov, A. A., 1965, Nekotoryye osobennosti
    geologicheskogo razvitiya severnoy chasti arkhipe-
    laga Shpitsbergen, *in* Materialy po geologii Shpits-
    bergena: Leningrad, Nauchno-Issled. Inst. Geologii
    Arktiki, p. 29–44.
———— 1969, Kaledonskiye intruzii arkhipelaga Shpits-
    bergen: Nauchno-Issled. Inst. Geologii Arktiki,
    Uchenyye Zapiski, Regional'naya Geologiya, no. 16,
    p. 62–68.
———— A. Ya. Krylov, and O. A. Alyapyshev, 1964, O
    vozraste nekotorykh granitoidnykh porod i gneysov
    severnoy chasti arkhipelaga Shpitsbergen: Akad.
    Nauk SSSR Doklady, v. 159, no. 4, p. 796–799.
Kulling, O., 1934, The "Hecla Hoek formation" round
    Hinlopenstretet, Pt. XI *of* Scientific results of the
    Swedish-Norwegian Arctic expedition in the summer
    of 1931: Geog. Annaler, arb. 16, no. 4, p. 161–254.
Livshitz, Yu. Ya., 1967, Tretichnyye otlozheniya zapad-
    noy chasti arkhipelaga Shpitsbergen, *in* Materialy po
    stratigrafii Shpitsbergena: Leningrad, Nauchno-Is-
    sled. Inst. Geologii Arktiki, p. 185–204.
———— 1970, Osnovnyye etapy formirovaniya platfor-
    mennykh struktur Shpitsbergena, *in* Mat-ly 1 k
    nauchn. konf. asp. geologov.: Leningrad, Vses. Nauch-
    no-Issled. Geol. Inst. Trudy i "NTO Gornoy," p.
    8–10.
Orvin, A. K., 1940, Outline of the geological history of
    Spitsbergen: Skr. om Svalbard og Ishavet, no. 78, 57
    p.
Sandford, K. S., 1956, The stratigraphy and structure
    of the Hecla Hoek formation and its relationship to
    a subjacent metamorphic complex in North-East
    Land (Spitsbergen): Geol. Soc. London Quart.
    Jour., v. 112, pt. 3, no. 447, p. 339–362.
Semevsky, D. V., 1965, K voprosu o vozraste vulkana
    Sverre, *in* Materialy po geologii Shpitsbergena: Len-
    ingrad, Nauchno-Issled. Inst. Geologii Arktiki, p
    272–275.
Sokolov, V. N., A. A. Krasil'shchikov, and Yu. Ya.
    Livshitz, 1968, The main features of the tectonic
    structure of Spitsbergen: Geol. Mag., v. 105, no. 2,
    p. 95–115.
Winsnes, Th. S., 1966, The Precambrian of Spits-
    bergen and Bjørnøya, *in* Kalervo Rankama, ed., The
    Precambrian (The geologic systems), v. 2: New York
    Interscience Pub. (John Wiley and Sons).
Yanshin, A. L., 1965, Tektonicheskoye stroyeniye Yev-
    razii: Geotektonika, no. 5, p. 7–36.

Middle Paleozoic Reefs of Siberian North: Potential Oil and Gas Reservoirs[1]

D. K. PATRUNOV and **YU. G. SAMOILOVICH**[2]

Leningrad, USSR

Abstract Main criteria for predicting the presence of ancient reefs are paleoclimatic, paleotectonic, and lithologic. The paleoclimatic criterion is used to identify warm climatic zones, restricted to the equatorial belt of the globe, where reef formation was possible. Regions of differential tectonic movements, which are the essential factors for reef formation, are located by use of the paleotectonic criterion. The lithologic criterion distinguishes marine sedimentary complexes associated with reefs. By use of these criteria, three middle Paleozoic reef provinces have been distinguished in the Soviet Arctic—the Pechora–Novaya Zemlya, Taymyr–Tungusska, and East Siberia–Chukchi regions.

The Pechora–Novaya Zemlya province contains Silurian-Devonian reefs. In the Novaya Zemlya–Urals area, reef complexes are confined to edges of geosynclinal downwarps and tectonic scarps in the outer part of a miogeosynclinal area. In the Pechora depression, Upper Devonian reef masses formed on tectonic scarps bordering trenchlike troughs of the platform. In Vaygach, Silurian reefs belong to the sedimentary complex of a shallow carbonate platform. A Devonian reef massif up to 2,000 m thick formed along a trough margin including part of northeastern Pay-Khoy and reaching southeastern Vaygach. Facies changes from reef to nonreef deposits may be decisive in formation of stratigraphic oil and gas traps. The aim of prospecting in the Pay-Khoy–Novaya Zemlya region is to search for high-porosity zones in reef massifs among petroliferous black shales and limestones.

Almost the whole spectrum of Silurian-Devonian deposits, especially rich in clay, clayey carbonate, and sulfate rocks, is represented on the sides of the Tungusska synclise and in the northern Taymyr margin of the Siberian platform. Bioclastic skeletal and biogenic limestones also are present. Carbonate sedimentation in the Tungusska basin was closely related to transgressions and regressions of the sea. Association of coral-stromatoporoid limestones of varied thickness with shales suggests the possibility of oil traps in Wenlockian deposits. Devonian reefs are probably present at the juncture of the Tungusska and Taymyr basins and in the Yenisey-Khatanga trough.

In the East Siberia–Chukchi reef province, Silurian and Devonian carbonate deposits with indications of reef formation are located north of the continental margin. Most paleotectonic reconstructions for the northeast margin of the USSR indicate the transition from a eugeosyncline at the south to a miogeosyncline and, at the north, the Hyperborean platform. The outer part of the miogeosyncline underwent differential tectonic movements favorable for reef formation. Reefs might also have been formed at the edges of troughs within the Hyperborean platform. Localized occurrences of reeflike limestones in volcanic sequences of the eugeosynclinal zone of the Koryak upland could have formed as atolls on submarine volcanic cones.

[1] Manuscript received, August 1, 1972.
[2] Research Institute of the Geology of the Arctic.

INTRODUCTION

Because of rapid technical development, exploitation of natural resources in the Arctic will soon be profitable on land and sea. There is little doubt now that the Arctic is rich in oil and gas. Among the prospective oil reservoirs, the middle Paleozoic reefs are most important. Their importance is substantiated by the fact that oil and gas fields have already been established and exploited in middle Paleozoic reefs within the regions adjacent to the Arctic (Pre-Urals, Western Canada). Oil is produced from the top of the Upper Devonian reefs in the Timan-Pechora oil province. The search is also facilitated by the possibility of predicting reef position.

CRITERIA FOR PREDICTION OF ANCIENT REEFS

The main criteria for predicting the presence of ancient reefs may be considered to be paleoclimatic, paleotectonic, and lithologic. The first two reflect general premises for reef formation. The lithologic criterion takes into consideration real reef features.

The paleoclimatic criterion is the most general. It allows determination of past climatic conditions where reef formation would have been possible. In each epoch, reefs were formed in warm climatic zones and were restricted to the equatorial belt of the globe. The middle Paleozoic reef tract, which is present throughout the Arctic, is developed in the Soviet Arctic from Novaya Zemlya to the eastern margin of the Chukchi Sea (Fig. 1).

The paleotectonic criterion permits location of regions of differential tectonic movements, which are the essential factors of reef formation. These regions are confined to the margins of platforms and geosynclines, anticlinoriums within geosynclines, margins of basins, and zones of deep-seated faults. Older tectonic structures controlling reef formation are widespread in the Arctic, though they are not always clearly revealed (Fig. 2).

The lithologic criterion distinguishes marine sedimentary complexes that are associated with reefs and biogenic structures, or sedimentary facies related genetically to reefs (bioclastic

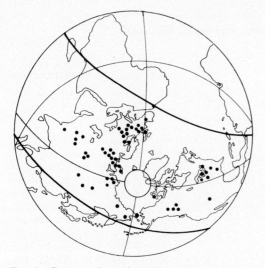

Fig. 1—Concentrations of Middle Paleozoic reefs of Siberian North.

limestones of reef-talus "dumps," carbonate sandstones, *etc.*). The establishment of sedimentary facies which accompany reefs may be of primary importance. Black calcareous shales, including thin graptolitic shales, are commonly associated with reefs, because they accumulate in depressions in front of reef structures.

On the basis of the paleotectonic criterion, including consideration of reef manifestation and accompanying facies, reef provinces are distinguished where middle Paleozoic reefs may be the object of the search for oil and gas. These provinces are the Pechora–Novaya Zemlya, Taymyr-Tungusska, and East Siberia–Chukchi regions.

PECHORA–NOVAYA ZEMLYA REEF PROVINCE

The Pechora–Novaya Zemlya reef province covers Novaya Zemlya, Vaygach Island, and adjacent areas of the Kara Sea, Pay-Khoy, and the Pechora depression. In different parts of this province, where a fairly detailed study was carried out, Silurian-Devonian reefs were found. This tectonically heterogeneous province was characterized in the middle Paleozoic by geologic and paleogeographic conditions exceptionally favorable for reef formation.

Reef complexes of Pay-Khoy, Vaygach, and Novaya Zemlya are located in regions parallel with recent anticlinoriums and shorelines. They are limited to edges of ancient geosynclinal downwarpings and tectonic scarps in the outer part of a miogeosynclinal area in the Novaya

Zemlya–Urals geosynclinal area. Only fragments of the belts are exposed. These reefs extend into the sea and under the thick Permian shale terrane of a periclinal depression in the southern island of Novaya Zemlya. Within the Pechora depression, Upper Devonian reef masses formed on tectonic scarps bordering trench-like troughs of the platform (Kushnareva and Matviyevskaya, 1969).

Reefs south of Novaya Zemlya and in Vaygach have been more completely studied. At present, these locations may be considered as key sections for the whole Soviet Arctic.

In Vaygach, biogenic structures and reefs are known to be present in the Silurian and Lower and Upper Devonian. In the Silurian they belong to the sedimentary complex of a shallow carbonate platform that occupied almost the whole territory of Vaygach, except its southeastern end, where shales are predominant. In the Wenlock or lower Ludlow of Vaygach, stromatoporoid-algal biostromes and flattened bioherms surrounded by algal, amphiporous, and microcrystalline limestones, and by sedimentary dolomites, are widespread. At the Silurian-Devonian boundary, light-gray coral-stromatoporoid-algal bioherms up to 20 m in height occur at the base of the Vaygach Horizon. They are surrounded by rims of bioclastic limestone and carbonate sandstone. Thin-layered detrital black limestone encloses the whole complex.

In Vaygach, reef development was greatest at the end of the Early Devonian and possibly at the beginning of the Eifelian, when a reef massif up to 2,000 m thick formed southeast of the island (Cape Sukhoy Nos). Confined to the west margin of the trough, this massif occupied the central northeastern part of Pay-Khoy and stretched almost along the meridian to the north, "touching" the southeastern part of Vaygach. The Lower Devonian reef massif northwest of Pay-Khoy (Cape Belyy Nos) may be related to the western edge of this synclinorium.

The reef southeast of Vaygach is composed of light-gray and cream-colored, predominantly algal limestones containing abundant incrustations. In the center of some incrustations, accumulations of black crystalline anthraxolite are found among columnar calcite.

Beneath the reef, at an interval up to 500 m, the section grades into Ludlovian black graptolite shale. Within this part of the section, a stage preceding the culmination of reef formation is marked by a 100-m-thick tongue of carbonate turbidites and breccias in association with shales and clayey limestones. The breccias are composed predominantly of platy fragments of reef limestones—*i.e.,* algal, brachiopodal-crinoidal, oolitic, *etc.* At this level, corresponding to the Silurian-Devonian boundary, bioherms were found by S. V. Cherkesova along the outcrop for several kilometers from the main exposure. The available data show that the first small reefs originated on a shale base. It may be expected that where they are buried they are sealed in shales and are prospective reservoirs of oil. This association is important, because the black shales contain 3 percent organic material.

A series of reefs in the subsurface on the western edge of the Pay-Khoy–Kara folded trough in the Kara Sea is very promising for oil and gas.

Bioherms 5–10 m thick are present southwest of Vaygach in the middle Frasnian. They are present in limestone strata, including algal varieties, and are found 100 m higher than the basal shale-sandstone unit. North of Vaygach, within the section of thicker and more shaly

Frasnian deposits, a unit of thin clayey black limestones (50–60 m) corresponds in age to the bioherms. Organic structures of the middle Frasnian have formed on the carbonate platform, which was only a little higher than a trough situated to the east. The platform boundary passed along Vaygach and somewhat north of the south shore of Novaya Zemlya, where its strike changed to east-west.

The southern island of Novaya Zemlya contains abundant Devonian reef deposits, and the reefs are developed very graphically. Devonian deposits form an almost continuous section as thick as 3,000 m; reefs are present in the Lower Devonian, Eifelian, Givetian, and Frasnian. Reefs are associated with a zone of shallow-water carbonate facies striking along the shoreline of the southern island. North of this zone are predominantly calcareous-argillaceous deposits, and shale-carbonate deposits, including dolomites, are widespread on the south. The width of this zone varies from a few to tens of kilometers; it was smallest during the periods of intensive reef formation. This zone was a belt of banks and low islands. Only during the Fras-

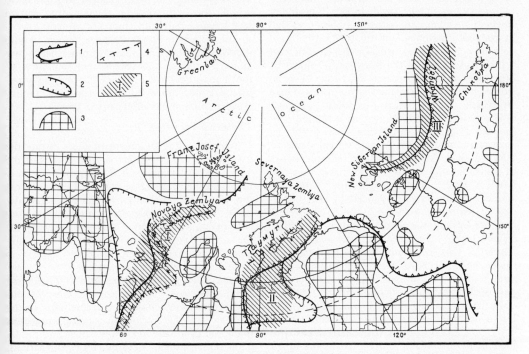

Fig. 2—Middle Paleozoic reef provinces in Soviet Arctic. I. Pechora–Novaya Zemlya; II. Taymyr-Tungusska; III. East Siberian–Chukchi. 1. Boundaries of platforms with geosynclines. 2. Boundaries of troughs within platforms. 3. Frasnian landmass (period of greatest Devonian transgression). 4. Location of relatively stable boundaries between zones of carbonate and clay sedimentation. 5. Reef provinces. Materials used are from "Atlas of the Lithologic-Paleogeographic Maps of the USSR" (Vinogradov *et al.,* 1968).

nian was it near the land which existed at the location of the present Pechora Sea; it paralleled the shoreline.

Reefs south of Novaya Zemlya are characterized by moderate sizes (tens and rarely hundreds of meters). They are usually formed by bioherm intergrowths and biostromes, as thick as 5–10 m, in which remnants of stromatoporoids, corals, and calcareous algae prevail. Reef formation took place in several stages. A stage began with the growth of a small organic structure on which other structures grew upward and outward. As a result, a complex reef massif formed with a cross-section shape of an assymmetric beaker with a great upward broadening. From this massif, "wings" or sets of small organic structures spread, predominantly on the lee sides. The upper "wings" are most widespread.

Organic structures are present in a complex of bedded detrital skeletal limestones of predominantly reef origin. Among the types of deposits present are varieties of reef "dumps," carbonate sandstones of different degrees of maturity, and calcisiltite. In this rock complex, primary dolomites and chemical and biochemical limestones change facies to reef limestones. Reefs and separate bioherms may be enveloped by bedded limestones, but this relation is found only in a few places, even in the case of reef breccias. As a whole, the thickness of bioclastic limestones is much greater than that of limestones present in organic structures. (These structures, formed as a "meadow" of reef-building organisms, were usually scattered over the sea floor and thus were extensively destroyed.) The thicknesses of forereef deposits, adjacent shale deposits, and reef complexes are of the same order, and it is probable that reef barriers were 20–40 m high. Reef formation was discontinuous as evidenced by the separation of carbonate deposits by units of forereef deposits—essentially shales—and by a wedge-shaped section of interbedded reef and forereef deposits. This carbonate rock–shale relation might be a decisive factor in formation of stratigraphic oil and gas traps in the arched part of the Vaygach anticlinorium.

In the northern island of Novaya Zemlya, Silurian deposits are widespread, and are apparently over 2,000 m thick. Devonian deposits in most of the island are represented by the upper series only (Gramberg, 1967). The Silurian and Devonian deposits include widely distributed clastic beds with coarse sediments and limestone units with features of shallow-marine bioclastic and biogenic carbonate formations.

The Caledonides probably were the source of clastic material, which was transported eastward and deposited on the site of the present northern island. The steep slope of the sea bottom which generally is present near a mountainous shore should have favored reef formation, which probably was slowed somewhat by an irregular inflow of clastic material. There currently is only a theoretical basis for assuming the presence of reefs in Silurian and Devonian rocks of the northern island of Novaya Zemlya.

Silurian and Devonian petroliferous black shales with an organic content up to 7 percent are widespread in Pay-Khoy, Vaygach, and Novaya Zemlya. They probably were oil-generating deposits. In Eifelian sandstones of Pay-Khoy, in Devonian limestones of Vaygach and south of Novaya Zemlya, and in Upper Silurian limestones of the northern island of Novaya Zemlya, bitumen shows occur in the form of liquid oil drops and extractions; accumulations of anthraxolite also are present. All these facts are direct evidence for the presence of oil and gas in these deposits. The aim of prospecting in the Pay-Khoy–Novaya Zemlya region is to search for high-porosity zones within buried reef massifs. Such oil traps are already known in the adjacent Timan-Pechora region, within the West Tabuk region, and in other nearby regions. The Upper Devonian reef structures of the Timan-Pechora oil- and gas-bearing province are not discussed here, for their importance as oil and gas reservoirs is known.

TAYMYR-TUNGUSSKA REEF PROVINCE

Widespread development of reefs during the middle Paleozoic is inferred on the sides of the Tungusska syneclise and in the northern Taymyr margin of the Siberian platform. Almost the whole spectrum of Silurian-Devonian deposits, which are especially rich in shale, clayey carbonate, and sulfate rocks, is represented there. Bioclastic skeletal limestones and biogenic limestones, which in places appear to contain reef rock, are also found.

Carbonate sedimentation in the Tungusska basin was closely related to sea transgressions and regressions, which were repetitious in the Silurian and Devonian. In general, however, this basin gradually became smaller, and the lagoon environment became more important. Biogenic and bioclastic carbonate formations were widely developed during transgressive periods in the Silurian, but were confined to the shallow shelf outlining the central, relatively deep part of the basin.

In Wenlockian time, a sequence of coral-stromatoporoid limestones up to 120 m thick formed. Study of the northwest part of the Tungusska basin shows these limestones to be dolomitized and silicified, and to include algal limestones, bioclastic rocks, breccias, and carbonate sandstones. They also contain algal bioherms up to 2.5 m in diameter. Bgatov and Matukhina (1969, p. 101–103) suggest that some deposits of the barrier-reef type are present; however, information about them is inconclusive. For coral-stromatoporoid limestones, significant permeability (up to 40 md), tests which recovered abundant water, and gas shows are recorded. The association of these carbonate strata of varied thickness with clay deposits suggests the possibility of oil traps.

In Devonian time, the facies zonation was more sharply marked at the area where the shallowing Tungusska basin and the stable, subsiding Taymyr basin join. Favorable conditions for reef formation, interrupted by intensive shale deposition, may have occurred. There are remarkable indications of reef origin of some limestones from the upper parts of the Lower Devonian on the Tareya River, the northern tributary of the Pyassina River. As the Taymyr sea extended farther south, the main fairway of Devonian reefs probably was within the Yenisey-Khatanga trough.

East Siberian–Chukchi Reef Province

The geology of this province is very problematic; however, because of large-scale geologic processes which took place in the northeastern USSR, extensive reef formation may be expected there. The possibility of reef formation is indicated by carbonate deposits containing reef rock in the Silurian and Devonian north of the vast territory from the Indigirka River to the edge of the Chukotsk Peninsula. A paleotectonic and paleogeographic analysis of this region also confirms this suggestion.

Most paleotectonic reconstructions for the northeastern margin of the USSR are based on the presence of sublatitudinal tectonic features which, from south to north, represent a eugeosyncline, a miogeosyncline, and the ancient Hyperborean platform (Tilman, 1963). For the geosynclinal zones, great amplitudes of tectonic subsidence are evident. In the miogeosynclinal zone, subsidence was aided by an intensive influx of clastic material. The clastic sediment probably derived from island uplifts in the eugeosyncline and the inner part of the miogeosyncline (cf. Churkin, 1969). It is possible that the current of detrital material was somewhat weakened near the outer part of the miogeosynclinal zone and did not hinder reef formation at the juncture of this region with the platform. This region was favorable for reefs because of the differential character of tectonic movements. It was situated within the limits of the south continental shelf of the East Siberian and Chukchi Seas. The Silurian graptolite shales east of the New Siberian archipelago might be deposits of the forereef trough. Reefs could also be present at the sides of the troughs within the Hyperborean platform itself. Thus, the whole shelf of these ancient seas is of economic interest with respect to oil exploration.

Middle Paleozoic limestones of reeflike appearance occur in sequences of clastic volcanic rocks of the eugeosynclinal zone of the Koryak upland. Exposures of such limestones are localized there. According to observations of one of the writers, such reefs could form as small atolls on submarine volcanic cones.

Conclusions

It may be suggested that middle Paleozoic reefs and related bioclastic limestones which are potential reservoirs for oil and gas are widely distributed in the Arctic. Further progress in the study of these possible reefs may be reached in the process of target investigations. One of the methods for studying new reefs would be comparison with known reefs that are in a similar geologic environment.

References Cited

Bgatov, V. I., and V. G. Matukhina, 1969, Zakonomernosti osadkonakopleniya v ordovike i silure severozapadnoy chasti Sibirskoy platformy: Sibir. Nauchno-Issled Inst. Geologii, Geofizikii Mineral'nogo Syr'ya Trudy, no. 52, 123 p.

Churkin, M., 1969, Paleozoic tectonic history of the Arctic basin north of Alaska: Science, v. 165, p. 549–555.

Gramberg, I. S., ed., 1967, Paleogeografiya Sovetskoy Arktiki: Nauchno-Issled. Inst. Geologii Arktiki Trudy, no. 150.

Kushnareva, T. I., and N. D. Matviyevskaya, 1969, Rifogennyye struktury Pechorskoy depressii i perspektivy ikh neftegazonosnosti: Geologiya Nefti i Gaza, no. 8, p. 30–33.

Tilman, S. M., 1963, K voprosu o tektonicheskom razvitii severo-vostochnoy okrainy Azii i Alyaski v paleozoyskoye vremya, in B. Kh. Egiazarov, ed., Geologiya Koryakskogo nagorya: Moscow, Nauchno-Issled. Inst. Geologii Arktiki, p. 133–142.

Vinogradov, A. P., gen. ed.; V. N. Vereshchagin; and A. B. Ronov, ed., 1968, Atlas litologo-paleogeograficheskikh kart SSSR; tom 3, Triasovyy, yursky i melovoy periody (Atlas of the lithologic-paleogeographic maps of the USSR; Volume 3, Triassic, Jurassic and Cretaceous): Moscow, Akad. Nauk SSSR, 75 sheets.

Graptolite Zonation and Correlation of Ordovician Deposits of Northeastern USSR[1]

A. M. OBUT[2]

Leningrad, USSR

Abstract The basic biostratigraphic unit of the Ordovician of the northeastern USSR is the horizon. Subdivisions of the horizons, termed "zones," are proposed on the basis of graptolite occurrences. These zones are correlated with the unified standard graptolite scale of the USSR and with graptolite scales of other regions.

Graptolite zones are not established for the Tremadoc and most of the Arenig series. Graptolite development in upper Arenig rocks of the northeastern USSR is very similar to that of North America, China, and Australia, which are assigned to the Pacific Zoogeographic Province. In these areas, the genera *Isograptus*, *Cardiograptus*, and *Phyllograptus* are widely developed, whereas in England *Didymograptus* prevails.

The Llanvirn of the northeastern USSR, North America, China, and Australia is characterized by the graptolite genera *Americograptus*, *Paraglossograptus*, and *Cardiograptus*, as well as the abundant *Didymograptus*. In England these genera are absent, and the *Didymograptus bifidus* Zone is difficult to distinguish from the overlying *D. murchisoni* Zone (together composing the Llanvirn). In the Landeilo and lower Caradoc, graptolite development is more uniform throughout the world. Provincial isolation is distinctly expressed again from the middle Caradoc through the Ashgill sequence. Graptolite associations indicate that the northeastern USSR, North America, China, and Australia were a single Pacific paleozoogeographic province in the Ordovician. England and the other European countries are assigned to the Atlantic Province.

In the northeastern USSR, Ordovician deposits are represented by four types of stratigraphic sections—predominantly carbonate, terrigenous-carbonate, volcanic-terrigenous, and transitional.

The predominantly carbonate sequence is confined to the central part of the Omulëvka Mountains, El'genchak Mountains, the middle of the Yasachnaya River basin, Tas-Khayakhtakh Ridge, Sette Daban Ridge, and Chukotsk Peninsula. The main rock types of this sequence are various limestones with remnants of corals, brachiopods, ostracods, and trilobites.

The terrigenous-carbonate section is developed in the Omulëvka uplift (the Eryekhe River basin and the Omulëvka River near the mouth of the Eryekhe River). It is represented by siltstone-limestone and schists with graptolites, and also by bands of limestones and clay-

limestones containing scarce brachiopods and ostracods.

Volcanic-terrigenous deposits are known in the central region of the Rassokha River (Serechen River). They consist of tuffs, trachybasalt, and trachyandesite interspersed with bands of siliceous rock, clay schists, and siltstone-limestone. Schists and limestones contain graptolites, a few corals, and brachiopods (Merzlyakov, 1967).

The transitional type of section is developed in the Omulëvka uplift (the eastern slope of the northwestern Omulëvka Mountains and the upper part of the Yasachnaya River) and in the middle Kolyma River area. The transitional type is represented by vertical alternation of terrigenous and terrigenous-carbonate strata containing graptolites and carbonate strata containing a benthonic fauna. Terrigenous-carbonate rocks and transitional strata are the rock sequences which provide the foundation for the correlation of different facies sequences.

The fundamental subdivision of the Ordovician biostratigraphic chart in the northeastern USSR is the horizon (Oradovskaya and Preobrazhensky, 1968; Kanygin et al., 1970). Within the horizons of the terrigenous-carbonate, volcanic-terrigenous, and transitional types of sections, a series of subdivisions termed "zones" is proposed on the basis of graptolite occurrences. On the basis of similarity of graptolite associations, the zones are correlated with the unified standard graptolite scale of the USSR and graptolite scales of other regions. Presence of graptolites in some horizons which otherwise contain mainly benthonic fauna allows the correlation of not only terrigenous, but also carbonate deposits.

In terms of thickness, horizons correspond to a few graptolite zones or to stages of the unified standard graptolite scale. The Tremadoc Stage and most of the Arenig Stage are recognized only in the sections with carbonate rocks. On the basis of brachiopods, Lower Ordovician deposits were divided by Oradovskaya (1964) into two horizons—the Inanya and Khita Horizons, which are respectively correlated with the

[1] Manuscript received, August 1, 1972.

[2] Research Institute of the Geology of the Arctic.

Tremadoc and Arenig Stages of the unified standard scale. In the northwestern part of the Omulëvka Mountains, the Layminskaya (below) and Zhurskaya unfossiliferous formations belong to the Inanya Horizon. In the central part of these mountains, the Omulëvka Formation corresponds to the Inanya Horizon, and in the basin of the middle Yasachnaya River the Biykskaya sequence also corresponds to this horizon. The Sekdekunskaya Formation of the Selennyakh Ridge tentatively is assigned to the Inanya Horizon. Maximum thickness of the horizon is 1,500 m.

On the northwestern part of the Omulëvka Mountains, the Uol'chanskaya and Syenskaya Formations correspond to the Khita Horizon. The Khita Formation in the central part of the Omulëvka Mountains and in the basin of the middle Yasachnaya River corresponds to it also. The Uchugeyskaya Formation of the Tas-Khayakhtakh Ridge is tentatively assigned to the Khita Horizon, and the Unginskaya Formation and the lower part of the Tarynyuryakhskaya Formation of the Selennyakh Ridge also belong to this horizon. On the Sette Daban Ridge, the lower and middle members of the Sakkyryrskaya Formation correspond to the Khita Horizon.

In all the areas mentioned, the Khita Horizon is established only on the basis of benthonic fauna. A late Arenigian age for the upper half of the horizon is established on the basis of the combined occurrences of ostracods and brachiopods, which are common for the Khita Horizon, and of late Arenigian graptolites in the lower part of the Eryekhe sequence in the basin of the Eryekhe River. Graptolites of late Arenigian age are also known in the Serechen basin, where they mark the upper part of the Ichenskaya sequence and the overlying Biykskaya sequence. Late Arenigian graptolites are also present in the middle area of the Kolyma River.

Complexes of graptolite species described from these deposits are distinguished as the *Cardiograptus morsus* local zone, corresponding to the *Isograptus gibberulus* and *Didymograptus hirundo* Zones of the unified standard.

The most complete graptolite assemblage of the *Didymograptus hirundo* Zone occurs on the Eryekhe River, where the zone is represented by *Americograptus pussilus* (Rued.), *Pendeograptus fruticosus* (J. Hall), *Loganograptus logani* (J. Hall), *Phyllograptus typus* (J. Hall), *P. angustifolius* (J. Hall), *P. anna longus* Rued., *Trigonograptus ensiformis ensiformis* (J. Hall), *T. ensiformis minor* Mu and Lee, *Atopograptus magadanicus* Sob., *Isograptus chinghaensis* Hsu, and *Glyptograptus dentatus* (Brongn.).

The most closely related graptolite species to the above are in the Biykskaya sequence within the Serechen-Biyk interfluve, where, besides *Tetragraptus* (*Eotetragraptus*) *quadribrachiatus* (J. Hall), also *T.* (*E.*) *shejiangensis* Geh, *Isograptus gibberulus* (Nich.), *T. walcottorum* Rued., *Oncograptus* sp., *Trigonograptus ensiformis ensiformis* (J. Hall), and *Expansograptus pennatulus* (J. Hall) are present. In the middle valley of the Kolyma River, *Caveliograptus morsus* H. and K. also is present. The thickness of the rocks assigned to this zone is 100–120 m.

In Texas and the Great Basin region of the United States and in Western Canada, the *Isograptus caduceus* Zone corresponds to the *Didymograptus hirundo* Zone. Jackson (1964, 1966) and Berry (1960) recorded the appearance at this level of such species as *Oncograptus* sp., *Trigonograptus ensiformis ensiformis, Cardiograptus morsus, Glossograptus acanthus.* and *Isograptus walcottorum*, which are also found in the northeastern USSR (see Fig. 1). In China, the equivalent of the *Didymograptus hirundo* Zone is the *Isograptus caduceus* Zone, where, along with endemic species, there are such species as *Loganograptus logani, Phyllograptus anna longus, Trigonograptus ensiformis ensiformis, T. ensiformis minor, Isograptus chinghaensis*, and *Tetragraptus* (*E.*) *shejiangensis*, which are similar to northeastern USSR species. In Australia the *Isograptus* Zone (Castlemain Series) and *Oncograptus* and *Cardiograptus* Zones (Yapeen Series), where they include species common to the northeastern USSR, correspond to the *C. morsus* Zone. Complexes with common features are found in Taymyr in contemporaneous deposits (*I. gibberulus* Zone) and in Kazakhstan (*I. gibberulus* and *D. hirundo* Zones).

The *Isograptus gibberulus* Subzone and *Didymograptus hirundo* Zone of England correspond to the *C. morsus* Zone of northeastern Russia. This correlation is based on species common to two regions, including *Isograptus gibberulus, Phyllograptus angustifolius, P. typus*, and *Glossograptus acanthus*. The *Isograptus gibberulus* Zone corresponds to the *Didymograptus hirundo* Zone in Sweden.

Middle Ordovician deposits are widespread, and carbonate sections have the greatest thickness (about 2,000 m). Three horizons are

System	Series	Stage member	Graptolite zones of the USSR (A. M. Obut, 1969)	horizon	North-East USSR (A. M. Obut, 1964; R. F. Sobolevskaya, 1970)
Ordovician	Upper	Ashgill	*Climacograptus supernus* and *Dicellograptus complanatus*		*Dicellograptus ornatus* and *Climacograptus supernus*
Ordovician	Upper	Caradoc upper	*Orthograptus quadrimucronatus*		*Orthograptus quadrimucronatus*
Ordovician	Middle	Caradoc middle	*Dicellograptus caduceus* and *Climacograptus caudatus*	Kharkindzha	*Diplograptus ingens wellingtonensis* and *Dicranograptus clingani*
Ordovician	Middle	Caradoc middle	*Climacograptus tubuliferus*	Kharkindzha	
Ordovician	Middle	Caradoc lower	*Climacograptus peltifer*	Kharkindzha	*Climacograptus peltifer*
Ordovician	Middle	Caradoc lower	*Nemagraptus gracilis*	Kharkindzha	*Nemagraptus gracilis*
Ordovician	Middle	Llandeilo	*Glyptograptus teretiusculus*	Lachug	*Glyptograptus teretiusculus*
Ordovician	Middle	Llanvirn upper	*Didymograptus murchisoni*	El'genchak	*Paraglossograptus etheridgei* and *Cardiograptus crawfordi*
Ordovician	Middle	Llanvirn lower	*Didymograptus bifidus*	El'genchak	
Ordovician	Lower	Arenig	*Didymograptus hirundo*	Khita	*Cardiograptus morsus*
Ordovician	Lower	Arenig	*Isograptus gibberulus*	Khita	
Ordovician	Lower	Arenig	*Phyllograptus elongatus* and *Phyllograptus densus*	Khita	Not established
Ordovician	Lower	Arenig	*Tetragraptus appoximatus*	Khita	
Ordovician	Lower	Tremadoc	*Triograptus canadensis*	Inanya	Not established
Ordovician	Lower	Tremadoc	*Clonograptus tenellus*	Inanya	
Ordovician	Lower	Tremadoc	*Dictyonema flabelliforme* and *Dictyonema graptolithinum*	Inanya	
Ordovician	Lower	Tremadoc	*Dictyonema parabola* and *Dictyonema sociale*	Inanya	

FIG. 1—Zonal chart of Ordovician of northeast USSR and correlation with charts of other regions (this page and 2 following pages).

known in the Middle Ordovician: the El'genchak Horizon, corresponding to the Llanvirn; the Lachug Horizon, corresponding to the Llandeilo; and the Kharkindzha Horizon, corresponding to the early-middle Caradoc.

In a carbonate section the El'genchak Horizon is characterized by brachiopods, trilobites, and ostracods, which permit correlation of the section with the Whiterock Stage in North America. The El'genchak Formation, composed of limestones and clay-limestones with trilobites, brachiopods, and ostracods, is assigned to the El'genchak Horizon in the central part of the Omulëvka Mountains, the El'genchak Mountains, and in the middle area of the Yasachnaya River. The Usunskaya Formation conditionally belongs to the El'genchak Horizon in the Tas-Khayakhtakh Ridge. In the Selennyakh Ridge, the upper member of the Tarynyuryakhskaya Formation and the lower member of the Volchinskaya Formation also belong to it. In the Sette Daban Ridge, the upper member of the Sakkyryrskaya Formation, containing ostracods and brachiopods, corre-

Taymyr (A. M. Obut, R. F. Sobolevskaya, 1964)	Western Canada Jackson, Lenz, 1962; Jackson, 1964	Stage	Texas, Great Basin (Berry, 1960-1966, 1967; Jackson, 1964)
Not established	Dicellograptus complanatus var. ornatus	Richmond	Dicellograptus complanatus
Orthograptus quadrimucronatus	Orthograptus quadrimucronatus	Mays-Edenville	Orthograptus quadrimucronatus
Dicellograptus caduceus	Dicranograptus clingani	Trenton-Wilderness	Orthograptus truncatus var intermedius
?	?		
Climacograptus peltifer			Climacograptus bicornis
Nemagraptus gracilis	Nemagraptus gracilis	Porter-field	Nemagraptus gracilis
Not established	Glyptograptus euglyphus	Ashby	Glyptograptus cf. Glyptograptus teretiusculus
	? Paraglossograptus etheridgei	Marmor	Paraglossograptus etheridgei
		Whiterock	
Isograptus gibberulus	Isograptus caduceus		Isograptus caduceus
Not established	Didymograptus protobifidus	Canadian	Didymograptus protobifidus / Tetragraptus fruticosus 3 and 4-ranched
	Didymograptus extensus		Tetragraptus fruticosus 4-branched
Tetragraptus approximatus	Tetragraptus approximatus		Tetragraptus approximatus
Triograptus canadensis	Bryograptus and Clonograptus		Clonograptus - Adelograptus
Dictyonema flabelliforme and Dictyonema graptolithinum	Staurograptus		Anisograptus - Staurograptus
Dictyonema parabola and Dictyonema sociale	Dictyonema		

sponds to the El'genchak Horizon; in the Chukotsk Peninsula, the lower part of the Issetenskaya Formation also is assigned to this horizon.

A Llanvirnian age for the El'genchak Horizon is based on combined occurrences of brachiopods and ostracods, which are common for the horizon, and on the presence of Llanvirnian graptolites, which are known in the upper part of the Eryekhe sequence in the Eryekhe River basin.

One *Paraglossograptus etheridgei–Cardio-graptus crawfordi* local zone in graptolite-bearing terrigenous-carbonate and volcanic-terrigenous deposits corresponds to the El'genchak Horizon.

Llanvirnian deposits with graptolites are known to occur in the same areas as upper Arenigian deposits. Llanvirnian deposits also are present in the Krivun Creek basin and the Kharkindzha River (left tributaries of the Omulëvka River) region of the northwestern part of the Omulëvka Mountains. There, the Mokrinsky Formation (500 m) and the lower mem-

Series	Australia (Harris and Thomas,1938; Davies, 1950; Thomas, 1960)	China (My, 1954, 1957, 1963; My, Chen Schyi et al., 1965)	NN Zon	Norway (Bulman, 1954; Berry, 1964; Henningsmoen, 1957, 1959)	England (Zones according to Geological Survey of England, 1960; Bulman,1970)
Bolind	Dicellograptus cf. complanatus	Dicellograptus szechuanensis	5a,б	Dicellograptus anceps and Dicellograptus complanatus	Dicellograptus anceps / Dicellograptus complanatus
Bolind	Pleurograptus linearis	Pleurograptus lui and Climacograptus papilio	4cd, у	Pleurograptus linearis and Climacograptus styloideus	Pleurograptus linearis
Easton	Dicranograptus hians	Climacograptus geniculatus	4бв	Dicranograptus clingani	Dicranograptus clingani
Easton	Climacograptus baragwanathi	Amplexograptus gansuensis	4бу	Amplexograptus vasae	(Diplograptus multidens) Climacograptus wilsoni
Gisborn	Climacograptus peltifer	Amplexograptus peltifer	4б,в	Diplograptus molestus	Climacograptus peltifer
Gisborn	Nemagraptus gracilis	Nemagraptus gracilis	4аβ	Nemagraptus gracilis	Nemagraptus gracilis
Darriwil	Glyptograptus teretiusculus	Glyptograptus teretiusculus	4ад₄	Glyptograptus teretiusculus	Glyptograptus teretiusculus
Darriwil	Diplograptus decoratus	Pterograptus elegans	4ад₃ / 4ад₂	Didymograptus murchisoni	Didymograptus murchisoni
Darriwil	Glyptograptus intersitus / Cardiograptus	Ampl. confertus / Cardiograptus yini / Paraglossograptus typicalis	4ад₁	Didymograptus bifidus	Didymograptus bifidus
Yapeen / Castlemaine	Oncograptus	Didymograptus hirundo	3c / 3бв	Orthoceratites limestone / Didymograptus hirundo	Didymograptus hirundo
Chewton	Isograptus caduceus				(Didymograptus extensus) Subzone Isograptus gibberulus
Chewton	Didymograptus proto-bifidus	?	3бβ	Lower Didymograptus shale	Subzone Didymograptus nitidus / Subzone Didymograptus deflexus
Chewton	Tetragraptus fruticosus	Didymograptus deflexus	3бγ / 3бβ		Subzone Tetragraptus
Bendigo	Tetragraptus approximatus	Dichograptus separatus	3бα		
Bendigo	Bryograptus	Clonograptus tenellus	3аγ		
Bendigo			3аβ / 3ад	Ceratopyge series	Transition beds with Clonograptus tenellus, Dictyonema flabelliforme anglicum
Llancefield	Staurograptus	Dictyonema flabelliforme			Dictyonema flabelliforme flabelliforme
Llancefield			2cβ / 2cд	Dictyonema flabelliforme	Dictyonema flabelliforme sociale

ber of the Krivun Formation (300–400 m) belong to the Llanvirnian. In the Eryekhe River region and in the Omulëvka River basin, near the mouth of the Eryekhe River, the upper part of the Eryekhe sequence (100 m) is Llanvirnian. In the Serechen River basin, the greater part (500 m) of the Gorelyshevskaya sequence also is Llanvirnian. In the middle region of the Kolyma River, a sequence 35–50 m thick containing *Pterograptus* sp., *Didymograptus* cf. *geminus* (His.), *Phyllograptus* aff. *typus* (J. Hall), *Glyptograptus dentatus* (Brongn.), and *Trigonograptus ensiformis ensiformis* (J. Hall) corresponds to the Llanvirn. The common graptolite assemblage of this zone is represented by the following species: *Americograptus pussilus* (Rued.), *Pendeograptus fruticosus* (J. Hall), *Phyllograptus nobilis* (H. and T.), *P. typus* (J. Hall), *Cardiograptus crawfordi* Harr., *C. vicinus* n. sp., *Trigonograptus ensiformis ensiformis* (J. Hall), *Tylograptus geniculiformis flexilis* Mu, *Glyptograptus austrodentatus austrodentatus* (H. and K.), *G. dentatus* (Brongn.), *Cryptograptus tricornis schaeferi* Lapw., and *Paraglossograptus etheridgei* (Harr.).

A common feature of the Llanvirn in the northeastern USSR, North America, China, and Australia is the presence of the graptolite genera *Americograptus, Paraglossograptus, and Cardiograptus*. The genus *Tylograptus* is also present in the first three regions. The genera mentioned above are characteristic of the Pacific Zoogeographic Province (Mu, 1963), and they are not known in the type section of England. The *P. etheridgei–C. crawfordi* Zone is well correlated on the basis of common graptolite assemblages with the *Paraglossograptus etheridgei* Zone in Texas and Western Canada and with the *Amplexograptus confertus* and *Pterograptus elegans* Zones in China. In Australia, the greater part of the Darriwil Series, which contains *Glyptograptus austrodentatus, Glyptograptus intersitus*, and *Diplograptus decoratus*, corresponds to the *P. etheridgei–C. crawfordi* Zone.

Americograptus pussilus, Tylograptus geniculiformis flexilis, Trigonograptus ensiformis ensiformis, Cardiograptus crawfordi, Cryptograptus tricornis schaeferi, Glossograptus hincksi, and *Paraglossograptus etheridgei* are some of the common Llanvirnian species in the northeastern USSR and North America. Almost all the species listed occur in contemporaneous deposits of China and Australia, where *Phyllograptus nobilis* is also known. *Phyllograptus nobilis* is found in the northeastern USSR but is not known in North America.

In Taymyr, Llanvirnian deposits are unfossiliferous, but in Kazakhstan the *Didymograptus bifidus* Zone (Kopalin Horizon) and the *D. murchisoni* Zone (Karakan Horizon) correspond to the Llanvirn.

In England, according to work by I. Strachan (1960), the *D. bifidus* Zone is not everywhere clearly distinguished from the overlying zone of the Llanvirnian *Didymograptus murchisoni*. In the Wales region the *D. extensus* and *D. murchisoni* Zones are well recognized. The *D. bifidus* Zone and the *D. murchisoni* Zone are mainly characterized by pendent forms of *Didymograptus*. However, between these zones are many transitional species, and it is difficult to recognize the zones without some of the characteristic species.

In Sweden and Norway, "upper *Didymograptus*" schists correspond to the Llanvirn. *Didymograptus bifidus* occurs there, and the equivalents of the *D. murchisoni* Zone are characterized by *Didymograptus murchisoni* var. *geminus, Janograptus* sp., and *Pterograptus* sp. Species common with those of England are scarce, although there are similar genera.

The Lachug Horizon, proposed by Kanygin,

Oradovskaya, and Sobolevskaya (1970), is assigned to the Llandeilo Stage to replace the present Darpirsky and Mokrinsky Horizons. It is mainly represented by carbonate deposits with benthonic fauna. In the basin of the middle branch of the Yasachnaya River and in the El'genchak Mountains, the Lachug Formation corresponds to the Lachug Horizon; in the Tas-Khayakhtakh Ridge, the Taganyinskaya Formation is tentatively assigned to the horizon also. In the Selennyakh Ridge, the upper member of the Volchinskaya Formation and the lower member of the Kalychan Formation are assigned to the Lachug Horizon. In the Sette Daban Ridge, the lower member of the Labystakhskaya Formation corresponds to the Lachug Horizon, and in the Chukotsk Peninsula the middle and upper parts of the Issetenskaya Formation correspond to it also.

Ostracods which are common in the Lachug Horizon and Llandeilian graptolites in the Minutka sequence of the Eryekhe River basin may provide indirect indications that the Lachug Horizon belongs to the Llandeilo Stage.

In graptolite facies, Llandeilian deposits, as determined by the *Glyptograptus teretiusculus* Zone, are not yet clearly defined. Occurrences of graptolites (*Climacograptus* sp. undet. and *Glyptograptus* aff. *euglyphus*) in the upper member of the Krivun Formation on Mokryy Creek (northwestern part of the Omulëvka Mountains) are suggestive of Llandeilian deposits. Graptolites characteristic of the Llandeilo Stage are also found in the lower part of the Minutka sequence (80 m) of the Eryekhe River basin and in the upper part of the Gorelyshevskaya sequence (300 m) in the Serechen-Biyk interfluve. The total list of graptolites in these areas is the following: *Glyptograptus euglyphus* (Lapw.), *Cryptograptus tricornis schaeferi* Lapw., and *Glossograptus hincksi robustus* Hsu. In the basin of Krivun Creek, the upper half of the Krivun Formation (300–350 m) and the overlying Darpirsky Formation, which are characterized by benthonic fauna, apparently correspond to the *Glyptograptus teretiusculus* Zone.

Beyond northeastern USSR, the Llandeilo is represented by the *Glyptograptus teretiusculus* Zone, except in Western Canada, where the *Glyptograptus euglyphus* Zone is its equivalent. Abundance of long-rhabdosome forms of *Glyptograptus* ex gr. *teretiusculus*, as well as *G. euglyphus, Cryptograptus tricornis schaeferi*, and *Glossograptus hincksi robustus*, is typical of this zone. Also typical is the complete absence of *Tetragraptus* and *Phyllograptus*. Forms of *Didymograptus* occur sporadically. In Texas this zone, according to Berry (1960) and Jackson (1964), contains *Glyptograptus* ex gr. *teretiusculus, G. euglyphus, Climacograptus riddelensis, Amplexograptus confertus,* and *A.* aff. *differtus.* A closely related complex is known in Western Canada. This zone has not been recognized in China. In Australia the upper part of the Darriwil Series corresponds to the *G. teretiusculus* Zone. In Taymyr this zone is not clearly expressed, but in Kazakhstan the lower half of the Tselinograd Horizon corresponds to it. In England the *Glyptograptus teretiusculus* Zone is characterized by absence of pendent forms of *Didymograptus* and presence of two-ranked biserial species. In Sweden the lower part of the *Dicellograptus* schists corresponds to the *G. teretiusculus* Zone, and in Norway schists with *Ogygiocaris* correspond to it.

The Kharkindzha Horizon, corresponding to the lower and middle Caradoc Stage, is indicated by graptolites in the Omulëvka uplift as well as in the Tas-Khayakhtakh and Selennyakh Ridges. The type section of the horizon is the Kharkindzha Formation, located in the northwestern part of the Omulëvka Mountains and containing abundant graptolites of the lower and middle Caradoc Stage. The cosmopolitan *Nemagraptus gracilis* and *Climacograptus peltifer* Zones are established in the lower Caradoc Stage. One local zone, *Diplograptus ingens wellingtonensis–Dicranograptus clingani,* is established in the middle Caradoc.

On the eastern slope of the Omulëvka Mountains, the lower part of the Kharkindzha Horizon, known as the Sono Formation, is represented by carbonate rocks containing brachiopods and ostracods. Terrigenous-carbonate rocks containing graptolites of the *C. peltifer* Zone and the *D. ingens wellingtonensis–D. clingani* zone of the A-E beds (local terminology; total thickness of 400 m) are above it. The carbonate Sono Formation corresponds to the lower part of the horizon in the central part of the Omulëvka Mountains and in the upper Yasachnaya River, and in the El'genchak Mountains the Snezhninskaya sequence also corresponds to it. In the Eryekhe River basin, the upper part of the Minutka sequence (100 m), which contains graptolites of the lower Caradoc Stage, corresponds to the lower half of the Kharkindzha Horizon; in the middle Rassokha River basin, the graptolite-bearing Bulkutskaya sequence (1,000 m) corresponds to the whole horizon; and, in the Tas-Khayakhtakh

Ridge, most of the lower part of the "Kharkindzha" formation also corresponds to the Kharkindzha Horizon. In the Selennyakh Ridge, the upper member of the Kalychan Formation, composed of carbonate rocks containing benthonic fauna, corresponds to the lower part of the horizon. Higher in the section is the Syachan Formation (250 m), which contains graptolites of the lower and middle Caradoc. In the Sette Daban Ridge, the middle and upper members of the Labystakh Formation, which consists of limestones and clay-limestones containing ostracods and brachiopods, correspond to the Kharkindzha Horizon.

Within the territory studied, *Nemagraptus gracilis* (J. Hall), *Dicellograptus divaricatus divaricatus* (J. Hall), *D. divaricatus* var. *bicurvatus* Rued., *D. intortus* Lapw., *D. sextans exilis* E. and W., *D. smithi* Rued., *Dicranograptus nicholsoni nicholsoni* Hopk., *D. nicholsoni diapason* Gurl., *D. nicholsoni geniculatus* Rued. and Deck., *Climacograptus bicornis bicornis* (J. Hall), *Glossograptus hincksi robustus* Hsu, and *Retiograptus geinitzianus* (J. Hall *et al.*) are the most common forms in the *Nemagraptus gracilis* Zone. The thickness of beds corresponding to this zone is about 250 m.

Almost all the listed species of graptolites also occur in other regions, especially in North America. In Australia the lower half of the Gisborn Series corresponds to the *N. gracilis* Zone. In Taymyr and Kazakhstan, graptolites of this zone have many common features with the *N. gracilis* Zone of the northeastern USSR.

Beds assigned to the *Climacograptus peltifer* Zone yield abundant graptolites in the central and northwestern parts of the Omulëvka Mountains, in the middle of the Omulëvka River region, and in the upper area of the Yasachnaya River. Occurrences of graptolites belonging to this zone are also known in the Selennyakh Ridge. Along with the species listed above, the following are also known in the *N. gracilis* Zone: *Dicellograptus divaricatus rigidus* Lapw., *Dicranograptus bungei* Obut and Sob., *D. kirki* Rued., *D. latiangulatus* Sob., *D. nicholsoni geniculatus* Rued. and Deck., *D. tripartitus* Sob., *D. ziczac* Lapw., *Climacograptus longicornis* Sob., *C. membraniferus* Obut and Sob., *C. peltifer* (Lapw.), *C. tridentatus* Lapw., *Pseudoclimacograptus scharenbergi* (Lapw.), *Glyptograptus euglyphus* (Lapw.), *Diplograptus multidens* E. and W., *D. rarithecatus* Sob., and *Amplexograptus perexcavatus* (Lapw.). *Orthograptus whitfieldi* (J. Hall) occurs in the *C. peltifer* Zone. In addition, *Ruedemanno-*

graptus rectangularis (Rued.), *Aspidograptus rarus* Sob., and *Desmograptus turriformis* Sob. occur with the above complex at Mirnyy Creek. The thickness of this zone is about 50 m.

In the northeastern USSR the *C. peltifer* Zone is well correlated with the zone of the same name in China, Australia, Taymyr, and Scotland. In North America (Texas and the Great Basin) the *Climacograptus bicornis* Zone corresponds to it; in Norway the *Diplograptus molestus* Zone is correlative.

In Great Britain the *C. peltifer* Zone is well expressed in Scotland only. The *C. peltifer* and *C. wilsoni* Zones cannot be distinguished in the rest of the territory because the rocks contain "surviving" fauna (Strachan, 1960). The *C. wilsoni* Zone is characterized by graptolites which may occur in the lower Caradoc. *Climacograptus bicornis bicornis, Pseudoclimacograptus scharenbergi,* and *Dicranograptus nicholsoni nicholsoni* belong to the lower Caradoc. In the Omulëvka uplift the species *Climacograptus wilsoni* was found in the upper part of the *N. gracilis* Zone. It was necessary therefore to distinguish a *Diplograptus ingens wellingtonensis–Dicranograptus clingani* local zone within the middle Caradoc in the territory studied. The most typical species of this zone, except zonal species, are *Dicranograptus tealei* H. and T., *Climacograptus spiniferus* (Rued.), *C. raricaudatus* R. and B., *Diplograptus pulcher* Obut and Sob., *Orthograptus colymaensis* sp. nov., and *Rectograptus kelleri* Sob.

Beds belonging to the middle Caradoc reach a thickness of 160 m. The related graptolite complex is known as the *Orthograptus truncatus* var. *intermedius* Zone in Texas and the Great Basin; in Western Canada the middle Caradoc is included in the *D. clingani* Zone. W. B. N. Berry has noted the abundance of *Rectograptus* in this zone and also the presence of *Dicranograptus tealei,* first established in the middle Caradoc of Australia. In the Omulëvka uplift, the American species *Climacograptus spiniferus* (Rued.) and *C. raricaudatus* R. and B. are assigned to the middle Caradoc, thus permitting reliable correlation of these deposits between the two areas. In Australia the upper two zones of the Easton Series—*Climacograptus baragwanathi* and the overlapping *Dicranograptus hians* Zones—correspond to the middle Caradoc. Both these zones are characterized by the abundance of *Rectograptus,* and *Dicranograptus tealei* is noted in the upper part of the *D. hians* Zone.

The presence of common typical species, primarily *Diplograptus ingens wellingtonensis* and *Dicranograptus tealei,* allows reliable correlation of the middle Caradoc between the territory studied and Australia. In the middle Caradoc of China, two zones are known—the *Amplexograptus gansuensis* (below) and *Climacograptus geniculatus.* Because they are mainly described by endemic species, their correlation with the middle Caradoc of England is particularly tentative. In England, only the upper part of the middle Caradoc, represented by the *Dicranograptus clingani* Zone, is distinctly determined. The *Climacograptus wilsoni* Zone has a mixed complex of graptolites.

In the northeastern USSR the *Orthograptus quadrimucronatus* Zone is recognized in the upper Caradoc, whereas one local zone, *Dicellograptus ornatus,* and the *Climacograptus supernus* Zone make up the whole of the graptolite facies of the Ashgill.

Lithology of the rocks of the Upper Ordovician is not uniform, and the series is represented mainly by carbonate sediments containing benthonic fauna. Terrigenous-carbonate sediments with graptolites, brachiopods, and corals are locally distributed. The Upper Ordovician is well exposed in the northwestern part of the Omulëvka Mountains. It is composed of aleurolites, aleuritic and clayey limestones, and shales with graptolites of Late Ordovician age.

In the eastern slope of the Omulëvka Mountains, limestones, marlstones, and shales of the F-L tongues (local terminology) containing graptolites and ostracods belong to the upper Caradoc, and rocks of the M-P tongues containing relict graptolites, brachiopods, ostracods, corals, and trilobites belong to the Ashgill. In the upstream part of the Yasachnaya River basin, the Dolzhinskaya carbonate formation and the lower part of the Iryudyskaya Formation, both containing brachiopods and corals, correspond to the upper Caradoc. The rest of the Iryudyskaya Formation, also containing brachiopods and corals, and the overlapping part of the Lukavinskaya Formation, containing Ashgillian graptolites, correspond to the Ashgill Stage. In the middle of the Rassokha River region, the Serechen sequence —which is defined on the basis of scarce brachiopods, corals, and crinoids—corresponds to the Upper Ordovician. In the Tas-Khayakhtakh Ridge the upper part of the "Kharkindzha" formation is unfossiliferous. In the Selennyakh Ridge the Nal'chanskaya Formation, containing brachiopods and scarce graptolites, corresponds to the upper Caradoc, and the Sakynd-zhinskaya Formation, containing brachiopods, corresponds to the Ashgill Stage. In the Sette Daban Ridge the carbonate Kulonskaya Formation and the overlying Taskanskaya Formation belong to the Upper Ordovician. In the Chukotsk Peninsula, the Chegitun'skaya Formation, with brachiopods, corals, and ostracods, is of Late Ordovician age.

Deposits containing graptolites of the *Orthograptus quadrimucronatus* Zone of the upper Caradoc are known only in the Omulëvka uplift (Mirnyy Creek, Drevnyaya River, Levaya Khekanda River, and Lukavyy Creek). On Mirnyy Creek, upper Caradoc relict brachiopods, ostracods, and trilobites occur along with upper Caradoc graptolites. The most complete known graptolite assemblage of the *O. quadrimucronatus* Zone is from the Drevnyaya River, Levaya Khekanda River, and Lukavyy Creek regions. The zone includes *Dicellograptus pumpilus* Lapw., *Climacograptus angustus* Sob., *C. hastatus hastatus* (T. S. Hall), *C. hsuei* Sob., *Orthograptus quadrimucronatus* (J. Hall), and *Rectograptus* aff. *truncatus pauperatus* E. and W. On Mirnyy Creek the thickness of the *O. quadrimucronatus* Zone is about 500 m, and on the Drevnyaya River it is 120–130 m.

In the USA and Western Canada the upper Caradoc zone is quite similar to that in the northeastern USSR, as shown by identical and characteristic species. Thus, correlation of contemporaneous deposits in these regions is made with confidence.

In China the *Pleurograptus lui–Climacograptus papilio* local zone, described by an abundant graptolite complex, is in the upper Caradoc. Known species which occur there include *Leptograptus* cf. *flaccidus*, *Climacograptus putillus*, *Orthograptus quadrimucronatus*, and *Rectograptus truncatus pauperatus*. In Australia the lower part of the Bolind Series (the *Pleurograptus linearis* Zone, which contains graptolites with close affinity to North American and Kolyma species) corresponds to the upper Caradoc. Among the common species the following are significant: *Climacograptus hastatus hastatus*, *C. caudatus*, *Leptograptus* ex gr. *flaccidus*, *Dicellograptus forchammeri*, and *Retiograptus pulcherrimus*.

A graptolite assemblage similar to that mentioned above is known in Kazakhstan. In England the *Pleurograptus linearis* Zone corresponds to the upper Caradoc. It contains fewer graptolites than contemporaneous deposits of North America, Australia, and China. How-ever, the presence of *Leptograptus flaccidus* and *Orthograptus quadrimucronatus* in this zone and their presence in other regions permit correlation of contemporaneous deposits.

The *Dicellograptus ornatus–Climacograptus supernus* local zone is recognized within the Ashgill deposits. Both of these species, which are found in the Omulëvka uplift, have narrow vertical but wide geographic distribution. Rocks with graptolites corresponding to this zone are known on the eastern slope of the Omulëvka Mountains (Mirnyy Creek and In River), in the upper Yasachnaya River basin, and in the Selennyakh Ridge. The most complete assemblage of graptolites is established on Mirnyy Creek, where the following species are present: *Dicellograptus ornatus* E. and W., *Climacograptus bicornis longispinus* (T. S. Hall), *C. lamellicornis* Sob., *C. angustus* Sob., *C. crassispinus* Mu and Shang., *C. hastatus hastatus* (T. S. Hall), *C. hsuei* Sob., *C. hvalross* R. and B., *C. kravtchunensis* Sob., *C.* aff. *papilio* Mu and Shang., *C. rossberryi* Sob., *C. supernus* E. and W., *Fenhsiangographtus extraordinarius* Sob., *Lasiograptus tardus* Sob., and *Arachniographtus chuchlensis* (Pv.).

In the upper Yasachnaya River basin (Drevnyaya River, Levaya Khekanda River and Lukavyy Creek), this zone is recognized by the presence of species of the preceding graptolite assemblage, though it contains fewer species. Present are such species as *Dicellograptus complanatus arkansasensis* Rued., *D.* aff. *pumilus* Lapw., *Climacograptus bicornis longispinus* (T. S. Hall), *C. angustus* Sob., *C. hastatus hastatus* (T. S. Hall), *C. hsuei* Sob., *C. hvalross* R. and B., *C. rossberryi* Sob., *Glyptographtus tenuissimus* R. and B., and *Lasiograptus tardus* Sob.

Among all the listed species of this zone, only *Dicellograptus ornatus* and *Climacograptus supernus* have wide geographic distribution. They are known in England, North America, China, Australia, and Kazakhstan. The rest of the species, except *Climacograptus angustus* Sob., *C. hsuei* Sob., and *C. hastatus hastatus* (T. S. Hall), occur in Ashgillian deposits only in North America, Australia, and China.

Among graptolites found in the Ashgill Stage in the northeastern USSR, it is important to note the different species of the genus *Climacograptus*. This genus has many common species with the Ashgillian *Climacograptus* from China, Australia, and, to a smaller degree, North America. Thus, of 11 species of this genus found in the northeastern USSR, five species are new and the rest are known in the

Ashgill of China, Australia, or North America or in all three of these regions. Occurring with *Climacograptus* in the Ashgill of the northeastern USSR, North America, and Australia are *Dicellograptus complanatus arkansasensis* and *Glyptograptus tenuissimus,* previously known from North American sections only. The similarities of the graptolite assemblages permit reliable correlation of Ashgill deposits in these regions.

On Mirnyy Creek, abundant corals and brachiopods corresponding to species of the 5b beds in Norway (Fig. 1) and of the Ashgill Stage in Kazakhstan occur together with graptolites. Because the exposures at Mirnyy Creek form a continuous section of Ordovician-Silurian rocks from the base of the Ashgill upward through the *Coronograptus cyphus* Zone of the lower Llandovery, they may be called the type section. The thickness of the Ashgill deposits on Mirnyy Creek is about 200 m; on Lukavyy Creek and the Levaya Khekanda River, it is about 100 m.

Analysis of graptolite assemblages from Ordovician deposits in marginal uplifts of the Kolyma stable region has shown that they have many common species with Ordovician graptolites of North America, China, and Australia. Previous investigations by American stratigraphers (Kindle and Whittington, 1958; Jackson, 1964; Berry, 1966) have noted that Ordovician graptolite assemblages of North America and Australia are very similar and that they belong to one zoogeographic province. The Chinese investigator A. T. Mu (1963) assigned these territories, including China, to the Pacific Zoogeographic Province. Study of Ordovician graptolites from the territory of marginal uplifts in the Kolyma massif permits assignment of this region to the Pacific Province. Thus, in all four listed regions the late Arenigian is characterized by widespread development of representatives of the genera *Isograptus, Cardiograptus,* and *Phyllograptus;* in the type section of England, however, *Didymograptus* prevails.

The presence of the genera *Americograptus, Tylograptus, Cardiograptus,* and *Paraglossograptus* in the Llanvirn of the northeastern USSR, North America, Australia, and China is peculiar, because they are absent in the type section of England, where the main graptolites are pendent forms of *Didymograptus.* The provincial isolation is less distinctly expressed in the Llandeilo and lower Caradoc. It is distinct, however, from the middle Caradoc to the Ashgill, inclusive. These associations suggest that the territories of the northeastern USSR, North America, China, and Australia were a single Pacific Paleozoogeographic Province during the Ordovician. England and other European countries are assigned to the Atlantic Province. The territory of Soviet Central Asia is apparently the "connecting link" between the Pacific and Atlantic Provinces.

SELECTED REFERENCES

Berry, W. B. N., 1960, Graptolite faunas of the Marathon region, West Texas: Univ. Texas Pub. 6005, p. 1–179.

———— 1964, The Middle Ordovician of the Oslo region, Norway, No. 16, Graptolites of the Ogygiocaris series: Norsk Geol. Tidsskr., v. 44, no. 1, p. 61–170.

———— 1966, A discussion of some Victorian Ordovician graptolites: Royal Soc. Victoria Proc., v. 79, pt. 2, p. 415–443.

———— 1967, Comments on correlation of the North American and British Lower Ordovician: Geol. Soc. America Bull., v. 78, no. 3, p. 419–428.

Bulman, O. M. B., 1954, The graptolite fauna of the *Dictyonema* shales of the Oslo region: Norsk Geol. Tidsskr., v. 33, no. 1–2, p. 1–40.

———— 1970, Graptolithina, pt. 5 *of* R. C. Moore, ed., Treatise on invertebrate paleontology: Geol. Soc. America and Univ. Kansas Press, p. 1–163.

Chugayeva, M. N., and Kh. S. Rozman, 1964, K voprosu o raschlenenii ordovikskikh otlozheny Severo-Vostoka SSSR: Akad. Nauk SSSR Yakut., Trudy Soveshchaniya po Stratigrafii YaASSR, Mater. po Geol. i Polezn. Iskop. YaASSR, no. 13, p. 292–300.

Elles, G. L., and E. M. R. Wood, 1901–1918, Monograph British graptolites: London, Palaeont. Soc., p. 1–526.

Harris, W. J., and D. E. Thomas, 1935, Victorian graptolites, pt. 3: Royal Soc. Victoria Proc., v. 47, p. 288–312.

———— and ———— 1938, A revised classification and correlation of the Ordovician graptolite beds of Victoria: Mining and Geol. Jour., v. 1, no. 3, p. 62–72.

Jackson, D. E., 1964, Observation on the sequence and correlation of Lower and Middle Ordovician graptolite faunas of North America: Geol. Soc. America Bull., v. 75, no. 6, p. 523–534.

———— and A. C. Lenz, 1962, Zonation of Ordovician and Silurian graptolites of northern Yukon, Canada: Am. Assoc. Petroleum Geologists Bull., v. 46, no. 1, p. 30–45.

Kanygin, A. V., M. M. Oradovskaya, and R. F. Sobolevskaya, in press, O stratigraficheskikh podrazdeleniyakh ordovika na Severo-Vostoke SSSR: Geologiya i geofizika.

Kindle, C. H., and H. B. Whittington, 1958, Stratigraphy of the Cow Head region, western Newfoundland: Geol. Soc. America Bull., v. 69, no. 3, p. 315–342.

Merzlyakov, V. M., 1967, Novyy tip razreza ordovika na Kolymskom massive: Kolyma, no. 7, p. 44–46.

Mu, A. T., 1954, On the Wufeng shale: Acta Palaeontologica Sinica, v. 2, no. 2, p. 153–170.

———— 1957, Some new or little known graptolites from the Ninkuo shale (Lower Ordovician) of Changshan, Western Chekiang: Acta Palaeontologica Sinica, v. 5, no. 3, p. 406–437.

———— 1963, Research in graptolite faunas of Chilianshan: Sci. Sinica, v. 12, no. 3, p. 341–371.

Mu En-Chzhi, Chen-Shuy, *et al.*, 1965, Atlas kitayskikh graptolitov: Peking, Izd. Paleont. In-ta Kitayskoy, p. 1–95.

Nikolayev, A. A., 1959, Skhema stratigrafii nizhnego i srednego paleozoya Omulevskikh gor: Trudy Mezhved. Soveshchaniya po Razrabotke Unif. Stratigr. Skhem Severo-Vostoka SSSR, p. 38–43.

Obut, A. M., 1964, Graptolity, *in* D. V. Obruchev, ed., Osnovy paleontologii, spravochnik dlya paleontologov i geologov SSSR, t. Iglokozhiye: Moscow, Akad. Nauk SSSR, p. 284–357.

———— and R. F. Sobolevskaya, 1964, Graptolity ordovika Taymyra: Moscow, Akad. Nauk SSSR Sibirskoye Otdeleniye, Inst. Geologii i Geofiziki–Nauchno-Issled. Inst. Geologii Arktiki, 86 p.

Oradovskaya, M. M., 1964, Skhema stratigrafii ordovika yugo-vostochnoy chasti Kolymskogo massiva: Akad. Nauk Yakut, Trudy Soveshchaniya po Stratigrafii YaASSR, Mater. po Geol. i Polezn. Iskop., no. 13, p. 357–361.

———— and B. V. Preobrazhensky, 1968, Kratky ocherk stratigrafii ordovikskikh otlozheny Severo-Vostoka SSSR: Magadan, Polevoy Atlas Ordovikskoy Fauny Severo-Vostoka SSSR, p. 5–16.

Pruvost, Pierre, director, 1960, Lexique stratigraphique international, v. 1, pt. 3a V: Paris, Internat. Geol. Cong. Comm. Stratigraphy, Centre Natl. Recherche Sci., p. 4–296.

Sobolevskaya, R. F., 1969, Novyye pozdneordovikskiye graptolity Omulevskikh gor: Paleontologichesky Zhur., no. 1, p. 115–118.

———— 1970, Biostratigrafiya srednego i verkhnego ordovika okrainykh podnyaty Kolymskogo massiva po graptolitam: Novosibirsk, Avtoref. dissert., p. 1–26.

———— 1971, Novyye ordovikskiye graptolity v Omulevskikh gorakh: Paleontologichesky Zhur., no. 11, p. 82–87.

Strachan, I., 1960, The Ordovician and Silurian graptolite zones in Britain: Copenhagen, 21st Internat. Geol. Cong. Rept., pt. 7, p. 109–113.

Thomas, D. E., 1960, The zonal distribution of Australian graptolites: Royal Soc. New South Wales Jour. and Proc., v. 94, pt. 1, p. 4–58.

Middle and Upper Cambrian Strata of North-Central Siberia[1]

N. P. LAZARENKO[2]

Leningrad, USSR

Abstract Widespread Cambrian deposits in Northern Siberia are notable for the absence of stratigraphic breaks within the sequences and for the abundance of fossils. Middle Cambrian rocks conformably overlie those of the Lenian Stage. The boundary is determined by the disappearance of Protolenidae and the appearance of Oryctocephalidae, Agnostidae, and Paradoxididae. The Middle Cambrian is divided into the Amginian and Mayian Stages. Amginian rocks range from limestone to black shale, but they contain similar trilobite assemblages and are divisible into three zones. The Amginian-Mayian boundary is fixed by the disappearance of typical Amginian species and the appearance of Anomocariodes, Metanomocare, Anopolenus, Dorypyge, and Linguagnostus. Mayian deposits show little facies variation, grading upward from red argillaceous limestone to green and gray limestones. Distinct changes in trilobite assemblages allow division into three zones. The Middle-Upper Cambrian boundary is located in a continuous section on the basis of the disappearance of Lejopyge, Anomocarina, and Bonneterrina, and the appearance of species of Agnostus, Homagnostus, Damesella, Buttsia, Proceratopyge, and other genera. Although lithologically varied, Upper Cambrian rocks are generally rhythmic clastic-carbonate strata. Trilobite assemblages allow division of the Upper Cambrian into six zones.

A trend toward uniformity of environments prevailed from the end of Early Cambrian time through the first half of the Mayian Age. By the end of Middle Cambrian time, shallowing and partial separation of the marine basin caused formation of different facies sequences and local development of the Upper Cambrian faunal assemblages.

INTRODUCTION

Cambrian deposits are widespread in Siberia, north of the Arctic Circle. Several sections showing continuous deposition from the Early Cambrian through the Ordovician Period have been recognized (Fig. 1). Because of the absence of stratigraphic breaks within sequences and the presence of abundant fossils, Cambrian stratigraphic sections of Northern Siberia may be considered unique. Many sections have been studied in detail (Sobolevskaya and Lazarenko, 1965; Makarov et al., 1966; Lazarenko, 1966; Datsenko and Lazarenko, 1968; and others). Within the territory from the Yenisey River on the west to the eastern side of the Lena River on the east, both vertical and horizontal facies variations of Cambrian deposits have been es-

tablished. Within this territory during the Cambrain Period there were basins where predominantly dolomite or limestone beds accumulated. Transitional types of sediments were deposited in very shallow water and behind sedimentary barriers. Lithologic and biostratigraphic subdivisions have been recognized on the basis of the rock composition and contained fossils (Fig. 2).

The Middle Cambrian deposits are underlain conformably by rocks belonging to the Lenian Stage, which in Northern Siberia includes three faunal zones (Lazarenko, 1962). The boundary between the Lower and Middle Cambrian Series is marked by the disappearance of Protolenidae and an assemblage of associated genera and species, and by a mass appearance of Oryctocephalidae, Agnostidae, and Paradoxididae.

AMGINIAN STAGE

The Middle Cambrian is divided into the Amginian and Mayian Stages (Resheniya, 1959; 1963). Deposits of the Amginian Stage are represented by dolomite, gray and greenish-gray argillaceous bioclastic limestone, black shale, and limestone. Despite their varied nature, Amginian deposits are characterized by similar trilobite assemblages; the Amginian is divided into three zones (Demokidov et al., 1959). The Orictocephalidae Zone is characterized by the genera Cheiruroides, Oryctocephalops, Oryctocephalus, Oryctocara, Tonkinella, Pagetides, Kounamkites, Chondraomocare, Burlingia, Ptarmigania, Pagetia ferox, Paradoxides ex. gr. pinus, Peronopsis anabarensis, Triplagnostus praeccurens, and others.

The Triplagnostus gibbus Zone contains an impoverished trilobite assemblage. In addition to the zonal species, there are other common species of Triplagnostus which do not occur below. Tomagnostus fissus, T. perrugatus, Peronopsis fallax, and Paradoxides sp. are present in this zone. The top of the zone is marked by a thin stratum of thinly laminated, combustible shale, an excellent marker bed which is present throughout the region (Fig. 2c).

The Amginian Stage is capped by the Pseudanomocarina aojiformis–Peronopsis bifurcatus Zone. In addition to the zonal species,

[1] Manuscript received, August 1, 1972.
[2] Research Institute of the Geology of the Arctic.

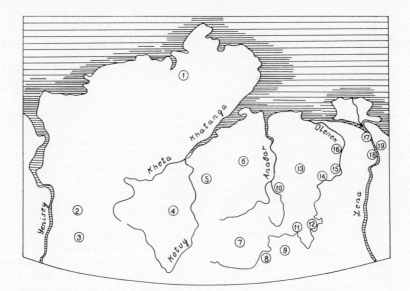

FIG. 1—Scheme of main Cambrian section localities over territory of north-central Siberia. (Numbers 1–19 indicate locations of main sections on Figure 2.)

several other common species of *Paradoxides* and *Pseudanomocarina* are present, as well as *Kootenia amgensis, Corynexochus tersus, Eodiscus punctatus, Hartshillia clivosa, Bailiaspis dalmani,* and *Dawsonia.*

MAYIAN STAGE

The boundary of the Amginian Stage with the Mayian Stage is fixed by the disappearance of species characteristic of the Amginian and the appearance of representatives of *Anomocarioides, Metanomocare, Anopolenus, Dorypyge,* and *Linguagnostus.*

The Mayian deposits are almost everywhere (except where dolomite occurs) uniform in facies. During the first half of the Mayian Age, accumulation of red argillaceous limestone predominated. Later deposits are characterized by green and gray limestones. Trilobite assemblages within the Mayian deposits are varied. Distinct changes in trilobite assemblages allow division of the stage into three zones.

The lower *Dorypyge olenekensis–Corynexochus perforatus* Zone, in addition to zonal forms, is characterized by the presence of *Linguagnostus gronwalli, Phalacroma longifrons, Anomocarioides divulgatus, Metanomocare petaloides, Anopolenus henrici, Solenopleura magna,* and scarce *Hydrocephalus, Dasometopus,* and *Centropleura.*

The trilobite assemblage characteristic of the *Anomocarioides* Zone is diverse. Within the lower portion of the zone, along with surviving zonal species, are numerous *Centropleura* in association with *Dasometopus breviceps, Elyx laticeps, Anomocarioides limbatus, A. limbataeformis, Diplagnostus planicauda, Triplagnostus elegans, Belagnostus longus,* and *Dolichoagnostus admirabilis.* In deposits of the upper part of the zone, different species of *Anomocarina, Forchhammeria, Goniagnostus, Clavagnostus,* and *Phalacroma,* as well as *Phalagnostus glandiformis, Ptychagnostus acualeatus, Pianaspis attenuata, Schoriella optata,* and others, are characteristic.

The *Lejopyge armata–Maiaspis mirabilis* Zone comprises the upper third of the Mayian Stage. The characteristic feature of the zone is the abundance of *Lejopyge, Maiaspis, Aldanaspis, Buitella, Koldiniella, Bonneterrina, Rina, Cyclolorenzella, Siligacites, Tgazkiella, Rontcastina, Oidalagnostus trispinifer, Phoidagnostus bituberculatus, Linguagnostus kjerulfi, Belovia calva,* and others.

UPPER CAMBRIAN

The Middle–Upper Cambrian boundary in Northern Siberia is stratigraphically conformable because sedimentation was continuous at the time of transition. The boundary is estab-

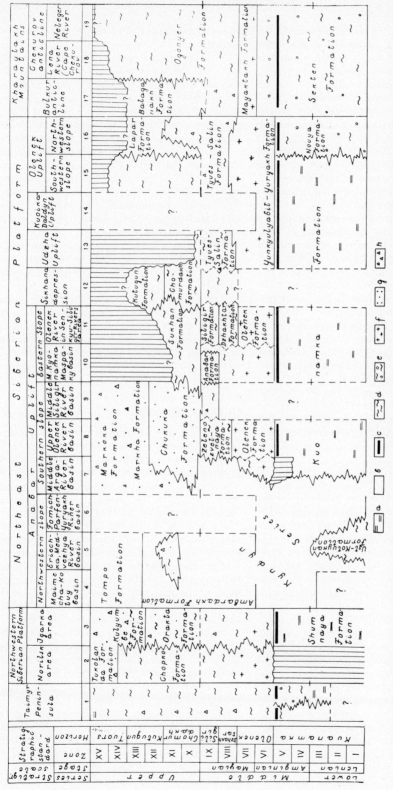

FIG. 2—Correlation chart of sections and rock-stratigraphic units of Middle and Upper Cambrian in north-central Siberia. Compiled by Lazarenko (1970). **a**, black shale, argillaceous limestone; **b**, light colored dolomite, rare limestone; **c**, marker horizon; **d**, gray and green limestone, argillaceous and silty limestone, siltstone, marl and shale bands; **e**, gray and green bioclastic limestone; **f**, variegated, argillaceous, and dolomitized limestone; marl (redbeds predominate); **g**, calcareous sandstone; arenaceous, dolomitized, argillaceous limestone; **h**, variegated dolomite; dolomitized, argillaceous, stromatolitic, and oolitic limestone containing bands and lenses of conglomerate and breccia.

I, *Bergeroniellus expansus–Pagetiellus ultimus*. **II**, *Neopagetina venusta*. **III**, *Anabaraspis cylindrica–Micmacca tumida*. **IV**, *Oryctocephalidae*. **V**, *Triplagnostus gibbus*. **VI**, *Pseudanomocarina aojiformis–Peronopsis bifurcatus*. **VII**, *Dorypyge olenekensis–Corynexochus perforatus*. **VIII**, *Anomocarioides*. **IX**, *Lejopyge armata–Maiaspis mirabilis*. **X**, *Agnostus pisiformis–Homagnostus fecundus*. **XI**, *Glyptagnostus stolidotus*. **XII**, *Glyptagnostus reticulatus–Olenaspella evansi*. **XIII**, *Irvingella–Cedarellus felix*. **XIV**, *Plicatalina perlata*. **XV**, *Promegalaspides*.

lished on the basis of the disappearance of *Lejopyge, Anomocarina, Aldanaspis, Bonneterrina,* and *Rina* and the appearance of various *Agnostus, Homagnostus, Buttsia, Damesella, Proceratopyge,* and *Nganasanella.*

The Upper Cambrian deposits are lithologically varied. In general, these rocks are clastic-carbonate strata of rhythmic nature formed in relatively shallow water by abruptly changing geologic conditions. The trilobite assemblages of the deposits are different in composition, but their relative contemporaneity with the clastic-carbonate strata is easily determined because of the presence of common species.

Upper Cambrian trilobites are grouped in three major assemblages; the duration of their evolution corresponds to an age. A grouping of species and genera is established within each assemblage, and six zones are recognized.

The *Agnostus pisiformis–Homagnostus fecundus* Zone is characterized by the zonal species plus *Buttsia pinga, Toxotis? venustus, Damesella? eremita, Proceratopyge nathorsti, Pedinocephalina divulgata, Acrocephalinella borealica, Homagnostus paraobsus, Acmarhachis acutus, Oedorhachis tridens, Peconopsis insignis,* and *Agnostacus longus.*

The trilobite assemblage of the *Glyptagnostus stolidotus* Zone includes *Glyptagnostus stolidotus, Olenus proximus, Damesella? dispara, Paleodates florens, Acidaspidella limata, Aspidagnostus laevis, Homagnostus abesus,* and others.

The *Glyptagnostus reticulatus–Olenaspella evansi* Zone contains an impoverished assemblage of trilobites, which are confined to the zone. Those which are abundant include *Glyptagnostus reticulatus, Pseudagnostus idalis, Olenaspella evansi, O.? borealica,* and *Acrocephalaspis orientalis* in association with scarce *Aspidagnostus lunulosus, A. cugosus, Agnostus inexpectans, Maspakites occidentalis, Proceratopyge capitasa, Ecyxanium sentum,* and others.

The *Irvingella–Cedarellus felix* Zone is characterized by an abundant and varied trilobite assemblage which contains *Irvingella major, I. oblonga, Cedarellus felix, Elvinia roemeri, Tagenarella eniseica, Amorphella modesta, Parabolina spinulosa, Parabolinina edita, Parabolinella? fortunata, Protopeltura incerta, Catuniella? monstruosa, Proceratopyge tenuita, P. fragilis, P. portentosa, Kazelia* sp., *Onchonetellus abnormis, Agnostus captiosus, Agnostotes inconstans, Cyclopagnostus orientalis, Glyp-*

tagnostotes elegans, and varied forms of *Pseudagnostus.*

The *Plicatolina perlata* Zone is determined by zonal species in association with *Plicatolina lucida, Protopeltura holtedali, Parabolina angusta, Iwayaspis caelata, Eoacidaspis amplicauda, Pseudagnostus communis,* and *Ctenopyge* sp. Also present are representatives of a new genus of Olenidae similar to *Leptaplastus.*

The *Parabolinites rectus–Acerocare tulbergi* Zone caps the Upper Cambrian and is characterized by a peculiar trilobite assemblage wherein different species of *Promegalaspides, Plicatolina, Parabolinites, Parabolina, Skljarella, Hedinaspis, Lotagnostus, Pseudagnostus,* and *Geragnostus* predominate.

The Upper Cambrian zones are combined in pairs into major stratigraphic units called "horizons," which in rank and importance are equal to stages.

It is difficult to determine the upper boundary of the Cambrian in continuous sections because of the monotonous character of the rocks and the faunal peculiarity of the transitional beds. The solution of the problem, however, is reliably obtained by complex lithostratigraphic studies of the sections.

GENERAL CONCLUSIONS

The tendency toward uniformity of geologic environments in Northern Siberia, which began by the end of Early Cambrian time, was most pronounced at the end of the Amginian Age. This trend continued during the general marine transgression in the first half of the Mayian Age. By the end of the Middle Cambrian, there was a general shallowing of the Cambrian marine basin, and it was partially separated into several depositional environments. This separation permitted the formation of different facies sequences and resulted in distinct local development at the species level, and commonly at the generic level, of faunal assemblages which characterize the Upper Cambrian deposits.

Analysis of a trilobite assemblage from the Middle and Upper Cambrian deposits confirms the fact that sedimentary environments became more uniform at the end of the Amginian Age. This uniformity coincides with the almost complete separation of the Northern Siberian marine basin from the Pacific basins and, at the same time, a wide exchange of water masses with seas of the Atlantic paleozoogeographic area. During the Late Cambrian Epoch, the remaining connections with the Pacific basins became weaker or ceased to exist as a result of differential tectonic movements and corresponding structural regeneration of the territory of Northern Siberia. Geologic data show clearly that Northern Siberia had connections with such southern basins as the Altai-Sayan, Tien-Shan, China, and Australia basins.

Owing to the combined presence in the fossil assemblages of forms characteristic of different paleozoogeographic areas, the Middle and Upper Cambrian deposits of Northern Siberia are well correlated with coeval formations both within the USSR and outside its territory.

REFERENCES CITED

Datsenko, V. A., and N. P. Lazarenko, 1968, Biostratigrafiya kembryskikh otlozheny severo-zapada Sibirskoy platformy: Nauchno-Issled. Inst. Geologii Arktiki Trudy, v. 155, p. 12–115.

Demokidov, K. K., et al., 1959, Stratigrafiya sinyskikh i kembryskikh otlozheny severo-vostoka Sibirskoy platformy: Nauchno-Issled. Inst. Geologii Arktiki Trudy, v. 101, p. 53–206.

Lazarenko, N. P., 1962, Novyye nizhnekembryskiye trilobity Sovetskoy Arktiki: Leningrad, Sb. Stat. po. Paleont. i Biostrat., no. 29, p. 29–37.

———— 1966, Biostratigrafiya i nekotoryye novyye trilobity verkhnego kembriya Olenekskogo podnyatiya i Kharaulakhskikh gor: Nauchno-Issled. Inst. Geologii Arktiki, Uchenyye Zapiski, Paleont. i Biostrat., no. 2, p. 33–38.

Makarov, K. K., N. P. Lazarenko, and S. S. Filatov, 1966, Novoye v stratigrafii kembryskikh otlozheny zapadnoy chasti yuzhnogo kryla Anabarskoy anteklizy: Vses. Neft. Nauchno-Issled. Geol.-Razved. Inst. Trudy, no. 249, p. 7–17.

Resheniya Mezhvedomstvennogo Soveshchaniya po razrabotke unifitsirovannykh stratigraficheskikh skhem Sibiri, 1959, Gosgeoltekhizdat: Moscow, Interdepartmental Stratigraphic Committee, p. 5–10, tables XII–XIII.

Resheniya Mezhvedomstvennogo Soveshchaniya po razrabotke unifitsirovannykh stratigraficheskikh skhem Yakutskoy ASSR, 1963, Gosgeoltekhizdat: Moscow, Interdepartmental Stratigraphic Committee, p. 3–8, table 3.

Sobolevskaya, R. F., and N. P. Lazarenko, 1965, Stratigrafiya kembriya Vostochnogo i Tsentralnogo Taymyra: Nauchno-Issled. Inst. Geologii Arktiki Trudy, v. 145, p. 35–36.

Arctic Mesozoic Floras[1]

N. D. VASILEVSKAYA[2]

Leningrad, USSR

Abstract Mesophytic floras (Late Triassic–Early Cretaceous) of the Arctic are most complete for the Upper Jurassic and Lower Cretaceous. Late Triassic floras exist in many areas, but Early and Middle Jurassic floras are scarce in the Arctic.

Mesozoic floras of Arctic islands are not isolated from continental ones. Late Triassic floras of Svalbard, Franz Josef Land, and East Greenland are assigned to the European paleofloristic province. The early Liassic flora of East Greenland is also included in the European province. Early Liassic floras in the areas of the Kolyma and Vilyuy Rivers are assigned to the Siberian paleofloristic region, but a separate Kolyma province is postulated. Late Jurassic floras traceable from the Lena River basin to the Kolyma River basin are typical of the Siberian region. Early Cretaceous floras of most of the Arctic, except West Greenland, belong to the Siberian paleofloristic region. The West Greenland flora belongs to the Indo-European region. Presence of Late Triassic floras on both the continent and the Arctic islands, in and between marine deposits, suggests unstable marine conditions. Floral similarity indicates a possible land connection between Svalbard and East Greenland and Western Europe in Late Triassic time. East Greenland was undoubtedly connected with Western Europe in Early Jurassic time also.

Late Triassic floras of Svalbard and the Aldan River area indicate warm and rather humid climatic conditions, and a hot climate existed in East Greenland in the Early Jurassic. A Siberian temperate flora apparently formed in the Vilyuy depression and the southern Yakutsk basin in Early Jurassic time. This flora spread during Middle and Late Jurassic time, and in the Early Cretaceous it flourished in vast areas of the Arctic and Subarctic regions.

INTRODUCTION

Analysis of the Mesophytic floras (Mesozoic floras which range in age from Late Triassic to Early Cretaceous, inclusive)[3] of the Arctic shows that in this region the most complete floral history is of the Mesophytic second phase. This second phase corresponds in age to the Late Jurassic and Early Cretaceous. Within this range the Early Cretaceous floras are best preserved, most widespread, and best known. The reverse is true for the floras of the Mesophytic first phase. In this phase, floras representing vegetation of the first period of the phase (Late Triassic–Early Jurassic) dominate, and very

---

[1] Manuscript received, August 1, 1972.

[2] Research Institute of the Geology of the Arctic.

[3] The Mesophytic range is accepted in the sense of Vakhrameyev (1966, p. 8).

few traces of vegetation of the second period of the phase (Middle Jurassic) are present.

To obtain a general picture of the history of Arctic Mesophytic vegetation, it is necessary to extend the discussion of floras from regions north of the Arctic Circle to include a consideration of those from adjacent Subarctic areas. Mesozoic floras are found mainly in continental or lagoonal-continental strata, and only rarely in marine formations.

LATE TRIASSIC FLORAS

Late Triassic floras are known from many Arctic regions. Some examples are the Rhaetion flora (the *Lepidopteris* Zone) of East Greenland; the middle Keuper (Carnian(?)-Norian) flora of Svalbard (Spitsbergen, Barentsøya, and Edgeøya islands); the middle(?) Keuper (in writer's opinion) flora of Franz Josef Land (Kap Stepan on George Land); floras of the Pechora basin (Nar'yan Mar and the Synya River areas), Pay-Khoy (the Khey-Yaga River), central Taymyr (the Fad'yu-Kuda River), eastern Taymyr (Cape Tsevetkov), Kotel'nyy Island, and the lower Aldan River (the Rumara River basin); and the Norian flora of the Anyuy River basin (east tributary of the Kolyma River).

Among the floras mentioned, the Rhaetian flora of East Greenland (Harris, 1937, 1961) is the best known. The writer (Vasilevskaya, 1972) described a collection of the middle Keuper flora from Svalbard that was obtained by workers of the Research Institute of the Geology of the Arctic expedition.

The Late Triassic flora of Svalbard is of great interest because it is accompanied by invertebrate faunas (Vasilevskaya, 1965). In some areas (the Viman River in the Isfjorden area of Spitsbergen and Cape Neger on Edgeøya), marine deposits containing the ammonites *Nathorstites gibbosus* Stolley, *N. lenticularis* (Whit.), and *N. tenuis* Stolley and the pelecypod *Halobia zitteli* Lindstr.—all characteristic of the lower Carnian—underlie beds with plant remains (Korchinskaya *et al.*, 1967). Above the plant-bearing strata are marine deposits containing *Meleagrinella* ex gr. *antiqua* Tozer, *Halobia* ex gr. *norica* Mojs., *Anodontophora* ex gr. *munsteri* Wissm., and other forms which indicate a Norian age. In other sections (Uich Bay area, Spitsbergen; Vosse Bay, Barentsøya), a bed containing remains of the fern *Asterotheca merianii* lies within Carnian marine deposits. On the east side of the Kolyma River, plant impressions are present in Norian marine deposits with *Monotis ochotica* (Keys.) and other forms. Present knowledge of the floras discussed does not support or disprove a Late Triassic botanico-geographic zonation of the Arctic.

An undoubted relation between the middle Keuper floras of Svalbard (Spitsbergen, Edgeøya, and Barentsøya) and those of Switzerland (Basel) and Austria (Lunz) is established by the following elements: *Neocalamites merianii* (Brongn.) Halle, *Asterotheca merianii* (Brongn.) Stur., *Danaeopsis marantacea* Presl.; representatives of *Clathropteris*, *Distyophyllum*, *Cladophlebis*, *Pterophyllum brevipenne* Kurr, *P. jaegeri* Brongn.; and representatives of *Glossophyllum*. It is probable that the floras belonged to a single paleofloristic province—the European—which apparently began to be isolated as far back as Late Triassic or perhaps in the Middle Triassic (because the main body of the Late Triassic flora began to form in Western Europe as early as the end of the Middle Triassic). In subsequent epochs, separation became more pronounced (Vakhrameyev, 1964). It is difficult to say how far in the Arctic the European province spread during Late Triassic time. Its northeastern boundary may have been somewhere in Franz Josef Land. This boundary location is evidenced by the content of the Late Triassic flora from George Land and Franz Josef Land, where the same *Neocalamites merianii* and representatives of *Paratatarina* and *Glossophyllum*(?) existed, and also by woods from the Upper Triassic deposits of Wiener-Neustadt, Heiss, and Spitsbergen islands. A relative abundance of *Paratatarina*-type pteridosperms in the Svalbard flora and their presence in the flora of George Land, whereas they are absent in Western Europe, permit assignment of these floras to an individual region of the European paleofloristic province. The pteridosperms connect these flora with those of the eastern Urals and southeastern Asia (China), where plants of similar type were widespread. The Svalbard flora has no elements related to the middle Keuper flora of southern Primor'ye (Srebrodolskaya, 1964); the middle Keuper flora belongs to the East Asian province (Vakhrameyev and Vasina, 1966). The flora of

East Greenland differs considerably in content from that of Svalbard and shows the next stage in the history of Late Triassic plants, a stage corresponding to the Rhaetian or late Keuper. This flora includes such characteristic species as *Dictyophyllum exile* (Brauns.) Nath., *Lepidopteris ottonis* (Goepp.) Schimp., *Furcula granulifer* Harris, and *Ptilozamites nilssonii* Nath. The East Greenland flora, like the West European Rhaetian floras, is assigned to the European paleofloristic province of the Indo-European region (Vakhrameyev, 1964).

EARLY JURASSIC FLORAS

In the Arctic, occurrences of Early Jurassic floras are scarce. Only the early Liassic flora (the *Thaumatopteris* Zone) of East Greenland has been studied in detail (Harris, 1937, 1961). Some plants were found (Samylina and Yefimova, 1968) along with ammonites in Liassic deposits on the east side of the Kolyma River (the Korkodon, Anyuy, and Omolon River basins). Most of the occurrences are located a little south of the Arctic Circle. A small assemblage of the early Liassic flora was also found outside the Arctic Circle in the Vilyuy depression in the vicinity of the upper Vilyuy River. The early Liassic flora of East Greenland, with the index species *Thaumatopteris schenkii* Nath. and *T. brauniana* Popp., belongs to the European province of the Indo-European region, whereas the Kolyma and Vilyuy floras are assigned to the Siberian paleofloristic region (Vakhrameyev, 1964; Samylina and Yefimova, 1968). The presence in the Kolyma flora of such Indo-European elements as *Thaumatopteris schenkii* Nath., *Sagenopteris*, and *Ptilophyllum*, which are typical Early Jurassic floras of the Siberian region, permits postulation of the existence of a separate Kolyma province (Samylina and Yefimova, 1968). It is probable that the provinces began to separate as early as Late Triassic time, because the remains of *Sagenopteris* are known from Norian deposits of the Anyuy River basin.

MIDDLE JURASSIC FLORAS

Middle Jurassic floras are almost unknown within the Arctic. A single occurrence in the lower Yenisey River area is confined to fossiliferous deposits located between Bajocian and Callovian beds (Sachs and Ronkina, 1957). It yields a small amount of plant remains containing characteristic elements (*Coniopteris* ex gr. *hymenophylloides* (Brongn.) Sew., *Raphaelia diamensis* Sew., and *Pityophyllum*) of the Siberian paleofloristic region.

LATE JURASSIC FLORAS

Late Jurassic floras are widespread south of the central Lena River basin (Zhigansk village) and are traceable along the Arctic Circle eastward into the Zyryanka River basin and along the east side of the Kolyma River (the Anyuy and Omolon river basins). In some sections (near Zhigansk and on the Sytoga, lower Aldan, and Anyuy Rivers) the stratigraphic position of Late Jurassic floras is determined by their position between marine Bathonian and lower Volgian deposits or within Upper Jurassic marine deposits. The Late Jurassic flora of the areas is a typical flora of the Siberian paleofloristic region (Vakhrameyev, 1964) and is surprisingly uniform in content. The associated fern species *Cladophlebis aldanensis* Vachr., *C. serrulata* Samyl., and *Raphaelia diamensis* Sew. compose a Late Jurassic index assemblage which is characteristic of almost all occurrences. The only variation in the complex is a somewhat higher content of cycadophites in the Upper Jurassic rocks from the Anyuy River basin.

EARLY CRETACEOUS FLORAS

Early Cretaceous floras are abundant in the Arctic, mainly in association with coal-bearing deposits. The floras are known from the following areas: West Greenland (Nûgssuaq peninsula), Svalbard (Isfjorden area of Spitsbergen, Sørkapp island, Agardbukt, and Kong Karls Land), Franz Josef Land (Nortbruk island and Salisbury), Severnaya Zemlya (October Revolution Island), the Ust'-Yenisey region (Yakovlevka River area), the Khatanga depression (Bol. Begichev Island and the Boyarka, Maymecha, and Kotuy River regions), Lena River basin, Polousnyy Ridge (Uyandina depression), the Indigirka River region, the Zyryanka River basin, Kotel'nyy Island, Koryak Range (the upper Anadyr' River and Velikaya River areas), Chukotsk Peninsula, and Alaska (Cape Lisburne and the Chandler and Colville River region). The age of flora from Andøya island (near the northeastern coast of Norway) is not quite clear. Mesozoic deposits preserved there in a small graben (Ørvig, 1953) are subdivided into several groups, and, on the basis of invertebrate-fossil content, range in age from earliest Late Jurassic to middle Neocomian (up to Hauterivian), inclusive. Plant remains found within the lower part of the deposits, which are

dated as Late Jurassic, are similar to typical Early Cretaceous floras of the Arctic.

The Early Cretaceous floras of Spitsbergen, the Lena River basin, and Alaska are the most important ones stratigraphically. In Spitsbergen, a sequence with plant remains is dated as Barremian; it is underlain in several sections by deposits yielding the late Hauterivian ammonite *Simbirskites* ex gr. *decheni* (Roemer) and overlain by deposits containing the Aptian ammonite *Tropaeum arcticum* Stolley, the pelecypod *Leda angulatostriata* Bodyl., and other forms indicative of an Aptian age.

There are complete Lower Cretaceous sections in the Lena River basin where the change in plant content can be traced in strata ranging in age from Early Cretaceous to Albian, inclusive. The lower contact of the strata containing plant remains is recognized in the area of the lower Lena River (Vasilevskaya and Pavlov, 1963) at the top of Valanginian marine deposits containing ammonites such as *Neotollia? anabarensis* (Pavl.), *Polyptychites ramulicosta* (Pavl.), and *Astieriptichites astieriformis* (Voron.).

In the Chandler-Colville River region of Alaska (Smiley, 1969), beds with plant remains are limited to deposits yielding a middle Albian fauna. A study of floras from this region will help in refining the time boundaries of floristic assemblages derived from the upper Lower Cretaceous deposits elsewhere in the Arctic, and, in turn, will help in resolving the question about the change from Mesophytic to Cenophytic floras.

The Early Cretaceous floras of the Arctic regions listed above, with the exception of the West Greenland floras, belong to the Siberian paleofloristic region. The flora from the Kome Formation, West Greenland, belongs to the Indo-European paleofloristic region (Vakhrameyev, 1964).

Ferns, cycadophytes, Ginkgoales, Czekanowskiales, and conifers are important in the Early Cretaceous vegetation of the Arctic. The role of these plant groups during Neocomian time was somewhat different than during Aptian-Albian time. Ferns were more varied and abundant in Aptian-Albian time because of widespread development of younger forms. The number of cycadophytes decreased during that time. Ginkgoales and Czekanowskiales decreased somewhat in number of genera and species in comparison with other groups, but some species were exceptionally abundant. They were a little more numerous in Neocomian than in Aptian-Albian time. Only a few representatives of *Czekanowskia* were present in Aptian-Albian time. The proportion of conifers during Neocomian time as compared with Aptian-Albian time was almost the same, but the number of genera was greater in the second half of the Early Cretaceous. Since late Albian time, angiosperms have increased in importance. In general, the Neocomian complex is characterized by *Coniopteris burejensis* (Zal.) Sew., *C. setacea* (Pryn.) Vachr., many species of *Cladophlebis* (*C. lenaensis* Vachr.), *Jacutiella amurensis* (Novop.) Samyl., species of *Tyrmia* (*Pterophyllum*?) and *Aldania*, numerous *Ctenis, Ginkgo* with relatively dissected leaves, abundant *Sphenobaiera* (*S. pulchella* [Heer] Fl.), *Pseudoltorellia nordenskioldii* (Heer) Fl., *Phoenicopsis mirabilis* (Fl.) Samyl., *Podozamites angustifolius* (Eichw.) Heer, and *Elatides* ex gr. *curvifolia* (Dunk.) Nath.

The Aptian-Albian assemblage contains numerous forms. Common forms include the following: species of *Osmunda*; *Coniopteris onychioides* Vasilevsk. and K.-M.; species of *Adiantopteris* and *Arctopteris*; *Asplenium dicksonianum* Heer; *A. rigidum* Vasilevsk.; species of *Scleropteris*; *Sphenopteris petiolipinnulata* Vasilevsk. (probably a new genus); *Anomozamites arcticus* Vasilevsk.; *Neozamites verchojanensis* Vachr.; *Ginkgo* ex gr. *adiantoides* (Ung.) Heer; *Sphenobaiera biloba* Pryn.; *S. flabellata* Vasilevsk.; platyphyllous *Phoenicopsis; Podozamites eichwaldii* Schimp.; *P. latifolius* (Heer); *Pityophyllum arcticum* Vasilevsk.; species of *Cephalotaxopsis, Sequoia,* and *Paratoxodium; Cyparissidium gracile* Heer; and, in the Albian, small-leaved angiosperms. The complexes listed have been studied extensively in the Lena (Vakhrameyev, 1958; Vasilevskaya and Pavlov, 1963; Samylina, 1963; Kirichkova and Slastenov, 1966, 1968) and Zyryanka (Samylina, 1967) basins and elsewhere in the Arctic. In the Lena River basin, more detailed floristic assemblages are recognized. The Neocomian and especially the Aptian-Albian assemblages from Franz Josef Land are somewhat different in content (Sveshnikova and Budantsev, 1969); the latter is characterized by more abundant cycadophytes.

CONCLUSIONS

Examination of the Mesophytic floras of the Arctic leads to the following conclusions. Discoveries of Late Triassic plant remains in many Arctic regions, both on the continent and on the Arctic islands, in and between marine deposits, suggest unstable marine conditions. The similarity of Svalbard and Greenland Late Triassic floras to those from Western Europe indicates a possible land connection between these territories. The presence of a giant belt of alluvial plains and subaerial deltas which stretched along the northern periphery of the continent (Dibner and Ageyev, 1960) seems probable.

The content and nature of the Svalbard flora indicate that plants of this territory during the Late Triassic were more or less tropical. The presence of Dipteridaceae and Marattiaceae and cycadophytes is indicative of a warm, possibly hot, and rather humid climate. There are remains of warm-climate plants of Late Triassic age in the Aldan River area where the fern *Bernoullia* (Abramova, 1960) grew.

In Early Jurassic time, a hot climate existed in East Greenland, which then, as in Late Triassic time, undoubtedly was connected with Western Europe. There probably was no water barrier between Greenland and Western Europe in the Late Triassic or in the Late Jurassic. Floras (especially late Liassic and Toarcian) collected from the east side of the Kolyma River contain Indo-European elements which give evidence for their relation to both southern Asian floras and southern Alaska floras. Floras from the upper Matanuska River (Knowlton, 1917) are indicative of a warm climate. The floras from the east side of the Kolyma River apparently grew on islands and were influenced by currents coming from the south. The Early Jurassic flora of southern Alaska also appears to be an island type.

The early Liassic flora of the Vilyuy depression suggests a less hot climate. In this region and throughout the southern Yakutsk basin, a Siberian temperate flora appears to have formed in Early Jurassic time. In the Arctic, this flora later became pronounced in a Middle Jurassic flora of the lower Yenisey River; in Late Jurassic and especially in Early Cretaceous time, it flourished and spread over vast areas of the Arctic and Subarctic regions.

During periods of maximum regression in the Early Cretaceous Epoch, a connection was possible between floras over vast areas of the continent and floras in the Arctic islands. Island floras (Spitsbergen, Kong Karls Land, Franz Josef Land, Severnaya Zemlya, Kotel'nyy Island) were not isolated from those on the continent. The climate in the Arctic from Late Triassic to Early Cretaceous time changed from rather hot and very humid to temperate warm and humid. A general decrease of temperature has occurred since the Middle Jurassic Epoch. However, climatic conditions were more or less the same in separate regions at the end of the Late Jurassic, with a few exceptions (*e.g.*, a possibly warmer climate in the Anyuy River basin), and in the second half of the Early Cretaceous (except in Franz Josef Land, as indicated by the Aptian-Albian flora with cycadophytes). A change in climate and in the nature of flora in Mesophytic time is well exemplified by Late Triassic and Early Cretaceous floras of Spitsbergen. The Late Triassic flora there belongs to subtropical floras of the Indo-European region, and the Early Cretaceous flora of Spitsbergen corresponds to floras of the Siberian paleofloristic region grown under moderately warm climatic conditions.

SELECTED REFERENCES

Abramova, L. N., 1960, Nakhodka paporotnika *Bernoullia* v triasovykh otlozheniyakh Sibiri: Sb. Statey po Paleont. i Biostratig. Inst. Geologii Arktiki, no. 22, pp. 68–70.

Dibner, V. D., and K. M. Ageyev, 1960, Mesozoyskiye otlozheniya ostrovov Severnoy Zemli: Inst. Geologii Arktiki Inf. Byull., no. 18, p. 9–18.

Harris, T. M., 1937, The fossil flora of Scoresby Sound, East Greenland: Medd. om Grønland, v. 112, no. 2, 114 p.

——— 1961, Rhaeto-Liassic flora of Scoresby Sound, central East Greenland, *in* Geology of the Arctic, v. 1: Toronto, Univ. Toronto Press, p. 269–273.

Kirichkova, A. I., 1966, O nakhodke nizhneyurskoy flory v Vostochnoy Sibiri: Vses. Neft. Nauchno-Issled. Geol.-Razved. Inst. Trudy, no. 249, p. 120–128.

——— and Yu. L. Slastenov, 1966, Stratigrafiya i flora nizhnemelovykh otlozheny r. Lepiske (Zapadnoye Priverkhoyanye): Vses. Neft. Nauchno-Issled. Geol.-Razved. Inst. Trudy, no. 249, p. 147–181.

——— and ——— 1968, K stratigrafii kontinentalnykh otlozheny apta i alba Priverkhoyanskogo progiba i Vilyuyskoy sineklizy: Akad. Nauk SSSR Doklady, v. 181, no. 1, p. 171–174.

Knowlton, F. H., 1917, A Lower Jurassic flora from the upper Matanuska Valley, Alaska: publication data unavailable.

Korchinskaya, M. V., B. A. Klubov, and T. M. Pchelina, 1967, O granitse srednego i verkhnego triasa na Shpitsbergene (the middle-upper Triassic boundary in Spitsbergen), *in* Materialy po stratigrafii Shpitsbergena: Leningrad, Nauchno-Issled. Inst. Geologii Arktiki, p. 159–169.

Ørvig, T., 1953, On the Mesozoic field on Andøya, I, Notes on the ichthyosaurian remains collected in 1952, with remarks on the age of the vertebrate-bearing beds: Acta Borealia, A, Scientia, no. 4, 31 p.

Sachs, V. N., and Z. Z. Ronkina, 1957, Yurskiye i melovyye otlozheniya Ust-Yeniseyskoy vpadiny: Nauchno-Issled. Inst. Geologii Arktiki Trudy, v. 90, 330 p.

Samylina, V. A., 1963, Mesozoyskaya flora nizhnego techeniya r: Paleobotanika (Akad. Nauk SSSR, Bot. Inst. Trudy, ser. 8), no. 4, p. 57–139.

——— 1967, Mesozoyskaya flora levoberezhya r.

Kolymy (Zyryansky uglenosnyy basseyn); chast' II, Ginkovyye, khvoynyye, obshchiye glavy (Mesozoic flora of the left bank of the Kolyma river [Zyryanka coal basin]; part 2, Gingkos, conifers, general chapters), *in* Problemy izucheniya iskopayemoy flory uglenosnykh otlozheny SSSR: Paleobotanika (Akad. Nauk SSSR Bot. Inst. Trudy, ser. 8), no. 6, p. 133–175.

——— and A. F. Yefimova, 1968, Pervyye nakhodki ranneyurskoy flory v basseyne r. Kolymy (First finds of an Early Jurassic flora in the Kolyma river basin): Akad. Nauk SSSR Doklady, v. 179, no. 1, p. 166–168.

Smiley, C. J., 1969, Cretaceous floras of Chandler-Colville region, Alaska: stratigraphy and preliminary floristics: Am. Assoc. Petroleum Geologists Bull., v. 53, no. 3, p. 482–502.

Srebrodolskaya, I. N., 1964, Pozdnetriasovaya (mongugayskaya) flora Primorya i etapy yeye razvitiya: Vses. Nauchno-Issled. Geol. Inst. Trudy, new ser., v. 107, p. 54–61.

Sveshnikova, I. N., and L. Yu. Budantsev, 1962, Iskopayemyye flory i yeye znacheniye dlya stratigrafii i paleogeografii triasa Primorya (Dalny Vostok): Leningrad, Aftoref. kand. dissert.

——— and ——— 1969, Iskopayemyye flory Arktiki; I, Paleozoyskiye i mesozoyskiye flory zapadnogo Shpitsbergena, Zemli Frantsa Iosifa i ostrova Novaya Sibir' (Fossil flora of the Arctic; 1, Paleozoic and Mesozoic flora of West Spitsbergen, Franz Joseph Land, and Novaya Sibir island): Leningrad, Izd. "Nauka," Leningrad Otdel., 129 p.

Vakhrameyev, V. A., 1958, Stratigrafiya i iskopayemaya flora yurskikh i melovykh otlozheny Vilyuyskoy vpadiny i prilegayushchey chasti Priverkhoyanskogo krayevogo progiba, *in* Regionalnaya stratigrafiya SSSR, v. 3: Moscow, Akad. Nauk SSSR Geol. Inst., 137 p.

——— 1964, Yurskiye i rannemelovyye flory Yevrazii i paleo-floristicheskiye provintsii etogo vremeni: Akad. Nauk SSSR Geol. Inst. Trudy, no. 102, 261 p.

——— 1966, Botaniko-geograficheskaya zonalnost v geologicheskom proshlom i evolyutsiya rastitelnogo mira: Paleontologicheskiy Zhurn., no. 1, p. 6–18.

——— and M. P. Doludenko, 1961, Verkhneyurskaya i rannemelovaya flora Bureinskogo basseyna i yeye znacheniye dlya stratigrafii: Akad. Nauk SSSR Geol. Inst. Trudy, no. 54, 135 p.

——— and R. A. Vasina, 1966, Mesozoyskiye flory SSSR i stratigrafiya kontinentalnykh otlozheny (Mesozoic faunas of the USSR and the stratigraphy of continental deposits): Itogi Nauki, Ser. Geol., no. 10, p. 80–100.

Vasilevskaya, N. D., 1957, Novyye dannyye o mezozoyskoy flore o. Kotelnogo: Akad. Nauk SSSR Doklady, v. 112, no. 6, p. 1101–1103.

——— 1959, Stratigrafiya i flora mesozoyskikh uglenosnykh otlozheny Sangarskogo rayona Lenskogo uglenosnogo basseyna: Nauchno-Issled. Inst. Geologii Arktiki Trudy, v. 105, p. 17–43.

——— 1965, O novykh nakhodkakh iskopayemoy flory na arkhipelage Shpitsbergen, *in* Materialy po geologii Shpitsbergena: Leningrad, Izd. Nauchno-Issled. Inst. Geologii Arktiki, p. 209–221.

——— 1972, Pozdnetriasovaya flora Svalbarda: *in* Mezozoyskiye otlozheniya Svalbarda: Leningrad, Nauchno-Issled. Inst. Geologii Arktiki, p. 27–63.

——— and V. V. Pavlov, 1963, Stratigrafiya i flora melovykh otlozheny Leno-Olenekskogo rayona Lenskogo uglenosnogo basseyna: Nauchno-Issled. Inst. Geologii Arktiki Trudy, v. 128, 96 p.

Geologic Structure of Novaya Zemlya, Vaygach, Pay-Khoy, Polar Urals, and Northern Pechora[1]

V. I. BONDAREV, S. V. CHERKESOVA, V. S. ENOKYAN, and B. S. ROMANOVICH[2]

Leningrad, USSR

Abstract The late Paleozoic–early Mesozoic fold system of the Urals–Novaya Zemlya region and the Paleozoic-Cenozoic Pechora depression formed on folded pre-Mesozoic basement. The fold system may be divided into the Polar Ural and Pay-Khoy anticlinoriums and the structures of Novaya Zemlya. In the inland part of the Ural region, at the juncture of the fold system and the depression, a set of foredeep basins is recognized.

A complex of Precambrian, Paleozoic, and early Mesozoic (within the foredeep) sedimentary and volcanic rocks is involved in the formation of the Ural–Novaya Zemlya fold system. The thickness of Precambrian formations exceeds 3,000 m; that of Paleozoic rocks is over 10,000 m. Paleozoic (Ordovician and higher) strata transgressively and unconformably overlie the older formations. Important hiatuses in the Paleozoic section are recognized in pre–Late Devonian (Novaya Zemlya) and in Late Carboniferous rocks (Pay-Khoy, Novaya Zemlya).

Volcanic strata of predominantly mafic composition form a considerable part of the Precambrian (Polar Urals, Novaya Zemlya, Pay-Khoy) and Late Devonian sequences. Volcanic rocks of late Mesozoic–early Paleozoic age are found in northeastern Pay-Khoy. The following intrusive complexes are found in this area: an ancient pre-Ordovician and partially pre-Silurian ultramafic to acidic intrusive complex (Polar Urals, Pay-Khoy, Novaya Zemlya), a Caledonian (Silurian-Devonian) complex of ultramafic, mafic, and acidic intrusions (Polar Urals and Novaya Zemlya), and Hercynian mafic and acidic intrusions (Novaya Zemlya and the Polar Urals).

INTRODUCTION

The study area includes the northern part of the Paleozoic–early Mesozoic Novaya Zemlya–Ural fold area and the Paleozoic-Cenozoic Pechora depression, formed on the folded Precambrian basement (Fig. 1).

The arctic portion of the Novaya Zemlya fold area consists of the Polar Ural and Pay-Khoy anticlinoriums and a set of structures in Novaya Zemlya. At the juncture of the fold area and the Pechora depression, the Vorkuta and Korotaikha troughs of the Pre-Ural foredeep are recognized. The Novaya Zemlya–Ural fold area has a complex origin and varied relations with adjacent structures.

The Polar Urals region is characterized by a typical joining of Urals fold structures with a platform; a foredeep occupies the junction zone. The Pay-Khoy anticlinorium is a separate structure that was formed during the final stage of late Variscan tectogenesis; it divides the otherwise continuous Permian marginal trough in the northern Urals.

The Novaya Zemlya region, in contrast to the Urals region, is joined on the west not only by the platform, but also by the Caledonian geosynclinal structures of the eastern Barents Sea. The region comprises the territory of the Novaya Zemlya archipelago and Vaygach Island. The following anticlinoriums are distinguished: North Novaya Zemlya, Pakhtusov, and South Novaya Zemlya–Vaygach; synclinorial structures divide the anticlinoriums.

NORTH NOVAYA ZEMLYA ANTICLINORIUM

The North Novaya Zemlya anticlinorium, made up of Paleozoic sedimentary and partly volcanic strata, is typical of the anticlinoriums. At the base of the section is a clastic sequence of Middle and Upper Cambrian rocks more than 1,000 m thick; these rocks crop out in the Matochkin Shar Strait area. In more northern areas, nonfossiliferous metamorphosed shale that forms the core of the structure is arbitrarily assigned to the Cambrian. Within the anticlinorium, Ordovician fossils were found only in northern Novaya Zemlya, where they are represented by remains of trilobites. Unfortunately, the position within the section of the fossils collected has not been precisely determined.

In the Matochkin Shar area, Upper Cambrian rocks are transgressively overlain by Ordovician–Lower Silurian(?) strata up to 2.2 km thick. In the middle part of the section is a thick unit (400 m) of coarse conglomerate interbedded with sandstone. These strata are overlain by Llandoverian and Wenlockian carbonate deposits with a total thickness of more than 300 m. The overlying Upper Silurian deposits of the Ludlow Series and Greben Horizon comprise a mainly clastic sequence made up of gritstone, sandstone, and shale, as well as

[1] Manuscript received, August 1, 1972.

[2] Research Institute of the Geology of the Arctic.

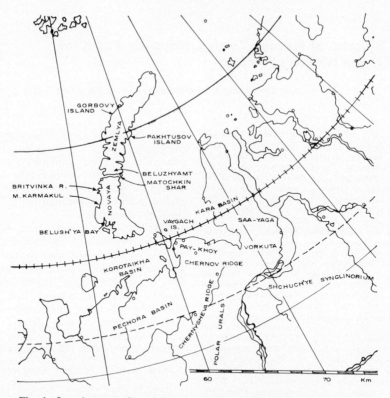

Fig. 1—Location map for geologic structure of Novaya Zemlya, Vaygach,
Pay-Khoy, Polar Urals, and northern Pechora.

units of carbonate rocks containing a benthonic fauna. The thickness of Upper Silurian deposits is 700–800 m. In northern Novaya Zemlya the Silurian is represented by a predominantly terrigenous sequence containing Llandoverian, Wenlockian, and Ludlovian graptolites, and in the Zhelaniya Cape area the sequence is composed mainly of coarse-grained clastic rocks. The thickness of the sequence is more than 1,000 m. Upper Devonian volcanic, clastic, and carbonate rocks reach 2,200 m in thickness and in places lie on a deeply eroded surface. Lithologic content and thickness of Middle and Upper Devonian deposits, as well as Silurian rocks, are extremely varied.

Carboniferous deposits on the western flank of the North Novaya Zemlya anticlinorium are represented mainly by carbonate rocks, and, on the eastern flank, by carbonate and clastic rocks. Lower, Middle, and Upper Carboniferous strata are distinguished. Local erosional unconformities are noted in many areas, and Lower Carboniferous deposits which are present in most of the area are, in places, completely absent. The maximum thickness of Carboniferous rocks is in the northwest in the Gorbovy Island area, where it reaches 2,500 m, but near Matochkin Shar Strait it is only 200 m.

Permian deposits, in most places, lie transgressively on Carboniferous rocks. The Permian section is composed of clastic rocks totaling 1.5–2 km in thickness. In places, these strata contain marine fossils of Early and Late Permian age.

Mesozoic deposits are present mainly in the form of reworked boulders and other rock fragments which contain marine fossils ranging in age from Middle Jurassic to Early Cretaceous, inclusive. Near the mouth of the Britvinka River, continental Late Triassic–Early Jurassic deposits may be present *in situ*.

Thin Neogene(?) conglomerates and breccias found near Belush'ya Bay are considered to be the oldest Cenozoic deposits. The stratigraphic section is usually capped by thin upper Pleistocene and Holocene marine, glacial, alluvial, talus, and eluvial (weathered residue) deposits. Mesozoic and Quaternary rock types are more or less consistent throughout the entire area of investigation. An important characteristic feature of Quaternary strata overlying structures of the North Novaya Zemlya anticlinorium is the presence of thick (up to 130 m) morainal units and thick talus deposits. The latter are typical of the Polar Urals.

Magmatic bodies are significant in the structure of the North Novaya Zemlya anticlinorium. The oldest of them are thin sheets of intensely altered mafic rocks of Silurian age. The largest granitoid intrusions on the western shore of Novaya Zemlya south of Matochkin Shar Strait possibly formed shortly before Middle Devonian time. An early Frasnian complex of extrusive and intrusive rocks is of spilite-diabase composition. The largest intrusive bodies in the complex are sills which can be traced for tens of kilometers, whereas extrusive bodies are 300–500 m thick and may cover an area of several hundred square kilometers. The limbs of the anticlinorium are broken by numerous small granitoid intrusions of Late Permian–Early Triassic and Late Triassic–Early Jurassic age. The northernmost part of the structure is amagmatic.

The North Novaya Zemlya anticlinorium has been greatly complicated by intense folding and faulting that are especially well manifested in a central part that is rather highly metamorphosed. On the western limb of the anticlinorium, recurrent deep-seated faulting is indicated by several features.

PAKHTUSOV ANTICLINORIUM

The Pakhtusov anticlinorium is situated on the eastern side of the northern island of Novaya Zemlya and is the least known among Novaya Zemlya structures. In its axial zone, Upper Silurian and Lower Devonian carbonate rocks with a total thickness up to 1,000 m are exposed. The overlying rocks are predominantly terrigenous strata about 500 m thick; they have been dated arbitrarily as Early and Middle Devonian, but they are probably Middle Devonian. The Devonian section is capped by transgressive Upper Devonian strata consisting of variegated carbonate and terrigenous rocks and a few sheets of mafic extrusives. The thickness of Upper Devonian deposits is less than 1,000 m. The Lower Carboniferous in the Pakhtusov anticlinorium is represented by carbonate rocks up to 500 m thick. They are overlain transgressively by a complex of terrigenous deposits about 2,000 m thick that range in age from Middle Carboniferous to Permian.

Magmatic rocks of the Pakhtusov anticlinorium are represented by Late Devonian basic extrusives and intrusives, as well as by cataclastic plagiogranite (P_2-T_1) and unaltered microcline granite and aplite-like granite (T_3-J_1) which form a large stock on the eastern side of Zivolko Bay. The intensity of folding and faulting within the anticlinorium is great, but not as great as in Novaya Zemlya.

SOUTH NOVAYA ZEMLYA–VAYGACH ANTICLINORIUM

The South Novaya Zemlya–Vaygach anticlinorium is exposed on Vaygach Island and southern Novaya Zemlya. Because it is situated between the Pay-Khoy and central Novaya Zemlya structures, it is considered to be a transitional structure. The base of the stratigraphic section is made up of volcanic-terrigenous strata more than 1,500 m thick. The strata are presumed to be Precambrian except for the upper part, which is probably Cambrian. The strata are strongly deformed, and their strike in southern Novaya Zemlya is sublatitudinal, in contrast to the overlying rocks, which strike northwest-southeast. The latter are Ordovician terrigenous and carbonate rocks that vary considerably in composition and thickness. The maximum thickness of Ordovician rocks is 2,500 m, and the minimum is several hundred meters. Ordovician deposits are conformably overlain by Silurian strata in which Llandoverian (600 m), Wenlockian (700 m), and Ludlovian (Khatanzeya Horizon, 400 m; and Greben Horizon, 200–300 m) strata are distinguished. In the Greben Horizon an admixture of fine clastic material is abundant, especially in the Belush'ya Bay area on Novaya Zemlya. The Silurian sequence of the South Novaya Zemlya–Vaygach anticlinorium is conformably overlain by Devonian rocks in which all three series are distinguished. The Lower Devonian is represented by a variegated facies and partially reefoid carbonate strata reaching a maximum thickness of 1,000 m in Novaya Zemlya. In southeastern Vaygach Island the thickness of the Lower Devonian reef facies is probably greater, whereas in the southwestern part of the island the exposed thickness of the Lower Devonian is 150 m.

The Middle Devonian is represented also by heterogeneous, predominantly carbonate rocks which are locally reefoid. The amount of sandy terrigenous material increases northwestward. Thickness of the Middle Devonian in southern Novaya Zemlya reaches 800–900 m. Upper

Devonian strata within the limits of the North Novaya Zemlya anticlinorium lie transgressively on underlying deposits. Depth of erosion into underlying strata is comparatively small. At the base of the Upper Devonian deposits are terrigenous rocks which consist of coarse clastic material in Novaya Zemlya; conglomerate and sandstone are interbedded with mafic extrusives and associated tuffs in northwestern sections, and variegated shale grades into sandstone in southwestern Vaygach. The higher sections of the Frasnian and the Famennian are represented mainly by carbonate deposits. Thickness of Upper Devonian rocks in southern Novaya Zemlya reaches 1,600 m, and in Vaygach it is 1,000 m. The Carboniferous deposits within the South Novaya Zemlya–Vaygach anticlinorium lie conformably on Upper Devonian strata. The Lower Carboniferous deposits, represented by a thick sequence of exclusively carbonate rocks, are the most widespread. In southeastern Novaya Zemlya, thickness of these strata reaches 1,200 m, decreasing westward and northwestward to 100 m in the Belush'ya Bay area. Middle Carboniferous deposits are of limited distribution and are represented by a thin limestone unit. In some areas of Novaya Zemlya, Carboniferous rocks are absent because of erosion.

Permian deposits have a transgressive contact with underlying strata. The Permian is represented by a flyschlike complex of terrigenous rocks and is subdivided into lower and upper series. The thickness of the lower series exceeds 2,000 m, and that of the upper is 1,000 m.

The general nature of the Mesozoic and Quaternary rocks was mentioned in the description of the North Novaya Zemlya anticlinorium. In southern Novaya Zemlya, Neogene(?) conglomerates and breccias are present.

Igneous rocks within the South Novaya Zemlya–Vaygach anticlinorium are represented by pre-Ordovician and Late Devonian complexes of basic intrusives and extrusives, the former located in southern Novaya Zemlya and northern Vaygach, and the latter in the northwestern part of the anticlinorium.

The South Novaya Zemlya–Vaygach anticlinorium is a symmetric anticlinorium of great structural complexity, but the structural deformation, especially faulting, is considerably less than that of the North Novaya Zemlya anticlinorium. Between these structures is the wide Karmakul synclinorium. It is made up of folded Lower Permian sandstone, shale, and argillite with a total thickness of about 2,000 m. The middle part of the synclinorium is complicated by a large brachyanticline composed of predominantly terrigenous deposits of post–Middle Devonian age.

PAY-KHOY ANTICLINORIUM

The junction of the South Novaya Zemlya–Vaygach and Pay-Khoy anticlinoriums is located at a fault with vertical displacement up to 3.5 km. The core of the Pay-Khoy anticlinorium is exposed in the northwestern part of the structure. It consists of highly deformed Proterozoic rocks that are assigned to a greenschist facies. Three sequences are distinguished in the Proterozoic section. The lower sequence, with an exposed thickness ranging from 1,500 to 2,000 m, is composed of conglomeratic, arenaceous, and siliceous chlorite schists and, in the lower part, mafic extrusives. These rocks are overlain by limestone containing Vendian microphytolites and by dolomite. The thickness of the carbonate deposits is 2,000–2,500 m. The deposits are, in places, replaced by extrusives of a rhyolite-basalt formation and the associated tuffs (porphyries, spilite, albitophyre or albitite, and others). Total thickness of the volcanic assemblage is 1,500–2,000 m.

The Proterozoic section is capped by variegated carbonate-clastic strata 1,500–2,000 m thick, separated from underlying formations by basal conglomerates. Predominantly mafic extrusives and associated tuffs are present in some areas.

Cambrian deposits of the Pay-Khoy anticlinorium lie with angular unconformity on Proterozoic rocks and are represented by a 40-m-thick conglomerate unit underlying variegated conglomerate, sandstone, and siltstone with a total thickness of 200 m. Among terrigenous deposits are lenses of limestone containing Late Cambrian trilobites.

Ordovician and older rocks compose an axial zone of the Pay-Khoy anticlinorium. The Ordovician section is clearly divided into two rock types. In the lower part of the section is a terrigenous sequence 2,000 m thick composing, together with Cambrian rocks, a single transgressive sequence. The Cambrian-Ordovician boundary is drawn at the base of beds containing trilobites and brachiopods of a Tremadocian aspect. The Upper Ordovician sequence is conformably overlain by Lower Silurian deposits and is composed almost completely of limestones. The limestone sequence, 500 m thick, contains trilobites, corals, and other fossils of Middle-Late Ordovician age.

Silurian–Lower Carboniferous sequences of Pay-Khoy are represented by two rock types— carbonate and terrigenous. The first type is observed on the southwestern limb of the Pay-Khoy anticlinorium; the second occurs on the northeastern limb in the area of the junction of the anticlinorium with Ural structures. During the Early Carboniferous Epoch, facies differences were eliminated, and limestone became the predominant lithologic type until the end of the Middle Carboniferous.

Abundant corals, brachiopods, and other fossils collected from carbonate type sections permit stratigraphic subdivision as far as stages and, in several cases, biostratigraphic horizons. In addition, this abundance of fossils allowed recognition of several local stratigraphic breaks. Thickness of carbonate sections is as follows: Lower Silurian, 1,200–1,700 m; Upper Silurian, 500 m; Lower-Middle Devonian, more than 700 m; Upper Devonian, more than 600 m; Lower Carboniferous, more than 250 m; and Middle Carboniferous, more than 50 m.

Terrigenous type sections of Silurian–Early Devonian rocks are represented by a sequence of siliceous shales with some limestones. Within the sequence, series and stages 470–600 m thick are established by use of graptolites. The overlying Middle Devonian sandstone, 500–600 m thick, contains impressions of continental flora. A 100-m-thick unit of nonfossiliferous siliceous shales, the youngest deposits in terrigenous type sections, is assigned tentatively to the Upper Devonian. Above are limestones with a total thickness of about 400 m which contain abundant fossils of Early and Middle Carboniferous marine faunas. On the basis of these fossils, stratigraphic subdivisions and interformational breaks have been established. Carboniferous deposits are transgressively overlain by a Lower Permian sequence, at the base of which is a thin unit containing an Asselian-Sakmarian fauna. The Lower Permian sequence is composed mainly of shale, argillite, siltstone, and sandstone. The lower part of the section contains limestone, and coaly seams are present in the upper part. Higher in the section, marine fossils are replaced by freshwater forms and terrestrial fossils.

The Early Permian deposits are the youngest in the Pay-Khoy anticlinorium. These rocks are locally eroded and absent. On the northeastern limb they underlie the vast Kara trough.

Mesozoic, or more precisely Upper Cretaceous, sandstone and siltstone were found only on the northeastern slope of the Pay-Khoy anticlinorium in the Saa-Yaga basin. Paleogene(?) tuff, breccia, and andesite lavas, with a total thickness up to 40 m, fill a caldera-shaped depression on the Kara seashore and represent the oldest Cenozoic formations. The Pay-Khoy section is capped by a thin cover of loose clastic sediments that began to form as early as the Neogene.

The magmatic activity within the Pay-Khoy anticlinorium was manifested mainly in the axial zone by the intrusion of a few comparatively small bodies of diabase and gabbro-diabase, probably Late Devonian in age.

Inner structure of the symmetric Pay-Khoy anticlinorium is comparatively simple except for the area of the junction with Ural structures, where intensely folded and faulted structures are present. Several longitudinal faults on the anticlinorium limbs are remarkable because of their length.

POLAR URAL ANTICLINORIUM

The Polar Ural anticlinorium is the northern termination of the exceedingly complex Ural mega-anticlinorium. The widespread development of Proterozoic strata is a peculiar feature here. The Polar Ural stratigraphic section of Proterozoic rocks is distinguished from that of Pay-Khoy by two main features. First, in the Polar Urals, highly metamorphosed rocks—i.e., amphibolites, mica-garnet schists, and granite gneisses that are considered to be equivalent in age to the oldest clastic and volcanic rocks of Pay-Khoy—are present at the base of the section. Second, in the Polar Urals, limestones and dolomites do not compose a separate thick sequence in the middle part as they do in Pay-Khoy.

Unquestioned Cambrian deposits have not been found in the Polar Urals. Some investigators assign to the Cambrian several sequences with rather different rock content (Shchokurin, Manya, and Oyuyakhin Formations) which contain scarce archaeocyathids, hyolithids, and the brachiopod *Billingsella*. The fossils are poorly preserved. Some geologists consider assignment of the deposits to the Cambrian to be doubtful, for the fossils obviously may be late Proterozoic (Vendian) or Ordovician. Age of a shaly formation 600–800 m thick is more certain. Limestone bands contain *Billingsella* shells of undoubtedly early Paleozoic forms, most likely Late Cambrian.

These sequences of uncertain age lie with transgressive or even angular unconformity on the underlying rocks, so it is difficult to recognize the Proterozoic-Paleozoic boundary.

The western and eastern slopes of the Polar Urals differ greatly in Paleozoic rock types, starting with the Ordovician strata. Sections on the western slope have much in common with those of Pay-Khoy and are represented by two main types of rock—terrigenous in the inner part of the Polar Ural anticlinorium and carbonate on its outer side. The eastern slope is characterized by widespread volcanic formations. On both slopes, structural-stratigraphic zones are distinguished by a general northeast strike along the anticlinorium axis. In the junction area of the Ural and Pay-Khoy structures, however, several zones appear to have a northwest-southeast strike due to later tectonic movements.

Polar Ural sequences, composed chiefly of limestones and dolomites from Ordovician to Carboniferous age, are similar in composition and thickness to coeval sequences in Pay-Khoy. They differ from those in Pay-Khoy by comparatively minor facies peculiarities.

Sections of terrigenous Ordovician deposits on the western slope of the Polar Urals, in comparison with equivalent formations in Pay-Khoy, are more varied lithologically and are poorly fossiliferous. Thus, it is essential to recognize certain lateral and vertical facies changes.

Thickness of the Ordovician structural-stratigraphic zones ranges from 1,700 to 3,100 m, increasing westward. In sections of the eastern slope, a sequence of volcanic and metamorphic schists containing bands and lenses of marble is tentatively assigned to the Ordovician.

Silurian terrigenous strata on the western limb of the Polar Ural anticlinorium differ from those in Pay-Khoy by the presence of thin covers of mafic extrusives and associated tuffs. On the eastern limb of the structure, the Silurian is represented almost exclusively by basic to acidic extrusives and associated tuffs. Also present are bands of schists and shales, as well as limestones containing brachiopods.

On the western slope of the Polar Urals, Lower and Middle Devonian terrigenous sections are generally similar to those in Pay-Khoy, but in eastern sections there are basic and intermediate extrusives. A sequence 400–1,000 m thick composed of limestone and lime-

stone lenses is assigned to the Upper Devonian.

On the eastern slope of the Polar Urals, a sequence made up of basic extrusives, tuffs, shales, and limestone lenses containing scarce brachiopods and crinoids is dated as Early-Middle Devonian. Northward along strike the sequence is replaced by Early Devonian and partly Middle Devonian limestones. The rock complex is overlain by a volcanic-carbonate-terrigenous sequence, which is Late Devonian in age. The maximum thickness of Devonian formations is several thousand meters.

In Pay-Khoy, Carboniferous strata are made up chiefly of carbonate rocks; however, on the western slope of the Polar Urals, synchronous strata with a thickness as great as 1,000 m are of a very different lithology. The boundary with the Permian is drawn tentatively within a monotonous sandstone-shale sequence, whose lower part yields Middle Carboniferous foraminifers and whose upper part contains a Permian flora. A motley lithology is characteristic also of a sequence on the eastern slope of the Polar Urals which differs from underlying formations chiefly by the absence of volcanic beds. These rocks, the youngest of which are Middle Carboniferous, cap the Paleozoic section.

Within the Polar Ural anticlinorium, Proterozoic and Paleozoic intrusions are related to the axial zone and the eastern limb. The axial zone contains small bodies of ultrabasic to acidic igneous rocks. Among Paleozoic intrusions, the foremost are large massifs of ultramafic, mafic, and granitic rocks of Silurian and Early Devonian age. In addition, there are small intrusions of early and late Paleozoic granitoids as well as early Paleozoic mafic rocks.

The Polar Ural anticlinorium is characterized by a very complex structure resulting from numerous folds and faults. It is possible to distinguish two structural units—the Pre-Uralides and the Uralides—which correspond to the Baykalides and the Hercynides. Structures in the pre-Ordovician volcanic-sedimentary sequence belong to the Pre-Uralides. In the axial zone of the anticlinorium they are raised in a tectonic wedge bordered on the west by the principal Ural fault. This fault, to which large intrusions are related, divided the Paleozoic geosyncline into mio- and eugeosynclinal zones, which are well illustrated by the stratigraphic sections on the eastern and western slopes of the Urals. The fault turns northeastward and intersects the Shchuch'ye synclinorium, which is composed of Paleozoic strata of the eugeosynclinal zone. These strata are extensively overlain by mildly deformed Triassic deposits. Within the miogeosynclinal zone a submeridional deep fault separates Ural structures from the Pay-Khoy structure. The northern part of the Polar Ural anticlinorium is marked by a change of trend from northwest to northeast.

KOROTAIKHA, VORKUTA, AND PECHORA DEPRESSIONS

In the west, the Pay-Khoy and Polar Ural anticlinoriums join the Korotaikha and Vorkuta depressions. There are two viewpoints about the tectonic nature of the depressions: their origin is either related to that of the Pre-Ural foredeep or to that of the Kara depression. The Kara, Korotaikha, and Vorkuta basins may have been one basin in the Permian. Such a basin may have occupied a position on a periclinal termination of the Ural mega-anticlinorium, situated entirely on middle Paleozoic structures of geosynclinal type, whereas the inner side of the foredeep is developed on a platform margin.

The Korotaikha and Vorkuta depressions are filled mainly with Lower and Upper Permian rocks with total thickness up to 6–8 km. Upward in the section, marine deposits are replaced by continental strata. The Permian sequence is underlain by middle Paleozoic deposits, predominantly carbonate in the east and terrigenous in the west. This facies variation is indicated by comparison of the Pay-Khoy and Ural sections with those of the Pechora Sea islands and the Chernov and Chernysheva Ridges. The ridges bordering the depressions on the west are composed of middle and upper Paleozoic deposits that were folded and extensively faulted. Tectonic structures of the ridges are genetically related to movements along a deep fault.

The Vorkuta depression is characterized by the presence of thick coal seams (up to 30 m) in the upper part of the section. In the Korotaikha depression a Permian sequence is overlain transgressively by Triassic continental deposits with a total thickness of 2,200–2,400 m. The base of the Triassic sequence is composed of variegated rocks and two basalt sheets 10–12 and 16–19 m thick. On the uplift dividing the depressions, a similar basalt sheet 37 m thick was found in a borehole. The stratigraphic section is capped by Pliocene-Holocene sediments, mainly marine and glacial-marine sandy loam, but partly sands and clays. The total thickness of Cenozoic deposits reaches 200 m.

Permian rocks of the Vorkuta depression are overlain in a large area by Upper Cretaceous sandstones up to 250 m thick. Above is a thin cover of Pliocene-Holocene sediments similar in composition and thickness to those of the Korotaikha depression, but glacial deposits are also present.

The Pechora depression is a typical platform area with its northern part joining the Vorkuta and Korotaikha depressions. We shall consider only this poorly known northern part of the depression. A platform cover of 4–6 km overlies the basement. Of the several opinions regarding the structure and age of this feature, two theories are most widely accepted. The first is that the basement in the area is made up of folded structures of the Baykal eugeosyncline. According to the second theory, the platform cover lies on crystalline rocks of the pre-Baykal massif.

The lithology, thickness, and age of the basal sequence of the platform cover in the northern part of the depression are problematic. The prevailing opinion is that it has a clastic composition and a maximum thickness of 750 m. The sequence is correlated with the Izhma-Zyryanka complex encountered in boreholes in the southern part of the depression. The age of the Izhma-Zyryanka complex is approximately dated as Vendian-Ordovician.

The terrigenous deposits are believed to be overlain transgressively by a carbonate-clastic sequence which began to form in the Silurian or Middle Ordovician and was completed in the Early Permian. In addition to local erosional surfaces, there appears to be a Tournaisian-Viséan regional break in the sequence. It is assumed that, in the northern Pechora depression, unlike more northern and eastern areas, siltstone-shale facies are more widespread in the Devonian, dolomites are most common in the Carboniferous, and evaporites and limestones are widespread in the Permian sequence. The overlying rocks are a Lower Permian–Triassic sequence composed of marine beds and overlying continental deposits; this sequence is similar in composition to coeval rocks of the Pre-Ural trough. In contrast with the latter, however, thickness of the Permian sequence in the northern part of the depression decreases to 1 km. In the most complete sections the thickness of the Triassic sequence is almost the same, and the sequence is overlain transgressively by Middle Jurassic–Lower Cretaceous shales and sandstones with a total thickness of less than 450 m. The stratigraphic section is capped by Neogene-Quaternary deposits which, in composition, origin, and total thickness, are similar to synchronous formations in the Korotaikha depression.

In the basement of the Pechora depression, the fault systems are orthogonal and diagonal (the main systems have predominant northwest-southeast faults). In the northern part of the depression, block movements of the basement are reflected in a pre-Jurassic sequence primarily in the form of tectonic uplifts and elongate northwest-southeast-striking troughs; some of the faults extend into the platform cover. During formation of the pre-Jurassic sequence, the depression was tilted mainly eastward. In the Mesozoic, north-northwestward tilting changed the structural framework of a less deformed Middle Jurassic–Lower Triassic sequence. Neotectonic structures are mainly inherited from more ancient structures and are more evident in the northern part of the depression than in the south. In general, the structures are less pronounced than those of Pay-Khoy and especially those of the Polar Urals.

Ordovician of Soviet Arctic[1]

V. I. BONDAREV,[2] A. Z. BURSKY,[2] E. M. KRASIKOV,[2]
L. V. NEKHOROSHEVA,[2] and M. M. ORADOVSKAYA[3]

Leningrad and Magadan, USSR

Abstract Ordovician rocks are widely represented in the Soviet Arctic. They are known in Novaya Zemlya, Vaygach Island, Pay-Khoy, Severnaya Zemlya, the northern Siberian platform, the New Siberian Islands, and the northeastern USSR. In the western Arctic (Polar Urals–Novaya Zemlya), Ordovician deposits are represented by a very thick and varied complex of clastic-carbonate rocks.

The Ordovician is at the base of the stratigraphic column in Severnaya Zemlya; on Taymyr Peninsula and on the Siberian platform, the Cambrian and Ordovician rocks form a continuous sequence. Ordovician deposits in the region are represented by predominantly carbonate rocks as thick as 2,000 m in basins; in the northern part of the Taymyr Peninsula, the Ordovician consists of clastic-carbonate rocks as thick as 1,000 m containing graptolites. The Ordovician of Severnaya Zemlya is represented by variegated clastic-carbonate rocks about 2,000 m thick.

Within the eastern Arctic, Ordovician deposits are a part of the folded margin of the Kolyma massif and the Mesozoides of the northeastern Chukotsk Peninsula. Ordovician strata in the northeastern USSR are represented by carbonate, clastic-carbonate, and clastic sequences. The relations with underlying rocks are uncertain. Thicknesses are widely varied and reach 5,500 m in places.

Ordovician deposits have been studied in more detail in southern Novaya Zemlya, Vaygach Island, northern Pay-Khoy, central Taymyr, in the district of Noril'sk, and within the limits of the folded margin of the Kolyma massif. The Ordovician of northern Novaya Zemlya, Severnaya Zemlya, and the New Siberian Islands is less well known.

Even where Ordovician sections have been investigated comprehensively and are richly fossiliferous, however, the Lower-Middle Ordovician and Ordovician-Silurian boundaries are uncertain because of geologic peculiarities of the region, and no definite solution to the Cambrian-Ordovician boundary problem has been found. Varied sedimentary facies and diverse zoogeographic provinces make regional and interregional correlations difficult. Nevertheless, recognition of transitional sequences in fold areas of the Soviet Arctic and the wide interregional distribution of some faunal elements during climaxes of marine transgression (late Tremadoc and middle Caradoc) permit rather definite correlations for the solution of practical biostratigraphic problems and correlation with standard sequences elsewhere.

INTRODUCTION

Ordovician deposits are widespread in the Soviet Arctic. They are present in the Ural–

[1] Manuscript received, August 1, 1972.
[2] Research Institute of the Geology of the Arctic.
[3] Northeastern Geological Division.

Novaya Zemlya fold area, in Severnaya Zemlya, and in the New Siberian Islands. They form the folded structures of mountainous Taymyr and fringe the Kolyma and Omolon stable regions. They are present also in northeastern Chukotsk Peninsula and are exposed in vast areas of the northern Siberian platform (Table 1).

URAL–NOVAYA ZEMLYA FOLD AREA

Ordovician rocks of the region have been studied in detail in northern Pay-Khoy, Vaygach, and southern Novaya Zemlya. Outcrops of Ordovician rocks are also known in central Novaya Zemlya (Gribovaya Bay–Matochkin Shar area) and northward (Cape Spory Navolok), where clastic strata up to 1,000 m thick crop out. However, fossil content of the latter is indeterminate. In Pay-Khoy, Vaygach, and southern Novaya Zemlya, the basal contact of Ordovician formations is transgressive and unconformable, and the upper contact with Silurian deposits is conformable. A peculiar characteristic of the Ordovician is its striking regional variation in lithology and thickness. Two types of Ordovician sections are clearly distinguished in the region—carbonate-shale rocks containing trilobites and graptolites and clastic-carbonate rocks containing benthonic fossil assemblages. Carbonate-shale sections occur on the east flank and in the axial zone of the Pay-Khoy anticlinorium; clastic-carbonate sections are clearly represented in Vaygach Island and in southern Novaya Zemlya. The Ordovician deposits in the first type of section are 1,500 m thick, and deposits of the second type exceed 2,500 m.

As a result of investigations concerning development of Ordovician sedimentary basins in the region studied, a detailed stratigraphic standard has been formulated. The Ordovician strata of the trough (or basin) which occupied the present area of Novaya Zemlya and Vaygach Island are subdivided into the Rusanova and Loginova Series. The first corresponds in general to the Lower Ordovician, and the second to both Middle and Upper Ordovician. The sequences exhibit a transgressive relation in the margins of the trough and a normal deposi-

Table 1. Correlation Chart of Ordovician Deposits of Soviet Arctic

Stratigraphic Standard	North Ural-Novaya Zemlya Fold Area	Taymyr Fold Area — Northern Zone	Taymyr Fold Area — Southern Zone	Siberian Platform	Severnaya Zemlya	New Siberian Islands — Kotel'nyy Island	New Siberian Islands — Bennetta Island	North-eastern USSR
Upper — Ashgill: *Dicellograptus anceps* / *Dicellograptus complanatus*	Loginova Series — Varnek Subseries: Stadolskogo Horizon	Beds with *Rectograptus truncatus abreviatus*	Korotkaya Horizon	Keta Stage	B'ergov Formation	Sandstone with *Calapoecia, Catenipora delicatulus*	?	Iryuda Horizon
Middle — Caradoc Upper: *Pleurograptus linearis* / *Dicranograptus clingani*	Lyamchina Subseries: Yugorskiy Horizon	Beds with *Dicellograptus pumilis* / *Dicellograptus caduceus* / ?	Taymyr Horizon	Dolbor Stage	Komsomol'skiy Formation		Kharkindzha Horizon	Kharkindzha Horizon
Caradoc Middle: *Climacograptus wilsoni* / *Climacograptus peltifer*		*Climacograptus peltifer*	Tolmacheva Horizon	Mangazeya Stage — Baksan Horizon / Chertov Horizon		Sandstone with *Mimella panna*	Shale with *Glyptograptus dentatus*	Darpirsky Horizon
Caradoc Lower: *Nemagraptus gracilis*	Yun'yakha Horizon	*Nemagraptus gracilis*	Engelhardt Horizon	Krivolutsk Stage		?		Mokrinsky Horizon
Llandeilo: *Glyptograptus teretiusculus*		Beds with *Glyptograptus eugliphus, Phyllograptus, anna* and others	Tollya Horizon / ?				*Didymograptus murchisoni*	El'genchak Horizon
Llanvirn: *Didymograptus murchisoni* / *Didymograptus bifidus*	Reyneke Horizon / ? / Korsakova Horizon	*Isograptus gibberulus* / ? / *Tetragraptus approximatus*	Beds with *Angarella* / Beds with *Imbricatia russanovi* / ?	Chuna Stage	Kruzhilikha Formation		Shale with *Azigograptus, Didymograptus*	Khita Horizon
Lower — Arenig: *Didymograptus hirundo* / *Didymograptus extensus* / *Dichograptus*	Petukhovskiy Horizon	*Clonograptus* spp. / *Triograptus canadensis*		Ust'Kut Stage				Inanya Horizon
Tremadoc: *Bryograptus* / *Dictyonema flabelliforme*	Lakorsale Horizon	*Dictyonema graptolithinum* / *Dictyonema sociale*	?					?
Underlying deposits	PCm	Cm₃	Cm₃	Cm₃	Cm₃		Cm₃	

Series (North Ural-Novaya Zemlya): Loginova Series (Varnek Subseries, Lyamchina Subseries); Rusanova Series (Neljdova Subseries, Sokoliy Subseries).

tional relation in its axial zone. The Rusanova Series is more than 60 m thick, and the Loginova Series is as thick as 2,300 m. Each series is divided into subseries. Within the Rusanova Series the Sokoliy and Nelidova Subseries are distinguished. The Sokoliy Subseries is divided into the Lakorsale and Petukhovskiy Horizons. The Lakorsale Horizon (lower) represents a transgressive stage in the development of the basin, and in Pay-Khoy it yields fossils characteristic of *Syntrophopsis magna* and *Dekelokephalina* beds (Bondarev *et al.*, 1968). The Petukhovskiy Horizon, present on the sides of the trough, shows a regressive stage of basin development; in Pay-Khoy it comprises the *Nyaya*, *Apatokephalus serratus*, and *Megalaspides* beds (Bondarev *et al.*, 1968). In Novaya Zemlya the thickness of the Sokoliy Subseries of clastic strata is 285 m; in Pay-Khoy the Sokoliy consists of 100 m of carbonate deposits. The Sokoliy Subseries may be correlated with the Tremadoc and the lowest Arenig on the basis of its abundant fossils.

The Nelidova Subseries, similarly to the Sokoliy Subseries, reflects a complete subcycle of sedimentary-basin development and may be divided into two horizons. The Korsakova Horizon (lower) was formed during a transgressive period; it is represented in Novaya Zemlya by calcareous-clastic rocks 100 m thick containing benthonic fauna and in Pay-Khoy by carbonate-shale strata 250 m thick. Beds containing *Tetragraptus approximatus*, the lower beds of the *Phyllograptus* shale, and beds containing *Eorobergia* and *Phyllograptus* aff. *densus* are assigned to the Korsakova Horizon in Pay-Khoy. The Reyneke Horizon (upper) reflects a regressive stage of the basin; in Novaya Zemlya it consists of clastic rocks containing *Angarella*, whereas in Pay-Khoy it includes carbonate rocks and shales comprising the *Megistaspis limbata* and *Trigonograptus ensiformis* beds (Bondarev *et al.*, 1968). The Nelidova Subseries correlates in general with the Arenig.

The Loginova Series includes two subseries. The Lyamchina Subseries is subdivided into the Yun'yakha (Yunoyaga), Yugorskiy, and Stadolskogo Horizons, which correspond to transgressive, stable, and regressive stages, respectively, in the basin. The Yun'yakha Horizon in Vaygach is represented by a clastic sequence 1,000 m thick; it yields a benthonic faunal assemblage that permits its correlation with the Llanvirn. In Pay-Khoy the horizon is clastic and is several meters thick. It contains graptolites that also permit correlation with the

Llanvirn. The Yugorskiy Horizon (= Dyrovat + Yugorskiy Horizons of the 1968 standard) is calcareous; in Novaya Zemlya, Vaygach Island, and northwestern Pay-Khoy, it contains abundant and varied fossils of benthonic faunas which permit correlation of the deposits with the early and middle Caradoc. In eastern Pay-Khoy, synchronous strata yield early Caradocian graptolites. The thickness of the Yugorskiy Horizon in the region has a wide range, reaching 750 m on Vaygach Island. In the uppermost Lyamchina Subseries, the Stadolskogo Horizon is represented by variegated calcareous-clastic strata in Novaya Zemlya and by tuffaceous rocks in southern Vaygach. Thickness of the horizon reaches 130 m. A coral assemblage from the horizon proves it to be Late Ordovician.

The Varnek Subseries, at the top of the Loginova Series, is well exposed only in its lower part and reflects a transgressive stage of the basin. In Novaya Zemlya and Vaygach Island, the Varnek Subseries consists of carbonate strata 250–300 m thick that yield corals, brachiopods, bryozoans, and other fossils.

TAYMYR FOLD AREA

Ordovician deposits within the Taymyr fold area are exposed in the axial zones and on the flanks of intensely faulted linear structures.

According to recent data (Bondarev *et al.*, 1968; Obut and Sobolevskaya, 1962; 1964), the Ordovician deposits in Taymyr are represented by two greatly different types of sections —thin, predominantly argillaceous strata in the north and thicker carbonate rocks in the south.

Ordovician stratigraphic units in the southern zone show the stages of basin development. In the northern zone, the stages of development are not so distinct, and stages of the Ordovician standard are therefore recognized on the basis of graptolite evolution. Local stratigraphic zones are used for more detailed classification.

Lower Ordovician rocks of the southern structural-stratigraphic zone occur in isolated outcrops in central Taymyr. A Lower Ordovician carbonate unit with an exposed thickness of 200 m yields *Apheoorthis* sp. and *Imbricatia russanovi* V. Bond. The upper part of the sequence is also known there (Tareya River), where it is represented by a sequence of limestone, dolomite, and shale more than 600 m thick. The lower contact of the sequence is not exposed. The deposits contain *Angarella* sp., *Biolgina* sp., and *Remopleurides* sp.

Within the northern structural-stratigraphic

zone, Ordovician deposits are known from central and eastern Taymyr. The Tremadoc is composed of limestone and shale totaling 200 m in thickness. It includes three local zones: (1) *Dictyonema sociale–Dictyonema parabola,* (2) *Dictyonema graptolithinum,* and (3) *Triograptus canadensis.*

The Arenig is represented by carbonate-argillaceous rocks in which the following zones were recognized on the basis of graptolites: (1) *Clonograptus* spp. and (2) *Tetragraptus approximatus* in the lower part and *Isograptus gibberulus* in the upper part of the section. The middle Arenig is not exposed in the Taymyr Peninsula. The thickness of the Arenig reaches 350 m.

Middle Ordovician rocks are widespread in the Taymyr Peninsula. In the southern zone, Middle Ordovician deposits are subdivided into three horizons. The Tollya Horizon includes calcareous shale and aphanic limestone comprising a transgressive phase of the sedimentary cycle. The following fossils were found in the deposits: *Robergia* sp., *Cybele* sp., *Remopleurides* sp., *Triarthrus* sp., and *Telephus* sp. The relation of the horizon to underlying deposits is unknown. The thickness of the Tollya Horizon is about 450 m. The Engelhardt Horizon (a regressive phase of the sedimentary cycle) is represented in the lower part by silty bioclastic limestone and in the upper part by bioclastic algal limestone. The following fossils were found: *Lichenaria prima* Okul., *Billingsaria lepida* Sok., *Trematopora njuensis* Modz., *Pachydictya* aff. *fimbriata* Ulr., *Atelelasma peregrinum* (Andr.), *Lonchodomas rostratus* (Sars and Boeck), *Ampyx depressus* (Ang.), and *Illaenus depressicapitatus* Brad. The thickness of the Engelhardt Horizon is about 500 m. The Tolmacheva Horizon, representing a transgressive phase of the sedimentary cycle, is composed of alternate limestone and shale, partly variegated. Fossils found are *Tetraporella minor* (Troeds.), *Fletcheria* sp., *Nicholsonella polaris* Modz., *N. vaupeliformis* Modz., *Atelelasma carinatum* (Andr.), *Mimella panna* Andr., and *Isotelus gigas* Dekay. The thickness of the horizon ranges from 300 to 500 m.

Within the northern structural-stratigraphic zone, Middle Ordovician classification is not so distinct. A limestone-shale unit 100 m thick corresponds to the Llanvirn and Llandeilo. *Phyllograptus* aff. *anna* Hall, *P. angustifolius* Hall, *Glossograptus acanthus* Elles and Wood, and *Hallograptus echinatus* (Rued.) are present in its lower part, and *Glyptograptus eugly-*

phus (Lapw.) occurs in the upper part. Caradoc deposits in eastern Taymyr are subdivided into: (1) siltstone, silt, limestone, and shale (25–50 m thick) with *Nemagraptus gracilis* (Hall) and other forms; (2) claystone and shale (49 m) with *Climacograptus peltifer* (Lapw.) and *Diplograptus multidens* (Elles and Wood; and (3) shale, claystone, and limestone (75 m) with *Dicellograptus caduceus* Lapw., *D. pumilus* Lapw., and *Retiograptus pulcherrimus* Koble and Harris. Obut and Sobolevskaya (1962, 1964) considered these subdivisions to be local zones. The stratigraphic extent of the latter zone is indefinite.

The Upper Ordovician within the southern structural-stratigraphic zone is subdivided into two horizons. The Taymyr Horizon is composed of dolomite and calcareous dolomite and is 220 m thick in the type section. *Catenipora tollinoides* Zhizh., *C.* cf. *gracilis* (Hall), *C.* cf. *delicatulus* Wil., and other fossils are found there. The Korotkaya Horizon is represented by limestone and dolomite yielding *Catenipora* cf. *robustus* (Wil.), *Paleofavosites* cf. *amoenus* Smirn., *Sibiriolites* cf. *sibiricus* Sok., *Phaenoporella anastomosa* Nekh., *Boreadorthis asiaticus* Nikif., and *Glyptorthis* cf. *katangaensis* Nikif. The horizon is 200 m thick in the type section. Within the northern structural-stratigraphic zone the Upper Ordovician is not classified. A claystone–clayey limestone unit about 100 m thick is assigned to this series and is considered to be situated higher than the middle Caradoc and lower than the lowest Llandovery rocks. *Dicellograptus pumilus* Lapw., *Climacograptus minimum* (Carr.), *Rectograptus barcovaensis* Obut and Sob., *R.* ex gr. *truncatus* (Lapw.), and *Retiograptus pulcherrimus* Koble and Harris were found in the lower part of this unit.

SIBERIAN PLATFORM

On the northern Siberian platform there are two vast areas of Ordovician deposits. In the northwestern part of the platform, Ordovician rocks form structures of the Rybinsk and Kureyka-Letnyaya uplifts (Datsenko, 1968); in the northeastern part, these rocks compose the southwestern flank of the Anabar anticlise (Nikiforova and Andreyeva, 1961). On the basis of sedimentologic study and typical faunal assemblages related to sedimentary stages, the Ordovician of the Siberian platform is subdivided into three series and six local stages.

The Lower Ordovician, subdivided into the Ust'-Kut and Chuna Stages, is represented in the northwestern part of the platform (Andreyeva, 1967; Vysotsky and Andreyeva, 1967; Mikutsky, 1967; and others), where maximum total thickness is about 800 m (Kulyumbe River basin). The Ust'-Kut Stage is composed of a monotonous sequence of predominantly gray dolomite alternating with limestone that conformably overlies similar Upper Cambrian rocks. The total thickness of the Ust'-Kut Stage reaches 400 m in the Igarka-Noril'sk region and decreases to 80 m southward. The Chuna Stage is represented by gray and variegated carbonate-clastic and clastic rocks as thick as 370 m. The characteristic fauna of the stage is *Cryptolichenaria, Angarella, Pseudomera, Giolgina, Tolmachovia,* and *Moyeronia.* The boundary between the Ust'-Kut and Chuna Stages is conformable.

In the northeastern part of the platform, the Lower Ordovician in most sections, excluding the Moyero River basin, is composed chiefly of calcareous rocks totaling 180–215 m in thickness, but it has not yet been subdivided into the Ust'-Kut and Chuna Stages.

The Upper Cambrian–Lower Ordovician boundary problem—and, therefore, the problem concerning the stratigraphic extent of these series—has not been solved (Andreyeva, 1967; Datsenko and Lazarenko, 1968; Rozova and Yadrenkina, 1967). Most workers draw the boundary at the place in a section where *Syntrophopsis arkansasensis* Ulr. and Coop. and *Dictyonema* first appear.

The Middle Ordovician is subdivided into the Krivolutsk and Mangazeya Stages. The Krivolutsk Stage is represented by clastic and clastic-carbonate rocks lying paraconformably on eroded Chuna deposits. Three horizons are distinguished within the stage—the Volginsk, Kirensk, and Kudryusk (Andreyeva, 1959). In the northwestern part of the platform, only the Volginsk Horizon, 30–35 m thick, is clearly recognized; it consists of gray argillaceous-silty limestone with interbedded dolomite, gypsum, and anhydrite. *Atelelasma peregrinum* (Andr.), *Rafinesquina amara* Andr., *Evenkina lenaica* (Gir.), *Homotellus lenaensis* Z. Max., *Billingsaria lepida* Sok., and other fossils are found in the limestone. The overlying unit, 45–65 m thick, is represented by variegated claystone, siltstone, dolomite, and sandstone. It yields ostracods and may be correlated with both the Kirensk and Pudrinsk Horizons.

In the northeastern part of the platform, sections of the Krivolutsk Stage are composed of variegated clastic rocks 35–60 m thick containing typical Krivolutsk faunal assemblages. In the Moyero River basin, all three horizons are distinguished. The other regions are insufficiently studied.

Lithologically, the Mangazeya Stage is generally uniform, and it is represented chiefly by limestone. On the basis of faunal-assemblage characteristics, the stage is subdivided into the Chertov and Baksan Horizons (Andreyeva, 1959; Nikiforova and Andreyeva, 1961). In the northwestern Siberian platform, the Mangazeya deposits lie conformably on the Krivolutsk rocks. Complete sections of the Mangazeya rocks are not established there. The thickest known section (80–100 m) is in the Kulyumbe River basin, where both horizons are recognized.

In the northeastern regions of the platform, the Mangazeya deposits are not subdivided into horizons, except in the Moyero River basin, where a 13-m-thick marlstone and limestone unit yielding *Nicholsonella polaris* Modz., *N. vaupeliformis* Modz., *Mimella panna* Andr., *Ceraurinus icarus* (Bill.), and other fossils is assigned to the Chertov Horizon. An overlying 21-m-thick unit of rocks with similar lithology, but yielding *Tetradium fibratum* (Saff.), *Phaenopora elegans* Nekh., *Eurydictya mojerensis* Nekh., *Rostricellula transversa* Coop., *R. subrostrata* Nikif., and *Carinopyge fracta* Z. Max., belongs to the Baksan Horizon.

The Upper Ordovician is divided into the Dolbor and Keta Stages (Tesakov, 1967; Rozman and Fomin, 1967). The Middle-Upper Ordovician boundary in most places is not marked lithologically, but is drawn according to the change of faunal assemblages or is located tentatively. The upper boundary of the Ordovician is an erosional unconformity distinctly traceable throughout the region. In the northern Siberian platform, only the lowest Dolbor deposits are known. In the northwestern regions of the Kulyumbe River basin, a 12-m marl unit containing *Opikina gibbosa* Andr. and *Bumastus* aff. *holli* Foerste is assigned to the Dolbor Stage. In the northeast, in the Moyero River basin, the Dolbor Stage is represented by argillaceous-marly rocks 23 m thick containing abundant *Boreadorthis asiatica* Nikif., *Strophomena lethaea* Nikif., and other fossils. The uppermost Dolbor and the Keta Stages are absent in the northern part of the platform because of pre-Silurian erosion.

SEVERNAYA ZEMLYA

In Severnaya Zemlya, Ordovician deposits are widespread (Bondarev, 1960). They lie unconformably on underlying strata and are transgressively overlain by Silurian rocks. The section is represented by a complex of variegated clastic-carbonate strata, commonly containing gypsum and yielding scarce fossils. In ascending order, the following units are recognized in the section: the Kruzhilikha, Komsomol'skiy, and Bergov Formations. The Kruzhilikha Formation consists of clastic and carbonate members and totals 450 m in thickness. *Angarella* sp. is found in the formation. The Komsomol'skiy Formation includes variegated clastic-carbonate strata containing gypsum in places and totaling more than 1,300 m in thickness. Middle Ordovician gastropods were found among fossils in this part of the section. The Bergov Formation consists of limestone (containing gypsum in places), dolomite, and sandstone 500–600 m thick.

New Siberian Islands

In the New Siberian Islands the Ordovician is known on Bennetta and Kotel'nyy Islands. Fine clastic strata are developed on Bennetta Island. They contain Cambrian fauna in the lower part and graptolite fossils of Early Ordovician and Llanvirnian age in the middle and upper parts. The thickness of the strata assigned to the Ordovician is 1,000 m.

On Kotel'nyy Island the Ordovician forms the basal part of the geologic column of the island and is represented by calcareous rocks of the upper Middle and Upper Ordovician. The Ordovician rocks yield a benthonic fauna approximately coeval with fauna from the Siberian platform. The thickness of the Middle Ordovician is 300–350 m, and that of the Upper Ordovician is 800–1,000 m.

Northeastern USSR

Ordovician deposits in the northeastern USSR are widespread mainly in the Omulëvka, Polousnyy, and Tas-Khayakhtakh marginal uplifts of the Kolyma stable region. They are also known from the Sette-Daban uplift on the Siberian platform margin, in the Okhotsk and Omolon stable regions, and on the Uelen uplift in the Chukotsk Peninsula area (Oradovskaya, 1969; Chugayeva *et al.*, 1964; Chugayeva and Rozman, 1969; Polevoy Atlas, 1968).

The Ordovician sections have a maximum thickness of 5,500 m in the Kolyma River basin and in the Omulëvka and El'genchak Mountains; in Selennyakh Ridge their thickness is 4,500–5,000 m, in Sette-Daban Ridge it is about 4,000 m, and in the Chukotsk Peninsula,

where the section is discontinuous, it is 780 m. Ordovician deposits are represented by different facies, of which the most characteristic are carbonate, clastic-carbonate, and sedimentary-volcanic. The carbonate facies contains a peculiar assemblage of benthonic fauna unknown from European sections but similar to faunas from North America; clastic-carbonate sections are correlated on the basis of graptolites with the stratigraphic standard. The regional standard is compiled on the basis of carbonate facies. Different types of sections are recognized in the Omulëvka uplift area and the Kolyma River basin, where Ordovician deposits are more completely studied and where transitional sections are also present. In the latter, carbonate deposits with benthonic fauna alternate with graptolite shale, and this combination of faunas in some cases permits fairly precise dating of the regional units. The Inanya and Khita Horizons are recognized within the Lower Ordovician; the Middle Ordovician contains the El'genchak, Mokrinsky, Darpirsky,[4] and most of the Kharkindzha Horizons; and in the Upper Ordovician the Iryuda Horizon (Iryudyskaya Formation of Obut, this volume) has been distinguished.

The Lower Ordovician is well known in the El'genchak Mountains, where type sections of both horizons are located. The Inanya Horizon is represented by calcareous siltstone, limestone, and calcareous-argillaceous shale as thick as 850 m. The fauna of the horizon, which is not abundant, includes *Clarkella calcifera* (Bill.), *Nanorthis hamburgensis elegenchatica* Orad., *Apatokephalus globosus* Tschug., and *Protopliomerops longus* Tschug. The Khita Horizon is composed almost exclusively of limestone up to 600 m thick. The faunal assemblage consists of *Finkelnburgia tscherskyi* Orad., *Nanorthis* sp. undet., *Hesperonomia fontinalis* (White), *Archaeorthis canadensis* Ulr. and Coop., *Tritoechia typica bona* Orad., *T. efimovae* Orad., *Tetralobula rugosa* Orad., *Syntrophia grande* Orad., *Apatokephalus globosus* Tschug., *Biolgina maximovae* Tschug., and others.

The Middle Ordovician has been studied in more detail in the El'genchak and Omulëvka Mountains. The El'genchak Horizon (lower) includes deposits of different facies with thicknesses which range from 270 to 1,000 m. The benthonic fauna which dates the horizon has

---

[4] The names for the Mokrinsky and Darpirsky Horizons are being revised; see manuscript by Obut in this volume.

been collected from the formation of the same name in the El'genchak Mountains. It contains *Orthidiella sienica* Orad., *Hesperonomia antelopensis* Coop., *Polytoechia russkaja* Orad., *Porambonites? ovalis* Orad., *Xenelasmella graciosa* Rozm., *Rhysostrophia occidentalis asiatica* Orad., *Onychoplecia* aff. *kindlei* Coop., *Eoroberia plana* Tschug., *Pliomera fischeri asiatica* Tschug., and others. Lower Llanvirnian graptolites were found in clastic-carbonate deposits of the El'genchak Horizon in the Omulëvka Mountains.

The Mokrinsky Horizon, equivalent to the Mokrinsky Formation in the Omulëvka Mountains, has conformable contacts with underlying deposits; its lower boundary was determined on the basis of appearance of new faunal assemblages. The horizon is composed of limestone, marlstone, shale, and siltstone containing the following brachiopods and ostracods: *Hesperorthis brachioporus* (Coop.), *Atelelasma peregrinum* (Adr.), *Opikina amara* (Andr.), *Strophomena simplex* Adr., *Soanella maslovi* (V. Ivan.), *S. rara* (V. Ivan.), and *Egorovella compacta* V. Ivan. The Lachug Formation in the El'genchak Mountains, the Volchinskaya Formation in Selennyakh Ridge, and the lower Issetenskaya Formation on the Chukotsk Peninsula correspond to the Mokrinsky Horizon.

The Darpirsky Horizon is a widespread Middle Ordovician subdivision in the northeastern USSR. The Krivun[5] and Darpirsky Formations of the northwestern Omulëvka Mountains, the Sonskiy Formation of the central Omulëvka Mountains, and the Kolychan Formation of Selennyakh Ridge are assigned to the horizon. Typical rocks of the Darpirsky Horizon are massive aphanic limestones containing abundant gastropods, trilobites, and crinoids in the Sonskiy Formation, and varied brachiopods in the Kolychan Formation. The total thickness of the horizon is 1,400 m.

The Kharkindzha Horizon lies conformably on limestone of the Darpirsky Horizon in places; at other locations the contact is tectonic. The horizon is composed of carbonate-clastic rocks 250–800 m thick yielding abundant Caradocian graptolites. The Kharkindzha Formation, which is widespread in the Omulëvka Mountains and can be traced in Tas-Khayakhtakh Ridge, is the type section of the horizon. The lower part of the horizon in the northwestern Omulëvka Mountains (Krivun Creek)

is characterized by lower Caradocian graptolites of the *Nemagraptus gracilis* (Hall.) and *Climacograptus peltifer* Lapw. Zones. In the Inanya basin (central Omulëvka Mountains), the lower part of the horizon is represented by carbonate rocks with *Plectorthis inanjensis* Orad., *Hesperorthis australis* Cooper, *Camarella oklachomensis* Orad., and other fossils. In the middle part of the horizon, graptolites of two zones, *Climacograptus wilsoni* and *Dicranograptus clingani*, were found. The uppermost beds of the Kharkindzha Horizon yield an Upper Ordovician fauna. The Middle-Upper Ordovician boundary is drawn within the horizon at the base of the *Rectograptus* ex gr. *truncatus* (Lapw.) beds.

Within the upper Kharkindzha Horizon and the Iryuda Horizon, the Upper Ordovician is considered to be represented by deposits of different facies. The Iryuda Horizon corresponds to the formation of the same name in the upper Yasachnaya River area and is represented by a 480-m sequence of gray coral limestone overlain by muddy shale containing graptolites of Ordovician and Silurian aspect. In the Omulëvka Mountains the Iryuda Horizon is represented by rhythmic alternation of limestone and graptolite shale; the Chegitun'skaya Formation in the Chukotsk Peninsula and the Nal'chanskaya Formation in the Selennyakh Ridge are equivalents of the horizon.

The Ordovician-Silurian boundary in the region is marked lithologically and may be drawn at the base of the *Akidograptus acuminatus* beds (graptolite facies) and at the top of the *Conchidium? unicum* A. Nik., *Calapoecia* sp., and *Catenipora admira* Prbz. beds (carbonate facies).

REFERENCES CITED

Andreyeva, O. N., 1959, Stratigrafiya ordovika Angaro-Okinskogo rayona: Mater. Vses. Nauchno-Issled. Geol. Inst. Trudy, new ser., no. 23, p. 79–108.

—— 1967, Nizhneordovikskiye otlozheniya severa Sibirskoy platformy: Vses. Nauchno-Issled. Geol. Inst. Trudy, new ser., v. 129, no. 3, p. 12–26.

Bondarev, V. I., 1960, Ordovik Sovetskoy Arktiki (The Ordovician System in the Soviet Arctic): 21st Internat. Geol. Cong., Doklady Sovet Geol., Probl. 7, p. 95–106.

—— et al., 1968, Ordovikskiye otlozheniya Taymyra: Nauchno-Issled. Inst. Geologii Arktiki, Uchenyye Zapiski, Paleont. i Biostrat., no. 24, p. 5–32.

—— A. Z. Bursky, and L. V. Nekhorosheva, 1968, A stratigraphical classification of the Ordovician of the Arctic regions of the Ural-Novaya Zemlya fold area and its correlation with Ordovician standards of North Europe: Czechoslovakia, 23rd Internat. Geol.

---

[5] Llandeilo graptolites were collected from the Krivun Formation.

Cong. Rept., Proc. Sec. 9, p. 85–95.

Chugayeva, M. N., and Kh. S. Rozman, 1969, K voprosu o raschlenenii ordovikskikh otlozheny Severo-
Vostoka SSSR: Mat. po Geol. i Polezn. Iskop. Yakutskoy ASSR, no. 13, p. 292–300.

—— —— and V. A. Ivanova, 1964, Sravnitelnaya
biostratigrafiya ordovikskikh otlozheny Severo-Vostoka SSSR: Akad. Nauk SSSR Geol. Inst. Trudy,
no. 106, p. 5–233.

Datsenko, V. A., 1968, Korrelyatsiya razrezov ordovika
severo-zapada Sibirskoy platformy, *in* Geologiya i
polezn. iskop. Norilskogo gornoprom. rayona:
Noril'sk, p. 28–32.

—— and N. P. Lazarenko, 1968, K voprosu o
verkhney granitse kembryskoy sistemy na severo-zapade Sibirskoy platformy: Nauchno-Issled. Inst.
Geologii Artktiki Trudy, v. 155, p. 109–113.

Mikutsky, S. P., 1967, Nizhny i sredny ordovik Sibirskoy platformy, *in* Stratigrafiya paleozoya Sredney
Sibiri: "Nauka," Sibirskoye Otd., p. 44–52.

Nikiforova, O. I., and O. N. Andreyeva, 1961, Stratigrafiya ordovika i silura Sibirskoy platformy i yeye
paleontologicheskoye obosnovaniye: Vses. Nauchno-
Issled. Geol. Inst. Trudy, new ser., v. 56, no. 1, p.
3–410.

Obut, A. M., and R. F. Sobolevskaya, 1962, Graptolity
rannego ordovika na Taymyre: Nauchno-Issled. Inst.

Geologii Arktiki, v. 127, no. 3, p. 65–96.

—— and —— 1964, Graptolity ordovika Taymyra: Izd. "Nauka," p. 3–92.

Oradovskaya, M. M., 1969, Skhema stratigrafii ordovika yugo-vostochnoy chasti Kolymskogo massiva:
Mat. po Geol. i Polezn. Iskop. Yakutskoy ASSR, no.
13, p. 355–360.

Polevoy Atlas Ordovikskoy Fauny Severo-Vostoka
SSSR, 1968: Magadanskoye Knizhn. Izdat., p. 3–
144.

Rozman, Kh. S., and Yu. M. Fomin, 1967, K biostratigrafii pozdneordovikskikh otlozheny basseyna r. Pod-
kememmaya Tunguska: Akad. Nauk SSSR, Izv. Ser.
Geol., no. 3, p. 92–104.

Rozova, A. V., and A. G. Yadrenkina, 1967, Biostratigrafiya i brakhiopody verkhnego kembriya i nizhnego ordovika razreza r. Kulyumbe (Sibirskaya
platforma), *in* Novyye dannyye po biostratigrafii
nizhnego paleozoya Sibirskoy platformy: Izd.
"Nauka," p. 12–44.

Tesakov, Yu. I., 1967, Verkhny ordovik i silur Sibirskoy platformy, *in* Stratigrafiya paleozoya Sredney
Sibiri: Izd. "Nauka," Sibirskoye Otd., p. 53–67.

Vysotsky, A. A., and O. N. Andreyeva, 1967, Razrez
ordovika na r. Kulyumbe (Sibirskaya platforma):
Vses. Nauchno-Issled. Geol. Inst. Trudy, v. 112, p.
68–82.

Tectonic Map of Earth's Polar Regions and Some Aspects of Comparative Analysis[1]

B. KH. EGIAZAROV, I. P. ATLASOV, M. G. RAVICH, G. E. GRIKUROV,
R. M. DEMENITSKAYA, G. Z. ZNACHKO-YAVORSKY, A. M. KARASIK,
YU. N. KULAKOV, A. P. PUMINOV, and B. S. ROMANOVICH[2]

Leningrad, USSR

Abstract The "Tectonic Map of the Polar Regions of the Earth" has been compiled on the scale 1:10,000,000, and structural regions have been distinguished on the basis of genesis and age. The map is accompanied by sketches of geotectonic zonation, neotectonic data, and geophysical characteristics reflecting deep features of the Arctic and Antarctic regions.

The North and South Polar regions have had different histories since Proterozoic time, and their deep-seated structures differ. The Arctic and Antarctic, although both are regions where the Pacific and Atlantic structural segments join, did not have similar geosynclinal and tectono-magmatic development.

In the Arctic, the stable Precambrian platform underwent fragmentation which gave rise to smaller platforms and central stable regions fringed by fold systems such as the Baykalides, Caledonides, Hercynides, and Mesozoides. The asymmetrical structure of the Arctic is evidenced by the differing degrees of stability of its western and eastern segments. The Antarctic, in contrast to the North Polar region, represents a heterogeneous pre-Riphean platform of a Gondwana type similar to the platforms of Africa, South America, Australia, and India. In West Antarctica the platform is fringed by the Antarctandes, which belong to the Pacific mobile belt. The Archean and Proterozoic magmatic complexes of the two Polar regions are almost the same type. The Antarctic is characterized by a widely developed charnockite formation.

The earth's crust in the Arctic is of complex structure and greatly varied thickness. In the Arctic basin, three areas may be distinguished: "normal ocean," transoceanic ridge area (Lomonosov and Mendeleyev-Alpha ridges), and the Canada basin. The Antarctic continent has mainly continental crust, but subcontinental crust is present at the West-East Antarctica juncture. The South Ocean is underlain by oceanic crust with some complications within the submarine ridges.

It is postulated that the thickness and crustal structure have changed abruptly in the Arctic during geologic history but were more stable in the Antarctic. The youngest tectonic event is marked by reactivation of structural features which determine the modern relief forms. Block movements are significant in the Antarctic. Besides these movements of opposite sense, a concentric distribution of the main structural features about the geographic poles is apparent in the polar regions.

INTRODUCTION

Long ago the geographic contrast between the earth's polar regions attracted the attention of researchers. The main problem is to determine whether these contrasts are the reflection of the modern phase of the earth's evolution or whether they have resulted from the factors associated with the geotectonics of the Arctic and Antarctic regions. Consideration of this problem raises questions concerning polar wandering in some geologic periods, stability of the Antarctic platform and its relation to other Gondwana continents, and the evolution of geosynclinal systems of the Arctic regions and their relations to the Pacific and the Atlantic geosynclinal systems. The best method for investigating these questions seems to be a comparative analysis of the tectonics and deep-seated structure of the earth's polar regions, but only some of the questions can be solved by this approach. In this connection we have compiled the "Tectonic Map of the Polar Regions of the Earth"[3] on the scale 1:10,000,000 (in 4 sheets) with equal-azimuth Lambert projections, a general legend, and a tectonic history. Oceanic, continental, and intermediate structures, as characterized by the corresponding crustal types, are shown on the polar tectonic map. The structures are shown at the various stages of development. Ages are indicated for continental structural features. The tectonic subdivisions of the Arctic and Antarctic, those of the deep crust, the seismic and other physical features of the upper mantle, and other geophysical data are given on special inset maps at scales of 1:25,000,000 and 1:50,000,000. Recent continental and oceanic structures are shown on the neotectonic maps of the Arctic (1:25,000,000) and Antarctic (1:40,000,000). In the general legend, these structures are assigned to structural regions on the basis of the direction and intensity of the most recent tectonic movements. This article deals only with the main problems of the comparative analysis of polar-region tectonics.

The Arctic and Antarctic regions are located

[1] Manuscript received, August 1, 1972.

[2] Research Institute of the Geology of the Arctic.

[3] Egiazarov, B. Kh., et al., 1971, Tectonic map of the polar regions of the earth: Leningrad, Research Institute of the Geology of the Arctic.

317

at the structural juncture of the Altantic and Pacific crustal segments. However, during a considerable part of the history of their development, the character of the tectonic-element juncture as well as some features of the tectono-magmatic processes were different in the Arctic and the Antarctic.

ARCTIC REGION

Continental Structures

Both continental and oceanic structures are widespread in the North Polar region. The continental structures are represented by several groups of tectonic elements, indicated below in reverse order of the stages of development of the earth's crust.

The young fold systems are absent in the area studied. However, a Cenozoic system—the Olyutorskiy–East Kamchatka fold system—is situated close to the continental-oceanic boundary, and its development is associated with the Arctic tectogenesis.

The fold systems in the postgeosynclinal stage of development (areas of completed folding) include the Baykalides (Carolinides) of East and North Greenland and Ellesmere Island; the Caledonides of Norway, Severnaya Zemlya, Spitsbergen, East Greenland, and Cornwallis and Axel Heiberg Islands, and the supposed Caledonides beneath the Barents and Beaufort Seas; the Hercynides of the Urals, Novaya Zemlya, Taymyr, and northern Canada; and the Mesozoides of the Verkhoyansk-Chukotsk area and Alaska.

Older fold systems that have undergone postgeosynclinal development form the platform basement. They are exposed as the Baltic, Canadian, and Greenland shields and as the smaller Timan projection and the East Spitsbergen, Anabar, East Kara, and Anadyr'-Seward massifs. The formation of the plates—the volcanic-sedimentary covers overlying the fold structures—is associated with the evolution of these fold systems. According to basement ages, the plates are divided into pre-Baykalian, Baykalian, and post-Baykalian. In the Arctic the pre-Baykalian category is represented by the Russian, East Siberian, North American, and Hyperborean plates. The Pechora plate is of Baykalian age. The Barents-Kara and West Siberian plates are post-Baykalian, and the submarine Lomonosov and Mendeleyev Ridges and the Alpha plateau must be synchronous.

Between the postgeosynclinal areas are the plates represented by the Cis-Urals, Cis-No-vaya Zemlya, Cis-Verkhoyansk, and North American foredeeps. The Cis-Taymyrian foothills trough and the pericratonic Peary-Ellesmere trough belong to the same group.

A special group of structures is represented by the parageosynclinal depressions located completely or partially on the craton and on the other types of stable regions. These depressions, characterizing one of the last stages of the development of the continental structures, are located on land in places where the crust is relatively thin and on the Arctic shelf. According to the age of the basement folding, the pre-Baykalian (in the Kolyma, Omolon, and Anadyr'-Seward stable regions, and in the block of the Laptev Sea) and the post-Baykalian (Sverdrup, North Siberian, Novosibirsk, and East Siberian Sea) depressions may be distinguished.

Oceanic Structures

In the Arctic the oceanic structures are represented (in order of their formation) by the Nansen, Amundsen, Greenland, Lofoten (Norway), North Iceland, and Canada oceanic basins; the Greenland-Iceland and Marvin oceanic trenches; and the midoceanic volcano-tectonic ridges, including the Arctic (Gakkel), Knipovich, and Mohn rift zones. The oceanic basins are bordered by extensive zones of deep-seated faults. In addition to the tectonic elements listed above, a wide zone of tectono-magmatic activization, manifested between the continental and oceanic structures, is shown on the map. This zone is marked by volcanic flows of acidic, intermediate, and mixed composition which compose the lower layer of the Okhotsk-Chukotsk volcanic belt, and by plateau basalts which form the upper layer of the same belt as well as the Transarctic volcanic belt.

The Arctic and Subarctic fold systems, which differ in history of development, morphostructures, and formational complexes, make up Arctides, Arcto-Atlantides, Pacifides, and Arcto-Pacifides. The Paleozoides and Mesozoides which border the fragments of the Hyperborean platform belong to the Arctides, whereas the Caledonides which surround the Eria platform and the Barents massif, as well as the Hercynides of Novaya Zemlya, are considered to be part of the Arcto-Atlantides. Part of the Pacifides is represented by the Mesozoides and Cenozoides of the northern Pacific areas, located on the margin of the Pacific thalasso-craton. The Kolyma megablock (Yana-Kolyma region), located between the Arctides and Pacifides proper, is related hypothetically to the Arcto-Pacifides.

ANTARCTIC REGION

The Antarctic is mainly a heterogeneous Epibaykalian (Epirossian) platform of the Gondwana type, which is similar in its structure and history of development to the platform areas of Australia, South America, Africa, and India. The Mesozoides of the South American Andes, composing the Pacific mobile belt, are present only in West Antarctica, especially within the Antarctic Peninsula.

The pre–late Proterozoic stabilization of the Antarctic continental crust was completed by formation of the crystalline basement, which is the projection of the ancient pan-Antarctic platform. In late Proterozoic time, this platform broke into several large stable fragments— geoblocks—which were characterized by platform conditions during the ensuing continental history (including the Holocene) and in which the typical features of the ancient platforms are preserved.

In late Proterozoic time, an activization of the crystalline basement occurred in the zones between the blocks. This basement, which was downwarped, served as the basement for Riphean geosynclinal belts. In East Antarctica, as well as in the greater part of West Antarctica, these Riphean belts formed the intracratonic belts, whereas the late Proterozoic geosynclinal belt of the Antarctic Peninsula was apparently already a part of the Pacific mobile belt. Another variety of mobile region of the crystalline basement is represented by mountains similar to those of Queen Maud Land (Dronning Maud Land), which underwent repeated uplift in the Proterozoic. The older rheomorphic charnockite intrusions, as well as the younger and more scarce granitic intrusions, are associated with this area.

In mobile areas, the late Proterozoic regeneration of the crystalline basement probably became more intense with time and culminated by early Paleozoic time, i.e., in the Rossian (Baykalian) tectonic epoch. The Rossian orogeny, specifically the folding that climaxed it at the end of the Precambrian, was the last event which affected the whole continent and transformed its greater part into the completely stabilized folded basement of the Antarctic platform.

In the Pacific coastal area of West Antarctica, the Rossian folding apparently did not terminate in late Proterozoic time; geosynclinal

development seems to have proceeded in separate zones at different times. During middle-late Paleozoic time, geosynclinal volcanic and sedimentary formations accumulated on the Rossian basement and were later subjected to folding during Triassic–Early Jurassic time. Since Devonian time, deformation of a typical Gondwana platform cover has led to the enlargement of the older platform complexes. These complexes developed within the stable geoblocks of the post–middle Proterozoic "panplatform." The early Mesozoic folding of the Antarctandes (Antarctic extension of the Andean chain) on the Antarctic platform resulted in intensive trap magmatism.

After Middle Jurassic time, the late Mesozoic evolution of the Antarctandes corresponded to the orogenic stage of development of the fold system. The most intense orogeny and the accompanying granitic magmatism occured at the transition from Early to Late Cretaceous time and in the middle Paleogene. The Neogene-Quaternary history of the Pacific coastal part of Antarctica has been characterized by extensive marginal belts of basaltic and alkalic volcanism; eruptions have been associated with markedly differentiated block movements and rifting.

The neotectonic activization of the Antarctic platform is manifested mainly in areas which were formerly subjected in some manner to the Rossian orogeny and which were abruptly uplifted to form the higher modern epiplatform mountain systems. The stable-platform geoblocks have preserved the appearance of plains or have experienced isostatic subsidence near the neotectonic epiplatform orogens.

The Antarctandes may be considered as a part of the Pacific segment, but their main folding phase (early Mesozoic) was not synchronous with that of the typical Mesozoides of the Pacific mobile belt. They also differ from the typical Pacific Mesozoides by the great time span of their orogenic development. The most important tectonic events of the western and eastern parts of the Pacific belt (Nevadan and Laramide orogenies of the North American Cordillera; the Andean folding, the "Rangitata orogenesis" of New Zealand; and orogenic episodes of other parts of the Circum-Pacific belt, including the Antarctandes) are comparable in age to events which took place within the Circum-Pacific Mesozoic geosynclines.

Comparison of the Antarctic platform to other Gondwana platforms of the Atlantic segment reveals a common disparity in time of stabilization of different parts of the folded basement. This disparity results from the general tectonic heterogeneity of its structural framework, which has, to a great extent, been inherited from the ancient pre-Riphean framework of the crystalline basement. The formation of the basement was caused by the same general conditions which now are established for the tectonic evolution of the granitic-metamorphic crustal layer on the other continents. In the Antarctic this layer was subjected to very deep erosional truncation as a result of great uplifts of the crystalline basement in late Proterozoic and succeeding time.

Magmatic Activity

Magmatic activity in Antarctica is similar to the magmatism of other Gondwana platforms of the Southern Hemisphere. Formation in Antarctica of the world's greatest charnockite province during the Archean and Proterozoic is considered to be an established fact. However, the oldest valid isotopic age determination for magmatic rocks in the South Polar area is 2,000 m.y., whereas, in the Arctic territory, the presence of the oldest magmatic bodies in the earth's crust (3,500 m.y.) is definitely established.

In upper Proterozoic rocks of the Arctic, diverse intrusive activity is manifested by the large plutons of alkalic rocks (Gremyachka-Vyrmes, Gardar), rapakivi granites, *etc*. In the Antarctic the synchronous intrusive complex is represented by granitic rocks exclusively. An extensive development of upper Proterozoic volcanic rocks in western Queen Maud Land is characteristic of the Antarctic platform. During early Paleozoic time, magmatism in the Arctic was characterized by a wide range of composition (from alkaline granitic to ultramafic rocks) and by great extent, mainly in the Atlantic structural blocks. In Antarctica the only igneous rocks are granodiorites and granites, except in the Atlantic (Gondwana) segment, where granite-syenites also occur. At the time of the Hercynian orogeny, magmatic activity in the Arctic was diverse in composition and form. Small syenitic intrusions were formed in Antarctica (Queen Maud Land) during the same time. Significant in the structure of both the polar regions is the global Triassic-Jurassic formation of trap rocks. In the Cretaceous and Paleogene, extrusive magmatism was prevalent in the Arctic as a result of the activization of the marginal parts of the North American and Eurasian continents. Mesozoic geosynclinal magmatism in circumpolar parts of the Pacific belt was characterized both by similar composition and by contemporaneity of igneous activity. However, magmatism in the Antarctic areas appears to have been more intense.

In late Cenozoic time the Antarctic volcanic belt was formed in West Antarctica. According to the character of volcanism, this belt may, to some extent, be comparable to the Asiatic volcanic belt, but it differs from the latter in age and extent.

Geophysical Data

The contrast between the earth's polar regions is reflected both in the crustal structure and in geophysical differences between the Arctic and Antarctic. With respect to the thickness of the crust, the Antarctic continent may be clearly subdivided into West and East Antarctica. In West Antarctica the crustal thickness ranges from 20 to 50 km, and almost all of the thicker values are in the northern part of the area. In East Antarctica the range of crustal thickness is 35–50 km. In East Antarctica the crust is uniform and has an average thickness of 40 km, whereas in West Antarctica it is less uniform and has an average thickness of 45 km.

The Lomonosov submarine ridge divides the abyssal part of the Arctic Ocean into two basins—the Eurasian and Amerasian—which antipodally correspond to the divisions of the Antarctic Ocean. On the unusually wide shelf of Eurasia the crustal thickness seems to be almost normal for continents. According to geophysical and geomorphologic data, the crustal structure of the Eurasian basin may be supposed to be similar to that of the Atlantic Ocean basin; however, in the Amerasian (Canada) basin, suboceanic and, probably, subcontinental crust occur together with oceanic crust. The crust of the Eurasian basin may have been formed by the process of spreading from the basin axis.

According to data from the study of the regularly banded magnetic field of the Eurasian basin, the actual rate of sea-floor movement is determined as 1 cm/year. The basin is divided into deep-water basins by the aseismic Lomonosov and Mendeleyev-Alpha rises. Most of the the basin is characterized by a heterogeneous magnetic field, which exceeds by several times the intensity of the Eurasian-basin magnetic anomalies. The mosaic and poorly regulated character of the magnetic field shows that complex deformation and faulting have occurred in the Amerasian basin. The bridge of continental crust which separates the Arctic Ocean basin from the Pacific Ocean basin suggests independent development of the Amerasian basin.

The Antarctic magnetic-field structure of West Antarctica indicates magnetic and, most likely, petrologic heterogeneity of the platform basement, as well as a complicated tectonic history. The magnetic anomalies of West Antarctica are consistent with the idea of extensive recent volcanism, indicating that the magnetic products of the latter reach the surface of the bedrock.

The earth's polar regions are also very different seismically. The Antarctic is practically aseismic, but several seismic zones of various nature are found in the Arctic. The narrow linear Arctic belt with shallow earthquake foci which forms the Arctic extension of the oceanic rift system is confined to the rift zone and to transform faults of the Gakkel midoceanic ridge. Several earthquake epicenters in the Barents Sea may indicate the influence of Atlantic rifting on the northern European continental margin.

The zone of scattered earthquake epicenters on the southern extension of the Arctic seismic belt is thought to be related to the hypothetical continental extension of the Gakkel Ridge. Several epicenters extend into the margin of the Arctic Ocean from the Alaskan zone of deep-foci earthquakes.

Thus, seismic evidence indicates that Antarctica belongs to one lithospheric geoblock, whereas the Arctic is divided into two parts—belonging to different geoblocks—by the axis of the Gakkel midoceanic ridge.

NEOTECTONIC HISTORY

The modern stage of tectonic development has been marked by the activization of structural elements, including ancient stable areas. This tectonism has determined the main topographic features of the earth's polar regions. The locations of the main vertical movements are shown on the neotectonic maps. The following structural areas have been distinguished: platform areas (continental and oceanic), orogenic areas (epiplatform continental and oceanic areas, epigeosynclinal areas), modern geosynclines, and rift zones. Crustal tension appears to account for movement in these zones.

Modern structural movements have created considerable contrast between the earth's polar regions, primarily by heterogeneous movement in circumpolar regions (mainly subsidence in the Arctic and uplift in the Antarctic) and by displacement along the concentric (relative to geographic poles) fault zones marked by the continental slope.

CONCLUSIONS

Preliminary analysis of the "Tectonic Map of the Polar Regions of the Earth" suggests several conclusions concerning structural and historical features.

1. During Archean–early Proterozoic time in the polar regions, pan-Arctic and pan-Antarctic platforms formed part of a global set of ancient cratons.

2. The Arctic area is characterized by diverse geosynclinal processes, which have resulted in the formation of the Baykalides, Caledonides, Hercynides, and Mesozoides as the geosynclinal environments migrated from Atlantic to Pacific segments, causing subsequent rejuvenation of the fold systems. The Arctic mobile belt (Arctides) and transitional areas, *i.e.,* the Arcto-Atlantides and Arcto-Pacifides, seem to be independent structural systems located at the juncture between the Atlantic and Pacific segments. As a result of crustal evolution in the Arctic, the ancient stable elements (plates and central stable regions) were fragmented and were bordered by fold systems and zones of different degrees of stability.

3. Only the Rossides, which in mode of formation are related to the late Baykalides, occur in East and partially in West Antarctica (in the Atlantic segment). Throughout most of the Phanerozoic, this part of the Antarctic, in contrast to the North Polar region, remained a platform and was part of the Gondwana area of the southern hemisphere. The Mesozoic orogeny of Antarctica was manifested only in West Antarctica and resulted in the formation of the Antarctandes, the features of which are characteristic of the Andean geosynclinal system of the Pacific mobile belt.

4. The northern and southern polar regions differ by the nature, intensity, and time of magmatic activity. Charnockite intrusions are widely distributed, permitting recognition of the conspicuous Antarctic charnockite province. Triassic-Jurassic trap magmatism has been clearly manifested in both areas.

5. The crust in the Arctic is of intricately differentiated structure and is considerably varied in thickness. Continental crust is present on land areas and on the shelf, and oceanic and subcontinental crust are present in the Arctic

basin and in the circumpolar part of the Atlantic Ocean. In the latter area it is possible to trace the zones of magmatic activization, the oceanic depressions and trenches, the rift zones of midoceanic rises, and also the submarine block ridges with reduced crust thickness and a "granitic" layer. In the Antarctic the crust is mainly continental and has a great range in thickness. Subcontinental crust is present only in the areas of juncture of the East and West Antarctic structures, and oceanic crust, with some complications within submarine ridges, is present in the South Ocean. There is evidence to suggest that the depth and the structure of the crust in the Arctic have undergone considerable changes in the course of geologic history, whereas in the Antarctic the crust has been more stable. Several seismic zones are present in the Arctic, but the Antarctic is almost aseismic.

6. The contrasting development of the polar regions, which has existed since Proterozoic time, is emphasized not only by their modern structure, but also by the differing character and intensity of the latest tectonic movements. Subsidence is prevalent in the Arctic, and uplift is characteristic in the Antarctic.

If we consider that these features originated during Mesozoic time, it seems doubtful that considerable polar migration has occurred since the late Mesozoic.

Main Tectonic Features of North Pacific Mobile Belt[1]

B. KH. EGIAZAROV,[2] B. V. ERMAKOV,[2] V. A. VAKAR,[2] N. G. ZAGORSKAYA,[2]
G. I. KAMENEVA,[2] T. N. KOPYLOVA,[2] E. M. LITVINOV,[2] G. K. PICHUGINA,[2]
N. P. ANIKEYEV,[3] I. E. DRABKIN,[3] V. A. TITOV,[3] D. E. GERSHANOVICH,[4]
M. I. ITSIKSON,[5] and V. I. BERGER[5]

Leningrad and Magadan, USSR

Abstract The Koryak-Kamchatka-Kuril and Alaska-Aleutian areas form the northern part of the Pacific mobile belt (Pacifides). The Koryak-Kamchatka-Kuril system represents the polycyclic migration areas of eu- and miogeosynclinal style of development and the general migration of geosynclinal systems (Mesozoides, Cenozoides, modern Kuril geosyncline) in a southeast direction from the continent to the ocean. This migration is emphasized by a system of reentrant angles formed by the intersection of zones of deep-seated faults which border the geosynclines. The bisectors of the reentrant angles show the general direction of migration of the geosynclinal processes which occurred along and across the general trend of the area.

The Alaska-Aleutian area represents the polycyclic type of eu- and miogeosynclinal development. The migration of the geosynclinal processes occurred along the Cordilleran belt (early Mesozoides, late Mesozoides, modern Aleutian geosyncline). The fact that geosynclinal formations synchronous to the Cenozoides of the Olyutorskiy–East Kamchatka system are absent in Alaska reflects the asymmetric structure of the northern part of the Pacifides. The character of the junction of the Aleutian arc with the Kamchatka Cenozoides (through the Komandorskiy Islands) in the west and with the Alaska Mesozoides in the east also shows the asymmetry. The development of the geosynclinal systems of the northern part of the eastern Asian–coastal Pacific zones are mainly associated with tensional tectonic movements. Systems of North America have compressional movements. This fact is confirmed by the structural-formational and tectonic-magmatic features of the development of the geosynclinal systems of the northern part of the Pacific belt.

The fold systems of the adjoining areas of the Arctic mobile belt (Arctides)—North Alaska and Novosibirsk-Chukotsk—join the Pacifides along the zone of the Mackenzie-Lena deep-seated faults. The systems are characterized by monocyclic and miogeosynclinal types of development.

The metallogenic character of the Pacifides and adjoining Arctides is one of diverse late Mesozoic and Cenozoic ores (gold, mercury, copper, and polymetals, and tin and tungsten—in the Arctides especially); low-temperature ores prevail. It may be assumed that the possible oil and gas basins of Arctic Canada, North Alaska, the Chukotsk Peninsula, and the Chukchi and East Siberian Seas compose a single hydrocarbon belt timed tectonically to the Arctides. The existence of a North Pacific belt of oil and gas accumulations, including the oil and gas basins of the Kamchatka-Koryak and the Cordilleran-Alaska areas, is also assumed.

[1] Manuscript received, August 1, 1972.

[2] Research Institute of the Geology of the Arctic, Leningrad.

[3] Northeastern Regional Geological Office, Magadan.

[4] All Union Institute of Fishery and Oceanology, Leningrad.

[5] All Union Research Geology Institute, Leningrad.

The Koryak-Kamchatka-Kuril and Alaska-Aleutian areas constitute the North Pacific mobile belt. Fold systems of the Arctic mobile belt (North Alaskan and Novosibirsk-Chukotsk regions) form a part of the Amerasian segment of the Arctides and join the Pacifides along the Mackenzie-Lena fracture zone. Problems concerning the recognition of the Arctides and the Pacifides, as well as transitional areas such as the Arcto-Pacifides and the Arcto-Atlantides, have been discussed in previous papers (Egiazarov, 1969; Egiazarov and Kameneva, 1970; Berger and Itsikson, 1972). Herein, we shall discuss the most important evolutionary features of the geosynclinal system of the North Pacific area and adjacent Arctic territories on the basis of formational, tectonic, magmatic, and mineralogic-genetic correlations.

In regard to the types of deposits and the stages of geosynclinal development, we follow the divisions of Shatsky (1965, p. 175–991), Kheraskov (1967, p. 317–321, 375–400), and Khain (1964). Two periods, geosynclinal and postgeosynclinal, are distinguished in the development of a complete fold area. The geosynclinal period is subdivided into a geosynclinal and an orogenic stage.

In general, the four steps which are recognized for geosynclinal periods are early, middle, late, and final. The first two of these steps correspond to the main geosynclinal stage, and the third and fourth belong to the orogenic stage. Ancient complexes of gneisses and schists are considered to be protogeosynclinal complexes of pre-Paleozoic basement in the Mesozoides and Cenozoides.

There are two main geosynclinal cycles in the structural history of the Koryak–West Kamchatka system—the Paleozoic–early Mesozoic and the late Mesozoic–Cenozoic cycles. In the Paleozoic–early Mesozoic cycle, only early and middle stages, characterized by the Penzhino (miogeosynclinal) and Pikaswayama (eugeosynclinal) zones, are present. In the first zone the beginning of the geosynclinal cycle is assigned to the Late Ordovician and the second zone is assigned to the Late Silurian. The end of the geosynclinal cycle in both zones can be dated as Late Jurassic. The vertical sequence of formations in the Pikaswayama zone is characterized by volcanic-siliceous rocks (middle-upper Paleozoic) and graywacke (Triassic–Middle Jurassic). Formations within the Penzhino zone are the following: slate (Ordovician-Silurian), an incomplete volcanic-siliceous sequence (Middle Devonian), and graywacke (Carboniferous–Middle Jurassic). These rocks correspond to the early and middle stages of the geosynclinal cycle. Manifestations of pre-Jurassic folding are evident in the early Mesozoides structures. The Paleozoic–early Mesozoic geosyncline did not undergo all the common stages of geosynclinal development; thus, it is "incomplete" (Kheraskov, 1967). Structures of the cycle are considered as early Mesozoic (the early Koryakides).

The late Mesozoic–Cenozoic geosynclinal cycle of the Koryak-West Kamchatka fold system is characterized by a complete geosynclinal sequence. Different zones, within which age ranges vary somewhat, are characterized by slate and volcanic-siliceous formations (Late Jurassic–Valanginian), graywacke (Hauterivian-Barremian), andesitic rocks (Hauterivian), flysch (Aptian-Turonian and, in places, Barremian–early Cenomanian), lower molasse strata (Cenomanian, Senonian-Eocene), and upper molasse strata (Paleogene–early Neogene). These units correspond to main geosynclinal and orogenic stages. The postgeosynclinal period was marked by the accumulation of terrestrial-volcanic formations (late Neogene-early Quaternary) and, in late Cenozoic depressions, unconsolidated deposits.

Analysis of the available data suggests the following conclusions concerning the late Mesozoic–Cenozoic Koryak–West Kamchatka geosynclinal system. (1) The system is characterized by complete development. During Late Jurassic–late Cenozoic time, after all stages of geosynclinal development had been completed, it became a consolidated mountain fold system. (2) In contrast to the early Koryakides geosynclinal cycle, the earliest stage (Late Jurassic–Valanginian) of the later Koryakides geosynclinal cycle was of shorter duration and resulted in a comparatively thin volcanic-siliceous sequence. (3) Deposition of the lower molasse beds was approximately coeval (beginning of Late Cretaceous) with the deformation stage of the Koryak–West Kamchatka system. (4) There was almost ubiquitous manifestation of the folding phase, which marked the completion of the early orogenic epoch and the general attenuation of geosynclinal processes at the end of the Late Cretaceous–early Paleogene. Until that time the main features of the fold system were synchronous in time of formation to the North American Laramides. A widespread upper molasse complex is indicative of the final stage of development of the geosynclinal system. (5) Peculiar orogenic magmatism was represented mainly by intrusions (subbatholitic granodiorite intrusions) within the Okhotsk-Chukotsk volcanic belt. (6) Almost synchronous with formation of the Cenozoides of the Olyutorskiy–East Kamchatka system was the formation of a late Pliocene–early Quaternary subformation of plateau basalts and plateau andesites. Thus, peneplanation of the geotectonic area and, at the end of the geosynclinal cycle, complete transformation of almost the entire Koryak-Kamchatka fold area into a system of consolidated structures are indicated.

On the basis of the age of folding of the youngest strata of the lower molasse sequence, the Koryak–West Kamchatka system is assigned to the late Mesozoides. It is suggested that this structural system be recognized as a separate tectonotype named the "late Koryakides." The early and late Mesozoides correspond to two geosynclinal cycles and may be united under a common name, the Koryakides, where referring to the whole Koryak–West Kamchatka system as a single tectonic unit.

Formational analysis allows the recognition of several peculiar features of the early Mesozoides of the South Alaskan fold system. These peculiarities are reflected in: (1) duration (early Paleozoic–Middle Triassic and, in places, early Paleozoic–Jurassic) of the early stage of the geosynclinal cycle; (2) the presence of widespread, thick volcanic-siliceous and carbonate formations; (3) short duration (Late Triassic and, in places, Early Jurassic) of the middle stage; (4) small thicknesses of graywacke and limestone formations; and (5) distinct manifestations of the Nevadan folding phases and the accompanying formation of Jurassic molasse complexes and granitoid intrusions. As in the Koryak–West Kamchatka system, a protogeosynclinal complex of early Mesozoides basement is established in the South Alaskan fold system.

The late Mesozoic–Cenozoic cycle of the late Mesozoides of the South Alaskan system is characterized by: (1) short duration of an early stage (Late Jurassic–Valanginian), (2) an incomplete formational sequence, (3) absence of a record of the middle stage of development in the vertical sequence of formations,

(4) intense granitic magmatism (forming batholiths) during an Early Cretaceous hiatus, (5) a prolonged early orogenic stage during which a thick lower molasse section was formed, (6) distinct manifestations of Laramide movements and Late Cretaceous intrusive magmatism, and (7) considerable late Cenozoic terrestrial volcanism, marking a transition of the South Alaskan system into the postgeosynclinal period. On the basis of their development, the Mesozoides of the South Alaskan system are properly distinguished as a separate tectonotype which may be termed the "Alaskides."

Unlike fold systems of the North Pacific belt, the Arctic Mesozoides of the North Alaskan and eastern part of the Novosibirsk-Chukotsk system are characterized by a completely miogeosynclinal sedimentary environment, absence of repetition of the same type of formations in vertical series, widespread Late Jurassic–Early Cretaceous deposits, and Cretaceous and Paleogene-Neogene molasse complexes which fill the Colville, Umiat, and Chukchi basins. In development, sedimentary environment, mode of magmatism, and general structural framework, the Mesozoides of the Arctic belt differ greatly from the Mesozoides of the North Pacific area.

The Olyutorskiy–East Kamchatka fold system underwent all the stages of the geosynclinal cycle within a relatively short period of time (Late Cretaceous–Cenozoic); during the transitional period from Neogene to Quaternary time, it developed into a mountain fold system. In the vertical sequence of formations there are slates (Coniacian-Campanian and, in places, up to Eocene, inclusive), siliceous-volcanic rocks (Santonian-Paleogene), flysch with flyschoid and tuffaceous flysch subformations (Maestrichtian, Danian, Oligocene), andesite (Oligocene–early Miocene), lower molasse strata (Paleogene, Miocene), upper molasse strata (late Miocene, Pliocene), and terrestrial-volcanic rocks (late Pliocene, Pleistocene). A change of age ranges of formational complexes implies a migration of tectono-sedimentary processes in time and space.

Formational analyses establish the following relations concerning the Cenozoic development of the Olyutorskiy–East Kamchatka system: (1) short duration of the geosynclinal cycle (Late Cretaceous–Cenozoic) and complete formational series which correspond to all stages of development of the system; (2) thick volcanic-siliceous formations (up to 11,000 m), which accumulated only during Late Cre-

taceous time, implying considerable downwarping and high rates of sedimentation during the early stage of the geosynclinal cycle; (3) relatively short duration (Paleogene–early Miocene) of the middle stage; (4) great thickness (up to 8,500 m) and diversity of formational composition, implying mobility of sedimentary environments and presence of different tectono-sedimentary environments in different parts of the Olyutorskiy–East Kamchatka system; (5) short duration (middle-late or only late Miocene) of the late stage and great thicknesses (3,000–10,000 m) of lower molasse complexes, with only insignificant amounts of intrusive magmatism; and (6) clear manifestations of terrestrial volcanism. On the basis of the age of strata belonging to the lower molasse sequence (late Miocene), the Olyutorskiy–East Kamchatka system is related to Cenozoic folding. It is suggested that structures of the Olyutorskiy–East Kamchatka system be considered as a separate tectonotype termed the "Kamchatides."

Peculiar features of the modern structural framework of the Koryakides of the northern Koryak–West Kamchatka fold system are as follows: (1) linearity and great extent of main structural elements, *i.e.,* anticlinoriums, synclinoriums, and troughs; (2) persistence of general northeast strike of structures and bifurcation into two branches—southeast and north-northwest—which are affected by the western Anadyr'-Seward stable region; (3) development of two main northeast- and northwest-striking fault systems, reflecting the orientation of regional fracture zones which delineate the northern Koryak–West Kamchatka system (Intersection of the fracture zones north of the region discussed forms a reentrant angle of the system.); (4) ancient fractures that are significant in controlling the location of later tectonic and magmatic activity; (5) confinement of granitoid intrusions to marginal parts of the fold system and to the junction zone with the Okhotsk-Chukotsk volcanic belt; and (6) confinement of volcano-tectonic uplifts to areas of deep-seated faults in the northwest, governing the formation of the structural framework, separation of late Mesozoic–early Cenozoic troughs, and formation of late Cenozoic basins and depression.

The Kamchatides of the Olyutorskiy–East Kamchatka fold system occupy the southeastern part of the Koryak-Kamchatka area. This relation reflects the migration of the late Mesozoic-Cenozoic geosyncline from the continent toward the ocean. The modern framework of the Kamchatides is a combination of linear and brachyform structures, volcano-tectonic uplifts, and late Cenozoic depressions. Major linear structures which have a northeast strike in the Kamchatides gradually curve toward the southeast and become the structural framework of the Koryakides. Areal position of the structures was also influenced by such fracture zones as the Parapol'skiy, Ukelayat, Vivnik, and Karaginskiy-Pakhacha. As in the Koryakides, there are structures of a postgeosynclinal period— i.e., volcano-tectonic uplifts and a late Cenozoic depression filled with unconsolidated sediments.

The structural framework of the Kamchatides shows the following characteristics. (1) The main structural elements are linear, and arclike northeast- and northwest-curving deep-seated faults form an outer border of the Kamchatides system. Intersection of these faults forms a reentrant angle in the late Mesozoic–Cenozoic Olyutorskiy–East Kamchatka system. (2) the Il'pinskiy, Karaginskiy-Pakhacha, and Pylgovayam faults are subordinate to the Vivnik fault; their tectonic control is reflected in the change of dimension and orientation of structures in the inner part of the Olyutorskiy trough. (3) Relatively small basins are filled by an orogenic molasse complex. (4) Insignificant orogenic magmatism produced small granodiorite-diorite intrusions. (5) Approximately synchronous formation of volcano-tectonic uplifts in the Kamchatides and in the Koryakides area indicates close similarity of tectonic environments during the final stages of their development.

Vertical repetition of formations of the same lithology but different age, as well as successive lateral migration of geosynclinal systems (Mesozoides-Cenozoides, and the modern geosyncline), suggests that the Koryak-Kamchatka-Kuril area has had a polycyclic migration history with eu- and miogeosynclinal modes of development. This successive migration from continent toward ocean is stressed by systems of reentrant angles formed by interaction of fracture zones which mark the outer limits of geosynclinal troughs.

The bisector of the angles, we suggest, shows the general direction of migration of geosynclinal processes which occurred both along and across the general strike of the Koryak-Kamchatka-Kuril area. A generally southeast migration of the Koryak-Kamchatka-Kuril geosynclinal system is supported also by changes in

thickness of the earth's crust in the same direction.

The Koryak-Kamchatka fold area, which is especially exemplified by the Koryak Range, is characterized by a threefold (middle–late Paleozoic, Late Jurassic–Early Cretaceous, and Late Cretaceous) manifestation of mafic-ultramafic intrusive magmatism, pronounced extrusive activity at different stages of fold-system development, and small-scale granitoid magmatism. These factors, taken together, suggest that the development of the Koryak-Kamchatka fold area is related mainly to tectonic movements of a compressional type which caused extensive faulting and a peculiar type of magmatism.

It is noteworthy to consider the following observations. Along the projection of the reentrant-angle bisector of the Koryakides into the Pekul'ney anticlinorium, numerous ultramafic-mafic intrusions are located along a fracture zone. Along the projection of the reentrant-angle bisector of the Kamchatides, the volcano-tectonic Shirshov uplift has been formed with submarine volcanoes confined to its fault-bounded southwest side. Furthermore, the bisector of the reentrant angle of the modern Aleutian-Komandorskiye and Kuril-Kamchatka geosynclines is the site of the Obruchev uplift (Emperor Seamount Chain) and of the Hawaiian submarine volcanic ridge. Such physiographic and magmatic similarities do not appear to be accidental. Apparently, the association is indicative of a certain regular relation which is reflected in the fact that reentrant-angle bisectors correspond to extension-zone directions. Such extensional movements are, in general, characteristic of the northern part of the East Asiatic–Pacific area throughout geologic history.

The general structural framework, position, and configuration of some folded branches of the Koryak-Kamchatka area were predetermined by the presence of the Okhotsk, mid-Kamchatka, Anadry'-Seward, and Taygonos stable regions. The structural framework of the Kamchatides is subordinate to that of the Koryakides. In the northeast, the Kamchatides stretch along the Bering shelf and, being truncated at faults of the continental slope, do not continue to southwest Alaska.

The South Alaskan system is characterized by a twofold repetition of units of the same lithology but different age which represent the early and late stages of two geosynclinal cycles; however, this system shows no fold-zone migration toward the Pacific Ocean. Accumulation of sediments took place in eu- and miogeosynclinal environments. Present data permit assignment of the South Alaska system (Alaskides) to systems of a polycyclic, inherited type with a eu- and miogeosynclinal mode of development. Peculiar evolutionary features of the Alaskides were predetermined by regional location between the Anadyr'-Seward and Yukon massifs on the north and northeast margins of the Pacific thalassocraton. Inner limits of the South Alaskan system were the Rocky Mountain and Mackenzie-Lena fracture zones, separating the South Alaskan system from the North Alaskan fold system and from the Rocky Mountain uplifts. At the intersection of the two fracture zones, a reentrant angle of the Alaskides is formed similar to that of the Koryakides. The absence in Alaska of Late Cretaceous–Neogene geosynclinal formations that can be correlated with units of the Kamchatides is indicative of the peculiar development of the Alaskan Pacifides and the asymmetric structure of the North Pacific belt.

The South Alaskan system is characterized by the accumulation of thick molasse complexes corresponding to the Jurassic, Cretaceous, and Paleogene-Neogene orogenic stages of the Alaskides development, and also by extensive granitoid magmatism. These phenomena are possibly related to compressional tectonic movements. Differences in extensional movements in the west and compressional movements in the east during a long period of time must have led to major faulting in the earth's crust. One such fault may be the submeridional Bering fault. The existence of such a major fault, which has resulted in the displacement of the Chukotsk-Koryak-Kamchatka block with respect to that of Alaska, is indicated by linear zones of gravity and magnetic anomalies.

General structural framework and changes in strike of major folded structures of the Pacifides were predetermined by the locations of the North Pacific thalassocraton, intergeosynclinal and marginal stable regions, and the systems of deep-seated faults and genetically related but subordinate structures of varying strikes. The presence of transverse fracture zones (Lewis-Clark, Bruin-Ogilvie, Bering, and Aleutian-Lena in combination with a system of longitudinal fracture zones (Denali, Rocky Mountain, Mackenzie-Lena, Olyutorskiy-Kamchatka, and others) governs the block structure of the North Pacific belt. Such structural control supports the concepts of Krasny (1966) and King (1969) about block structure of the Pacific crustal segment.

The Mesozoides of the North Alaskan system, which form a link in a chain of folded structures of the Arctic mobile belt, are characterized by a complete sequence of units that corresponds to stages of development of a single geosynclinal cycle. Within a sequence of formations there is no repetition of units of the same lithology but different age; such repetition is characteristic of geosynclinal systems of the Pacifides. Furthermore, no volcanic-siliceous and ophiolite complexes are present, and evidence of gabbroic and granitic magmatism is local and scattered. The few intrusions present are, as a rule, confined to fault zones or to the boundary zone of the Arctides and the Pacifides. In comparison to the history of geosynclinal systems of the Pacifides (South Alaskan and Koryak–West Kamchatka), Late Jurassic–Early Cretaceous time in the North Alaskan system was not marked by the formation of a new geosynclinal trough, but by the beginning of deposition of a lower molasse sequence, the accumulation of which continued in the Colville trough in Cretaceous, Paleogene, and Neogene time.

Main features of geosynclinal development of the North Alaskan system are characteristic also of the adjacent eastern part of the Novosibirsk-Chukotsk fold system. One difference is that intrusive and extrusive rocks, which are mainly the result of influence of the Okhotsk-Chukotsk volcanic belt, are widespread in the Novosibirsk-Chukotsk fold system. A general latitudinal and sublatitudinal structural framework of the Arctides part of this fold zone was determined by its location between the Mackenzie scarp on the east; the Yukon, Anadyr'-Seward, and Kolyma massifs on the south and southwest; and the Hyperborean platform on the north. Characteristic structural features provide the basis for assigning the North Alaskan and Novosibirsk-Chukotsk geosynclinal systems to epicratonic systems of monocyclic type and miogeosynclinal mode of development.

The nature of magmatic activity in the North Pacific mobile belt was significant in development of the structural-stratigraphic and tectonic features of the Arctides and the Pacifides. The Arctides are characterized by a sublatitudinally striking gabbro-diabase intrusive complex. Rocks of the complex in North Alaska are Jurassic, whereas those in the Chukotsk Peninsula are dated as Triassic. Individual granitoid

stocks of Devonian age which are located in
eastern North Alaska are confined to faults in
the junction zone of the North and South Alaskan systems, and are considered to be genetically related to those faults. In the writers'
opinion, Cretaceous granite-granodiorite intrusions and comagmatic liparite-andesite volcanic
rocks of Chukotsk are assigned to formations of
the Okhotsk-Chukotsk volcanic belt, because
they are similar in age, composition, type of
chemical activity, and mode of occurrence.

The North Pacific–Koryak–Kamchatka and
South Alaskan systems show the effects of eugeosynclinal magmatism and have features indicative of asymmetric structure and development. The similarities are reflected by the presence of two geosynclinal magmatic cycles, the
earlier stages of which are marked by mafic-ultramafic intrusions closely associated with volcanic-siliceous formations.

On the basis of geologic position, petrogra-
phy-mineralogy, chemical features, and metallogenic characteristics of mafic-ultramafic formations in the South Alaskan and Koryak-
Kamchatka fold belts, two groups of formations may be distinguished. The first group is a
calcareous-magnesian formation and the second is a magnesian formation which has different calcium oxide, magnesium oxide, and iron
oxide ratios, indicating similarity of these rocks
to basalt and peridotite magma. The magnesian
group is characterized by low ferruginous content, sparse mafic minerals, high magnesian
content, low calcium oxide content, and higher
silica content.

The ultramafic intrusions are Paleozoic or
early Mesozoic in age. They are situated in
outer zones of fold systems of the North Pacifides and are closely associated with volcanic-siliceous formations. The intrusions, of mainly
dunite-harzburgite composition, have a layered
structure. Among the predominant mafic minerals are orthopyroxenes; clinopyroxene is almost absent. Characteristic features are extensive serpentinization and local weathering
crusts.

In the area of Alaska and British Columbia,
an ultramafic belt which is 500 km long and
which ranges in age from Devonian to Triassic
is assigned to this group. The belt extends
northwestward along the Alaska-Yukon
boundary into central British Columbia. Intrusive bodies of the belt are associated with volcanic-siliceous rocks of the Sylvester Group
(Devonian–Lower Mississippian).

In the Koryak Range, Paleozoic and Early

Cretaceous ultramafic belts in the eastern and
northern parts of the region are assigned to the
group of magnesian formations. All these intrusions are within volcanic-siliceous sequences,
and all strike northeast. Intrusive rocks of the
group have not been recognized in Kamchatka.

Rocks and minerals of the calcareous-
magnesian group are highly ferruginous (17–
21 percent) and have high calcium oxide content and low silica content (parameter $S = 29.9$
percent). Ultramafic intrusions of the unit are
Late Cretaceous and Middle Jurassic in age.
They are situated within fold systems of the Pacifides which are adjacent to the ocean. Volcanic-siliceous formations are not everywhere
associated with them. Ultramafic intrusions
have chiefly dunite-wehrlite composition and
cylindrical-zonal structures with dunite cores.
Among mafic minerals, clinopyroxene of diopside to diopside-augite composition predominates. Serpentinization is mild.

In accordance with the characteristics listed,
two ultramafic belts are assigned to the calcareous-magnesian group in Alaska and British Columbia. The first belt, situated in southeastern
Alaska, is 640 km long and 48 km wide. It is
Jurassic-Cretaceous in age. The second belt,
which is Middle Jurassic in age, is situated in
central British Columbia; it is known as the Polaris ultramafic complex.

The corresponding belts in the USSR are
(1) the Vatyna mafic-ultramafic complex (Late
Cretaceous), which extends southwestward as a
narrow band 500 km long from Anastasiya Bay
to Kamchatka Isthmus, and, tentatively, (2) the
Late Cretaceous intrusions of ultramafic-gab-
broic composition present in the Iruney Series
in Kamchatka.

The recognition of the calcareous-magnesian
and magnesian groups of formations in the
North Pacific mobile belt leads to some conclusions about the nature of the parent magma.
The predominance of ultramafic rocks over
mafic rocks, the high magnesium content of
mafic minerals, and the absence of iron concentrations in the magnesian group suggest that the
magnesian group is a derivative of a peridotite
magma. The calcareous-magnesian group,
which is more ferruginous and richer in calcareous-magnesian minerals and has a predominance of ultramafic rocks over mafic rocks, is
also believed to be derived from a peridotite
magma.

Despite a sharply different scale of magmatic
activity during middle and late stages of geosynclinal development in the Koryak-Kam-

chatka and South Alaskan fold systems, there is a markedly similar, regular distribution of alkali and silica content within these intrusive complexes. A calc-alkalic group of formations may be distinguished in these regions. This rock group is characterized by intrusions of quartz diorite, diorite, granodiorite, and plagiogranite composition. This group of rocks occurs in fold zones of the Pacifides which are adjacent to the ocean. The boundary of calc-alkalic formation distribution within the Alaska-Columbian area is J. G. Moore's (1959) "quartz diorite line." The Roddick "quartz monzonite line" is a southward continuation. In a recent paper (Reed and Lanphere, 1969, p. 23–44), this line separating the calc-alkalic rocks from the alkalic rocks is extended along the northern part of the Alaska and Aleutian Ranges. In the American part of the Pacifides the calc-alkalic unit is represented by a major batholithic belt (3,000 km long). There is no equivalent belt within the East Asiatic–Pacific area, although the Koryak-Kamchatka Pacifides are characterized by the same regular distribution of calc-alkalic and alkalic units. The boundary of calc-alkalic rock occurrence is represented in the Koryak Range mainly by small diorite, granodiorite, and plagiogranite intrusions; it extends along the Murgal anticlinorium.

The main distinguishing features of magmatism in the Koryak-Kamchatka fold area are a weak manifestation of intrusive magmatism and intense extrusive activity, as well as predominance of mafic-ultramafic intrusions and absence of large batholiths. The South Alaskan fold area was characterized by intense extrusive activity only at early, but long-lasting, stages of geosynclinal development. Intrusive magmatism is extremely widespread. Among intrusive bodies, granitoid batholiths are predominant both in scale and number.

Geophysical, geological, and geomorphological data provide information for reconstructing the structural development of the suboceanic area within the North Pacific mobile belt and adjacent ocean floor. Two types of processes appear to be involved. Geosynclinal processes caused the extension of a continental block and its submarine projections and resulted in their displacement toward the oceanic basin. "Geomarginal" processes acted in the opposite direction and determined the formation of the downwarped zone near the continental margin, which is morphologically reflected in sea-floor topography as the continental slope. Tectonically, this zone may be charac-

terized as the "geomargin." Geosynclinal and geomarginal processes have resulted in the most complex geologic relations in a transitional zone in the northernmost Pacific Ocean. This transitional zone has different structures west and east of the meridian of the Alaska Bay head. This zone is apparently one of the most important structural boundaries in the northeastern Pacific, for west of it the belt of marginal Pacific seas ends. Within these marginal Pacific seas, the transition from continent toward ocean is expressed as abyssal basins, island arcs, and abyssal trenches. Such a classic sequence is observed in the Bering and Okhotsk Seas. East of the zone the continental block and basin are separated only by a continental slope. There are no marginal seas, but the continental rise is extensive. The complex bottom topography of abyssal areas is related mainly to deep-seated volcanism.

The head of the Alaska Bay is distinguished not only by the fact that it is crossed by the structural transitional-zone boundary, but also by the nearby change of direction of all structural elements, both on land and on the ocean floor.

In the formation of most bottom structures, both within the Pacific mobile belt and along its ocean margin, Cenozoic geologic history was of utmost importance. During the Cenozoic, consolidation of the more mobile elements of the submarine projection of the continental block bordering the more ancient and stable core occurred. Numerous structural features of the transitional zone appeared and later underwent significant changes. Deep-seated faults played the most important role. In the Neogene the Bering Sea became completely separated from the Okhotsk Sea. Formation of the Aleutian island arc led to the division of the northernmost Pacific into the Bering Sea and the Gulf of Alaska, and submarine ridges in the deep part of the Bering Sea led to the formation of its suboceanic basins (Kamchatka, Bowers, and Aleutian). The continental slope received its distinct morphologic appearance; its most ancient part forms the continental rise, and the younger part forms the continental slope, which contains numerous submarine canyons. In the oceanic zone, development of structural elements was determined mainly by deep-seated faults, volcanism, and, in the periphery (as in the Bering Sea basins), by the accumulation of sedimentary deposits.

Analysis of available data allows discussion of metallogenic specialization of the North Pa-

cifides and the adjacent Arctides. Main endo-
genic metallogenic features of the Arctides and
Pacifides were predetermined by peculiar features of the development of deep-seated structure, as well as by geotectonic style and mode
of development.

Metal associations which have resulted in ore
concentrations in each megaprovince may be
considered in two main groups. The Arctides
are characterized by tin and tungsten. The Pacifides contain copper, pyrite ores, chromium,
asbestos, nickel, and, in lesser amounts, platinum.

Gold shows surround the North Pacific area
and adjacent parts of the Arctides, forming a
subglobal belt which can be traced from Transbaykal to Oregon and California. These occurrences are independent of the crustal type and
geotectonic features within the territories
crossed. This relation has previously permitted
outlining of the great North Pacific gold-bearing arc (Itsikson *et al.*, 1960), in which gold
deposits were formed at various times from the
early Precambrian to the Miocene. Berger and
Itsikson (1972) suggested that parts of an associated mercury-bearing arc may also be recognized. Partially associated gold-bearing and
mercury-bearing arcs are apparently related to
fault systems extending deep into the mantle
along borders of the Pacific and Arctic segments of the earth. This system, in general, appears to correspond to a hexagonal Transpacific
system of deep-seated faults proposed by Egiazarov. These faults were formed at least as
early as late Precambrian time. The deep-seated
faults predetermined the location and development of geosynclinal areas bordering the Pacific Ocean. A similar hexagonal Transarctic
system of deep-seated faults is outlined for the
Arctic segment (the Hyperborean region and
surrounding Arctides).

Copper and tin in large amounts occur separately in the Arctides and Pacifides. They obviously originate from deep sources. Metallogenic specialization is due to differences in
crust type and characteristic features of each
area's geologic history. The epicratonic character of the Arctides predetermined the development of metallogenic associations of the "crustal" elements (tin and tungsten) within them.
The development of the near-oceanic Pacifides
on the suboceanic (basaltic) crust predetermined a femic pattern of mineralization and
manifestation of deeper metal associations—
i.e., copper, iron, tungsten, and, in a lesser degree, chromium, platinum, and nickel.

Certain differences, as well as some similarities, in areal distribution of prospective oil
structures and stratigraphic ranges of oil- and
gas-bearing rock units can be mentioned. In the
Pacifides area, within the northern part of the
Koryak-Kamchatka area and on the adjacent
shelf, there are two groups of intermountain
troughs situated in the Koryakides and Kamchatides areas. These troughs, which developed
at different times, contain sequences of varied
oil potential.

In Koryakides troughs the strata are Neogene, and those of the Kamchatides are Paleogene-Neogene. Oil shows are found not only in
deposits of molasse complexes, but also in formations of a typical geosynclinal nature. Thus,
the possibility of oil and gas accumulations is
suggested, both in predominantly porous reservoirs of an orogenic complex and in fracture
reservoirs in the folded basement of the troughs
and depressions. The most promising region
within the Koryakides (with the exception of
the Anadyr' trough) is the Penzhino trough, especially its southwestern part (including Penzhino Bay). The Middle Anadyr' trough,
within the northeastern Penzhino trough, is also
promising. Within the Kamchatides, the Khatyrka trough and adjacent shelf are of interest
in view of exploration results.

Intermountain troughs of the Koryakides
(Anadyr' and Penzhino troughs), on the basis
of their structural position and of age ranges of
potential oil reservoirs, are correlative with
similar troughs within the Mesozoides of the
South Alaskan fold system (Kuskokwim, Koyukuk, and Cook Inlet). The Anadyr' trough
and the Koyukuk and Kuskokwim troughs on
the Bering shelf form the single Anadyr'-Se-
ward depression. Its tectonic position and contained deposits, together with other evidence,
points to the Bering shelf as one of the most
important areas of oil exploration. A peculiar
feature of the Cook Inlet trough (comparable
with that of Penzhino) is the presence of a
thick molasse complex of Jurassic age, in addition to a Cretaceous-Paleogene complex.

Troughs and depressions of northern Alaska
form an extensive oil- and gas-bearing province
which differs from the Koryak Range and central and southern Alaska in its tectonic position
and age of deposits. The stratigraphic range of
known oil- and gas-bearing deposits (Carbonif-
erous-Cretaceous) of North Alaska is explained by a miogeosynclinal environment of
sedimentation and monocyclic mode of development of the North Alaskan system, as well as

by its tectonic position between the Yukon massif in the south and the Hyperborean platform in the north. The projection of the North Alaskan oil- and gas-bearing provinces to the west is to be sought within the Chukchi and East Siberian shelves. It is possible to suggest that potential oil- and gas-bearing troughs and depressions of Arctic Canada, North Alaska, Chukotsk, and the Chukchi and East Siberian Seas form a single Arctic belt of oil and gas accumulations which are tectonically confined to the Arctides. Also recognized is a North Pacific oil- and gas-producing belt including oil- and gas-bearing troughs and depressions of the Koryak-Kamchatka and Cordillera-Alaska provinces and adjacent shelves.

References Cited

Berger, V. I., and M. I. Itsikson, 1972, Osnovnyye cherty metallogenii severo-vostochnoy chasti Tikhookeanskogo poyasa: Sovetskaya Geologiya, no. 1, p. 90–105.

Egiazarov, B. Kh., 1969, Arktidy-osobaya geostruktura Zemli, in Mezozoysky tektogenez: Magadan, p. 17–20.

———— 1969, Geologicheskoye stroyeniye Alyaski i Aleutskikh ostrovov: Sravnitelnaya kharakteristika s sopredelnymi regionami severo-vostoka Azii: Leningrad, Izd. "Nedra," 264 p.

———— and G. I. Kameneva, 1970, Geosinklinalnyy magmatizm Alyaski i Koryakskogo nagorya, in Materialy i konferentsii po paleovulkanizmu Sredney Sibiri: Krasnoyarsk, p. 33–36.

Itsikson, M. I., et al., 1960, Osnovnyye cherty metallogenii severo-zapadnoy chasti Tikhookeanskogo rudnogo poyasa: Geologiya Rudnykh Mestorozhdeny, no. 1, p. 16–44.

Khain, V. Ye., 1964, Geosinklinalnyy protsess i evolyutsiya tektonosfery: Akad. Nauk SSSR, Izv. Ser. Geol., no. 12, p. 3–16.

Kheraskov, N. P., 1967, Tektonika i formatsii: Moscow, Izd. "Nauka," p. 317–321, 375–400.

King, Philip B., 1969, Voprosy tektoniki Severnoy Ameriki (Problems relating to the tectonics of North America): Moscow, Izd. Moscow Univ., 179 p.

Krasny, L. I., 1966, Osnovnyye cherty geologicheskogo stroyeniya, in Geologicheskoye stroyeniye severo-zapadnoy chasti Tikhookeanskogo podvizhnogo poyasa: Moscow, Izd. "Nedra," p. 24–30.

Moore, J. G., 1959, The quartz diorite boundary line in the western United States: Jour. Geology, v. 67, no. 2, p. 198–210.

Reed, B. L., and M. A. Lanphere, 1969, Age and chemistry of Mesozoic and Tertiary plutonic rocks in south-central Alaska: Geol. Soc. America Bull., v. 80, no. 1, p. 23–43.

Shatsky, N. S., 1965, Izbrannyye trudy, v. 3, Geologicheskiy formatsii i osadochnyye poleznyye iskopayemyye: Moscow, Izd. "Nauka," 348 p.

Features of Sedimentary Layers Beneath Arctic Ocean[1]

R. M. DEMENITSKAYA, G. I. GAPONENKO, YU. G. KISELEV, and S. S. IVANOV[2]

Leningrad, USSR

Abstract Part of the earth's crust surrounded by three pre-Paleozoic platforms (East European, Mid-Siberian, and Greenland-Canadian) was the site of origin and development of the Arctic Ocean. Arctic Ocean structures are discordant with the structures of the coast and continental shelf. According to tectonic data, present shelf regions represent vast parageosynclinal basins of nearly isometric shape filled with varied sedimentary sequences. Sedimentary history of the shelf is closely related to development of megablocks of the earth's crust in this region. The Barents-Kara, Laptev, East Siberian–Chukotsk, and Alaska megablocks are recognized on the basis of geophysical data. Sequential rejuvenation of the megablocks and sedimentary cover seems to have occurred in a west-east direction.

Rocks of the central Arctic basin are unconsolidated sediments (first layer) with seismic velocities of 1.6–2.5 km/sec, consolidated sediments (second layer) with velocities of 3.0–4.5 km/sec, pre-oceanic folded basement (third layer) with velocities of 5.0–6.2 km/sec, and crystalline basement (fourth layer) with velocities of 5.7–6.3 km/sec for granitic composition and 6.4–6.7 km/sec for basalts. In the western part of the Arctic basin, the second and third layers are usually found only in the periphery; in the central parts, unconsolidated sediments lie directly on basaltic basement. In most of the eastern part of the basin, a continuous section is present. In both sectors, thickness of unconsolidated sediments is less on uplifts and ridges (0.1–0.5 km) than in adjacent troughs (1–2 km). Thickness distribution of the second layer generally does not conform to the present structural configuration. Thus, the most significant vertical movement in the inner Arctic Ocean basin occurred mainly in late Mesozoic–Cenozoic time, during deposition of the sediments of the first layer. During that time the present configuration of the Arctic Ocean basin was attained.

INTRODUCTION

A part of the earth's crust that was limited by three large pre-Paleozoic platforms (East European, Mid-Siberian, and Greenland-Canadian) was the initial site for the origin and development of the Arctic Ocean. The existence of these platforms and surrounding folded zones controlled conditions in the inner regions of the ocean area. During the evolution of the Arctic Ocean, its boundaries and dimensions were not constant. At times, areas which now are shelves, or even extensive deep-sea areas, were exposed and extensively eroded (Sachs, 1960). Evidence for these periods of

emergence is based on recent paleogeographic studies of the Arctic continental margins and shelf islands (Bondarev et al., 1967; Gramberg et al., 1967; Ronkina et al., 1967) and on seismic data on angular discordance of sedimentary layers in inner oceanic regions (Kiselev, 1966; Demenitskaya and Kiselev, 1968; 1969).

One of the characteristic features of the Arctic Ocean structure is its discordance both to coastal structural features and to those of the submarine continental margin. Structural features which intersect at the ocean margins are indicated to have different ages and different histories of development. The structures of the continent and of its margin are similar in origin, but no genetic unity is found between structures of central oceanic regions and those of the Arctic shelf areas. The structural features of central regions of the ocean are mainly neogenetic; their surficial and deep structure reflect stages of ocean formation. All these facts are directly reflected in the structure and distribution of different sedimentary sequences both on the shelf and in central parts of the ocean.

ARCTIC SHELF OF EURASIA

According to tectonic data, oceanic margins —the regions of the present shelf—represent vast parageosynclinal basins of nearly isometric shape, filled by thick sedimentary layers of different ages and composition. The sedimentary framework of the shelf is the result of structural development of the central Arctic basin and adjacent continents, as well as of certain megablocks of the earth's crust that were formed within the peripheral oceanic zone.

The results of regional geological and geophysical investigations on the Arctic shelf of Eurasia provide a basis for recognizing the Barents-Kara, Laptev, East Siberian–Chukotsk, and Alaska megablocks (Gaponenko, 1969).

There is evidence for sequential rejuvenation of megablocks and sedimentary cover (except for the Alaska megablock, which is believed to have been consolidated in pre-Paleozoic or Paleozoic time) in a west-east direction. All the megablocks are limited by a continental slope on the north and by a coastline or by regions of recent mountain building on the south, and are

[1] Manuscript received, August 1, 1972.
[2] Research Institute of the Geology of the Arctic.

separated by north-south-trending deep fracture zones. Thus, the history of formation of sedimentary sequences on the Eurasian Arctic shelf is closely connected with the history of development of the megablocks themselves, especially during Mesozoic-Cenozoic time.

Barents-Kara Megablock

Within the Barents-Kara megablock there are two major sedimentary basins, the Barents and Kara Seas. The latter has not been extensively studied, but it is supposed that sedimentary layers on the Kara shelf are as thick as 10–12 km in some localities. Seismic data on the Barents Sea suggest that the sedimentary thickness reaches 15–18 km in the central part (Litvinenko, 1968) and includes at least three structural stages. It is thought that the formation of the sedimentary cover and crustal structural features was greatly influenced in this area by the process of midocean rifting (Ivanov et al., 1970).

Laptev Megablock

The Laptev megablock is the least studied of the four megablocks. However, it is evident that the sedimentary cover of the block has undergone two periods of deformation, and its general thickness ranges from 2 to 8 km. The greatest thickness of sedimentary rocks is observed within the South Laptev trough (up to 8 km) and in the Lena graben. It is obvious that the principal sedimentary sequences of the Laptev shelf are rather complicated as a result of the continuation of the Mid-Arctic Ridge from the Eurasian basin to the Moma trough on the continent. This continuation is apparent also from geophysical data.

East Siberian–Chukotsk Megablocks

The East Siberian and Chukotsk megablocks, according to geophysical data, appear to have been a single megablock in late Peleozoic–early Mesozoic time. Due to the development of structures in the central Arctic basin, this major block was divided by the Mendeleyev-Kolyma fracture zone into two different megablocks. Both blocks are characterized by three distinct layers within the sedimentary sequence, by a rather thick unconsolidated layer, and by marked subsidence during the present stage of development.

The upper layer of unconsolidated sediments, with seismic velocities ranging from 1.8 to 2.3 km/sec, is consistently present. Its thickness ranges from 0.5 km (northwestern part of East Siberian Sea) to 1.5 km (central East Siberian Sea and northeastern part of Chukchi Sea). Unconsolidated sedimentary sequences are underlain by consolidated rocks with seismic velocities of 3.5–4.0 km/sec. The greatest thickness of consolidated sediments is within the East Siberian depression (5–7 km).

Consolidated rock sequences are underlain by folded basement rocks ("Epi-Mesozoic platform"). The seismic velocity of these rocks appears to be 5.5–5.7 km/sec. The crystalline basement within the East Siberian megablock has been studied only in isolated localities. The basement is characterized by seismic velocities of 6.0–6.3 km/sec and depths from 9 km (northwestern part of East Siberian Sea) to 12 km (East Siberian depression).

The sedimentary framework of the Chukotsk megablock is similar to that of the East Siberian megablock with the exception of the northeastern part, where the sedimentary sequence has two principal layers.

A marginal shelf uplift and a trough that can be traced along the continental slope from Alaska to Severnaya Zemlya are the principal regional structures of the sedimentary rocks of the East Siberian shelf. The marginal shelf trough is characterized by asymmetric structure; the gentle flank faces toward the shelf and the steep one toward the continental slope. Thicknesses of sedimentary sequences within this trough range from 1–2 km (marginal shelf trough of the Laptev Sea with carbonate deposits) to 5–8 km (marginal shelf trough of the Chukchi Sea with terrigenous-volcanic deposits).

The structure of the marginal uplift is little known. Undoubtedly, it is formed by uplifted crystalline basement broken into numerous blocks of various levels. The inner (relative to the ocean) blocks probably are submerged.

A characteristic feature of the sedimentary sequence in the East Siberian Sea is the relation between thickness of the sedimentary sequence and isostatic conditions of the earth's crust within certain structures. Analysis of geophysical data shows that isostatic disequilibrium is generally observed on structures of the first and second orders where thickness of the sedimentary cover is more than 7–8 km. In these areas, a lack of compensation is evident which corresponds to prevailing subsidence. Supposedly, these areas, where intensive accumulation of sediments presently is occurring, are the sites of future development of other first- and second-order structures. The East Siberian depression, the marginal shelf trough of the East Siberian shelf, and some trenches and zones of present block movements on the boundaries of mega-blocks (Lomonosov-Svyatonos, Mendeleyev-Beringovskiy, *etc.*) are examples of first- and second-order structures.

CENTRAL ARCTIC

Principal elements of sea-floor topography of the Arctic basin are the Nansen basin, the Mid-Arctic Ridge, the Amundsen basin, the Lomonosov Ridge, the Makarov basin, the Toll basin (Podvodnikov), the Mendeleyev-Alpha ridges, and the Beaufort (Canadian) Trough (Treshnikov *et al.*, 1967). Such structures as the Chukchi Cape, the Northwind uplift, and the Chukchi abyssal plain (Demenitskaya and Kiselev, 1969), which represent relatively recent submergence of the former shelf, may also be considered as features of the central Arctic sea floor.

A great variety is apparent in the structure of sedimentary series of these structural units. There is considerable variation in the thickness of the unconsolidated sedimentary sequence (the first layer). The thickness of the consolidated sedimentary rocks (the second layer) is not well known but has been measured in places. Angular discordance between the first and second layers is quite evident in some places and obscure in others. In some places the rocks of the second structural stage apparently are absent, and the positions they occupied are occupied by rocks similar to those of the first stage. In some basins of long duration, no discontinuity is evident between the structural layers, and they are distinguished only by velocity differences.

In the regions where the horizontal or sub-horizontal sequence of rocks of the second layer is traced with certainty, a complex disturbed sequence is clearly seen beneath the sedimentary beds. This sequence is attributed to the third layer, of mainly terrigenous sedimentary origin, which is believed to be a pre-oceanic folded basement. Lower in the section are rocks of the crystalline basement that have either granitic or basaltic composition.

Rocks of the first layer have seismic velocities from 1.6 to 2.5 km/sec, depending on their location and thickness, whereas rocks of the second and third layers have velocities from 3.0 to 4.5 km/sec and from 5.0 to 6.2 km/sec, respectively. Crystalline basement of granitic composition has seismic velocities from 5.7 to 6.3 km/sec; the basalts have a seismic velocity of 6.4–6.7 km/sec.

CONCLUSIONS

The deep-seated structures of the western part of the Arctic basin differ sharply from those of the eastern part. In the western part (Eurasian subbasin) the rocks of the second and third layers are present, as a rule, only in the periphery. Unconsolidated sediments in flank areas of the basin overlie the complexly faulted and folded rocks, and in the central parts of the basin the unconsolidated sediments lie directly on the basaltic basement (Rassokho *et al.*, 1967). In the eastern part of the Arctic Ocean (Amerasian subbasin) the relation with the deep layer is different. Here, except in some central regions of the Beaufort basin, the continuous section is clearly seen. Both in the eastern and western sectors of the Arctic basin, the thickness of unconsolidated sediments on the ridges and large uplifts is less than in the adjacent troughs. Thickness ranges from 0.1–0.5 km on the ridges to 1–2 km in the troughs. The thickness of the second layer also differs. It is thin (0.5–1 km) in the uplifted parts of the Chukchi Cape and the Mendeleyev Ridge, but it exceeds 1 km in thickness in the Toll and Makarov basins and on the Lomonosov Ridge.

The thickness distribution of the second layer generally does not conform to the present structural configuration. For example, in some basins and in some regions of recent structural uplift, thicknesses may be the same. This fact suggests that the most significant vertical movement in the inner Arctic Ocean basin occurred mainly in late Mesozoic–Cenozoic time, during deposition of the sediments of the first layer. At that time, the present configuration of the Arctic Ocean was attained.

Further study of the sedimentary framework of the area, in both the inner and outer regions of the ocean, is expected to reveal how the Arctic Ocean was formed, as well as how this process affected crustal regeneration and formation of new rocks.

SELECTED REFERENCES

Bondarev, V. I., *et al.*, 1967, Ranne-srednepaleozoysky etap paleograficheskogo razvitiya, *in* Paleografiya tsentralnoy chasti Sovetskoy Arktiki: Moscow, Izd. "Nedra," p. 38–122.

Demenitskaya, R. M., and Yu. G. Kiselev, 1968, Osobennosti stroyeniya morfologii i osadochnogo chekhla tsentralnoy chasti khrebta Lomonosova po dannym seysmicheskikh issledovany, *in* Geofizicheskiy metody razvedki v Arktike, no. 5: Leningrad,

Nauchno-Issled. Inst. Geologii Arktiki, p. 33–46.

——— and ——— 1969, Chukotsky kupol i yego vzaimootnosheniya s mezozoidami Chukotsko-Alyaskinskoy zony (po materialam seysmicheskikh issledovany), *in* Tezisy doklady 7th sessii Nauchnogo soveta po tektonike Sibiri i Dalnego Vostoka: Magadan, p. 183–184.

——— and ——— 1970–1971, Osnovnyye cherty tektonicheskogo stroyeniya Chukotskogo kupola i prilegayushchikh k nemu rayonov, *in* Tektonika Sibiri i Dalnego Vostoka, v. 5: Novosibirsk, Akad. Nauk SSSR Sibirskoye Otdeleniye.

Gaponenko, G. I., 1969, O vozmozhnosti vydeleniya mezozoyskikh struktur shelfa po geofizicheskim dannym v oblastyakh proyvaleniya noveyshey blokovoy tektoniki, *in* Tezisy doklady 7th sessi Nauchnogo soveta po tektonike Sibiri i Dalnego Vostoka: Magadan, p. 243–244.

Gramberg, I. S., *et al.*, 1967, Pozdnepaleozoysko-rannemezozoysky etap paleograficheskogo razvitiya, *in* Paleografiya tsentralnoy chasti Sovetskoy Arktiki: Moscow, Izd. "Nedra," p. 123–196.

Ivanov, S. S., A. M. Karasik, and V. N. Sokolov, 1970, Seysmologicheskiye dokazatelstva vliyaniya sredinnookeanicheskogo khrebta na severo-zapadnuyu okrainu Yevropeyskogo kontinenta (Seismological data on the effect of the Mid-Atlantic Ridge on the northwestern margin of the European continent), *in* 10th Yevropeyskaya Seysmologicheskaya Komissiya, Trudy, v. 2: Moscow, Akad. Nauk SSSR, Sov. Geofiz. Kom., p. 103–117.

Kiselev, Yu. G., 1970, Nekotoryye cherty sovremennogo morfotektonicheskogo stroyeniya khrebta Lomonosova po dannym seysmicheskikh issledovany (Some features of the present-day morphotectonic structure of the Lomonosov Ridge based on seismic surveys), *in* Morskaya geologiya i geofizika, v. 1: Riga, Vses. Nauchno-Issled. Inst. Morskoy Geologii i Geofiziki, p. 84–87.

Litvinenko, I. V., 1968, Osobennosti glubinnogo razreza zemnoy kory severo-zapadnoy chasti Kolskogo poluostrova i yuzhnoy chasti Barentseva morya, *in* Geologiya i glubinnoye stroyeniye vostochnoy chasti Baltyskogo shchita: Leningrad, p. 94–96.

Rassokho, A. I., *et al.*, 1967, Podvodnyy Sredinnyy Arktichesky khrebet i yego mesto v sisteme khrebtov Severnogo Ledovitogo okeana: Akad. Nauk SSSR Doklady, v. 172, no. 3, p. 659–662.

Ronkina, Z. Z., *et al.*, 1967, Pozdnemezozoysky etap paleograficheskogo razvitiya, *in* Paleografiya tsentralnoy chasti Sovetskoy Arktiki: Moscow, Izd. "Nedra," p. 193–276.

Sachs, V. N., 1960, Geologicheskaya Istoriya severnogo Ledovitogo okeana na protyazhenii mezozoyskoy ery (The geological history of the Arctic Ocean during the Mesozoic Era): 21st Internat. Geol. Cong., Dokl. Sovet. Geol., Probl. 12, p. 108–124.

Treshnikov, L. F., *et al.*, 1967, Geograficheskiye naimenovaniya osnovnykh chastey relyefa dna Arkticheskogo basseyna: Problemy Arktiki i Antarktiki no. 27, p. 5–9.

Main Geologic Structures of the Arctic[1]

B. V. TKACHENKO, B. KH. EGIAZAROV, I. P. ATLASOV, V. M. LAZURKIN,
F. G. MARKOV, Y. I. POLKIN, M. G. RAVICH, B. S. ROMANOVICH,
and V. N. SOKOLOV[2]

Leningrad, USSR

Abstract The fold belts of northern Greenland, Arctic Canada, northern Alaska, Chukotsk, and the Siberian Arctic coast (up to the mouth of the Lena River) form the latitudinal Arctic belt of the Baykalides, Caledonides, Hercynides, and Mesozoides. Its location was influenced by the presence of the Hyperborean and Greenland-Canadian platforms, as well as by the central Yukon, Anadyr'-Seward, and Kolyma massifs, at the close of the Proterozoic and the beginning of the Paleozoic. It is suggested that the fold belts of the Arctic be considered as a special geostructural zone—the Arctides—in contrast to the structures of the Pacific and the Atlantic—the Pacifides and the Atlantides. The Arctides are mainly characterized by a miogeosynclinal regime of sedimentation, and the Pacifides are characterized by a eugeosynclinal regime.

The Arctides may be divided into two segments: American (from eastern Greenland to the Mackenzie River) and Amerasian (from the Mackenzie River to the Lena River); these systems differ by age of folding. The Caledonian and Hercynian fold systems developed in the American segment. The Mesozoic geosynclinal cycle was most important in development of the Amerasian segment (the Mesozoides of North Alaskan and Novosibirsk-Chukotsk fold systems).

The juncture of the Arctides and Pacifides occurs along the zone of the Mackenzie-Lena latitudinal and sublatitudinal deep faults. The nature of the Arctides juncture with the fold systems of Taymyr, Severnaya Zemlya, Novaya Zemlya, and Spitsbergen is not clear. Hypothetically, this deep-lying border may be drawn from the continental slope of Greenland to the mouth of the Lena River.

The great Kolyma megablock, limited by zones of deep-seated faults, is an area of mutual influence of Arctides and Pacifides types of development. It is suggested that this megablock be considered as a transitional geostructural area—the Arcto-Pacifides.

It is suggested that the Taymyr–Severnaya Zemlya and Novaya Zemlya fold area; structures of Timan, Spitsbergen, and East Greenland bordering the Barents Sea platform; and the Kora Sea massif are spatially and genetically associated with the Atlantic segments and occupy an intermediate position between the Atlantides and the Arctides. They may be called the "Arcto-Atlantides."

Many investigators have made attempts to study the structural framework of the Arctic and the nature of the junction of the Arctic, Pacific, and Atlantic segments of the earth (C. Schuchert, H. Stille, O. Holtedahl, D. V. Naliv-

kin, W. S. Shatsky, V. N. Sachs, T. P. Atlasov, A. J. Eardley, N. P. Kheraskov, and others). Tectonic and geologic maps compiled during the last 10 years for large regions and continents are important to the solution of the problem. Some of the maps are those by Atlasov *et al.* (1966), Bogdanov *et al.* (1966), Geological Survey of Canada (1969), Egiazarov (1970), King (1969), Krasny (1967), Markov (1966a, 1966b), Pushcharovsky (1963), Pushcharovsky and Udintsev (1970), Shell Oil Company (1959), Spizharskiy (1966), and Yanshin (1968).

Information concerning the presence of a peculiar Arctic latitudinal structural belt was explained in 1963 by Kheraskov (1967). He considered that circular and semicircular distribution of Arctic fold systems is caused by the submerged Hyperborean platform within the central Arctic basin. He also stressed the importance of the northward merging of the Atlantic and Ural-Siberian meridional belts of the Atlantic segments. Atlasov *et al.* (1968), in studies of tectonic problems of the polar regions of the earth, noted that the Arctic is at the juncture of the Pacific and Atlantic segments.

Following Kheraskov's concepts, Egiazarov (1969), on the basis of the formational analysis, characteristic structural features, and classification of fold systems of the North Pacific belt and adjacent territories of the Arctic, concluded that the Arctic mobile belt (Arctides) is a separate geostructure of the earth, apart from the Pacific mobile belt (Pacifides), and that it differs in history of development by complex and yet-unknown relations. He also suggested that the Arcto-Pacifides and Arcto-Atlantides be recognized as transitional areas.

We think that such fold systems as those of North Greenland, Arctic Canada, North Alaska, the Chukotsk Peninsula, the Soviet Arctic coast (up to the mouth of the Lena River), and the New Siberian Islands form the Arctic mobile belt—consisting of the Baykalides, Caledonides, Hercynides, and Mesozoides. Cenozoic movements of different intensity, in-

[1] Manuscript received, August 1, 1972.

[2] Research Institute of the Geology of the Arctic.

cluding the neotectonic stage (Puminov and Grachev, 1969), are also indicative of the geostructural mobility manifested there. The locations of geosynclinal systems of the Arctic mobile belt probably were influenced at the close of the Precambrian by the presence of the Hyperborean (Arctic) platform, the Greenland-Canadian platform, and the Yukon, Anadyr'-Seward, and Kolyma stable regions. Fragments of the Hyperborean platform—Chukchi dome and Alpha Cordillera (North rise)—are recognizable on the basis of geophysical data obtained by Soviet and American investigators, and existence of the platform is proved beyond any doubt. In a discussion of problems of the Paleozoic tectonic history of the Arctic basin north of Alaska, Churkin (1969) distinguishes a Circum-Arctic and a Circum-Pacific geosynclinal belt, and he assigns the Franklin, North Alaska, and Chukchi (Chukotsk) geosynclinal systems to the first and the Koryak and Kamchatka geosynclines and cordillera to the second belt.

The Arctides are characterized by a general latitudinal structural framework of mainly monocyclic development and miogeosynclinal sedimentation. They may be divided into segments —American (from East Greenland to the Mackenzie River) and Amerasian (from the Mackenzie River to the Lena River). Differences in age of fold systems suggest that asymmetric structures of the Arctides, Baykalides, Caledonides, and Hercynides geosynclinal systems developed within the American segment, and it appears that the Hercynides underwent the whole cycle of development. The Mesozoides are absent in this area or are poorly developed. In the Amerasian segment the Paleozoic cycle is manifested but the sequence is incomplete. The formation of the Paleozoides was not accompanied by significant orogenic movements or by development of molasse complexes. The Mesozoic geosynclinal cycle culminated in the formation of the Mesozoides of North Alaska. Development of the Novosibirsk-Chukotsk fold systems was the event of major significance in the Amerasian segment of the Arctides.

The Arctides are characterized mainly by continental crust 39–40 km thick on continents and 30–35 km thick on shelves; generally this 30–40-km crust includes a "basalt" layer 10–15 km thick overlain by a "granite" layer 13–15 km thick (Fotiadi et al., 1969). High gradients of gravity anomalies on continents and weakly differentiated gravity fields on shelves are typical. These areas have weak, varied, mainly negative magnetic fields.

We assign the Mesozoides, the Cenozoides, and recent geosynclinal systems of the North Pacific mobile belt (Koryak-Kamchatka and Alaska-Cordillera fold areas, as well as Aleutian-Komandorskiy and Kuril-Kamchatka recent geosynclines) to the North Pacifides. The North Pacifides are characterized by a polycyclic migrational style of development, a general sublongitudinal structural framework predetermined by a Pacific thalassocraton, and stable platform regions in the continental part of East Asia and North America adjacent to the Pacific Ocean.

The North Pacifides are characterized by complex structure of the crust, which ranges from oceanic to continental type and from 10 to 40 km thick. Complex, generally intense, linear magnetic and gravity anomalies are observed. Direct relations between the structure and gravity and magnetic anomalies are typical (Borisov, 1967).

The junction of the Arctides and Pacifides in the Amerasian segment follows a zone of deep-seated latitudinal and sublatitudinal faults from the Mackenzie River mouth, along the southern margin of the North Alaskan fold system (Brooks Range), past the south termination of the Novosibirsk-Chukotsk system and the northern margin of the Kolyma stable region, to the Lena River mouth. The zone of deep faults, called the Mackenzie-Lena zone (Egiazarov, 1969), is determined by geophysical data and is represented by Chukotsk and Oloysko-Lyakhovskiy volcanism. Farther from the Bering Strait, along the southern slope of the Brooks Range and up to the Mackenzie River mouth, displacement is discernible on airborne-magnetometer surveys made by American geophysicists (Elvers et al., 1967). The Mackenzie-Lena deep fault zone is, in all probability, a transregional structure—a peculiar "geostep" of the earth's crust along which the Arctides and Pacifides are joined. It is possible that the zone is an independent element or that it forms a part of the Arctic belt of deep faults (Nikolayevsky, 1967). Fold systems of Arctic Canada and North Greenland that join the Canadian-Greenland platform may also follow deep fault zones that are a part of a boundary system of the Arctides. The system is complicated by longitudinal and sublongitudinal faults, such as the Bering shear zone, the Okhotsk fault zone (and associated volcanogenesis), and the

Lena-Aleutian lineament (Vashchilov, 1963; Atlasov *et al.*, 1970), which differ in type and amount of displacement.

The major Kolyma megablocks (or "geoblocks"; after Krasny, 1966)—the Kolyma stable region, the fringing Yano-Kolyma Mesozoides, and structures of the Kolyma-Omolon fold-belt area that are bounded by deep fault zones (Okhotsk, Mackenzie-Lena, Lena-Aleutian zones)—represent an area of mutual influence and interaction between Arctic and Pacific types and styles of development. Because the megablock on the slope of the Arctic mantle dome (Nikolayevsky, 1967) differs in geologic structure and history from the Arctides and Pacifides and occupies an intermediate position between them, it is suggested that it be considered an independent geostructural area—the Arcto-Pacifides. Following Nikolayevsky (1967), we consider that the Okhotsk fault zone appears to reflect a deep-seated junction of the Arctic and Pacific mantle domes. The fault zone is characterized by an abrupt change in thickness of the earth's crust from 30 to 40–45 km; in places the gradient reaches 100 m/km. A gravitational nose along the fault zone separates an area of the Koryak-Kamchatka region which generally yields gravity maximums from the block-folded structures of the Kolyma-Omolon region where low gravity values occur.

In geophysical parameters, the Arcto-Pacifides have features resembling those of both the Arctides and the Pacifides. They are characterized by continental crust 40–45 km thick with a somewhat thicker (15–20 km) "basalt" layer in comparison with the "granite" layer (13–15 km). Mainly negative, weak magnetic fields and intense gravity fields are typical of the Arctides. However, on the site of the Kolyma block and east of it, zones of intense positive magnetic anomalies and intense gravity anomalies typical of eugeosynclinal areas of the Pacifides are recognized.

Late Caledonian and late Hercynian folded structures in the Atlantic sector of the North Polar area which formed a part of the Atlantic and Ural-Mongolian mobile belts—situated between the North American, East European, and Siberian platforms—are assigned to the Arcto-Atlantides. The arrangement of the Arctic late Caledonides and late Hercynides within a recent structural framework follows the previously established relation (Atlasov *et al.*, 1970) with respect to "rejuvenation" of Phanerozoic fold systems from the Atlantic toward the Pa-

cific Ocean. Paleotectonic reconstruction of the Arcto-Atlantides is hypothetical to a certain degree, because oceanic basins were already developed in Mesozoic time, and a considerable part of their area was underwater. Nevertheless, it is evident that the Arcto-Atlantides differ considerably in structural and formational features from synchronous fold systems farther south that properly belong to the Atlantides. A principal characteristic is the general northward decrease in tectonism.

The nature of the Arctides junction with fold systems of the Arcto-Atlantides is not quite clear. Hypothetically, as was explained in 1963 by Kheraskov (1967), the boundary is deep-seated and may be drawn along the continental slope from Greenland to the Lena River mouth. The Lena-Aleutian lineament may be considered as a continuation of the junction. It is related to the development of the Yano-Kolyma geosynclinal system, which constitutes a Pacific metastasis into the Arctides and Arcto-Atlantides. Considering the relation of the Mesozoides of the Verkhoyansk area and of southern Taymyr, it is apparent that the structure of the latter constitutes a branch of a Mesozoic fold area of northeast Asia or an area of diminishing intensity of folding of the Pacific Mesozoides belt. The Taymyr–Severnaya Zemlya area appears to be a peculiar boundary area affected by both Atlantic and Pacific systems.

The Arcto-Atlantides display geophysical features which are characteristic both in the Arctides and in the Atlantides. The Atlantides are characterized by continental crust which is thicker (maximum thickness, 45–50 km) than that of the Arctides (Demenitskaya *et al.*, 1967), by approximately equal thickness of "basalt" and "granite" layers, by intense positive magnetic anomalies, and by abrupt gravity anomalies which have linear trends along the folded belt. The intermediate nature of the Arcto-Atlantides is most clearly demonstrated by magnetic data, which indicate that, along the Pay-Khoy–Novaya Zemlya and Taymyr–Severnaya Zemlya fold areas of typical Arctides miogeosynclinal development, there are thick eugeosynclinal zones of metastasis in the Norwegian Caledonides typical of the Atlantides. The Arcto-Atlantides generally are characterized by a weak negative magnetic field and an intense positive gravitational field (negative for Taymyr), but the Caledonides have an intense, linear, positive magnetic field and gravitational anomalies.

Major platforms and plates such as the Hyperborean, Greenland-Canadian, Siberian, East European, and Eria, as well as the Pacific thalassocraton, have predominantly influenced the position and structural history of fold systems of the Arctic and adjacent regions of the Pacific mobile belt and transitional areas (Arcto-Pacifides, Arcto-Atlantides).

The Hyperborean platform is situated in the Pacific part of the Arctic basin. As stated by Stille (1943), in early Precambrian time the platform formed a single unit with the Canadian shield. At present the Hyperborean platform does not exist as a single structural element. It is represented by relics of a platform structure that form a heterogeneous basement of irregularly raised submarine blocks separated by abyssal basins. The raised blocks are the South Hyperborean and North Hyperborean (including the Shatsky massif) blocks, horst structures of the Lomonosov and Mendeleyev Ridges, and the Alpha Cordillera.

Three structural complexes are established by geophysical data in the raised block structures, which are characterized by subcontinental crust. The upper complex (platform complex) is correlated with Mesozoic-Cenozoic formations of land areas; the middle complex (folded complex) is on the Lomonosov and Mendeleyev Ridges, partly on the Alpha Cordillera, and on platform complexes elsewhere. This middle complex is believed to consist of terrigenous strata of Paleozoic and late Precambrian age. The lower complex appears to consist of crystalline rocks. In areas where it is believed to be exposed on the ocean floor, samples of gneiss and schist of presumed early and middle Precambrian age were dredged. The Toll, Makarov, and Canadian abyssal basins which separate the horstlike structures have suboceanic and oceanic crust.

The Arctic mobile belt (Arctides) includes the Novosibirsk-Chukotsk, North Alaskan, Cornwallis–Axel Heiberg, and Innuitian fold systems.

The Novosibirsk-Chukotsk Mesozoic fold system is the Asiatic link with the Amerasian segment of the Arctides. It is situated on the Arctic shore of northeastern Asia and on the shelf of the Laptev, East Siberian, and Chukchi Seas.

Five tectonic stages are recognized in the structural history of the Novosibirsk-Chukotsk fold system. They are the early-middle Proterozoic stage, during which a crystalline basement of the Mesozoides formed (Chukotsk Peninsula, Bol. Lyakhovskiy Island); the late Proterozoic stage (no late Proterozoic rocks are present); the early-middle Paleozoic stage, the late Paleozoic–Mesozoic stage, and the Mesozoic-Cenozoic stage.

The early-middle Paleozoic stage was characterized by terrigenous sedimentation (up to 1,600 m) during the Cambrian–Middle Ordovician carbonate deposition (up to 3,600 m) in the Late Ordovician–Middle Devonian, and carbonate-terrigenous deposition (up to 3,800 m) in Late Devonian–Middle Carboniferous time, including coarse red sediments that were deposited at the close of the Devonian.

Sedimentation in the west took place in a subgeosynclinal regime (with two breaks between Silurian and Devonian and between the Early and Middle Carboniferous). In the east, deposition was presumably in a geosynclinal environment. Some data on Wrangel (Vrangelya) Island suggest incomplete folding at the close of middle Paleozoic time.

The late Paleozoic–Mesozoic tectonic stage of miogeosynclinal development is revealed by terrigenous formations in which several stratigraphic units are absent from the section. In the southwest (Bol. Lyakhovskiy Island), deposits tentatively assigned to the Permo-Triassic (2,000–3,000 m thick) are metamorphosed. In the northwest (Kotel'nyy Island), these strata are represented by Triassic argillites (2,000–3,000 m) lying unconformably on Paleozoic rocks. In the west the upper part of the complex consists of an arenaceous-argillaceous sequence (up to 1,900 m) of Early Cretaceous age. Upper Carboniferous and Permian deposits are absent on Kotel'nyy Island, and upper Paleozoic deposits are absent on Wrangel Island. The Jurassic (up to 2,900 m) occurs only in the littoral part of the continent. The late Paleozoic–Mesozoic stage of folding culminated in the Early Cretaceous.

The Mesozoic-Cenozoic stage is characterized by a postgeosynclinal tectonic regime during which horsts, grabens, arches, and domelike uplifts were formed in the superposed and inherited depressions.

Magmatic rocks are represented by peridotite and pyroxenite found in early Precambrian schists, by Paleozoic mafic and granitic intrusions (Wrangel Island), by late Mesozoic granitoids and basalts, and by late Mesozoic–Cenozoic liparites and basalts.

The Novosibirsk-Chukotsk fold system in the west is monocyclic. In the east it begins presumably with a middle Paleozoic stage of incomplete folding and is characterized by a decrease of thickness and reduction of folded structures toward the Hyperborean platform.

The North Alaskan Mesozoic fold system is situated on the eastern flank of the Amerasian segment of the Arctides. In the south, along the deep-seated Mackenzie-Lena fault zone, the fold system borders the Anadyr'-Seward depression (located in the Anadyr'-Seward stable region) and the Yukon massif. The Dave Lord Creek arch, where Precambrian metamorphic and crystalline schists are exposed, is related to the Kuskokwim-Mackenzie fault zone in the eastern part of the system. North of the Mesozoides of the North Alaskan system is the southern margin of the Hyperborean platform. It is possible that the fold zone of the Caledonides(?) strikes along the edge of the North Alaska continental slope. The Mesozoides of the North Alaskan system are represented by a Riphean-Mesozoic structural complex divided into several structural stages and substages. An accumulation of thick (up to 10–11 km) carbonate, carbonate-shale, and terrigenous formations typical of a miogeosynclinal tectono-sedimentary environment corresponds to a geosynclinal stage (Ordovician–Middle Jurassic) of its structural history. The orogenic stage was marked by the formation of thick (6–12 km) Upper Jurassic–Valanginian and Cretaceous petroliferous molasse units which filled the Colville foredeep. In a superposed depression (Umiat and Chukchi) of the postgeosynclinal stage, mildly deformed deposits of Paleogene-Neogene age are 600–2,100 m thick. General lateral strike of the Mesozoides of the North Alaskan system is emphasized by major faults, mostly thrust faults, which complicate the linear structures of the Brooks Range. The system discussed is essentially amagmatic; only gabbro-diabase intrusions of tentatively Jurassic age and Devonian and Jurassic(?) minor granitoid masses have been found. The intrusives commonly are located along fault zones or at the points of their intersection. As a whole, the North Alaskan fold area represents a monocyclic system with a completed miogeosynclinal style of development. Its relations with the eastern flank of the Novosibirsk-Chukotsk area are complicated by the nearly north-trending Bering strike-slip fault (Egiazarov, 1969), which is known from geological and geophysical evidence.

The Caledonides with approximately northward strike are represented by a Riphean-Silurian structural complex. The Sverdrup parageosynclinal basin (Tozer and Thorsteinsson, 1964) is fringed by Hercynian structures of the Innuitian system. The Innuitian system consists of upper Paleozoic–Cenozoic rocks as thick as 15 km. Linear broken folds and diapiric domes are developed there. The domes are distributed in the eastern part of the basin. According to the data of several workers, manifestations of hypabyssal magmatism are recognized in this area. Diapirism, nature of magmatism, and some structural features suggest that the Cornwallis–Axel Heiberg fold extends under the eastern part of the Sverdrup basin.

As was mentioned, the Arcto-Pacifides are recognized as a separate geostructural area. The Arcto-Pacifides are a complex of the major structural elements of the Verkhoyansk-Chukotsk fold area which are joined in the Kolyma geoblock. The latter consists of the Kolyma stable region and the fringing Indigirka-Kolyma fold zone, containing elements of eugeosynclinal development. The Verkhoyansk-Chukotsk and the Indigirka-Kolyma fold zones merge into the Yano-Kolyma fold system.

The Kolyma stable region and the Indigirka-Kolyma fold zone are situated in the middle Indigirka and Kolyma basins, and in the Alazeya headwaters.

Boundaries of the massif, its nature, and its age are not precisely established and, therefore, are interpreted differently. Some workers consider surrounding mountain ranges, such as the Polousnyy and Cherskiy, and the highly faulted anticlinoriums in the northwestern Yukagirskiy plateau to be boundaries of the stable region; others consider them to be raised blocks of the margin of a folded basement in the stable region. The Kolyma stable region is considered as a platform by some, as a stable region by others, and as a block of a Mesozoic fold area which subsided in Meso-Cenozoic time by still others. There is also no single opinion about the age of folded basement; it is variously dated as early Precambrian to middle Paleozoic. The Kolyma massif is fringed by anticlinoriums (or horsts-anticlinoriums) which include Polousnyy in the north, Tas-Khayakhtakh in the west, Moma in the south, and the Pre-Kolyma in the southeast, all of which are structural elements of the Indigirka-Kolyma fold zone.

Part of the stable region, where exposed on the Alazeya plateau, has an anomalously thin cover of sediments. Some workers consider this to be the central area; other workers interpret this area to be a geosynclinal uplift of a Mesozoic folded structure called the "Alazeyan uplift."

In the structural history of the stable region, as exemplified by the Indigirka-Kolyma fold zone, five tectonic stages are recognized on the basis of differences in structural framework and formations present.

Rocks of the middle Proterozoic stage are mainly schists and gneisses.

The late Proterozoic stage was a time of initiation of major trough formation, as indicated by increased thicknesses of metamorphosed sedimentary rocks—phyllite, marble, and quartzite—which are more than 500 m thick in the Alazeyan uplift and which increase in thickness toward the fold zone (to 2,000 m northward and northwestward and to 5,000 m eastward).

The early-middle Paleozoic stage was initiated by sedimentation which began in the east and in the west of the Indigirka-Kolyma zone in Ordovician time and, in the north, in Devonian time. The stage was terminated at the end of middle Paleozoic time by an incomplete episode of folding. Sedimentation was manifested in the formation of carbonate and terrigenous strata (as thick as 11 km in the west, as thick as 4.5 km in the east). A break in sedimentation during pre-Devonian time is recorded throughout the area, but a pre-Carboniferous unconformity is apparent only in the western area. At the end of the stage, thin covers of acidic extrusives and spilites were formed in the northern part of the area. On the Alazeyan uplift, rocks of the early-middle Paleozoic stage are represented by a Devonian volcanic sequence of mixed composition (300–400 m); it is replaced toward the fold zone by a terrigenous-carbonate sequence. Thickness of the terrigenous-carbonate rocks (1,500–1,700 m in the west and north and 2,500 m in the southeast) is several times greater than that of the volcanic assemblage.

The late Paleozoic–late Mesozoic tectonic stage started in the Middle Carboniferous and ended in Early Cretaceous time with linear folding in the Indigirka-Kolyma zone and linear faulting and folding on the Alazeyan uplift. The stage is characterized by volcanic-sedimentary formations with predominantly intermediate extrusives. The formations, which range in thickness from 6.3 km in the east to 14 km in the west, are related to a fold zone formed in an area of mixed eugeosynclinal and miogeosynclinal regime. On the Alazeyan uplift, however, a geanticlinal region prevailed, and the thickness there is only 2,350 m. The stage is divided into three parts according to breaks which oc-

curred in pre–Late Triassic and pre-Volgian and, locally, in pre-Cretaceous time.

The late Mesozoic–Cenozoic tectonic stage corresponds to a postgeosynclinal period of fold-system development. On the Alazeyan uplift, as well as in northern and eastern regions of the Indigirka-Kolyma fold zone, the stage is represented by mildly faulted terrigenous and volcanic strata (200–900 m) filling basins and grabens situated between elevated blocks.

Magmatic activity, apart from extrusive complexes, is represented by intrusions of differing age and composition. Among them are presumably middle Proterozoic mafic sills and dikes (altered into amphibolites) and masses of altered granitoids; late Proterozoic bodies of ultramafic rocks and granitoids; Triassic stocks and lens-shaped bodies with compositions from ultramafic to alkalic-acidic; Late Jurassic gabbroid masses and minor granitoid bodies; Early Cretaceous granitoids; Late Cretaceous and Paleogene granitoids; and alkalic granitoids, monzonites, and gabbroids.

The Verkhoyansk fold zone, which is the westernmost structural element of the complex Yano-Kolyma fold system, is situated between the Indigirka-Kolyma fold zone and the Siberian platform. The border is marked by deep-seated faults.

The Verkhoyansk miogeosyncline, of monocyclic development, was formed in late Paleozoic time and was converted into a folded structure at the end of the Early Cretaceous. Late Proterozoic carbonate-terrigenous, Vendian–middle Paleozoic terrigenous-carbonate, and late Paleozoic–Mesozoic terrigenous (Verkhoyansk complex) formations reflect tectonic stages of structural development and compose part of the structures of the Verkhoyansk fold zone.

Late Proterozoic carbonate-terrigenous formations are most widespread south of the Verkhoyansk fold zone, where they reach great thicknesses (8 km). The rocks are substantially thinner (2 km) in the northern part. An equivalent pattern is established for terrigenous-carbonate formations of the Vendian–middle Paleozoic stage. Their complete section (12–13 km thick) is known from the south Verkhoyansk area, where essentially terrigenous deposits form the lower part, and terrigenous rocks, gypsum, and anhydrite form the upper part. Thickness of strata of similar composition in the north Verkhoyansk area decreases to 2.5 km. Late Proterozoic–middle Paleozoic formations of the Verkhoyansk fold zone are a direct continuation of coeval formations of the Siberian platform and form the basement of the Verkhoyansk miogeosyncline.

Terrigenous formations of the late Paleozoic–Mesozoic stage reflect the structural history of the Verkhoyansk miogeosyncline. Three periods of sedimentation are distinguished—late Paleozoic, Triassic, and Jurassic–Early Cretaceous—wherein marine argillaceous and arenaceous-argillaceous sediments are dominant at the beginning of each period and lagoonal-marine, paralic, and continental deposits are dominant at the end.

Late Paleozoic formations (10–11 km thick) are widespread within the Verkhoyansk mega-anticlinorium. Triassic rocks are 5–7 km thick within the Yano-Indigirka mega-anticlinorium. Jurassic and Late Cretaceous formations in the Lena trough, which represents a western-most structure of the Verkhoyansk miogeosyncline, are about 5.5 km thick; in the Inyali-Debin synclinorium, these rocks are about 3.9 km thick.

The Verkhoyansk fold area includes a combination of major anticlinal and synclinal structures with different, commonly low degrees of rock deformation. Within this fold area, a set of long-lived major faults commonly forms the margins of large-scale structures. In the south, northwest, and northeast of the Verkhoyansk zone, changes in trend of the main folding are apparent. A larger northwest virgation goes through the Laptev Sea shelf and, in a reduced form, reaches the Taymyr fold area.

Magmatic activity in the Verkhoyansk fold zone is manifested only by intrusives which formed during the second half of the Devonian and in Early Triassic time as intersecting and layered diabase bodies, and in late Mesozoic time as granitoid masses. The former are an equivalent of Siberian platform trap rocks, whereas the latter are related to eastern and southern peripheries of the fold zone formed during orogenic and postorogenic stages of structural development. Equivalents of volcanic-plutonic formations of adjacent eugeosynclinal areas are also manifested.

The Arcto-Atlantides are represented by structures of the late Caledonides of Greenland, Spitsbergen, northern Scandinavia, and Scandinavia–Novaya Zemlya (where they are almost completely submerged), and by the Hercynides of Novaya Zemlya, Vaygach Island, Pay-Khoy, Taymyr, and Severnaya Zemlya. Stable regions—the Eria platform and Barents massif—which may be considered as vast basement blocks of the Grampian mobile belt, are enclosed within the Caledonian geostructure.

The Eria platform—more precisely, its basement exposures in the form of the Archean-Lewisian complex—in northern Scotland and the Hebrides was partly regenerated by the middle Proterozoic (Laxfordian) tectogenesis. It is assumed that a larger part of the platform is submerged in the Atlantic Ocean. However, because its existence is doubtful and its boundaries are not precisely determined, it is not discussed in this paper.

The Barents stable region is situated in the northern part of the Barents Sea. Surrounding it are the Caledonides and structures of the stable region in the north, which are truncated by a continental slope bordering the Nansen basin. The stable region crops out in Nordaustlandet, where it is composed of a pre-Riphean granite-gneiss complex. The complex, which completely underlies Belyy Island, presumably crops out on the ocean bottom between the island and Spitsbergen. Throughout the rest of the area, the stable region is under the platform cover and forms the basement of the Barents plate. Based on present knowledge, a working hypothesis suggests that the whole basement is pre-Baykalian. The most deeply buried parts of the basement surface presumably reach depths of 5–7 km. Four main structural forms within the platform cover are suggested: the Franz Josef Land uplifted block, Klenov syncline, Labrov Beach ridge, and Olgin trough. The platform cover is composed chiefly of late Paleozoic and Mesozoic deposits but also contains Early Cretaceous basalts. Deposition of sedimentary beds probably began during the Late Devonian Epoch.

The junction of the ancient Barents stable region and the Caledonides of Spitsbergen with structures of the northern shore of the European continent remains unclear. Significant formational and structural differences of the Greenland-Spitsbergen and British-Scandinavian Caledonides, a different structural history of geosynclinal troughs which were present at the sites where the Caledonides developed, and data on Bear Island geology cast doubt on the continuation of the fold systems between Scandinavia and Spitsbergen. More probably, they were separated by an ancient stable region. There is much evidence in favor of a Caledonides branch in the Barents Sea extending from Scandinavia to Severnaya Zemlya. However, it is accepted that the Norwegian Caledonides terminated near the northeastern end of Scandinavia. It is possible that basement structures of the Pechora plate project into a northern part of the Barents shelf.

The Caledonides of Spitsbergen and East Greenland are situated northwest of the Barents stable region and form a geosynclinal belt separating the East European and Greenland-Canadian ancient platforms. Analysis of the Caledonian history of Spitsbergen implies formational and structural similarity with East Greenland. Both areas are characterized by continuous miogeosynclinal development during late Precambrian and early Paleozoic time.

Three structural-stratigraphic complexes are distinguished in Caledonides structures. They are the crystalline basement, the main geosynclinal complex, and the orogenic complex of inner and superposed basins. The pre-Riphean crystalline basement exposed in Spitsbergen and in cores of the Caledonian anticlinoriums is composed of highly metamorphosed volcanic-sedimentary formations formed of plagiogneiss, amphibolite, quartzite, marble, and schist. In East Greenland, crystalline rocks of the basement crop out in outliers and in thrust blocks (Haller, 1964).

The formation of the major geosynclinal complex in Spitsbergen had three stages. During the early Riphean stage, predominantly shale sequences less than 5 km thick accumulated. During the middle Riphean, lower terrigenous-carbonate transgressive units and upper terrigenous regressive formations (including tillite-like rocks) with total thickness of 5–7 km accumulated. This stage was climaxed by general uplift and peneplanation. In East Greenland a thick sequence of terrigenous and carbonate rocks (10–12 km) accumulated during the late Precambrian. The early Paleozoic stage in both regions was a time of mild tectonic activity and deposition of quartz sands and shallow-water carbonate sediments. The total thickness is 2–3 km. The sedimentary environment was nearly that of a subplatform.

A general inversion of the Caledonian geosyncline took place in early Paleozoic–Silurian time. Emplacement of granite and subalkalic intrusions and associated metamorphism resulting in "rejuvenation" of the Caledonides crystalline basement protrusion are related to the inversion (Krasil'shchikov, 1965). During the Devonian orogenic period, grabenlike basins were formed. They are filled with terrigenous variegated molasse strata up to 6.5 km thick in the northern part of West Spitsbergen. Equivalent formations of "Old Red"-type sandstone are characteristic of the Caledonides of East Greenland, where their thickness increases to 8–10 km.

Folded structures of the Caledonides of Spitsbergen later formed the basement of a young mobile platform. During a period of platform development, which began in the Early Carboniferous, four stages are distinguished. These stages coincide with the main sedimentary cycles and are separated by epochs of uplift and peneplanation. The stages are late Paleozoic, Mesozoic, early Cenozoic, and late Cenozoic. During these times a sedimentary cover was formed with a total thickness which in places of greatest downwarping of the Caledonian basement reaches 5–7 km (West Spitsbergen trough).

The Scandinavian Caledonides stretch northeastward along the Norwegian Sea and form a part of the structure of the adjacent shelf, where deposits are 50–150 km thick. Miogeosynclinal and eugeosynclinal zones of a more complex structure than that of the Caledonides of Spitsbergen are recognized.

The Scandinavian geosyncline was deformed at the beginning of the late Proterozoic, and numerous folds were developed in the eugeosynclinal zone (Strand, 1961). It is supposed that the closing phase of Caledonian tectogenesis (Silurian–Middle Devonian) in the eugeosyncline was earlier than in the miogeosynclinal zone. Because of southeastward movements along low-angle faults, structures of the miogeosynclinal zone commonly are overthrust onto the platform cover; furthermore, the Baykalides of the East European platform commonly are overlain by cover structures of the eugeosynclinal zone. Width of the Caledonian deformation zone decreases greatly northward. Largest displacements (up to 100 km) are established near the Arctic Circle, and it is reasonable to consider the region as transitional between the Arcto-Atlantides and the Atlantides. The formation of structures was accompanied by intrusions of different size and composition and a wide range of metamorphic processes of different types.

Formational composition of the miogeosynclinical zone is rather simple. A well-known Riphean sparagmite formation (7 km thick) represented predominantly by sandstones and conglomerates is situated at the base. Northward in the Riphean section, shales and dolomites are fairly abundant. Riphean deposits are conformably overlain by a much thinner carbonate-terrigenous Cambro-Silurian sequence.

Sections of the eugeosynclinal zone are more complex. There, the Cambro-Silurian sequence (up to 4–5 km) unconformably lies on the sparagmitic units and crystalline basement. The zone is characterized by high-grade metamorphic rocks and the presence of basic flows and tuffs (forming a part of a terrigenous-volcanic complex up to 2.5 km thick). Trondheim (volcanic-terrigenous) and Nordland (volcanic-carbonate-terrigenous) facies types are distinguished. The first occur both in the south and in the north and correspond to the eugeosynclinal trough. The Nordland facies are distributed only in the north and are absent in the Arctic Circle region. It is suggested that the Nordland facies formed in a geanticlinal environment within a eugeosynclinal zone.

Southern regions of the Scandinavian Caledonides differ from northern regions by the presence of orogenic basins (troughs, depressions) filled with redbeds. Large intrusive and extrusive igneous bodies are associated with the largest depression (Oslo graben), whereas equivalent structures developed in the Caledonian Arcto-Atlantides are not characterized by igneous rocks.

The Caledonides of Scandinavia–Severnaya Zemlya are poorly known because they are mostly submerged. In addition, over extensive areas they are overlain by a sedimentary cover. The tectonic structure thus is problematic.

Stretching sublatitudinally from Finnmark, the Scandinavia–Severnaya Zemlya Caledonides separate the Barents stable region from the East European platform. In the Barents Sea they widen, forming northeast and southwest branches, on the western parts of which the late Hercynides of the Pay-Khoy–Novaya Zemlya fold system are developed. The northeast branch enters the Kara Sea, where its southwest margin turns northward and crops out in eastern Severnaya Zemlya. Branching of Caledonian folds from northwest to northeast is observed. The Caledonian folds are composed of a Cambro-Silurian sequence up to 9 km thick almost devoid of magmatic formations. Inherited depressions filled with a Devonian carbonate-terrigenous sequence up to 1,400 m thick are developed on Caledonian structures. In some sections the sequence is clear: terrigenous Cambrian formations at the base, Ordovician and Silurian carbonate formations, Early and Middle Devonian evaporites, and Late Devonian terrigenous redbeds. Eastward attenuation of Caledonian structural movements is evident

from structural studies. Though the rest of the Scandinavia–Novaya Zemlya fold zone is poorly known from comparative tectonic studies, it is possible to suggest that it is broadly comparable to the Scandinavian Caledonides, having the same type of development but in a milder form.

The late Hercynian Pay-Khoy–Novaya Zemlya fold system is situated between the Scandinavia–Severnaya Zemlya Caledonides and the submarine projection of the Epihercynian West Siberian plate and the Epibaykalian Pechora plate, which is the northernmost element of the East European platform. The system is a part of the Ural–Novaya Zemlya fold area. Structures of the Urals belong to the Atlantides, and those of Novaya Zemlya are assigned to the Arcto-Atlantides. The Arcto-Atlantides differ from the Atlantides in structural form, formation sequences, magmatism, and time of completion of folding. For example, miogeosynclinal and eugeosynclinal zones which are present in the Urals are absent in the Pay-Khoy–Novaya Zemlya fold system. In the latter, the southern half has a different structure from that of the northern half because of the heterogeneity of the Hercynides basement. In the southern half of the Pay-Khoy–Novaya Zemlya fold system, the structures were formed mainly on Baykalides similar to the Hercynides of the Urals. In the northern half the structures are situated along the periphery of the Caledonian geosynclinal system. Among the structural features common to the systems mentioned are foredeep-type structures and a major axial deep fault in each system.

Since Cambrian time the southern half of the Pay-Khoy–Novaya Zemlya fold system has been developing monocyclically like the Ural miogeosynclinal zone. The sedimentary sequence (more than 9 km thick) contains formations which range from terrigenous at the base to Lower Permian flyshlike strata. Middle Paleozoic intrusive and extrusive basic rocks are most abundant. The main structures are two anticlinoriums joined *en échelon* along a major fault.

General structure of the northern half of the region is a complex anticlinorium. Abrupt facies changes, local erosional and angular unconformities, and numerous folds and faults are observed there. Two structural stages are divided into substages corresponding to Caledonian and Hercynian periods of development.

The anticlinorium core exposes a Cambro-Silurian terrigenous formation more than 3.2 km thick in which a few thin sheets of mafic extrusives are present. Next above is a Silurian–Early Devonian terrigenous-carbonate sequence with a total thickness of about 2.6 km. It is overlain by Middle Devonian molasse-like deposits more than 1 km thick. Their sedimentation, together with the intrusions of Middle Devonian granitoids, climaxed the Caledonian stage of development.

The Hercynian stage began with the formation of an early Frasnian volcanic-sedimentary complex as thick as 2.2 km. Basic flows and associated tuffs, as well as comagmatic intrusions, were widespread. The next event, which lasted till the end of the Carboniferous, was deposition of a carbonate-terrigenous sequence with a total thickness of about 3 km. Sedimentation of carbonate rocks took place mainly in the western regions. In the Early Permian, a flyschlike sequence was deposited. In central Novaya Zemlya, it underlies a major synclinorium where thickness of Lower Permian rocks is about 2–2.5 km. An orogenic stage was marked by intense folding, appearance of Late Permian molasse, and granitic (P_2-T_1) intrusion. At the beginning of a post-geosynclinal period, intense block movements and small injections of granite magma (T_3-I_1) took place. Sedimentary beds of corresponding age are not of great importance in the general structure of the Pay-Khoy–Novaya Zemlya fold system.

The Taymyr–Severnaya Zemlya fold area is the easternmost geostructure of the Arcto-Atlantides. It unites structures of Taymyr and the Novaya Zemlya archipelago, as well as adjacent structures of the western part of the Kara Sea. Formation of the Taymyr–Severnaya Zemlya geostructure took place in different ways. The following main tectonic stages are distinguished: Precambrian, early middle Paleozoic, late Paleozoic–early Mesozoic, and late Mesozoic–Cenozoic.

The basement of folded structures of Taymyr and Severnaya Zemlya is made up of differently deformed and metamorphosed sequences of presumed late Archean and Proterozoic terrigenous, terrigenous-carbonate, and extrusive formations with a total thickness of more than 16 km. The sequence is more complete on the north side of Taymyr, whereas, on Bol'shevik and October Revolution Islands, only the upper part of the section crops out. Accumulation of the sequences took place in a vast, almost north-striking geosyncline which began to form as early as the late Archean; inversion of the geosyncline is assigned to the end of the Proterozoic. Repeated magmatic activity resulted in the formation of mainly granitic intrusions; however, some basic intrusives of different ages and composition are present.

The oldest rocks—all of them affected by tectonic processes, magmatic activity, and deep-seated magmatism—are various types of gneiss and schist, mainly of amphibolite facies, which are characteristic of the lower and middle parts of the Precambrian section. Ultrametamorphism led to the formation of migmatite fields and "shadow" granitoids; the original structures and textures are barely preserved in some places.

The subsequent early-middle Paleozoic stage was marked by development of the subplatform environment in Taymyr, where the accumulation of carbonate and terrigenous-carbonate deposits with a total thickness of 4-6 km took place. In the Severnaya Zemlya archipelago area, different terrigenous, terrigenous-carbonate, and salt-bearing sequences with a total thickness of about 10 km were deposited under unstable conditions in a miogeosyncline during Cambrian-Devonian time. Caledonian folding was manifested rather distinctly in pre-Ordovician, pre-Silurian, and Devonian time, resulting in formation of linear north- and northwest-striking folded structures. Magmatism was manifested in the formation of small intrusive and subintrusive bodies. These Caledonian movements were only indirectly manifested in Taymyr.

Subsequent development of the Taymyr–Severnaya Zemlya fold-area structural framework during the Paleozoic–early Mesozoic and late Mesozoic–Cenozoic stages is revealed only in geologic data from Taymyr; definitely dated Carboniferous, Permian, and Triassic deposits have not been recognized in the Severnaya Zemlya archipelago.

The late Paleozoic and early Mesozoic sequences of Taymyr have a generally similar structural framework and are separated from underlying rocks by an unconformity. In this area, Middle Carboniferous tectonic activity predetermined the emplacement of the sublatitudinal Taymyr trough, which was limited in the north by a deep fault zone along the southern side of the rising Kara stable region. The Kara stable region is situated not only within the limits of the Kara Sea, but also includes the northern side of Taymyr and the Severnaya Zemlya archipelago. Subsidence of the Taymyr trough was greatest (up to 10 km) in the fault zone. In the south the basin merged with an epicontinental sea which covered the northern margin of the Middle Siberian plateau. During Late Permian time, deep faults appeared along the northern flank of the upland and in its western part. It is possible that the Taymyr miogeosynclinal trough projected eastward and was linked with the Verkhoyansk miogeosyncline.

Initially, marine carbonate and terrigenous formations were deposited under miogeosynclinal conditions. Later, as a result of irregular oscillatory movements in the south of the basin, environments favorable for accumulation of paralic and limnic coal-bearing formations were established sporadically. In the central and eastern parts of the Taymyr trough, however, conditions remained favorable for accumulation of marine terrigenous and, locally, paralic coal-bearing deposits. Sequences 5–8 km thick were formed. Near the end of the Permian Period, a tendency toward arching of the Kara stable region caused the appearance of numerous faults within the region, and the faults served as paths for granitic and partially basic intrusions. In areas adjacent to the south miogeosynclinal trough and on the northern margin of the Siberian platform, the faults served as routes (channels) for intrusions of sills and trap magma.

During the first half of the Triassic Period, inversion of the trough took place. Folded structures which were formed joined the southern and southeastern sides of the Kara arch, making a vast arc belt. Former structures, which had been considerably changed in orientation, were involved in intensive tectonic movements. The creation of intermontane depressions is related to an orogenic stage wherein the Triassic molasse was deposited. During the final stage of the deformation, alkalic granitoid intrusions were formed.

In the Triassic Period the structural framework of Taymyr took its final shape, which was only slightly complicated later by block-fault movements.

The late Mesozoic–Cenozoic stage of development of the Taymyr–Severnaya Zemlya fold area was characterized by differential structural movements which resulted in subsidence of separate blocks and allowed marine transgressions into the subsiding area. Development of a major Yenisey-Lena trough bordering the Taymyr fold system in the south began at this time. In Early Cretaceous time, separation into the Ust'-Yenisey, Khatanga, and Lena-Anabar depres-

sions took place, and terrigenous sequences accumulated. Cretaceous deposits are coal-bearing. Locally, they form gentle structures of platform type.

References Cited

Atlasov, I. P., *et al.*, eds., 1966, Tectonic map of the Arctic and Subarctic: 22d Internat. Geol. Cong., India, Comm. Geol. Map World, Sci. Commun., p. 121–128.

—— *et al.*, 1968, Sravnitelnaya tektonika polyarnykh oblastey Zemli, *in* Orogenicheskiye poyasa: Moscow, Izd. "Nauka," p. 22–25.

—— *et al.*, 1970, Obyasnitelnaya zapiska k tektonicheskoy karte Arktiki i Subarktiki masshtaba 1: 5,000,000 (Explanatory text for the tectonic map of the Arctic and Subarctic, scale 1:5,000,000): Moscow, Izd. "Nedra," 44 p.

Bogdanov, A. A., *et al.*, eds., 1966, Tectonic map of Europe, *in* On the preparation of the first international tectonic map of the world: 22d Internat. Geol. Cong., India, Comm. Geol. Map World, Sci. Commun., p. 135–139.

Borisov, A. A., 1967, Glubinnaya struktura territorii SSSR po geofizicheskim dannym: Moscow, Izd. "Nedra," 303 p.

Canada Geological Survey, 1969, Geological map of Canada: Canada Geol. Survey Map 1250A, scale 1:5,000,000.

Churkin, Michael, Jr., 1969, Paleozoic tectonic history of the Arctic basin north of Alaska: Science, v. 165, no. 3893, p. 549–555.

Demenitskaya, R. M., A. M. Karasik, and Yu. G. Kiselev, 1967, Novyye dannyye o geologicheskom stroyenii dna Severnogo Ledovitogo okeana po materialam geofizicheskikh issledovany, *in* Metodika, tekhnika i rezultaty geofizicheskoy razvedki: Moscow, Izd. "Nedra," p. 31–38.

Egiazarov, B. Kh., 1969, Arktidy-osobaya geostruktura Zemli, *in* Mezozoysky tektogenez: Magadan, Izd. SVKNII, p. 17–20.

—— *et al.*, 1971, Tectonic map of the polar regions of the earth: Leningrad, Research Inst. of the Geology of the Arctic, 4 sheets, scale 1:10,000,000.

Elvers, Douglas, George Peter, and Robert Moses, 1967, Analysis of magnetic lineations in the North Pacific (abs.): Am. Geophys. Union Trans., v. 48, no. 1, p. 89.

Fotiadi, E. E., *et al.*, 1969, Geofizicheskoye izucheniye tektonicheskogo stroyeniya i glubinnoy struktury zemnoy kory vneshney zony Tikhookeanskogo podvizhnogo poyasa na Vostoke SSSR, *in* Stroyeniye i razvitiye zemnoy kory na Sovetskom Dalnem Vostoke: Moscow, Izd. "Nauka," p. 6–20.

Haller, John, 1964. Geologischen Einfuhrung, *in* Zur petrographie von Nordhoeks Bjergund Nördlunds Alper, Hudson Land (zentral Ostgrönland): Medd om Grønland, v. 168, no. 5, p. 9–19.

Kheraskov, N. P., 1967, Tektonika i formatsii: Moscow, Izd. "Nauka," 404 p.

King, Philip B., compiler, 1969, Tectonic map of North America, scale 1:5,000,000: Washington, D.C., U.S. Geol. Survey, 2 sheets.

Krasil'shchikov, A. A., 1965, Nekotoryye osobennosti geologicheskogo stroyeniya severnoy chasti arkhipelaga Shpitsbergen, *in* Materialy po geologii Shpitsbergena: Leningrad, Izd. Nauchno-Issled. Inst. Geologii Arktiki, p. 29–44.

Krasny, L. I., 1966, Osnovnyye cherty geologicheskogo

stroyeniya, *in* Geologicheskoye stroyeniye severo-za-padnoy chasti Tikhookeanskogo podvizhnogo po-yasa: Moscow, Izd. "Nedra," p. 24–39.

—— ed., 1967, Geological map of the northwestern part of the Pacific mobile belt: Moscow.

Markov, F. G., ed., 1966a, Geologicheskaya karta Ark-tiki i Subarktiki (Geologic map of the Arctic and Subarctic): Moscow, Min. Geol.–Nauchno-Issled. Inst. Geol. Arktiki, scale 1:5,000,000.

—— ed., 1966b, Tectonic map of the northeast of the USSR: Moscow.

Nikolayevsky, A. A., 1967, Glubinnoye stroyeniye severo-vostoka po geofizicheskim dannym: Trudy Severo-Vostoch. Kompleksnogo Nauchno-Issled. Inst., no. 30, p. 39–43.

Puminov, A. P., and A. F. Grachev, 1969, Karta no-veyshey tektoniki Arktiki i Subarktiki, *in* Noveyshiye dvizheniya, vulkanizm i zemletryaseniya materikov i dna okeanov: Moscow, Izd. "Nauka," p. 177–183.

Pushcharovsky, Yu. M., 1963, Tectonic map of the Arctic: Moscow.

—— and G. B. Udintsev, eds., 1970, Tektoniche-skaya karta Tikhookeanskogo segmenta Zemli (Tec-tonic map of the Pacific segment of the earth): Moscow, Akad. Nauk SSSR, Geol. Inst.–Okeanol.

Inst., 6 sheets, scale 1:10,000,000.

Shell Oil Company, 1959, Map of tectonic elements of the North Polar region.

Spizharskiy, T. N., and L. I. Borovikov, 1966, Tectonic map of the Soviet Union on a scale of 1:2,500,000: 22d Internat. Geol. Cong., India, Comm. Geol. Map World, Sci. Commun., p. 111–119.

Stille, Hans, 1943, Tektonische probleme in der Neuen und der Alten Welt: Deutsch Geol. Gessel. Zeitschr., v. 95, no. 1–2, p. 33–46.

Strand, Trygve, 1961, The Scandinavian Caledonides: a review: Am. Jour. Sci., v. 259, no. 3, p. 161–172.

Tozer, E. T., and R. Thorsteinsson, 1964, Western Queen Elizabeth Islands, Arctic Archipelago: Can-ada Geol. Survey Mem. 332, 242 p.

Vashchilov, Yu. A., 1963, Glubinnyye razlomy Yano-Kolymskoy skladchatoy zony i Okhotsko-Chaun-skogo vulkanogennogo poyasa i ikh rol v obrazova-nii intruzy i v formirovanii struktur (po geofiziches-kim dannym): Sovetskaya Geologiya, no. 4, p. 54–72.

Yanshin, A. L., 1966, Tectonic map of Eurasia: 22d Internat. Geol. Cong., India, Comm. Geol. Map World, Sci. Commun., p. 103–109.

Specific Character of Magnetic Field and Development of Oceanic Ridges in Arctic Ocean Basin: Summary[1]

A. M. KARASIK, R. M. DEMENITSKAYA, and V. G. SHCHELOVANOV[2]

Leningrad, USSR

The Eurasian basin, which includes the mid-ocean Gakkel Ridge and the abyssal Nansen and Amundsen basins, is the only region of the world's oceans where the magnetic field has been thoroughly studied. Systematic surveys have also been made over the Lomonosov and Mendeleyev Ridges and in intervening basins adjacent to the Eurasian coast of the Arctic Ocean. Being so well surveyed, the Arctic basin is particularly useful for studying the relation of magnetic anomalies to complex oceanic regions.

The magnetic pattern of the Eurasian basin is undoubtedly related to the global paleomagnetic-reversal sequence, but some special characteristics include the following: (1) a subdued intensity of anomaly amplitudes; (2) relative displacement between magnetic-anomaly zones and morphologic boundaries; (3) poor contrast between positive and negative anomalies; (4) many transversely oriented breaks with apparent offsets of the magnetic-anomaly pattern; (5) cases of disappearance of distinct anomalies or separate groups of anomalies; (6) poor fit between observed profiles and those generated from models where a constant spreading rate has been assumed; and (7) a relatively low degree of bilateral symmetry.

The analysis of these characteristics provides insight into processes of sea-floor spreading that opened the Arctic Ocean and formed the structures of the Eurasian basin.

The magnetic character of the Lomonosov Ridge suggests that it drifted away from the axes of opening of the Eurasian basin.

Magnetic profiles over the Mendeleyev Ridge and adjacent basins show anomalies of typically oceanic intensity. However, there is a poor degree of correlation of linear anomaly patterns. This irregular anomaly pattern can be interpreted in the context of global ocean-floor spreading only if a pattern of complex and disjunctive tectonics is assumed for the region. The rather high-intensity magnetic field over the Mendeleyev Ridge and in the Makarov and Podvodnikov basins contrasts with the smoother field in the Eurasian basin, thus indicating sharp differences in magnetization of the floor of the two areas. Calculated depths to the source of anomalies are similar for the two areas.

[1] Manuscript received, August 1, 1972.

[2] Research Institute of the Geology of the Arctic.

Regional Arctic Geology of Alaska

Tectonic Framework of Northern and Central Alaska[1]

ERNEST H. LATHRAM[2]

Menlo Park, California 94025

Abstract The tectonic framework of Alaska in use through 1969 was based on Payne's map, "Mesozoic and Cenozoic Tectonic Elements of Alaska," on which he showed and described positive structures (geanticlines) and negative linear areas (geosynclines) established by Mesozoic earth movements and basins containing Tertiary clastic rocks. King, on his 1969 "Tectonic Map of North America," added Precambrian and Paleozoic data and stressed the nature of tectonic materials, reclassifying all deposits by type and age of orogeny. In the plethora of plate-tectonic speculations which have appeared since 1968, so bewildering an array of possible crustal movements has been postulated that the tectonic history has been confused rather than clarified.

The essential skeletal elements of the observable tectonic framework consist of (1) a Precambrian and early Paleozoic Arctic (Innuitian) fold belt in the Brooks Range and northward; (2) a Precambrian and early Paleozoic "Cordilleran" fold belt south of the Yukon River and along the front of the Alaska Range; (3) a late Paleozoic (Permian) and Mesozoic Yukon eugeosyncline between the older fold belts and beneath the southern Bering Sea, plus associated miogeosynclinal or shelf sedimentary strata over the Brooks Range and northward; (4) the western edge of the Yukon shelf, stable through Precambrian and Paleozoic time; and (5) the Seward Peninsula block, a stable shelf in Paleozoic time but the site of eugeosynclinal sedimentation and deformation in Precambrian time. Superimposed on these primary elements on land and on the continental shelf are Cretaceous and Tertiary basins containing the detritus of late Mesozoic, Laramide, and younger uplifts. The location and form of these basins are controlled by older structures which have been reactivated.

Two conclusions seem apparent: (1) Observable tectonic elements have inherited their form and position from Paleozoic and possibly Precambrian structures, and the history of their development shows a close relation between them and adjacent elements. (2) Alaska is not formed from segments which were rifted from other continents and drifted to a final resting place; instead, it is a continental mass formed by the accretion of fold belts caused by interaction between the Canadian and Siberian shields and the crust of the ancient Arctic and Pacific oceans in Precambrian and most of Paleozoic time, and between the resulting larger continental mass and the crust of an ancient Pacific ocean (including the present Bering Sea area) since late Paleozoic time.

Introduction

The framework of Alaskan tectonic elements in use prior to 1969 was formalized by Payne

[1] Manuscript received, September 20, 1971. Publication authorized by the Director, U.S. Geological Survey.

[2] U.S. Geological Survey.

(1955), who developed and enlarged on the work of Mertie (1930), Smith (1939), Eardley (1948), and Cady et al. (1955). This framework dealt primarily with elements established as a result of Mesozoic and Cenozoic tectonism; however, it has been used extensively as a frame of reference in discussions of earlier earth movements. The primary tectonic elements identified were geosynclines and geanticlines—i.e., the large, linear negative elements predominantly occupied by Mesozoic strata (the sites of deposition) and the linear positive elements chiefly occupied by Paleozoic and older rocks (the sites of erosion or nondeposition)—as well as superimposed smaller, sublinear to nonlinear troughs and basins, mostly sites of Cenozoic deposition. The general geology of the elements was described by Miller et al. (1959), and the tectonic history reflected in this framework was summarized by Gates and Gryc (1963) and Gates et al. (1968).

Because of the paucity of firm data on pre-Mesozoic events, few attempts were made to systematize pre-Mesozoic tectonics prior to compilation of the "Tectonic Map of North America" by King (1969a). Unlike Payne (1955), who stressed structural features, King stressed the nature of the rock materials. In addition, King successfully classified not only Cenozoic and Mesozoic, but also Paleozoic and Precambrian, deposits by type and by age of orogeny.

Both Payne's and King's syntheses, as well as their tectonic summaries, were based on the hypothesis that, during Paleozoic time, all of Alaska was a part of the Cordilleran geosyncline. Deposition of strata south of the Brooks Range was considered to have been in the eugeosynclinal zone; deposition in the Brooks Range and northward was probably in the miogeosynclinal realm. The northern border of the miogeosyncline was considered to be a platform or shield. This general hypothesis was questioned by Jeletzky (1962), Ziegler (1967), Churkin and Brabb (1967), Churkin (1969, 1970a, b), and Tailleur (1969), all of whom presented evidence that the pre-Mississippian rocks of northern Alaska, because they were

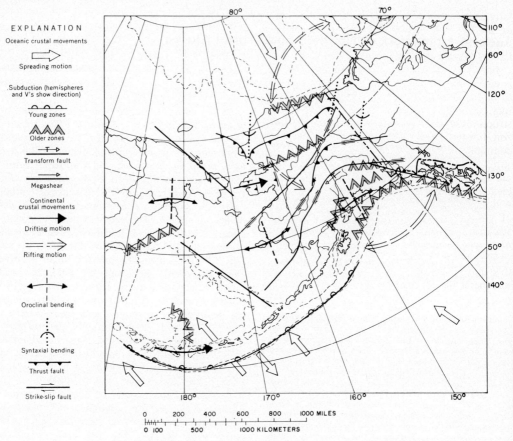

EXPLANATION

Oceanic crustal movements

⇨

Spreading motion

Subduction (hemispheres
and V's show direction)

Young zones

Older zones

Transform fault

Megashear

Continental
crustal movements

Drifting motion

Rifting motion

Oroclinal bending

Syntaxial bending

Thrust fault

Strike-slip fault

0   200   400   600   800   1000 MILES
0   100   500   1000 KILOMETERS

FIG. 1—Compilation of proposed crustal movements affecting Alaska.

deposited in a domain different from that of the Cordilleran geosyncline, probably are part of the Innuitian fold belt. King (1969b, p. 53) also recognized the possibility that the Innuitian fold belt may be related to early Paleozoic structures of the Brooks Range.

The concept of continental as well as oceanic mobility of the "new global tectonics" (Izacks et al., 1968) and the strategic location of Alaska with respect to postulated motions of the American, Pacific, and Eurasian plates have resulted in a stream of papers since 1968. Together, these papers present such a bewildering array of possible crustal movements in Alaska (Fig. 1) that the tectonic history has been confused rather than clarified. Most postulations are highly speculative, and it is difficult to assess their value in the absence of supporting factual data.

Despite the confusion engendered by the proposed crustal movements, the hypothesis of

plate tectonics has opened new and exciting areas for the study of tectonic processes. As Coney (1970) has pointed out, this new hypothesis requires a reassessment of older concepts and a revision in the classic nomenclature. Such an exercise is not appropriate for this paper, but some clarification of the usage of terms is necessary. "Eugeosyncline" will be used to characterize the area of active interplay between oceanic crust and continental masses and the resultant volcanic, volcanogenic, and related deposits formed in that area, whether in single or multiple troughs, welts, or arcs. The eugeosyncline is not half of a structurally downwarped couple, but is simply the border of an active continental margin. Nor is its floor necessarily entirely oceanic crust; there are numerous examples of younger eugeosynclinal deposits on older continental crust in Alaska and elsewhere (Rast, 1969, and others). Miogeosynclinal or shelf deposits are those formed totally on continental crust near either an active or an inactive margin but in a nonvolcanic, passive domain of vertical or extensional (not laterally compressive) movement.

Payne's (1955) terminology of geanticlines is widely recognized and is useful in discussions of the distribution of strata and of tectonic history. Because the term "geanticline" implies structural warping of strata, the positive Mesozoic linear elements to which he applied it are commonly expected to display a structural or stratigraphic symmetry—which they may not actually possess. Payne recognized this fact and clearly limited his usage of the term to ". . . a belt of relatively old rocks flanked by belts of younger rocks." However, to minimize the structural connotation, herein the positive element will be referred to as a "geanticline."

With this background, it is the purpose of this paper to identify the essential skeletal members that make up the observable tectonic framework of northern and central Alaska, to describe briefly their character and interrelations, and to make some observations with respect to the application of plate-tectonic concepts in deciphering the tectonic history of Alaska.

SIMPLIFIED TECTONIC FRAMEWORK

In the most simplified sense, northern and central Alaska are dominated by three major eugeosynclinal terranes. Two of these are represented in the remnants of old fold belts—a Precambrian and early Paleozoic fold belt in northern Alaska and a Precambrian and early Paleozoic fold belt south of the Yukon River. The third is represented by the deposits of the late Paleozoic and Mesozoic Yukon eugeosyncline which lie between exposures of the older fold belts (Fig. 2). Two areas of lesser extent have been generally stable throughout much of Alaska's history and have, to a certain extent,

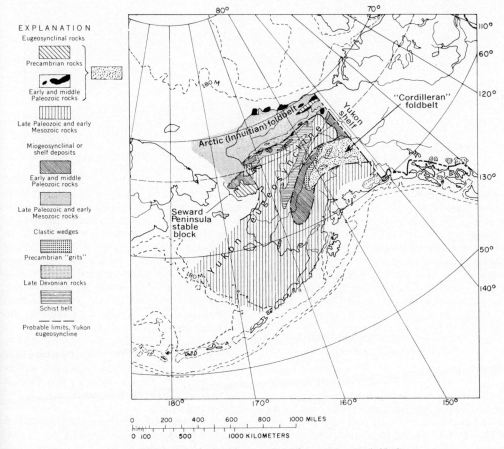

FIG. 2—Primary tectonic elements of northern and central Alaska.

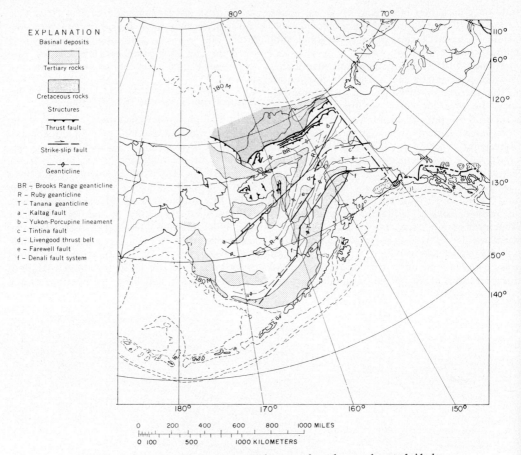

EXPLANATION
Basinal deposits

Tertiary rocks

Cretaceous rocks

Structures

Thrust fault

Strike-slip fault

Geanticline

BR – Brooks Range geanticline
R – Ruby geanticline
T – Tanana geanticline
a – Kaltag fault
b – Yukon-Porcupine lineament
c – Tintina fault
d – Livengood thrust belt
e – Farewell fault
f – Denali fault system

FIG. 3—Basinal deposits and structural features of northern and central Alaska.

constrained the boundaries of the major elements; these areas are the Seward Peninsula block and the western edge of the Yukon shelf. Superimposed on these five primary elements are (1) Cretaceous clastic basins, which represent the erosional products of folding or rejuvenation of the fold belts in late Mesozoic time, and (2) Tertiary basins, which are more restricted and contain the detritus generated by Laramide and younger uplifts (Fig. 3).

EARLY PALEOZOIC AND PRECAMBRIAN ARCTIC (INNUITIAN) FOLD BELT

Early Paleozoic rocks in northern Alaska generally have been found to be the remnants of an old fold belt rather than miogeosynclinal or shelf strata deposited against a northern stable shield (Fig. 2).

The buried Arctic platform, where it has been penetrated by drilling at and south of

Point Barrow and eastward along the Arctic coast, is underlain by a sequence of deformed and moderately metamorphosed argillite, on which rocks as old as Middle Devonian lie unconformably (Brosgé and Tailleur, 1970). Locally, the argillites contain sponge spicules and, hence, are younger than Precambrian; however, one whole-rock radiogenic age of 592 m.y. suggests that older rocks may be present (Lanphere, 1970). Gravity data indicate that this basement high parallels the Arctic coast and continental shelf from Barrow to Banks Island (Wold et al., 1970), suggesting that these rocks form an arc extending eastward and are continuous with similar rocks in the Franklinian geosyncline, as postulated by Churkin (1969) and others.

In the Romanzof Mountains, at least two episodes of pre-Mississippian folding can be recognized. A sequence of quartz wacke, phyllite, and semi-schist, locally exhibiting several stages of deformation, is intruded by Silurian granitic rocks (431 m.y.); this sequence is the oldest part of the Neruokpuk Formation and is probably of Precambrian age (Reiser, 1970; Dutro, 1970). The sequence is overlain unconformably by a more widespread sequence of Paleozoic (Middle Devonian and older) deformed and locally metamorphosed carbonate, volcanic, and volcaniclastic rocks; chert and argillite; and some mafic intrusive rocks. Unconformably overlying the intrusive rocks are Mississippian shelf carbonate rocks (Brosgé and Tailleur, 1970; Dutro, 1970; Reiser, 1970).

In the central Brooks Range, phyllite, volcanic rocks, and chert, intruded by Middle Devonian gabbro (373 m.y.), are overlain unconformably by Mississippian carbonate rocks (Lanphere, 1965); in the southeastern Brooks Range, pelitic schists which underlie Mississippian strata have been intruded by Late Devonian (354 m.y.) or Early Mississippian (335 m.y.) granites (Brosgé and Tailleur, 1970).

Although the fold belt is known only east of the longitude of Barrow, magnetic anomalies in possibly pre-Middle Devonian basement (Brosgé and Tailleur, 1970) are recognized as far west as the 160th meridian, suggesting that the fold belt underlies the western area as well.

The wide distribution of this evidence of eugeosynclinal deposition and mobility indicates that prior to Mississippian time, as suggested by Churkin (1969, 1970a, b), Ziegler (1967), and Jeletzky (1962), northern Alaska was not the miogeosynclinal part of the Cordilleran geosyncline. Moreover, Silurian and Devonian clastic rocks grade into a carbonate facies southward, as shown in plates of carbonate strata of the Baird Group which are thrust northward over clastic rocks of equivalent age in the central and southern Brooks Range (Tailleur et al., 1967). Thus, it is suggested that miogeosynclinal or shelf sedimentation occurred toward the south in Silurian-Devonian time. Such a geometry is similar to that of the Franklinian geosyncline of the Innuitian fold belt (Brosgé and Tailleur, 1970) and opposite to that of the Cordilleran geosyncline. Furthermore, this entire eugeosynclinal terrane was uplifted and deformed in Late Devonian time, yielding a clastic wedge which was shed southward from the axis of folding and uplift in a pattern similar to that of the Franklinian geosyncline (Brosgé and Tailleur, 1970). Hence, northern Alaska, prior to Mississippian time, was a separate mobile belt, and it is equated

more logically with the Innuitian fold belt than with the Cordilleran.

EARLY PALEOZOIC AND PRECAMBRIAN "CORDILLERAN" FOLD BELT

King (1969b, p. 65) used the term "Cordilleran" for the fold belt along the western side of North America whose climactic orogenies took place in Mesozoic time but whose history of sedimentation and deformation stretches back into early Paleozoic time. The Mesozoic orogenies of this tectonic cycle, and later episodes of deformation, have affected most of Alaska, largely concealing evidence of earlier fold belts and leading to the assumption that all or most of Alaska was a part of the Cordilleran geosyncline throughout its history. The fold belt south of the Yukon River was formed from deposits in the Cordilleran geosyncline but may have had its climactic deformation in Late Devonian time. It represents either a stage of, or a precursor to, the Cordilleran fold belt of King. Accordingly, this fold belt will be referred to herein in quotes—as the "Cordilleran" fold belt—in order to indicate a limited usage of the term and yet call attention to the identity of the fold belt with the Cordilleran tectonic regime.

This fold belt occupies an arcuate area which is south of the Yukon River and extends through the Yukon-Tanana upland and westward along the northern margin of the Alaska Range (Fig. 2). In the core is a polymetamorphic, multideformed sequence of gneiss, amphibolite, schist, marble, and ultramafic rocks from which radiogenic ages recording Ordovician, Devonian, possibly Permian, and Jurassic and Cretaceous thermal events have been obtained (Foster et al., this volume). The nature of these rocks and the recorded ages of metamorphism suggest a Precambrian–middle Paleozoic history of eugeosynclinal deposition and deformation. In late Precambrian time, this area was the site of a fold belt that was the source of a thick sequence of distinctive clastic materials (the "grit" unit) deposited northeastward in the Selwyn basin in Yukon Territory (Gabrielse, 1967). Strata of comparable lithology in Alaska flank the uplift, mainly along the northern margin. Overlying these strata along the north and northwest flank of the uplift, and particularly around the southwestern nose, is a sequence of Cambrian through Devonian thin limestone beds and graptolitic shale; the sequence is transitional between possibly miogeosynclinal sediments on the north and the eugeosynclinal ones on the south (Churkin, 1970b). Superimposed on these earlier strata northwest of the Fairbanks area is a belt of Late Devonian clastic deposits that were probably shed from a Late Devonian fold belt on the south (Brosgé and Dutro, this volume). The sequence of events in this belt is similar to that of northern Alaska, but the direction of facies change in early Paleozoic and Late Devonian sequences is opposite to that of equivalent strata in the Brooks Range.

The metamorphic complex of the uplift continues southeastward into the Yukon Plateau of Yukon Territory and British Columbia; the overlying grit sequence, early to middle Paleozoic limestone and shale, and the Late Devonian clastic sequence can be traced (with interruption by the Tintina fault) around the arc of the schist into strata of the Cordilleran geosyncline in Canada. These data, coupled with the difference in tectonic regime in northern Alaska, clearly indicate that, prior to Mississippian time, northern Alaska and the Cordilleran geosyncline were separate tectonic entities.

Yukon Eugeosyncline

The area between the Arctic and "Cordilleran" fold belt is the site of the Yukon eugeosyncline of late Paleozoic (Permian) and Mesozoic age. Most deposits of the eugeosyncline lie within the area bounded by a belt of phyllite, quartzite, and pelitic schist that extends eastward from the Seward Peninsula along the southern margin of the Brooks Range and then southwestward along the Ruby "geanticline" of Payne (1955), forming a recumbent "V" in outline. Within this area, no rocks older than Permian are known, and Patton (1970a, p. E20) suggested that the floor may be oceanic crust, a conclusion not incompatible with available gravity data (David Barnes, oral commun., 1970). Deposits of the eugeosyncline lie unconformably on the schist belt and, where they overstep it, on unmetamorphosed Devonian and older strata. Mississippian strata seem to be absent.

The schists within the belt have not been firmly dated, but Devonian fossils were found associated with them in the Kuskokwim area (Mertie and Harrington, 1924), and Brosgé and Tailleur (1970) reported that field evidence in the western Brooks Range suggests the presence of metamorphosed fine-grained distal equivalents of the more northerly Upper Devonian clastic wedge. The schist belt may represent the intersection of two old fold belts, but

W. W. Patton (oral commun., 1970) suggested that the distinctive lithologic bands which compose it may wrap around the apex of the "V." The schist belt may be the metamorphosed equivalent of Upper Devonian and Carboniferous argillaceous sediments deposited along the continental margin of the Yukon eugeosynclinal sea in the early stages of its formation. Such an assumption is logical because of (1) the possible presence of Late Devonian fine-grained sedimentary rocks, (2) the absence of argillites of Carboniferous age that would be expected because of southward facies changes from Brooks Range carbonate rocks (Brosgé and Tailleur, 1970), and (3) the spatial relation of the belt to the general outline of the eugeosyncline. Another possibility is that the belt represents a high of older rocks such as underlies many modern continental margins. Because of the presence of early Paleozoic carbonate sequences north and southeast of the schist belt, Churkin (1969, 1970a, b) has suggested that the area of the Yukon eugeosyncline may be floored by a carbonate shelf that connected the Yukon shelf and the Seward Peninsula; however, in view of the predominantly pelitic nature of the schists and the indication that continental crust is absent, this suggestion seems unlikely.

Permian through Lower Cretaceous marine volcanic rocks and volcanogenic units form the bulk of the deposits in the eugeosyncline. Volcanism continued into Late Cretaceous, Tertiary, and Quaternary time but was subaerial. Along the margins of the schist belt, Jurassic, Triassic, and possibly older ultramafic and mafic rocks, spilites, chert, and argillite of the "ophiolite" suite are commonly exposed (Reiser et al., 1966; Patton and Miller, 1970; Patton, 1970b). The eugeosynclinal deposits occur mainly within the "V" of the schist belt, but they must have formerly occupied a greater area, because outlying remnants are found across the western and central Brooks Range (largely in thrust sheets) and around the perimeter of the Yukon Flats. They extend under the Flats—as shown by aeromagnetic surveys (Brosgé et al., 1970)—crop out in the Rampart area (Brosgé et al., 1969), and occur locally southwestward along the crest of the Ruby "geanticline." Data from continuous seismic profiles in the Bering Sea suggest that rocks beneath acoustic basement in the Bering Sea and the Aleutian basin represent deformed Cretaceous and older strata (Cameron and Stone, 1970; Hopkins et al., 1969; Scholl et al., 1968; Stone, 1968), possibly deposits of the Yukon eugeosyncline. In the Bristol Bay area the eugeosyncline probably was coextensive with similar terrane in southern Alaska, forming a continuous volcanic province.

Northward in the Brooks Range, miogeosynclinal or shelf carbonate deposits covered the area of the older Arctic fold belt from Mississippian through Triassic time. The Arctic platform, foreland for the late Paleozoic and younger seas, formed on an uplifted part of the old Arctic fold belt, and the area of a southward facies change from predominantly carbonate to predominantly chert-argillite in the central Brooks Range (Ziegler, 1967; Brosgé and Tailleur, 1970) lay close to the margin between shelf and oceanic regions during late Paleozoic time. In Jurassic and Early Cretaceous time, uplift and thrusting in the shelf-margin area separated a shale basin in the north from the active eugeosyncline in the south (Brosgé and Tailleur, 1970).

Yukon Shelf

As pointed out by Jeletzky (1962), Churkin and Brabb (1967), and Churkin (1969), the Yukon shelf seems to have been a stable, though negative, area of carbonate and shale deposition throughout late Precambrian, Paleozoic, and early Mesozoic time. Precambrian through Paleozoic carbonate and shale and later clastic units in the southern part of the area grade into deposits of the Cordilleran geosyncline to the south and east. However, carbonate, clastic, and mafic intrusive and extrusive rocks on the north and west indicate transitions with the Paleozoic Arctic geosyncline on the north and the late Paleozoic and Mesozoic Yukon eugeosyncline on the west.

Seward Peninsula Block

Like the Yukon shelf, the Seward Peninsula was an area of shelf carbonate deposition during most of the Paleozoic. The carbonate strata, however, overlie highly deformed and metamorphosed eugeosynclinal rocks that represent remnants of at least two periods of folding, both of Precambrian age; the older fold episode is dated as about 750 m.y. (Sainsbury et al., 1970). The relation of these Precambrian rocks to those of the Arctic and "Cordilleran" fold belts is unknown; they may be more closely related to Precambrian representatives of the Chukotsk Peninsula (Churkin, 1970a, p. G9, G10).

Cretaceous Sedimentary Basins

Superimposed on the older fold belts are broad, linear basins (the geosynclines of Payne [1955], in part, and successor basins of King [1969a, b]; Fig. 3). Although the classifications of exogeosyncline, autogeosyncline, foredeep, and marginal basin could be variously applied, the basins are not categorized herein but are referred to simply as sedimentary basins. They contain the marine and nonmarine clastic detritus eroded from uplifts within and marginal to the Yukon eugeosyncline. They range from Neocomian to Maestrichtian in age, though most are Albian through Campanian. The areal extent of these basins and the thickness of the deposits increase generally northward, westward, and southwestward, away from the rising east and central parts of the state. The southernmost Albian deposits in the Colville basin in northern Alaska overlie north-directed thrusts or gravity slides resulting from Late Jurassic and Early Cretaceous uplift in the Brooks Range (Martin, 1970; Brosgé and Tailleur, 1970; Lathram and Gryc, 1966). The distribution of these basins, as many authors have pointed out, is controlled by the major early Mesozoic structures recognized by Payne (1955)—the Brooks Range, the Ruby and Tanana "geanticlines," and the Seward Peninsula stable block.

Little is known concerning the distribution of Cretaceous basins on the continental shelf. In the Chukchi Sea, north of the subsea continuation of the Brooks Range thrust belt, is a thick sequence of acoustically coherent strata which Grantz (Grantz et al., 1970) interpreted as a continuation of the Cretaceous basin onshore. In the southern Bering Sea, Campanian fossils have been dredged from exposures of the bedrock underlying the Tertiary basin near Pribilof Island (Hopkins et al., 1969), and stratified sedimentary rocks underlying the southwest margin of the Bristol Bay Tertiary basin are believed to be Cretaceous (Hatten, 1971).

Tertiary Basins

Superimposed on all older tectonic elements are basins containing the detritus eroded from early and middle Tertiary uplifts (Fig. 3). With the exception of the Sagavanirktok basin on the north coast of Alaska, all onland basins are nonmarine, and their shape does not appear to be controlled by older structures; exceptions are the small linear basins that occupy the trenches of the Tintina, Denali, and Kaltag faults (Gates *et al.*, 1968). Basins on the continental shelf, including those discovered in recent years by marine geologic studies (all containing strata more than 1 km thick), are mostly marine. These offshore basins and the Sagavanirktok basin are controlled by the Mesozoic structures. The Sagavanirktok basin is superimposed on deposits of the Colville basin and is the farthest northeast in the series of sequential foredeep basins that migrated northeastward from the rising and northward-thrusting Brooks Range. Basins in the Bering and Chukchi Seas lie between the offshore continuations of the Brooks Range and the Ruby and Tanana "geanticlines," or between one of these and either the Seward Peninsula stable block or older folds paralleling the continental margin. Strata within basins on the continental shelf may include deposits of latest Cretaceous and Quaternary age, though most of the strata are believed to be of Tertiary age.

Fault Systems

The major faults of northern and central Alaska are the thrust belts of the Brooks Range, the Seward Peninsula, the western Yukon-Koyukuk province, and the Livengood area, mostly Late Cretaceous and early Tertiary in age, and the series of extensive strike-slip faults of equivalent and younger age that cut obliquely across both young orographic and older tectonic elements (Grantz, 1966). These strike-slip faults have resulted in gross offset of facies trends in rocks of all ages, according to Grantz (1966), Churkin and Brabb (1967), Patton and Hoare (1968), and others. The most extensive and best recognized of the strike-slip faults, together with the known thrust belts that generally trend obliquely to them, seem to define a series of continental blocks that have been translated large distances. Part of the lateral movement along the strike-slip faults may have been dissipated by foreshortening in the thrust belts. Along the Kaltag fault–Yukon-Porcupine lineament, the northern block seems to have been translated 60–80 mi (96–128 km) to the northeast past the Yukon shelf buttress—as suggested by Brosgé and Tailleur (1970)—possibly in response to eastward crowding from the Seward-Chukotsk block. On the Tintina fault, northwestward translation of the southwest block, postulated to be as much as 260 mi (418 km; Roddick, 1967), may have been accomplished partially by northwestward thrusting on the Livengood belt, which may join the Farewell

fault on the west (Brosgé and Dutro, this volume). Along this front, Precambrian and early Paleozoic rocks have been translated over schists of the Ruby "geanticline." Movement along the Denali fault seems varied, and vertical movement is indicated at numerous points. Generally, however, this fault system seems to have offset the Tanana "geanticline" and to have emplaced Permian and younger eugeosynclinal rocks on the southern flank of the early Paleozoic and Precambrian ("Cordilleran") fold belt. This movement suggests crowding from the south, perhaps from Pacific movements.

Observations on Application of Mobile Concepts

One of the most powerful concepts of the "new global tectonics" is that the eugeosynclinal realms represent zones of active interplay between oceanic and continental plates and that these mobile areas are the precursors of fold belts. Two of the major tectonic elements of Alaska are (1) an early Paleozoic and Precambrian Arctic (Innuitian) fold belt concentric with the Canada basin and (2) a similar "Cordilleran" fold belt concentric with the Pacific Ocean. These two elements have a divergent facies symmetry with respect to each other and to the Yukon shelf and the Canadian shield. The Late Devonian uplift and the ultimate accretion of these fold belts into the continental mass, together with the converging symmetry of subsequent deposition and of the resultant facies changes between them, set the stage for the development of the Yukon eugeosyncline. In late Paleozoic and Mesozoic time, interaction between the continental mass formed by these fold belts and the ancient Pacific ocean (including the present Bering Sea area) resulted in eugeosynclinal deposition in the Yukon area. Northward, largely vertical and secular movements of the continental interior permitted miogeosynclinal or subsiding-shelf deposition across northern Alaska. The areas of deposition in late Mesozoic and in Tertiary time were controlled by (1) uplift of the older fold belts, of the margins of the Yukon eugeosyncline, and of welts within it, and (2) the continuing positive nature of the Yukon shelf and the Seward Peninsula block.

From these observations, two conclusions seem apparent.

1. The form and position of the tectonic elements recognized in Alaska are, in general, inherited from elements established in Paleozoic

and possibly in Precambrian time. Each has an essential unity throughout history and the history of each is closely interrelated with that of adjacent elements. Consequently, in considering movements of continental plates or segments of plates which affect Alaska, we cannot postulate the removal or addition of a segment of crust or a segment of the stratigraphic column without thoroughly considering how this might modify the history of adjacent segments.

2. Alaska is not the "graveyard" of segments rifted from other continents and drifted together thousands of miles from the north, west, and south, as some workers have proposed. Rather, it is a continental mass accreted between the Canadian and Siberian shields by the interaction of these shields with ancient oceans, which then interacted with the expanding continental mass; these oceans have occupied their present relative positions in the Arctic and in the Pacific from at least Precambrian time, but their margins have become more separated as the continental mass has overridden their basins through accretion. The present dislocation of continental segments that is evident is only on the order of hundreds of miles or less, and reflects internal adjustments in response to the continued pressure of the expanding floors of these two oceans.

SELECTED REFERENCES

Adkison, W. L., and M. M. Brosgé, eds., 1970, Proceedings of the geological seminar on the North Slope of Alaska: Los Angeles, Pacific Sec. Am. Assoc. Petroleum Geologists, 201 p.

Brosgé, W. P., and I. L. Tailleur, 1970, Depositional history of northern Alaska, in W. L. Adkison and M. M. Brosgé, eds., Proceedings of the geological seminar on the North Slope of Alaska: Los Angeles, Pacific Sec. Am. Assoc. Petroleum Geologists, p. D1–D17.

―――― E. E. Brabb, and E. R. King, 1970, Geologic interpretation of reconnaissance aeromagnetic survey of northeastern Alaska: U.S. Geol. Survey Bull. 1271-F, p. F1-F12.

―――― et al., 1969, Probable Permian age of the Rampart Group, central Alaska: U.S. Geol. Survey Bull. 1294-B, p. B1-B18.

Cady, W. M., et al., 1955, The central Kuskokwim region, Alaska: U.S. Geol. Survey Prof. Paper 268, 132 p.

Cameron, C. P., and D. B. Stone, 1970, Outline geology of the Aleutian Islands with paleomagnetic data from Shamya and Adak Islands: Alaska Univ. Geophys. Inst. Rept. UAG R-213, 153 p.

Churkin, Michael, Jr., 1969, Paleozoic tectonic history of the Arctic basin north of Alaska: Science, v. 165, p. 549–555.

―――― 1970a, Fold belts of Alaska and Siberia and drift between North America and Asia, in W. L. Adkison and M. M. Brosgé, eds., Proceedings of the geological seminar on the North Slope of Alaska:

Los Angeles, Pacific Sec. Am. Assoc. Petroleum Geologists, p. G1-G12.

―――― 1970b, Paleozoic and Precambrian rocks of Alaska and their role in its structural evolution: U.S. Geol. Survey Open-File Rept., 131 p.

―――― and E. E. Brabb, 1967, Devonian rocks of the Yukon-Porcupine Rivers area and their tectonic relation to other Devonian sequences in Alaska, in D. H. Oswald, ed., International symposium on the Devonian system, v. 2: Calgary, Alberta Soc. Petroleum Geologists, p. 227–258.

Coney, P. J., 1970, The geotectonic cycle and the new global tectonics: Geol. Soc. America Bull., v. 81, p. 739–748.

Dutro, J. T., Jr., 1970, Pre-Carboniferous carbonate rocks, northeastern Alaska, in W. L. Adkison and M. M. Brosgé, eds., Proceedings of the geological seminar on the North Slope of Alaska: Los Angeles, Pacific Sec. Am. Assoc. Petroleum Geologists, p. M1–M7.

Eardley, A. J., 1948, Ancient Arctica: Jour. Geology, v. 56, p. 409–436.

Gabrielse, H., 1967, Tectonic evolution of the northern Canadian Cordillera: Canadian Jour. Earth Sci., v. 4, no. 2, p. 271–298.

Gates, G. O., and George Gryc, 1963, Structure and tectonic history of Alaska, in O.E. Childs and B. W. Beebe, eds., Backbone of the Americas: Am. Assoc. Petroleum Geologists Mem. 2, p. 264–277.

―――― Arthur Grantz, and W. W. Patton, Jr., 1968, Geology and natural gas and oil resources of Alaska, in B. W. Beebe and B. F. Curtis, eds., Natural gases of North America—Part 1, Natural gases in rocks of Cenozoic age: Am. Assoc. Petroleum Geologists Mem. 9, v. 1, p. 3–48.

Grantz, Arthur, 1966, Strike-slip faults in Alaska: U.S. Geol. Survey Open-File Rept., 82 p.

―――― et al., 1970, Geology of the Chukchi Sea as determined by acoustic and magnetic profiling, in W. L. Adkison and M. M. Brosgé, eds., Proceedings of the geological seminar on the North Slope of Alaska: Los Angeles, Pacific Sec. Am. Assoc. Petroleum Geologists, p. F1–F28.

Hatten, C. W., 1971, Petroleum potential of Bristol Bay basin, Alaska, in I. H. Cram, ed., Future petroleum provinces of the United States—their geology and potential: Am. Assoc. Petroleum Geologists Mem. 15, v. 1, p. 105–108.

Hopkins, D. M., et al., 1969, Cretaceous, Tertiary and early Pleistocene rocks from the continental margin in the Bering Sea: Geol. Soc. America Bull., v. 80, p. 1471–1480.

Izacks, B., J. Oliver, and L. R. Sykes, 1968, Seismology and the new global tectonics: Jour. Geophys. Research, v. 72, p. 5855–5900.

Jeletzky, J. A., 1962, Pre-Cretaceous Richardson Mountains trough—its place in the tectonic framework of Arctic Canada and its bearing on some geosynclinal concepts: Royal Soc. Canada Trans., 3d ser., v. 56, sec. 3, pt. 1, p. 55–84.

King, P. B., compiler, 1969a, Tectonic map of North America: U. S. Geol. Survey, scale 1:5,000,000.

―――― 1969b, The tectonics of North America—a discussion to accompany the Tectonic Map of North America, scale 1:5,000,000: U.S. Geol. Survey Prof. Paper 628, 94 p.

Lanphere, M. A., 1965, Age of Ordovician and Devonian mafic rocks in northern Alaska, in Geological Survey research 1965: U.S. Geol. Survey Prof. Paper 525-A, p. A101–A102.

—— 1970, Discussion *of* Michael Churkin, Jr., Fold belts of Alaska and Siberia and drift between North America and Asia, *in* W. L. Adkison and M. M. Brosgé, eds., Proceedings of the geological seminar on the North Slope of Alaska: Los Angeles, Pacific Sec. Am. Assoc. Petroleum Geologists, p. G16.

Lathram, E. H., and George Gryc, 1966, New look at geology and petroleum potential of northern Alaska (abs.): Am. Assoc. Petroleum Geologists Bull., v. 50, no. 3, p. 622.

Martin, A. J., 1970, Structure and tectonic history of the western Brooks Range, De Long Mountains and Lisburne Hills, northern Alaska: Geol. Soc. America Bull., v. 81, p. 3605–3622.

Mertie, J. B., Jr., 1930, Mountain building in Alaska: Am. Jour. Sci., 5th ser., v. 20, p. 101–124.

—— and G. L. Harrington, 1924, The Ruby-Kuskokwim region, Alaska: U.S. Geol. Survey Bull. 754, 129 p.

Miller, D. J., T. G. Payne, and George Gryc, 1959, Geology of possible petroleum provinces in Alaska, with an annotated bibliography by E. H. Cobb: U.S. Geol. Survey Bull. 1094, 131 p.

Patton, W. W., Jr., 1970a, Discussion *of* I. L. Tailleur and W. P. Brosgé, Tectonic history of northern Alaska, *in* W. L. Adkison and M. M. Brosgé, eds., Proceedings of the geological seminar on the North Slope of Alaska: Los Angeles, Pacific Sec. Am. Assoc. Petroleum Geologists, p. E20.

—— 1970b, Petroleum possibilities of the Yukon-Koyukuk province, Alaska: U.S. Geol. Survey Open-File Rept., 13 p.

—— and J. M. Hoare, 1968, The Kaltag fault, west-central Alaska, *in* Geological Survey research 1968: U.S. Geol. Survey Prof. Paper 600-D, p. D147–D153.

—— and T. P. Miller, 1970, Preliminary geologic investigations in the Kanuti River region, Alaska: U.S. Geol. Survey Bull. 1312-J, p. J1–J10.

Payne, T. G., 1955, Mesozoic and Cenozoic tectonic elements of Alaska: U.S. Geol. Survey Misc. Geol. Inv. Map I-84.

Rast, Nicholas, 1969, Orogenic belts and their parts, *in* P. E. Kent *et al.*, eds. Time and place in orogeny: London Geol. Soc., p. 197–213.

Reiser, H. N., 1970, Northeastern Brooks Range—a surface expression of the Prudhoe Bay section, *in* W. L. Adkison and M. M. Brosgé, eds., Proceedings of the geological seminar on the North Slope of Alaska: Los Angeles, Pacific Sec. Am. Assoc. Petroleum Geologists, p. K1–K10.

—— M. A. Lanphere, and W. P. Brosgé, 1966, Jurassic age of a mafic igneous complex, Christian quadrangle, Alaska, *in* Geological Survey research 1966: U.S. Geol. Survey Prof. Paper 525-C, p. C68–C71.

Roddick, J. A., 1967, Tintina Trench: Jour. Geology, v. 75, no. 1, p. 23–33.

Sainsbury, C. L., R. G. Coleman, and Reuben Kachadoorian, 1970, Blueschist and related greenschist facies rocks of the Seward Peninsula, Alaska, *in* Geological Survey research 1970: U.S. Geol. Survey Prof. Paper 700-B, p. B33–B42.

Scholl, D. W., E. C. Buffington, and D. M. Hopkins, 1968, Geologic history of the continental margin of North America in the Bering Sea: Marine Geology, v. 6, p. 297–330.

Smith, P. S., 1939, Areal geology of Alaska: U.S. Geol. Survey Prof. Paper 192, 100 p.

Stone, D. B., 1968, Geophysics in the Bering Sea and surrounding areas: a review: Tectonophysics, v. 6, no. 6, p. 433–460.

Tailleur, I. L., 1969, Rifting speculation on the geology of Alaska's North Slope: Oil and Gas Jour., v. 67, no. 39, p. 128–130.

—— W. P. Brosgé, and H. N. Reiser, 1967, Palinspastic analysis of Devonian rocks in northwestern Alaska, *in* D. H. Oswald, ed., International symposium on the Devonian system, v. 2: Calgary, Alberta Soc. Petroleum Geologists, p. 1345–1361.

Wold, R. J., T. L. Woodzick, and N. A. Ostenso, 1970, Structure of the Beaufort Sea continental margin: Geophysics, v. 35, no. 5, p. 849–861.

Ziegler, P. A., 1967, Guidebook for Canadian Cordillera field trip: Alberta Soc. Petroleum Geologists, Internat. Symposium on the Devonian System, Calgary, 1967, 66 p.

Paleozoic Rocks of Northern and Central Alaska[1]

WILLIAM P. BROSGÉ[2] and J. THOMAS DUTRO, JR.[2]

Menlo Park, California, and Washington, D.C.

Abstract Cambrian through Middle Devonian fossiliferous rocks define three sets of depositional elements in Alaska: (1) a carbonate platform near the craton in the Porcupine Plateau and north of the northeast Brooks Range; (2) shale-chert-volcanic basins south and west of this platform in the Ogilvie Mountains, Yukon-Tanana upland, northeast Brooks Range, and probably along the Arctic coast; and (3) two linear segments of an outer carbonate platform—one trending westward from the southern Brooks Range to Seward Peninsula and St. Lawrence Island, and the other southwestward from the Yukon-Tanana upland to the lower Kuskokwim River. Early Paleozoic orogeny in the northeast Brooks Range is indicated by Silurian (430 m.y.) granite and a post-Cambrian unconformity within pre-Mississippian rocks.

A thick wedge of Upper Devonian terrigenous clastic strata in the Brooks Range north and east of Upper Devonian carbonate beds indicates a Late Devonian orogeny farther north. The regional angular unconformity beneath Mississippian rocks and a Late Devonian granite mark the orogenic belt along the Arctic coast, northeast Brooks Range, and the northern Porcupine Plateau. Upper Devonian turbidite conglomerates also indicate uplift south of the Porcupine Plateau and in the Yukon-Tanana upland.

Mississippian and Pennsylvanian carbonate beds lap northward and eastward from the Brooks Range across a platform of folded Precambrian(?) to Devonian rocks on the Arctic coast and the northern Porcupine Plateau. Permian uplift along the Arctic coast is indicated by the fact that coarse Permian clastic sediments were shed southward into the Brooks Range area. A regional unconformity beneath Permian quartzose clastic beds indicates other uplifts in the Porcupine Pleateau and on part of the former carbonate platform on the upper Kuskokwim River. The Permian uplift on the Kuskokwim is bordered on the southeast by thick Mississippian and Permian volcanic rocks of the Alaska Range and on the northwest by Permian volcanic rocks and chert along the Yukon and lower Kuskokwim Rivers. Permian eugeosynclinal rocks may extend farther north, because Permian terrigenous clastic rocks in the Brooks Range grade southward into chert and argillite, and Permian(?) mafic intrusive rocks are present on St. Lawrence Island.

Introduction

The largest exposures of Paleozoic rocks in Alaska are north of the Arctic Circle (Fig. 1). To place these rocks in a regional setting, we have included the rocks in central Alaska and have used the regional syntheses for the Yukon

[1] Manuscript received, September 20, 1971. Publication authorized by the Director, U.S. Geological Survey.

[2] U.S. Geological Survey.

Territory by Gabrielse (1967), Bassett and Stout (1967), Douglas *et al.* (1963), Jeletzky (1962), Martin (1959), Norford (1964), and Norris (1967) as a base for correlation with the Alaskan tectonic elements (Fig. 2). The major Paleozoic elements in Alaska have been outlined by Churkin (1969, 1970), and most of the stratigraphic data summarized here have been discussed by him in more detail. The sources of the data are cataloged by locality and geologic system at the beginning of the reference list.

Early Paleozoic Tectonic Elements

The major tectonic elements inferred from late Precambrian through Middle Devonian deposits are two shallow-water arches defined by carbonate deposits; two deep-water basins defined by deposits of shale, chert, and volcanic rocks; and a fold belt defined by granite and a major unconformity within the northern basin. The northern basin is part of the ancestral Brooks geosyncline inferred by Churkin (1969, 1970). It may have been connected to the Richardson trough of the Yukon, but it contains volcanic rocks whereas the Richardson trough does not. The southern basin is a direct westward continuation of the Selwyn basin of the Yukon, offset somewhat by the Tintina fault. The two arches correspond to the northern and southern limits of the possible broad, stable shelf across central Alaska suggested by Churkin (1969, 1970) and Jeletzky (1962).

Mesozoic plutonism and metamorphism have obscured the record in the Ruby geanticline and Yukon platform. The pelitic metasedimentary rocks of the Ruby geanticline are poorly known and are shown as defining a possible early Paleozoic basin between the carbonate arches of northern and southern Alaska. However, these same metasedimentary rocks might be part of an early Paleozoic uplift, as some evidence suggests that they were folded before either Devonian or Ordovician time. Probably much of the Alaskan part of the Yukon platform was originally within the Selwyn basin. In addition to probably Precambrian gneiss, the Yukon platform rocks include crinoidal Paleo-

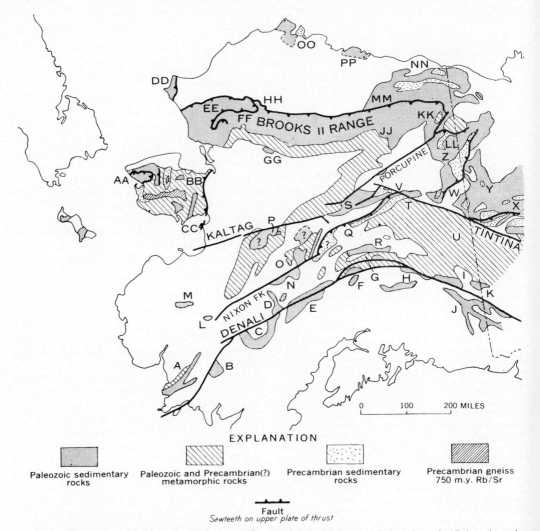

EXPLANATION

Paleozoic sedimentary rocks | Paleozoic and Precambrian(?) metamorphic rocks | Precambrian sedimentary rocks | Precambrian gneiss 750 m.y. Rb/Sr

Fault
Sawteeth on upper plate of thrust

FIG. 1—Index map showing major faults and outcrops of Precambrian and Paleozoic rocks. Paleozoic rocks shown on Arctic Coast are from drill data. Letter symbols A through QQ show localities in reference list. Modified from King (1969).

zoic greenschist and marble and a distinctive Precambrian(?) grit unit typical of the Selwyn basin.

UPPER PRECAMBRIAN ROCKS

South of the Tintina fault and in the Selwyn basin, the oldest sedimentary rocks are red and green argillite and gritty feldspathic sandstone with conspicuous granules of blue quartz (Figs. 3, 4). The grit in the Selwyn basin has been correlated tentatively with the upper Proterozoic Windermere Series (Gabrielse, 1967); associated trace fossils in Alaska suggest that the

grit could also be earliest Cambrian in age. Precambrian dolomite and quartzite of the lower Tindir Group represent shelf deposits that are probably older than the grit. They overlie slate and argillite on Ogilvie arch and, presumably, also overlie the slate and phyllite exposed on the axis of Dave Lord Creek arch. The equivalent of the grit is probably the upper Tindir beds, which are similar to the Rapitan Formation of Canada. On Ogilvie arch these beds contain pillow basalts and polymictic cobble conglomerates that may be either glacial debris or slide debris from nearby uplifts. The known

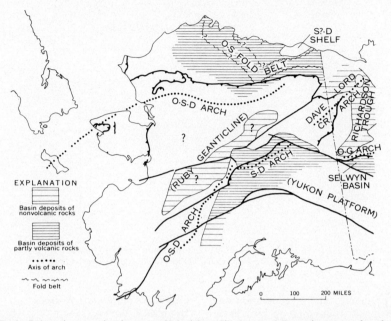

FIG. 2—Early Paleozoic tectonic elements. Ordovician, Silurian, and Devonian ages of arches and of fold belt are indicated by letter symbols. O-G arch is Ogilvie arch. Ruby geanticline and Yukon platform are Mesozoic elements exposing possibly lower Paleozoic metasedimentary rocks. Tectonic elements in Canada are from Gabrielse (1967).

occurrences of this basalt and conglomerate adjacent to the Selwyn basin suggest uplift at the basin edge, and the basalt may indicate rifting at a newly-formed continental margin (Stewart, 1971).

North of Dave Lord Creek arch, probably Precambrian quartz wacke and red and green phyllite in the northeast Brooks Range, as well as red and green phyllite on the Arctic coast that was dated as Precambrian by K-Ar whole-rock analysis, indicate another basin similar to the Selwyn basin.

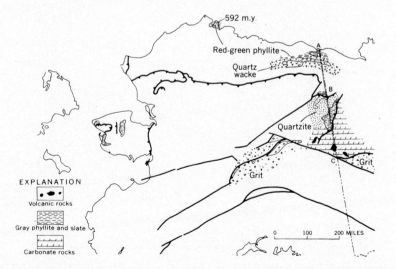

FIG. 3—Upper Precambrian and possibly lowest Cambrian rocks. For section ABC, see Figure 4.

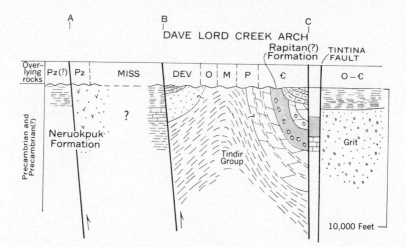

FIG. 4—Restored section of upper Precambrian and possibly lowest Cambrian rocks along U.S.-Canada boundary. Section offset about 170 mi (275 km) along Tintina fault. Age of overlying Paleozoic rocks shown by letter symbols. For location, see Figure 3.

The only positively dated Precambrian high-grade metamorphic rocks are on the Seward Peninsula, where late Precambrian paragneiss and orthogneiss in the core of the greenschist terrane (Fig. 1) suggest a Precambrian basement for the lower Paleozoic carbonate shelf.

CAMBRIAN THROUGH MIDDLE DEVONIAN ROCKS

Basinal sequences are pronounced in both Cambrian and Ordovician rocks. They are less pronounced in the Silurian and Devonian section, in which thick carbonate rocks overlie

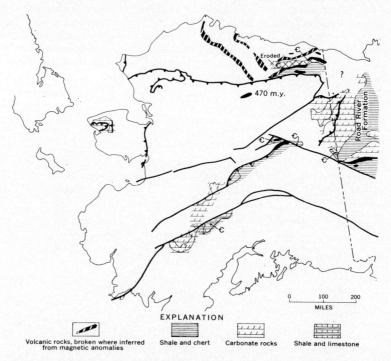

EXPLANATION

Volcanic rocks, broken where inferred from magnetic anomalies · Shale and chert · Carbonate rocks · Shale and limestone

FIG. 5—Cambrian and Ordovician rocks. Six known Cambrian fossil and trace-fossil localities are indicated by Є.

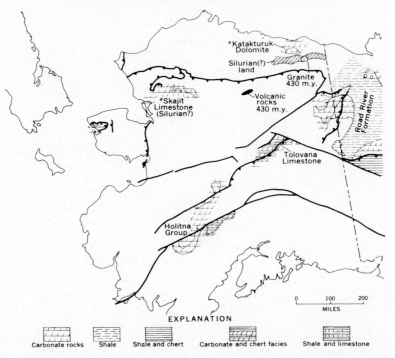

FIG. 6—Silurian rocks. *Assignment of Katakturuk and lower part of Skajit to Silurian(?) System in this paper is interpretative and should not be construed as a revision of their previously published age assignments.

some of the Cambrian and Ordovician basinal deposits.

Nonvolcanic basinal sequences of Late Cambrian through Silurian age are represented partly by graptolitic shale and chert of the Road River Formation in the Richardson trough and partly by interbedded graptolitic shale, siltstone, and limestone at the Denali fault (Figs. 5, 6). The volcanic basinal sequences are represented by Lower Ordovician argillite and chert and Middle Ordovician andesite in the Selwyn basin and its westward exten-

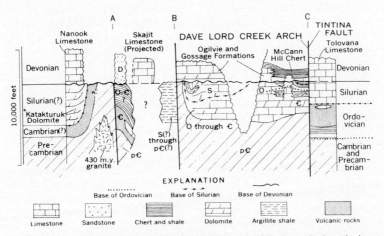

FIG. 7—Restored section of lower Paleozoic (Cambrian through Middle Devonian) rocks in northeast Brooks Range and along U.S.-Canada boundary. Section offset about 170 mi (275 km) along Tintina fault. For location, see Figure 8. *Assignment of Katakturuk to Silurian(?) System is interpretative and should not be construed as a revision of its previous Middle Devonian or older age assignment.

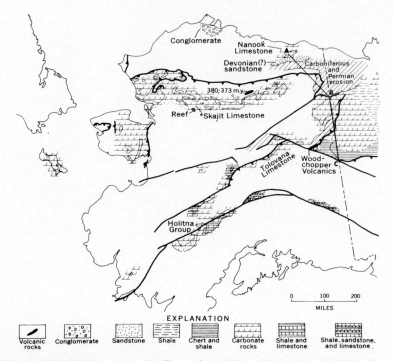

FIG. 8—Lower and Middle Devonian rocks. For section ABC, see Figure 7. *Assignment of part of Skajit to definite Middle Devonian is interpretative and should not be construed as a revision of its previously published Middle(?) and Late Devonian age.

sion (Figs. 5, 7), and by Lower Cambrian, Upper Cambrian, and possibly Ordovician shale, chert, volcanic rocks, and carbonate rocks in the northeast Brooks Range. In addition, the volcanic rocks in the central Brooks Range yield a scatter of K-Ar dates indicating Ordovician, Silurian, or Middle Devonian ages.

The main carbonate shelves are represented by continuous carbonate deposits of Ordovician through Devonian age that are more than 12,000 ft (3,660+ m) thick on Seward Peninsula, more than 6,000 ft (1,830+ m) thick in southwest Alaska, and perhaps 3,000–4,000 ft (915–1,220 m) thick on Dave Lord Creek arch. A southeastward transition from these carbonate beds to the graptolitic facies of Selwyn basin and its westward extension is shown by intertonguing of the two facies south of Dave Lord Creek arch (Fig. 7), and by downward gradation of Middle Ordovician limestone into shale and limestone at the edge of the basin along the Denali fault in southwest Alaska. Northward overlap of Ordovician carbonate beds onto older basinal deposits is suggested at the north end of the carbonate outcrop along Nixon Fork fault (Fig. 5), where

several thousand feet of Upper Ordovician limestone is reported to lie unconformably on the schist of the Ruby geanticline.

Silurian and Devonian carbonate deposition advanced beyond the area of Ordovician carbonate deposition and into former basins. The Middle Silurian to Middle or Upper Devonian Tolovana Limestone (Figs. 7, 8) overlies Middle Ordovician volcanic rocks in the westward extension of the Selwyn basin; and the Katakturuk Dolomite, which we infer to be Silurian(?), and the Nanook Limestone of Middle Devonian age overlie the volcanic rocks near the Arctic coast. Outliers of Middle Devonian limestone apparently lie on the schist in the eastern Seward Peninsula and also in the Ruby geanticline near the Kaltag fault and beyond the southwest end of the Denali fault (Fig. 8).

Silurian or Early Devonian uplift and erosion are evident on Dave Lord Creek arch and in the northern basin. On the south flank of Dave Lord Creek arch, Silurian rocks are absent locally beneath the Lower Devonian basal limestone of the McCann Hill Chert (Fig. 7), whereas, on the north flank of the arch, Devonian dolomite lies unconformably on Precambrian quartzite. Near the Arctic coast, a major uplift of probably Silurian age is evident (Figs. 6, 7, 8) where Precambrian rocks in the northeast Brooks Range are intruded by a granite stock dated as earliest Silurian, and Ordovician(?) cherts are overlain with angular unconformity by Lower or Middle Devonian sandstone. Farther northwest, near Barrow, Middle or Lower Devonian plant-bearing conglomerate suggests continued uplift. This uplift might account for the establishment of the Silurian(?) to Middle Devonian carbonate shelf in the former basin.

UPPER DEVONIAN ROCKS

Upper Devonian rocks are absent in large areas because of late Paleozoic uplift and erosion, but are thick and varied within the Brooks Range.

South of the Brooks Range the Upper Devonian is represented mainly by the Nation River Formation and correlative chert-pebble conglomerate and graywacke as thick as 4,000 ft (1,220 m); the latter are probably of early Late Devonian age (Fig. 9). South of the Tintina fault, this conglomerate locally lies with apparent unconformity on diorite and serpentine; it contains clasts of those rocks, thus suggesting major Devonian thrusting and uplift on the Yukon platform.

In the Brooks Range a regional unconformity within the lower Upper Devonian separates the Hunt Fort Shale from an underlying sequence of three units—the uppermost beds of the Skajit Limestone; interbedded limestone and siltstone; and a mixture of chloritic phyllite, conglomerate, graywacke, limestone, and pyroclastic rocks (Figs. 9, 10). Because the limestone is the oldest, its position on the map marks broad pre-unconformity uplifts. Evidence as to source direction is meager, but the chloritic phyllite and graywacke seem to interfinger southward into the limestone and siltstone, and the limestone-siltstone seems to grade southward into thin beds of limestone and dolomite.

In the western Brooks Range, lower Upper Devonian limestone is present in the upper part of an allochthonous carbonate sequence and is probably represented by the lower 1,000 ft (305 m) of the Kugururok Formation (Fig. 9). This limestone is inferred to grade eastward into the limestone and siltstone, but may persist southwestward in the limestones of possibly early Late Devonian age on the Seward Peninsula and St. Lawrence Island.

North of the Brooks Range is a fold belt that contains Late Devonian granite; in this belt, Precambrian through Middle Devonian rocks are overlain with marked angular unconformity

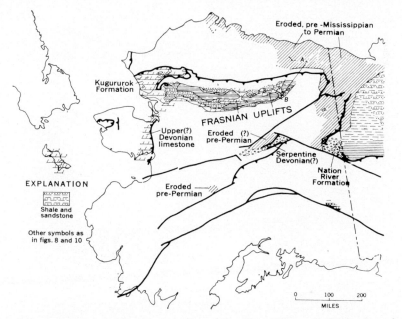

FIG. 9—Lower Upper Devonian (Frasnian) rocks. For section AB, see Figure 10. Rocks shown in eastern and central Brooks Range are directly beneath sub–Hunt Fork unconformity.

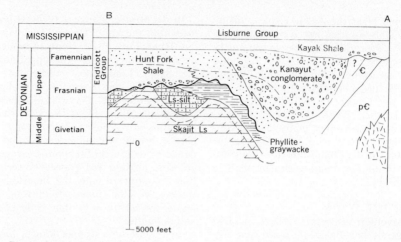

Fig. 10—Restored section of Upper Devonian rocks in eastern Brooks Range. For location, see Figure 9.

by the Mississippian (Figs. 10, 11).

The Hunt Fork Shale and Kanayut Conglomerate form a thick wedge of clastic rocks derived from this Late Devonian tectonic land. The conglomerate grades downward and southward into sandstone in the upper part of the Hunt Fork; this sandstone extends over most of the northern and western Brooks Range. However, in the southeast the sandstone grades into lithic graywacke (Fig. 11), and, in the same region, the underlying shale becomes cherty southeastward. These facies changes suggest that, although the clastic wedge was derived from the land to the north, it was not derived from the land around the large granite body just to the east.

Mississippian rocks generally lie concordantly on the Upper Devonian rocks of the clastic

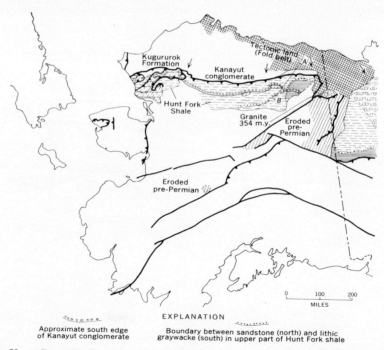

Fig. 11—Upper Upper Devonian (Frasnian and Famennian) rocks. Arrows show direction of sediment transport.

wedge. However, in small areas, all or part of the clastic wedge has been removed by pre-Mississippian erosion.

The Upper Devonian limestone in the western Brooks Range is allochthonous with respect to the rocks of the clastic wedge. The actual extent of latest Devonian limestone in the thrust plates is known only in the northern part, where the upper 500 ft (150 m) of Kugururok limestone is the same age (Famennian) as the Kanayut and upper Hunt Fork.

CARBONIFEROUS ROCKS

Most of the Brooks Range is south of the Late Devonian fold belt, and clastic deposition there was generally continuous from Late Devonian into Early Mississippian time. Within the fold belt the basal Mississippian rocks are conglomeratic where they lie discordantly on older rocks (Fig. 10); a shoreline near the Arctic coast is indicated by sandstone and redbeds near Barrow (Fig. 12).

Above the basal clastic beds the Mississippian and Lower Pennsylvanian are mostly carbonate rocks of the Lisburne Group, which overlap northward and eastward (Figs. 12, 13). Carbonate deposition south of the fold belt began in Early Mississippian time. It did not begin within the fold belt until the Late Mississippian, but it continued there during the Early Pennsylvanian, as is shown by very shallow-water deposits of that age. In the area of Lower and Upper Mississippian carbonate rocks south of the fold belt, three facies are distinguished. A predominantly clean, open-marine carbonate facies extends over most of the Brooks Range. In the western Brooks Range, an anomalous dark, shaly and cherty facies suggests deeper water to the north, whereas a mixed facies that contains elements of the other two, plus a basal unit of Lower Mississippian quartzite and limestone, suggests a nearby source. The base of the carbonate sequence becomes younger westward. Locally, the lowest carbonate units on the west coast are Upper Mississippian, and the lowest carbonate rocks on the Seward Peninsula and St. Lawrence Island are apparently also Upper Mississippian, suggesting overlap on a shoreline in the west as well as in the north.

Another shoreline southeast of the Brooks Range is shown by the unconformable overlap of Upper Mississippian rocks on the schist intruded by Late Devonian granite just north of

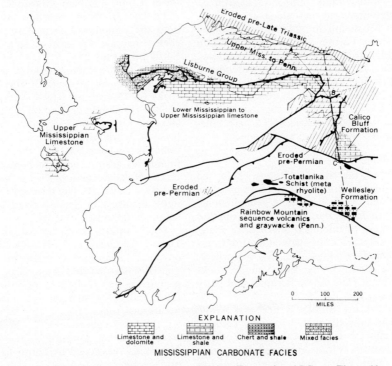

FIG. 12—Mississippian and Lower Pennsylvanian. For section ABC, see Figure 13.

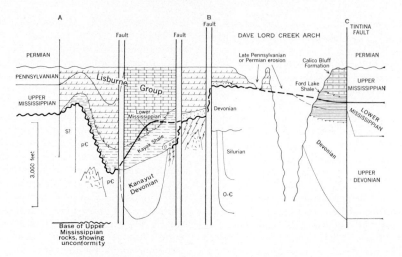

FIG. 13—Restored section of Mississippian and Lower Pennsylvanian rocks in northeast Brooks Range and along U.S.-Canada boundary. For location, see Figure 12.

the Porcupine fault (*B*, Fig. 13). South of that fault a thinner section of Carboniferous limestone and sandstone lies with slight unconformity on Devonian shelf carbonate beds on the north flank of Dave Lord Creek arch.

In contrast, on the south flank of the arch, near the Tintina fault, Upper Mississippian deeper water limestone and shale grade down into Lower Mississippian and Upper Devonian chert and shale. Farther south, near the Denali fault, the Mississippian is probably represented by more than 12,000 ft (3,660+ m) of submarine rhyolite flows of the Totatlanika Schist, and the mid-Pennsylvanian is represented by about 7,000 ft (2,135 m) of marine andesite and dacite, tuffaceous clastic rocks, and limestone of the Rainbow Mountain sequence.

PERMIAN ROCKS

In most of the Brooks Range, only the Lower Permian is present. It is represented in the south and west by varicolored siltstone, chert, and shale of the Siksikpuk Formation and, in the east, by unnamed interbedded shale, limestone, and calcareous shale along the International Boundary (Figs. 14, 15). Elsewhere, north of the Alaska Range, only younger rocks of mid-Permian (late Early Permian and early Late Permian) age may be present.

In the northeast Brooks Range and Arctic Coast region, only the mid-Permian is present. It is represented by the two facies of the Echooka Member. A transgressive shallow-water sandstone facies which lies with erosional unconformity on the Lisburne Group was derived from the north; a deeper water siliceous siltstone and shale facies is present to the southwest.

The exact relation between the Siksikpuk and the Echooka is not known. However, the lower Upper Permian sandstone facies of the Echooka probably overlaps unconformably onto the unnamed Lower Permian calcareous shales that are the eastern equivalents of the Siksikpuk (Fig. 15).

South of the Porcupine fault, a great unconformity is evident beneath the mid-Permian rocks on Dave Lord Creek arch, where chert-pebble conglomerate and conglomeratic limestone lie discordantly across the entire Precambrian to Carboniferous section. A comparable uplift is suggested by the thick mid-Permian limestone, arkose, and conglomerate sequence of the Nuka Formation that is found locally in the Brooks Range, but the location of such an uplift is uncertain because all of the Nuka may be allochthonous.

Other uplifts southwest along strike from Dave Lord Creek arch are indicated (1) by an erosional unconformity between mid-Permian quartz sandstone and the schists of the Ruby geanticline in a small area near the Nixon Fork fault, and (2) by the apparent absence of Carboniferous rocks beneath the Rampart Group. All the fossil collections near the Rampart that were previously assigned to the Mississippian have been reassigned by Dutro to the Permian or Devonian.

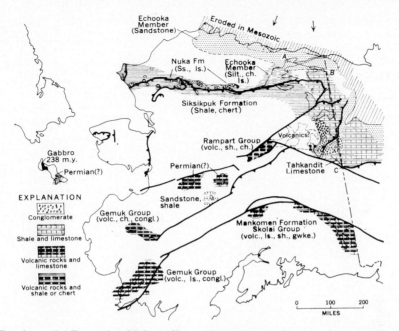

FIG. 14—Permian rocks. For section ABC, see Figure 15. Questioned volcanic rocks east of Rampart Group are inferred from magnetic data.

Except on these arches, most of the known Permian rocks south of the Brooks Range are volcanic sequences. Along the Denali fault these beds are 4,000–10,000 ft (1,220–3,050 m) thick; they consist of mafic flows interbedded with clastic rocks and limestone lentils as thick as 1,000 ft (305 m). The depositional setting was probably an island arc. North of the Denali fault, chert seems to be more common in the volcanic deposits; in the Rampart Group,

limestone is scarce, suggesting generally deeper water north of the Denali fault. On St. Lawrence Island the possibly Permian sedimentary rocks are like the Siksikpuk, and a large mafic intrusive body is dated as Permian.

An Arctic platform along the present Arctic coast was the source of the Permian nearshore sands, which were deposited on a shelf that probably extended as far south as the underlying Carboniferous carbonate rocks and in-

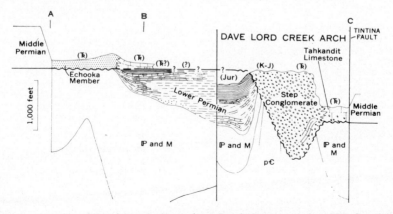

FIG. 15—Restored section of Permian rocks in northeast Brooks Range and along U.S.-Canada boundary. For location, see Figure 14. Pre-Echooka rocks locally include Pennsylvanian shale north of Porcupine fault. Age of rocks that overlie Permian is shown by letter symbol in parentheses.

cluded Dave Lord Creek arch. The cherty and volcanic rocks surround the inferred projection of the shelf southwest of Dave Lord Creek arch, but their relation to the broader shelf of Arctic Alaska is not known.

SELECTED REFERENCES

Letters refer to localities shown on Figure 1; numbers refer to the publications listed below.

Upper Proterozoic: Q-40, 74; T-29, 62; W-9, 11; X-46, 47; Y-69; Z-8, 26; AA-91; LL-18; OO-20; NN-39, 76.

Cambrian: E-79; V-31, 62; W-6, 11, 31; X-47; Y-67; AA-90; OO-102; NN-39.

Ordovician: D-89; E-14, 77, 78, 79; N-24; O-40; Q-74; T-29, 30, 62; W-6, 9, 11, 32; X-47; Y-67, 69; Z-8, 26; AA-90, 91; II-56; LL-18.

Silurian: C-25; D-89; E-79; N-24; O-40; Q-74; S-29, 44, 62; T-29, 30, 62; V-62; W-6, 9, 11, 26, 32; X-47; Y-67, 68, 69; Z-8, 26; AA-90; FF-98; LL-18, 26; NN-38, 39, 80.

Middle and Lower Devonian: A-52; C-25; D-89; E-14, 77, 79; G-28; I-42, 65; N-24, 64; O-40; P-61, 64; Q-74; S-29, 62; T-29, 30, 62; V-62; W-9, 11, 32; Y-68; Z-8, 26; BB-48, 55; CC-48, 94; EE-98; FF-98; GG-45, 98; II-22, 56; JJ-16, 17, 22; LL-18, 26, 33; NN-38, 39; OO-34; QQ-71, 72.

Crinoidal metasedimentary rocks: U-41, 43, 62.

Lower Upper Devonian: I-65; S-29, 44, 60, 62, 101; W-9, 10, 11; Y-68; CC-94; EE-88, 98; II-99; JJ-16, 17, 22; QQ-71, 72.

Upper Upper Devonian: W-7, 8, 9; Y-68; EE-58, 88, 98; FF-58, 98; II-5, 75, 98; JJ-15, 16, 17, 22; KK-18; LL-4, 18.

Carboniferous: H-65, 85, 87; K-13; R-100; W-7, 9, 10, 11; X-47; Y-59, 66; Z-8; AA-95; DD-1, 27, 96; EE-1, 58, 88; HH-97, 99; II-5, 75; JJ-17, 20, 22; KK-18; LL-18; MM-2, 20; NN-2, 20, 22; OO-2, 34; PP-2, 84; QQ-71, 72.

Permian: A-50, 52; B-50, 52, 63; F-86; H-73, 81, 82, 85, 87; J-83, 92; L-51; M-49; O-24; P-61, 64; S-23, 29, 62; V-21; W-7, 11, 12; X-47; Y-3, 66; Z-8, 26; DD-27; EE-58; HH-37, 58, 97, 99; II-70, 75; JJ-17, 22; KK-18; LL-18, 57; MM-54; NN-22, 35; OO-34; PP-84; QQ-71, 72.

(1) Armstrong, A. K., 1970, Carbonate facies and the lithostrotionid corals of the Mississippian Kogruk Formation, De Long Mountains, northwestern Alaska: U.S. Geol. Survey Prof. Paper 664, p. 1–38.

(2) ——— and B. L. Mamet, 1970, Biostratigraphy and dolomite porosity trends of the Lisburne Group, in W. L. Adkison and M. M. Brosgé, eds., Proceedings of the geological seminar on the North Slope of Alaska: Los Angeles, Pacific Sec. Am. Assoc. Petroleum Geologists, p. N1–N15.

(3) Bamber, E. W., and M. S. Barss, 1969, Stratigraphy and palynology of a Permian section, Tatonduk River, Yukon Territory: Canada Geol. Survey Paper 68–18, 39 p.

(4) Bassett, H. G., and J. G. Stout, 1967, Devonian of Western Canada, in D. H. Oswald, ed., International symposium on the Devonian System, v. 1: Calgary, Alberta Soc. Petroleum Geologists, p. 717–752.

(5) Bowsher, A. L., and J. T. Dutro, Jr., 1957, The Paleozoic section in the Shainin Lake area, central Brooks Range, Alaska: U.S. Geol. Survey Prof. Paper 303-A, p. A1–A39.

(6) Brabb, E. E., 1967, Stratigraphy of the Cambrian and Ordovician rocks of east-central Alaska: U.S. Geol. Survey Prof. Paper 559-A, p. A1–A30.

(7) ——— 1969, Six new Paleozoic and Mesozoic formations in east-central Alaska: U.S. Geol. Survey Bull. 1274-I, p. I1–I26.

(8) ——— 1970, Preliminary geologic map of the Black River quadrangle, east-central Alaska: U.S. Geol. Survey Misc. Geol. Inv. Map I-601, scale 1:250,000. Includes Cairnes collections.

(9) ——— and Michael Churkin, Jr., 1965, Preliminary geologic map of the Eagle D-1 quadrangle, east-central Alaska: U.S. Geol. Survey Open-File Map, scale 1:63,360.

(10) ——— and ——— 1967, Stratigraphic evidence for the Late Devonian age of the Nation River Formation, east-central Alaska, in Geological Survey research 1967: U.S. Geol. Survey Prof. Paper 575-D, p. D4–D15.

(11) ——— and ——— 1969 (1970), Geologic map of the Charley River quadrangle, east-central Alaska: U.S. Geol. Survey Misc. Geol. Inv. Map I-573, scale 1:250,000.

(12) ——— and R. E. Grant, 1971, Stratigraphy and paleontology of the revised type section for the Tahkandit Limestone (Permian) in east-central Alaska: U.S. Geol. Survey Prof. Paper 703.

(13) Brooks, A. H., 1900, A reconnaissance in the Tanana and White River basins, Alaska, in 1898: U.S. Geol. Survey 20th Ann. Rept., pt. 7, p. 427–509.

(14) ——— 1911, The Mount McKinley region, Alaska: U.S. Geol. Survey Prof. Paper 70, p. 1–234, map scale 1:625,000.

(15) Brosgé, W. P., and H. N. Reiser, 1962, Preliminary geologic map of the Christian quadrangle, Alaska: U.S. Geol. Survey Open-File Map, scale 1:250,000.

(16) ——— and ——— 1964, Geologic map and section of the Chandalar quadrangle, Alaska: U.S. Geol. Survey Misc. Geol. Inv. Map I-375, scale 1:250,000.

(17) ——— and ——— 1965, Preliminary geologic map of the Arctic quadrangle, Alaska: U.S. Geol. Survey Open-File Map, scale 1:250,000.

(18) ——— and ——— 1969, Preliminary geologic map of the Coleen quadrangle, Alaska: U.S. Geol. Survey Open-File Map, scale 1:250,000.

(19) ——— and I. L. Tailleur, 1970, Depositional history of northern Alaska, in W. L. Adkison, and M. M. Brosgé, eds., Proceedings of the geological seminar on the North Slope of Alaska: Los Angeles, Pacific Sec. Am. Assoc. Petroleum Geologists, p. D-1–D17.

(20) ——— and ——— 1971, Northern Alaska petroleum province, in I. H. Cram, ed., Future petroleum provinces of the United States—their geology and potential: Am. Assoc. Petroleum Geologists Mem. 15, v. 1, p. 68–99.

(21) ——— E. E. Brabb, and E. R. King, 1970, Geologic interpretation of reconnaissance aeromagnetic survey of northeastern Alaska: U.S. Geol. Survey Bull. 1271-F, p. F1–F14.

(22) ———— et al., 1962, Paleozoic sequence in eastern Brooks Range, Alaska: Am. Assoc. Petroleum Geologists Bull., v. 46, no. 12, p. 2174–2198.

(23) ———— et al., 1969, Probable Permian age of the Rampart Group, central Alaska: U.S. Geol. Survey Bull. 1294-B, p. B1–B18.

(24) Brown, J. D., 1926, The Nixon Fork country: U.S. Geol. Survey Bull. 783-D, p. 97–144, map scale 1:250,000.

(25) Cady, W. M., et al., 1955, The central Kuskokwim region, Alaska: U.S. Geol. Survey Prof. Paper 268, 132 p., map scale 1:250,000.

(26) Cairnes, D. D., 1914, The Yukon-Alaska International Boundary: Canada Dept. Mines Geol. Survey Mem. 67, Geol. Ser., no. 49, p. 1–161.

(27) Campbell, R. H., 1967, Areal geology in the vicinity of the Chariot site, Lisburne Peninsula, northwestern Alaska: U.S. Geol. Survey Prof. Paper 395, 71 p.

(28) Capps, S. R., 1940, Geology of the Alaska Railroad region: U.S. Geol. Survey Bull. 907, 201 p., map scale 1:250,000.

(29) Chapman, R. M., F. R. Weber, and Bond Taber, 1971, Geologic map of the Livengood quadrangle: U.S. Geol. Survey Open-File Map.

(30) Church, R. E., and M. C. Durfee, 1961, Geology of the Fossil Creek area, White Mountains, Alaska: Unpub. MS thesis, Univ. Alaska, College.

Churkin, Michael, Jr., 1969, Paleozoic tectonic history of the Arctic Basin north of Alaska: Science, v. 165, p. 549–555.

———— 1970, Paleozoic and Precambrian rocks of Alaska and their role in its tectonic history: U.S. Geol. Survey Open-File Rept., 131 p.

(31) ———— and E. E. Brabb, 1965a, Occurrence and stratigraphic significance of *Oldhamia,* a Cambrian trace fossil, in east-central Alaska, *in* Geological Survey research 1965: U.S. Geol. Survey Prof. Paper 525-D, p. D120–D124.

(32) ———— and ———— 1965b, Ordovician, Silurian, and Devonian biostratigraphy of east-central Alaska: Am. Assoc. Petroleum Geologists Bull., v. 49, no. 2, p. 172–185.

(33) ———— and ———— 1967, Devonian rocks of the Yukon-Porcupine Rivers area and their tectonic relation to other Devonian sequences in Alaska, *in* D. H. Oswald, ed., International symposium on the Devonian System, v. 2: Calgary, Alberta Soc. Petroleum Geologists, p. 227–258.

(34) Collins, F. R., 1958, Test wells, Topagoruk area, Alaska: U.S. Geol. Survey Prof. Paper 305-D, p. D265–D316.

(35) Detterman, R. L., 1970, Sedimentary history of Sadlerochit and Shublik Formations in northeastern Alaska, *in* W. L. Adkison and M. M. Brosgé, eds., Proceedings of the geologic seminar on the North Slope of Alaska: Los Angeles, Pacific Sec. Am. Assoc. Petroleum Geologists, p. O1–O13.

Douglas, R. J. W., et al., 1963, Geology and petroleum potentialities of northern Canada: Canada Geol. Survey Paper 63–31, 28 p.

(36) Dutro, J. T., Jr., 1953, Stratigraphy and paleontology of the Noatak and associated formations, Brooks Range, Alaska (abs.): Geol. Soc. America Bull., v. 64, no. 12, pt. 2, p. 1415.

(37) ———— 1961, Correlation of the Arctic Permian, *in* Geological Survey research 1961: U.S. Geol. Survey Prof. Paper 424-C, p. C225–C228.

(38) ———— 1970, Pre-Carboniferous carbonate rocks, northeastern Alaska, *in* W. L. Adkison and M. M. Brosgé, eds., Proceedings of the geological seminar on the North Slope of Alaska: Los Angeles, Pacific Sec. Am. Assoc. Petroleum Geologists, p. M1–M7.

(39) ———— W. P. Brosgé, and H. N. Reiser, 1972, Significance of recently discovered Cambrian fossils and reinterpretation of Neruokpuk Formation, northeastern Alaska: Am. Assoc. Petroleum Geologists Bull., v. 56, no. 4, p. 808–815.

(40) Eakin, H. M., 1918, The Cosna-Nowitna region, Alaska: U.S. Geol. Survey Bull. 667, 54 p.

(41) Foster, H. L., 1969, Reconnaissance geology of the Eagle A-1 and A-2 quadrangles, Alaska: U.S. Geol. Survey Bull. 1271-G, p. G1–G30, map scale 1:63,360.

(42) ———— 1970, Reconnaissance geologic map of the Tanacross quadrangle, Alaska: U.S. Geol. Survey Misc. Geol. Inv. Map I-593, scale 1:250,000.

(43) ———— and T. C. Keith, 1968, Preliminary geologic map of the Eagle B-1 and C-1 quadrangles, Alaska: U.S. Geol. Survey Open-File Map, scale 1:63,360.

(44a) Foster, R. L., 1966, The petrology and structure of the Amy Dome area, Tolovana mining district, east-central Alaska: PhD thesis, Univ. Missouri, Columbia.

(44b) ———— 1968, Potential for gold deposits in the Livengood Gold Placer district, east-central Alaska: U.S. Geol. Survey Circ. 590, p. 1–18.

(45) Fritts, C. E., 1970, Geology and geochemistry of the Cosmos Hills, Ambler River and Shungnak quadrangles, Alaska: Alaska Div. Mines and Minerals Geol. Rept. 39, 69 p.

(46) Gabrielse, H., 1967, Tectonic evolution of the northern Canadian Cordillera: Canadian Jour. Earth Sci., v. 4, p. 271–298.

(47) Green, L. H., and J. A. Roddick, 1962, Dawson, Larsen Creek, and Nash Creek map areas, Yukon Territory: Canada Geol. Survey Paper 62–7, 20 p.

(48) Gryc, George, et al., 1967, Devonian of Alaska, *in* D. H. Oswald, ed., International symposium on the Devonian System, v. 1: Calgary, Alberta Soc. Petroleum Geologists, p. 703–716.

(49) Hoare, J. M., 1961, Preliminary geology along the lower Yukon River, Alaska: U.S. Geol. Survey Open-File Map, scale 1:500,000 (OF: 221).

(50) ———— and W. L. Coonrad, 1959a, Geology of the Bethel quadrangle, Alaska: U.S. Geol. Survey Misc. Geol. Inv. Map I-285, scale 1:250,000.

(51) ———— and ———— 1959b, Geology of the Russian Mission quadrangle, Alaska: U.S. Geol. Survey Misc. Geol. Inv. Map I-292, scale 1:250,000.

(52) ———— and ———— 1961, Geologic map of the Goodnews quadrangle, Alaska: U.S. Geol.

Survey Misc. Geol. Inv. Map I-339, scale 1: 250,000.

(53a) Hummel, C. H. L., 1962a, Preliminary geologic map of the Nome C-1 quadrangle, Seward peninsula, Alaska: U.S. Geol. Survey Mineral Inv. Field Studies Map MF-247, scale 1: 63,360.

(53b) ——— 1962b, Preliminary geologic map of the Nome D-1 quadrangle, Seward peninsula, Alaska: U.S. Geol. Survey Mineral Inv. Field studies Map MF-248, scale 1:63,360.

Jeletzky, J. A., 1962, Pre-Cretaceous Richardson Mountains trough: its place in the tectonic framework of Arctic Canada and its bearing on some geosynclinal concepts: Royal Soc. Canada Trans., 3d ser., v. 56, sec. 3, pt. 1, p. 55–84.

(54) Keller, A. S., R. H. Morris, and R. L. Detterman, 1961, Geology of the Shaviovik and Sagavanirktok Rivers region, Alaska: U.S. Geol. Survey Prof. Paper 303-D, p. D169–D222.

(55) Kindle, E. M., 1911, The faunal succession in the Port Clarence limestone, Alaska: Am. Jour. Sci., ser. 4, v. 32, p. 349.

King, P. B., 1969, Tectonic map of North America: U.S. Geol. Survey, scale 1: 5,000,000.

(56) Lanphere, M. A., 1965, Age of Ordovician and Devonian mafic rocks in northern Alaska, in Geological Survey research 1965: U.S. Geol. Survey Prof. Paper 525-A, p. A101–A102.

(57) Maddren, A. G., 1912, Geologic investigations along the Canada-Alaska boundary: U.S. Geol. Survey Bull. 520, p. 297–314.

(58) Martin, A. J., 1970, Structure and tectonic history of the western Brooks Range, De Long Mountains and Lisburne Hills, northern Alaska: Geol. Soc. America Bull., v. 81, no. 12, p. 3605–3622.

(59) Martin, L. J., 1959, Stratigraphy and depositional tectonics of north Yukon–lower Mackenzie area, Canada: Am. Assoc. Petroleum Geologists Bull., v. 43, no. 10, p. 2399–2455.

(60) McAlester, A. L., 1962, A new Devonian pelecypod from Alaska and its bearing on pterioid phylogeny: Yale Univ. Peabody Mus. Postilla, no. 58, p. 1–13.

(61) Mertie, J. B., Jr., 1937a, The Kaiyuh Hills, Alaska: U.S. Geol. Survey Bull. 868-D, p. D145–D178, map scale 1:500,000.

(62) ——— 1937b, The Yukon-Tanana region, Alaska: U.S. Geol. Survey Bull. 872, 276 p., map scale 1:500,000.

(63) ——— 1938, The Nushagak district, Alaska: U.S. Geol. Survey Bull. 903, 96 p., map scale 1:250,000.

(64) ——— and G. L. Harrington, 1924, The Ruby-Kuskokwim region, Alaska: U.S. Geol. Survey Bull. 754, 129 p.

(65) Moffit, F. H., 1954, Geology of the eastern part of the Alaska Range and adjacent area: U.S. Geol. Survey Bull. 989-D, p. D65–D218, map scale 1:250,000.

(66) Nelson, S. J., and C. E. Johnson, 1968, Permo-Pennsylvanian brachythyrid and horridonid brachiopods from the Yukon Territory, Canada: Jour. Paleontology, v. 42, no. 3, p. 715–746.

(67) Norford, B. S., 1964, Reconnaissance of the Ordovician and Silurian rocks of northern Yukon Territory: Canada Geol. Survey Paper 63–39, 139 p.

(68) Norris, A. W., 1967, Devonian of northern Yukon Territory and adjacent District of Mackenzie, in D. H. Oswald, ed., International symposium on the Devonian System, v. 1: Calgary, Alberta Soc. Petroleum Geologists, p. 753–780.

(69) Norris, D. K., R. A. Price, and E. W. Mountjoy, 1963, Geology of northern Yukon Territory and northwestern District of Mackenzie: Canada Geol. Survey Map 10-1963, scale 1:1,000,000.

(70) Patton, W. W., Jr., 1957, A new upper Paleozoic formation, central Brooks Range, Alaska: U.S. Geol. Survey Prof. Paper 303-B, p. B41–B45.

(71) ——— and Béla Csejtey, Jr., 1971, Preliminary geologic investigations of western St. Lawrence Island, Alaska: U.S. Geol. Survey Prof. Paper 684–C, map scale 1:250,000.

(72) ——— and J. T. Dutro, Jr., 1969, Preliminary report on the Paleozoic and Mesozoic sedimentary sequence on St. Lawrence Island, Alaska, in Geological Survey research 1969: U.S. Geol. Survey Prof. Paper 650-D, p. D138–D143.

(73) Petocz, R. G., 1970, Biostratigraphy and Lower Permian Fusulinidae of the upper Delta River area, east-central Alaska Range: Geol. Soc. America Spec. Paper 130, 94 p.

(74) Péwé, T. L., Clyde Wahrhaftig, and F. R. Weber, 1966, Geologic map of the Fairbanks quadrangle, Alaska: U.S. Geol. Survey Misc. Geol. Inv. Map I–455, scale 1:250,000.

(75) Porter, S. C., 1966, Stratigraphy and deformation of Paleozoic section at Anaktuvuk Pass, central Brooks Range, Alaska: Am. Assoc. Petroleum Geologists Bull., v. 50, no. 5, p. 952–980.

(76) Reed, B. L., 1968, Geology of the Lake Peters area, northeastern Brooks Range, Alaska: U.S. Geol. Survey Bull. 1236, 132 p.

(77) ——— and R. L. Elliott, 1968a, Geochemical anomalies and metalliferous deposits between Windy Fork and Post River, southern Alaska Range: U.S. Geol. Survey Circ. 569, 22 p.

(78) ——— and ——— 1968b, Lead, zinc, and silver deposits at Bowser Creek, McGrath A-2 quadrangle, Alaska: U.S. Geol. Survey Circ. 559, 17 p.

(79) ——— and ——— 1970, Reconnaissance geologic map, analyses of bedrock and stream sediment samples, and an aeromagnetic map of parts of the southern Alaska Range: U.S. Geol. Survey Open-File Rept., map scale 1: 250,000.

(80) Reiser, H. N., 1970, Northeastern Brooks Range —a surface expression of the Prudhoe Bay section, in W. L. Adkison and M. M. Brosgé, eds., Proceedings of the geological seminar on the North Slope of Alaska: Los Angeles, Pacific Sec. Am. Assoc. Petroleum Geologists, p. K1–K13.

(81) Richter, D. H., 1966, Geology of the Slana district, south-central Alaska: Alaska Div. Mines and Minerals Geol. Rept. 21, 51 p., map scale 1:63,360.

(82) ——— 1967, Geology of the Upper Slana–Mentasta Pass area, south-central Alaska:

Alaska Div. Mines and Minerals Geol. Rept. 30, 27 p., with maps, scale 1:63,360.

(83a) ———— 1970a, Reconnaissance geologic map and section of the Nabesna A-3 quadrangle, Alaska: U.S. Geol. Survey Open-File Maps.

(83b) ———— 1970b, Reconnaissance geologic map and section of the Nabesna B-4 quadrangle, Alaska: U.S. Geol. Survey Open-File Maps.

(83c) ———— and D. L. Jones, 1970, Structure and stratigraphy of eastern Alaska Range (abs.): Am. Assoc. Petroleum Geologists Bull., v. 54, p. 2502.

(84) Rickwood, F. K., 1970, The Prudhoe Bay field, in W. L. Adkison and M. M. Brosgé, eds., Proceedings of the geological seminar on the North Slope of Alaska: Los Angeles, Pacific Sec. Am. Assoc. Petroleum Geologists, p. L1–L11.

(85) Rose, A. W., 1966, Geological and geochemical investigations in the Eureka Creek and Rainy Creek areas, Mt. Hayes quadrangle, Alaska: Alaska Div. Mines and Minerals Geol. Rept. 20, 37 p.

(86) Ross, C. P., 1933, Mineral deposits near the West Fork of the Chulitna River, Alaska: U.S. Geol. Survey Bull. 849-E, p. 289–333, map scale 1:125,000.

(87) Rowett, C. L., 1969, Upper Paleozoic stratigraphy and corals from the east-central Alaska Range, Alaska: Arctic Inst. North America Tech. Paper 23, 120 p.

(88) Sable, E. G., and J. T. Dutro, Jr., 1961, New Devonian and Mississippian formations in De Long Mountains, northern Alaska: Am. Assoc. Petroleum Geologists Bull., v. 45, p. 585–593.

(89) Sainsbury, C. L., 1965, Previously undescribed Middle(?) Ordovician, Devonian(?) and Cretaceous(?) rocks, White Mountain area, near McGrath, Alaska, in Geological Survey research 1965: U.S. Geol. Survey Prof. Paper 525-C, p. C91–C95.

(90) ———— 1969, Geology and ore deposits of the central York Mountains, western Seward peninsula, Alaska: U.S. Geol. Survey Bull. 1287, 101 p.

(91) ———— R. G. Coleman, and Reuben Kachadoorian, 1970, Blueschist and related greenschist facies rocks of the Seward peninsula, Alaska, in Geological Survey research 1970: U.S. Geol. Survey Prof. Paper 700-B, p. B33–B42.

(92) Smith, J. G., and E. M. MacKevett, Jr., 1970, The Skolai Group in the McCarthy B-4, C-4 and C-5 quadrangles, Wrangell Mountains,

Alaska: U.S. Geol. Survey Bull. 1274-Q, p. Q1–Q26, map scale 1:96,000.

(93) Smith, P. S., 1917, The Lake Clark–Central Kuskokwim region, Alaska: U.S. Geol. Survey Bull. 655, 162 p., map scale 1:250,000.

(94) ———— and H. M. Eakin, 1911, A geologic reconnaissance in southeastern Seward peninsula and the Norton Bay-Nulato region: U.S. Geol. Survey Bull. 449, 146 p., map scale 1:250,000; and unpub. faunal lists.

(95) Steidtmann, Edward, and S. H. Cathcart, 1922, Geology of the York tin deposits, Alaska: U.S. Geol. Survey Bull. 733, 130 p., map scale 1:250,000.

Stewart, J. H., 1971, Late Precambrian (< 750 m.y.) continental separation in western North America—possible evidence from sedimentary and volcanic rocks (abs.): Geol. Soc. America Abstracts with Programs, v. 3, no. 2, p. 201.

(96) Tailleur, I. L., 1963, Northern Alaska, in Geological Survey research 1963: U.S. Geol. Survey Prof. Paper 475-A, p. A99.

(97) ———— and E. G. Sable, 1963, Nuka Formation of Late Mississippian to Late Permian age, new formation in northern Alaska: Am. Assoc. Petroleum Geologists Bull., v. 47, no. 4, p. 632–642.

(98) ———— W. P. Brosgé, and H. N. Reiser, 1967, Palinspastic analysis of Devonian rocks in northwestern Alaska, in D. H. Oswald, ed., International symposium on the Devonian System, v. 2; Calgary, Alberta Soc. Petroleum Geologists, p. 1345–1361.

(99) ———— B. H. Kent, Jr., and H. N. Reiser, 1966, Outcrop/geologic maps of the Nuka-Etivluk region, northern Alaska: U.S. Geol. Survey Open-File Maps, map scale 1:63,360.

(100) Wahrhaftig, Clyde, 1968, Schists of the central Alaska Range: U.S. Geol. Survey Bull. 1254-E, p. E1–E22.

(101) Weber, F. R., and Bond Taber, 1964, Stratigraphy revised in Livengood and Christian quadrangles, in Geological Survey research 1964: U.S. Geol. Survey Prof. Paper 501-A, p. A118.

(102) Woolson, J. R., et al., 1962 (1963), Seismic and gravity surveys of Naval Petroleum Reserve No. 4 and adjoining areas, Alaska: U.S. Geol. Survey Prof. Paper 304-A, 25 p.

Ziegler, P. A., 1969, The development of sedimentary basins in western and Arctic Canada: Calgary, Alberta Soc. Petroleum Geologists, 89 p.

Mesozoic Sequence in Arctic Alaska[1]

ROBERT L. DETTERMAN[2]

Menlo Park, California

Abstract Early Mesozoic rocks in Arctic Alaska reflect a continuation of deposition in the late Paleozoic Cordilleran geosyncline. Starting in Early Jurassic time, the broad Cordilleran geosyncline was warped into three small geosynclines: the Colville, Koyukuk, and Kandik, separated by the east-trending Brooks Range geanticline and the narrow southwest-trending Ruby geanticline. These structural highs and lows were areas of erosion and deposition throughout the remainder of the Mesozoic.

Orogeny was widespread in the Cretaceous. One major orogeny took place during the Aptian; as a result, all post-Aptian strata lie with angular discordance on earliest Cretaceous to Devonian beds. Orogeny continued in Cenomanian time, and, by Late Cretaceous, folding was largely completed in the Koyukuk and Kandik geosynclines. The Brooks Range was uplifted at the end of Cretaceous time, and the rocks of the Colville geosyncline were moderately to intensely deformed. Major thrust plates developed, and the strata were thrust northward, so that rocks of similar age but widely different facies were commonly juxtaposed.

Early Triassic beds are primarily confined to northeastern Alaska, where 500–1,000 ft (150–300 m) of strata show a distinct northward coarsening of clastic components, indicating a source in that direction. Middle and Late Triassic time are represented by widespread deposits of black phosphatic limestone, calcareous shale, and chert totaling several hundred feet in thickness. These shelf deposits are similar to, and largely concordant with, the underlying Paleozoic strata.

During the Jurassic the Colville and Kandik geosynclines received 2,000–10,000 ft (610–3,050 m) of monotonous dark pyritic shale, siltstone, and graywacke. At the same time, mafic igneous flows and tuffs were accumulating in the Koyukuk area. These rocks are largely discordant on older strata and locally discordant between successive Jurassic units.

The depositional pattern established in the Jurassic continued into the Early Cretaceous, when 5,000–15,000 ft (1,525–4,570 m) of mainly flysch-type sediments accumulated in the geosynclines. By middle Albian time, conditions favoring deposition of subgraywacke prevailed. Shifting shorelines caused better sorting in the 3,000–10,000 ft (915–3,050 m) of interfingering marine and nonmarine clastic rocks deposited during the remainder of Cretaceous time.

INTRODUCTION

Early Mesozoic rocks in Arctic Alaska reflect a continuation of the depositional pattern established during the late Paleozoic. The Cordilleran geosyncline occupied much of central

[1] Manuscript received, September 20, 1971. Publication authorized by the Director, U.S. Geological Survey.

[2] U.S. Geological Survey.

and southern Alaska and was bordered on the north by the Yukon platform (Ziegler, 1969). Along the northern edge of Alaska, the main tectonic elements were the Arctic Alaska basin (Tailleur, 1969) and the Arctic platform (Payne, 1955); this northern positive area was the source for most of the early Mesozoic sediments now preserved in Arctic Alaska.

TRIASSIC

Lower Triassic rocks are positively identified only in north-central and northeastern Alaska (Figs. 1, 2A). Rocks that may be partly coeval, but are of an entirely different facies, are tentatively identified on St. Lawrence Island and near Point Hope in western Alaska. Many well-exposed sections of clastic sedimentary rocks of the Ivishak Member of the Sadlerochit Formation have been measured along the north flank of the Brooks Range in northeastern Alaska (Keller *et al.*, 1961; Detterman, 1970b); the same sequence of beds is present in the subsurface along the north coast.

The section exposed in the northeast Brooks Range is mainly a clastic wedge, 500–1,000 ft (150–300 m) thick, consisting of locally conglomeratic quartzitic sandstone, siltstone, and shale. These rocks were deposited in a nearshore deltaic environment. Prodeltaic shale and siltstone beds become more numerous southward, and the sandstone and conglomerate become coarser grained and more abundant northward, indicating a source area in that direction. Depositional features preserved on bedding planes suggest that the direction of sediment transport was from N30°–40°E. Rocks present in the subsurface along the north coast were deposited mainly in a nonmarine to littoral environment.

Beds of the Ivishak Member lie conformably on strata of the Echooka Member (Late Permian) of the Sadlerochit Formation in the Brooks Range. Along the north coast, these same beds unconformably overlie Mississippian to pre-Devonian(?) carbonate and clastic rocks. Most of the Scythian Stage of the Lower Triassic is represented by the fossils *Otoceras, Claraia, Ophiceras,* and *Euflemingites.*

Middle and Upper Triassic rocks are present

in nearly all parts of Arctic Alaska. The Middle-Late Triassic was a time of slow deposition; the condensed section is generally no more than 200–300 ft (60–90 m) thick. The dark-gray to sooty-black calcareous shale, siltstone, limestone, and chert are abundantly fossiliferous and form a distinctive unit. Dark-gray calcareous to siliceous sandstone locally forms a minor but prominent marker at the top of the section in the northeast. Phosphate nodules and pebbles are locally abundant (Detterman, 1970a), and the rocks have a high organic content that probably was the source for at least part of the petroleum found there. These rocks are best exposed north of the Brooks Range and are mapped across northern Alaska as the Shublik Formation (Fig. 1). Middle and Upper Triassic rocks are poorly exposed south of the range except between the Yukon and Porcupine Rivers, adjacent to the International Boundary, where about 100 ft (30 m) of limestone and shale, including minor oil shale, is present in the lower part of the Glenn Shale (Brabb, 1969). Upper Triassic rocks are also mapped along the Coleen River and Monument Creek and on St. Lawrence Island.

The depositional environment of the Shublik Formation was that of an open, stable shelf where water depth increased southwestward. The source area was on the northeast, and the apparently slow detrital input probably indicates a low landmass rather than one far removed. Glauconite is abundant at some localities. Dark fine-grained sandstone is limited to the northeastern part of Arctic Alaska, near the source area, and limestone and chert become more abundant southwestward, indicating deeper water. The source of the Glenn Shale is not known definitely but was probably on the northeast. Volcanic rocks commonly associated with Triassic strata in southern Alaska and elsewhere in the world are absent in Arctic Alaska.

Fossils from the Middle and Upper Triassic rocks indicate that the European Anisian, Ladinian, Karnian, and Norian Stages are present. The Anisian Stage is represented by *Leiophyllites;* the Ladinian Stage by *Daonella frami* and *D. degeeri;* the Karnian by *Leptochondria, Halobia zittelli, Arctosirenites,* and *Tropites;* and the Norian by *Monotis typica, M. pinensis, M. ochotica ochotica,* and *Halobia fallax.*

The Shublik Formation conformably overlies Lower Triassic strata in northeastern Alaska; westward along the north front of the Brooks Range and in the subsurface at Point Barrow

and Cape Simpson, the formation unconformably overlies pre-Devonian(?) to Lower Permian rocks. The Glenn Shale also unconformably overlies Permian strata.

JURASSIC

The tectonic framework that had persisted throughout the late Paleozoic and early Mesozoic was warped into negative and positive areas of deposition and erosion starting in Early Jurassic time (Fig. 2B). Geosynclines and successor basins that formed in the negative areas are the sites of all middle and late Mesozoic rocks in Arctic Alaska. Detritus for these rocks was obtained from the intervening positive terranes. The time of folding cannot be stated precisely, and it probably did not occur everywhere at the same time. Tectonic activity probably started during the Hettangian Stage, at the beginning of the Jurassic Period, and first involved interior Alaska, where Triassic and older strata were gently upwarped and subjected to erosion.

The Colville geosyncline in northern Alaska apparently started to form during the Early Jurassic by a gentle downwarping, and deposition was nearly continuous throughout the Early Jurassic (Fig. 3). The record for the Hettangian Stage is fragmentary, but this time span is probably represented by largely unfossiliferous, dark, fissile paper shale with clay-ironstone cannonball concretions at the base of the Kingak Shale. About 600–800 ft (185–245 m) of these paper shales is preserved locally in northeastern Alaska; the shales have yielded specimens of *Psiloceras.* Farther west, along the north side of the Brooks Range in a disturbed belt, these dark shales are represented by a condensed section no more than 100 ft (30 m) thick. The paper-shale sequence lies under several hundred to a thousand feet of clay shale, including clay-ironstone concretions and interbeds of siltstone and silty shale. The rocks, which are included in the Kingak Shale, contain *Arietites, Otapiria, Amaltheus, Dactylioceras,* and *Pseudolioceras,* suggesting that all stages of the Lower Jurassic are present.

Glauconitic sandstone in the subsurface along the north coast suggests that the source of the sediments was still on the north. The presence of distal shale—mapped as part of the Glenn Shale (Brabb, 1969)—in the Kandik area between the Yukon River and the International Boundary indicates a southward extension of this basin.

During Middle and Late Jurassic time,

Series	European stages	Age: Base of stage in millions of years [1/]	Characteristic megafossils [2/]	West — Lisburne Peninsula southern foothills [3/]	Utukok R. to Etivluk River northern and southern foothills [4/]	Killik R. to Itkillik River northern and southern foothills [5/]	Point Barrow to Umiat coastal plains-subsurface [6/]	Sagavanirktok R. to Canning River northern foothills [7/]	Sadlerochit M... to Jago R... northern fo... [8/]
Overlying beds				Quaternary	Quaternary	Quaternary	Quaternary	Quaternary / Tertiary	Quaternary
Upper Cretaceous	Maestrichtian	70	Inoceramus patootensis				Kogosukruk Tongue / Sentinel Hill Mbr	Sandstone and shale	Siltstone, and sandst
	Campanian	76	Inoceramus steenstrupi			Kogosukruk Tongue / Sentinel Hill Mbr / Schrader Bluff Fm / Barrow Trail Mbr / Prince Creek Fm / Rogers Creek Mbr	Sentinel Hill Mbr / Schrader Bluff Fm / Barrow Trail Mbr / Prince Creek / Rogers Creek Mbr		Sandstone an
	Santonian	82						Tuff, siltstone, and shale	Tuff and
	Coniacian	88	Inoceramus cuvieri	Prince Creek Formation		Tuluvak Tongue / Ayiyak Mbr	Tuluvak Tongue / Ayiyak Mbr	Organic shale and bentonite	Probably Organic and ber
	Turonian	94	Scaphites delicatulus / Borissjakoceras sp. / Inoceramus labiatus	Probably absent		Seabee Fm / Shale Well Mbr	Seabee Fm / Shale Well Mbr		
	Cenomanian	100	Inoceramus dunveganensis	Corwin Formation	Niakogon Tongue / Chandler Fm / Ninuluk Fm / Killik Tongue / Tuktu Fm	Niakogon Tongue / Chandler / Ninuluk Fm / Killik Tongue / Tuktu Fm	Ninuluk Formation / Grandstand Fm	Ninuluk / Ignek Formation (lower part) / Chandler Fm / Tuktu Fm	
Lower Cretaceous	Albian — Upper		Inoceramus altifluminsis	Kukpowruk Formation	Torok Fm	Torok Fm	Topagoruk Fm	Torok Fm	Sandstor siltst
	Albian — Middle	106	Paragastroplites spiekeri	Torok Fm					Graywa (cong
	Albian — Lower		Cleoniceras tailleuri / Beudanticeras affine	Fortress Mountain Fm	Fortress Mountain Fm	Fortress Mountain Fm	Oumalik Formation	Fortress Mountain Fm	
	Aptian	112							
	Barremian	118	Colvillia crassicostata						
	Neocomian — Hauterivian	124							
	Valanginian	130	Buchia crassicollis / Buchia sublaevis	Kisimilok Formation	Okpikruak Formation	Okpikruak Formation	Pebble shale	Okpikruak Formation	Pebble sha
	Berriasian	136	Buchia okensis / Buchia subokensis					Kemik Ss Mbr	Sandsto
Upper Jurassic	Portlandian	146	Buchia piochii / Buchia rugosa	Telavirak Formation	Gabbro	Varingated shale, siltstone, sandstone, and chert	Probably absent	Pebble shale, and glauconitic sandstone	Probably a
	Kimmeridgian	151	Buchia mosquensis / Buchia concentrica		Graywacke conglomerate, siltstone, and shale			Kingak Shale (Locally contains a sandstone and siltstone facies)	
	Oxfordian	157	Buchia spitiensis / Amoeboceras (Prionodoceras)	Ogotoruk Formation		Possibly present	Possibly present in part		Kingak S
Middle Jurassic	Callovian	162	Cardioceras sp. / Scarburgiceras sp.						
	Bathonian	169	Reineckeia stueboli / Pseudocadoceras greywingki / Arcticoceras kochi				Possibly present		
	Bajocian	172	Inoceramus ambiguus		Tuffaceous graywacke, siltstone, and shale	Pyritic clay shale			Kingak S
Lower Jurassic	Toarcian	178	Inoceramus lucifer / Tmetoceras sp. / Pseudolioceras sp.			Possibly present			
	Pliensbachian	183	Dactylioceras / Amaltheus sp.			Clay shale, siltstone, and sandstone		Kingak Shale	Probably in p
	Sinemurian	188	Otapiria tailleuri / Arietites bucklandi						Clay sh
	Hettangian	190=195	Caloceras sp. / Monotis pachypleura				Possibly present		
Upper Triassic	Rhaetian		Monotis ochotica / Halobia fallax / Monotis pinensis						Sandstone
	Norian		Monotis typica / Arctosirenites canadensis	Shublik Formation	Shublik Formation	Limestone member / Chert member / Shublik Fm	Limestone, siltstone, and glauconite / Shublik Fm	Shublik Formation	Shublik Fo
	Karnian	205	Halobia ornatissima / Halobia zitteli / Leptochondria nationalis						
Middle Triassic	Ladinian		Daonella degeeri / Daonella frami / Nathorstites gibbosus	Possibly present		Shale member			
	Anisian	215	Leiophyllites gibbosus / Euflemingites romunderi						Lower siltsto
Lower Triassic	Scythian	225	Ophiceras sp. / Claraia stachei / Otoceras sp.					Ivishak Member	Ivishak
Underlying beds				Lower Permian	Lower Permian	Lower Permian	Devonian / Permian	Upper Permian	Upper

Nonmarine sedimentary rocks   Marine sedimentary rocks

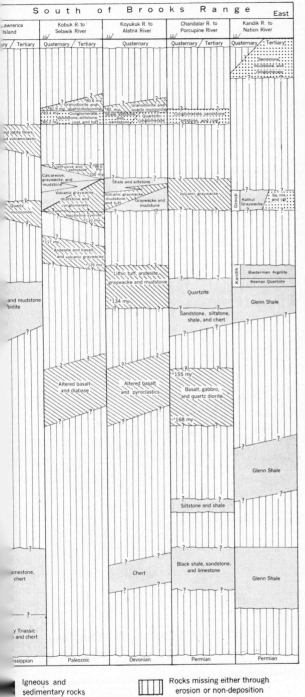

FIG. 1—Arctic Mesozoic correlation chart. Asterisks indicate position of rocks dated by K-Ar method.

[1] Age of stages from Harland *et al.*, 1964.

[2] Fossils identified by: Cretaceous—Jones, D. L., and R. W. Imlay; Jurassic—Imlay, R. W.; Triassic—Silberling, N. J.

Sources for geologic data:

[3] Campbell, R. H., 1967; Chapman, R. M., and E. G. Sable, 1960.

[4] Chapman, R. M., and E. G. Sable, 1960; Chapman, R. M., R. L. Detterman, and M. D. Mangus, 1964.

[5] Detterman, R. L., R. S. Bickel, and George Gryc, 1963; Patton, W. W., Jr., and I. L. Tailleur, 1964.

[6] Bergquist, H. R., 1966; Brosgé, W. P., and C. L. Whittington, 1966; Collins, F. R., 1958a, b, c, 1959, and 1961; Robinson, F. M., 1956, 1958a, b, 1959a, b, and 1964.

[7] Keller, A. S., R. H. Morris, and R. L. Detterman, 1961.

[8] Adkison, W. L., and M. M. Brosgé, 1970; Leffingwell, E. de Koven, 1919; Reed, B. L., 1968; Reiser, H. N., W. P. Brosgé, J. T. Dutro, Jr., and R. L. Detterman, unpublished field data.

[9] Patton, W. W., Jr., and J. T. Dutro, Jr., 1969.

[10] Patton, W. W., Jr., 1967; Patton, W. W., Jr., and T. P. Miller, 1968; Patton, W. W., Jr., T. P. Miller, and I. L. Tailleur, 1968.

[11] Patton, W. W., Jr., and T. P. Miller, 1966; Patton, W. W., Jr., 1966.

[12] Brosgé, W. P., and H. N. Reiser, 1964 and 1969.

[13] Brabb, E. E., 1969; Brabb, E. E., and Michael Churkin, 1969.

[14] Upper-Middle Jurassic boundary after Arkell *et al.*, 1957.

Compiled November 1970 by R. L. Detterman.

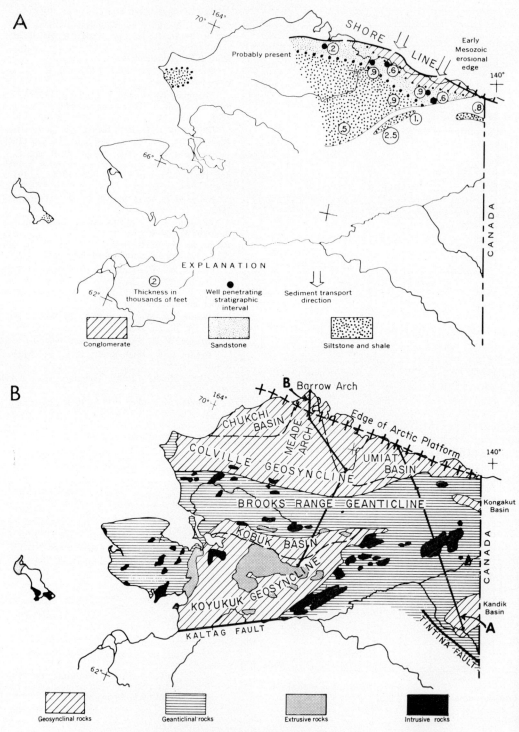

FIG. 2—**A.** Distribution of Lower Triassic rocks. **B.** Mesozoic tectonic elements. A and B indicate lines of cross section (Fig. 3).

downwarping of the Colville geosyncline continued, accompanied by uplift of the Brooks Range geanticline. Downwarping was greatest along the present west coast, near Point Hope and Cape Lisburne, where at least 10,000 ft (3,050 m) of flysch-type graywacke, mudstone, shale, and siltstone was deposited (Campbell, 1967); these rocks are mapped as the Ogotoruk and Telavirak Formations (Fig. 1). The Jurassic age cannot be proved, but directly overlying strata contain basal Neocomian fossils. A similar section about 2,500 ft (760 m) thick is exposed on St. Lawrence Island (Patton and Dutro, 1969).

The landmass off the north coast of Alaska subsided contemporaneously with the development of the Colville geosyncline, but the area of the Barrow arch remained positive at least through the Bajocian Stage of the Middle Jurassic. Glauconitic sandstone 120 ft (35 m) thick in the subsurface at Barrow contains a *Tmetoceras* fauna of early Bajocian age (Collins, 1961).

Two dissimilar coeval facies of Jurassic rocks are present locally along the north flank of the central and western Brooks Range. A coarse clastic facies of graywacke and conglomerate, locally tuffaceous, is found adjacent to a fine clastic siltstone, shale, and chert section in a structurally disturbed belt. The coarse-grained rocks apparently were deposited a considerable distance to the south and were thrust northward to their present location by an Early Cretaceous orogeny. Clay shale, silty shale, and siltstone, all locally pyritic, were deposited in northeastern Alaska during the Middle and Late Jurassic. The rocks are lithologically similar to the Lower Jurassic sequence in that area, but siltstone becomes more abundant and slightly coarser grained in a southerly direction. This fact suggests a southern source area for at least some of the rocks included in the upper part of the Kingak Shale. Disconformities and diastems are abundant throughout the Jurassic section in northern Alaska; one major break covering most of the Callovian and Bathonian Stages may represent the shift from a northern to a southern source area.

Faunal remains are locally abundant and represent all stages of the Middle and Upper Jurassic (Imlay, 1955). The fauna includes *Tmetoceras, Inoceramus lucifer, I. ambiguus, Arcticoceras, Pseudocadoceras, Reineckeia, Scarburgiceras, Cardioceras, Amoeboceras, Buchia spitiensis, B. concentrica, B. mosquensis, B. rugosa,* and *B. fischeri piochii.*

South of the Brooks Range, Middle and Upper Jurassic rocks are poorly defined and imperfectly known. Most of the record consists of radiometrically dated extrusive and intrusive rocks (Reiser *et al.*, 1965). Volcanism was particularly prevalent in the west-central part of the range and probably was a source for some of the tuffaceous graywacke sediments in the disturbed belt on the north side of the range. Minor sedimentary rocks are recorded from the Middle and Upper Jurassic sequence on the south flank of the range; most of them are in the southeast, where sandstone, siltstone, shale, and minor chert are found in the Chandalar area. Distal shales are mapped with the Glenn Shale in the Kandik area.

Early Cretaceous

By earliest Cretaceous (Neocomian) time, Mesozoic tectonic elements were well established (Gates and Gryc, 1963; Brosgé and Tailleur, 1970), and detritus from the Brooks Range geanticline was being shed both to the north and the south. Graywacke and mudstone turbidites as thick as 5,000 ft (1,525 m), mapped as the Kisimilok Formation (Fig. 1), were deposited conformably on older rocks near Point Hope and Cape Lisburne; the same rocks are possibly present on St. Lawrence Island. Similar graywacke and mudstone turbidites were deposited unconformably on Jurassic to Devonian rocks in the bordering foredeep in western and central northern Alaska. Volcanic graywacke and tuff were deposited in parts of the Koyukuk and Kobuk basins on the south side of the range (Fig. 4). In northern Alaska these rocks are mapped as the Okpikruak Formation. A condensed dark shale unit containing pebbles and floating quartz grains is present in the subsurface along the north coast (Collins, 1961) and locally along the north flank of the Brooks Range; this is a distal facies of the Okpikruak Formation. This shale laps unconformably onto the basement high just south of Barrow and locally contains thin stringers of glauconitic sand, suggesting that the Arctic platform still influenced deposition along the north side of the basin. A quartzose sandstone about 100 ft (30 m) thick—the Kemik Sandstone Member of the Okpikruak Formation (Keller *et al.*, 1961)—directly underlies the condensed, pebbly, dark shale unit in northeastern Alaska.

A distal shale facies was deposited in the Kongakut and Kandik basins adjacent to the Canada–United States boundary. In the Kongakut basin the shale unconformably overlies

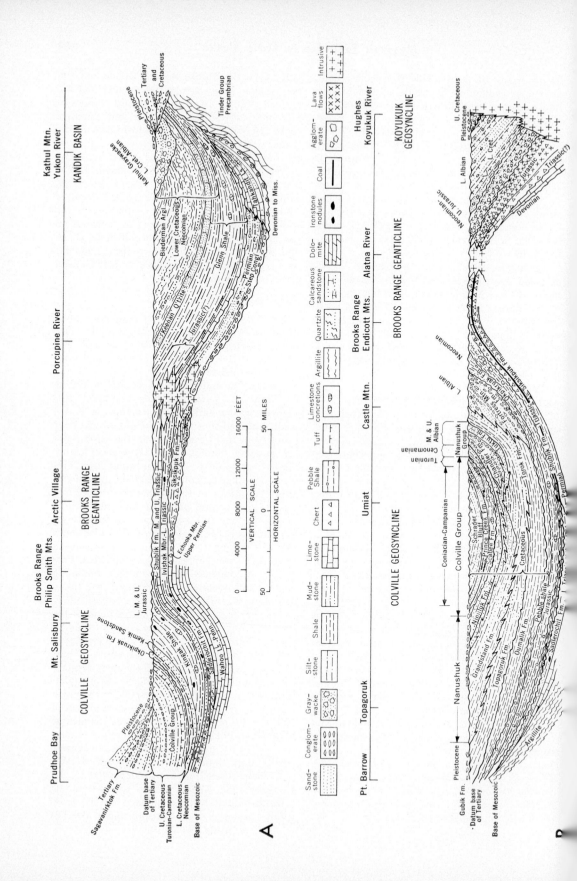

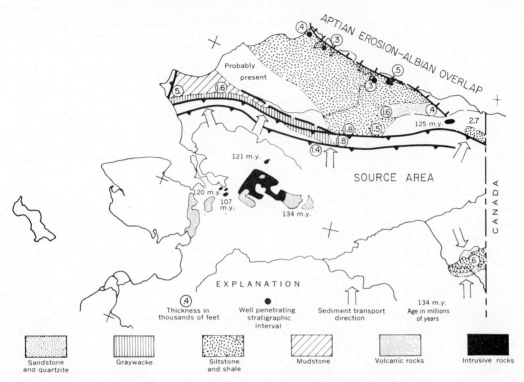

EXPLANATION

④ Thickness in thousands of feet

● Well penetrating stratigraphic interval

⇧ Sediment transport direction

134 m.y. Age in millions of years

| Sandstone and quartzite | Graywacke | Siltstone and shale | Mudstone | Volcanic rocks | Intrusive rocks |

Fig. 4—Distribution of Lower Cretaceous (Neocomian) rocks.

Lower Triassic to Upper Jurassic rocks; in the Kandik basin this shale is included as the upper part of the Glenn Shale. A normal siltstone and shale sequence about 2,500 ft (760 m) thick conformably overlies the condensed shale in the Kongakut basin; however, in the Kandik basin the Keenan Quartzite overlies the shale and is, in turn, overlain by the Biederman Argillite, which is as thick as 5,000 ft (1,525 m).

Faunal remains in these Lower Cretaceous rocks are almost exclusively of the pelecypod *Buchia* and are primarily confined to calcareous layers in the shale sections; locally, the fossils form coquina beds. The Berriasian Stage is represented by *Buchia subokensis* and *B. okensis*, and the Valanginian Stage by *B. sublaevis* and *B. crassicollis*. Faunal remains are absent in Arctic Alaska for the Hauterivian, Barremian, and Aptian Stages of the Lower Cretaceous,

←≪≪

Fig. 3—**A.** Stratigraphic diagram, Prudhoe Bay to Kathul Mountain, Alaska. **B.** Stratigraphic diagram, Point Barrow to Hughes, Alaska.

and, in all probability, these rocks are missing from the sedimentary record there. Extrusive and intrusive rocks dated by the potassium-argon method at 107–121 m.y. (Patton, 1967; Patton and Miller, 1968; Patton *et al.*, 1968) cover large areas of the Koyukuk geosyncline and are the only record of these stages. A date of 125 m.y. on a granitic rock from the Romanzof uplift in northeastern Alaska probably records a remobilization of an older intrusive rather than an intrusion at that time (Sable, 1965).

A thick and well-defined lower Albian sequence overlies the Neocomian beds throughout Arctic Alaska. Flysch-type deposits consisting of graywacke, polymictic conglomerate, mudstone, and shale were deposited along both sides of the Brooks Range geanticline, and as much as 10,000 ft (3,050 m) of coarse clastic sediments accumulated adjacent to the range. In northern Alaska these rocks, mapped as the Fortress Mountain Formation (Fig. 1), unconformably overlie several different Mesozoic and Paleozoic sequences in the disturbed belt. The Fortress Mountain grades northward rather abruptly into the predominantly shale sequence of the Torok Formation; both formations contain a lower Albian fauna at their base and are presumed to be contemporaneous.

The Torok shale thins northward, particularly where it onlaps the platform at Barrow. Most of the thinning is in the upper part of the formation and in beds equivalent to the Nanushuk Group; these beds are mapped locally in the subsurface as the Topagoruk Formation. A change in depositional pattern and direction between the upper and lower parts of the Torok Formation is indicated by subsurface data from near Barrow and along the north coast. The lower part thins northward and unconformably onlaps older rocks at the edge of the platform; the upper part is a prodeltaic sedimentary deposit that thins northeastward and lies unconformably on the lower part as well as on older rocks.

A volcanic graywacke and igneous pebble-conglomerate equivalent to the Fortress Mountain Formation is present along the south flank of the Brooks Range geanticline. The deposit is locally 5,000–10,000 ft (1,525–3,050 m) thick in the Koyukuk area, but it thins eastward; about 1,500 ft (455 m) is preserved in the Kandik basin, where these beds are mapped as the Kathul Graywacke.

The flysch deposits contain a meager fauna of early Albian age (Imlay, 1961) that is found primarily in the basal parts of the formations. Main elements of this fauna include the ammonites *Colvillia, Beudanticeras,* and *Grantziceras.*

By middle Albian time the foredeeps were largely filled, and succeeding beds were deposited mainly as a clastic deltaic wedge by marine transgressions and regressions. The shifting shorelines caused better sorting of the clastic debris and deposition of subgraywacke. This sequence of beds is well exposed in the foothills north of the Brooks Range and is mapped as the Nanushuk Group, which is divided into several formations, largely on the basis of the marine or nonmarine character of the rocks (Figs. 1, 5A). Cenomanian strata are included within the Nanushuk Group, primarily on the basis of lithologic similarity and a continuous depositional sequence.

Nonmarine rocks decrease in abundance northward away from their source in the Brooks Range; the greatest thickness is near the present west coast. The intertonguing marine and nonmarine strata are primarily confined to a northwest-trending belt across northern Alaska in which the shoreline progressed northeastward with time. The area roughly equivalent to the Umiat basin contains an all-marine sequence in the Nanushuk Group.

The basal contact of the Nanushuk Group with the older Cretaceous strata is considered to be conformable or gradational except in the northeast, where the Nanushuk strata were largely removed by Late Cretaceous erosion and the depositional relation with the older rocks is uncertain. A small area containing beds equivalent to the basal Nanushuk Group is preserved east of the Sadlerochit Mountains, where it unconformably overlies Jurassic strata.

Middle and upper Albian rocks are not positively known from south of the Brooks Range, although they may be included with a nonmarine-transitional sequence mapped in the Koyukuk area. Presumably contemporaneous intrusive and extrusive igneous rocks dated at 98.6 and 100 m.y. suggest that most of these calcareous graywackes are Cenomanian rather than Albian in age. Volcanic activity south of the Brooks Range was probably the source for the bentonite and ashstone found in the contemporaneous Cenomanian strata in northern Alaska.

Faunal remains in the Nanushuk Group are primarily a facies-controlled nearshore suite of pelecypods. A few ammonites, present in fine clastic rocks near the base, include *Cleoniceras* and *Paragastroplites.* Diagnostic elements of the pelecypod fauna include *Inoceramus anglicus, I. altifluminsis,* and *I. dunveganensis.* The nonmarine rocks contain an abundant and diversified flora suggestive of a middle Albian to Cenomanian age (Smiley, 1969a, b).

LATE CRETACEOUS

The last cycle of Mesozoic deposition began in middle Turonian time following a period of uplift and erosion that locally removed part or all of the Nanushuk Group in northern Alaska (Fig. 5B). A major unconformity exists in outcrops and in the subsurface between the marine transgressive rocks of the Seabee Formation, at the base of the Colville Group, and the underlying strata (Fig. 1). Upper Cretaceous rocks are essentially confined to the Umiat structural basin and are absent across the Meade arch. A few hundred feet of nonmarine strata, equivalent to a part of the Colville Group, is preserved in the Chukchi basin near the west coast.

The basal strata of the Colville Group are dark, fissile clay shale, in part organic, with bentonite and limestone indicative of slow deposition in moderately deep water. As much as 1,500 ft (455 m) was deposited in the foredeep

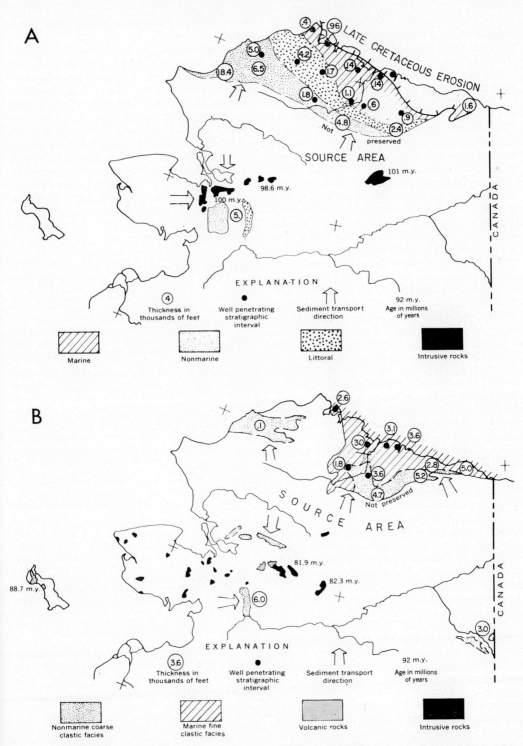

FIG. 5—**A.** Distribution of upper Lower and lower Upper Cretaceous Nanushuk Group and equivalent rocks. **B.** Distribution of Upper Cretaceous Colville Group and equivalent rocks.

adjacent to the western margin of the basin. The organic shales are restricted to the lowest few hundred feet, and the entire sequence thins abruptly. The shale of the Seabee is overlain by a thin but widespread marine sandstone of the Ayiyak Member.

The final phase of late Mesozoic deposition was a period of abrupt marine regressions and transgressions starting in the Coniacian and continuing throughout the remainder of the Cretaceous. Massive conglomerate and sandstone units with interbeds of siltstone, shale, coal, and bentonite were deposited in a nonmarine environment that intertongues with marine sandstone, siltstone, shale, and tuff; the tuff is present both as individual beds and as a detrital constituent of the other rocks. The Late Cretaceous nonmarine rocks are included in the Prince Creek Formation, and the marine strata are assigned to the Schrader Bluff Formation; the formations are further divided into members and tongues (Fig. 1). In northeastern Alaska, equivalent strata are included with the upper part of the Ignek Formation.

Several thousand feet of Late Cretaceous conglomerate, sandstone, mudstone, shale, coal, and tuff is preserved south of the Brooks Range. These rocks are entirely nonmarine; no evidence of a marine transgression into central Alaska in Late Cretaceous time has been found. Intrusive and extrusive igneous activity accompanied the filling of the Koyukuk basin, and volcanic detritus is locally a major part of the sedimentary pile (Patton and Miller, 1966, 1968; Patton et al., 1968). This volcanic activity probably supplied the ash and bentonite found in the rocks north of the range.

The source of the molasselike Late Cretaceous detritus was primarily the Brooks Range, although some was undoubtedly supplied by folded early Mesozoic strata in the modern foothill belt. Rocks exposed along the Meade arch may have supplied some of the detritus for the nonmarine strata along the northwest coast.

Faunal remains are locally abundant in northern Alaska and exhibit the greatest diversity in the Seabee Formation at the base of the Colville Group. Ammonites and pelecypods present in this major marine transgressive sequence include *Borissjakoceras, Scaphites, Inoceramus labiatus,* and *I. cuvieri.* A few pelecypods occur in nearshore deposits of late Santonian and early Campanian age; the main elements of this assemblage are *Inoceramus steen-*

strupi and *I. patootensis* (Jones and Gryc, 1960).

Late Cretaceous rocks are poorly consolidated as compared to Early Cretaceous and other Mesozoic strata. The subgraywacke sandstones are moderately well sorted and considerably cleaner than the older beds, although most have a tuffaceous matrix. The contact between Late Cretaceous and early Tertiary rocks cannot be located with any degree of certainty in Arctic Alaska. The beds are for the most part structurally conformable across the contact, although a hiatus of considerable magnitude may be represented. No significant change has been noted in clastic constituents, degree of induration, or coloration between Late Cretaceous and Tertiary strata.

SELECTED REFERENCES

Adkison, W. L., and M. M. Brosgé, eds., 1970, Proceedings of the geological seminar on the North Slope of Alaska: Los Angeles, Pacific Sec. Am. Assoc. Petroleum Geologists, 201 p.

Arkell, W. J., et al., 1957, Treatise on invertebrate paleontology, part L, Mollusca 4, Cephalopoda, Ammonoidea: Geol. Soc. America–Univ. Kansas Press, Lawrence, Kansas, 490 p.

Bergquist, H. R., 1966, Micropaleontology of the Mesozoic rocks of northern Alaska: U.S. Geol. Survey Prof. Paper 302-D, p. 93–227.

Brabb, E. E., 1969, Six new Paleozoic and Mesozoic formations in east-central Alaska: U.S. Geol. Survey Bull. 1274-I, p. I1–I26.

—— and Michael Churkin, Jr., 1969 (1970), Geologic map of the Charley River quadrangle, east-central Alaska: U.S. Geol. Survey Misc. Geol. Inv. Map I-573.

Brosgé, W. P., and H. N. Reiser, 1964, Geological map and sections of the Chandalar quadrangle, Alaska: U.S. Geol. Survey Misc. Geol. Inv. Map I-375.

—— and —— 1969, Preliminary geologic map of the Coleen quadrangle, Alaska: U.S. Geol. Survey Open-File Rept., scale 1:250,000.

—— and I. L. Tailleur, 1970, Depositional history of northern Alaska, in W. L. Adkison and M. M. Brosgé, eds., Proceedings of the geological seminar on the North Slope of Alaska: Los Angeles, Pacific Sec. Am. Assoc. Petroleum Geologists, p. D1–D18.

—— C. L. Whittington, and R. H. Morris, 1966 (1967), Geology of the Umiat-Maybe Creek region, Alaska: U.S. Geol. Survey Prof. Paper 303-H, p. H501–H638.

Campbell, R. H., 1967, Areal geology in the vicinity of the Chariot site, Lisburne Peninsula, northwestern Alaska: U.S. Geol. Survey Prof. Paper 395, p. 71.

Chapman, R. M., and E. G. Sable, 1960, Geology of the Utukok-Corwin region, northwestern Alaska: U.S. Geol. Survey Prof. Paper 303-C, p. C47–C167.

—— R. L. Detterman, and M. D. Mangus, 1964, Geology of the Killik-Etivluk Rivers region, Alaska —Exploration of Naval Petroleum Reserve No. 4 and adjacent areas, northern Alaska, 1944–53—Pt.

3, Areal geology: U.S. Geol. Survey Prof. Paper 303-F, p. F325–F407.

Collins, F. R., 1958a, Test wells, Umiat area, Alaska: U.S. Geol. Survey Prof. Paper 305-B, p. B71–B206.

———— 1958b, Test wells, Topagoruk area, Alaska: U.S. Geol. Survey Prof. Paper 305-D, p. D265–D316.

———— 1958c (1959), Test wells, Meade and Kaolak areas, Alaska: U.S. Geol. Survey Prof. Paper 305-F, p. F341–F376.

———— 1959, Test wells, Square Lake and Wolf Creek areas, Alaska: U.S. Geol. Survey Prof. Paper 305-H, p. H423–H484.

———— 1961, Core tests and test wells, Barrow area, Alaska: U.S. Geol. Survey Prof. Paper 305-K, p. K569–K643.

Detterman, R. L., 1970a, Analysis of Shublik Formation rocks from Mt. Michelson quadrangle, Alaska: U.S. Geol. Survey Open-File Rept., 4 sheets.

———— 1970b, Sedimentary history of Sadlerochit and Shublik Formations in northeastern Alaska, in W. L. Adkison and M. M. Brosgé, eds., Proceedings of the geological seminar on the North Slope of Alaska: Los Angeles, Pacific Sec. Am. Assoc. Petroleum Geologists, p. O1–O13.

———— R. S. Bickel, and George Gryc, 1963, Geology of the Chandler River region, Alaska: U.S. Geol. Survey Prof. Paper 303-E, p. E231–E300.

Gates, G. O., and George Gryc, 1963, Structure and tectonic history of Alaska, in O. E. Childs and B. W. Beebe, eds., Backbone of the Americas: Am. Assoc. Petroleum Geologists Mem. 2, p. 264–277.

Harland, W. B., A. G. Smith, and B. Wilcock, eds., 1964, The Phanerozoic time-scale; a symposium: Geol. Soc. London Quart. Jour., supplement to v. 120, p. 260–262.

Imlay, R. W., 1955, Characteristic Jurassic mollusks from northern Alaska: U.S. Geol. Survey Prof. Paper 274-D, p. D69–D96.

———— 1961 (1962), Characteristic Lower Cretaceous megafossils from northern Alaska: U.S. Geol. Survey Prof. Paper 335, 74 p.

Jones, D. L., and George Gryc, 1960, Upper Cretaceous pelecypods of the genus *Inoceramus* from northern Alaska: U.S. Geol. Survey Prof. Paper 334-E, p. E149–E165.

Keller, A. S., R. H. Morris, and R. L. Detterman, 1961, Geology of the Shaviovik and Sagavanirktok Rivers region, Alaska: U.S. Geol. Survey Prof. Paper 303-D, p. D169–D222.

Leffingwell, E. de K., 1919, The Canning River region, northern Alaska: U.S. Geol. Survey Prof. Paper 109, 251 p.

Patton, W. W., Jr., 1966, Regional geology of the Kateel River quadrangle, Alaska: U.S. Geol. Survey Misc. Geol. Inv. Map I-437.

———— 1967, Regional geologic map of the Candle quadrangle, Alaska: U.S. Geol. Survey Misc. Geol. Inv. Map I-492.

———— and J. T. Dutro, Jr., 1969, Preliminary report on the Paleozoic and Mesozoic sedimentary sequence on St. Lawrence Island, Alaska: U.S. Geol. Survey Prof. Paper 650-D, p. D138–D143.

———— and T. P. Miller, 1966, Regional geologic map of the Hughes quadrangle, Alaska: U.S. Geol. Survey Misc. Geol. Inv. Map I-459.

———— and ———— 1968, Regional geologic map of the Selawik and southeastern Baird Mountains quadrangle, Alaska: U.S. Geol. Survey Misc. Geol. Inv. Map I-530.

———— and I. L. Tailleur, 1964, Geology of the Killik-Itkillik Rivers region, Alaska: U.S. Geol. Survey Prof. Paper 303-G, p. G409–G500.

———— T. P. Miller, and I. L. Tailleur, 1968, Regional geologic map of the Shungnak and southern part of the Ambler River quadrangles, Alaska: U.S. Geol. Survey Misc. Geol. Inv. Map I-554.

Payne, T. G., 1955, Mesozoic and Cenozoic tectonic elements of Alaska: U.S. Geol. Survey Misc. Geol. Inv. Map I-84.

Reed, B. L., 1968, Geology of the Lake Peters area, northeastern Brooks Range, Alaska: U.S. Geol. Survey Bull. 1236, 132 p.

Reiser, H. N., M. A. Lanphere, and W. P. Brosgé, 1965, Jurassic age of mafic igneous complex, Christian quadrangle, Alaska, in Geological Survey research 1965: U.S. Geol. Survey Prof. Paper 525-C, p. C68–C71.

Robinson, F. M., 1956, Core tests and test wells, Oumalik area, Alaska: U.S. Geol. Survey Prof. Paper 305-A, p. A1–A70.

———— 1958a, Test wells, Gubik area, Alaska: U.S. Geol. Survey Prof. Paper 305-C, p. C207–C264.

———— 1958b, Test well, Grandstand area, Alaska: U.S. Geol. Survey Prof. Paper 305-E, p. E317–E339.

———— 1959a, Test wells, Titaluk and Knifeblade areas, Alaska: U.S. Geol. Survey Prof. Paper 305-G, p. G377–G422.

———— 1959b, Core test, Sentinel Hill area (USGS) and test well, Fish Creek area, Alaska: U.S. Geol. Survey Prof. Paper 305-I, p. I485–I521.

———— 1959c, Test wells, Simpson area, Alaska: U.S. Geol. Survey Prof. Paper 305-J, p. J523–J568.

———— 1964, Core tests, Simpson area, Alaska: U.S. Geol. Survey Prof. Paper 305-L, p. L645–L730.

Sable, E. G., 1965, Geology of the Romanzof Mountains, Brooks Range, northeastern Alaska: U.S. Geol. Survey Open-File Rept., 218 p.

Smiley, C. J., 1969a, Cretaceous floras of Chandler-Colville region, Alaska: stratigraphy and preliminary floristics: Am. Assoc. Petroleum Geologists Bull., v. 53, p. 482–502.

———— 1969b, Floral zones and correlations of Cretaceous Kukpowruk and Corwin Formations, northwestern Alaska: Am. Assoc. Petroleum Geologists Bull., v. 53, p. 2079–2093.

Tailleur, I. L., 1969, Speculations on North Slope geology: Oil and Gas Jour., v. 67, no. 38, p. 215–220.

Ziegler, P. A., 1969, The development of sedimentary basins in western and arctic Canada: Calgary, Alberta Soc. Petroleum Geologists, 89 p.

Regional Geology of Yukon-Tanana Upland, Alaska[1]

HELEN L. FOSTER,[2] FLORENCE R. WEBER,[3] ROBERT B. FORBES[4]
and EARL E. BRABB[2]

Menlo Park, California 94025, and College, Alaska 99701

Abstract The basic geologic framework of the Yukon-Tanana upland, Alaska, a mountainous region of about 30,000 sq mi (77,700 sq km) between the Yukon and Tanana Rivers, was delineated primarily by L. M. Prindle and J. B. Mertie, Jr., in the early part of this century. The subsequent recognition of large-scale offset along the Tintina fault, which bounds the eastern upland on the north, has required a reconsideration of the regional stratigraphic and structural relations.

The northwestern part of the upland is predominantly underlain by a sedimentary sequence consisting of rocks which range in age from Cambrian to Mississippian. Cretaceous and Tertiary sedimentary rocks unconformably overlie the older sequence. The Cambrian is apparently underlain by a thick section of grits, quartzites, phyllites, and quartz-mica schists. Pre-Silurian volcanic rocks, mafic and ultramafic rocks of probably Devonian age, and Permo-Triassic diabase and volcanic rocks are also present. These sedimentary and igneous rocks are cut by granitic plutons of Cretaceous and Tertiary age.

The central and eastern parts of the upland are underlain by a metamorphic complex of rocks which range from lower-greenschist to amphibolite facies. Fossils date the parent sediments of some greenschist-facies rocks as Paleozoic. Radiometric dates from several localities in the metamorphic complex indicate that Precambrian, Ordovician, and Jurassic-Cretaceous thermal events are recorded in the metamorphic history. Mesozoic granodiorite and quartz monzonite batholiths and smaller granitic plutons of Mesozoic and Tertiary age intrude the crystalline schists. Locally, unmetamorphosed Cretaceous and/or Tertiary sedimentary rocks are in unconformable or fault contact with the older rocks. Tertiary volcanic rocks ranging in composition from rhyolite to basalt overlie the older rocks in small but significant parts of the eastern upland. Ultramafic intrusions, mostly small and serpentinized, also occur.

Work has progressed to the point where the sedimentary rocks in the upland can reasonably be correlated with those in other parts of Alaska, but interregional correlation of the metamorphic terranes must await additional clarification of structural and petrologic relations.

Introduction

The Yukon-Tanana upland is a hilly and mountainous region about 30,000 sq mi (77,700 sq km) in area which lies between the

[1] Manuscript received, September 20, 1971. Publication authorized by the Director, U.S. Geological Survey.

[2] U.S. Geological Survey, Menlo Park.

[3] U.S. Geological Survey, College.

[4] University of Alaska, College.

Yukon and Tanana Rivers (Fig. 1). Rounded, fairly smooth-topped ridges with gentle side slopes are characteristic, but rugged peaks occur in places. The region is unglaciated except in the highest parts, where small Pleistocene alpine glaciers have steepened the valley walls. In contrast, loess mantles large areas, particularly in the Livengood and Fairbanks quadrangles, and tends to smooth and subdue the relief. Altiplanation terraces, stone polygons, stone stripes, and solifluction lobes are common features at higher altitudes. Thaw lakes and pingos occur in valleys. The entire region is in the zone of discontinuous permafrost.

All drainage eventually reaches the Yukon River, either from the south via the Tanana River or from the east and north by other tributaries. Rock exposure in most of the region is poor because of vegetation and loess and colluvial and alluvial cover. Even in the higher areas, outcrops are scarce and bedrock mapping is based largely on rubble.

Geologic Setting

The Yukon-Tanana upland is primarily a region of complexly deformed metamorphic rocks which have been intruded by Mesozoic batholiths and smaller Mesozoic and Tertiary plutons. However, in the northwestern part of the upland there is a sequence of sedimentary and metasedimentary rocks of Precambrian (or Cambrian) to Tertiary age along with felsic to mafic intrusive bodies. Thus, the upland consists of two different parts—a metamorphic complex in the eastern and central part and the relatively unmetamorphosed northwestern part.

The southern physiographic boundary of the Yukon-Tanana upland is the Tanana River. It separates the upland from the Alaska Range and is possibly a structural boundary as well, because, in places in the Tanana valley, there is geomorphologic evidence of faulting. However, metamorphic and granitic rocks similar to those in the upland are present in the Tanana valley and south of it in the Alaska Range, and the most distinct change in lithology is south of the Denali fault system. The Denali fault system separates the metamorphic rocks on the north from mostly unmetamorphosed late Paleozoic and Mesozoic rocks on the south. Little is known about the kind and time of movement along this sector (sector shown on Fig. 1) of the Denali fault, but topographic expression and offset of topographic features and rock formations suggest right-lateral movement, possibly mostly in Tertiary time. Fresh local scarps also indicate some Holocene vertical movements.

The upland is bounded on the north by the Tintina fault zone and the Yukon Flats. Like the Denali fault system, in most places in Alaska the Tintina separates metamorphic rocks from unmetamorphosed or relatively unmetamorphosed rocks. Right-lateral movement along the Tintina fault zone has been postulated by Roddick (1967, p. 28), largely on the basis of geologic relations in Canada. He estimated that there may have been 40 mi (64 km) of lateral offset in Paleozoic time and an additional 220 mi (354 km) in Mesozoic time. Several faults have been mapped in the northwestern part of the upland (Fig. 1), one or more of which may indicate an extension of the Tintina fault zone.

Metamorphic Terranes

Metamorphic terranes, composed of rocks of both igneous and sedimentary parentage, underlie about three fourths of the Yukon-Tanana upland and continue southeastward into Canada. Metamorphic grade ranges from lower-greenschist to upper-amphibolite facies.

In mapping the metamorphic rocks in the late 1800s and early 1900s, Spurr (1898), Prindle (1905), Cockfield (1921), and other geologists, both in Alaska and Canada, used several formational names such as "Fortymile Series," "Klondike Series," "Yukon Group," "Nasina Series," "Pelly Gneiss," and others. The relation of some of the metamorphic rock units to one another was determined, but the paucity of structural and stratigraphic control did not permit definite age assignment; a given unit may have been referred by some authors to the Paleozoic and by others to the Precambrian.

Mertie (1937, p. 48), in his classic work on the Yukon-Tanana upland, virtually abandoned the previous classifications and applied the name "Birch Creek Schist" to ". . . all the older Precambrian metamorphic rocks that were originally of sedimentary origin." He specifically excluded the schists and gneisses of igne-

ous parentage from his definition of the Birch Creek Schist, but "for convenience" mapped them within this unit. He also mapped two other units that include metamorphic rocks of sedimentary parentage—a "pre-middle Ordovician" unit and an "undifferentiated Devonian" unit. He stated (1937, p. 51) that the presence of biotite and muscovite was used to distinguish the Birch Creek Schist from highly altered Paleozoic rocks, which are likely to contain a higher proportion of the brittle micas and chloritic minerals.

No type section for the Birch Creek Schist has been designated, but it is evident from a report by Spurr (1898, p. 140–145), who originally referred to the Birch Creek "series," that the type area is in the headwaters of Birch Creek about 80 mi (130 km) northeast of Fairbanks. Mertie (1930, p. 18), however, considered the entire Yukon-Tanana region as the type area.

Mertie (1937, p. 55–56) considered the Birch Creek Schist to be of early Precambrian age because of lithologic differences from, and supposed stratigraphic relation to, the Tindir Group. That group comprises a series of late Precambrian sedimentary and volcanic rocks as thick as 25,000 ft (7, 620 m) in the Eagle area. Mertie pointed out that, although the two groups of rocks are almost in contact along the Yukon River, they are different in lithology. The Tindir Group consists of dolomite, limestone, shale, slate, quartzite, redbeds, and basic lavas, whereas the Birch Creek Schist in this vicinity contains few calcareous rocks and no redbeds. Mertie believed that it would be impossible, through metamorphism, to transform the rocks of the Tindir Group into rocks similar to those which constitute the Birch Creek Schist; he thus reasoned that the Birch Creek Schist must be older. The juxtaposition of the two differing rock sequences can now be explained by the fact that the Tintina fault zone separates the Tindir Group from the Birch Creek Schist (Brabb and Churkin, 1965, 1969). Thus, the proposed Precambrian age of the Birch Creek Schist as determined from its apparent relation to the Tindir Group does not have a firm geologic basis. The degree of metamorphism is also an uncertain criterion for determining the age of the metamorphic rocks and for distinguishing the Birch Creek Schist throughout the upland, as Mertie recognized (1937, p. 67). Chloritic minerals are common in rocks mapped by Mertie as Birch Creek Schist, and some rock types common in the

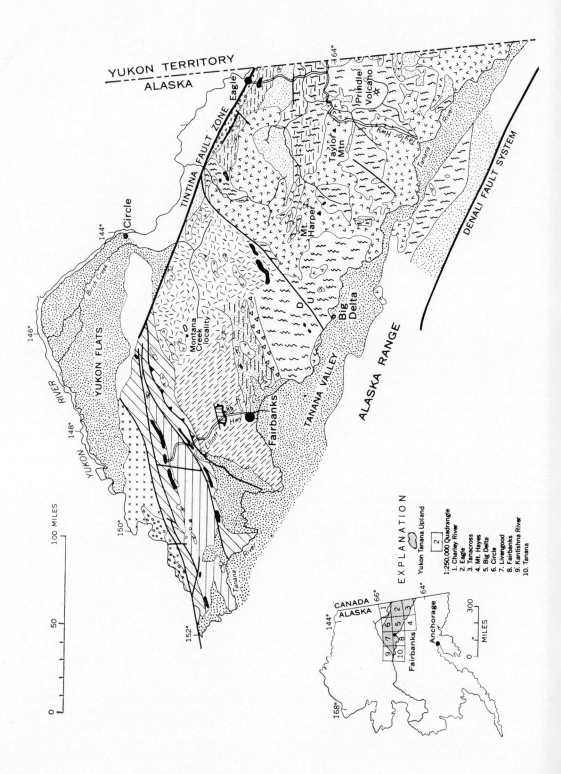

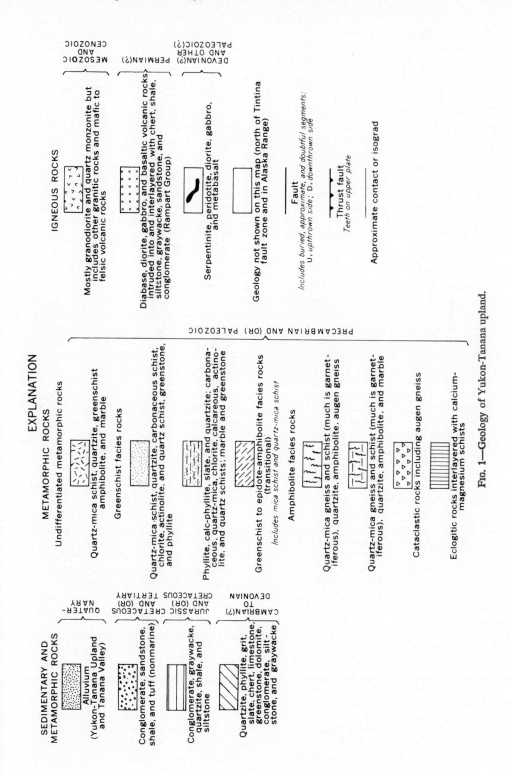

EXPLANATION

SEDIMENTARY AND METAMORPHIC ROCKS

QUATERNARY
Alluvium (Yukon-Tanana Upland and Tanana Valley)

JURASSIC CRETACEOUS AND (OR) CRETACEOUS TERTIARY
Conglomerate, sandstone, shale, and tuff (nonmarine)

Conglomerate, graywacke, quartzite, shale, and siltstone

CAMBRIAN(?) TO DEVONIAN
Quartzite, phyllite, grit, slate, chert, limestone, greenstone, dolomite, conglomerate, siltstone, and graywacke

METAMORPHIC ROCKS

Undifferentiated metamorphic rocks

Quartz-mica schist, quartzite, greenschist amphibolite, and marble

Greenschist facies rocks

Quartz-mica schist, quartzite, carbonaceous schist, chlorite, actinolite, and quartz schist, greenstone, and phyllite

Phyllite, calc-phyllite, slate, and quartzite; carbonaceous, quartz-mica, chlorite, calcareous, actinolite, and quartz schists; marble and greenstone

Greenschist to epidote-amphibolite facies rocks (transitional)
Includes mica schist and quartz-mica schist

Amphibolite facies rocks

Quartz-mica gneiss and schist (much is garnetiferous), quartzite, amphibolite, augen gneiss

Quartz-mica gneiss and schist (much is garnetiferous), quartzite, amphibolite, and marble

Cataclastic rocks including augen gneiss

Eclogitic rocks interlayered with calcium-magnesium schists

PRECAMBRIAN AND (OR) PALEOZOIC

IGNEOUS ROCKS

MESOZOIC AND CENOZOIC
Mostly granodiorite and quartz monzonite but includes other granitic rocks and mafic to felsic volcanic rocks

PERMIAN(?)
Diabase, diorite, gabbro, and basaltic volcanic rocks intruded into and interlayered with chert, shale, siltstone, graywacke, sandstone, and conglomerate (Rampart Group)

DEVONIAN(?) AND OTHER PALEOZOIC(?)
Serpentinite, peridotite, diorite, gabbro, and metabasalt

Geology not shown on this map (north of Tintina fault zone and in Alaska Range)

Fault
Includes buried, approximate, and doubtful segments: U, upthrown side; D, downthrown side

Thrust fault
Teeth on upper plate

Approximate contact or isograd

FIG. 1—Geology of Yukon-Tanana upland.

Birch Creek, such as quartzite, quartz schist, marble, and carbonaceous schist, are also abundant in sequences of known Paleozoic age.

In summary, we believe that the term "Birch Creek Schist" has doubtful value as a rock-stratigraphic unit and recommend that it be abandoned. Therefore, we shall divide the metamorphic complex of the Yukon-Tanana upland (that is, the metamorphic rocks between the Tintina fault zone and the Tanana River and from the northeast-trending thrust 40 mi [64 km] north of Fairbanks east to the Canadian border) primarily on the basis of metamorphic facies and characteristic lithologies, and shall describe them in two geographic groups: the rocks of the Fairbanks–Big Delta region and the rocks of the Fortymile-Eagle region.

Fairbanks–Big Delta Region

The metamorphic rocks in the Fairbanks–Big Delta region form several northeast-trending belts (Fig. 1). One belt of highly deformed greenschist-facies rocks characterized by slate and calc-phyllite is traceable through the central part of the Fairbanks region. To the south is a zone of cataclastic rocks which separates the greenschist-facies rocks from crystalline schists of the amphibolite facies. The rocks in the amphibolite facies include biotite schists and various gneisses. The fabric indicates that they are polymetamorphic; amphibolite-facies metamorphism was followed in palces by a retrograde event that resulted in the formation of assemblages belonging to the greenschist facies.

North of the greenschist-facies belt are mica schists transitional between greenschist and epidote-amphibolite facies. In this zone of metamorphic rocks (Fig. 1), Prindle (1913, p. 62–64) discovered an eclogite-bearing terrane about 15 mi (24 km) north of Fairbanks. Recent study of these rocks by Forbes et al. (1968a, b) indicates that younger pelitic schists and subordinate greenschists have been thrust over the older and more highly deformed eclogitic rocks.

The thrust zone, where exposed along the Elliott Highway, is defined by coarse-grained garnetiferous calc-mylonites, which appear to be cataclastically deformed, and by retrograded calc-silicate rocks. Eclogitic rocks intercalated with calcium-magnesium schists are characterized by the assemblage clinopyroxene-garnet-carbonate-sphene (with or without quartz). Mineral assemblages in adjacent rock units suggest that the eclogitic rocks were actually recrystallized under conditions of the amphibolite rather than granulite or eclogite facies.

Fortymile-Eagle Region

The northeast-trending belts of metamorphic rocks of the Fairbanks–Big Delta region cannot be traced eastward into the Fortymile-Eagle region because they are cut by large granitic batholiths in the vicinity of Mt. Harper and the Charley River, and also by faults. Belts with distinct lithologies and trends of isograds are less definable in most parts of the Fortymile-Eagle region than in the Fairbanks–Big Delta region. In the northern part of the Fortymile-Eagle region, however, belts of greenschist, marble, and phyllite trend northwestward subparallel with the Tintina fault zone (Fig. 1).

The metamorphic rocks of the Fortymile-Eagle region consist of a wide variety of metasedimentary and meta-igneous rocks which range from lower-greenschist to upper-amphibolite facies. In the southern part of the region (Tanacross quadrangle), characteristic rock types are quartz-biotite schist and quartz-biotite and augen gneiss. Marble is absent. To the north, in the Eagle and Charley River quadrangles, quartz-biotite schist and quartz-biotite gneiss are major rock types, but augen gneiss is scarce. Quartzite and marble are abundant. In much of the eastern part of the upland, few distinct separations of rocks of different metamorphic facies are apparent, but, along the Taylor Highway north of the Fortymile River, amphibolite-facies rocks are distinctly separated from greenschist-facies rocks by a fault (Foster and Keith, 1968). These greenschist-facies rocks are mostly quartzites and quartz-graphite schists, and they contain little carbonate. Farther north, however, are greenschists with abundant calcareous layers and intercalated marble beds. Both groups of greenschist-facies rocks are cut by massive greenstone. There are also several areas of slaty to phyllitic rocks. The largest appears to be parallel with the Tintina fault zone in the Charley River quadrangle (Brabb and Churkin, 1969). Amphibolite-facies rocks and some greenschist-facies rocks are polymetamorphic, and evidence of retrogradation is found in many of them.

Age of Metamorphic Rocks

Only a few poorly preserved and nondiagnostic fossils have been found in the metamorphic rocks. Crinoid columnals have been collected at several different localities south of Eagle, mostly from marble interlayered in green-schist-facies rocks; bryozoans also have been found at one of these localities. In the central part of the Eagle quadrangle, crinoid columnals occur in marble interlayered with rocks of higher metamorphic grade (amphibolite or epidote-amphibolite facies) than those near Eagle. This occurrence suggests that perhaps all or most of the metamorphosed sedimentary rocks in the Eagle quadrangle, particularly those containing interlayered marble and quartzite, are of Paleozoic age.

Radiometric dating methods were first applied to the metamorphic rocks of the Yukon-Tanana upland by Wasserburg et al. (1963, p. 259). A phyllitic schist collected near Montana Creek in the north-central part of the upland provided a whole-rock Rb^{87}-Sr^{87} age of 1,020 m.y., but muscovite separated from the schist gave a Rb^{87}-Sr^{87} age of 511 m.y. and a discordant K^{40}-Ar^{40} age of 111 m.y. The whole-rock data yielded the only Precambrian radiogenic age from the rocks or constituent minerals in the metamorphic complex. According to Wasserberg, Eberlein, and Lanphere (oral commun., 1969), however, the age determined may be that of the clastic mica and feldspar of a parent rock and not truly indicative of time of deposition or metamorphism.

Radiogenic age determinations of amphiboles and micas from the Fairbanks district (Forbes, 1971, unpub. data) primarily define the polymetamorphic origin of the metamorphic terrane. For instance, hornblende extracted from an eclogitic rock in the older metamorphic sequence (under the thrust plate) in the Fairbanks district gave a K^{40}-Ar^{40} age of 470 ± 35 m.y.; muscovite from a garnet-mica schist sampled at the same locality provided a radiogenic age of 115.5 ± 2.6 m.y. Muscovite from a garnet-mica schist believed to belong to the upper plate or younger sequence gave a K^{40}-Ar^{40} age of 100 ± 3 m.y.

Rubidium-strontium ages on biotite from the Eagle-Tanacross area range from 180 to 187 m.y. (Wasserburg et al., 1963, p. 258), which is very close to the similarly determined 190-m.y. age on biotite from the Taylor Mountain batholith. These ages are believed to be indicative of thermal imprinting at the time of the intrusion of the Taylor Mountain batholith and other plutons which may have been intruded at about that time.

No acceptable proof of a Precambrian thermal event has yet been found in any of the metamorphic rocks, but the possibility cannot be ruled out, particularly for rocks in the older thrust plate in the Fairbanks district and northward in the greenschist-facies belt along the margin of the northeasterly-trending thrust fault (Fig. 1).

Northwestern Upland

The northwestern part of the upland differs from the remainder of the region in having a sequence of only slightly metamorphosed sedimentary rocks that appear to be underlain by a thick section of grits, quartzites, and quartz-mica schists. The schists seem to decrease in grade to the northwest and probably represent the northwestern margin of the metamorphic complex which was described above. This area may be the only place in the upland where relatively unmetamorphosed Paleozoic rocks are in contact with crystalline schists, and it is, in part, a fault contact.

The older units in the relatively unmetamorphosed sedimentary sequence are possibly of very late Precambrian and/or Cambrian age and include quartzite, phyllite, grit, slate, and chert. Some limestone and greenstone also are present. The Cambrian trace fossil *Oldhamia* (Churkin and Brabb, 1965, p. D123) has been recognized in an olive slate. Maroon and green slate and dark limestone are distinctive rock types.

Rocks of probably Ordovician age are represented by gray slate, siliceous shale, chert, very fine-grained light-colored quartzite, platy limestone, white dolomite, greenstone, and tuff. Chert is a characteristic rock type and composes a large part of the section, although volcanic rocks are locally abundant.

A prominent limestone—the Tolovana—is believed to be Silurian and/or Devonian, but most of the known Devonian consists of chert-pebble conglomerate, shale, siltstone, graywacke, and quartzite.

Chert, shale, siltstone, graywacke, tuff, sandstone, and conglomerate intruded by, or interlayered with, diabase, diorite, gabbro, and basaltic volcanic rocks compose the Rampart Group of Permian(?) age (Brosgé et al., 1969). The igneous rocks compose about 70 percent of the Rampart Group.

A considerable area in the northwestern upland is underlain by polymictic conglomerate, graywacke, quartzite, shale, and siltstone. These rocks are dated as Jurassic or Cretaceous on the basis of fossil content. These clastic units are probably older than, and are different in origin and lithology from, the sedimentary rocks of possibly Late Cretaceous or early Tertiary age in the eastern part of the upland.

Tertiary nonmarine conglomerate, sandstone, shale, and coal are also present in the north-western part of the upland, but the relation of these rocks to scattered occurrences of bedded Tertiary rocks elsewhere in the upland is not known (Fig. 1).

IGNEOUS ROCKS

Plutonic rocks ranging in composition from granite to gabbro occur throughout most of the upland; the largest granitic plutons, predominantly granodiorite and quartz monzonite, are in the eastern part.

Volcanic eruptions have occurred through-out the geologic history of the upland. Paleo-zoic, Tertiary, and Holocene volcanic rocks are abundant in the eastern upland, and Paleozoic and Mesozoic volcanic rocks in the northwest. In the east, felsic tuffs, including welded tuffs, cover many square miles. The most recent vol-canism is exemplified by a small isolated basal-tic cone—Prindle Volcano—of Holocene age. The lava and ejecta of this cone contain inclu-sions of peridotite and granulite (Foster *et al.*, 1966).

Ultramafic rocks also occur in many places in the upland. One ultramafic body studied in the Livengood quadrangle (Foster, 1967) has alpine-type serpentinite affinities and contains tectonically transported inclusions. In the east-ern part of the upland the ultramafic rocks crop out as bodies up to 1 sq mi (2.59 sq km) in area, but most are small masses, commonly only a few square feet in area. Many are ser-pentinized, and some contain chrysotile asbes-tos fiber. In the western upland, the outcrops of ultramafic bodies have a northeasterly trend; in most places, trends and relations to major faults are obscure.

CONCLUSION

Most of the Yukon-Tanana upland was a site of deposition, probably in large part eugeosyn-clinal, from late Precambrian to middle or late Paleozoic time. Deposition from late Precam-brian into Cambrian time may have been con-tinuous. Isotopic dates and the stratigraphic se-quence indicate that the major Paleozoic oro-genic events occurred in the Ordovician, the Early or Middle Devonian, and the Pennsylva-nian and Permian. Major Paleozoic mafic vol-canic and intrusive activity occurred in the Late Ordovician, Devonian, and Permian. At least some of the ultramafic bodies were emplaced in

the Devonian. There is no record of Triassic sedimentation, although there was igneous ac-tivity at that time. By Late Jurassic or Early Cretaceous time, geosynclinal-type deposits again accumulated in parts of the upland re-gion; Late Cretaceous and Tertiary deposits are nonmarine. Intrusive and volcanic activity was widespread from Late Triassic or Early Jurassic through the latest Cretaceous and into the Ter-tiary, particularly in the eastern upland. Isoto-pic age dates confirm Jurassic, Cretaceous, and Tertiary thermal events.

At present, the upland can be considered to consist of two entities—the large metamorphic complex and the smaller, relatively unmeta-morphosed area of Precambrian(?), Paleozoic, and Mesozoic rocks. The two are probably sep-arated from each other, as well as from other parts of interior Alaska, by major faults. Je-letzky (1962, p. 61) included the Yukon-Ta-nana metamorphic complex in his geosynclinal belt of the southern Yukon and considered it the northern extension of the Cordilleran geo-syncline. The relatively unmetamorphosed northwestern part of the upland, along with the area north of the Tintina fault zone, was part of his Yukon stable block. King (1969, p. 66) pointed out that there may be no stable block as envisioned by Jeletzky because, he believes, the Cordilleran fold belts were continuous into northern Alaska. Such an assumption would imply that the old unmetamorphosed rocks were also involved in the Cordilleran orogenic activity, and that the orogenic and thermal events which affected various parts of the up-land so differently are mostly pre-Cordilleran.

The Tintina fault zone also came into exis-tence in pre-Cordilleran time, because Roddick (1967, p. 30) recognized probably early Paleo-zoic transcurrent movement. Roddick (1967, p. 32) has compared the Tintina fault zone with the San Andreas fault zone, but he believes the Tintina is older. If this is a reasonable compari-son, the Tintina could be an old transform fault.

REFERENCES

Brabb, E. E., 1967, Stratigraphy of the Cambrian and Ordovician rocks of east-central Alaska: U.S. Geol. Survey Prof. Paper 559-A, p. A1–A30.
———— and M. Churkin, Jr., 1965, Preliminary geo-logic map of the Eagle D-1 quadrangle, east-central Alaska: U.S. Geol. Survey Open-File Rept., 2 p.
———— and ———— 1969, Geologic map of the Charley River quadrangle, east-central Alaska: U.S. Geol. Survey Misc. Geol. Inv. Map I-573.
Brosgé, W. P., E. E. Brabb, and E. R. King, 1970, Geologic interpretation of reconnaissance aero-

magnetic survey of northeastern Alaska: U.S. Geol. Survey Bull. 1271-F, p. F1–F14.

—— et al., 1969, Probable Permian age of the Rampart Group, central Alaska: U.S. Geol. Survey Bull. 1294-B, p. B1–B18.

Churkin, Michael, Jr., 1969, Paleozoic tectonic history of the Arctic basin north of Alaska: Science, v. 165, p. 549–555.

—— 1970, Fold belts of Alaska and Siberia and drift between North America and Asia, in W. L. Adkison and M. M. Brosgé, eds., Proceedings of the geological seminar on the North Slope of Alaska: Los Angeles, Pacific Sec. Am. Assoc. Petroleum Geologists, p. G1–G17.

—— and E. E. Brabb, 1965, Occurrence and stratigraphic significance of Oldhamia, a Cambrian trace fossil, in east-central Alaska, in Geological Survey research 1965: U.S. Geol. Survey Prof. Paper 525-D, p. D120–D124.

Cockfield, W. E., 1921, Sixtymile and Ladue Rivers area, Yukon: Canada Geol. Survey Mem. 123, 60 p.

Forbes, R. B., H. D. Pilkington, and D. B. Hawkins, 1968a, Gold gradients and anomalies in the Pedro Dome–Cleary Summit area, Fairbanks district, Alaska: U.S. Geol. Survey Open-File Rept., 47 p.

—— R. C. Swainbank, and D. C. Burrell, 1968b, Structural setting and petrology of eclogite-bearing terrane near Fairbanks, Alaska (abs.): Am. Geophys. Union Trans., v. 49, no. 1, p. 345.

Foster, H. L., 1967, Geology of the Mount Fairplay area, Alaska: U.S. Geol. Survey Bull. 1241-B, p. B1–B18.

—— 1969a, Asbestos occurrence in the Eagle C-4 quadrangle, Alaska: U.S. Geol. Survey Circ. 611, 7 p.

—— 1969b, Reconnaissance geology of the Eagle A-1 and A-2 quadrangles, Alaska: U.S. Geol. Survey Bull. 1271-G, p. G1–G30.

—— 1970, Reconnaissance geologic map of the Tanacross quadrangle, Alaska: U.S. Geol. Survey Misc. Geol. Inv. Map I-593.

—— and T. C. Keith, 1968, Preliminary geologic map of the Eagle B-1 and C-1 quadrangles, Alaska: U.S. Geol. Survey Open-File Rept.

—— R. B. Forbes, and D. M. Ragan, 1966, Granulite and peridotite inclusions from Prindle Volcano, Yukon-Tanana upland, Alaska, in Geological Survey research 1966: U.S. Geol. Survey Prof. Paper 550-B, p. B115–B119.

Foster, R. L., 1967, Tectonic inclusions from a serpentinite, east-central Alaska: U.S. Geol. Survey Prof. Paper 575-D, p. D120–D122.

Gabrielse, H., 1967, Tectonic evolution of the Northern Canadian Cordillera: Canadian Jour. Earth Sci., v. 4, p. 271–298.

Green, L. H., and J. A. Roddick, 1962, Dawson, Larsen Creek, and Nash Creek map areas, Yukon Territory: Canada Geol. Survey Paper 62-7, 20 p.

Holmes, G. W., 1965, Geologic reconnaissance along the Alaska Highway, Delta River to Tok Junction, Alaska: U.S. Geol. Survey Bull. 1181-H, p. H1–H19.

—— and H. L. Foster, 1968, Geology of the Johnson River area, Alaska: U.S. Geol. Survey Bull. 1249, 49 p.

Jeletzky, J. A., 1962, Pre-Cretaceous Richardson Mountains trough: its place in the tectonic framework of Arctic Canada and its bearing on some geosynclinal concepts: Royal Soc. Canada Trans., 3d ser., v. 56, sec. 3, pt. 1, p. 55–84.

King, P. B., 1969, The tectonics of North America—a discussion to accompany the tectonic map of North America, scale 1:5,000,000: U.S. Geol. Survey Prof. Paper 628, 94 p.

Matzko, J. J., H. W. Jaffe, and C. L. Waring, 1958, Lead-alpha age determinations of granitic rocks from Alaska: Am. Jour. Sci., v. 265, no. 8, p. 529–539.

Mertie, J. B., Jr., 1930, Geology of the Eagle-Circle district, Alaska: U.S. Geol. Survey Bull. 816, 168 p.

—— 1937, The Yukon-Tanana region, Alaska: U.S. Geol. Survey Bull. 872, 276 p.

Prindle, L. M., 1905, The gold placers of the Fortymile, Birch Creek and Fairbanks region, Alaska: U.S. Geol. Survey Bull. 251, 89 p.

—— 1913, A geologic reconnaissance of the Fairbanks quadrangle, Alaska: U.S. Geol. Survey Bull. 525, 220 p.

Ragan, D. M., and J. W. Hawkins, Jr., 1966, A polymetamorphic complex in the eastern Alaska Range: Geol. Soc. America Bull., v. 77, p. 597–604.

Richter, D. H., 1967, Geology of the Upper Slana–Mentasta Pass area, south-central Alaska: Alaska Div. Mines and Minerals Geol. Rept. 30, 25 p.

Roddick, J. A., 1967, Tintina Trench: Jour. Geology, v. 75, p. 23–32.

Spurr, J. E., 1898, Geology of the Yukon gold district, Alaska: U.S. Geol. Survey 18th Ann. Rept., pt. 3, p. 87–392.

St. Amand, P., 1957, Geological and geophysical synthesis of the tectonics of portions of British Columbia, the Yukon Territory and Alaska: Geol. Soc. America Bull., v. 68, no. 10, p. 1343–1370.

Wahrhaftig, C., 1965, Physiographic division of Alaska: U.S. Geol. Survey Prof. Paper 482, 52 p.

—— 1968, Schists of the central Alaska range: U.S. Geol. Survey Bull. 1254-E, p. E1–E22.

Wasserburg, G. J., G. D. Eberlein, and M. A. Lanphere, 1963, Age of the Birch Creek Schist and some batholithic intrusions in Alaska (abs.): Geol. Soc. America Spec. Paper 73, p. 258–259.

Stratigraphic and Tectonic Development of Cook Inlet Petroleum Province[1]

C. E. KIRSCHNER and C. A. LYON[2]

San Francisco, California

Abstract The Cook Inlet basin in south-central Alaska is an intermontane half-graben about 200 mi (325 km) long and 60 mi (95 km) wide. The basin contains roughly 20,000 cu mi (84,000 cu km) of Tertiary sedimentary rocks estimated to have at least 1.5 billion bbl of proved reserves recoverable by present production techniques and 5 trillion cu ft of proved gas reserves in place, possibly 70 percent of which are recoverable.

This paper concerns the more extensively explored northern part of the basin. The stratigraphic and tectonic development of the basin includes three Mesozoic cycles of marine sedimentation and two Tertiary cycles of estuarine to nonmarine sedimentation. Each cycle was closed by an orogenic episode accompanied by a major geographic shift in the depocenter for the succeeding cycle and generally by some increase in the relative land area; thus, progressively more extensive land areas and a more restricted basin of deposition were produced. The stratigraphic succession in the basin includes a cumulative total of more than 40,000 ft (12,195 m) of Mesozoic sedimentary rocks and up to 30,000 ft (9,150 m) of Tertiary sedimentary beds.

The structural trend of the basin between its confining mountain borders is approximately N30°E. The enclosed Tertiary sedimentary beds are deformed into en échelon anticlines with more northerly trends diverging from the basin margin about 15°. The folds are concentric in habit and contain Mesozoic sedimentary and volcanic rocks in their cores. They have an essentially westward asymmetry, except along the northwest margin of the basin, where the structural development is influenced by the basin-bounding Castle Mountain fault system. In that system there is evidence for a right-lateral component of movement. Northwesterly-directed continental underthrusting along the Aleutian Trench could be an adequate mechanism to account for the structural shortening evident in the basin.

INTRODUCTION

The purpose of this paper is to present an interpretation of the stratigraphy and structure of the Cook Inlet basin as it bears on the tectonic development of south-central Alaska.

Since the discovery of commercial oil in

[1] Manuscript received, September 20, 1971.

[2] Standard Oil Company of California, Western Operations, Inc.

The writers' knowledge of exploration in the Cook Inlet basin was by reason of their employment with Standard in Anchorage during the period 1962 to the present. We are indebted to Standard for permission to present this paper. We also gratefully acknowledge the helpful comments and criticisms of our co-workers at Standard and of R. L. Detterman, with the U.S. Geological Survey in Menlo Park, California. The illustrations were prepared in the drafting section of Standard's Anchorage office by J. R. Russell.

Cook Inlet in 1957, the subsequent oil and gas development in the basin has furnished a large volume of subsurface information that can be related to the geology of the surrounding upland areas in order to evolve a reasonable integrated tectonic history. Although it is still incomplete and speculative in many respects, some facets of the history have an interesting bearing on adjacent provinces in Alaska.

GEOGRAPHY

The Cook Inlet basin in south-central Alaska (Figs. 1, 2) is an intermontane basin 200 mi (325 km) long and 60 mi (95 km) wide which lies between the metamorphic and igneous terrane of the southern Alaska Range on the northwest and the metavolcanic slate and graywacke terrane of the Kenai Mountains and Chugach Mountains on the southeast. The lowland and submarine area of the basin thus occupies about 12,000 sq mi (30,000 sq km).

The marine waters of Cook Inlet and its tributary bays cover about 70 percent of the basin. The southwestern offshore part of the basin, which comprises about 40 percent of the basin area, is relatively unexplored. The average density of significant exploratory wildcats in the basin is one per 100 sq mi (259 sq km). The north end of the basin is approximately defined by the Castle Mountain fault.

STRATIGRAPHY

The stratigraphic succession in the basin includes a cumulative total of 40,000 ft (12,195 m) of Mesozoic marine strata and up to 30,000 ft (9,145 m) of Tertiary estuarine and nonmarine strata. Three Mesozoic cycles of sedimentation and two Tertiary cycles are recognized (Fig. 3). Each cycle was closed by an orogenic pulse accompanied by a geographic shift of the depocenter for the succeeding cycle and by some increase in the relative area of land emergence. Therefore, progressively more extensive land areas and a more restricted basin of deposition were produced.

Early Mesozoic

The early Mesozoic was a time of eugeosynclinal deposition that can be separated into

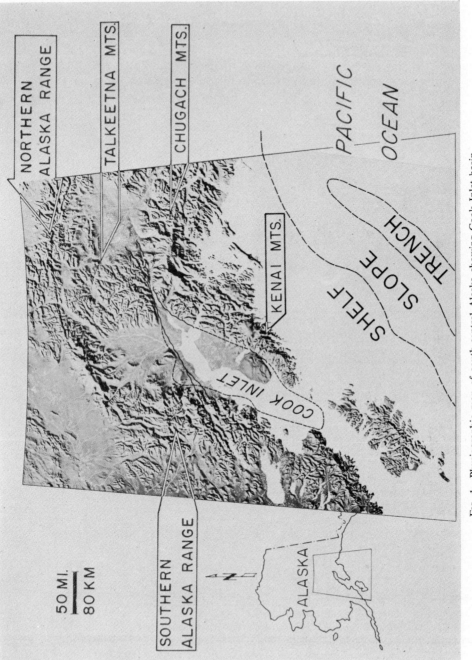

Fig. 1—Physiographic map of south-central Alaska showing Cook Inlet basin.

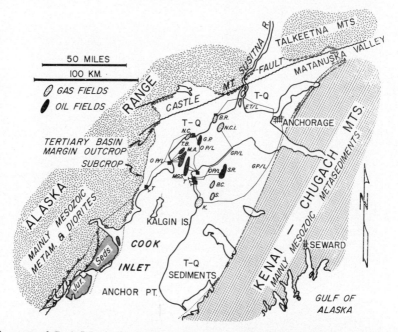

FIG. 2—Outline map of Cook Inlet basin showing major oil and gas fields, *etc.* OP/L, oil pipeline; ET/L, electric transmission line; GP/L, gas pipline; T, terminal facilities.

Gas Fields
B. R.   Beluga River
N.C.I.   North Cook Inlet
N.C.   Nikolai Creek
B.C.   Beaver Creek
S.   Sterling
K.   Kenai

Oil Fields
G.P.   Granite Point
T.B.   Trading Bay
M.A.   MacArthur River
M.G.S.   Middle Ground Shoal
S.R.   Swanson River

two distinct phases (Fig. 4). Pre-flysch and associated volcanic-arc sediments were deposited during Permo-Triassic to Early Jurassic time, and a regressive clastic sequence was deposited during Middle and Late Jurassic time.

Early phase—Rocks in the early phase are the oldest known rocks in the region and include sediments of Permo-Triassic and Early Jurassic age; the sequence is many thousands of feet thick. The rocks crop out in the southern Cook Inlet region (Detterman and Hartsock, 1966) and are present also in the subsurface in wells along the eastern and western margins of the basin, where they are unconformable beneath onlapping Tertiary beds (Fig. 5). The suite contains pelagic, pre-flysch, and ophiolite deposits in the Lower Triassic that grade upward into flyschlike and volcanic-arc deposits in the Upper Triassic–Lower Jurassic. The best-known exposures consist of Upper Triassic black fossiliferous marine metalimestones and chert—the Kamishak Formation—and associated thick se-

quences of Triassic(?) to Lower Jurassic metavolcanic, ultramafic, and volcaniclastic rocks— the Talkeetna Formation.

These early Mesozoic rocks in the Cook In-

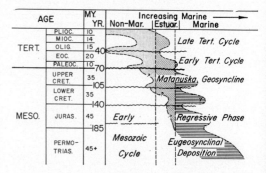

FIG. 3—Depositional cycles in Cook Inlet basin. Three Mesozoic cycles of deposition and two Tertiary cycles are recognized. Each cycle was closed by an orogenic episode followed by a geographic shift in depocenter for succeeding cycle.

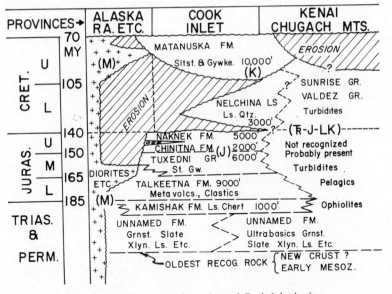

FIG. 4—Mesozoic correlation chart of Cook Inlet basin.

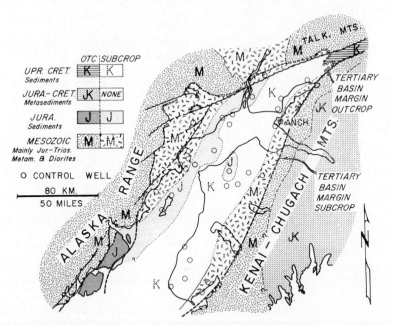

FIG. 5—Distribution of Mesozoic rocks in Cook Inlet basin. Early Mesozoic metasedimentary and meta-volcanic rocks intruded by diorites flank basin on northwest and crop out in Alaska Range and Talkeetna Mountains. Early Mesozoic to Cretaceous metavolcanic rocks, "slates," and graywackes flank basin on southeast and crop out in Kenai-Chugach Mountains. Jurassic and Cretaceous marine sedimentary beds that are locally petroliferous subcrop beneath Tertiary in central or axial part of basin.

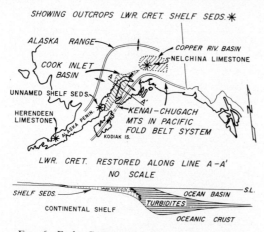

FIG. 6—Early Cretaceous is postulated to be represented by both a marine shelf and a coeval continental-rise or turbidite suite as shown in restored cross section. Shelf sedimentary units crop out at isolated localities northeast and southwest of trend of Cook Inlet basin, and turbidites crop out in Kenai-Chugach Mountains fold belt.

let region apparently formed a segment of a volcanic archipelago and trench that has, through deformation—probably by underflow of the oceanic crust—been accreted to the continent.

This episode of eugeosynclinal sedimentation was phased out with the initiation of a mid-Jurassic "Alaska Range" orogeny, during which diorites of the southern Alaska Range batholith and the Talkeetna Mountains batholith were emplaced (Detterman *et al.*, 1965).

Late phase—The late regressive phase of the early cycle is represented by clastic rocks of late Early, Middle, and Late Jurassic age (Fig. 4); the beds probably were deposited as a clastic wedge in a linear marine trough in front of the rising Alaska Range orogen.

These rocks are well exposed in southwestern Cook Inlet as the Tuxedni Group and the Chinitna and Naknek Formations, which are at least 13,000 ft (3,965 m) thick. They have also been penetrated in the subsurface in several wells in the basin proper, but coeval sediments in the thick turbidite suites of the Kenai-Chugach Mountains have not been recognized.

The Middle Jurassic Tuxedni Group consists primarily of interbedded, dark gray, fossiliferous siltstone and volcanic graywacke. In the conglomerate tongues of Late Jurassic age, 40 percent of the clasts are diorite, which indicates unroofing of the Alaska Range batholith in the rising orogen. With this uplift was initiated the

deposition of thick feldspathic-quartzitic graywackes of the Upper Jurassic Naknek Formation—the final regressive phase of the cycle.

Late Mesozoic

Early Cretaceous cycle—The Early Cretaceous cycle is postulated to be represented by both a marine continental-shelf facies and a coeval, ensimatic, turbidite or continental-rise suite, probably somewhat comparable to the Great Valley and Franciscan model of west-central California (Fig. 6).

The shelf-facies sediments are represented by the Nelchina Limestone of the Copper River basin, the Herendeen Limestone of the Alaska Peninsula, and similar unnamed sedimentary units southwest of Cook Inlet (Jones and Detterman, 1966). Erosional remnants of these shelf sediments could be present in the subsurface of the Cook Inlet basin. The coeval sediments were thick turbidite suites that are now extensively exposed as the Sunrise and Valdez Groups in the geanticlinal welt of the Kenai-Chugach Mountains (Fig. 4; Moffitt, 1954).

Dating is insufficient to prove the contemporaneity of the Early Cretaceous shelf and turbidite suite as postulated. The model is considered valid, but positive dating could modify the concept of when the cycle was initiated and terminated.

Orogenesis beginning in the late Early to early Late Cretaceous initiated collapse of the turbidite–continental-rise prism against the continent and began to modify the continental-shelf and rise relations.

Late Cretaceous cycle—The Late Cretaceous cycle is represented by at least 10,000 ft (3,050 m) of marine siltstone and sandstone (Fig. 4); the sediments were deposited in the Matanuska geosyncline (Payne, 1955). The Matanuska Formation (Fig. 7) is extensively exposed in the Matanuska Valley and has been penetrated in many wells in the Cook Inlet basin. The formation consists primarily of siltstone with thin basal transgressive and upper regressive sandstone members. Polymictic conglomerates derived from the Kenai-Chugach Mountains are recognized locally in the Cenomanian to Turonian, whereas quartzitic graywackes derived from the Alaska Range and the Talkeetna Mountains are present in the Senonian, suggesting relative stability of the northwestern trough margin (Grantz, 1960).

The Late Cretaceous cycle terminated with the initiation of the Laramide orogeny. This orogenic episode compressed the Upper Cretaceous sedimentary beds into tight folds and cul- minated in the accretion of the Lower Creta- ceous continental-rise prism to the continent. A thick section of Upper Cretaceous rocks is pre- served in the central part of the basin and is flanked by older Mesozoic sedimentary and metasedimentary rocks, all of which are over- lain unconformably by Tertiary rocks (Fig. 5).

The Mesozoic strata penetrated in the sub- surface of the Cook Inlet basin have not dem- onstrated significant oil potential to date.

Tertiary

We propose a Tertiary model (Fig. 8) in which sediments were deposited in a broad, lin- ear intermontane trough (or troughs) confined between the Kenai-Chugach Mountains on the southeast and the southern Alaska Range on the northwest. Climatic conditions were warm to temperate, and the confining borderlands had low to moderate relief. Drainages reached as far north as the eastern Interior province of Alaska or adjacent Western Canada. A large volume of sediment influx from these drainages confined the encroachment of marine waters to the distal end of the trough, where deltaic, es- tuarine, and floodplain conditions prevailed. The predominant sediment source was a remote one on the north in the early Tertiary, but, dur- ing an Oligocene hiatus and in the late Tertiary, the dominant sources were the nearby high- lands.

Tertiary deposition in the trough is repre-

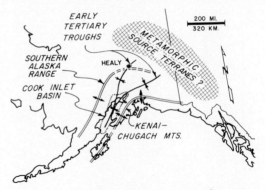

FIG. 8—Early Tertiary paleogeography, Cook Inlet basin.

sented by two cycles of sedimentation: an early cycle during which the depocenter was north- east of the present Cook Inlet basin and a late cycle during which the depocenter was in the present upper Cook Inlet area. Dating of these predominantly nonmarine sedimentary beds has been primarily on the basis of their rich mega- flora and microflora.

Early Tertiary cycle—During the Paleocene and Eocene Epochs, several thousand feet of nonmarine to estuarine sediments accumulated (Fig. 9) in a downwarp northeast of the pres- ent Cook Inlet basin.

The Chugach Mountains were the source of coarse lithic and volcanic detritus deposited along the southern margin of the downwarp. The Talkeetna Mountains batholith on the north contributed coarse arkosic detritus which formed the Arkose Ridge Formation (Grantz and Wolfe, 1961) that occurs along the north- ern margin of the trough. However, most of the sediment deposited in the trough is represented by the Chickaloon Formation, which consists of several thousand feet of garnetiferous quart- zitic graywacke sandstone and micaceous and carbonaceous siltstone with interbedded coal. The Chickaloon appears to have been derived largely from a different, probably remote, high- grade metamorphic terrane (Fig. 8).

This cycle ended in the late Eocene to early Oligocene as a result of uplift, folding, and erosion.

Oligocene hiatus—The Oligocene orogenic episode (Fig. 9) is indicated by an abrupt change in sedimentary regimen and a regional unconformity between Chickaloon and post- Chickaloon sedimentary units. This uncon- formity is evident in the outcrop and in several wells at the north end of the Cook Inlet basin.

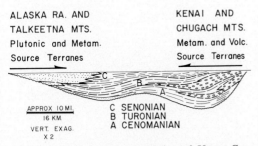

ALASKA RA. AND TALKEETNA MTS. Plutonic and Metam. Source Terranes	KENAI AND CHUGACH MTS. Metam. and Volc. Source Terranes

APPROX 10 MI.
16 KM.
VERT. EXAG.
X 2

C SENONIAN
B TURONIAN
A CENOMANIAN

FIG. 7—Diagrammatic cross section of Upper Cre- taceous strata in Matanuska geosyncline (Payne, 1955), restored to approximate close of Cretaceous time. Orogenic polymictic conglomerates were derived locally from Kenai-Chugach Mountains; quartzitic gray- wackes are represented in a thin basal transgressive sandstone and regressive Late Cretaceous sandstones derived from Alaska Range and Talkeetna Mountains, suggesting relative stability along northern and western trough margin. This interpretation is patterned pri- marily after outcrop data in Matanuska valley (Grantz, 1960). Limited subsurface data (Fig. 6) suggest this pattern of sedimentation was also present in Cook Inlet area of Matanuska geosyncline.

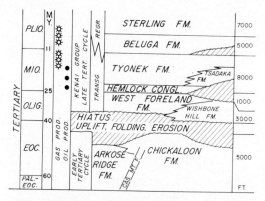

FIG. 9—Tertiary correlation chart of Cook Inlet basin (Calderwood and Fackler, 1972). West Foreland Formation, Hemlock Conglomerate, Tyonek Formation, Beluga Formation, and Sterling Formation are new names proposed by Calderwood and Fackler. Arkose Ridge Formation, previously considered to be Cretaceous (Grantz and Wolfe, 1961), is now believed to be early Tertiary and to be correlative with Chickaloon Formation (Grantz and Wolfe, personal commun.).

Late Tertiary cycle: general statement—The late Tertiary cycle is represented by the Kenai Group (Calderwood and Fackler, 1972), which consists of about 25,000 ft (7,620 m) of estuarine and nonmarine clastic sedimentary rocks in the Cook Inlet basin (Fig. 9). On the basis of the lithologic and mineralogic character of the sediments, the cycle is divisible into three phases: an Oligocene-Miocene transgressive phase, a brief late Miocene culmination, and a Pliocene regressive phase.

Oligocene-Miocene: The Oligocene-Miocene transgressive phase includes deposition of the West Foreland Formation, the Hemlock Conglomerate, and the lower part of the Tyonek Formation (Fig. 10).

The West Foreland Formation ranges in thickness from a few hundred to more than 1,000 ft (305+ m) and consists of poorly sorted polymictic conglomerate, graywacke, and siltstone with interbedded tuffs and local subaerial basalt flows. The basal beds tend to reflect the lithology and the mineralogy of the underlying Mesozoic terrane.

Deposition of the West Foreland Formation covered the midbasin area and leveled it by filling in topographic and structural lows. The West Foreland is absent because of nondeposition along the eastern basin margin and crops out along the foothills of the Alaska Range (Fig. 11). In outcrop the formation is con-

glomeratic, indicating a significant sediment contribution from the southern Alaska Range.

The Hemlock Conglomerate and the sandstones and conglomerates of the Tyonek Formation, which are approximately 7,000 ft (2,135 m) thick, consist predominantly of quartzitic, conglomeratic graywacke interbedded with siltstone and coal. Fluvial to deltaic deposition took place in the central basin area. The maximum sandstone development is along the western edge of the basin (Fig. 11); these sandstones are equivalent to silty floodplain sandstones and interbedded coals along the eastern margin of the basin. The conglomerates contain mainly white quartz and black chert clasts in contrast to the more common dark, poorly sorted, polymictic clasts in the conglomerates that are characteristic of the underlying West Foreland Formation and the overlying Beluga and Sterling Formations. The occurrence of radiolarians, sponge spicules, and saline connate waters together with the spores and pollen indicates deposition in estuarine waterways flowing through swampy forested lowlands.

The heavy-mineral suite contains a high percentage of garnet. The high garnet content and the lithologic characteristics of the sandstones and conglomerates suggest derivation from a high-grade metamorphic source terrane similar to that for the Chickaloon Formation (Fig. 8). Neither the terranes of the Kenai-Chugach

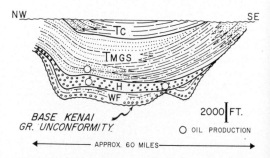

FIG. 10—Diagrammatic stratigraphic cross section of Cook Inlet basin showing transgressive sedimentary units of lower Kenai Group and deposits of mid-Kenai culmination. **WF,** West Foreland Formation; characterized by polymictic conglomerates, tuffaceous siltstone and graywacke, and local subaerial basalts. **H,** Hemlock Conglomerate; characterized by quartz-chert conglomerate and quartzitic, garnetiferous sandstone. **TMGS,** Lower and middle part of Tyonek Formation; characterized by conglomerate and sandstone similar to Hemlock Formation; interbedded with coaly and carbonaceous siltstone. **TC,** Upper part of Tyonek Formation; characterized by silty sandstone, carbonaceous siltstone, and abundant thick coal beds.

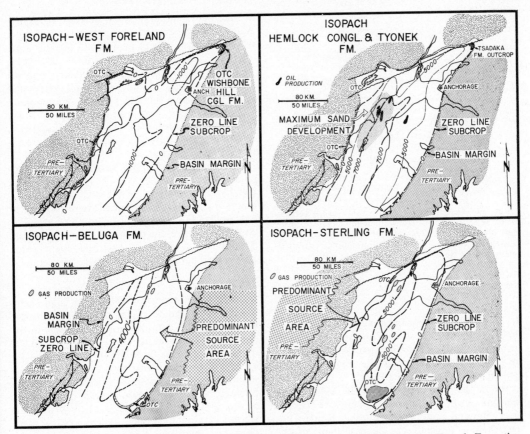

F<small>IG</small>. 11—Generalized isopach maps of West Foreland Formation, Hemlock Conglomerate–Tyonek Formation, Beluga Formation, and Sterling Formation.

Mountains nor those of the southern Alaska Range appear likely as sources for these sediments. Little evidence has been found for coarse clastic wedges or tongues along either margin of the basin during deposition of these formations, and, as discussed in a subsequent section, the mineralogy from these nearby terranes is different. It appears probable, therefore, that the source terranes were in east-central Alaska or Western Canada northeast of the present central Alaska Range.

This concept is supported by data from Wahrhaftig *et al.* (1969) which indicate that the central Alaska Range in the Healy area did not begin to rise until about 8–12 m.y. ago, which is roughly coincident with the Miocene-Pliocene transition and with a major change in sedimentation in both the Healy and the Cook Inlet Tertiary basins.

The bulk of the oil production from the major oil fields in the Cook Inlet basin is from sandstones of the Hemlock Conglomerate and the Tyonek Formation (Fig. 10).

Late Miocene culmination: In late Miocene time a short transitional period of low-energy sedimentation occurred in the central Cook Inlet basin; during this period, deposition was largely of siltstone, carbonaceous shale, and coal, present in the upper part of the Tyonek Formation, and siltstone and coal beds in the lower part of the Beluga Formation (Figs. 9, 12).

Deposition of sandy sediments of the Tyonek Formation diminished, presumably as a result of the initiation of uplift in the central Alaska Range which resulted in stream capture and elimination of the source for the quartz-rich garnetiferous sandstones. Concurrently, orogenic uplift in the Kenai-Chugach Mountains initiated the final regressive phase of the cycle.

Pliocene regression: The Pliocene regressive phase is represented by about 12,000 ft (3,660

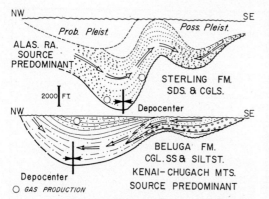

FIG. 12—Diagrammatic stratigraphic cross sections of Cook Inlet basin showing sedimentation during regressive phase of deposition of upper Kenai Group. During deposition of Beluga Formation, polymictic fanglomerates were derived predominantly from Kenai-Chugach Mountains. During deposition of Sterling Formation, conglomerates and sands were derived predominantly from Alaska Range.

m) of conglomerate, sandstone, and siltstone of the Beluga and Sterling Formations, derived from the rising Kenai-Chugach Mountains and the Alaska Range, respectively (Figs. 11, 12).

The early phase of regression is represented in the mineralogic character of the Beluga Formation. A predominance of epidote in the heavy-mineral suite indicates that Kenai-Chugach source terranes on the east flank of the basin provided the sediment which was swept across the basin to the foothills of the Alaska Range on the west. These foothills apparently stood in low relief and only contributed a minor amount of sediment during the early phase of regression (Fig. 11). A thick sequence of rhythmically alternating thin sands, silts, and coals was deposited in the northwestern part of the basin; the sequence is equivalent to the fanglomerates on the east flank of the basin (Fig. 12).

The final phase of regression is represented by the Sterling Formation, which has conglomeratic facies on the margins coeval with thick-bedded sandstones in the central part of the basin (Fig. 12). The depocenter was shifted somewhat eastward from its position during deposition of the Beluga Formation, reflecting a stronger, more positive source in the Alaska Range on the west during the terminal phase of regression than in the initial phase when the Kenai-Chugach Mountains on the east were the more positive source (Fig. 11). This shift is confirmed by the predominance of hornblende

in the heavy-mineral suite derived from the Alaska Range diorites, in contrast to epidote, which is scarce except in wells on the east side. Another common heavy mineral is hypersthene, which increases in abundance upward in the Pliocene section, reflecting increasing volcanism during the late Tertiary regression.

Significant dry-gas production occurs from the upper sandstones of the Beluga Formation and the basal sandstones of the Sterling Formation (Fig. 12).

In summary, the upper Tertiary sequence includes more than 15,000 ft (4,570 m) and roughly 18,000 cu mi (75,000 cu km) of sedimentary rocks. These strata are estimated to contain 1.5 billion bbl of proved oil reserves recoverable by present production techniques and 5 trillion cu ft of proved gas reserves, of which possibly 70 percent are recoverable (Fig. 13).

STRUCTURE

Structurally, the Cook Inlet basin is an asymmetric intermontane graben or half-graben with a steeper, more complex northwest flank in the north end of the basin (Fig. 14). The general trend of the basin, N30°E, is subparallel with its confining mountain borders. The Tertiary sedimentary beds in the basin have been deformed into an *en échelon* series of anticlines of varied structural amplitude. A horizon in the Hemlock Conglomerate along section *A-A'* (Fig. 15) has been shortened about 6 percent, or 5 mi (6 km), from a total of 72 mi (115 km) by late Tertiary to Holocene orogenesis.

Trends of individual folds in the northern part of the basin are more northerly than the general trend of the basin. Folds on the northwest flank of the basin trend slightly east of north and are truncated by the Castle Mountain fault. The eastward bend on some axial traces of folds adjacent to the Castle Mountain fault suggests right-lateral drag (Fig. 16), and offset of stream drainages, such as shown by the Susitna River, further suggests a component of right-lateral movement along the fault.

This right-lateral component of movement is dissipated in several splays in the Trading Bay area. The Castle Mountain fault does not appear to extend, with any significant strike-slip motion, to the southwest of this area. A similar pattern of structural development has been described by Grantz (1960) at the northeast end of the Castle Mountain fault system in the Sheep Mountain area of the Nelchina district, where the right-lateral movement in the Matanuska valley on the southwest is dissipated in

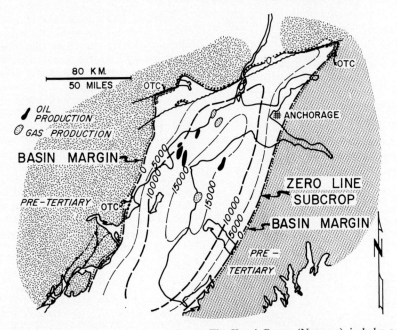

FIG. 13—Generalized isopach map of Kenai Group. The Kenai Group (Neogene) includes a maximum of more than 15,000 ft (4,570 m) and roughly 18,000 cu mi (75,000 cu km) of sedimentary rocks. All oil and gas production in basin is from these strata.

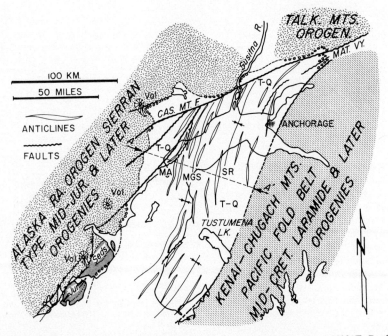

FIG. 14—Generalized tectonic map of Cook Inlet basin. Trend of basin is about N30°E. Predominant trend of structures within basin is more northerly than trend of basin, except south of Tustumena Lake. This change in trend suggests late Tertiary warping or late fold development south of Tustumena Lake.

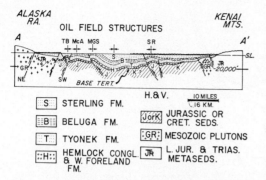

FIG. 15—Cross section of Cook Inlet basin (see Fig. 14). Oil-field structures (Alaska Geol. Soc., 1969) are: **TB**, Trading Bay field; **McA**, MacArthur River field; **MGS**, Middle Ground Shoal field; **SR**, Swanson River field.

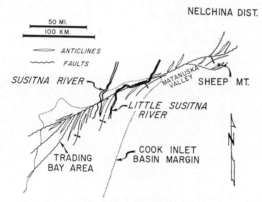

FIG. 16—Sketch map showing structural pattern of Castle Mountain fault system. Offset of river drainages and drag on structural trends suggest a strong component of right-lateral movement. This movement appears to be dissipated in a series of splays and associated folds, horsts, and grabens in Trading Bay and Sheep Mountain areas.

several splays, each with a predominant vertical or dip-slip component of displacement.

Virtually all the anticlines in the basin have the same structural configuration; the asymmetric structures have steeper west flanks that are commonly faulted on the high-relief parts of the major folds (Fig. 17). The only exceptions to this habit are a few high-relief folds adjacent to the Castle Mountain fault zone—*e.g.*, the Trading Bay fold. In such cases, we believe that late movements along the Castle Mountain fault or along splays of the Castle Mountain system have reversed the normal westward asymmetry. Nearly all folds are concentric in habit and involve pre-Tertiary strata in their cores at depth.

South of Tustumena Lake (Fig. 14), the anticlinal folds appear to have a structural development similar to those described for the northern part of the basin, except that their trends are more northeasterly, possibly owing to late Tertiary warping.

In addition to the transcurrent or rift faulting along part of the Castle Mountain system and the predominantly dip-slip thrust faulting related to the higher relief folds, normal faulting is also documented, as on the Swanson River anticline (Fig. 18). These normal faults evidently are tensional and probably are due to stretching along the longitudinal axis of the fold. The fact that similar faults paralleling the axis of the fold are scarce could be a result of active tectonic compression in a northwesterly or cross-basin direction.

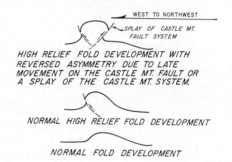

FIG. 17—Fold development in Cook Inlet basin. All folds are asymmetric with a steeper northwest flank except those adjacent to Castle Mountain fault, where late movement has reversed normal asymmetry. All folds are concentric in habit and most involve pre-Tertiary rocks in their cores.

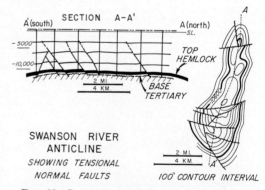

FIG. 18—Structure contour map and longitudinal section of Swanson River anticline showing tensional normal faults developed as a result of stretching along longitudinal axis of fold. Faults appear to involve pre-Tertiary rocks and to diminish in throw and die out upward in section.

It is suggested that Plafker's (1969) concept of continental underthrusting along the Aleutian Trench could be an adequate model to account for the Tertiary structural deformation in the Cook Inlet basin.

SELECTED REFERENCES

Alaska Geological Society, 1969, West to east stratigraphic correlation section, West Foreland to Swan Lake, upper Cook Inlet basin, Alaska: Anchorage, scale 1 in. = 500 ft.

Calderwood, K. W., and W. C. Fackler, 1972, Proposed stratigraphic nomenclature for Kenai Group, Cook Inlet basin, Alaska: Am. Assoc. Petroleum Geologists Bull., v. 56, no. 4, p. 739–754.

Carter, R. D., and W. L. Adkison, 1972, Correlation of subsurface Tertiary rocks, Cook Inlet basin, Alaska: U.S. Geol. Survey Open-File Rept.

Clark, Sandra, 1972, Reconnaissance bedrock geologic map of the Chugach Mountains near Anchorage, Alaska: U.S. Geol. Survey Map MF-350.

Crick, R. W., 1971, Potential petroleum reserves, Cook Inlet, Alaska, *in* I. H. Cram, ed., Future petroleum provinces of the United States—their geology and potential: Am. Assoc. Petroleum Geologists Mem. 15, v. 1, p. 109–119.

Detterman, R. L., and J. K. Hartsock, 1966 (1967), Geology of the Iniskin-Tuxedni region, Alaska: U.S. Geol. Survey Prof. Paper 512, 78 p.

——— B. L. Reed, and M. A. Lanphere, 1965, Jurassic plutonism in the Cook Inlet region, Alaska: U.S. Geol. Survey Prof. Paper 525-D, p. D16–D21.

Grantz, A., 1960, Generalized geologic map of the Nelchina area, Alaska, showing igneous rocks and larger faults: U.S. Geol. Survey Misc. Geol. Inv. Map I-312.

——— and D. L. Jones, 1960, Stratigraphy and age of the Matanuska Formation, south-central Alaska: U.S. Geol. Survey Prof. Paper 400-B, art. 159, p. B347–B350.

——— and J. A. Wolfe, 1961, Age af the Arkose Ridge Formation, south-central Alaska: Am. Assoc. Petroleum Geologists Bull., v. 45, no. 10, p. 1762–1765.

Hartman, D. C., G. H. Pessel, and D. L. McGee, 1972, Preliminary report on stratigraphy of Kenai Group, upper Cook Inlet basin, Alaska: Alaska Div. Mines and Minerals Spec. Rept. 5.

Jones, D. L., and R. L. Detterman, 1966, Cretaceous stratigraphy of the Kamishak Hills, Alaska Peninsula: U.S. Geol. Survey. Prof. Paper 550-D, p. D53–D58.

Moffitt, F. H., 1954, Geology of the Prince William Sound region, Alaska: U.S. Geol. Survey Bull. 989-E, p. 225–310.

Parkinson, L. J., 1962, One field, one giant—the story of Swanson River: Oil and Gas Jour., v. 60, no. 13, p. 180–183.

Payne, T. G., 1955, Mesozoic and Cenozoic tectonic elements of Alaska: U.S. Geol. Survey Misc. Geol. Inv. Map I-84.

Plafker, George, 1969, Tectonics of the March 27, 1964, Alaska earthquake: U.S. Geol. Survey Prof. Paper 543-I, p. I1–I74.

Wahrhaftig, Clyde, *et al.*, 1969, The Coal-Bearing group in the Nenana coal field, Alaska: U.S. Geol. Survey Bull. 1274-D, p. D1–D30.

Structure and Stratigraphy of Eastern Alaska Range, Alaska[1]

D. H. RICHTER[2] and D. L. JONES[2]

Anchorage, Alaska 99501, and Menlo Park, California 94025

Abstract The eastern Alaska Range, between 141°W (International Boundary) and 145°W long. in south-central Alaska, provides clues to the tectonic development of northwestern North America.

The Denali fault system, a major structural feature extending in an arcuate path from the Bering Sea to the Gulf of Alaska, transects the eastern Alaska Range and separates extremely diverse geologic terranes. North of the Denali fault lies a widespread terrane of highly deformed, metamorphosed sedimentary and minor igneous rocks of Precambrian to Devonian age. South of the Denali fault system these rocks are absent, and the oldest rocks exposed are a heterogeneous series of Pennsylvanian(?) or Permian volcanic and volcaniclastic rocks derived from a late Paleozoic volcanic island arc probably built directly on oceanic crust. These rocks are overlain by a succession of Permian marine clastic beds and limestones; Triassic carbonaceous shales, subaerial tholeiitic basalt flows, and marine limestones; and Jurassic-Cretaceous argillite, graywacke, and conglomerate. The cumulative thickness of the succession locally exceeds 10,000 ft (3,050 m). Sedimentation culminated in middle(?) Cretaceous time with a short-lived and restricted episode of andesitic volcanism. Relatively undeformed continental sedimentary rocks of Cretaceous age, or younger, and late Cenozoic terrestrial volcanic flows overlie the older rocks with marked angular unconformity.

Linear bodies of serpentinized ultramafic rocks are present with the Permian rocks to the west in the central Alaska Range and to the east in Canada. In the eastern Alaska Range, ultramafic rocks have not been observed south of the Denali fault, but they do occur locally along the fault zone and in the older terrane just north of the fault.

All pre–Late Cretaceous rocks south of the Denali fault system have been cut by high-angle normal faults and by numerous reverse and thrust faults that dip north toward the Denali fault. The Jurassic-Cretaceous marine sedimentary rocks also exhibit complex folding, locally isoclinal, and fold axes plunge at low angles generally toward the northwest.

The geologic data suggest that the oceanic terrane south of the Denali fault collapsed against, and was added to, the continental American plate, probably in Early Triassic time. Since then, this terrane has undergone multiple deformation as later oceanic plates impinged against the continental margin. The Denali fault, which represents an ancient subduction zone, was reactivated as a ridge-arc dextral transform fault—probably during the early Pliocene—in response to a change in the direction of spreading in the North Pacific oceanic plate. The Totschunda fault system, which diverges from the Denali structure near 144°W long. and trends southeasterly toward the Fairweather fault in the Gulf of Alaska, is another major right-lateral strike-slip fault that may have developed as recently as the middle Pleistocene. At present, the Denali fault system apparently is inactive southeast of the Denali-Totschunda junction.

INTRODUCTION

The Alaska Range is a prominent, high arcuate mountain belt that extends from the Alaska Peninsula eastward into Canada. It merges along the Canadian border with the Wrangell Mountains on the south and the Kluane Range and St. Elias Mountains on the southeast. This study concerns the eastern part of the Alaska Range between 145°W long. and the Canadian border (Fig. 1), principally within the Nabesna quadrangle (scale 1:250,000). Because much of this region is still unexplored geologically, the present account must be regarded only as a preliminary summary of our current knowledge.

GENERAL STATEMENT

The dominant geologic feature in the eastern Alaska Range is the Denali fault, a major dextral strike-slip fault that separates the range into two distinct, markedly different geologic terranes (Fig. 2). North of the fault, metamorphic rocks of Devonian and older age are exposed; south of the fault, the rocks are late Paleozoic and younger. This paper emphasizes the structure and stratigraphy of the rocks south of the Denali fault. A brief description of the metamorphic rocks north of the fault is included to illustrate the significant contrast between the two terranes.

ROCKS NORTH OF DENALI FAULT

The terrane north of the Denali fault is part of an old dissected craton consisting chiefly of phyllite, quartz-mica schist, micaceous quartzite, metaconglomerate, marble, and greenstone. Most of the rocks exhibit a polymetamorphic texture within the greenschist metamorphic facies. A Devonian age for at least part of this metamorphic terrane is established by the presence of the stromatoporoid *Amphipora* in marble lenses that crop out in a relatively narrow belt within a few miles of the De-

[1] Manuscript received, September 20, 1971. Publication authorized by the Director, U.S. Geological Survey.

[2] U.S. Geological Survey.

nali fault. The metamorphic grade—and possibly the age of these rocks—increases northward beyond the eastern Alaska Range.

Rocks South of Denali Fault

South of the Denali fault, a section more than 45,000 ft (13,715 m) thick composed of sedimentary and volcanic rocks ranges in age from Permian to Holocene (Fig. 3). However, all units are not present in any one place, and their maximum thicknesses are attained in different areas. The oldest, most widespread, and probably the thickest sequence consists of volcanic flows, volcaniclastic rocks, and marine sedimentary rocks of Permian age. These beds are overlain disconformably by a Triassic assemblage of carbonaceous shale, amygdaloidal basalt, and marine limestone. The amygdaloidal basalt constitutes the bulk of the Triassic rocks and exhibits a consistent thickness throughout the area. Overlying the Triassic rocks are Jurassic and Cretaceous marine rocks that are predominantly turbidites. In the eastern part of the area, a local Cretaceous volcanic-volcaniclastic unit conformably overlies the Jurassic and Cretaceous marine sedimentary sequence. Continental sedimentary rocks of questionably Late Cretaceous age lie with angular unconformity chiefly on rocks of pre-Jurassic age in local basins scattered throughout the range. Above these and the older rocks, and separated by another angular unconformity, are the continental flows and tuffs of the Wrangell Lava of Miocene-Holocene age.

Intrusive Rocks

Four distinct periods of intrusive activity have been recognized south of the Denali fault (Fig. 3) on the basis of intrusive relations and several K-Ar dates obtained from a study now under way by Marvin Lanphere of the U.S. Geological Survey. The oldest known igneous rocks consist of extremely heterogeneous gneissic diorites, syenites and monzonites, and nonfoliated diorite and quartz monzonite that were emplaced during a tectonic event in Late Permian to Middle Jurassic time. A later plutonic event is recorded by large sills and dikes of gabbro within the Permian and the lower part of the Triassic sections. These rocks may be the hypabyssal equivalents of the amygdaloidal basalts; if so, they were emplaced during Middle to Late Triassic time. The most significant and widespread plutonic event occurred during middle Cretaceous time. This major event resulted in the emplacement of diorite, quartz diorite, granodiorite, and quartz monzonite in masses ranging from small stocks to complex

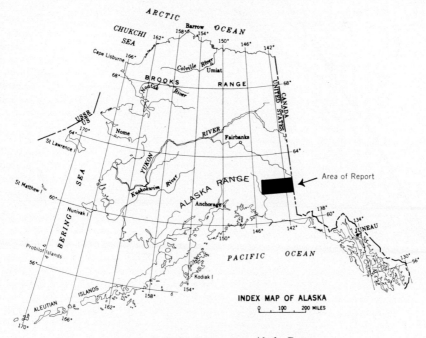

Fig. 1—Location map, eastern Alaska Range.

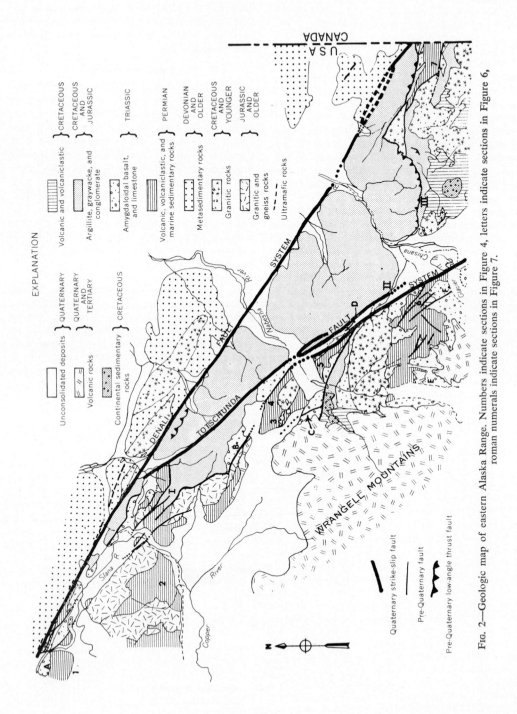

FIG. 2—Geologic map of eastern Alaska Range. Numbers indicate sections in Figure 4, letters indicate sections in Figure 6, roman numerals indicate sections in Figure 7.

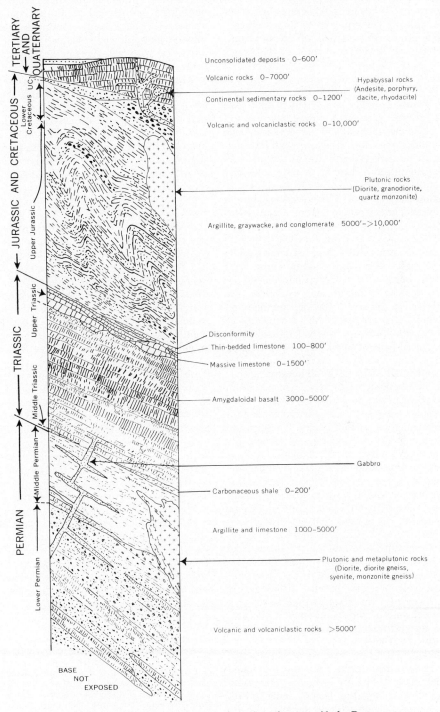

FIG. 3—Diagrammatic composite cross section of eastern Alaska Range.

batholiths. The fourth and youngest period of activity probably began in Miocene time, concurrent with the beginning of Wrangell volcanism, and produced a variety of epizonal porphyry intrusives throughout most of the range.

STRATIGRAPHY

Permian Rocks

The Permian rocks are divided into two main lithologic groups—a lower marine volcanic-volcaniclastic unit and an upper marine argillite-limestone unit. However, extreme heterogeneity of rock types is found within each unit. A generalized picture of the character and distribution of the Permian rocks is shown by the sections in Figure 4. These sections show a minimum thickness ranging from about 1,100 to 8,550 ft (335–2,600 m) along 132 mi (212 km) of the range; the strata—at least the marine sedimentary unit—thin eastward. The lower volcanic-volcaniclastic unit, whose base has never been observed, consists chiefly of massive volcanic mudflow and avalanche deposits, breccias, massive to bedded pumice and lithic lapilli tuffs, amygdaloidal to dense andesite flows with locally developed pillow structure, and bedded volcaniclastic rocks ranging from mudstone to cobble conglomerate. Thin chert and dark bioclastic limestone occur locally interbedded with the volcaniclastic rocks. The overlying marine sedimentary rocks are possibly separated from the volcanic unit by a slight angular unconformity. These younger Permian rocks contain no coarse volcanic material; they consist chiefly of black argillites and massive limestone. The massive limestone generally is present at the base of the marine unit but may be absent locally. In some places, such as at Mankomen Lake, more than one limestone unit is present. Meager fossil evidence indicates a Wolfcamp age for the volcanic and volcaniclastic unit and a late Leonard age for the marine sedimentary unit. However, a Pennsylvanian age for some of the older volcanic rocks is possible, because lithologically similar rocks of Pennsylvanian age have been found northwest of the Mankomen Lake section in the central Alaska Range (Hanson, 1963; Rowett, 1969).

At Gillett Pass in the eastern Alaska Range, a severely deformed dunite body and associated amphibolite-pyroxenite are in fault contact with Permian rocks along the Denali fault. Ultramafic rocks associated with Permian rocks are much more abundant both on the west and the east, as shown on Figure 5 (Rose, 1965; Mul-

ler, 1967). The ultramafic rocks are chiefly serpentinized dunites and peridotites and are generally associated with complexly deformed, massive and pillowed volcanic rocks and, at two localities, with glaucophane-bearing crystalline rocks (Rose, 1965).

The Permian rocks appear to be the vestiges of a late Paleozoic volcanic island arc.[3] Their close association with ultramafic rocks suggests that the arc was built directly on oceanic crust; and the juxtaposition of these rocks with the metamorphic terrane north of the Denali fault suggests that these two dissimilar suites have been brought together by large-scale horizontal movement.

Triassic Rocks

Locally, 200 ft (60 m) or less of discontinuous carbonaceous shales and minor limestones conformably overlies the Permian rocks (Fig. 6). These rocks, in turn, are overlain by a tremendous blanket, up to 5,000 ft (1,525 m) thick, of subaerial flood basalts composed of hundreds of flows ranging from a few inches to more than 50 ft (15 m) thick. Most flows are highly vesicular and tholeiitic in character. They extend far east into Canada, west into the central Alaska Range, and south to the southern flank of the Wrangell Mountains, where the equivalent Nikolai Greenstone is found. A conservative estimate of their volume is about 10,000 cu mi (42,000 cu km). Throughout the eastern Alaska Range, no pillows or other features indicative of submarine eruption have been observed. However, Muller (1967) reported that, eastward in the Kluane Range, equivalent flows locally exhibit pillow structures and are interbedded with marine deposits.

Massive micritic limestone, as much as 1,500 ft (455 m) thick, overlies the amygdaloidal basalt with local angular unconformity and represents the first deposits of a transgressive Late Triassic sea. The limestone occurs in crude beds as thick as 50 ft (15 m) that locally contain abundant chert nodules; diagnostic fossils are scarce.

---

[3] *Note added in proof:* Biostratigraphic studies of the "Permian" section at Mankomen Lake (see Fig. 4) in 1972 have shown that most of the volcanogenic sequence is Pennsylvanian in age, implying that similar strata elsewhere in the eastern Alaska Range are also Pennsylvanian. These new data suggest that the Permian volcanic arc, as referred to in this paper, developed during Pennsylvanian time and may have been virtually inactive by the Permian.

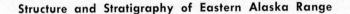

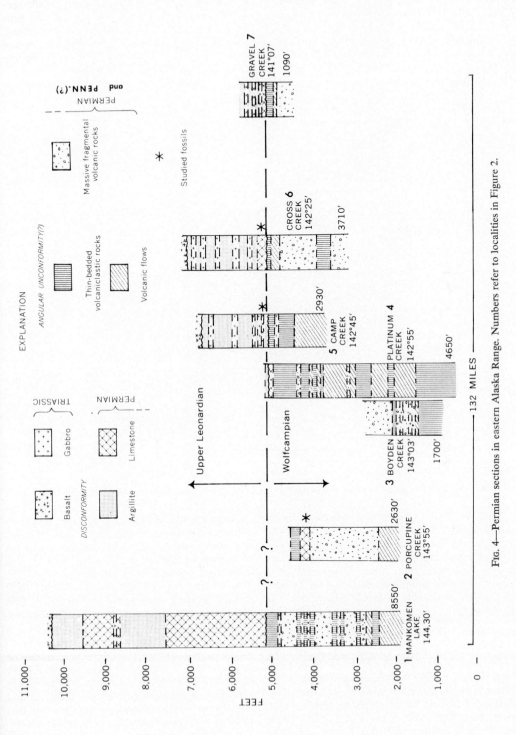

Fig. 4—Permian sections in eastern Alaska Range. Numbers refer to localities in Figure 2.

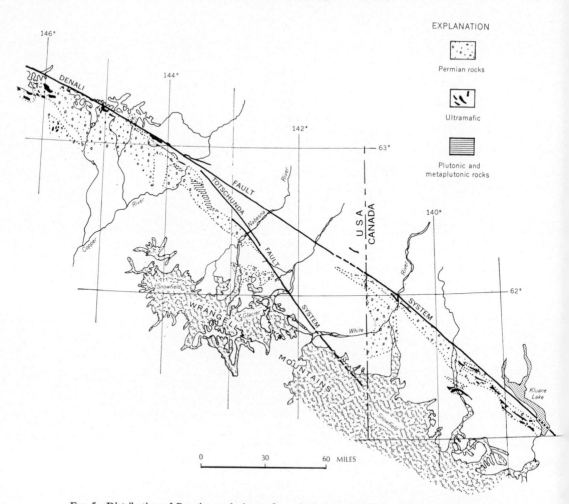

EXPLANATION

Permian rocks

Ultramafic

Plutonic and
metaplutonic rocks

FIG. 5—Distribution of Permian and ultramafic rocks in eastern Alaska Range and adjoining areas.

Thin beds of micritic and spiculitic lime-stones separated in some places by thinner beds of shale and cherty argillite overlie the massive limestone and represent deposition in a deeper marine environment. This limestone unit locally contains abundant specimens of *Mono-tis subcircularis* Gabb, of latest Triassic age.

Upper Jurassic and Lower Cretaceous Rocks

More than 9,000 ft (2,745 m) of argillite and flyschlike clastic sedimentary rocks of Late Jurassic and Early Cretaceous age disconform-ably overlie Triassic strata (Fig. 7). Rocks of Early and Middle Jurassic age are absent. The lower part of this unit consists of 3,000 ft (915 m) of dark argillite with thin lenses and nod-

ules of siltstone and minor graywacke and con-glomeratic beds containing large clasts of Trias-sic limestone. Scarce and poorly preserved specimens of *Buchia* in the lower part of this basal unit are indicative of Kimeridgian age. Toward the top of the basal argillite unit, graded bedding becomes more apparent, and there is a gradual upward transition to well-de-veloped, thin, graded beds of graywacke-silt-stone-argillite and interbeds of massive gray-wacke and extraformational pebble to cobble conglomerate. Very scarce specimens of *Buchia* in the graded beds also indicate a Kimeridgian age. The uppermost part of the Jurassic and Cretaceous clastic sequence comprises 3,000 ft (915 m) or more of argillite with minor calcar-eous siltstone and limestone that grade upward

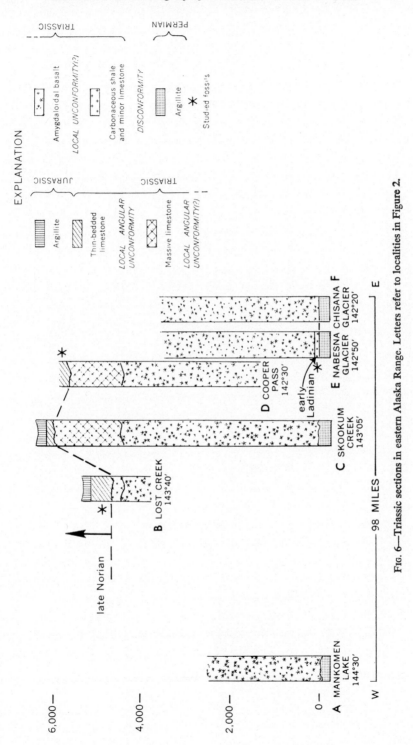

FIG. 6—Triassic sections in eastern Alaska Range. Letters refer to localities in Figure 2.

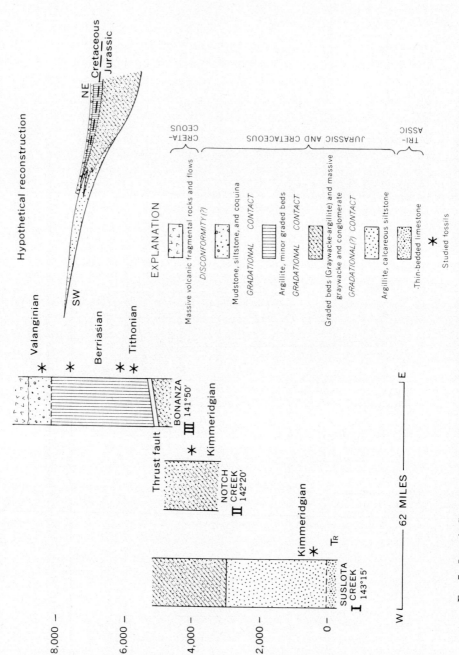

Fig. 7—Jurassic-Cretaceous sections in eastern Alaska Range. Roman numerals refer to localities in Figure 2.

into about 800 ft (245 m) of siltstone and tuff-aceous mudstone with coquina interbeds. *Buchia* faunas are extremely abundant locally throughout these two units, recording a complete sequence from Tithonian to Valanginian.

Cretaceous Volcanic Rocks

Between the Chisana River (142°W long.) and the Canadian border, a thick series of andesitic volcanic, volcaniclastic, and minor fine-grained marine and continental sedimentary rocks, as much as 10,000 ft (3,050 m) thick, conformably overlies the Jurassic and Cretaceous strata (Fig. 2). Massive submarine lahars or debris-avalanche deposits and volcanic conglomerates with interbedded crystal tuffs, tuffaceous mudstone, and argillite are abundant low in the section. Nondiagnostic *Inoceramus* prisms are locally abundant in the mudstone and argillite beds and also are scattered throughout many of the volcaniclastic beds. Marine sedimentary rocks decrease in abundance upward in the section; lenses of amygdaloidal andesitic volcanic rocks are common, and a few coalified wood fragments are found scattered through the volcaniclastic rocks. The sequence is intruded by the middle Cretaceous plutons and, hence, is post-Valanginian, pre–middle Cretaceous in age.

Cretaceous Nonmarine Rocks

Unconformably overlying the Cretaceous volcanic rocks in the eastern part of the range, and pre-Jurassic rocks elsewhere, is as much as 1,200 ft (365 m) of continental conglomerate and sandstone with minor shale and coaly beds. These rocks were deposited in small, local intermontane basins scattered throughout the range. Abundant and well-preserved floras suggest a Late Cretaceous age.

Cenozoic Volcanic Rocks

The Wrangell Lava unconformably overlies all older rocks in the eastern Alaska Range. The base of this volcanic pile is characterized by rhyodacite flows, endogenous domes, and pyroclastic cones. These silicic volcanic rocks are overlain by rocks erupted from several large shield volcanoes, some of which exhibit minor effusive activity today. The earliest products of the shield-building volcanoes were blankets of andesitic pumice that locally were reworked by fluvial action. Upon these pumiceous deposits lies a great thickness of basalt, andesite, and dacite flows that constitute the bulk of the volcanic rocks. A few K-Ar dates

suggest that this period of volcanic activity commenced in early Miocene time.

Cenozoic Glacial and Fluvial Deposits

Semiconsolidated tillites interbedded with the Miocene part of the Wrangell Lava in scattered exposures throughout the range show that major glacial activity preceded the Pleistocene Epoch by many millions of years.

Unconsolidated glacial, glaciofluvial, and fluvial deposits of Pleistocene and younger age mantle all older rocks in the range. Glaciofluvial outwash deposits of Wisconsin age locally exceed 600 ft (185 m) in thickness and form the bulk of the unconsolidated material in the area. These Wisconsin deposits are important as a time base in estimating rates of Holocene fault movement.

STRUCTURAL GEOLOGY

The eastern Alaska Range and contiguous terrane to the south and southwest have acted as a fairly cohesive block that, until late Cenozoic time, responded to variable rates of tectonic stress mostly directed northward. In general, these stresses have been relieved by rupture in the pre-Jurassic rocks and by plastic deformation in the thick basinal Jurassic and Cretaceous strata.

The effects of an assumed major tectonic event in Late Permian and Early Triassic time are now largely obscured by later structures or covered by younger rocks. However, development of foliation and cataclastic features in Triassic and older crystalline rocks and emplacement of alpine-type ultramafic bodies are strong evidence supporting such an event.

Three distinct types of faulting have been recognized in post–Middle Triassic rocks: (1) north- to northwest-trending high-angle reverse and normal faults generally with the southwest block down; (2) low-angle thrust faults with northeast dip; and (3) linear, northwest-trending, right-lateral strike-slip faults.

The high-angle reverse and normal faults offset rocks as young as Late Cretaceous and are probably related largely to a late Mesozoic and early Cenozoic tectonic event.

The low-angle thrust faults are confined to the Jurassic and Cretaceous rocks and, where relations can be seen, cut the steeply dipping faults. These faults probably formed during the final stages of the late Mesozoic and early Cenozoic tectonic event. The thrusts, which are associated with recumbent isoclinal folds, were of sufficient magnitude locally to move sedimen-

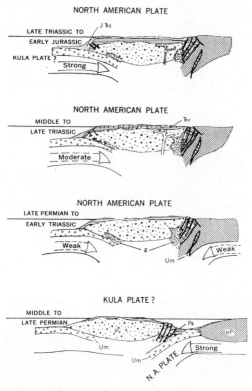

FIG. 8—Diagrammatic cross sections through eastern Alaska Range and south-central Alaska along 142°W long., Permian through Late Triassic. Symbols:

pP = Pre-Permian metamorphic rocks north of
       Denali fault
Pv = Permian volcanic rocks
Ps = Permian sedimentary rocks
Ŧ v = Triassic volcanic rocks
JŦ s = Jurassic and Triassic sedimentary rocks
Um = Ultramafic rocks
  g = Granitic rocks

tary rocks out of their basin in the form of flat-lying nappelike thrust sheets.

Strike-slip faulting is shown by the great Denali fault system and the related Totschunda fault system (Fig. 2). Both fault systems are geologically young structures exhibiting intense Quaternary right-lateral movement. The Denali fault system juxtaposes a Devonian and older metamorphic continental terrane against a late Paleozoic and younger terrane through the entire length of the eastern Alaska Range. The younger Totschunda fault system is confined to the late Paleozoic and younger rocks south of the Denali fault system. Offset Wisconsin glacial deposits indicate minimum average Holocene rates of movement of 0.5–1.5 in. (1.27–

3.81 cm) per year along most of the Totschunda-Denali structure. On the basis of plate-motion theory for the North Pacific region, the Denali fault system may have formed in Miocene and Pliocene time when a spreading ridge was consumed in an active trench (Atwater, 1970; Grow and Atwater, 1970). If constant motion since that time and an average rate of slip of 1 in. (2.54 cm) per year are assumed, the minimum total right-lateral separation would be about 200 mi (320 km). The younger Totschunda system exhibits only 6 mi (9.6 km) of right-lateral separation and may be no older than late Pleistocene. Thus, the Denali and Totschunda fault systems are young structures that apparently separate two major crustal plates.

INFERRED GEOLOGIC HISTORY

The geologic history of the terrane south of the Denali fault apparently began in Early Permian or possibly Late Pennsylvanian time with development of a volcanic island arc on the Kula (Grow and Atwater, 1970) or, possibly, some older oceanic plate (Figs. 8, 9). The arc was formed by the underthrusting of another plate—the North American plate, composed of Devonian and older continental rocks—with a leading edge of oceanic crust. By Middle and Late Permian time, much of the oceanic crustal part of the North American plate had moved into the active trench bordering the arc, and the arc and the continent had begun to impinge. Volcanic activity then waned, parts of the arc subsided, and marine sedimentation predominated.

As the result of continued plate motion and lithosphere subduction, the volcanic arc eventually collapsed against the continent on the North American plate. This collapse, probably during Late Permian to Middle Triassic time, was accompanied by uplifts, heterogeneous dioritic and syenitic intrusions, local metamorphism, and emplacement of alpine ultramafic rocks along the suture zone. Following collapse of the arc and cessation of underthrusting by the North American plate, the oceanic plate broke along its join with the volcanic arc and began to descend under the arc now coupled to the continent.

In Middle to Late Triassic time, following a general emergence of the continent, a tremendous volume of subaerial flood basalts poured over the Permian volcanic rocks and sediments along the continental margin. Removal of this vast quantity of volcanic material from the mantle apparently resulted in regional subsidence. Late Triassic seas transgressed the submerged continent, depositing thick carbonate muds and, later, thinner bedded limestone units.

During Jurassic and Cretaceous time an active subduction zone, in which the oceanic plate disappeared, existed along the continental margin, and the related trench received a thick section of clastic sediment. During this period of increasing tectonic stress, subsidence in the areas of the eastern Alaska Range was restricted to large linear basins generally far behind the continental margin. Locally, along the edge of the continent, the land emerged. Subsidence and basin sedimentation waned by the Early Cretaceous as the oceanic plate continued to push against and underneath the continent. As the edge of the continent was compressed and raised, overthrusting was initiated along the edge of this plate, and intense normal and reverse faulting ruptured the rocks. The local volcanism which occurred during this time probably represented the beginning of middle Cretaceous plutonic activity.

By the Late Cretaceous or early Tertiary, plutonic activity and marked deformation behind the trench had climaxed. In the deep Jurassic and Cretaceous basins, the sedimentary rocks had been severely deformed by folding and overthrusting. Most of the continental margin had emerged, but isolated marine basins continued to collect sediments. Terrestrial sediments were also accumulating in small intermontane basins. Along the trench, overthrusting may have accelerated during this period, effectively relieving the stress elsewhere along the plate margin. The thick clastic deposits along the trench were complexly deformed and mixed with oceanic crustal rocks as they were carried under the edge of the plate.

In early Miocene time, shallow plutonic activity was evident and, by the middle Miocene, large andesitic volcanoes were forming. Glaciers covered much of the area and thick marine tillites accumulated along the margin of the continent. Probably during middle and late Miocene time, the oceanic ridge separating the Kula plate from the Pacific plate migrated into the trench and disappeared. Underthrusting ceased, but the Pacific plate, with a slight change in direction and a relative reduction in rate of motion (Grow and Atwater, 1970), continued to impinge on the continent. The complete disappearance of the ridge and the resultant change in direction and rate of Pacific-

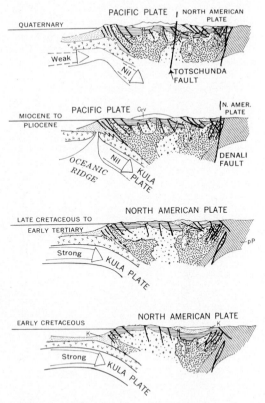

Fig. 9—Diagrammatic sections through southern Alaska approximately along 142°W long., Cretaceous through Quaternary. Symbols as in preceding figure, plus K = Cretaceous sedimentary volcanic rocks and Czv = Cenozoic volcanic rocks.

plate motion caused a transform fault or tear-transform fault to be generated along the old Permian arc–Devonian continent suture. This fault represented the beginning of the great strike-slip Denali fault system.

Through the late Tertiary and into the Quaternary, the Pacific plate apparently did not underthrust the continent in south-central Alaska. The compressional stresses imposed by the motion of the Pacific plate, however, were relieved by uplift and lateral movement along the Denali fault system, effectively decoupling a part of the North American plate. A second major strike-slip structure, the Totschunda fault system, began to form late in the Pleistocene, impeding movement along a large segment of the Denali fault system.

Presently, from the Denali-Totschunda fault system east of about 153°W long. southward to the Gulf of Alaska, this former part of the

North American plate is moving with the Pacific plate. Northwest of the junction of the Denali and Totschunda fault systems, plate motion is along the Denali fault. Southeast of the junction, the faults of the Denali system are passive and movement is along the Totschunda system and, possibly, the Fairweather fault.

REFERENCES CITED

Atwater, Tanya, 1970, Implications of plate tectonics for the Cenozoic tectonic evolution of western North America: Geol. Soc. America Bull., v. 81, p. 3513–3536.

Grow, J. A., and Tanya Atwater, 1970, Mid-Tertiary tectonic transition in the Aleutian Arc: Geol. Soc. America Bull., v. 81, p. 3715–3722.

Hanson, L. G., 1963, Bedrock geology of the Rainbow Mountain area, Alaska Range, Alaska: Alaska Div. Mines and Minerals Geol. Rept. 2, 82 p.

Muller, J. E., 1967, Kluane Lake map-area, Yukon Territory: Canada Geol. Survey Mem. 340, 137 p.

Rose, A. W., 1965, Geology and mineral deposits of the Rainy Creek area, Mt. Hayes quadrangle, Alaska: Alaska Div. Mines and Minerals Geol. Rept. 14, 50 p.

Rowett, C. L., 1969, Upper Paleozoic stratigraphy and corals from the east-central Alaska Range, Alaska: Arctic Inst. North America Tech. Paper 23, 120 p.

Plutonic Rocks of Alaska-Aleutian Range Batholith[1]

BRUCE L. REED and MARVIN A. LANPHERE[2]

Anchorage, Alaska 99501, and Menlo Park, California 94025

Abstract Potassium-argon mineral ages and reconnaissance mapping of the central and southern Alaska Range and Aleutian Range indicate that there were three major plutonic episodes during the Mesozoic and Cenozoic. The first began in the Early Jurassic about 180 m.y. ago and continued for about 25 m.y. Plutons of this age form an arcuate belt more than 500 mi (800 km) long that extends from Becharof Lake to the Talkeetna Mountains. The Jurassic plutonic rocks are largely diorite and quartz diorite with minor granodiorite. Late Cretaceous and Tertiary plutons occur locally within this belt but are largely confined to the northern part of the Alaska-Aleutian Range batholith, where they form north-trending belts transverse to the earlier tectonic elements and locally extend out into what was a more stable area bordering the earlier tectonic features. Composition of these plutons ranges from diorite through granite, but granodiorite and quartz monzonite predominate. Isolated granitic stocks intruded during the second episode also extend eastward into the central Alaska Range. The data suggest that this plutonic episode may be separated into Late Cretaceous (72–84 m.y.) and early Tertiary (50–65 m.y.) phases. The third episode is represented by middle Tertiary (34–40 m.y.) plutons that form a north-trending belt about 90 mi (145 km) long in the central part of the southern Alaska Range. These rocks are characteristically granites and quartz monzonites. Small plutons of middle Tertiary age are present locally in the Alaska Peninsula and the central Alaska Range. The chemical data that have thus far been accumulated on the rocks of these three plutonic episodes suggest progressive enrichment in alkali constituents with decreasing age.

Introduction

The area of study in the central and southern Alaska Range covers approximately 25,000 sq mi (64,750 sq km); the plutonic rocks which form the Alaska-Aleutian Range batholith (Fig. 1) are comparable in areal extent to the Sierra Nevada batholith of California. Geology of much of this part of Alaska is either unknown or poorly known. In some areas, geologic control is moderately good, but the recon-

[1] Manuscript received, September 20, 1971. Publication authorized by the Director, U.S. Geological Survey.

[2] U.S. Geological Survey.

The cooperation of geologists from oil and mining companies working in the region has been invaluable, particularly in providing samples; we are also grateful for their interest in the work as it progressed. R. L. Elliott, R. J. May, and M. B. Estlund assisted with field studies; and J. D. Luetscher, L. B. Schlocker, J. B. Von Essen, and H. C. Whitehead assisted with the age measurements.

naissance nature of our work has resulted in data which are, in general, widely scattered. Thus, in this preliminary synthesis we have drawn conclusions about the geology of the plutonic rocks of rather large areas for which we have little data.

This report is based on age measurements on 109 rock samples. Potassium-argon analyses were made on 88 biotite separates, 47 hornblende separates, and 3 muscovite separates. Age measurements for 34 of the rock samples have been reported previously (Reed and Lanphere, 1969). Additional studies on the rock chemistry and age measurements are also in progress, and new data may require revision of some aspects of the conclusions reached in this paper.

The precise information on the age of the plutonic rocks is based on potassium-argon age measurements. This dating method depends on the accumulation of radiogenic argon in a rock; the critical temperature at which accumulation of radiogenic argon begins is different for various minerals such as, for example, biotite and hornblende. Therefore, for those plutonic rocks on which concordant mineral ages have been measured, we infer that this measured age very closely approximates the time of crystallization of the rock from a melt, because a long cooling history probably would result in discordant mineral ages (Dalrymple and Lanphere, 1969). Reheating caused by subsequent intrusions or metamorphism also could produce discordant mineral ages.

Geologic Setting

Mesozoic plutonic rocks form an integral part of the Circum-Pacific region, and a thorough knowledge of the evolution of the granitic belts is essential to a complete understanding of the geologic history of the region. The Alaska-Aleutian Range, which lies on the northern part of the Circum-Pacific belt, underwent repeated deformation, batholithic intrusion, orogenic sedimentation, and volcanism during the Mesozoic and Tertiary.

The Alaskan-Aleutian Range batholith trends northeast essentially parallel with the mountain ranges (Fig. 1). The main batholithic mass is

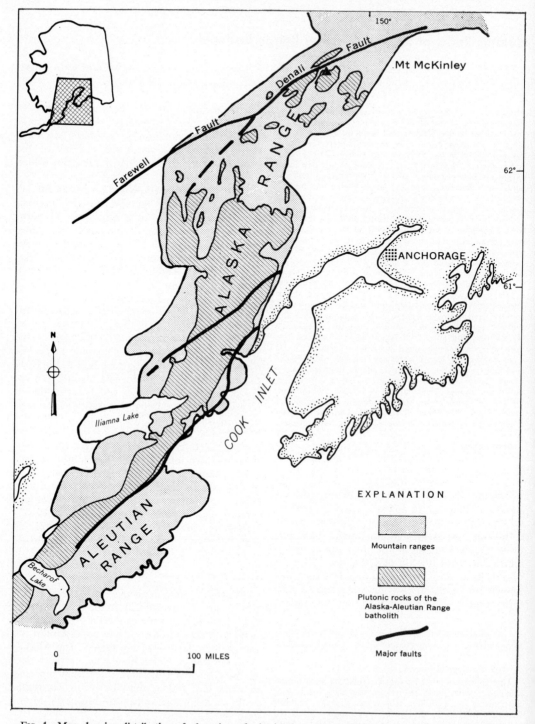

FIG. 1—Map showing distribution of plutonic rocks in Alaska and Aleutian Ranges. Alaska-Aleutian Range batholith includes plutonic rocks from vicinity of Becharof Lake northeast to approximate 62°N lat.

about 310 mi (500 km) long and 10–50 mi (15–80 km) wide. The apparent narrowing of the batholith in the Aleutian Range is due to a cover of Tertiary volcanic rocks on the west side. The main batholithic mass terminates rather abruptly at about 62°N lat. North and northeastward from this point into the Mount McKinley area, plutonic rocks occur as isolated bodies that range from a few tens of square miles up to 200 sq mi (520 sq km) in area. In general, contacts in the southern part of the batholith tend to be concordant with enclosing country rocks (although there are many exceptions), whereas, in the northern part of the batholith and in the isolated plutons on the north and east, contacts tend to be sharp and discordant.

From about 61°N lat. southward, the east side of the main batholith is flanked by early and middle Mesozoic volcanic and sedimentary rocks. The early Mesozoic rocks are eugeosynclinal, whereas the middle Mesozoic rocks are miogeosynclinal (Detterman and Hartsock, 1966). The west side of the southern part of the batholith is also flanked by the early Mesozoic eugeosynclinal rocks and, locally, by a Tertiary volcanic cover. A major fault (dashed line, Fig. 1) that trends northeast into the Denali fault appears to be the fundamental break of the Denali fault system in that it juxtaposes Mesozoic eugeosynclinal rocks on the south against Paleozoic miogeosynclinal rocks on the north (Reed and Elliott, 1970). This fault may be an extension of the ancient subduction zone in the eastern Alaska Range that Richter and Jones (1970) described. Later transcurrent movement along this major structural break produced a new break, the Farewell segment of the Denali fault system, a dextral fault which forms an escarpment on the north face of the Alaska Range and extends southwest to the Holitna fault (Grantz, 1966). Eastward along the Denali fault, in the direction of Mount McKinley, Paleozoic rocks occur generally north of the fault and are found south of the fault only locally.

Jurassic Plutonism

The oldest recognized period of plutonism in the Alaska-Aleutian Range began in the Early Jurassic about 180 m.y. ago and continued for about 25 m.y. Plutonism was coeval with, or closely followed, accumulation of a thick Lower Jurassic volcanic sequence, because plutonic and volcanic rocks are closely associated and extend northeast from Becharof Lake to the Talkeetna Mountains (Fig. 2), a distance of more than 500 mi (800 km; Grantz et al., 1963; Reed and Lanphere, 1969). Jurassic plutonism was, however, confined to a northeast-trending curved belt, whereas the Lower Jurassic eugeosynclinal sequence covers a much larger area. Rocks believed to be equivalent to the sequence are present in the Alaska Range southwest of Mount McKinley (Reed and Eberlein, 1972), an area where Jurassic intrusive rocks have not been found.

Jurassic plutonic rocks range in composition from gabbro to granodiorite, but rocks at the mafic end of the series—diorite and quartz diorite—are by far the most abundant. Most Jurassic plutons vary internally in composition and, wherever intrusive relations and K-Ar ages have been determined within an intrusive sequence, the older plutons are the more mafic and successively younger plutons the more felsic. Large plutons are elongate parallel with the northeast regional strike of the enclosing rocks, and many of the Jurassic intrusive sequences show primary foliations and are zoned compositionally. Contacts with country rocks are both concordant and discordant and locally show the effects of wall-rock deformation. Contact migmatites are present locally. At the present level of exposure of the Jurassic plutons, comparison of these features with those of younger plutons indicates that many of the Jurassic plutonic rocks may be considered as syntectonic plutons that were more forcefully intruded and perhaps emplaced at a greater depth than the Cretaceous or Tertiary plutonic rocks.

Late Cretaceous Plutonism

Plutonic rocks of Late Cretaceous age presently are known to occur in only three areas (Fig. 2), and the extent of these bodies is not well known. Small bodies of granodiorite and quartz monzonite occur on the west side of the main batholith north and south of Iliamna Lake; a body of quartz diorite occurs on the east side of the batholith west of Cook Inlet; and a series of isolated north-trending plutons is present in the northwest part of the batholith. The latter plutons have a relatively uniform composition of quartz diorite to granodiorite and contrast markedly with the bordering granites of early and middle Tertiary age. Some have well-developed platy and linear flow structures which are parallel with the enclosing rocks and suggest active magma emplacement. Flow structures are not found in the adjacent Tertiary plutons.

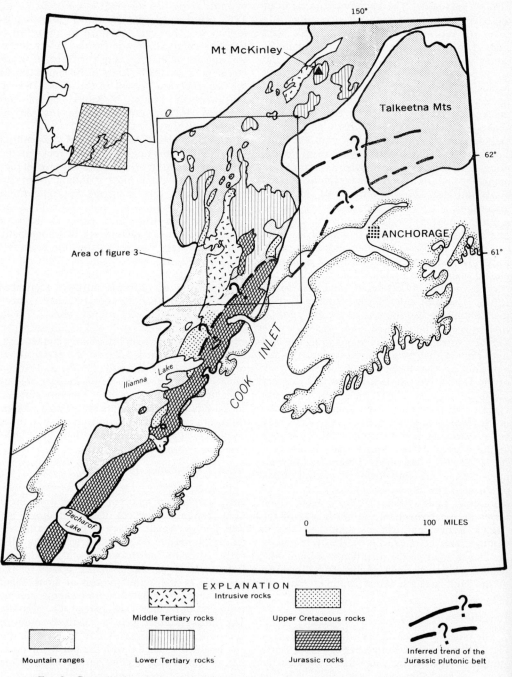

FIG. 2—Generalized geologic map of Alaska-Aleutian Range batholith and associated plutons.

TERTIARY PLUTONISM

Tertiary plutonic rocks in the Alaska and Aleutian Ranges are mainly confined to the northern part of the batholith and extend northeastward in the direction of Mount McKinley as isolated stocks, chiefly of granite composition (Fig. 2). Wherever sequences of intrusion of this group have been established, the more mafic phases were the first to be emplaced.

The Tertiary plutons characteristically are elongate transverse to the regional strike of the country rock and lack platy or linear flow structures. Contacts with country rocks are generally sharp and discordant, and the plutons have chilled border zones. Some plutons show evidence of passive emplacement, and the isolated stocks northeast of the batholith also show evidence of doming.

The distribution of plutonic rocks in the northern part of the batholith is shown in Figure 3. Many more K-Ar age measurements have been made in this area than are indicated on the figure; the ages shown are representative of a much larger group of data. A middle Tertiary granite pluton about 90 mi (145 km) long has locally caused argon loss that has led to younger or updated mineral ages in the adjacent plutonic rocks. The intrusive rocks in the central part of Figure 3 are thought to be Jurassic, because they are diorites and quartz diorites similar in chemical composition to Jurassic rocks on the south. The Jurassic rocks in the central part of Figure 3 are intruded on the east by early Tertiary granodiorite and quartz diorite and on the west by middle Tertiary granite. Mineral pairs of biotite and hornblende from the presumably Jurassic rocks show discordant ages, and the maximum age of 95 m.y. does not correlate with any plutonic event presently known in this part of Alaska.

The early Tertiary rocks in the north-central part of Figure 3 belong to a comagmatic sequence ranging in composition from quartz diorite to granite. The younger rocks of this sequence are the more felsic. The north-trending, two-pronged body in the western part of Figure 3 is a granite pluton. Biotite ages from the pluton range from 55 to 58 m.y. North of this pluton, there are two middle Tertiary granitic stocks, one of which was emplaced about 30 m.y. ago. This stock records the youngest plutonic event presently known in this part of the Alaska Range.

Middle Tertiary plutons form an elongate belt in the northern part of the batholith, an isolated stock in the Alaska Peninsula, and small bodies west of Mount McKinley. The northern part of the elongate middle Tertiary pluton is closely associated with volcanic rocks that are cut by the pluton. Reconnaissance mapping suggests that this part of the pluton vented explosively, erupting lava and pyroclastic rocks. This initial phase was followed by cauldron subsidence and a rise of magma through its own volcanic ejecta—i.e., this part of the pluton appears to have formed with no roof, other than a crust of its own material. Remnants of gently to moderately dipping volcanic rocks locally preserved near early Tertiary plutons suggest that these plutons may be the exposed roots of similar intrusive masses whose upper volcanic parts have been removed by erosion.

SUMMARY OF PLUTONIC EPISODES

The plutonic episodes of the Alaska-Aleutian Range batholith are diagrammed on Figure 4. This diagram shows part of the geologic time scale and the time and length of the plutonic episodes that have been recognized in the Alaska and Aleutian Ranges. A subjective representation of the areas underlain by plutonic rocks of a particular age is also shown. For example, the significance of Jurassic plutonism is shown by the curve which extends farther to the right of the time scale than that for the other plutonic events, because a larger part of the Alaska-Aleutian Range batholith is underlain by Jurassic rocks.

Jurassic plutonism began about 180 m.y. ago and continued for about 25 m.y. in this part of Alaska. No plutonic events have been identified for the interval between 84 and 155 m.y., although plutonic rocks about 110 m.y. old have been dated in the eastern Alaska Range (Richter and Jones, 1970).

Late Cretaceous plutonism began about 84 m.y. ago, and concordant biotite and hornblende ages suggest that this episode continued for about 12 m.y.

A major period of plutonic activity occurred in early Tertiary time. Differences in measured ages and rock chemistry suggest that magma was emplaced at different times.

Middle Tertiary plutonism is recorded by a minor event 25–30 m.y. ago and a major episode 34–40 m.y. ago. Age determinations on all of the rocks thought to fall in the 34–40-m.y. group have not been completed, but the available data suggest that more than one pe-

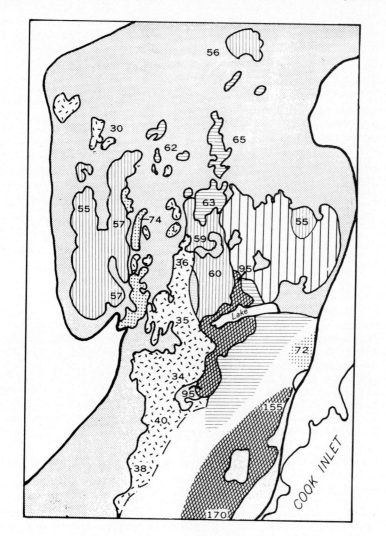

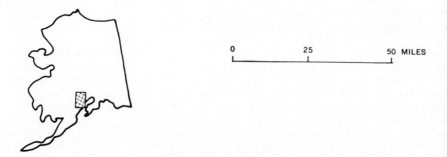

EXPLANATION

Mountain ranges

Middle Tertiary
Intrusive rocks

Lower Tertiary
Intrusive rocks

Undifferentiated
Tertiary intrusive rocks

Upper Cretaceous
Intrusive rocks

Jurassic
Intrusive rocks

35

K-Ar age

0   25   50 MILES

FIG. 3—Generalized geologic map of northern part of Alaska-Aleutian Range batholith.
K-Ar ages are in millions of years.

riod of magma generation occurred in this interval. The period of middle Tertiary plutonism correlates closely with the sedimentary hiatus and uplift recorded in the Cook Inlet basin (Kirschner and Lyon, 1970).

We believe that deformation in this part of Alaska ended by early Tertiary time and that the Tertiary plutonic rocks were emplaced at relatively shallow depths and belong in large part to a late or post-tectonic phase.

The Jurassic plutons occur largely within eugeosynclinal terranes, and it seems reasonable to postulate that the batholiths and the eugeosynclines may have had a related origin in which magma generation evolved through anatexis in geosynclinal roots. However, Jurassic plutonic rocks are confined to a rather narrow, northeast-trending, curved linear belt, whereas the associated eugeosynclinal rocks extend over a much broader region—even as far north as Mount McKinley. The remarkable linearity of the Jurassic plutonic belt may be related in some way to the convergence of two lithosphere plates involved in an arc-trench system, where magma was generated along an inclined subduction zone. Magma for Tertiary plutons was, however, generated beneath diverse geologic environments that included stable platform areas as well as regions of former eugeosynclines, in which deformation had essentially ceased.

CHEMICAL TRENDS

We previously noted (Reed and Lanphere, 1969) that plutonic rocks richest in K-feldspar

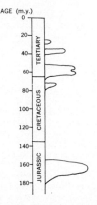

AGE (m.y.)

FIG. 4—Diagrammatic representation of plutonic episodes in Alaska-Aleutian Range batholith.

in south-central Alaska are in general of Cretaceous or Tertiary age. Additional data on the chemistry of the rocks of the Alaska-Aleutian Range batholith likewise indicate that the younger the rocks are, the richer they are in alkali constituents. On Figure 5, which is a comparison of potassium and sodium oxides with silica, rocks of each age group fall within discrete fields. Of course, the fields do overlap—e.g., the field defined by the Late Cretaceous rocks overlaps the Jurassic and early Tertiary fields, and alkali-silica trend lines for the middle Tertiary Foraker pluton (which lies west of Mount McKinley) and the small middle Tertiary stock in the Aleutian Range cross the field defined by Jurassic rocks. No doubt, as more data become available this simplistic diagram will be modi-

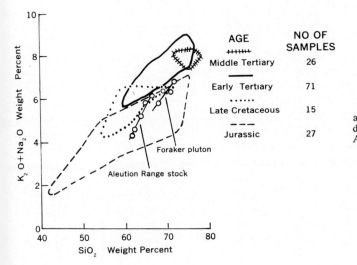

AGE	NO OF SAMPLES
┼┼┼┼┼ Middle Tertiary	26
Early Tertiary	71
･･････ Late Cretaceous	15
--- Jurassic	27

FIG. 5—K$_2$O + Na$_2$O plotted against SiO$_2$ for plutonic rocks for different age groups in Alaska and Aleutian Ranges.

fied; nonetheless, the present information indicates an age-related compositional trend for plutonic rocks in the Alaska-Aleutian Range batholith.

REFERENCES CITED

Dalrymple, G. B., and M. A. Lanphere, 1969, Potassium-argon age dating: San Francisco, California, W. H. Freeman and Co., 258 p.

Detterman, R. L., and J. K. Hartsock, 1966, Geology of the Iniskin-Tuxedni region, Alaska: U.S. Geol. Survey Prof. Paper 512, 78 p.

Grantz, A., 1966, Strike-slip faults in Alaska: U.S. Geol. Survey Open-File Rept., 82 p.

—— et al., 1963, Potassium-argon and lead-alpha ages for stratigraphically bracketed plutonic rocks in the Talkeetna Mountains, Alaska, in Geological Survey research 1963: U.S. Geol. Survey Prof. Paper 475-B, p. B56–B59.

Kirschner, L. E., and L. A. Lyon, 1970, Stratigraphic and tectonic development of Cook Inlet petroleum province (abs.): Am. Assoc. Petroleum Geologists Bull., v. 54, no. 12, p. 2490 (complete paper in this volume).

Reed, B. L., and G. D. Eberlein, 1972, Massive sulfide deposits near Shellabarger Pass, southern Alaska Range, Alaska: U.S. Geol. Survey Bull. 1342.

—— and R. L. Elliott, 1970, Reconnaissance geologic map, analyses of bedrock and stream sediment samples, and an aeromagnetic map of parts of the southern Alaska Range: U.S. Geol. Survey Open-File Rept., 145 p.

—— and M. A. Lanphere, 1969, Age and chemistry of plutonic rocks in south-central Alaska: Geol. Soc. America Bull., v. 80, p. 23–44.

Richter, D. H., and D. L. Jones, 1970, Structure and stratigraphy of eastern Alaska Range, Alaska (abs.): Am. Assoc. Petroleum Geologists Bull., v. 54, no. 12, p. 2502 (complete paper in this volume).

Comparisons in the North Atlantic Borders

Evolutionary Aspects of Precambrian of Northern Sweden[1]

PETER PADGET[2]

Stockholm, Sweden

Abstract This paper gives an account of present geologic activities in the northernmost part of Sweden and, in particular, of some newer ideas concerning the geologic evolution of the area. From more detailed geologic mapping, as well as several age determinations, the following have been established: (1) the existence of a cratonic nucleus dated at 2,700 m.y., or a little more, with a thick cover of geosynclinal strata (Karelian type); (2) two phases of orogenic activity (marked by folding and emplacement of granite, diorite, and syenite) separated by a phase of acidic volcanic activity at around 1,635 m.y. ago; and (3) post-granitic deformation marked by shearing, brecciation, and block faulting.

Introduction

The area under consideration lies mainly north of the Arctic Circle and is bounded by the Caledonides front on the west and by the state boundary with Finland on the east (Fig. 1). It forms the northern half of the county of Norrbotten, the Precambrian geology of which was described by Olof Ödman in 1957. Since the appearance of Ödman's map and description, further geologic investigations strongly supported by geophysical surveys have greatly extended our knowledge of this area. The purpose of this paper is to present some of the more interesting results of these investigations.

Historical Aspects

The area is well known internationally because of the presence of iron ores such as those at Kiruna and Malmberget and the more recently investigated deposits at Svappavaara. These iron-ore discoveries quickly attracted the attention of geologists and led to several publications, notably Geijer's (1910) description of the Kiruna ores and the geology in the vicinity, and Sundius' (1915) study of greenstones and certain alteration phenomena.

About 60 other iron-ore deposits are known from this northerly part of Sweden, and regional maps are of great value. Geijer (1931) compiled such a map for the Kiruna-Gällivare-Pajala triangle and included much valuable

[1] Manuscript received, October 18, 1971.

[2] Geological Survey of Sweden.

The Geological Survey of Sweden (Ore Investigation Department) is responsible for this work, and the author is grateful for information, much unpublished, from colleagues at this institution.

stratigraphic and petrologic data in the accompanying description. He was especially interested in deep-seated rocks and their part in the geologic history—a subject he discussed further in a recent article (1966) in Swedish. It remained for Ödman (1957) to extend these regional studies to the whole of Norrbotten, a task he completed by the mid-1950s. He postulated the existence of two major earth cycles—an older Svionian cycle and a younger Karelian cycle. In the area considered in this paper, the earlier cycle is characterized by acidic porphyries, the so-called Kiruna porphyries, and some sedimentary rocks. These rocks are intruded by granites, quartz diorites, and diorites. The later cycle comprises a variety of rocks including greenstone, quartzite, pelite, dolomite, and conglomerate intruded by granodiorite, dioritic gabbro, and monzonite in the early stage of orogenesis and by syenite and potassic granite in a later stage. These conclusions were reached by conventional geologic study unaided by age determinations. The commonly very small degree of exposure owing to water, vegetation, and moraine cover imposes severe limitations on conventional methods of geologic survey.

A completely new phase of investigation began in the early 1960s when money was voted for geologic mapping on a map-sheet basis and for aeromagnetic and radiometric surveying. Increased resources were also made available for diamond drilling and for ground geophysics. The airborne-magnetometer work has now been largely completed, and the results are being published on maps at a scale of 1:50,000. Because of the low flight altitude (30 m) and close line spacing (200 m), a very detailed picture was obtained, compensating to some extent for difficulties in geologic mapping and in making photogeologic interpretations of the terrane. Since Ödman's survey was completed, much has been learned about the distribution of rock types such as gabbro and granite, and also about folds and faults of regional significance. In addition, a few age determinations from the Geochronological Laboratory in Stockholm throw new light on the geologic history of the area.

To date, geological and geophysical maps at

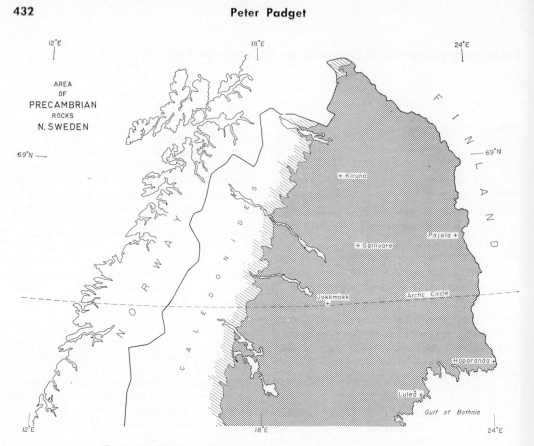

FIG. 1—Distribution of Precambrian rocks (stippled) in northern Sweden.

a scale of 1:50,000 are available only for the Kiruna, Tärendö, and Lainio sheets. Many others now in preparation will not appear for some time. For this reason, the views expressed in this paper are to be regarded as preliminary.

GEOLOGIC EVOLUTION

Seven main episodes can be distinguished in the geologic evolution of northernmost Sweden on the basis of field studies and age determinations. These are shown in Figure 2.

1. *Cratonic nucleus*—The oldest known rocks occur north of Kiruna (Fig. 3) and consist of a varied series of gneisses with a northerly trend. They apparently continue into Finland and Norway. Geologic evidence (Offerberg, 1967) shows that the gneisses occupy a low stratigraphic and structural position and form a basement for a thick sequence of layered rocks. Age determinations carried out by O. Kouvo of Finland, however, showed much older ages than expected. By use of the U-Pb

m.y.	Event	Rock type + radiom. age
7	Post-granitic deformation	Faulting, shearing, block movements
1500		
6	Granite emplacement	Lina 1540 ±90 Perthite granite 1535 ±30 Syenite 1565 ±25
1600		
5	Deformation : folding block-faulting. Some sedimentation	Vakko formation
4	Acidic volcanism	Kiruna 1605 ±65 K. Tjåurek 1635 ±90
1775		
3	Intrusion and deformation	Haparanda granite suite 1880 m.y., possibly with gabbroic differentiates
1900		
2	Major phase of deposition	Svecofennian rocks of sedimentary and volcanic character
2100 ?	Major unconformity	
1	Ancient Cratonic Nucleus 2700 m.y.	

FIG. 2—Main events in geologic evolution of northern Sweden. Partly after Welin (1970a).

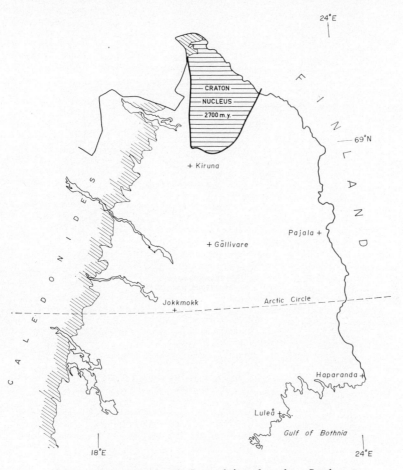

FIG. 3—Cratonic nucleus in Precambrian of northern Sweden.

method, ages of 2,700 m.y. or slightly more were obtained for zircons and sphenes in a quartz diorite (Welin, 1970b). The gneisses are thus to be regarded as a nucleus in the cratonic development of the Baltic shield. Some migmatization of this basement may have taken place later in Precambrian time, but its extent is still uncertain.

2. *Svecofennian rocks, Karelian type*—These rocks are very widespread in northern-most Sweden (Fig. 4) and have long interested geologists, partly because iron ores with a stratiform character occur at certain levels. The total section is thousands of meters thick and includes rocks of both sedimentary and volcanic origin. These rocks are geosynclinal in character and form part of the so-called Karelian zone which stretches southeastward into Finland.

An important aspect of recent mapping activity has been to determine the correct order of succession, in the absence of fossils. Accordingly, great use has been made of "way-up" structures such as crossbedding, pillow-lava morphology, and even the provenance of pebbly material in conglomerates.

The main elements of the succession in a broad zone between Kiruna and Pajala (1 in Fig. 4) are as follows:

d. Sedimentary-volcanic formations, still inadequately known and commonly gneissic;

c. Nonvolcanic rocks, mainly sandstone, shale, and conglomerate, locally uncon-formable on b;

b. Volcanic rocks, mainly greenstones of basic to semibasic composition with in-

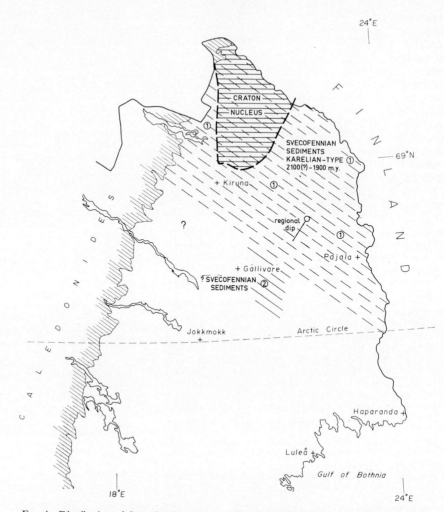

F<small>IG</small>. 4—Distribution of Svecofennian rocks of Karelian type (area 1) in northern Sweden. Younger beds are on south (area 2).

terbedded pelitic and graphitic units; upper part is iron-ore bearing;

a. Basal sandstones.

These rocks are commonly metamorphosed and their continuity is broken by granitic bodies and by faults.

Fuller details of the stratigraphy and correlations from area to area are contained in separate map-sheet descriptions (Offerberg, 1967; Padget, 1970; Witschard, 1970).

Because of the regional southerly dip, it seems likely that beds even younger than those listed should occur in this direction. If this is so, the metasedimentary rocks of the Gällivare area (2 in Fig. 4) can be taken as examples.

These rocks consist of a variegated sequence of pelites, psammites tending toward graywacke and arkose, and calc-silicate rocks. Description of them is in progress in connection with investigations on the Gällivare map-sheet area.

All the above rocks are thought by Welin (1970a) to have been deposited in the time interval from 2,100(?) to 1,900 m.y. ago. Rather similar rocks are reported from Finland and Norway.

3. *Intrusion and deformation*—A major contribution made by Ödman (1957) was the recognition of a suite of older intrusive rocks, which he called the "Haparanda Granite Series." Besides plagioclase granites, this suite includes many diorites, quartz diorites, and possibly

gabbros interpreted as early differentiates of the same magma. All were intruded into the Sveco-fennian rocks. Recent age determinations using the Rb-Sr method (Welin *et al.*, 1970) on selected rocks of this intrusive suite, including material from the type locality near Hapar-anda, gave an age of 1,880 m.y. for the time of emplacement. This time of intrusive activity is considered to represent the time of a major or-ogenic-type deformation which affected north-ern Sweden, particularly its eastern half (Fig. 5), and which is characterized also by folding and faulting of the Svecofennian strata. An interesting feature is that the more acidic members of the series are confined to the eastern-most part of the area and their western bound-ary, at least in the north, is quite sharp.

Of further significance is the fact that a quartz diorite belonging to the Haparanda Granite Series cuts and intrudes folded layers

of skarn iron ore in the Svecofennian sequence (Frietsch, 1967a). The origin of the iron ore and even of the skarn was therefore prior to 1,880 m.y. ago.

4. *Acidic volcanic phase*—Kiruna has long been famous for its porphyries, two of the main types of which occur in close proximity to the iron-ore body. They also occupy wide areas to the south and have been correlated with other major areas of porphyries such as those near Arvidsjaur. Common types are quartz por-phyry, syenite porphyry, and a dark andesitic syenite porphyry (Offerberg, 1967. The main distribution of rocks of this phase is fairly well defined (Fig. 6); the boundary on the east and north is abrupt. Two smaller areas of porphy-ritic rocks occur east of this boundary and could represent local centers of volcanic acitivity. The Kiruna map-sheet shows the porphyritic rocks to lie unconformably on the Svecofen-

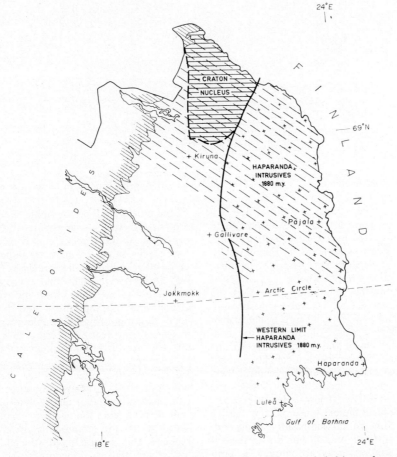

Fig. 5—Distribution of members of Haparanda Granite Series; gabbros excluded in northern Sweden.

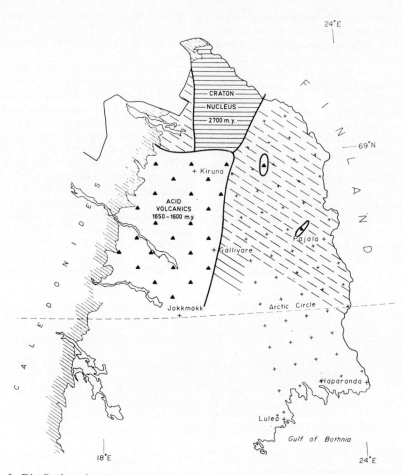

FIG. 6—Distribution of rocks of acidic volcanism phase (triangular pattern) in northern Sweden.

nian Karelian-type rocks. Therefore, the Kiruna rocks are younger than the Svecofennian rocks—as suggested by Geijer (1910, 1931)—rather than older, as believed by Ödman. This relation is further supported by Rb-Sr determinations carried out in Stockholm on samples of porphyry from the mine area (1,605 ± 65 m.y.) and from Kaska Tjåurek to west-southwest of Kiruna (1,635 ± 90 m.y.). These ages seem surprisingly young in view of the conformable relations of the rocks of the Kiruna sheet, but the Kiruna rocks are roughly comparable with the Dala porphyries of central Sweden (1,670 m.y.), according to Welin and Lundqvist (1970). These determinations, therefore, indicate the existence of an extensive north-south zone of predominantly acidic volcanism, the northern end of which is in the Kiruna area. Similar rocks are absent in both Norway and Finland.

Much field and petrographic work remains to be done before a true picture of the mode of formation of these rocks can be obtained. At some places, however, there are indications that the porphyries can be interpreted as tuffs.

5. *Deformation*—This phase was responsible for folding of the acidic volcanic rocks of the Kiruna and Vittangi areas and possibly for block faulting of considerable magnitude. A marked linear feature passing in a north to northeasterly direction through Gällivare (Fig. 7) was possibly activated during this period, and one possible effect was the formation of fault-controlled grabens subsequently filled with clastic material of quartzofeldspathic character derived from the nearby volcanic terrane. These strata are commonly of considerable thickness and are preserved at scattered localities, where they lie unconformably on other rocks. They are collectively referred to as the

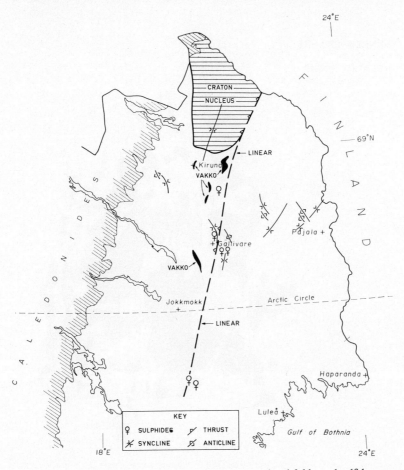

Fig. 7—Linear structure in relation to cratonic nucleus, some regional folds, and sulfide occurrences. Compare Figure 6.

Vakko Formation.

The lineament is also of interest from other points of view. It seems effectively to limit the cratonic nucleus on the east. It is also a line of overfolding and/or overthrusting with the sense of movement to the east. Sulfide ore is known to occur in several places on or near this feature. The feature is clearly evident on satellite photographs (H. Paarma, Finland, private commun.).

6. *Granite emplacement*—Granites and related rocks, distinctly potassic in composition but otherwise with a normal chemistry, are widespread in northern Sweden. At the present level of erosion, they occupy 50 percent or more of the total area (Fig. 8) and show both migmatitic and discordant relations to older rocks and structures. They are considered to

have been emplaced in the late or waning stages of a major orogeny. One of the commonest types is called the "Lina granite," which consists of reddish microcline, creamy white plagioclase, quartz, and a little biotite. It is normally coarse grained and crumbles readily on weathering. Pegmatites and aplites are commonly associated with it, particularly in marginal areas. Other types of granite with more syenitic compositions also belong to this phase.

Age determinations using the Rb-Sr method gave the following results: Lina granite (Lina is type locality), 1,540 ± 90 m.y.; perthite granite (Masugnsbyn), 1,535 ± 30 m.y.; and syenite (Sjaunja), 1,565 ± 25 m.y. These intrusions, therefore, evidently postdated other geologic events—a conclusion which is in good agreement with field observations.

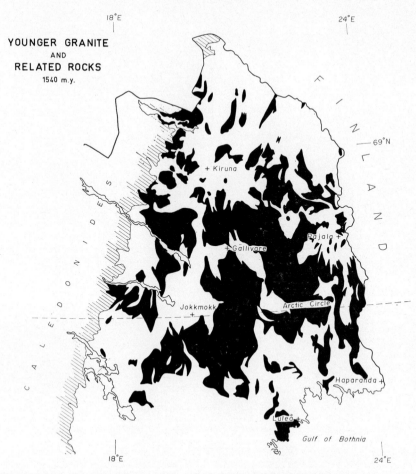

FIG. 8—Distribution of younger granites, mainly of potassic composition, in northern Sweden.

In his most recent papers, Welin (1970a, b) has indicated that some potassic granites yield older ages. The reason is not yet known, but perhaps more caution is required in referring all potassic granites to this phase, especially where contact relations cannot be checked.

7. *Post-granitic deformation*—By approximately 1,500 m.y. ago, relatively stable conditions had been achieved in this part of the Baltic shield. It is, however, becoming increasingly apparent that the late granites (phase 6) are commonly tectonized (Witschard, 1970; Padget, 1970). This tectonism may be apparent as breccia zones, micro-shearing with the development of sericite, slickensides on steeply dipping surfaces, or block faulting that resulted in segmentation of the crust.

These effects are not found everywhere but are sufficiently common to suggest that at least one phase of post-granitic deformation affected northern Sweden in Precambrian time. This possibility has not previously been given much attention in the geologic literature and still requires analysis over a greater area to determine whether the later deformation was epeirogenic or orogenic (*i.e.,* involving vestigeosynclinal development, or deformation in vestigial geosynclines) in origin. The operation of more than one phase is also possible.

CONCLUSIONS

The preceding exposé gives merely an outline of the main features of the geologic history as understood at present. Extended field studies coupled with an appropriate number of radiometric age determinations should clarify the sequence of events further. Already, the vast amount of new stratigraphic and tectonic information has caused a shift of interest from petrology and mineralogy—the traditional Swedish approach to Precambrian geology. In due course, a return to these aspects will be necessary in order to understand better the genesis of the Haparanda Granite Series, the Lina granite, and the Kiruna porphyries.

Little has been said in a systematic way about the origin of iron ores. Their present classification, however, into volcanic-sedimentary, metasomatic, and magmatic types (Frietsch, 1967b; 1970, p. 130) reflects the complicated history of their environment. Many have distinct stratiform character but are mineralogically and chemically modified by later metasomatic and metamorphic processes. Descriptions of individual bodies, utilizing a wealth of new drillhole and analytical data, are now in print (e.g., Frietsch, 1966; Lundberg, 1967), as are certain comparative studies (trace elements in ore minerals [Frietsch, 1970]). Further publications of this type are in preparation.

REFERENCES CITED

Frietsch, R., 1966, Berggrund och malmer i Svappavaar-afältet, norra Sverige (Geology and ores of the Svappavaara area, northern Sweden): Sveriges Geol. Undersökning, Årsb. 59, no. 4, ser. C, no. 604, 282 p.
—— 1967a, On the relative age of the skarn iron ores and the Haparanda granite series in the country of Norrbotten, northern Sweden: Geol. Fören. Stockholm Förh., v. 89, pt. 1, no. 528, p. 116–118.
—— 1967b, The relationship between magnetite and hematite in the iron ores of the Kiruna type and some other iron ore types: Sveriges Geol. Undersökning, Årsb. 61, no. 10, ser. C, no. 625, 28 p.
—— 1970, Trace elements in magnetite and hematite mainly from northern Sweden: Sveriges Geol. Undersökning Årsb., v. 64, no. 3, ser. C, no. 646, 136 p.

Geijer, P., 1910, Igneous rocks and iron-ores of Kiirunavaara, Luossavaara and Tuollavaara: Scientific and Practical Researches in Lappland.
—— 1931, Berggrunden inom malmtrakten Kiruna-Gällivare-Pajala: Sveriges Geol. Undersökning Årsb., ser. C, no. 366.
—— 1966, Cykeltänkandet och granitproblemen: Geol. Fören. Stockholm Förh., v. 87, pt. 4, no. 523, p. 455–583.
Lundberg, B., 1967, The Stora Sahavaara iron ore deposit, Kaunisvaara, northern Sweden: Sveriges Geol. Undersökning, Årsb. 61, no. 5, ser. C, no. 620, 37 p.
Ödman, O. H., 1957, Beskrivning till berggrundskarta över urberget i Norrbottens län (Description to map of the Precambrian rocks of the Norrbotten county): Sveriges Geol. Undersökning Årsb., ser. Ca, no. 41, 151 p.
Offerberg, J., 1967, Beskrivning till berggrundskart-bladen Kiruna NV, NO, SV, SO: Sveriges Geol. Undersökning Årsb., ser. Af 1–4.
Padget, P., 1970, Beskrivning till berggrundskartbladen Tärendö NV, NO, SV, SO (Description of the geologic map sheets Tärendö NW, NE, SW, SE): Sveriges Geol. Undersökning Årsb., ser. Af, no. 5–8, 95 p.
Sundius, N., 1915, Beiträge zur Geologie der Südlichen teils des Kirunagebiets: Vetens. Praktische Under-sogelse i Lappland, Geologie des Kirunagebiets 4.
Welin, E., 1970a, Den svecofenniska orogena zonen i norra Sverige; en preliminär diskussion (The Svecofennian orogenic zone, a preliminary discussion): Geol. Fören. Stockholm Förh., v. 92, pt. 4, no. 543, p. 433–451.
—— 1970b, Rb-Sr radiometric ages of extrusive and intrusive rocks in northern Sweden: Sveriges Geol. Undersökning Årsb., ser. C.
—— and T. Lundqvist, 1970, New Rb-Sr age data for the sub-Jotnian volcanics (Dala porphyries) in the Los-Hamra region, central Sweden: Geol. Fören. Stockholm Förh., v. 92, pt. 1, no. 540, p. 35–39.
—— K. Christiansson, and Ö. Nilsson, 1970, Rb-Sr age dating of intrusive rocks of the Haparanda suite: Geol. Fören. Stockholm Förh., v. 92, pt. 4, no. 543, p. 336–346.
Witschard, F., 1970, Description of the geological maps Lainio NV, NO, SV, SO: Sveriges Geol. Undersökning Årsb., ser. Af, no. 9–12, 116 p.

Caledonian Geology of Scoresby Sund Region, Central East Greenland[1]

NIELS HENRIKSEN[2]

Copenhagen, Denmark

Abstract The Geological Survey of Greenland has completed the first 3 years of a 5-year mapping campaign in the Scoresby Sund region, which includes the southernmost part of the Caledonian fold belt of East Greenland.

The preliminary results show that it is possible to distinguish the following main geologic units in the Caledonian fold belt: (1) a Precambrian crystalline basement with a cover of Precambrian metasedimentary and metavolcanic rocks; these rocks have been affected to varied degrees by Caledonian folding; (2) a metamorphosed but nonmigmatized supracrustal complex composed of psammitic and pelitic rocks containing scattered bands of calcareous rocks and totaling several kilometers in thickness; these rocks represent Caledonian geosynclinal deposits of miogeosynclinal aspect and are probably of very late Precambrian age; (3) a Caledonian infracrustal complex of mainly gneisses, migmatites, and synkinematic granites; this unit was formed by migmatization of Caledonian geosynclinal deposits; and (4) late to post-Caledonian intrusions mainly of granitic type.

Westward-directed thrust sheets with a displacement of several tens of kilometers are present along the western rim of the fold belt. They comprise largely Caledonian supracrustal rocks, but locally basement rocks are also incorporated in the thrust sheets. The central part of the north-south-directed fold belt is characterized by infracrustal rocks with simple low-dipping macroscopic structures; in some parts of the area these structures can be shown to be the limbs of major recumbent folds.

The Caledonian supracrustal rocks in the western part of the region were metamorphosed under high-pressure conditions and are characterized by kyanite-bearing rocks. In contrast, the rocks of the central migmatitic part of the region were formed under low-pressure conditions and are characterized by cordierite-bearing assemblages.

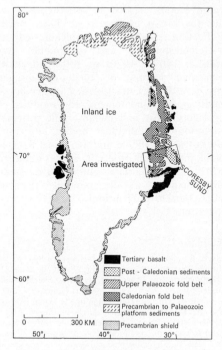

Fig. 1—Sketch map showing location of Scoresby Sund region.

Introduction

The Geological Survey of Greenland (GGU) in 1968 began a 5-year systematic mapping program in the Scoresby Sund region of East Greenland between 70° and 72°N lat. (Fig. 1). The region includes the southernmost exposed part of the East Greenland Caledonian fold belt, which on the south dips beneath a cover of Tertiary plateau basalts. Three summer field seasons in the region have been completed, and more than three fifths of the region has been mapped. The remaining areas comprise Liverpool Land and the southwestern part of the region, but parts of both of these areas have previously been described by members of "The Danish expeditions to East Greenland, 1926–58" or have been visited by prospectors from "Nordisk Mineselskab." It is therefore possible to present a preliminary description of the region, but modifications of the views expressed are to be expected in the coming years because work is still in progress.

The work of the Survey has been carried out as a team project in which 15 geologists have so far participated in the mapping of the crystalline complex. Each of these geologists is currently working on his material, and several detailed descriptions of areas will be published in the near future.

The Caledonian fold belt can be followed northward from the Scoresby Sund region for more than 1,100 km (Haller, 1970, p. 29, 67).

[1] Manuscript received, October 18, 1971.

[2] Geological Survey of Greenland. The writer thanks K. Ellitsgaard-Rasmussen, Director of the Geological Survey of Greenland, for permission to publish this paper. Appreciation is expressed to my colleagues in the Geological Survey for many ideas which are incorporated in this paper.

Nonmetamorphosed units deposited in the Caledonian geosyncline are present north of 72°N lat. and total more than 16,000 m in thickness. The Precambrian Eleonore Bay Group, which forms the lower part of this succession, comprises more than 8,000 m of argillaceous and arenaceous beds, 2,000 m of quartzose rocks, and 2,000 m of calcareous and dolomitic beds with argillaceous intercalations in the lower part. Eocambrian psammites with tillitic beds are succeeded by 3,000 m of Cambro-Ordovician calcareous sedimentary rocks which are the youngest deposits in the East Greenland geosyncline.

North of 72°N lat. the Caledonian geosynclinal strata can be traced continuously from a marginal position toward the inner part of the fold belt, where they have been transformed to supracrustal schists and gneisses. These rocks can be traced along their strike, although with interruptions, into the Krummedal supracrustal sequence south of 72°N lat. (Fig. 2). This latter sequence of schists and gneisses has lithologic similarities with the lower part of the Eleonore Bay Group. Except for a small isolated occurrence in the extreme northeast, nonmetamorphosed Caledonian strata do not occur in the Scoresby Sund region, and fossil remnants have not been found. The general chronologic interpretation of the Scoresby Sund region is therefore based largely on the validity of the indirect correlation of the Krummedal supracrustal sequence with rocks of the Eleonore Bay Group.

Previous and Present Investigations

Edvard Bay (1895, p. 145–176) presented the first description and a geologic sketch map of the crystalline rocks in the inner part of the Scoresby Sund region. In the early 1930s, H. Backlund, E. H. Kranck, Th. G. Sahlstein, and E. Wenk visited the region as members of "The Danish expeditions to East Greenland, 1926–58," led by Lauge Koch. The description of Liverpool Land by Kranck (1935) is the most significant work of this period.

Although the work of Lauge Koch's expeditions was concentrated farther north, some investigations were made during the 1950s in the northwestern part of the Scoresby Sund region (Vogt, 1965; Zweifel, 1959) and in the Gåseland area (Wenk, 1961). Wenk established the existence of pre-Caledonian basement rocks in a window in the southwesternmost part of the Caledonian fold belt.

The primary results of GGU's systematic mapping in the inner fjord zone and in the nunatak area north of 70°30′N lat. have been summarized by Henriksen and Higgins (1969, 1970, in prep.). These reports include acknowledgments of the work of all geologists who have participated in this GGU mapping project. More detailed accounts are available concerning the geology of southeastern Renland (Chadwick, 1971), the geology of the Bjørneøer (Kalsbeek, 1969), and the metamorphic relations of the Charcot Land area (Steck, in press). Radiometric age determinations from the region have been given by Hansen and Steiger (in prep.), Haller and Kulp (1962), and Larsen (1969).

Nordisk Mineselskab (The Northern Mining Company) has been prospecting in the Scoresby Sund region during the past 4 years and has prepared geologic sketch maps of certain hitherto unmapped areas. The results of unpublished investigations from the Fønfjord and Gåsefjord areas have kindly been made available to the author by E. Hintsteiner, of Nordisk Mineselskab, whose cooperation is gratefully acknowledged.

Central and Western Part of Fold Belt: Inner Fjord Zone and Nunatak Area

Three separate units of infracrustal rocks, all of supposedly pre-Caledonian age, occur in this part of the region. One unit is exposed in the autochthonous basement window in Gåseland which was not reworked during Caledonian diastrophism. The two others are the basement beneath the Charcot Land supracrustal sequence and the amphibolite gneisses which form the basement to the Krummedal supracrustal sequence; both were reworked together with their cover.

Thrust boundaries separate two distinct supracrustal sequences—the Charcot Land supracrustal sequence, which has equivalents in Gåseland, and the Krummedal supracrustal sequence; it has not been possible to demonstrate directly their age relations to each other. The Charcot Land sequence is, however, thought to have been laid down prior to the initial sedimentation in the Caledonian geosyncline. Traced northward, the Charcot Land supracrustal sequence with its reworked basement gradually grades into an infracrustal marble-amphibolite-gneiss series. The Krummedal supracrustal rocks occur in a belt along the inner part of the fjord zone and are traced eastward into the Caledonian migmatite zone of the central Scoresby Sund region. This zone of migma-

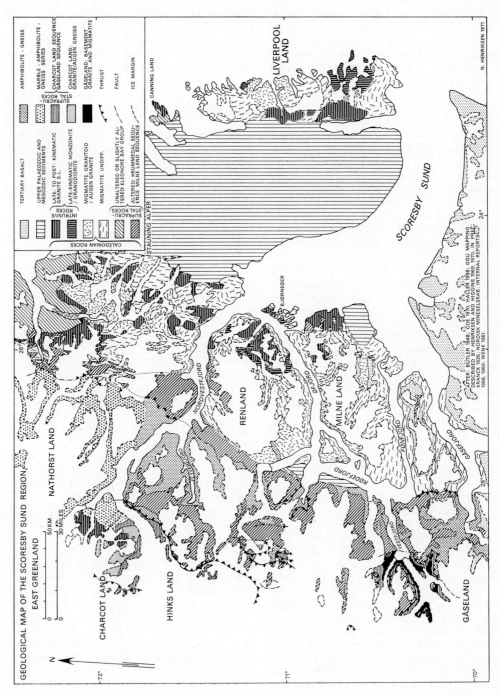

Fig. 2—Geologic map of Scoresby Sund region.

tites forms the locus of late- and post-kinematic plutonic activity.

Rocks of Pre-Caledonian Origin
Infracrustal Rocks

The three following units have been distinguished.

1. The autochthonous basement rocks described from Gåseland by Wenk (1961, p. 17–22) form a composite unit comprising amphibolitic banded migmatites and homogeneous microcline augen gneisses; these rocks are cut by discordant amphibolitic dikes, some of them garnet-andesine bearing. The supracrustal rocks lying unconformably in contact with these basement rocks are chlorite-sericite-bearing rocks; it can therefore be assumed that their deposition postdated the metamorphism of the discordant amphibolitic dikes. The basement complex was thus influenced by two plutonic episodes prior to the deposition of the first supracrustal units. Radiometric age determinations of these basement rocks indicate an age of at least 2,300 m.y. (Haller and Kulp, 1962, p. 63).

2. Infracrustal rocks underlie the Charcot Land supracrustal rocks and are conformably deformed with their cover. No unconformity between them has been recorded. In eastern Charcot Land the infracrustal rocks comprise homogeneous foliated augen gneisses, but toward the northwest they grade into gneisses with extensive amphibolite layers. Discordant amphibolitic dikes have not been recorded.

These infracrustal rocks probably represent the former basement to the Charcot Land supracrustal sequence.

3. The migmatitic amphibolite gneisses found beneath the Krummedal supracrustal sequence comprise mainly gray granodioritic biotite and hornblende gneisses containing abundant conformable bands and lenses of amphibolitic and ultramafic rocks. Scattered bands of mica schists and marbles also occur. This complex is dissected by swarms of folded discordant amphibolite dikes. This relation indicates that the host rocks were deformed and migmatized prior to intrusion of the dikes, and also that a further period of deformation and metamorphism occurred after the dikes were formed. The latest deformation of the basement took place when the Krummedal rocks and their infracrustal basement were involved in the Caledonian orogeny. The amphibolite gneisses have thus undergone at least two episodes of deformation and plutonism, though

the degree of deformation by Caledonian events is varied; the least deformed rocks are found around inner Nordvestfjord and Flyverfjord, where the basement is informally referred to as the "Flyverfjord infracrustal complex."

From Flyverfjord the infracrustal rocks can be traced southward into a discontinuous series of outcrops. In many places they are intricately folded with the Krummedal rocks; the earlier sets of basement structures have been heavily overprinted by Caledonian structures, and the discordant nature of the amphibolite dikes is in most places no longer demonstrable.

The age relations of the three units of supposed basement are uncertain because the different units are separated by Caledonian thrusts, but it is possible that all the units were once parts of a single extensive Precambrian infracrustal complex.

Charcot Land Supracrustal Sequence

A sequence of low-grade metamorphic supracrustal rocks—mainly greenschists, siliceous marbles, and pelitic rocks—can be traced discontinuously along the rim of the Inland Ice. In nearly all places they occur structurally below Caledonian thrust masses. The general lithologic character of the sequence makes it likely that they should be regarded as a single unit, as Wenk (1961, p. 35) suggested.

Steck (in press) has described a 2,000-m-thick sequence of metamorphosed limestones, siliceous dolomites, semipelites, quartzitic rocks, and associated mafic volcanic rocks and gabbroic sheets in the Charcot Land area that crop out beneath a major Caledonian thrust. There are pronounced lateral lithologic variations. In the north the sequence includes metamorphosed carbonate rocks, mafic volcanic rocks, and argillaceous beds in roughly equal proportions; whereas, in southern Charcot Land, metavolcanic rocks are dominant over metapelites, and several metagabbro intrusions are present. Relic contact metamorphic aureoles around some of the intrusions suggest that they were emplaced at a high crustal level before the sequence was exposed to a regional metamorphism of Barrovian type.

In the Gåseland area, Wenk (1961, p. 22–36) described a parautochthonous sequence of metasedimentary rocks lying with angular unconformity on the basement. At the base of the sedimentary sequence is a very locally distributed psephitic series up to 50 m thick which has been interpreted as tillite. Next is a 250-m-thick "marble-chlorite-phyllite series" and a further 1,000-m sequence of sericite phyllites grading upward into garnet-biotite phyllites. A flat-lying thrust separates the latter rocks from a succession of Caledonian kyanite-bearing mica schists. Wenk considered all these sedimentary units to be part of the same succession.

The supracrustal rocks in most of the nunatak area are of low metamorphic grade, but they become progressively more metamorphosed in the central and northern parts of the Charcot Land area. Steck (in press) reported a gradual northward increase in grade from stilpnomelane-bearing assemblages to kyanite-bearing assemblages over a distance of 30 km. Associated with the increase in grade is an increase in deformation affecting the supracrustal rocks and the underlying basement. The degree of deformation and metamorphism north of Nordvestfjord is such that distinction between basement and cover is no longer clear. In this area the rocks have been grouped together under the informal name of the "marble-amphibolite-gneiss series."

Marble-Amphibolite-Gneiss Series

The series comprises well-banded paragneisses, marbles, amphibolites, and minor quartzites interbanded conformably with homogeneous and veined gneisses. The amphibolites and quartzites may be several hundred meters thick; the marbles are generally thinner. The homogeneous and veined gneisses in places contain numerous thin amphibolitic layers; characteristically, they are plastically folded.

Locally discordant amphibolite dikes cut the gneisses. Such dikes have not been noted, however, in the Charcot Land supracrustal or basement rocks, but it is possible that other elements of basement have been welded and incorporated in the marble-amphibolite-gneiss series.

Age of Charcot Land Supracrustal Sequence

In western Charcot Land the supracrustal rocks are veined by a homogeneous medium-grained biotite granite. A small tillite unit lies unconformably on the granite and contains numerous boulders of the granite and of most rock types in the low-grade metamorphic part of the Charcot Land sequence (Steck, in press). The presence in the tillite of boulders of both supracrustal rocks and the granite which veins them shows that the original supracrustal sequence was consolidated and subjected to plutonism prior to accumulation of the tillite.

The isolated occurrence of the tillite makes determination of its age difficult. It is, however, most likely that it corresponds to the Eocambrian tillites best known in the central fjord zone north of the Scoresby Sund region about 180 km east-northeast of Charcot Land (Fränkl, 1953b, p. 25–29; Katz, 1954). If this correlation is correct, then the Charcot Land supracrustal sequence must be of Precambrian age.

Rocks of Caledonian Origin
Krummedal Supracrustal Sequence

The Krummedal sequence is found in the nunatak zone and in the innermost fjord zone and generally comprises rusty-brown schists and paragneisses. Much of the outcrop is not migmatized, but in places in the west there are migmatitic areas, and toward the east the rocks gradually become intensely migmatized. The sequence was recrystallized mainly under conditions of the Barrovian-type kyanite zone, but lower grades are evident locally and sillimanite assemblages occur in the eastern outcrops.

The lowest part of the Krummedal sequence lies directly on the "Flyverfjord infracrustal complex" in Hinks Land; the two disconformable units were deformed together. It is considered that the relation between infracrustal basement and supracrustal cover is of an "autochthonous" character, although no primary unconformity can now be distinguished. The sequence thus would represent the lowermost part of the Caledonian geosynclinal succession, which has not hitherto been identified with certainty in East Greenland.

In Hinks Land the base of the Krummedal sequence is represented by a series of leucocratic, siliceous paragneisses with quartzitic bands. Metabasaltic sills and scattered discordant sheets are characteristic. The thickness of this lowest part of the sequence is considerably varied. Maximum thickness is 1,000 m, but 100-m thicknesses are common and in places this part of the sequence is absent. The next unit in the sequence is a marble-amphibolite unit, which is succeeded by several thousand meters of rusty-red-weathered interbanded quartzites and mica schists, which pass upward into more massive garnet-kyanite mica schists. In some areas an uppermost, more siliceous sequence of quartzites and siliceous gneisses is distinguished.

West of Rødefjord, amphibolitic bands are found in places in the mica schists and biotite gneisses, and lenses of pyroxenite occur locally.

Farther south in Gåseland, mica schists and amphibolite are associated in the sequence. In the northeastern exposures of the Krummedal sequence, massive mica schists, scattered calcareous bands, and homogeneous banded quartzose gneisses and quartzites are distinguished.

There is clear evidence of considerable vertical and lateral variation in the Krummedal succession, but details of the variations are obscured by general pronounced deformation and, in some parts of the area, by migmatization.

A well-preserved but isolated sequence of supracrustal rocks in eastern Milne Land (Milne Land sequence) comprises alternations of mappable quartzite and mica schist units and a 150-m-thick marble. Although it is probably part of the Krummedal sequence, it is separated from the nearest comparable exposures by a wide zone of Caledonian migmatites and post-kinematic intrusions.

Synkinematic Plutonic Rocks

A wide north-south trending zone of migmatites occurs in the central part of the Scoresby Sund region; there is a gradual transition westward into the Krummedal supracrustal rocks.

Investigations of the migmatites of the Bjørneøer (Kalsbeek, 1969) and especially in southeastern Renland (Chadwick, 1971) have led to distinction of an early synkinematic phase and a late phase of migmatization. The two phases can be distinguished clearly only in the region around the entrance to Øfjord, where there has been an intervening development of intermediate intrusive rocks.

Synkinematic migmatites—The western and southern parts of the migmatite zone appear to be of synkinematic development. Typically, they comprise a banded sequence of rusty-brown-weathering rocks of which the paleosome is made up of garnet-biotite gneisses, siliceous biotite gneisses, and considerable amounts of quartzitic rocks. In the southern part of the zone, some amphibolitic rocks also occur. The neosome generally comprises leucocratic, fine- to medium-grained, garnet-biotite granites. Sillimanite is abundant in much of the migmatite zone.

Although paleosome components found in the northern part of the migmatite zone correspond closely to rock types found in the metasedimentary part of the Krummedal sequence, the presence of amphibolitic material in the southern part of the zone may be an indication

of the presence of reworked pre-Caledonian rocks.

In many places migmatization has been so intense that the neosome components dominate and the general banded structure is lost. Migmatites of this type commonly show plastic folds, and the paleosome inclusions in these rocks are commonly lensoid, largely digested, and rotated.

A zone of marble bands occurring in the eastern part of the migmatite zone can be traced for more than 100 km (Fig. 4). It is highly probable that these marbles are the southern continuation of the zone of calcareous rocks in the lower Eleonore Bay Group, which crops out in a nonmigmatized state directly northeast of the migmatite zone at 72°N lat. (Haller, 1958, p. 27).

Augen granites—In the area between central Nordvestfjord and northwestern Milne Land, sheets and other bodies of homogeneous garnet-biotite augen granites occur conformably within the synkinematic migmatites. The largest sheets are more than 1,000 m thick, and the most persistant bodies can be traced over several tens of kilometers.

Although generally conformable, the augen granites can be seen in detail to cut the structures in the migmatites: the granites evidently were emplaced as intrusive bodies, although they are now well foliated and have a gneissic structure. The foliation sweeps around the augen, which may be flattened and elongated.

The intrusion of the augen granites, their deformation into major recumbent folds, the formation of synkinematic migmatites, and regional metamorphism under conditions of the sillimanite zone—all are considered to be a related sequence of orogenic events.

Leucocratic garnet granites and coarse-grained homogeneous garnet-biotite granites, the latter type in independent bodies commonly of very large size, appear to be related to the augen granites.

Late- to Post-Kinematic Plutonic Rocks

Intermediate intrusive rocks—A monzonite body up to 500 m thick has been mapped in eastern Renland (Chadwick, 1971). The sheet forms a large saucer-shaped structure bordering an area of later migmatization and granite emplacement in the interior of the structure. The intermediate sheet, which is younger than the augen granites, was first emplaced after the phase of recumbent folding which deformed augen granites and migmatites. In addition to the main intrusion, there are several smaller, ir-regular-shaped, mafic intrusive bodies in the same region.

Chadwick has shown that the intermediate rocks have a charnockitic affinity. The main in-trusion has a paragenetic sequence: zoned pla-gioclase, orthoclase, orthopyroxene, clinopy-roxene, and biotite. The texture is without pre-ferred orientation. The boundary zones of the main sheet and the smaller irregular intrusions were influenced by late-stage migmatization during which the charnockitic assemblages be-came retrograded under amphibolite-facies conditions.

Toward the north, monzonitic rocks of the main sheet grade gradually into granodioritic rock types, which are lithologically identical to some isolated granite (s.l.) bodies mapped on the coast of Nordvestfjord and on the Bjør-neøer. In the Bjørneøer, Kalsbeek (1969) has described these rocks as "gray granite" and has shown them to be surrounded by a zone of in-tense migmatization. The timing of the late phase of migmatization, or alternatively the intrusive phase, appears to vary from area to area.

Late-stage migmatization and associated in-trusive granites—Within the late-orogenic sau-cer-shaped structure on eastern Renland, the rocks have been greatly influenced by a late phase of migmatization postdating the interme-diate intrusions. The migmatites are of a com-posite nature, containing traces of both the early-synkinematic phase of migmatization and of the late-kinematic phase. In the eastern part of Milne Land, two phases of migmatization also occurred, but the lack of intermediate in-trusions there makes it difficult to distinguish between them.

The late migmatitic phase was accompanied by the intrusion of numerous sheets of foliated biotite granite at a high level in eastern Ren-land. Chadwick (1971) termed these rocks "gray-pink granites." Among these granites, ho-mogeneous massive types are similar to some of the homogeneous intrusions known from the Stauning Alper area. The granitic sheets on eastern Renland range in thickness from 50 to 500 m. Similar sheets occur also in northeast-ern Milne Land.

Post-kinematic granites, s.l.—Clearly intru-sive post-kinematic granitic bodies occur in the Stauning Alper, in the northeastern part of Milne Land, and in Charcot Land.

The intrusions in the Stauning Alper are the most varied, comprising a range of rock types

and intrusive forms. Thin sheets and small bod-ies occur in abundance, and the largest bodies measure as much as 20 km across. These in-trusions correspond to the younger generation of granites of Haller (1958).

The Stauning Alper intrusions include fine-grained muscovite-biotite granites—the youngest type—and porphyritic biotite granites —the commonest rock type in the larger bod-ies. The central zones of some large intrusions are composed of hornblende syenite. The small intrusions are formed mainly of homogeneous biotite granites or granodiorites.

The summits of northeastern Milne Land are capped by intrusive granite sheets, and an intrusive complex is found along the coast south of Bjørneøer. The intrusive complex in-cludes a sequence of medium-grained grano-diorites, coarse-grained quartz syenites, and leucocratic granites. Some of these intrusions form outcrops 8 km by 15 km in area.

A post-kinematic granite 10 by 25 km in area crops out in central Charcot Land. The boundary zone is a several-kilometers-wide complex network of numerous pegmatites tran-secting the amphibolites and banded gneisses of the country rocks. Muscovite granite, com-monly coarse-grained or pegmatitic, is the prin-cipal rock type.

Structures

Both pre-Caledonian and Caledonian fold structures have been recognized in the Scoresby Sund region. Parts of the region, however, are incompletely mapped and many details of the structural history remain to be clarified.

In the Flyverfjord infracrustal complex, at least two phases of deformation predate the Caledonian reactivation. The most significant of these old phases is represented by major recumbent structures whose limb lengths ex-ceed 5 km. Caledonian structures are superim-posed on the basement structures to a varying degree.

In the Krummedal supracrustal cover rocks, tight to isoclinal folds of an early Caledonian phase can be distinguished from open folds with vertical axial planes that represent a later phase. The later of these Caledonian phases has had the greatest influence on the basement, and structures with amplitudes of several kilometers are apparent.

West of Rødefjord in the southwestern part of the region, the Caledonian deformation has been generally more intense, and pre-Caledo-nian structures in the basement are almost completely obliterated. The Caledonian folds comprise early macroscopic recumbent folds and later open to tight folds, both with east-west-trending axes; a third phase is represented by north-south-trending open folds with vertical axial planes.

The structures seen in the Charcot Land sequence in the northwestern part of the region represent an early phase which produced east-west- to northwest-southeast-trending folds and a later phase which produced open north-south folds. The Caledonian thrust separating these Charcot Land supracrustal rocks from rocks of the Krummedal sequence appears to cut obliquely through the structures on both sides. Therefore, it cannot be assumed that the folding in the two supracrustal sequences is of the same age.

In the marble-amphibolite-gneiss series northeast of Charcot Land, east-west-trending recumbent folds comparable in trend to those in the Charcot Land supracrustal rocks are present. Farther north in the "Migmatitkomplex Gletscherland" (Haller, 1955, p. 95–111), east-west-trending structures are also conspicuous. Between Charcot Land and Gletscherland, east-west structures are predominant, whereas the surrounding areas are characterized by north-south-trending folds. A possible hypothesis is that these east-west structures are a pre-Caledonian phase characterizing a pre-Caledonian block partly reworked in the Caledonian fold belt.

In the Caledonian migmatite zone, fold structures are observed in Renland and on Milne Land, but are uncommon in the area north of Nordvestfjord. Recumbent folds with limb lengths of up to 5 km and generally with east-west axes are the principal structures in places influenced by apparently synchronous superimposed folding (Chadwick, 1971). A later phase that produced commonly north-south-trending, large-scale, open to tight folds with vertical axial planes is recorded in the central part of the migmatite zone and also north of Nordvestfjord.

The western part of the Scoresby Sund region is characterized by low-angle thrusts separating units of very different lithologies and metamorphic grades. These thrusts, of late Caledonian age, were modified by later north-south-trending normal faults. In Gåseland, Wenk (1961) estimated the thrust displacement toward the west to be at least 20 km; in the Charcot Land area the displacement in the same direction is estimated at more than 40 km.

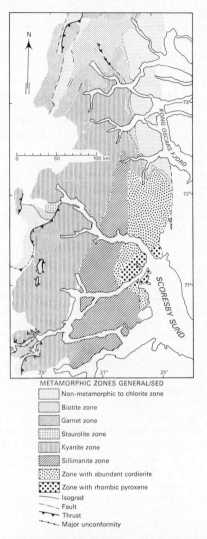

METAMORPHIC ZONES GENERALISED

☐ Non-metamorphic to chlorite zone

☐ Biotite zone

☐ Garnet zone

☐ Staurolite zone

☐ Kyanite zone

☐ Sillimanite zone

☐ Zone with abundant cordierite

☐ Zone with rhombic pyroxene

— Isograd

—··— Fault

⊤⊤⊤ Thrust

⋏⋏⋏ Major unconformity

FIG. 3—Metamorphic sketch map of Caledonian fold belt, central East Greenland. Compiled from publications by H. G. Backlund, B. Chadwick, S. Eha, E. Fränkl, J. Haller, N. Henriksen and A. K. Higgins, W. Huber, F. Kalsbeek, H. R. Katz, M. M. L. Parkinson and W. F. Whittard, M. Sommer, A Steck, E. Wenk, J. D. H. Wiseman, J. M. Wordie and W. F. Whittard, H. Zweifel, and others (see reference list). Metamorphic zones are not mapped as such, but are deduced by extrapolation of scattered observations.

Metamorphism

A map showing the general metamorphic features between 70° and 74°N lat. has been compiled from all the various descriptions of the region (Fig. 3). The material available is far from complete, and considerable interpretation has been necessary. The general picture which emerges shows a marked correlation between metamorphic zones and distribution of rock types.

In the region north of 72°N lat. the fold belt is symmetric about a central metamorphic complex characterized by the presence of kyanite (sillimanite not reported). The metamorphic zonation around this central metamorphic complex is unrelated to the fold structures in the supracrustal rocks (Wenk and Haller, 1953, p. 27; Fränkl, 1953a, p. 144–149).

The metamorphic zonation in the Scoresby Sund region, in contrast, is parallel with the general north-northeast trend of the fold belt, except in the Charcot Land area, where the isogrades trend approximately east-west in the zone below the late Caledonian thrust (Steck, in press).

Kyanite is present in a zone traceable from the central metamorphic complex in the north to Gåseland in the south. In the Scoresby Sund region it is characteristic of the Krummedal supracrustal rocks and the amphibolite gneisses. East of the kyanite zone is a sillimanite zone almost exclusively confined to the zone of extensive migmatization and granitization. It is thought that this metamorphic pattern developed during the main phase of deformation and migmatization.

Cordierite, in addition to sillimanite and garnet, commonly is found in the eastern part of the migmatite zone in the Scoresby Sund region. The distribution of the cordierite may be related to late-kinematic migmatization and granite emplacement.

In an area around easternmost Renland, minerals indicative of a relic hornblende-granulite-facies metamorphism have been preserved locally, especially in the intermediate intrusions (Kalsbeek, 1969; Chadwick, 1971). Both authors suggest that granulite-facies conditions occurred in this area shortly after the intrusion of the intermediate rocks, and that later retrogression took place with the subsequent migmatization.

Andalusite has been recorded from the northern part of the Stauning Alper, and also from the Bjørneøer (Oberlies, 1970, p. 38–42). Its occurrence is not a feature of contact metamorphism and may reflect a low-pressure stage in connection with the late plutonic activity in the region.

The east-west trends of the metamorphic isograds in the Charcot Land area (Steck, in press) do not fit well with the general Caledonian picture, although Steck considers the metamorphism to be of Caledonian age. The isograds parallel the fold axes in the region, which may be pre-Caledonian as was postulated herein, and, although this parallelism may be coincidental, it raises the possibility of a pre-Caledonian age for the metamorphism.

The following preliminary model for the Caledonian metamorphic evolution in the inner part of the Scoresby Sund region is suggested. A primary sillimanite- and kyanite-grade metamorphism took place simultaneously with the main phases of folding and main phase of migmatization. In the extreme east, granulite-facies conditions followed the intrusion of intermediate rocks. Late-stage migmatization and granite formation then took place under lower pressure conditions and were accompanied by cordierite and andalusite formation. This change from high- to low-pressure conditions may have taken place together with late-stage uplift of the fold belt.

EASTERN PART OF FOLD BELT: LIVERPOOL LAND

Kranck (1935) and Sahlstein (1935a, b) described the rocks of the southern and eastern parts of Liverpool Land, and these publications are still the primary source of information from this area. However, detailed mapping of Liverpool Land was begun by GGU in 1969 (Henriksen and Higgins, 1970, p. 5, 14–15) and is to be completed during 1971.

The larger part of Liverpool Land comprises migmatitic gneisses of which several units can be distinguished. Especially interesting are eclogitic garnet-pyroxene gneisses found in the southwestern corner of the area. Discordant basic dikes with an eclogitic affinity have been noted by Kranck in other gneiss units, and he considered the special mineral assemblages to have developed by metamorphic effects.

In northeastern Liverpool Land, conspicuous marble bands have been noted in association with rusty-weathering paragneiss bands. It is likely that they are the metamorphosed representatives of the Eleonore Bay Group, found unmetamorphosed on the peninsula north of Liverpool Land (Bütler, 1948, p. 21–33).

Late-synkinematic granodioritic intrusions and related slightly younger bodies of migmatitic granites cover extensive areas in southern Liverpool Land. The youngest plutonic rocks belong to the Hurry Inlet granite suite and make up post-kinematic high-level intrusions of mainly granitic rocks (Coe, 1970). An age determination on one of the granites is 435 m.y. (Hansen and Steiger, in prep.).

Kranck (1935) suggested there were traces of two "phases of orogenic activity" in the migmatitic gneisses of southern Liverpool Land. During the second the granodioritic and migmatitic granite bodies were thought to have developed and the gneisses to have been refolded and metamorphosed. The second phase was thought to be of Caledonian origin. However, it was also suggested that the "basal gneisses" might, at least in part, be of pre-Caledonian origin.

Age Determinations

An extensive age-determination program using a variety of methods on different rocks from the region is in progress. The first results from these investigations have been obtained by Hansen and Steiger (in prep.). Previous age determinations from the region were given by Haller and Kulp (1962) and by Larsen (1969).

Autochthonous basement rocks from Gåseland have yielded a K-Ar biotite age of 1,890 m.y. and an Rb-Sr microcline age of 2,290 m.y.[*] The most likely interpretation is that both of these are minimum ages of the last metamorphic event prior to the deposition of the overlying supracrustal rocks.

Two Rb-Sr ages on a discordant amphibolitic dike in reactivated basement in the "Flyverfjord infracrustal complex" indicate an age of 492 m.y.,[**] either corresponding to the age of the metamorphism of these dikes or representing a mixed age.

Schists and gneisses from the Krummedal supracrustal sequence have yielded K-Ar ages on mica of 406 m.y., 616 m.y., and 426 m.y.[†] The 616-m.y. age may indicate that "Caledonian" activity in the fold belt began very early.

Rocks from late-kinematic intrusions at the mouth of Øfjord yielded a K-Ar biotite age of 435 m.y.[†] and an Rb-Sr biotite age of 428 m.y.[**]

A homogeneous intrusive granite from the Stauning Alper has yielded an Rb-Sr biotite age of 481 m.y.,[**] and the post-kinematic Hurry

Inlet granite from Liverpool Land yielded an Rb-Sr biotite age of 435 m.y.[**]

The youngest event so far determined is the intrusion of a swarm of late pegmatites in the "Flyverfjord infracrustal complex." These pegmatites have yielded an Rb-Sr age on both biotite and K-feldspar of 395 m.y.[**]

From the Stauning Alper, several rather old ages have been obtained,[**] but their interpretation is presently very uncertain.

Regional Correlation

Figure 4 is a map showing a provisional correlation for the region between 70° and 74°N lat. The interpretation is not in agreement with previous views that the main part of the central metamorphic complex was formed from migmatized equivalents of the Eleonore Bay Group (Haller and Kulp, 1962, p. 21). The new interpretation is a consequence of extrapolation of the results of the mapping of the Scoresby Sund region, where basement gneisses older than the Caledonian supracrustal rocks have been identified. The probably pre-Caledonian Charcot Land supracrustal rocks and the marble-amphibolite-gneiss series have lithological and structural similarities with the "Migmatitkomplex Gletscherland" (Haller, 1955, p. 85), which has been provisionally reinterpreted as pre-Caledonian. Wegmann (1935, p. 39) reached a similar conclusion in referring to the deviating strike direction of the "Sylva-Maria group" as inherited from a pre-Caledonian basement. The occurrence of folded discordant dikes in the "Migmatitkomplex Gletscherland" (Haller, 1958, p. 106–110) and of vast amounts of amphibolite gneiss in the "Migmatitdecke Hagar" (Haller, 1955, p. 111–134) also suggests that highly reactivated basement rocks may be present. Such rocks are typical of the pre-Caledonian "Flyverfjord infracrustal complex," for example, but are virtually unknown in the migmatized rocks assumed to be equivalents of the Eleonore Bay Group.

The Krummedal supracrustal schists and gneisses do not contain any direct indication of their age, and it is not possible to make a detailed lithologic correlation between them and rocks of the Eleonore Bay Group. The main lithologic character of the Krummedal rocks is, however, generally comparable to the arenaceous and argillaceous rocks of the lower and middle part of the Eleonore Bay Group. The two areas of supracrustal rocks are separated by an area of Caledonian migmatites.

---

[*] Determination by Haller and Kulp (1962).
[**] Determination by Hansen and Steiger (in prep).
[†] Determination by Larsen (1969).

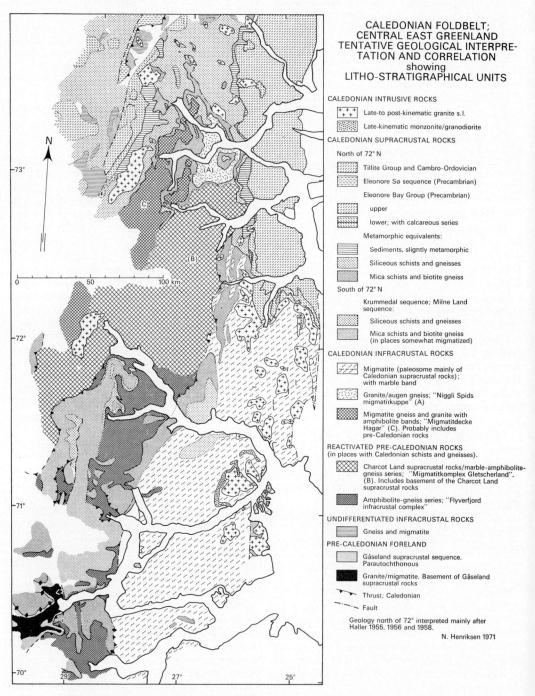

Fig. 4—Map showing tentative geologic interpretation and correlation of Caledonian fold belt in central East Greenland.

CONCLUSION

At the halfway stage of a systematic mapping program covering the southernmost part of the Caledonian fold belt in East Greenland, it has been possible to draw some preliminary conclusions concerning the general features of this part of the fold belt.

The Scoresby Sund region incorporates a 300-km-long cross section through the Caledonian fold belt of East Greenland. The westernmost part of the region comprises foreland rocks in autochthonous to parautochthonous position. They occur as tectonic windows below westward-directed late Caledonian thrust masses; the displacements on the thrusts are of the order of several tens of kilometers.

The pre-Caledonian foreland comprises an infracrustal migmatite complex with metamorphosed discordant basic dikes. The age of the infracrustal rocks is more than 2,300 m.y. The pre-Caledonian Charcot Land supracrustal sequence, at least 2,000 m thick, lies unconformably on basement rocks of the foreland. The supracrustal rocks comprise a greatly varied sequence of metasedimentary and metavolcanic rocks of eugeosynclinal aspect. Progressive metamorphism in the northernmost part of the region has transformed these supracrustal rocks and their basement into an infracrustal unit termed the "marble-amphibolite-gneiss series."

In the inner part of the fjord zone in the Scoresby Sund region, intensely deformed supracrustal schists and gneisses—the Krummedal supracrustal sequence—lie conformably on a reworked infracrustal migmatitic basement. These supracrustal rocks are the lowest deposits of the Caledonian geosyncline and comprise arenaceous and argillaceous rocks with very scattered volcanic intercalations. In general the sequence is of miogeosynclinal aspect. Both vertical and lateral lithologic variations have been recorded. The total thickness of the sequence is several thousand meters. The reworked basement below the Krummedal sequence probably corresponds in age to the infracrustal basement of the foreland and is probably also older than 2,300 m.y.

The Krummedal supracrustal rocks and their basement are both deformed by mesoscopic to macroscopic, recumbent, early isoclinal folds and later open to tight folds. Superimposed on these is a series of open north-south folds with vertical to steeply dipping axial planes. Kyanite is a widespread metamorphic mineral in these rocks.

A north-south-trending migmatite complex is present in the central part of the Caledonian fold belt in the Scoresby Sund region. The migmatites comprise a paleosome, almost exclusively derived from Krummedal-sequence rocks, and a granitic neosome. The neosome appears to be composed of anatectic components as well as introduced material and commonly dominates the paleosome completely. Thick sheets of synkinematic augen granites were intruded into the migmatites, probably as comformable, flat-lying sheets introduced at a low level of the crust. The migmatite complex is deformed by major isoclinal recumbent folds, generally with east-west-trending axes, and by open folds with vertical axial planes. The most widespread metamorphic mineral is sillimanite.

Late-kinematic intermediate intrusions, associated with the local development of granulite-facies conditions, separated the older synkinematic migmatites from a renewed phase of migmatization and injection of vast masses of granitic (s.l.) rocks in the easternmost part of the migmatite zone. These late granite intrusions include late-kinematic and post-kinematic types. Cordierite is ubiquitous in the zone of late- and post-kinematic migmatization and granite emplacement, and probably is indicative of low-pressure conditions during formation.

Liverpool Land, in the easternmost part of the region, is an infracrustal part of the Caledonian fold belt comprising migmatitic gneisses and orogenic plutonic rocks. The gneisses may contain relics of pre-Caledonian basement rocks, but this has not yet been demonstrated.

The existence of Caledonian infracrustal complexes both east and west of the extensive upper Paleozoic and Mesozoic sedimentary basin in the eastern part of the Scoresby Sund region demonstrates the intramontane character of this basin. Caledonian folded rocks are to be expected also offshore in the shelf region east of Scoresby Sund. Southward the fold belt disappears below the Tertiary basalts.

SELECTED REFERENCES

Backlund, H. G., 1930, Contributions to the geology of Northeast Greenland: Medd. om Grønland, v. 74, no. 11, p. 207–296.

Bay, E., 1895, Geologi, in C. Ryder, Den østgrønlandske ekspedition 1891–92 under ledelse af C. Ryder: Medd. om Grønland, v. 19, p. 145–176.

Bütler, H., 1948, Notes on the geological map of Canning Land (East Greenland): Medd. om Grønland, v. 133, no. 2, 97 p.

Chadwick, B., 1971, Preliminary account of the geology

of southeast Renland, Scoresby Sund, East Greenland: Grønlands Geol. Undersøgelse Rap. 34.

Coe, K., 1970, Faulting in the western part of Liverpool Land, East Greenland: Bull. Geol. Soc. Denmark, v. 20, no. 3, p. 260–264.

Eha, S., 1953, The pre-Devonian sediments on Ymers Ø, Suess Land, and Ella Ø (East Greenland) and their tectonics: Medd. om Grønland, v. 111, no. 2, 105 p.

Fränkl, E., 1951, Die untere Eleonore Bay Formation im Alpefjord: Medd. om Grønland, v. 151, no. 6, 15 p.

—— 1953a, Geologische untersuchungen in Ost-Andrées Land (NE-Grønland): Medd. om Grønland, v. 113, no. 4, 160 p.

—— 1953b, Die geologische karte von Nord-Scoresby Land (NE-Grønland): Medd. om Grønland, v. 113, no. 6, 56 p.

Frisch, W., and I. Thum, 1969, Über die Gebiete Vestfjord, westlicher Føhnfjord, Rødefjord, Rypefjord: Nordisk Mineselskab, Montangeologischer Bericht, Nordmine 1968, unpub. rept.

Haller, J. 1953, Geologie und petrographie von West-Andrées Land und Ost Frænkels Land (NE-Grönland): Medd. om Grønland, v. 113, no. 5, 196 p.

—— 1955, Die geologische karte von Suess Land, Gletscherland und Goodenoughs Land, pt. 1 of Der "Zentrale Metamorphe Komplex" von NE-Grönland: Medd. om Grønland, v. 73, no. 3, 174 p.

—— 1956, Geologie der nunatakker region von Zentral-Ostgrönland zwischen 72°30′ und 74°10′N.Br.: Medd. om Grønland, v. 154, no. 1, 172 p.

—— 1958, Die geologische karte der Staunings Alper und des Forsblads Fjordes, pt. 2 of Der "Zentrale Metamorphe Komplex" von NE-Grönland: Medd. om Grønland, v. 154, no. 3, 153 p.

—— 1970, Tectonic map of East Greenland (1: 500,000), in An account of tectonism, plutonism, and volcanism in East Greenland: Medd. om Grønland, v. 171, no. 5, 286 p.

—— and J. L. Kulp, 1962, Absolute age determinations in East Greenland: Medd. om Grønland, v. 171, no. 1, 77 p.

Hansen, B. T., and R. H. Steiger, in prep., The geochronology of the Scoresby Sund area: Grønlands Geol. Undersøgelse Rap. 37 (published 1971).

Henriksen, N., and A. K. Higgins, 1969, Preliminary results of mapping in the crystalline complex around Nordvestfjord, Scoresby Sund, East Greenland: Grønlands Geol. Undersøgelse Rap. 21, p. 5–20.

—— and —— 1970, Preliminary results of mapping in the crystalline complex of Renland, the southern Stauning Alper and southwest Liverpool Land, Scoresby Sund, East Greenland: Grønlands Geol. Undersøgelse Rap. 30, p. 5–17.

—— and —— in prep., Preliminary results of mapping in the crystalline complex around Rypefjord and Rødefjord, and on northern Milne Land, Scoresby Sund, East Greenland: Grønlands Geol. Undersøgelse Rap. 37 (published 1971).

Huber, W., 1950, Geologisch-petrographische untersuchungen in der innern fjordregion des Kejser Franz Josephs fjordsystems in Nordostgrönland: Medd. om Grønland, v. 151, no. 3, 83 p.

Kalsbeek, F., 1969, Preliminary report on the geology of Bjørneøer, Scoresby Sund: Grønlands Geol. Undersøgelse Rap. 26, 33 p.

Katz, H. R., 1952a, Zur geologie von Strindbergs Land (NE-Grönland): Medd. om Grønland, v. 111, no. 1, 150 p.

—— 1952b, Ein querschnitt durch die nunatakzone Ostgrönlands (ca. 74° n.B.): Medd om Grønland, v. 144, no. 8, 65 p.

—— 1954, Einige bemerkungen zur lithologie und stratigraphie der tillitprofile im gebiet des Kejser Franz Josephs Fjord: Medd. om Grønland, v. 72, no. 4, 63 p.

Kranck, E. H., 1935, On the crystalline complex of Liverpool Land: Medd. om Grønland, v. 95, no. 7, 122 p.

Larsen, O., 1969, K-Ar determinations: Grønlands Geol. Undersøgelse Rap. 19, p. 62–67.

Oberlies, F., 1970, Beziehungen zwischen migmatit und granit auf SW-Bjørne Ø I, Scoresby Sund, E. Grønland: Diplomarbeit, ETH, Zürich, unpub. manuscript.

Parkinson, M. M. L., and W. F. Whittard, 1931, The geological work of the Cambridge expedition to East Greenland in 1929: Geol. Soc. London Quart. Jour., v. 87, no. 20, p. 650–674.

Polegeg, S., and J. Koch, 1970, Prospektion im südlichen und östlichen Gaaseland sowie im westlichen Tiel der Danmark Ø: Nordisk Mineselskab, Montangeologischer Bericht, Nordmine 1969, unpub. rept.

Sahlstein, Th. G., 1935a, Petrographie der eklogitenschlüsse in den gneisen des südwestlichen Liverpool-Landes in Ost-Grönland: Medd. om Grønland, v. 95, no. 5, 43 p.

—— 1935b, Zur regelung der gesteine im kristallin von Liverpool-Land in Ostgrönland: Medd. om Grønland, v. 95, no. 6, 27 p.

Sommer, M., 1957, Geologie von Lyells Land (NE-Grönland): Medd. om Grønland, v. 155, no. 2, 157 p.

Steck, A., in press, Kaledonische metamorphose der Praekambrischen Charcot Land serie, Scoresby Sund, Ost-Grönland: Grønlands Geol. Undersøgelse Bull. 97 (published 1971).

Vogt, P., 1965, Zur geologie von Südwest-Hinks Land (Ostgrönland 71°30′N): Medd. om Grønland, v. 154, no. 5, 24 p.

Wegmann, C. E., 1935, Preliminary report on the Caledonian orogeny in Christian X's Land (North-East Greenland): Medd. om Grønland, v. 103, no. 3, 59 p.

Wenk, E., 1956, Alpines und Ostgrönlandisch—Kaledonisches kristallin, ein tectonisch-petrogenetischer vergleich.—Ostgrönlandisches Kaledon: Verh. Naturforsch Gesel Basel, v. 67, p. 95–99.

—— 1961, On the crystalline basement and the basal part of the Precambrian Eleonore Bay Group in the southwestern part of Scoresby Sund: Medd. om Grønland, v. 168, no. 1, 54 p.

—— and J. Haller, 1953, Geological explorations in the Petermann region, western part of Frænkels Land, East Greenland: Medd. om Grønland, v. 111, no. 3, 48 p.

Wiseman, J. D. H., 1932, A contribution to the petrology of the metamorphic rocks of East Greenland: Geol. Soc. London Quart. Jour., v. 88, no. 11, p. 312–349.

Wordie, J. M., and W. F. Whittard, 1930, A contribution to the geology of the country between Petermann Peak and Kjerulf Fjord, East Greenland: Geol. Mag., v. 67, no. 4, p. 145–158.

Zweifel, H., 1959, Geologie und petrographie von Nathorsts Land (NE-Grönland): Medd. om Grønland, v. 160, no. 3, 94 p.

Caledonian Geology of Arctic Norway[1]

RODNEY A. GAYER[2]

Cathays Park, Cardill, United Kingdom

Abstract Caledonian rocks form a north-south-trending orogenic belt along the western edge of Arctic Scandinavia and an east-west-trending belt in northernmost Norway. The change in direction of the belt separates two distinct regions of Caledonian geology.

Structurally, the two regions are similar. Both consist of a geosynclinal sequence broken into three distinct tectonic units, thrust easterly in the southern region and southeasterly in the northern region, over the autochthonous cover of the Archean Fennoscandian shield. The lower two units contain sequences similar to that of the autochthon; the sediments of the middle unit are mildly metamorphosed and overlie imbricated slices of basement. The upper unit contains highly metamorphosed geosynclinal sequences. In the south, this unit has been imbricated into a series of nappes. The eastern leading edges (in Sweden) are disjunctive on a brittle basement, whereas in the west (Norway) the trailing edges were drawn out when the rocks were hot and semiplastic; thus they thin progressively in a conjunctive, pseudo-autochthonous sequence deformed together with the "caledonized" basement.

Polyphase deformation and metamorphism is evident throughout the belt. The nappe folds and the initiation of thrusting developed during the first phase. Large quantities of differentiated mafic and ultramafic material, related to a geophysically detected zone of upthrust mantle rocks, were intruded along the western seaboard during the interval of maximum metamorphism between the first and second phases of deformation. The main transport of the nappes occurred during the second phase and was accompanied by intense flattening. The third and following phases deformed the thrust surfaces.

Historically, the two areas are distinct. Upper Precambrian to Lower Ordovician rocks form the autochthonous cover and the two lower tectonic units of both areas, although the northern rocks are much thicker (4,000–5,000 m and possibly 14,500 m). The geosynclinal sequences of the upper unit are composed of Ordovician to Silurian rocks containing thick volcanic sections in the south, but are composed of upper Precambrian to Upper Cambrian rocks in the north. The main period of metamorphism and the development of nappe folds occurred during the latest Silurian (396 ± 48 m.y.) in the south but during the latest Cambrian (530 ± 35 m.y.) in the north. The diachronous nature of the orogenic phases is interpreted as a migration along the continental margin of the point of collision of the lithospheric plate with the subduction zone.

INTRODUCTION

The Caledonian rocks of Arctic Scandinavia constitute the northward extension of the Ta-

[1] Manuscript received, October 18, 1971.

[2] Department of Geology, University College. The field work involved with the correlation of the Caledonides of Finnmark and north Troms was financed by a British Government Natural Environment Research Council grant.

conic-Caledonian fold belt, in a pre–continental-drift situation, from the eastern seaboard of North America through Britain into Scandinavia (e.g., see Wynne-Edwards and Hasan, 1970). The British-Scandinavian part of this belt was considered for many years to be formed from a single large geosyncline deformed essentially during one great orogeny of Late Silurian to Devonian age (see Bailey and Holtedahl, 1938). It now seems most likely that the sediments accumulated in several distinct geosynclinal troughs which were deformed individually at different times. A supposed evolution of the Appalachian-Caledonian orogen as far north as central Scandinavia has been outlined by Dewey (1969)

This review summarizes the stratigraphy and structure of the Caledonian orogen in northern Scandinavia, emphasizing the distinct evolution of the northernmost part of the belt. Unfortunately, no complete synthesis can yet be produced for the entire region, as the area linking the distinctive northern area of Finnmark and Troms with the south has not been mapped in detail. Much of the information used in this account has been published during the last decade; a complete bibliography of the earlier, largely reconnaissance work can be found in several of the references cited.

Geographically, the "axial" zone of the Caledonian belt lies along the western coast of Norway and includes extensive outcrops of "caledonized" basement rocks deformed together with an essentially concordant metasedimentary cover. The nappe fold structures of this "axial" area are developed eastward into disjunctive autochthonous thrust units; the thrust front crops out in northwest Sweden in the southern part of the belt and strikes north-northeast through a small extension of Finland into northernmost Norway, where the strike swings to east-northeast.

Four distinct tectonic zones can be recognized within the belt. In the east and southeast a marginal zone consists of an unmetamorphosed, autochthonous, late Precambrian to Ordovician sedimentary sequence lying on an Archean basement that forms part of the Fennoscandian shield. This basement, with or without

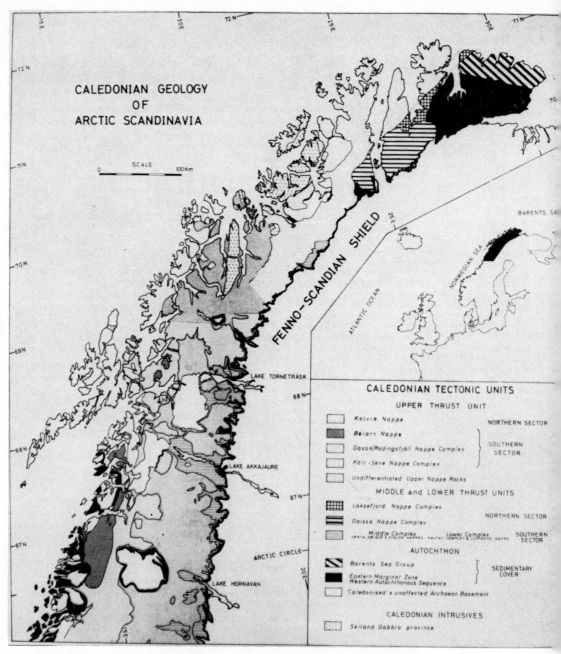

FIG. 1—Tectonic map of Caledonides of Arctic Scandinavia.

its autochthonous cover, reappears westward within the main fold belt, both as windows of unaltered Precambrian rock and, farther west, as eroded fold cores in "caledonized" basement. Three thrust units overlie the autochthonous zone. The lowermost unit appears to be the least displaced and to contain a sequence similar to that of the autochthon. The middle unit likewise has sequences similar to those of the autochthon, though they are mildly metamorphosed, and commonly contains imbricated slices of Archean basement in the lower portion. The individual thrust nappes of the lower two units occupy relatively narrow zones above and west of the eastern margin and cannot be traced for any great distance laterally. The uppermost tectonic unit consists of several distinct nappes, each containing characteristic metasedimentary sequences. The outcrop of these upper nappes is extensive; together with their westward counterparts, they occupy most of the area of the Caledonian orogenic belt.

STRATIGRAPHY

Although there are similarities between the sedimentary sequences developed in the tectonic units of the northern and southern sectors, the overall pattern of the two areas is basically different.

Southern Area

The autochthon—The eastern margin of the southern sector of the Caledonian orogen lies almost entirely within Sweden, crossing through Finland into Norway in the north.

The basement of this eastern margin is unaffected by Caledonian movements and consists largely of various Svecofennian and Karelian formations together with late Karelian intrusives (Geijer, 1963), forming the western edge of the Fennoscandian shield. Outcrops of similar basement rocks also occur within the Caledonian belt on the west as windows developed by the erosion of culminations of anticlines formed after thrusting. The two major windows of this category, both of which straddle the Norwegian-Swedish frontier, are the Rombak window (Reitan, 1960) in the north, and the Nasafjåll window in the south. Farther west in the Norwegian fjord area of the southern sector, numerous inliers of granite gneiss basement occur in the cores of both early and late folds; they are progressively more "caledonized" westward. The main examples are the Tysfjord and Rishaugfjell massifs (Nicholson and Rutland, 1969), the "caledonized" granite gneisses of the Heggmovatn antiform (Nicholson and Rutland, 1969), and the "caledonized" basement gneisses of the Glomfjord area (Rutland and Nicholson, 1965).

The autochthonous sedimentary cover of the eastern margin described by Kulling (1955, 1960, 1964) is relatively thin—up to 200 m in the north and only a few tens of meters in the south. At the base of the succession is the Eocambrian Sito Tillite Formation; it is overlain by arkosic sandstones of the Laisberg Formation, which in turn is overlain by inter-bedded shales and quartz sandstones of the Dividal Group (formerly *Hyolithes* Zone), which ranges in age from Eocambrian to latest Early Cambrian. Kulling (1964) regarded the Laisberg Formation as the lowest unit of the Dividal Group. South of the Arctic Circle in the south of the Våsterbotten Mountains, the succession is completed by thin sequences of the rest of the Cambrian and the Lower and Middle Ordovician. The entire succession is unmetamorphosed except for cataclasis directly beneath the overlying thrust units.

To the west, a relict Dividal Group sequence lies on the non-"caledonized" basement windows. Generally, only the Eocambrian part of the succession is preserved and is slightly metamorphosed (Kulling, 1960).

Around the "caledonized" basement inliers of the "axial" zone in the west, a series of thin metasedimentary sequences, the lowest portion closely associated with the basement gneisses, has been described by Nicholson and Rutland (1969). These sequences appear to be conformable with one another and with the basement and appear to retain their original stratigraphic arrangement. A typical example is that found around the basement gneisses of the Heggmovatn antiform (Nicholson and Rutland, 1969). The succession starts with schistose, feldspathic metasedimentary rocks of the lower Vågen Group, similar to the so-called "sparagmitic" metasedimentary rocks around other basement inliers in Nordland. The overlying upper Vågen Group and Saura Marble Group consist of a wide variety of abruptly alternating shelf-facies metasedimentary rocks. The calcareous quartzo-feldspathic schists of the Bodö Schist Group are thought to overlie this sequence. Eastward, individual units of the western autochthonous cover thicken and become perceptibly disjunctive, developing into the nappes of the upper thrust unit. Their present autochthonous nature must therefore remain in doubt. The lower Vågen Group is exceptional because it does not thicken eastward, and it may be the lateral equivalent of the Laisberg Sandstone Formation of the eastern margin autochthon.

Lower thrust unit—This unit occupies a narrow and discontinuous belt between the autochthon and the middle thrust unit on the west. In the south the unit consists of the Blaik nappe overlying the Fölinge nappe south of the Arctic Circle; in the north, around Lake Tornetrask, the Rautas nappe complex overlies the Luopakte nappe. The individual nappes generally consist of a lower imbricated portion containing cataclastically altered basement granites and syenites overlain by an almost unmetamorphosed sedimentary unit. In both the north and the south, the sedimentary sequences of the lowermost nappes are comparable with the sequence in the eastern autochthon; the Luopakte nappe consists of quartzites, phyllites, and lenses of limestone, forming the equivalent of the Laisberg Sandstone Formation and the Dividal Group of the autochthon. The limestones have a fauna denoting a latest Early Cambrian age (Kulling, 1964). The Blaik nappe has a fuller sequence than the lowermost nappes; it includes metasedimentary rocks of the lowest-greenschist facies. At the base of the succession are feldspar-rich shales, sandstones, and conglomerates of late Precambrian age overlain by the Långmarkberg Tillite Formation. This Eocambrian glacial zone, containing two separated tillites, is overlain by quartzites with subordinate slates and siltstones of the Ström Quartzite Formation. The various thrust units of the Rautas nappe complex in the northern Norrbotten Mountains contain a quartzite-slate sequence overlying imbricated basement; that sequence is very similar to the Ström Quartzite Formation farther south.

Middle thrust unit—Two main nappes are associated with the middle thrust unit; both contain metasedimentary rocks of the greenschist facies. In the south the Stalon nappe contains a late Precambrian feldspathic sandstone and conglomerate sequence overlain in the upper part of the nappe by a tillite and quartzite unit presumed to be the equivalent of the Långmarkberg Tillite and Ström Quartzite Formations of the lower thrust unit. The Abisco nappe in the north consists largely of cataclastically altered basement syenites and granites overlain by tectonically banded schistose psammites (the "Hårdskiffer" of the Swedish literature). In places the basement slice occupies extensive areas, as in the Akkajaure-Tysfjord culmination, where the boundary between the thrust basement of the Abisco nappe and the autochthonous basement to the west in the Tysfjord region is far from clear. Kulling (1964), for example, regards the basement rocks as autochthonous west of the Norwegian-Swedish boundary, whereas Nicholson and Rutland (1969), on the basis of similarity with adjacent, undisputed, autochthonous basement windows, place the allochthonous-autochthonous junction east of the International Boundary.

Upper thrust unit—Three main nappe complexes have been recognized in this unit, which is the largest of the four tectonic units. From east to west they are: the Seve-Köli nappe complex; the Gasak-Rödingsfjäll nappe complex, and the Beiarn nappe. Individual nappes within these complexes have been traced continuously across the area in only a few places.

The regional stratigraphy within each complex and correlation between complexes are extremely complicated, partly because of the tectonic complexity and high metamorphic grade of the rocks and partly because of insufficient detailed mapping. Nicholson and Rutland (1969) have attempted to construct a profile across the entire unit from the Norwegian coast at approximately 67°N lat. to the eastern edge north of Lake Akkajaure. This has been the only major attempt to correlate the stratigraphy of the different nappes. Zachrisson (1969) has suggested a correlation within the extensive outcrop of the Köli section of the lowest nappe complex in the Våsterbotten Mountains. Unfortunately, Zachrisson made no comment on Kulling's (1964) comparison between the Köli rocks of this area and those north of Lake Akkajaure. In Table 1 the stratigraphy of the various nappe complexes is outlined, and suggested comparisons are indicated.

The lowest of the three nappe complexes of the upper thrust unit—the Seve-Köli complex —is divided into a lower Seve unit, containing high-grade metamorphic rocks, and an upper Köli unit, containing lower grade metamorphic phyllites, schists, *etc.* In many places, a thrust can be recognized separating the two units, and several thrust nappes occur within the Köli unit. The Seve nappe contains a great variety of metamorphosed igneous rocks and high-grade gneisses and schists which, according to Asklund (1960), petrographically resemble the Archean rocks of southern and western Sweden and southeastern Norway. He regarded the Seve rocks as a thrusted Archean basement for the overlying Köli schists, but it appears possible that the Seve rocks are not basement. The Seve nappe thins to nothing in the west and north (Zachrisson, 1969).

The rocks of the Köli complex are best developed in the Våsterbotten Mountains (Kulling, 1933). They contain a thick sequence of calcareous mudstones, limestone, and conglomerates of lower metamorphic grade, together with substantial felsic and mafic volcanic rocks of both terrestrial and submarine aspect. Turbidites of presumably proximal type are also de-

Table 1. Comparative Lithostratigraphy Across Orogenic Belt of Southern-Sector Tectonic Units

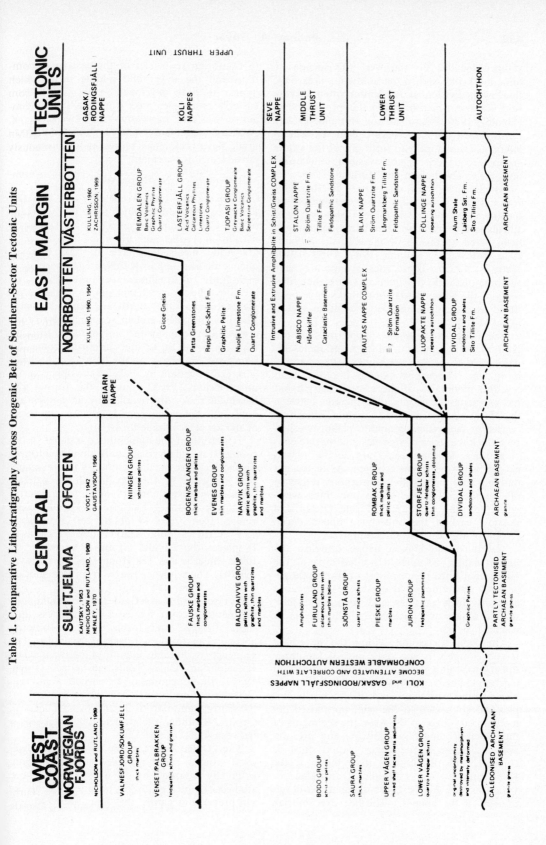

veloped locally. To the west the succession thins markedly, and in the Sulitjelma area only the lowest division of the Våsterbotten succession is present in a higher metamorphic facies (Henley, 1970; Nicholson and Rutland, 1969). Farther west the Köli rocks become extremely attenuated and appear to form one of the stratigraphic sequences in the western autochthonous cover (Nicholson and Rutland, 1969).

Fossils have been discovered in the Köli rocks at several localities in Sweden and at one locality in Norway. The Sjönstå and overlying Furuland Groups of the Sulitjelma region have been dated by means of these fossils as mid-Late Ordovician (Kulling, 1947, 1960, 1964; Katusky, 1953). These rock groups are near the base of the Köli sequence; and higher rock units in the Våsterbotten Mountains have been dated as Ashgillian and Early Silurian (Kulling, 1960).

The Gasak-Rödingsfjäll nappe overlies the Köli rocks and in general contains metasedimentary rock of a much higher state of metamorphism. The nappe extends into the main Swedish mountains of the eastern margin but has its greatest development in the area between the Norwegian fjords and Sulitjelma. The rocks consist of pelites and graphitic pelites overlain by a thick sequence of marbles and marble conglomerates. Volcanic rocks are notably absent except in northern Våsterbotten. As in the underlying Köli nappes, the sedimentary sequence of the Gasak-Rödingsfjäll nappe thins westward, forming the Saura Marble Group and possibly part of the underlying upper Vågen Group of the western autochthon.

The third and highest nappe complex, the Beiarn nappe, occupies a limited area of the Norwegian fjord region; most of the nappe apparently was removed by erosion. The sequence contains thick marbles and high-grade feldspathic schists and gneisses and thin layers of volcanic rocks.

The Köli succession within the Seve-Köli nappe complex is the only one of the three upper-thrust-unit complexes that can be dated paleontologically. Because both the Köli complex and the overlying Gasak-Rödingsfjäll complex are connected to the metamorphosed autochthonous cover in the west, the sediments of the Gasak-Rödingsfjäll complex, and presumably also those of the Beiarn nappe, must be equivalent to or younger than those of the Köli complex—i.e., Middle Ordovician or younger. (See Figure 2 for schematized development of the nappes.) The late Precambrian to Cambrian sequences of the eastern autochthon and the lower and middle thrust units appear to have developed in an independent easterly basin separated from the later, more active westerly basin by a positive area of Archean basement. The high-metamorphic-grade Seve rocks may represent the dislocated portion of this basement.

Northern Area

Autochthon—The Archean rocks of the Fennoscandian shield which form the basement of the Caledonian orogen along the southeast margin in Troms and Finnmark consist of a low-grade metasedimentary and volcanic sequence of late or post-Karelian age overlying a high-grade metasedimentary unit which, in turn, overlies a pre-Karelian migmatite complex (Reitan, 1960; Barth and Reitan, 1963). The late or post-Karelian sequence also crops out within two major tectonic windows through the Caledonian thrust units in north Troms and northwest Finnmark. In the latter, the Archean is directly overlain by rocks of the upper thrust unit (Reitan, 1963), but in the former the basement rocks are overlain by an autochthonous sedimentary cover and, in places, by rocks of the lower or middle thrust units.

The strata of the autochthonous cover in the southeast marginal zone can be divided into two distinct regions. In the southwest the relatively thin sequence of the Dividal Group extends from the southern area in Norrbotten to central Finnmark south of Laksefjord. The thickness ranges from zero to about 250 m (Føyn, 1967a); the variation is largely due to tectonism. In places the Dividal Group is underlain by tillite (Skjerlie and Tek Hong Tan, 1961; Føyn, 1967b). The sequence ranges from Eocambrian to earliest Cambrian in age.

Northeast of Laksefjord the autochthonous sedimentary cover increases in thickness in a short distance and forms a broad outcrop around Tanafjord and Varangerhalvöya. The sequence is divisible into three units: the late Precambrian "Older Sandstone Series" (Føyn, 1937), the Eocambrian to earliest Cambrian Vestertana Group (Banks et al., in press), and the Early Cambrian to Tremadocian Digermul Group (Reading, 1965). The total thickness is between 4,000 m and 5,000 m.

The "Older Sandstone Series" is well developed around Tanafjord, where the succession, originally described by Føyn (1937), has been studied east of the fjord by A. and S. Siedlecka (in press) and named the "Tanafjord Group."

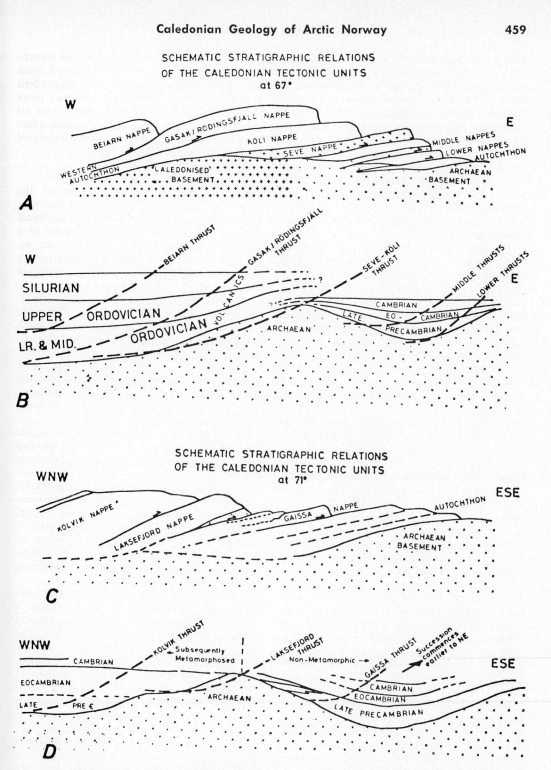

SCHEMATIC STRATIGRAPHIC RELATIONS
OF THE CALEDONIAN TECTONIC UNITS
at 67°

SCHEMATIC STRATIGRAPHIC RELATIONS
OF THE CALEDONIAN TECTONIC UNITS
at 71°

FIG. 2—Schematic cross sections through orogenic belt to show stratigraphic relations of main tectonic units. 2A and B, southern sector; 2C and D, northern sector; A and C, idealized sections of thrust nappes, ignoring post-thrusting folds; B and D, interpreted pre-thrusting stratigraphy.

The group there is 1,300 m thick and consists of interbedded shales and sandstones, both feldspathic and quartzitic, with a calcareous unit at the top. North of Varangerfjord the "Older Sandstone Series" is a sequence of interbedded sandstones and siltstones about 1,500 m thick (Røe, in press and personal commun.). The lowermost sediments were deposited in a shallow-marine environment but conditions oscillated about sea level to produce recurring estuarine and fluvial environments. Dominating a local southeasterly source of sediment supply was a distant westerly to northwesterly source (Banks et al., in press).

The overlying Vesterana Group, 1,600 m thick, contains, at the base, units indicating a glacially dominated regime and showing two main glacial advances (Føyn, 1937; Reading and Walker, 1966)—the first in the lower Smalfjord Tillite Formation and the second in the Upper Tillite Formation. A major interglacial period, represented by 200–400 m of the Nyborg Formation, separated these two advances. The Bigganjargga moraine, from which Reusch (1891) originally described the Varangian Eocambrian glacial beds, has been correlated with the Smalfjord Tillite Formation (Bjørlykke, 1967). An unconformity exists beneath both the Smalfjord and the Upper Tillite Formations and is attributed to the erosional nature of grounded ice. The upper part of the Vestertana Group represents sedimentation in a predominantly shallow-marine environment which produced quartzitic sandstones, siltstones, and mudstones. Trace fossils first appear in the upper part of the Vestertana Group about 400 m below the first occurrence of the Lower Cambrian zone-fossil *Platysolenites antiquissimus*. Upward in the section they increase greatly in abundance and diversity. The occurrence of *Platysolenites antiquissimus* allows correlation with the Dividal Group of the southwestern autochthon. This pattern of sedimentation continued through deposition of the 1,500-m-thick Cambrian to Tremadocian Digermul Group, which contains Lower, Middle, and Upper Cambrian and Tremadocian body fossils (Henningsmoen, 1960). Although the influence of a southern landmass is apparent for the glacially dominated regime, during deposition of the upper part of the Vestertana Group and the Digermul Group, a northerly or northeasterly positive area and sediment source was dominant (Banks et al., in press).

The north and northeastern part of Varangerhalvöya has been shown recently (A. and S.

Siedlecka, 1967) to consist of a distinct late Precambrian group, the Barents Sea Group, which has tectonic contact with the "Older Sandstone Series." This group is at least 9,500 m thick (A. and S. Siedlecka, in press) and consists of a lower turbidite sandstone and shale formation greater than 4,500 m thick (Kongsfjord Formation), overlain by 2,500 m of sandstones (Båsnaering Formation) and by more than 1,500 m of a multicolored carbonate-bearing unit (Båtsfjord Formation), and capped by 1,000 m of alternate red and gray sandstones and siltstones (Tyvjofjell Formation). A. and S. Siedlecka (1969) consider this sequence to be analogous to the late Precambrian Eleonore Bay Group of northeast Greenland and thus, presumably, to the Middle Hecla Hoek of Spitsbergen (*see* Harland et al., 1966). If this correlation is substantiated, the Barents Sea Group comprises in part the northern lateral equivalent of the "Older Sandstone Series" and in part a conformable lower sequence.

The presence of a thin autochthonous cover above the basement rocks of the Alta window gives an indication of the extent of post-metamorphism thrusting along the Kolvik thrust. The sequence has a 15 m lower unit of late Precambrian sandstones and shales overlain unconformably by tillite and 50 m of an upper unit of red and green sandstones and shales (Føyn, 1964).

Lower thrust unit—The thick autochthonous sedimentary cover of eastern Finnmark is detached from the basement around the head of Laksefjord; farther west, in the area of Porsangerfjord, a major thrust—the Gaissa thrust—is developed at its base. The precise relations between the allochthonous sequence of the Gaissa nappe and that of the eastern autochthon are not known; generally, however, the Gaissa nappe sequence represents the late Precambrian "Older Sandstone Series" of east Finnmark.

Holtedahl (1918) described the succession of "Porsanger Sandstone" overlain by Porsanger Dolomite and later established a late Precambrian age for the sequence (Holtedahl, 1931). White (1968a, b), in describing the petrology of the sandstone unit, drew attention to the tectonic contact between the dolomites and the sandstones; thus, only the dolomite, overlain by Eocambrian tillite (Føyn, 1960; Gayer and Roberts, in press), is conclusively Precambrian. Roberts (in press-a) has revised the stratigraphy of the nappe and (in press-b) has interpreted the sedimentation of the sequence.

The Gaissa Sandstone Formation (White's Porsanger Sandstone Formation) is 500–600 m thick and represents sedimentation in an initial fluvial environment followed by beach and estuarine environments and, finally, by a shallow-marine environment. The source area appears to have been on the south or southwest.

The Børselv Subgroup consists of 200 m of the Stabbursnes Formation overlain by 220 m of the Porsanger Dolomite Formation. The sedimentation of the lower part of the sequence suggests gradual emergence—from a shallow-marine environment that produced turbidite sandstones and siltstones. The upper, stromatolitic Porsanger Dolomite Formation indicates gentle submergence and a lack of detritus. The sedimentation reflects a positive area on the north or northwest (sabkha?). Gayer and Roberts (in press) suggest that the Børselv Subgroup is the lateral northwestern equivalent of the Gaissa sandstones and that sedimentation was controlled by northwestern and southern positive areas, respectively.

Middle thrust unit—Low-greenschist-facies metasedimentary rocks of the Laksefjord nappe overlie the lower thrust unit and autochthon in central and eastern Finnmark. The nappe consists of more than 6,000 m of Eocambrian metasedimentary rocks lying on an imbricated thrust sheet of highly metamorphosed basement rocks and plutonic intrusions. Generally, the metasedimentary rocks are thrust over the basement slices, but in places an original unconformable sedimentary contact is preserved (Laird, in press-a).

The metasedimentary sequence was described initially by Føyn (1960) in the Laksefjord area and named the "Laksefjord Group." He later extended his description to the rocks of the area between Laksefjord and Tanafjord (Føyn, 1969). A somewhat similar sequence has been recognized in the northwest of Varangerhalvöya—the Raggo Group (A. and S. Siedlecka, 1967). Laird (in press-b) has discussed the depositional history of the group. The 2,000-m Ifjord Formation consists of mainly terrestrial tillite in the south and west of the nappe, and grades northeastward into shallow-marine units containing scattered erratic boulders. Local slopes that developed in the northeast resulted in slumps and turbidites, whereas a fine-grained phyllite member suggests a lake in the south. After the Ifjord sediments were deposited, marine conditions resulted in the deposition of quartzitic sandstones of the Landersfjord Formation over all but the southwest-

ern part of the area, where rivers flowed to the north and northwest into the basin. The upper part of the Laksefjord Group consists of fine-grained sedimentary units of the Friarfjord Formation, marking the continued southerly retreat of the shoreline.

Upper thrust unit—The Kolvik thrust forms the base of the upper thrust unit throughout the area extending northeast through Troms and southwest Finnmark, and east-northeast through central and eastern Finnmark. Only one large disjunctive nappe has been recognized above this thrust—the late Precambrian to Cambrian Kolvik nappe. The lowest part of the nappe consists of a thick series of tectonically banded blastomylonites that is overlain by at least 5,000 m of metasedimentary rocks of the amphibolite facies. These metasedimentary rocks are generally very rich in both K- and Na-feldspars and form a sequence of alternate feldspathic psammites and feldspar subpelites. Sedimentary structures preserved in some of the psammitic units, together with the high clastic feldspar content, suggest a fluvial environment of deposition (Gayer, in press). Although these rocks have been referred to as "sparagmitic schists" (Padget, 1955; Skjerlie and Tek Hong Tan, 1961), the only resemblance to true sparagmite is the high feldspar content; nowhere in the wide outcrop of this unit have conglomeratic layers been found. The upper part of this feldspathic sequence is exposed in the island and fjord region of western Finnmark and northern Troms, where it has been named the "Klubben Psammite Group" (Ramsay, in press; formerly the Klubben Quartzite Group of Ramsay and Sturt, 1963) and the "Brynilen Psammite Group" (Hooper and Gronow, 1970), respectively. The discovery of Lower Cambrian archaeocyathids in the uppermost part of the Klubben Psammite Group in the Söröya area (Sturt and Ramsay, 1965), with the lack of any other evidence, suggests an Eocambrian to Early Cambrian age for the group.

The overlying Cambrian sequence, approximately 1,000 m thick, has been divided into four relatively thin groups (equivalent of formations[?]) by Ramsay (in press) and Armitage *et al.* (in press), showing a gradual submergence of the area of deposition from littoral and sublittoral through neritic to bathyal (Roberts, 1968; in press).

Stratigraphic relations between tectonic units —The chronostratigraphy of the four tectonic units is indicated in Table 2. Each of the units

Table 2. Comparative Stratigraphy of Northern-Sector Tectonic Units

AUTOCHTHON

		Age
DIGERMUL GROUP 1,530 m HERAJING 1966 BANKS et al. in press A. and S. SIEDLECKI 1967 and in press	BERLOGAISSA FM KISTEDAL FM DUOLBASGAISSA FM	CAMBRIAN
VESTERTANA GROUP 1,600 m	BREIVIK FM STAPPOGIEDDE FM UPPER TILLITE FM NYBORG FM SMALFJORD TILLITE FM	
TANAFJORD GROUP 1,300 m	GRASSDAL FM HANGLE CAERRO FM VAGGE FM GAMASFJELL FM DAKKOVARRE FM STANGENES FM GRØNNES FM	EOCAMBRIAN
BARENTS SEA GROUP 9,500 m	TYVJOFJELL FM BÅTSFJORD FM BÅSNAERING FM KONGSFJORD FM Base not seen	LATE PRECAMBRIAN

THRUST UNITS

LOWER WHITE 1969, GAYER and ROBERTS in press	MIDDLE FØYN, 1960, LAIRD, in press	UPPER RAMSAY and STURT, 1963, GAYER in press	Age
	LAKSEFJORD GROUP	HELLEFJORD SCHIST GP AAFJORD PELITE GP FALKENES MARBLE GP. STROEV SCHIST GP	CAMBRIAN
TILLITE PORSANGER DOLOMITE FM. STABBURSNES FORMATION GAISSA SANDSTONE FORMATION 500-600 m. members BØRSELV SUBGROUP 440-540 m. GAISSA THRUST	FRIARFJORD PHYLLITE FM. 1,200 m. LANDERSFJORD QUARTZITE FM. 2,600 m. IFJORD TILLITE FM. 2,700 m. EROSIONAL GAP	KLUBBEN PSAMMITE GROUP 2,300 m ALKEBERGET FM. 700 m FALKEBERGET FM. 900 m BILLEFJORD FM. 400-625 m. CADDAQAIVVE FM. 250 m NILPAVATN FM. 500 m. GAARADAKVATN FM. 1,200 m. TROLLHOLMSUNDET FM. 380 m.	EOCAMBRIAN
	BASEMENT LAKSE FJORD THRUST	KOLVIK THRUST	LATE PRECAMBRIAN

broadly covers the time span late Precambrian–Cambrian, and thus a hypothetical pre-thrusting arrangement of the units (Fig. 2) can be deduced using the sedimentology data given in the preceding paragraphs. In all four units the late Precambrian represents oscillating marine-fluvial conditions, and the Eocambrian to Cambrian represents gradually deepening marine conditions. These conditions can best be accounted for by the presence of a positive basement region north of the region of deposition of the "autochthon–lower thrust unit" and south of the region of the middle and upper thrust units. Portions of this positive basement region were caught up in the lower part of the middle thrust unit during the southeasterly-directed thrusting.

DEFORMATION AND METAMORPHISM

Much of the structural work carried out in the Caledonian rocks has been limited to the metamorphic rocks of the upper thrust units. It is within these rocks that details of a complex polyphase deformational and metamorphic history have been worked out. Detailed structural investigations that have been undertaken to prepare structural histories of more than limited areas within the region are as yet insufficient. Nevertheless, these accounts show a remarkably consistent deformational history.

The initial deformation (F_1 of most authors) produced complex recumbent folds; the folding either predated metamorphism (Wells and Bradshaw, 1970) or was accompanied by low-grade metamorphism and the development of an axial surface schistosity (e.g., Sturt and Ramsay, 1965). In the fjord region of the southern area and in the fjord and island region of the northern area, this early deformation, which has been shown to include more than one stage of movement (Nicholson and Rutland, 1969; Hooper, in press), produced the main nappe folds of these areas (Rutland and Nicholson, 1965; Hooper and Gronow, 1970). These nappe folds preserve the stratigraphic relations and are termed "conjunctive nappes" (Rutland and Nicholson, 1965). The movement of these early nappes appears to have been directed into structural depressions and away from F_1 anticlinal rises, which in the southern fjord region involve "caledonized" basement rocks. Rutland and Nicholson invoke gravity control to account for this arrangement.

Toward the eastern margin of the upper thrust unit, only small-scale recumbent folds of this early phase are present.

Throughout the belt, regional metamorphism reached its peak during a static recrystallization episode following the early deformation. During this stage, growth of porphyroblasts of high-grade minerals occurred. There is a general tendency for the metamorphic facies to be of higher grade toward the west, away from the thrust front. In the Sulitjelma area, Henley (1970) provides evidence that the principal movement of the Gasak nappe over the Köli nappe, which is conjunctive there, took place during this peak period of metamorphism.

The ensuing second phase of deformation (F_2 of most authors) produced intense flattening and extension, tightening of the earlier folds into more isoclinal folds, augenization of the statically grown porphyroblasts (Henley, 1970; Hooper, in press-a), and development of boudins in the more competent rock units. In general, metamorphism waned during this phase. In some places this phase of extension can be separated from a second episode of fold development (Henley, 1970), but generally the two phenomena are closely connected (Hooper, in press-a). These folds are generally recumbent structures and are developed in a complex history of movements (Gayer and Roberts, in press). Toward the thrust front the principal movement of the upper thrusts appears to have been accomplished during this second phase of deformation.

The third phase of deformation (F_3 of some authors, F_4 of others) produced open flexural-slip folds about steeply dipping axial surfaces, parallel with which a strain-slip cleavage is commonly developed. These folds are responsible for most of the tectonic windows through the eastern part of the upper thrust unit; they deform the earlier-formed thrusts. A variety of folds and faults was developed during a final episode of brittle deformation that is difficult to correlate from one area to another.

It seems clear that the movement of the nappes occurred earlier in the deformation history away from the thrust front. Diachronous tectonic phases from west to east with a fixed time for the movement of the nappes could be implied; however, a more likely alternative is that the nappes, initiated during the early deformation phase in the west, were transported eastward during successively later phases.

The deformation histories of the autochthon, the lower thrust unit, and the middle thrust unit are not so clear as that of the upper thrust unit. A polyphase deformation has been described in the lower thrust unit of the Porsangerfjord area, which can be presumed to have been linked with the structures of the upper thrust unit before movement along the Kolvik thrust (Gayer and Roberts, in press).

IGNEOUS ACTIVITY

Volcanic rocks—Volcanic rocks, both basaltic and keratophyric, are restricted to the Ordovician-Silurian sequences of the Köli nappe and possibly the Beiarn nappe in the southern sector of the belt. These volcanic rocks are described in the stratigraphy section (Table 1). The volcanic rocks do not appear to be associated with a deep-water geosynclinal facies, the majority of sediments apparently having been deposited in a nearshore environment.

Minor intrusions—Dikes and sheets of basaltic composition are of widespread occurrence throughout the belt. The age of intrusion relative to the deformation history varies considerably and, in several localities, intrusion of more than one set of dikes can be recognized; the dikes thus are used to distinguish various metamorphic and structural events (Gayer and Roberts, in press). In many places the composition of the dike rocks reflects a different affinity from nearby major plutons (Henley, 1970). Most of the dikes seem to be syntectonic, having been emplaced during or immediately before or after the static recrystallization period between the first two stages of deformation. One basaltic dike swarm on the island of Stjernöya in western Finnmark was intruded into the host rock while the latter was being actively deformed (Ramsay and Sturt, 1970b). Minor intrusions of acidic composition are far less abundant.

Major intrusions—Dominating the Caledonian igneous activity in Arctic Scandinavia is the Seiland gabbro province, represented by major mafic and ultramafic intrusions covering a wide area of the island and fjord region of northwest Norway. In this area, many plutons were emplaced at several stages during the orogenic development of the belt. Gabbros forming the earliest intrusions were emplaced during and immediately following the first phase of deformation (*e.g.*, the Sandland Gabbro—Hooper, in press-b; and the Hasvik Gabbro—Sturt, in press). The Hasvik Gabbro, intruded during the peak of almandine-amphibolite-facies regional metamorphism between the first and second deformation phases, has produced an Rb-Sr and an initial Sr^{87}/Sr^{86} isochron giving an age of 530 ± 35 m.y. for the intrusion of the gabbro (Pringle and Sturt, 1969).

In the latter groups of plutons, ultramafic rocks predominate and gabbroic bodies are commonly well layered, whereas, in the latest intrusions, alkalic rocks including nepheline syenites and carbonatites were emplaced (Robins, in press). The intrusive history ended during the later stages of the Caledonian deformation. The Seiland gabbro province has been shown to be connected with a pronounced positive Bouguer anomaly ($+100$ mgal) forming a culmination in a persistent positive-anomaly axis trending northwest-southeast off the coast of Finnmark and probably extending to the Lofoten-Vesterålen Islands (Brooks, 1970). Brooks interprets this anomaly as a zone of massive enrichment of the crust in mafic and ultramafic material.

In the southern sector of the belt, major intrusions are not so abundant. Gustavson (1969) described two suites of igneous rocks from the Ofoten and southern Troms areas. The first group consists of serpentinites, amphibolites, and meta-trondhjemites representing an early pre-metamorphism period of Caledonian magmatism connected with the geosynclinal stage of the orogeny. The second group, containing a mafic-ultramafic suite with subordinate granodiorites and trondhjemites, is late tectonic, but older than the latest fold movements.

The extensive areas of "Caledonian granites" shown on the geologic map of Norway (Holtedahl and Dons, 1960) in the Nordland area have been demonstrated to consist of "caledonized" basement gneisses and their metamorphosed sedimentary cover (Hollingworth et al., 1960; Rutland and Nicholson, 1965). Major igneous activity in this area is largely confined to gabbroic intrusions, the layered gabbro of Sulitjelma being the best example. Mason (1967) has shown that the Sulitjelma gabbro, like the gabbros of the Seiland province, was intruded during the peak of metamorphism between the first two phases of deformation, and was thrust eastward on the Gasak thrust prior to the second phase of deformation. In contrast to the Late Cambrian age for the intrusion of the northern Hasvik Gabbro, an Rb-Sr whole-rock isochron on the Furuland Granite in the south has shown that the metamorphic interval between the first two phases of deformation occurred here at 396 ± 48 m.y.

DISCUSSION—TECTOGENESIS

Age of sediments and later deformation—The southern sector of the belt contains sediments ranging in age from late Precambrian to Early Silurian, although the highly metamorphosed upper thrust units forming the bulk of this part of the belt are developed entirely within Middle Ordovician to Lower Silurian rocks. There is some doubt about the age of the metamorphosed western autochthon, which may include a thin late Precambrian to Cambrian sequence. The main development of the lower and middle thrust units was entirely within late Precambrian to Cambrian time, and the succession of the lower thrust unit appears to have been developed in a separate easterly basin. The main metamorphism, between the first two phases of deformation, occurred during the latest Silurian (396 ± 48 m.y.). It is possible that the older succession of the lower and middle thrust units was deformed earlier than the upper thrust unit, but there is no evidence for this.

The northern sector of the belt contains an entirely late Precambrian to Cambrian succession, and the bulk of the sediments was deposited in Precambrian time. Similar sequences are present in all four tectonic units, although there are strong indications that a positive area of basement rocks rose as a ridge parallel with the margin of the belt, separating the areas of deposition of the autochthon and the lower unit from those of the middle and upper units and forming the dominant source of sediment. The main metamorphism of this part of the belt occurred during the latest Cambrian (530 ± 35 m.y.); thus, the northern sequence was deformed and metamorphosed before most of the southern sequence had been deposited.

A conglomeratic and carbonate-bearing Lower Silurian sequence on Mageröya (Føyn, 1967c) appears to lie on the metamorphosed Kolvik nappe rocks of the northern upper thrust unit. The conglomerates, containing pebbles of metamorphic assemblages similar to the underlying Kolvik nappe lithologies, are themselves affected by a polyphase deformation (Ramsay and Sturt, 1970a), which must represent a later stage of the deformation history of the northern sector.

Despite the similarity of the deformational histories of the northern and southern sectors, the individual phases must be diachronous, the main deformation in the north occurring approximately 100 m.y. earlier than the equivalent stage in the south. The deformation of the lower thrust unit in the south may correspond to the Late Cambrian main deformation in the north, and the Silurian deformation on Mage-

röya may correspond to the main deformation in the south.

Direction of thrusting—The direction of tectonic transport is generally assumed to be perpendicular to the regional outcrop of the thrust front. A more accurate assessment can be made by studying the folds and linear structures in the rocks affected by the thrusting. Lindstrom (1958) attempted to synthesize these structures for the whole of the Scandinavian Caledonian chain, but his results are difficult to interpret in terms of deformation phases. What does emerge, as pointed out by Hooper (1968), is that the trend of the thrust plane in Arctic Scandinavia is perpendicular to an earlier set of overturned folds. In the northern part of the belt, these folds, where traced westward away from the thrust, swing into a regional north-south trend. There are several explanations for such an arrangement. It is possible that folds will develop both parallel with and perpendicular to the direction of transport (Lindstrom, 1958). Bryant and Reed (1969) have shown that earlier folds can be rotated by the thrust movements so that they lie either parallel with or perpendicular to the thrust. Hooper (1968) suggested that the direction of tectonic transport can be influenced by the presence of an earlier tectonic grain; thus, the thrust trend need not be perpendicular to the regional transport direction.

It is clear that tectonic transport directions do not give a simple movement pattern for this part of the orogenic belt, and a similarly ambiguous situation applies in the southern sector (Wells and Bradshaw, 1970). Perhaps the most significant structure of the northern part of the belt is the linear arrangement of the mafic and ultramafic intrusions of the Seiland gabbro province with the geophysically detected root zone trending northeast-southwest off the northwest coast of Norway. It is possible that this linear trend may represent a region of mantle rocks introduced along a subduction zone at the lithospheric-plate margin; it would therefore represent the true trend of the orogenic belt. The present attitude of the thrust front and the orientation of folds and other linear structures within the thrust rocks would then be related to the trend of this subduction zone. If this is the case, the direction of tectonic transport will be influenced by the movement direction of the underlying plate (not necessarily normal to the subduction zone) and by the position and attitude of the continental margin in collision with the subduction zone. It is possible to explain both the changing geometry and the diachronous nature of the fold belt in terms of an early collision with the subduction zone of an *east-northeast-trending continental margin* in the north and a later collision of a *north-south-trending continental margin* in the south. On the basis of this model, the attitude of early folds would be related to the actual direction of plate movement, whereas later folds and thrusts would be governed by the attitude of the continental margins. The timing of geosynclinal development and of the subsequent deformation would be controlled by the position of the continental margin with respect to the subduction zone. The northern east-northeast-trending continental margin would be the first to meet the subduction zone, followed progressively on the south by the north-south-trending margin.

Dewey (1969) has suggested that the Grampian (Early Ordovician) phase of the Caledonian orogeny was connected with movement on a subduction zone along the western and northwestern edges of a proto-Atlantic ocean, whereas the Late Silurian–Devonian phase occurred to the south and southeast during the final stages of closing of the proto-Atlantic. This view is not entirely different from the model suggested herein, but would require a northern early phase genetically distinct from the later southern phase. Moreover, there is no evidence in any part of the Arctic Scandinavian Caledonides that an oceanic crust forms the basement of the Caledonian geosyncline. Such an assumption would require the closing of the proto-Atlantic, if it existed here, before the onset of sedimentation.

Selected References

Armitage, A. H., et al. (in press), Stratigraphic correlation in the Caledonian rocks of SW Finnmark and North Troms, in Caledonian geology of northern Norway, Cardiff Symposium: Norges Geol. Undersokelse (published 1971).

Asklund, B., 1960, The geology of the Caledonian mountain chain and of adjacent areas in Sweden, in The description to accompany map of pre-Quaternary rock of Sweden: Sveriges Geol. Undersökning Årsb., ser. Ba, no. 16, p. 126–149.

Bailey, E. B., and O. Holtedahl, 1938, Northwestern Europe Caledonides, in Regionale Geologie der Erde: Leipzig, Akad. Verlaysgesellschaft, 76 p.

Banks, N. L., et al. (in press), Late Precambrian and Cambro-Ordovician sedimentation in East Finnmark, in Caledonian geology of northern Norway, Cardiff Symposium: Norges Geol. Undersokelse (published 1971).

Barth, T. F. W., and P. H. Retian, 1963, The Precambrian of Norway, in Kalervo Rankama, ed., The Precambrian (The geologic systems), v. 1: New York,

Interscience Publishers (John Wiley & Sons), p. 27–80.

Bjørlykke, K., 1967, The Eocambrian "Reusch Moraine" at Bigganjargga and the geology around Varangerfjord, northern Norway: Norges Geol. Undersokelse Skr., no. 251, p. 18–44.

Brooks, M., 1970, A gravity survey of coastal areas of West Finnmark, northern Norway: Geol. Soc. London Quart Jour., v. 125, p. 171–192.

Bryant, B., and J. C. Reed, Jr., 1969, Significance of lineation and minor folds near major thrust faults in the southern Appalachians and the British and Norwegian Caledonides: Geol. Mag., v. 106, no. 5, p. 412–429.

Dewey, J. F., 1969, Evolution of the Appalachian/Caledonian orogen: Nature, v. 222, p. 124–129.

Føyn, Sven, 1937, The Eo-Cambrian series of the Tana district, northern Norway: Norsk Geol. Tidsskr., v. 17, p. 65–164.

——— 1960, Tanafjord to Laksefjord, in Aspects of the geology of northern Norway, Guide to Excursion No. A3: 21st Internat. Geol. Cong., Norges Geol. Undersokelse Skr., no. 212, p. 45–57.

——— 1964, Den tillitførende formasjonsgruppe i Alta-en jeunføring med Øst-Finnmark og med indre Finnmark: Norges Geol. Undersokelse Skr., no. 228, p. 139–150.

——— 1967a, Dividal-gruppen ("Hyolithus-sonen") in Finnmark og dens forhold til de eokambrisk-Kambriske formasjoner: Norges Geol. Undersokelse Skr., no. 249, p. 1–84.

——— 1967b, Big boulders of tillite rock in Porsanger, northern Norway: Norges Geol. Undersokelse Skr., no. 247, p. 223–230.

——— 1967c, Stratigraphical consequences of the discovery of Silurian fossils on Magerøy, the island of North Cape: Norges Geol. Undersokelse Skr., no. 247, p. 208–222.

——— 1969, Laksefjord-gruppen ved Tanafjorden: Norges Geol. Undersokelse Skr., no. 258, p. 5–16.

Gayer, R. A. (in press), The stratigraphy of the Kolvik Nappe of West Porsanger, Finnmark, in Caledonian geology of northern Norway, Cardiff Symposium: Norges Geol. Undersokelse (published 1971).

——— and J. D. Roberts (in press), The structural relationships of the Caledonian nappes of Porsangerfjord, West Finnmark, northern Norway, in Caledonian geology of northern Norway, Cardiff Symposium: Norges Geol. Undersokelse (published 1971).

Geijer, P., 1963, The Precambrian of Sweden, in Kalervo Rankama, ed., The Precambrian (The geologic systems), v. 1: New York, Interscience Publishers (John Wiley & Sons), p. 81–143.

Gustavson, M., 1966, The Caledonian mountain chain of the southern Troms and Ofoten areas, Part I, Basement rocks and Caledonian meta-sediments: Norges Geol. Undersokelse Skr., no. 239, p. 1–162.

——— 1969, The Caledonian mountain chain of the southern Troms and Ofoten areas, Part II, Caledonian rocks of igneous origin: Norges Geol. Undersokelse Skr., no. 261, p. 1–110.

Harland, W. B., R. H. Wallis, and R. A. Gayer, 1966, A revision of the Lower Hecla Hoek succession in central North Spitsbergen and correlation elsewhere: Geol. Mag., v. 103, no. 1, p. 70–97.

Henley, K. J., 1970, The structural and metamorphic history of the Sulitjelma region, Norway, with special reference to the nappe hypothesis: Norsk Geol. Tidsskr., v. 50, no. 2, p. 97–136.

Henningsmoen, G., 1961, Cambro-Silurian fossils in

Finnmark, northern Norway: Norges Geol. Undersokelse, no. 213, p. 93–95.

Hollingworth, S. E., M. K. Wells, and R. Bradshaw, 1960, Geology and structure of the Glomfjord region, northern Norway: Copenhagen, 21st Internat. Geol. Cong. Rept., pt. 19, p. 33–42.

Holtedahl, O., 1918, Bidrag til Finnmarkens geologi: Norges Geol. Undersokelse Skr., no. 84, p. 1–314.

—— 1931, Additional observations on the rock formations of Finnmark: Norsk Geol. Tidsskr., v. 11, p. 241–279.

—— and J. A. Dons, 1960, The geological map of Norway, in The geology of Norway: Norges Geol. Undersokelse Skr., no. 208.

Hooper, P. R., 1968, The 'a' lineation and the trend of the Caledonides of northern Norway: Norsk Geol. Tidsskr., v. 48, p. 261–268.

—— (in press-a), A review of the tectonic history of SW Finnmark and North Troms, in Caledonian geology of northern Norway, Cardiff Symposium: Norges Geol. Undersokelse (published 1971).

—— (in press-b), The mafic and ultramafic rocks of SW Finnmark and North Troms, in Caledonian geology of northern Norway, Cardiff Symposium: Norges Geol. Undersokelse (published 1971).

—— and C. W. Gronow, 1970, The regional significance of the Caledonian structures of the Sandland Peninsula, West Finnmark, northern Norway: Geol. Soc. London Quart. Jour., v. 125, p. 193–217.

Kautsky, G., 1953, Der geologische Bau des Sulitjelma-Salojauregebietes in den Nordskandinavischen Kaledoniden: Sveriges Geol. Undersökning Årsb., ser. Ca, no. 528, p. 1–232.

Kulling, O., 1933, Bergbyggnaden inon Björkvattnet-Virisen-området i Västerbottensfjällens centrala del: Geol. Fören. Stockholm Förh., v. 55, no. 2, p. 167–422.

—— 1947, Aktuella fjällfrågor: Geol. Fören. Stockholm Förh., v. 69, no. 4, p. 475–486.

—— 1955, Den Kaledoniska fjallkedjans berggrund inon Våsterbottens Lan, Part 2 in Beskriuning till berggrundskarta over Våsterbottens Lan: Sveriges Geol. Undersökning Årsb., ser. Ca, v. 37.

—— 1960, On the Caledonides of Swedish Lapland, in Description to accompany map of pre-Quaternary rocks of Sweden: Sveriges Geol. Undersökning Årsb., ser. B, no. 16, p. 150–177.

—— 1964, Oversikt over Norra Norrbottensfjällens Kaledonberggrund: Sveriges Geol. Undersökning Årsb., ser. Ba, no. 19, p. 1–166.

Laird, M. G. (in press-a), The stratigraphy and sedimentology of the Laksefjord Group, Finnmark, Norway: Norges Geol. Undersokelse (published 1972).

—— (in press-b), Sedimentation of the late Precambrian Raggo Group, Varanger Peninsula: Norges Geol. Undersokelse (published 1972).

Lindstrom, M., 1958, Toward a further hypothesis on the Scandinavian Caledonides: Geol. Fören. Stockholm Förh., v. 80, p. 363–380.

Mason, R., 1967, The field relations of the Sulitjelma gabbro: Norsk Geol. Tidsskr., v. 47, p. 237–248.

Nicholson, R., and R. W. R. Rutland, 1969, A section across the Norwegian Caledonides: Bodo to Sulitjelma: Norges Geol. Undersokelse Skr., no. 260, p. 1–86.

Padget, P., 1955, The geology of the Caledonides of the Birtavarre region, Troms, northern Norway: Norges Geol. Undersokelse Skr., no. 192, p. 1–107.

Pringle, I. R., and B. A. Sturt, 1969, The age of the peak of the Caledonian orogeny in West Finnmark,

North Norway: Norsk Geol. Tidsskr., v. 49, p. 435–436.

Ramsay, D. M. (in press), The stratigraphy of Söröy, in Caledonian geology of northern Norway, Cardiff Symposium: Norges Geol. Undersokelse (published 1971).

—— and B. A. Sturt, 1963, A study of fold styles, their associations and symmetry relationships, from Söröy, North Norway: Norsk Geol. Tidsskr., v. 43, p. 411–430.

—— and —— 1970a, Polyphase deformation of a polymict Silurian conglomerate from Magerøy, Norway: Jour. Geology, v. 78, no. 3, p. 264–280.

—— and —— 1970b, The emplacement and metamorphism of a syn-orogenic dyke swarm from Stjernøy, northwest Norway: Am. Jour. Sci., v. 268, p. 264–286.

Reading, H. G., 1965, Eocambrian and lower Palaeozoic geology of the Digermul Peninsula, Tanafjord, Finnmark: Norges Geol. Undersokelse Årsb., no. 234, p. 167–191.

—— and R. G. Walker, 1966, Sedimentation of Eocambrian tillites and associated sediments in Finnmark, northern Norway: Palaeogeography, Palaeoclimatology, Palaeoecology, v. 2, p. 177–212.

Reitan, P. H., 1960, Precambrian of northern Norway, windows in the Caledonides in the Ofoten district, Troms and Finnmark, in Geology of Norway: Norges Geol. Undersokelse Skr., no. 208, p. 67–98.

—— 1963, The geology of the Komagfjord tectonic window of the Raipas suite, Finnmark, Norway: Norges Geol. Undersokelse Skr., no. 221, 71 p.

Reusch, H., 1891, Skurngsmerker og morenegrus ertervist i Finnmarken fra en periode meget eldre end "istiden": Norges Geol. Undersokelse Skr., no. 4, p. 78–85.

Roberts, D., 1968, Hellefjord Schist Group—a probable turbidite formation from the Cambrian of Söröy, West Finnmark: Norsk Geol. Tidsskr., v. 48, p. 231–244.

—— (in press), A conspectus of Eocambrian-Palaeozoic sedimentation on Söröya, in Caledonian geology of northern Norway, Cardiff Symposium: Norges Geol. Undersokelse (published 1971).

Roberts, J. D. (in press-a), The geology of South and East Porsanger, Finnmark, in Caledonian geology of northern Norway, Cardiff Symposium: Norges Geol. Undersokelse (published 1971).

—— (in press-b), Preliminary notes on sedimentation in South and East Porsanger, Finnmark, in Caledonian geology of northern Norway, Cardiff Symposium: Norges Geol. Undersokelse (published 1971).

Robins, B. (in press), Syenite-carbonatite relationships in the Seiland Gabbro Province, Finnmark, northern Norway, in Caledonian geology of northern Norway, Cardiff Symposium: Norges Geol. Undersokelse (published 1971).

Røe, S. L. (in press), Correlation between the late Precambrian Older Sandstone Series of the Tanafjord and Varangerfjord areas: Norges Geol. Undersokelse Skr. (published 1970).

Rutland, R. W. R., and R. Nicholson, 1965, Tectonics of the Caledonides of part of Nordland, Norway: Geol. Soc. London Quart. Jour., v. 121, no. 481, p. 73–109.

Siedlecka, A., and S. Siedlecki, 1967, Some new aspects of the geology of Varanger Peninsula, northern Norway: Norges Geol. Undersokelse Skr., no. 247, p. 288–306.

——— and ——— 1969, Some new geological observations from the inner parts of Varanger Peninsula, northern Norway, *in* Resumeer af Foredrag:
Nord. Geol. Vintermøde, no. 9, p. 54–55.

——— and ——— (in press), Late Precambrian sedimentary rocks of the Tanafjord-Varangerfjord
region of Varanger Peninsula, northern Norway, *in*
Caledonian geology of northern Norway, Cardiff
Symposium: Norges Geol. Undersokelse (published
1971).

Skjerlie, F. J., and Tek Hong Tan, 1961, The geology
of the Caledonides of the Reisa Valley area, Troms-
Finnmark, northern Norway: Norges Geol. Undersokelse Skr., no. 213, p. 175–196.

Sturt, B. A. (in press), The contact phenomena of the
syn-orogenic Hasvik Gabbro, Söröy, northern Norway, *in* Caledonian geology of northern Norway,
Cardiff Symposium: Norges Geol. Undersokelse
(published 1971).

——— and D. M. Ramsay, 1965, The alkaline complex of the Breivikbotn area, Söröy, northern Norway: Norges Geol. Undersokelse Skr., no. 231, p.
1–142.

——— J. A. Miller, and F. J. Fitch, 1967, The age of
the alkaline rocks from West Finnmark, northern
Norway, and their bearing on the dating of the Caledonian orogeny: Norsk Geol. Tidsskr., v. 47, p.
255–273.

Vogt, T., 1942, Trekk av Narvik-Ofotens-traktens geologi: Norsk Geol. Tidsskr., v. 21, p. 198.

Wells, M. K., and R. Bradshaw, 1970, Multiple folding
in the Sørfinnset area of northern Norway: Norges
Geol. Undersokelse Skr., no. 262, 89 p.

White, B., 1968a, The Porsanger Sandstone Formation
and subjacent rocks in the Lakselv district, Finnmark, northern Norway: Norges Geol. Undersokelse
Skr., no. 255, p. 59–85.

——— 1968b, A geological reconnaissance of Older-
eidhalvoya, Porsangerfjord, Finnmark, northern Norway: Norsk Geol. Tidsskr., v. 48, p. 187–200.

——— 1969, The Stabbursnes Formation and Porsanger Dolomite Formation in the Kolvik district,
northern Norway: the development of a Precambrian algal environment: Norges Geol. Undersokelse
Skr., no. 258, p. 79–115.

Wynne-Edwards, H. R., and Z. Hasan, 1970, Intersecting orogenic belts across the North Atlantic: Am.
Jour. Sci., v. 268, p. 289–308.

Zachrisson, E., 1969, Caledonian geology of northern
Jamtland-southern Vasterbotten-Koli, stratigraphy
and main tectonic outlines: Sveriges Geol. Undersökning Årsb., ser. C, no. 644, p. 1–33.

Devonian Stratigraphy of Greenland and Svalbard[1]

P. F. FRIEND[2]

Cambridge, England

Abstract In Greenland and Arctic Scandinavia, Devonian sedimentary rocks crop out in only two areas: (1) East Greenland between lat. 71½°N and 74½°N, and (2) Svalbard (Spitsbergen and possibly Bjørnøya).

The strata are nonmarine clastic units, and they are dated largely by their vertebrate fossils.

The Greenland succession has an aggregate thickness of 7,000 m and ranges in age from late Middle Devonian to late Late Devonian. The Spitsbergen succession has an aggregate thickness of 6,500 m and ranges in age from Silurian through early Early Devonian to late Middle Devonian. Both successions overlie deformed Ordovician or older rocks and unconformably underlie Carboniferous or younger rocks.

INTRODUCTION

In Greenland and Arctic Scandinavia, Devonian sedimentary rocks crop out in only two areas: (1) East Greenland between lat. 71½°N and 74½°N, and (2) Svalbard (Spitsbergen and possibly Bjørnøya).

The Devonian strata are nonmarine clastic units which are dated largely by their vertebrate fossils. Both successions lie on deformed Ordovician or older rocks and are unconformably overlain by Carboniferous or younger rocks.

Detailed analysis of Devonian sedimentation of Greenland and Spitsbergen is being carried out at present. The Greenland work is being done by P. D. Alexander-Marrack, J. Nicholson, A. K. Yeats, and myself. The Spitsbergen work is being carried out by M. Moody-Stuart and myself.

It would be premature to present any of the sedimentologic results of this work here. However, summaries of the stratigraphic schemes being used (Figs. 1, 2) and comments on the latest age determinations are included.

[1] Manuscript received, October 18, 1971.

[2] Scott Polar Research Institute.

Since submission of this article, the following papers have appeared:

Friend, P. F., and M. Moody-Stuart, 1972, Sedimentation of the Wood Bay Formation (Devonian) of Spitsbergen: regional analysis of a late orogenic basin: Norsk Polarinst. Skr., no. 157, 77 p.

Worsley, D., 1972, Sedimentological observations on the Grey Hoek Formation of northern Andrée Land, Spitsbergen: Norsk. Polarinst. Årb. 1970, p. 102–111.

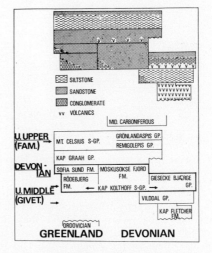

FIG. 1—Devonian lithostratigraphy and main Devonian rock types of Greenland.

GREENLAND

Recent reviews of the geology are by Bütler (1959, 1961) and Allen *et al.* (1967, p. 85).

The age determinations (Fig. 1) are from Jarvik (1961). The stratigraphic scheme outlined in Figure 1 involves some expansion and local modification of earlier schemes. Individually, the four major sedimentary units (Vilddal Group, Kap Kolthoff Supergroup, Kap Graah Group, and Mt. Celsius Supergroup) range between 1,000 and 3,000 m in thickness where fully developed. A reasonable estimate of aggregate thickness for the whole outcrop is 7,000 m.

SVALBARD

Recent reviews of the Devonian geology have been published by Friend (1961) and Allen *et al.* (1967, p. 87); the stratigraphy as summarized in Figure 2 involves no alteration of the scheme presented in the latter paper. An aggregate maximum thickness for the whole succession is 6,500 m.

The age determinations in this succession require comment in the light of recent work.

The earliest fossil faunas occur in the Fraenkelryggen Formation of the Red Bay Group.

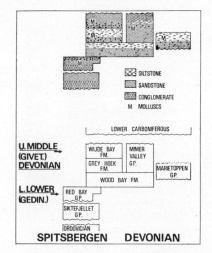

FIG. 2—Devonian lithostratigraphy and main Devonian rock types of Spitsbergen.

Their age has recently been discussed by Ørvig (1969a, p. 236), who concluded that it is equivalent to the age of the Symondsi and Leathensis zones of the Anglo-Welsh Old Red Sandstone succession. The international redefinition of the base of the Devonian system as the base of the *M. uniformis* zone will probably place a modified Downtonian Stage in the Anglo-Welsh Silurian (Martinsson, 1969). However, the Symondsi and Leathensis zones will remain in the Devonian. Ørvig (1969a, p. 238) suggested that the redefined base of the Devonian in Spitsbergen may occur in that part of the Red Bay Group which lies below the Fraenkelryggen Formation. I shall conclude, therefore, that the Siktefjellet and lower Red Bay Groups are probably Silurian, and that the upper Red Bay Group is lowermost Devonian.

Ørvig (1969b) has considered the position of the Emsian-Eifelian (Lower-Middle Devonian) boundary in the Spitsbergen succession; he suggested that it comes within the upper part of the Wood Bay Formation.

Halstead-Tarlo (1964) correlated the Mimer Valley Group and the Wijde Bay Formation, on the basis of psammosteids, with the Tartu and possibly part of the Narowa (late and possibly earlier Givetian) of the Baltic succession.

Bjørnøya is the southernmost island of the Svalbard group; it is not included in Figure 2. The lower part of the Ursa sandstone of Bjørnøya, which contains well-known macrofloras, has in recent years been regarded generally as Late Devonian in age (*e.g.*, Schweitzer, 1967, 1969). However, Cutbill and Challinor (1965, p. 422) have pointed to the close similarity of the succession in Spitsbergen, and this similarity has recently been confirmed in the field (J. Cutbill, personal commun.). Recent palynologic investigation (H. Schweitzer, personal commun.) may help to determine the age more precisely.

REFERENCES CITED

Allen, J. R. L., D. L. Dineley, and P. F. Friend, 1967, Old Red Sandstone basins of North America and Northwest Europe, *in* D. H. Oswald, ed., International symposium on the Devonian system, v. 1: Calgary, Alberta Soc. Petroleum Geologists, p. 69–98.

Bütler, H., 1959, Das Old Red Gebiet am Muskusoksefjord: Medd. om Grønland, v. 160, no. 5, 188 p.

——— 1961, Devonian deposits of central East Greenland, *in* G. O. Raasch, ed., Geology of the Arctic, v. 1: Toronto, Univ. Toronto Press, p. 188–196.

Cutbill, J. L., and A. Challinor, 1965, Revision of the stratigraphical scheme for the Carboniferous and Permian rocks of Spitsbergen and Bjørnøya: Geol. Mag., v. 102, p. 418–439.

Friend, P. F., 1961, The Devonian stratigraphy of north and central Vestspitsbergen: Yorks Geol. Soc. Proc., v. 33, p. 77–118.

Jarvik, E., 1961, Devonian vertebrates, *in* G. O. Raasch, ed., Geology of the Arctic, v. 1: Toronto, Univ. Toronto Press, p. 197–204.

Halstead-Tarlo, L. B., 1964, Psammosteiformes (Agnatha)—a review with descriptions of new material from the Lower Devonian of Poland, 1, General part: Palaeontologica Polonica, v. 13, 135 p.

Martinsson, A., 1969, The series of the redefined Silurian System: Oslo, Lethaia, v. 2, p. 153–161.

Ørvig, T., 1969a, The vertebrate fauna of the *primaeva* Beds of the Fraenkelryggen Formation of Vestspitsbergen and its biostratigraphic significance: Oslo, Lethaia, v. 2, p. 219–239.

——— 1969b, Vertebrates from the Wood Bay Group and the positions of the Emsian-Eifelian boundary in the Devonian of Vestspitsbergen: Oslo, Lethaia, v. 2, p. 273–328.

Schweitzer, H. J., 1967, Die Oberdevon-flora der Bäreninsel, 1. *Pseudobornia ursina* Nathorst: Palaeontographica Abt. B, v. 120, p. 116–137.

——— 1969, Die Oberdevon-flora der Bäreninsel, 2. *Lycopodiinae*: Palaeontographica Abt. B., v. 126, p. 101–137.

Devonian (Old Red Sandstone) Sedimentation and Tectonics of Norway[1]

TOR H. NILSEN[2]

Menlo Park, California 94025

(With a section on the Ringerike Series by J. H. McD. WHITAKER[3])

Abstract Devonian continental redbeds in Norway are of two distinct facies of the Old Red Sandstone: (1) coarse-grained fluvial sediments deposited in a series of separate intramontane basins, and (2) fine-grained fluvial sediments deposited on a broad extramontane alluvial plain. The intramontane facies is characterized by surprisingly thick accumulations of Lower and Middle Devonian breccias, conglomerates, and sandstones deposited as thick coalesced alluvial-fan complexes in structurally formed grabens and half-grabens. Penecontemporaneous uplift of surrounding provenance areas supplied abundant and varied detritus to the intramontane basins, including clasts of former eugeosynclinal metasedimentary and metavolcanic rocks, high-grade metamorphic schists, gneisses and amphibolites, and diverse mafic and felsic intrusive rocks. The largest of the structurally formed basins covers an area of approximately 2,000 sq km and has a continuous Devonian stratigraphic section with a maximum thickness of approximately 5,000 m.

The extramontane facies is characterized by the accumulation of as much as 1,250 m of red sandstones and siltstones of Late Silurian to Early Devonian(?) age. These sediments were deposited on a broad alluvial plain located approximately 250 m southeast of the intramontane basins, and they thin toward the southeast, grading laterally into intertidal sediments.

The intramontane basins developed in the former eugeosynclinal part of the Caledonian geosyncline, whereas the extramontane sediments were deposited on the former foreland. The geosyncline underwent major orogeny and uplift during the Late Silurian and Early Devonian, resulting in the formation of a major NE-SW-trending mountain system extending from Great Britain to Spitsbergen. Continued tectonic activity in the Devonian resulted in the formation of the intramontane basins, continued uplift of source areas, and subsequent folding and faulting of the Devonian sedimentary rocks. Devonian rocks locally have been thrust over surrounding older rocks; the original basin margins were probably high-angle normal faults, although strike-slip faulting is suggested locally. Paleocurrent patterns suggest transport of sediment from the surrounding highlands toward the central part of the intramontane basins, where longer rivers probably flowed parallel with the basin axes. The extramontane alluvial plain received sediments from the mountain chain on the northwest.

Introduction

Devonian rocks are known to crop out in four districts of Norway and, because of their unusual character, have been the subject of

[1] Manuscript received, October 18, 1971.

[2] U.S. Geological Survey.

[3] Department of Geology, Leicester University, Leicester, England.

many geologic studies dating back to the early 1800s (Fig. 1). This paper summarizes previous work on these rocks, much of which is not published in English, and outlines the Devonian tectonic and sedimentary history of Norway. The writer's task has been facilitated by reference to previous summaries by Holtedahl (1960) and Allen *et al.* (1967, p. 83–85).

Southern Norway consists largely of a Precambrian foreland over which deformed, metamorphosed and intruded rocks of the Caledonian geosyncline were thrust southeastward in a series of orogenic episodes that are collectively referred to as the "Caledonian orogeny" (Fig. 1). This orogeny apparently culminated in Norway during Late Silurian to earliest Devonian time (Downtonian), although tectonic activity probably took place intermittently from late in the Precambrian to at least the end of the Devonian. Vogt (1929b) called the extensive Devonian tectonism the "Svalbardian disturbance," by analogy with Devonian movements in Spitsbergen. The Svalbardian disturbance followed the uplift of a major chain of mountains in the area of the former Caledonian geosyncline and resulted in the deposition of surprisingly thick accumulations of terrestrial sediments that were derived from erosion of the newly uplifted mountains. The Devonian sediments were deposited as (1) alluvial-fan accumulations in structurally formed intramontane basins located in the former eugeosynclinal area, and (2) as broad, extramontane alluvial-plain accumulations on the former foreland area to the southeast.

Allen *et al.* (1967) distinguished three types of Devonian sedimentary rocks in the North Atlantic region: (1) sequences that are completely nonmarine and were deposited unconformably on older rocks, (2) sequences that are nonmarine but that grade conformably upward from underlying marine rocks, and (3) sequences composed primarily of marine rocks but including interbedded nonmarine redbeds. Each of these types of sequences is considered to be a facies of the Old Red Sandstone, and the land area on which the sediments were de-

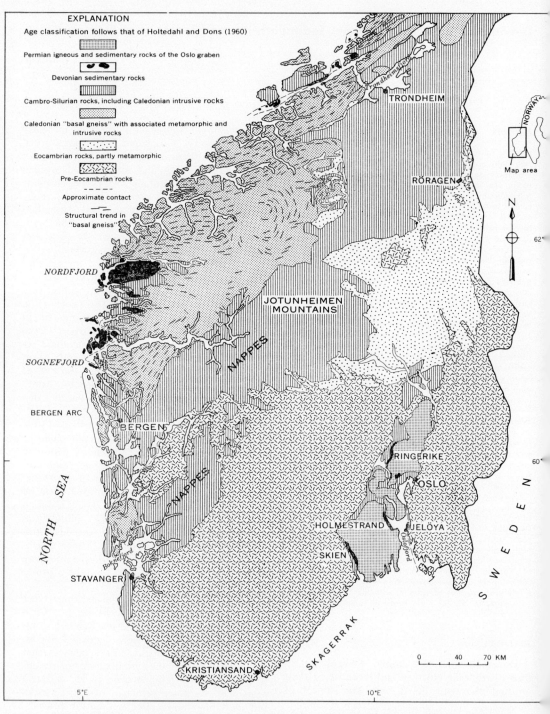

FIG. 1—Geologic map of southern Norway (modified from Holtedahl and Dons, 1960; Devonian of Oslo district is from J. H. McD. Whitaker, personal commun.).

posited is known as the "Old Red continent." Examination of Devonian rocks in Norway, Spitsbergen, East Greenland, Great Britain, Ireland, and North America strongly suggests a pre–continental-drift Devonian paleogeography that consisted of a linear central mountain chain flanked by coastal plains. The coastal plains passed laterally into shallow seas, and sediments were derived from streams eroding the mountains. The Old Red sedimentary rocks of the Nordfjord-Sognefjord, Trondheimsfjord, and Röragen districts are wholly nonmarine and have basal unconformities, whereas those of the Oslo district are conformable with underlying marine rocks and grade laterally southeastward into rocks deposited in the intertidal environment (Fig. 1). Following descriptions of the deposits of each district is a summary of the Old Red tectono-sedimentary history of Norway.

NORDFJORD-SOGNEFJORD DISTRICT

Devonian rocks along the west coast of Norway crop out in six separate sedimentary basins (Figs. 1, 2). These rocks form steep barren heights along the coast that have long interested geologists; they were first studied by Naumann (1824), who examined conglomerates in the Solund and Kvamshesten areas, and Keilhau (1838), who explored the Hornelen area. Irgens and Hiortedahl (1864) found more conglomerate in the Håsteinen area, published the first map of these basins, and suggested that the sediments were Devonian in age. They distinguished three levels of rocks along the coast: (1) a deepest gneiss ("basal gneiss"), (2) an intermediate mica schist–greenschist, and (3) a shallowest conglomerate-sandstone suite. More detailed studies of the sediments by Kjerulf (1879), Reusch (1881, 1912), and Helland (1881) contributed a wealth of information on the stratigraphy, structure, petrography, and sedimentology of these rocks.

Plant fossils found in the Hornelen area (C. Kolderup, 1904) finally proved a Devonian age for the sediments, and additional plant fragments were found later in the Kvamshesten, Buelandet-Vaerlandet, and Hornelen areas (C. Kolderup, 1915a, b, 1916a; Nathorst, 1915). The plant fossils, together with crossopterygian fish remains, convinced Kiaer (1918) that rocks of all the areas were Middle Devonian in age except those of Buelandet-Vaerlandet, which he thought to be Early Devonian. Fossils have not been found in the Håsteinen, Solund, or Byrknesoy-Holmengrå areas. C.

Kolderup's studies of each of the basins added a wealth of information on the Devonian rocks (1916b, 1923, 1925a, 1926a, 1927a, b), and N. Kolderup (1928) added complementary information about the underlying basement rocks. C. Kolderup (1925b, 1926b) also mapped some syndepositional intrusive or extrusive quartz keratophyres and some overthrust gabbro bodies within the Devonian conglomerates on Solund. Additional paleontologic studies were made on plants by Hoëg (1936) and on fish by Jarvik (1949). Each Devonian basin was restudied in the 1960s, thus providing many new ideas on the geologic development of these basins.

The Hornelen area was originally determined by C. Kolderup (1927a) to contain as much as 25,000 m of sedimentary rocks, primarily sandstone underlain by a basal breccia and conglomerate. Bryhni (1963, 1964a, b) suggested deposition in an east-west-trending graben and derivation of sediments from source areas on the north and south that were being uplifted contemporaneously. He inferred that the graben floor was tilted progressively westward along hinge faults and that the locus of sedimentation shifted progressively eastward with time; thus, the thickness of sediment accumulation at any particular locality would be considerably less than 25,000 m. The rocks were subsequently folded into an east-plunging syncline with tectonic contacts along the northern, eastern, and southern borders; an undisturbed basal unconformity is preserved in the west.

The Håsteinen area contains approximately 1,000 m of polymictic conglomerate with a coarse breccia at the base of the sequence and some sandstone in the uppermost part (C. Kolderup, 1925a). L. Osland (personal commun.) has suggested that the sediments were deposited in a basin that was infilled from all sides. The rocks are intensely faulted and may form a syncline; a basal unconformity is apparently preserved in the west, whereas the eastern contact is wholly tectonic.

The Kvamshesten area contains at least 4,000 m of Devonian sedimentary rocks, consisting of (1) 50–1,000 m of basal breccia and conglomerate, (2) 2,500 m of red and green sandstone, and (3) 700 m of red sandstone and polymictic conglomerate (F. J. Skjerlie and T. Höisaeter, personal commun.). The sediments are thought to have been deposited in a basin by streams eroding the surrounding source areas, which were undergoing uplift. The rocks were subsequently folded into an east-plunging

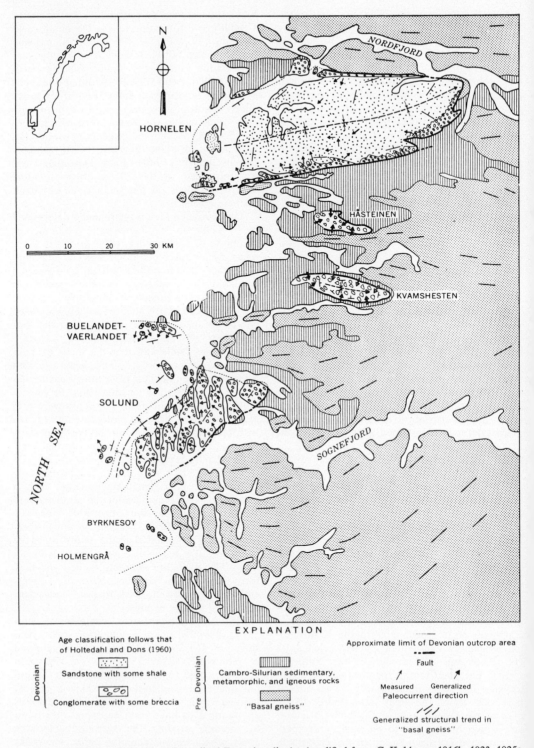

FIG. 2—Geology of Nordfjord-Sognefjord Devonian district (modified from C. Kolderup, 1916b, 1923, 1925a, 1926a, 1927a, b; N. Kolderup, 1928; Holtedahl and Dons, 1960; Bryhni, 1963, 1964a; F. J. Skjerlie, L. Osland, and T. Höisaeter, personal commun.; and Nilsen, 1968a, 1969).

syncline with subsidiary folds and faults of wide extent; the whole complex has apparently been thrust eastward, and only one portion of the western edge of the deposits retains an undisturbed basal unconformity.

The Buelandet-Vaerlandet area contains at least 3,400 m of sedimentary rocks, consisting of (1) a basal breccia up to 100 m thick and composed of fragments derived from the underlying greenschist, (2) 2,250 m of polymictic conglomerate, and (3) 1,050 m of sandstone (Nilsen, 1969). The sediments are thought to have been deposited as a coalesced alluvial-fan complex built southward by streams eroding a source area on the north that was undergoing uplift.

The Solund area contains 5,200 m of coarse polymictic conglomerate, including a thin basal breccia and lens-shaped interbeds of sandstone as thick as 700 m (Nilsen, 1967, 1968a, b). The sediments are thought to have been transported from southeast to northwest and deposited as a broad coalesced alluvial-fan complex. Along the southeastern margin of the basin the Devonian rocks have been thrust over basement rocks and also folded into a northeast-plunging anticline. The Solund deposits may grade laterally northward into the Buelandet-Vaerlandet deposits, thus forming a broader basin that may have originated as a graben. Nilsen (1968a) has suggested that the irregular gabbro bodies in the Solund deposits actually may be intrusive sills associated with the quartz keratophyre bodies noted by C. Kolderup (1925b, 1926a, b).

The Bryknesoy-Holmengrå outcrops consist primarily of polymictic conglomerate of undetermined thickness, but include some basal breccia and interbedded sandstone (C. Kolderup, 1927b). The strata lie unconformably on Cambro-Silurian schists of the Bergen arc; no transport directions for these rocks have been determined.

In summary, the Nordfjord-Sognefjord district consists of three northern basins containing Middle Devonian rocks that infilled separate grabens and were subsequently folded into east-plunging synclines and thrust eastward. Rocks of the southern areas may be younger in age, cannot be as clearly defined as graben deposits, and have undergone less postdepositional folding and faulting. Each of the basins is oriented parallel with older structural trends in the Caledonian "basal gneiss" and is filled with sedimentary units derived from the Cambro-Silurian sedimentary, igneous, and metamorphic rocks (including the "basal gneiss") that cropped out in the surrounding uplands.

TRONDHEIMSFJORD DISTRICT

North and west of the entrance to Trondheimsfjord, Devonian sedimentary rocks crop out as (1) a northeast-trending series of exposures up to 115 km long and 7 km wide, and (2) two small islands north of the village of Vallersund, about 20 km north of the first-named group of outcrops (Figs. 1, 3). Reusch (1914) first discovered the Devonian age of the rocks when he found fossil remains on Hitra that were identified as *Dictyocaris,* a phyllocarid crustacean thought to be Downtonian in age. Störmer (1935) collected additional specimens, including eurypterid fragments, from the same area and was able to identify the crustacean as *Dictyocaris slimoni,* a species indicative of a Downtonian age. Vogt (1924a, b, 1929a) collected Devonian plant fragments from Storfosen, and Höeg (1931, 1935, 1936) found many more Early Devonian plant fossils in the Trondheimsfjord district. He later found plant fossils on Örlandet which indicated most probably an Early Devonian age, but possibly also earliest Middle Devonian; in addition, he found plant fossils on the islands north of Vallersund which were typical of Middle Devonian flora and the first fossils of such age found in the Trondheimsfjord district (Höeg, 1945). D. Peacock (*in* Allen et al., 1967) more recently indicated an Early and Middle Devonian age for conglomerates on Smöla.

The Smöla and Hitra Devonian deposits crop out as a narrow belt of very steeply dipping beds up to 3.5 km wide that are exposed between Caledonian "basal gneiss" on the south and Caledonian intrusive rocks on the north. The Devonian rocks to the east, on Storfosen and Orlandet, have been folded into northeast-plunging synclines with outcrop widths up to 7 km.

Schetelig (1913) described the sedimentary rocks on Smöla and Hitra; Reusch (1914) published a more detailed description of the sequence on Hitra, which comprises (1) 20–30 m of basal breccia and conglomerate with clasts derived from the underlying diorite, and (2) several hundred meters of gray sandstone which contains interbeds of conglomerate composed of granitic clasts, as well as interbeds of fossil-bearing black shale. His paper also contains descriptions of such sedimentary features as conglomeratic channel-fills, "fining-upward" cycles, and rhythmic alternations of conglomer-

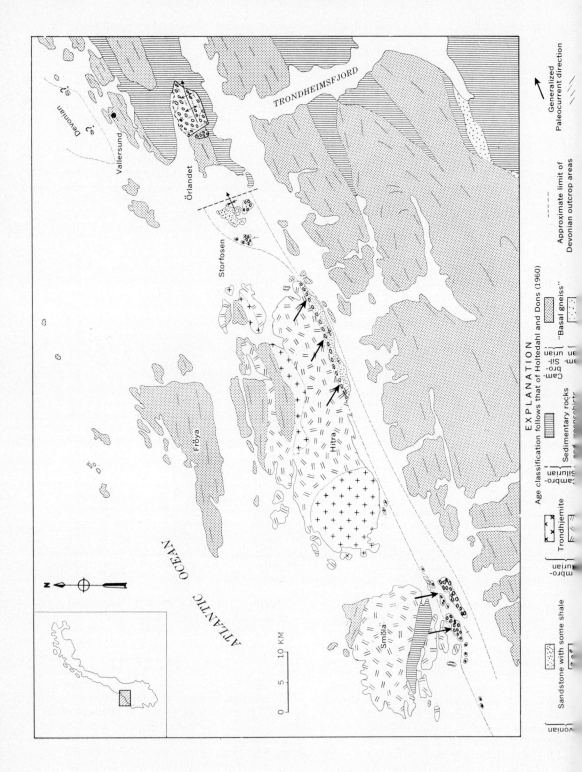

ate and sandstone. He suggested a westerly source for the gravels. Peacock subsequently measured an approximate thickness of 3,700 m of conglomerate on Smöla and judged these deposits to be younger (Early and Middle Devonian) than those on Hitra (latest Silurian or possibly Downtonian). Peacock (personal commun. and *in* Allen *et al.*, 1967) further concluded from stratigraphic and sedimentologic studies that the Smöla rocks were deposited on a broad alluvial piedmont by south-flowing streams.

The rock units on Storfosen and Örlandet were studied by Richter (1949, 1958). He measured a section of 1,800 m on Storfosen that consisted of a basal breccia, polymictic massive conglomerates, and, at the top, sandstone. Imbrication in the conglomerates suggested to him transport from south to north. In the Örlandet area, he described a section of 1,800 m that consists almost wholly of massive polymictic conglomerate, but the lower 50 m is more thinly bedded and contains some fossiliferous shale. Although no direction of transport for the conglomerates was given, he considered the deposits to have filled a graben and to have been deposited from Downtonian through Middle Devonian time. All the contacts of the Örlandet Devonian block with basement rocks are faulted.

The Trondheimsfjord Devonian rocks appear to be the remnants of what may once have been a larger northeast-trending intramontane valley, into which sediments were deposited by streams that were eroding highlands on the north and south. The nature of the sediments suggests that deposition took place primarily on alluvial fans built out into the valley, and that uplift of the source areas was penecontemporaneous with sedimentation. Transport of sediments in the center of the valley may have been primarily parallel with the axis of the valley. The valley may have originated as a post-orogenic graben following the main climax of the Caledonian orogeny, as suggested in part by Richter (1958). The fact that the valley is oriented approximately parallel with older Caledonian structural trends suggests some basement

control of the locus of basin formation. The small outcrops north of Vallersund are probably remnants of another Devonian basin of slightly younger age on the north.

RÖRAGEN DISTRICT

Goldschmidt (1913), on the basis of plant fossils found in the stratigraphically lower part of the exposed sequence (Fig. 1), mapped a small outlier of sedimentary rocks near the lake of Röragen in eastern Norway as Devonian. The district is located near the boundary between Precambrian and Eocambrian rocks on the southeast and Cambro-Silurian rocks on the northwest. Goldschmidt's fossils were examined by A. G. Nathorst, who suggested that the flora was indicative of the Middle Devonian (Goldschmidt, 1913); Halle (1916) collected additional specimens and concluded that the Röragen deposits were more likely to be Early Devonian in age. Höeg (1936) confirmed the Early Devonian age, primarily on the basis of the primitive characteristics of the *Psilophyton*-like flora.

Southwest of Röragen Lake, the Devonian sequence comprises (1) 80 m of basal conglomerate with moderate-sized pebbles composed of Eocambrian quartzite and trondhjemite; (2) 130 m of gray sandstone and shale with plant fossils, and (3) 10–20 m of red sandstone (Fig. 4). Northeast of the lake the sequence comprises (1) 10 m of a similar basal conglomerate, (2) gray sandstone and shale with interbedded red sandstone and conglomerate, and (3) at least 700 m of massive conglomerate and breccia composed of fragments of schist, phyllite, quartzite, and sparagmite derived from various sources. A serpentine breccia-conglomerate that is at least 200 m thick and is composed of angular serpentine fragments in a serpentine-rich groundmass crops out southwest of the main Devonian sedimentary sequence; it has heretofore been considered as Devonian (Holtedahl, 1960).

Goldschmidt (1913) mapped the boundary between the Devonian sedimentary rocks and Cambro-Silurian phyllite along the northwestern margin as a basal unconformity; he mapped the boundary along the northeastern margin as a fault contact. Goldschmidt thought the Devonian block had been downfaulted as a rigid body into the older basement rocks. Holtedahl (1960) emphasized the necessity for penecontemporaneous uplift of the surrounding source areas during active deposition in the Devonian basin, particularly because of the up-

←⫷⫷⫷

FIG. 3—Geology of the Trondheimsfjord Devonian district (modified from Holtedahl and Dons, 1960; Devonian lithologies and paleocurrents from Reusch, 1914; Richter, 1949; Allen *et al.*, 1967; and D. Peacock, personal commun.).

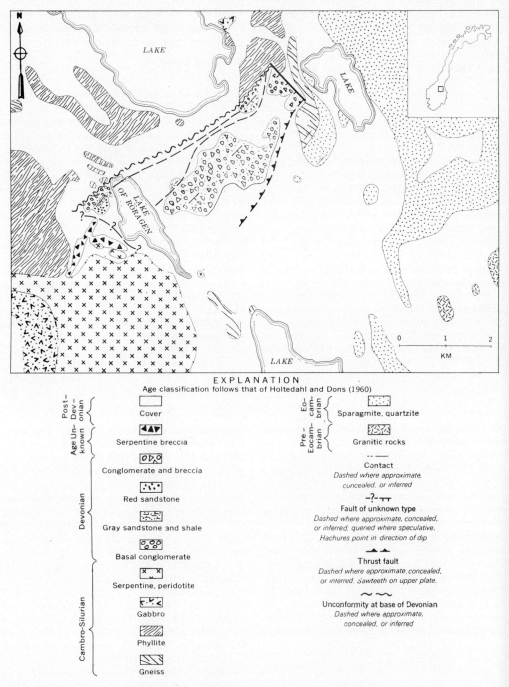

EXPLANATION
Age classification follows that of Holtedahl and Dons (1960)

Post-Dev-onian — Cover

Age Un-known — Serpentine breccia

Devonian — Conglomerate and breccia

Red sandstone

Gray sandstone and shale

Basal conglomerate

Cambro-Silurian — Serpentine, peridotite

Gabbro

Phyllite

Gneiss

Eo-cam-brian — Sparagmite, quartzite

Pre-Eocam-brian — Granitic rocks

Contact
Dashed where approximate,
concealed, or inferred

Fault of unknown type
Dashed where approximate, concealed,
or inferred, queried where speculative.
Hachures point in direction of dip

Thrust fault
Dashed where approximate, concealed,
or inferred. Sawteeth on upper plate.

Unconformity at base of Devonian
Dashed where approximate,
concealed, or inferred

Fig. 4—Geology of Röragen Devonian district (modified from Goldschmidt, 1913; Holtedahl, 1960; Holtedahl and Dons, 1960; and Holmsen, 1963).

ward persistence of coarse clasts in the stratigraphic sequence.

Holmsen (1963) reexamined the Röragen area and concluded that the Devonian rocks had been thrust over basement rocks along the drift-covered southeastern margin of the Devonian block. He also noted complex folding within the Devonian sequence, possible subsidiary thrust faults, and local low-grade metamorphism of the Devonian rocks. He reinterpreted the tectonic and sedimentary history of the Röragen Devonian as consisting of two episodes. The first included formation of a subsiding basin during a late phase of the Caledonian orogeny and syntectonic deposition of coarse clastic material in the basin (the direction of transport was not determined). He suggested that faulting probably controlled the formation of the basin and that uplift of the source area exposed progressively deeper parts of the pre-Devonian basement to erosion. The second episode consisted of postdepositional Svalbardian folding and faulting of the Devonian rocks along structural trends different from the earlier Caledonian trends—although the northeast-southwest orientation of the basin is generally parallel with the older structures. The writer suggests that the serpentine conglomerate may not be Devonian in age; instead, it may be either old landslide debris derived from the Caledonian serpentine and peridotites on the south or a tectonic breccia formed along a yet-unrecognized fault at the southwestern margin of the basin.

RINGERIKE SERIES OF OSLO DISTRICT[4]

The Ringerike Series, consisting of red sandstones and siltstones with scattered mud-flake breccias, of Late Silurian to Early Devonian(?) age, crops out at various localities in the Oslo graben (Fig. 1). Kiaer (1908, 1911, 1924, 1931) studied the series in the Oslo and Jelöya areas. Recently it has been studied near Oslo by Spjeldnaes (1966) and at Ringerike, Skien, and Holmestrand by Whitaker (1964, 1965, 1966). The fauna of eurypterids, phyllocarids, and fish is well known; the latest publication on the paleontology of the Ringerike Series is by Heintz (1969).

At Ringerike, about 1,250 m of redbeds have been gently arched into a broad anticline and are cut by several post-Permian faults, some

occupied by dikes. The lower beds consist of a large proportion of dark-red and green muddy siltstones, from which the above-mentioned fauna and trace fossils have been obtained. Ripple marks of various types, ripple-drift lamination, mudcracks, and other primary structures are seen.

Higher in the sequence, fine-grained sandstones, commonly micaceous, are more abundant, but many argillaceous layers with calcareous pellets and others with mudcracks, some showing diapiric characteristics, are present (Whitaker, 1964). Other structures include ripple marks, ripple-drift, parting lineation, and planar cross-stratification, slumps, ball-and-pillow structure, and sole markings of several types.

Mud-flake breccias are present at various levels in the Ringerike Series, as are crossbedded calcarenites that contain derived shelly fossils of Silurian type. Quartz, igneous, and metamorphic pebbles are completely absent, but scarce grains of antiperthitic feldspar suggest a source area in central Norway.

The uniformity of bedding, general fineness of grains, scarcity of channels, and absence of typical "fining-upward" cycles, together with the southerly thinning of the Ringerike Series (only 300 m at Skien) and with paleocurrent measurements, support the view that a source area about 200 km to the north-northwest and northwest supplied sediment to an extensive extramontane alluvial plain sloping gently toward the south-southeast; braided rivers probably flooded widely over the alluvial plain at times. Temporary lakes supported fish, eurypterids, and phyllocarids, leaving wide expanses of ripple-marked and mudcracked surfaces, some of which show the trails of these animals. Near Oslo, this alluvial plain passed into an intertidal area (Spjeldnaes, 1966).

SUMMARY AND CONCLUSIONS

The terrestrial Devonian rocks of the Nordfjord-Sognefjord, Trondheimsfjord, and Röragen districts were deposited in intramontane basins that were most likely formed as structural depressions of the graben or half-graben type. The rocks are preserved in only three areas where Cambro-Silurian rocks crop out adjacent to them; in the intervening areas, where only the "basal gneiss" is exposed, no Devonian rocks crop out (Fig. 1). The implication is that additional Devonian basins probably existed over a broader area of Norway but have subsequently been eroded during uplift of

---

[4] This section was contributed by J. H. McD. Whitaker.

the intervening areas that are presently underlain by "basal gneiss." Only small remnants of
the previously much more widespread Devonian intramontane basins remain.

Basin sedimentation began in Downtonian
time, if not earlier, and continued at least into
the Middle Devonian in some areas. Contemporaneity of uplift and sedimentation is indicated in each district. The orientation of the basins parallel with older Caledonian structural
trends suggests that rifting or graben formation
was controlled by preexisting structural lineaments. The extensive folding and faulting of
the Devonian areas, including eastward thrusting of the basins over basement rocks, indicate
intense tectonic activity during the Svalbardian
disturbance. The Svalbardian disturbance must
also have included, however, syndepositional
graben formation, repeated uplift of source
areas, and tectonic movements that date back
at least to the Downtonian; in fact, the formation of the Bergen arc may be a Svalbardian
event. Thus, the Svalbardian disturbance is
clearly in part coeval with tectonic episodes referred to the Caledonian orogeny. The distinction of Svalbardian events from the main phase
of the Caledonian orogeny, therefore, must be
based on different tectonic styles of deformation which possibly occurred simultaneously in
different parts of Norway.

The great thicknesses of sedimentary rocks
in relatively small basins suggest that erosion
and deposition proceeded vigorously, and that
abundant seasonal rainfall was capable of
transporting very coarse detritus into the sedimentary basins. Sedimentary structures and
stratigraphic relations indicate alluvial-fan deposition, whereby the finer grained sediments
accumulated on broad alluvial plains or in
lakes beyond the fan margins. Many of the intramontane basins may have been short-lived or
somewhat impermanent, because continued
tectonic activity and rapid infilling of the basins
shifted the loci of sedimentation. More widespread alluvial deposits are found east of the
central chain of mountains in the Oslo district.
These finer grained sediments (the coarse-
grained sediments of the intramontane basins
are absent) were probably transported by
through-flowing streams toward flanking
coastal plains. The distinct intramontane and
extramontane facies are also found in the Old
Red deposits of Great Britain and the Old
Red-type deposits of the Appalachian Mountains of North America.

REFERENCES CITED

Allen, J. R. L., D. L. Dineley, and P. F. Friend, 1967,
Old Red Sandstone basins of North America and
northwest Europe, in D. H. Oswald, ed., International Symposium on the Devonian System, v. 1:
Calgary, Alberta Soc. Petroleum Geologists, p. 69–
98.
Bryhni, Inge, 1963, Relasjonen mellom senkaledonsk
tektonikk og sedimentasjon ved Hornelens og Hås-
teinens devon (Engl. summ.): Norges Geol. Undersøkelse, no. 223 (Årb. 1962), p. 10–25.
──── 1964a, Migrating basins on the Old Red Continent: Nature, v. 202, p. 384–385.
──── 1964b, Sediment structures in the Hornelen series: Norsk Geol. Tidsskr., v. 44, p. 486–488.
Goldschmidt, V. M., 1913, Das Devongebiet am Röragen bei Röros mit einem Palaeobotanischen Bietrag:
Die Pflanzenreste der Röragen-Ablagerung, von
A. G. Nathorst: Skr. Videnskapsselskapet i Kristiania,
v. 2.
Halle, T. G., 1916, Some Devonian plants from Röragen in Norway: Kgl. Svenska Vetensk. Akad. Handl.,
57, p. 1–46.
Heintz, A., 1969, New agnaths from the Ringerike
Sandstone: Norske Vidensk-Akad. Skr., v. 1, no. 26,
p. 1–28.
Helland, A., 1881, Studier over konglomerater: Archiv
for Matematik og Naturvidenskab for 1880, 6B, 1H,
p. 1–80.
Höeg, O. A., 1931, Notes on the Devonian flora of
western Norway: Kgl. Norske Vidensk. Selsk. Skr.,
no. 6, p. 1–33.
──── 1935, Further contributions to the Middle Devonian flora of western Norway: Norsk Geol.
Tidsskr., v. 15, p. 1–17.
──── 1936, Norges fossile flora: Naturen, v. 60, p.
53–96.
──── 1945, Contributions to the Devonian flora of
western Norway III: Norsk Geol. Tidsskr., v. 25, p.
183–192.
Holmsen, P., 1963, On the tectonic relations of the
Devonian complex of the Röragen area, east-central
Norway: Norges Geol. Undersøkelse, no. 223, p. 127–
138.
Holtedahl, Olaf, 1960, Devonian, including Downtonian in the Hitra district, etc., in Olaf Holtedahl,
Geology of Norway: Norges Geol. Undersøkelse, no.
208 (Årb. 1962), p. 285–297.
──── and J. A. Dons, compilers, 1960, Geologisk kart
over Norge (bergrunnskart) (Geological map of
Norway [bedrock]): Norges Geol. Undersøkelse, no.
208.
Irgens, M., and Th. Hiortedahl, 1864, Om de geologiske forhold paa kyststrækningen af Nordre Ber-
genhus Amt. (French summ.), in Efter det academ-
iske Collegiums Foranstaltning udgivet som Univer-
sitetsprogram for andet halvaar 1864 ved Dr. Th.
Kjerulf: Christiania (Oslo), Brögger and Christies
Bogtrykkeri, p. 1–14.
Jarvik, E., 1949, On the Middle Devonian crossoptery-
gians from the Hornelen field in western Norway:
Univ. i Bergen Aarbok 1948, Naturvidensk. Raekke,
no. 8, 48 p.
Keilhau, B. M., 1838, Gaea Norvegica, von mehreren
Verfassen: Christiania (Oslo), Druck und Verlag
von Johann Dahl, 516 p.
Kiaer, J., 1908, Dar Obersilur in Kristianiagebiete:
Norske Vidensk.-Selsk. Skr., Matt.-Naturv. Kl., 2.

———— 1911, A new Downtonian fauna in the Sandstone Series of the Kristiania area: Norske Vidensk.-Selsk. Skr., Matt.-Naturv. Kl., 7.

———— 1918, Fiskerester fra den devoniske sandsten paa Norges vestkyst (Engl. summ.): Bergens Mus. Aarbok, Naturvidensk. Raekke, no. 7, p. 1–17.

———— 1924, The Downtonian fauna of Norway. I. The Anaspida: Norske Vidensk.-Selsk. Skr. 1, Matt.-Naturv. Kl., 6.

———— 1931, Hemicyclaspis murchisoni-faunaen i den Downtoniske sandsten på Jelöen i Oslofjorden: Norsk Geol. Tidsskr., v. 12, p. 419–434.

Kjerulf, Th., 1879, Fire felter af konglomerat og sandsten, in Udsigt over det sydlige Norges Geologi: Christiania (Oslo), Fabritius, 262 p.

Kolderup, C. F., 1904, Vestlandets devonisk lagraekker: Naturen, p. 270–276.

———— 1915a, Vestlandets devonfelter og deres plantefossiler: Naturen, p. 217–232.

———— 1915b, Das Vorkommen der Pflanzenreste: Bergens Mus. Aarbok 1914–1915, Naturvidensk. Raekke, no. 9, p. 1–11.

———— 1916a, Vestnorges devon: Förh. ved 16. Skand. Naturforskermötet, p. 499–507.

———— 1916b, Bulandets og Vaerlandets konglomerat og sandstensfelt (Engl. summ.): Bergens Mus. Aarbok 1915–1916, Naturvidensk. Raekke, no. 3, p. 1–26.

———— 1923, Kvamshestens devonfelt (Engl. summ.): Bergens Mus. Aarbok 1920–1921, Naturvidensk. Raekke, no. 4, p. 1–96.

———— 1925a, Haasteinens devonfelt (Engl. summ.): Bergens Mus. Aarbok 1923–1924, Naturvidensk. Raekke, no. 11, p. 1–32.

———— 1925b, En postorkadisk overskyvning i det vestlige Norge: Förh. ved. 17. Skand. Naturforskermötet, 1923, p. 173–179.

———— 1926a, Solunds devonfelt (Engl. summ.): Bergens Mus. Aarbok 1924–1925, Naturvidensk. Raekke, no. 8, p. 1–73.

———— 1926b, Vulkansk virksomhet og indpresning av aeldre bergarter i Vestlandets devon: Naturen, p. 129–142.

———— 1927a, Hornelens devonfelt (Engl. Summ.): Bergens Mus. Aarbok 1926, Naturvidensk. Raekke, no. 6, p. 1–56.

———— 1927b, Byrknesöyenes og Holmengraas devonfelter (Engl. summ.): Bergens Mus. Aarbok 1928, Naturvidensk. Raekke, no. 8, p. 1–18.

Kolderup, N.-H., 1928, Fjellbygningen i kystsröket mellom Nordfjord og Sognefjord (Engl. summ.): Bergens Mus. Aarbok 1928, Naturvidensk. Raekke, no. 1, p. 1–222.

Nathorst, A. G., 1915, Zur Devonflora des westlichen Norwegens: Bergens Mus. Aarbok 1914–1915, Naturvidensk. Raekke, no. 9, p. 12–23.

Naumann, C. F., 1824, Beyträge zur kenntniss Norwegens: v. 2, Leipzig.

Nilsen, T. H., 1967, Old Red sedimentation in the Solund district, western Norway, in D. H. Oswald, ed., International Symposium on the Devonian System, v. 2: Calgary, Alberta Soc. Petroleum Geologists, p. 1101–1115.

———— 1968a, The relationship of sedimentation to tectonics in the Solund Devonian district of southwestern Norway: Norges Geol. Undersøkelse, no. 259, 106 p.

———— 1968b, Sedimentary structures in Devonian fanglomerates, western Norway (abs.): Am. Assoc. Petroleum Geologists Bull., v. 53, p. 543.

———— 1969, Old Red sedimentation in the Buelandet-Vaerlandet Devonian district, western Norway: Sed. Geology, v. 3, p. 35–57.

Reusch, H. H., 1881, Konglomerat-sandstensfelterne i Nordfjord, Söndfjord og Sogn: Nyt Magazin for Naturvidenskaberne, v. 26, p. 93–170.

———— 1912, Bergenkystens devon: Naturen, p. 103–110.

———— 1914, Nogen bidrag til Hitterens og Smölens geologi (Engl. summ.): Norges Geol. Undersökelse, no. 69, p. 1–50.

Richter, M., 1949, Die Devonmolasse am Ausgang des Drontheimfjordes: Zeitschr. der Deutschen Geol. Gesell., v. 99, p. 1–7.

———— 1958, Die Halbinsel Orland am Ausgang des Trondheimfjordes: Geologie, v. 7, no. 3–6, p. 757–768.

Schetelig, J., 1913, Hitteren og Smölen (Engl. summ.); Et bidrag til den norske fjeldkjedes geologi: Norsk Geol. Tidsskr., p. 3–27.

Spjeldnaes, N., 1966, Silurian tidal sediments from the base of the Ringerike Formation, Oslo region, Norway: Norsk Geol. Tidsskr., v. 46, p. 497–509.

Störmer, L., 1935, *Dictyocaris salter*, a large crustacean from the Upper Silurian and Downtonian: Norsk Geol. Tidsskr., v. 15, p. 267–278.

Vogt, Th., 1924a, Undersökelser på Kartbladet Örlandet: Norges Geol. Undersøkelse, no. 122, p. 89–93.

———— 1924b, Plantefossiler fra Storfosens devoniske lagraekke: Naturen, p. 53–56.

———— 1929a, Undersökelser over den underdevoniske konglomerat-sandstensserie i Ytre Tröndelagen: Norges Geol. Undersøkelse, no. 133, p. 59–61.

———— 1929b, Den Norske Fjellkjedes revolusjons-historie: Norsk Geol. Tidsskr., v. 10, p. 97–115.

Whitaker, J. H. McD., 1964, Mud-crack diapirism in the Ringerike Sandstone of southern Norway: Norsk Geol. Tidsskr., v. 44, p. 19–30.

———— 1965, Primary sedimentary structures from the Silurian and Lower Devonian of the Oslo region, Norway: Nature, v. 207, no. 4998, p. 709–711.

———— 1966, The Silurian and Lower Devonian geology of Ringerike, southern Norway: Leicester, England, Univ. Leicester, unpub. Ph.D. thesis, 2 vols., 242 p. and 176 p.

Evolution of Arctic Ocean Basin

Geologic Concepts of Arctic Ocean Basin[1]

MICHAEL CHURKIN, JR.[2]

Menlo Park, California

Abstract Geologic concepts of the Arctic Ocean basin are that it is (1) a permanent or old feature of the earth's crust, dating from at least the early Paleozoic and probably from the Proterozoic, or (2) a relatively young feature, Mesozoic and/or Cenozoic, formed by subsidence of continental crust or by continental drift, through a process of rifting and/or sea-floor spreading. If the Arctic basin is considered as a whole, the great differences between parts of the basin indicate that its overall tectonic history has been far too complicated to be explained by either hypothesis.

Oceanographic and geophysical studies indicate that the Arctic Ocean basin is not a uniformly deep basin isolated from the world ocean system, but that it is divided into separate basins by submarine mountain ranges. The Eurasian basin, separated from the Canada basin by the Lomonosov Ridge, is connected to the northern Atlantic by a deep trough. The Gakkel Ridge, which crosses the Eurasian basin as an extension of the Mid-Atlantic Ridge, has volcanic and seismic activity that can be related to sea-floor spreading.

The shape of the Lomonosov Ridge shows a good fit with the continental margin of Eurasia, and the ridge appears to be a narrow fragment of Eurasia that has drifted passively into the center of the Arctic Ocean as the Eurasian basin spread.

The Canada basin, on the other side of the Lomonosov Ridge, contains the Alpha Cordillera, which is probably a dormant midocean ridge from an older period of sea-floor spreading. The opposite margins of the Canada basin do not have a good geometric fit.

Undeformed Cenozoic and, in places, Mesozoic deposits rimming both the Eurasian and the Canada basins indicate that no major movement has occurred between the floor of the Arctic Ocean basin and its continental margins since at least Early Cretaceous time.

Paleozoic rocks around the edges of the Arctic Ocean are generally much more deformed than Mesozoic and Cenozoic rocks. The Canada basin is rimmed on the south by a discontinuously exposed system of Paleozoic fold belts, elements of which seem to extend into both ends of the Lomonosov Ridge. The early development of geosynclines along the margins of the modern Canada basin —followed by deformation, metamorphism, granite intrusion, and major uplift and clastic-wedge sedimentation —indicates that a proto–Canada basin with continental-margin tectonics existed in the early Paleozoic.

The Eurasian basin appears to be a feature much younger than the Canada basin. No Paleozoic fold belts parallel its edges; instead, the Eurasian basin appears to truncate the Ural, Cherskiy, and Verkhoyansk fold belts.

The close similarity in the geology of Alaska and Siberia indicates that North America and Asia have been connected since the Paleozoic, and probably since the Precambrian, and that a proto–Canada basin, structurally separate from the Pacific and the Atlantic, can be identified as a center of Paleozoic marine sedimentation that served as an avenue for polar migration of faunas. Stratigraphic, structural, and petrologic features suggest that the boundary between the Paleozoic Cherskiy fold belt and the Mesozoic Verkhoyansk fold belt marks the suture of the Eurasian and North American continental plates that collided in Early Cretaceous time, perhaps as a consequence of opening of the Atlantic.

The available data are best explained by considering a series of stages in the development of the Arctic, beginning with development of a proto–Canada basin (Cambrian–Middle Devonian), which probably closed in Late Devonian–Early Mississippian time, followed by formation of successor basins (Mississippian-Triassic), opening of the modern Canada basin (Late Jurassic or Early Cretaceous), development of the deep Canada basin (Late Cretaceous), and opening of the Eurasian basin in connection with sea-floor spreading from Gakkel Ridge (Cenozoic).

INTRODUCTION

In addition to the tremendous increase in data since the First Symposium on Arctic Geology held in Calgary in 1960, there has been a revolution in ideas concerning the relations of oceans and continents. On the basis of data obtained mainly from the Atlantic and Pacific Ocean basins, the old ideas of continental drift have been reconsidered and subsequently incorporated into the new theory of sea-floor spreading and plate tectonics. The Arctic Ocean basin, however, appears to be a much smaller, isolated basin with several unusual features which should be investigated before the theory developed for the world ocean system can be applied to it.

Geologic concepts of the Arctic Ocean basin fall into two groups. One theory is that it is a relatively young feature formed by crustal subsidence or by continental drift through a process of rifting and/or sea-floor spreading during the Mesozoic and/or Cenozoic. Figure 1 illustrates the basic elements of the crustal-subsidence theory (Shatsky, 1935; Pushcharovsky, 1960; Atlasov, 1964).

This hypothesis is supported by the abrupt truncation of major fold belts which trend into the Arctic basin. Evidence of an ancient landmass in the basin area that shed clastic sediments into the regions rimming the basin has been found. This source area, thought to be a

[1] Manuscript received, September 20, 1971. Publication authorized by the Director, U.S. Geological Survey.

[2] U.S. Geological Survey.

FIG. 1—Theory of subsidence of continental crust (Shatsky, 1935); Pushcharovsky, 1960; Atlasov, 1964); hachures show deep-seated fault zones.

Precambrian platform (Shatsky, 1935), is believed to have sunk and formed the floor of the Arctic basin. However, the hypothesis does not explain conversion of sunken continental crust into oceanic crust (Pushcharovsky, 1960; Beloussov and Kosminskaya, 1968). Furthermore, the types of clastic sediments shed from the Arctic are coarse-grained chert-argillite conglomerate and sandstone that probably reflect tectonic uplift of an earlier Paleozoic geosyncline rather than a Precambrian platform or shield (Churkin, 1969).

Figure 2 illustrates the pattern of continental movements according to the rift theory (Carey, 1955; Tailleur and Brosgé, 1970; Rickwood, 1970). The oroclinal bend in southern Alaska

can be interpreted as a complementary feature of the tensional rifting in the Arctic basin (Carey, 1955; Tailleur and Brosgé, 1970. However, this hypothesis does not explain the submarine ridges that cross the basin at right angles to the direction of rifting and are not offset (Eardley, 1960). The Eurasian basin is elongated at right angles to the Canada basin, and its straight margin is a good geometric fit to the Lomonosov Ridge. The Canada basin, however, has a rather straight margin along the Canadian Arctic Islands, but on the Siberian side is the Chukchi Cap, a detached continental outlier (Churkin, 1973).

Figure 3 shows the positions of the various centers of spreading as proposed for the sea-

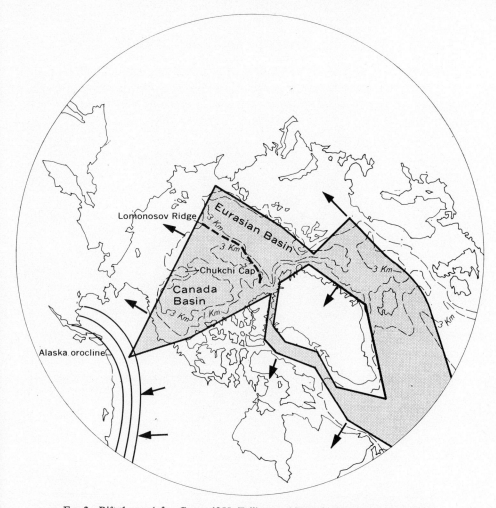

Fig. 2—Rift theory (after Carey, 1955; Tailleur and Brosgé, 1970; Rickwood, 1970).

floor-spreading theory; however, interpretation of the spreading rates is very preliminary, especially for the Alpha Cordillera. No spreading center is known to account for most of the deep part of the Canada basin north of Alaska.

The alternate theory suggests that the Arctic basin is a permanent or old feature of the earth's crust, dating from at least the Paleozoic, and probably the Precambrian. Supporting evidence for this supposition is said to be the Precambrian and Paleozoic evaporite distribution pattern in the Arctic (Meyerhoff, 1970). Another line of evidence that has been suggested to support a Paleozoic age for the Canada basin regards the early Paleozoic geosynclines along its margins. The geosynclinal sedimentation was followed by deformation, metamor-

phism, granite intrusion, and major uplifts within the resulting fold belts that shed wedges of clastic sediments; such a history is like that of other ancient ocean basins which are believed to have closed in the past (Churkin, 1969).

MODERN FEATURES AND GEOPHYSICAL DATA

The floor of the Arctic Ocean has subparallel submarine ridges which cross its long axis and divide its deeper parts into separate basins (Fig. 4). The Eurasian basin, separated from the Canada basin by the Lomonosov Ridge, is connected with the North Atlantic by a deep trough between Greenland and Spitsbergen (Ostenso, 1968). The Gakkel Ridge (Nansen Cordillera), which crosses the Eurasian basin

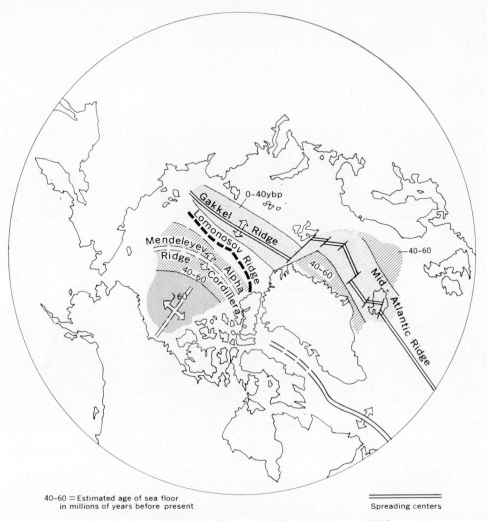

40-60 = Estimated age of sea floor
            in millions of years before present

Spreading centers

FIG. 3—Sea-floor-spreading theory (after Vogt and Ostenso, 1970).

midway between the Lomonosov Ridge and the continental margin of Eurasia, has volcanic centers and rift features (Atlasov, 1964), as well as seismic activity (Sykes, 1965) and a magnetic-anomaly pattern (Vogt *et al.*, 1970; Wold and Ostenso, this volume)—all of which can be related to sea-floor spreading on an Arctic extension of the Mid-Atlantic Ridge (Heezen and Ewing, 1961; Ostenso, 1968; Churkin, 1973).

An analysis of geophysical data suggests that the tensional tectonic conditions of the Gakkel spreading center do not end at the head of the Eurasian basin but extend into the continental framework of eastern Siberia (Demenitskaya and Karasik, 1969). The Sadko Trough, an un-

usually large submarine canyon at the head of the Eurasian basin, is aligned with the Gakkel Ridge, is the locus of earthquakes, and is reported to be a rift feature (Demenitskaya and Karasik, 1969; Fig. 4). The line of earthquake epicenters along the Gakkel Ridge and Sadko Trough continues across the Laptev Sea, where it splits into a southerly trend that follows the Verkhoyansk Mountains and a more southeasterly trend that follows the Cherskiy system of mountain ranges and depressions (Rezanov, 1964). According to Rezanov, very active Quaternary tectonic movements in the Cherskiy mountain system have produced large uplifts and depressions in this, the most active earthquake belt in the northeastern USSR. The

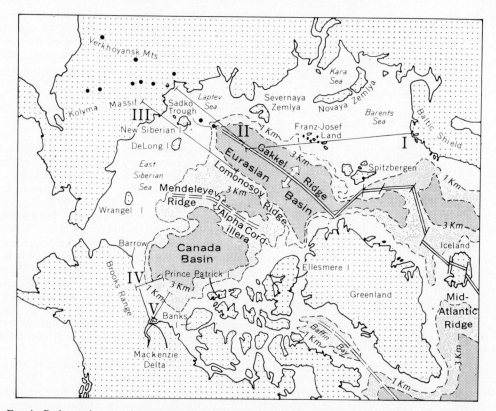

FIG. 4—Bathymetric map of Arctic Ocean showing submarine ridges and earthquake epicenters in Yakutia.

faulting and volcanism within the Cherskiy mountain system have been recognized as a landward extension of the sea-floor-spreading tectonics of the submarine Gakkel Ridge (Demenitskaya and Karasik, 1969). The crust in the Laptev Sea has been interpreted as transitional from continental crust into crust characteristic of midoceanic ridges (Demenitskaya *et al.*, 1968; Fig. 5). I believe that the available data from the Laptev Sea area suggest similar tectonic conditions to those in the Gulf of California, where faulting extends inland from the East Pacific Rise (Larson *et al.*, 1968).

Another prominent submarine feature is the Alpha Cordillera. Preliminary correlations of its magnetic profile with those of ridges in the northern Atlantic suggest that the Alpha Cordillera may have been a center of sea-floor spreading 40–60 m.y. ago, but that it now is dormant (Vogt and Ostenso, 1970; Ostenso and Wold, this volume; Fig. 3). Geophysical studies from ice station T-3, including seismic reflection profiling, support these results and show fractures and buried topography on the

Alpha Cordillera similar to those on the Mid-Atlantic Ridge (Hall, this volume).

The average thickness of unconsolidated sediments on the Alpha Cordillera is estimated to be nearly 400 m (Hunkins, 1961). If it is reasonable to extrapolate present rates of sedimentation in the area (Hunkins and Kutschale, 1965) much farther back in geologic time, it appears that the Alpha Cordillera could have been in existence since at least the Jurassic.

The Alpha Cordillera seems to be continuous with the Mendeleyev Ridge (Atlasov, 1964; Fig. 3). Their difference in trend may have resulted from displacement of the Alpha part of an originally more linear trend by impingement of the Lomonosov Ridge at the time of opening of the Eurasian basin.

The low heat flow ($\sim 1 \mu cal/cm^2/sec$) on the flank of the Alpha Cordillera suggests a low-conductivity crust such as that in an extinct midocean ridge, rather than a lagging remnant of a sunken continent (Lachenbruch and Marshall, 1969). Much higher heat flow (in the order of 3.0 $\mu cal/cm^2/sec$) across the Gakkel

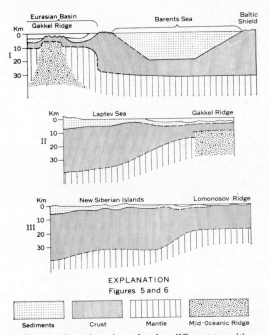

EXPLANATION
Figures 5 and 6

Sediments   Crust   Mantle   Mid-Oceanic Ridge

Fig. 5—Crustal sections showing different transitions between Eurasia and Arctic Ocean basin (after Demenitskaya *et al.*, 1968).

Ridge (Lyubimova *et al.*, 1969) supports the interpretation that this ridge is an active mid-ocean ridge. Heat-flow values on the Lomonosov Ridge (about 1.5–2.0 μcal/cm²/sec) are somewhat higher than the world average.

Recent surveys indicate a trend of high gravity along the continental margin of the Canada basin—from Barrow, Alaska, to Banks Island and beyond—which is broken by saddles of lower gravity offshore from the Colville, Mackenzie, and other river mouths (Wold *et al.*, 1970; Barnes, 1970; Sobzcak and Weber, this volume). These data suggest a thinning of the crust and the presence of a ridge in the basement rocks at about the 200-m isobath (Wold *et al.*, 1970). In comparison to continental margins elsewhere, Alaska has an unusually narrow transition from oceanic to continental crust; it occurs at 55–100 km from shore and at about the 200-m isobath, instead of at the 2,000-m isobath, as is the case for other continental margins. The possibility that an uncommonly thick accumulation of sediments may have displaced this transition zone landward implies a faster rate of sedimentation or a greater age for this continental margin than the world average (Wold *et al.*, 1970). Another explanation of this anomalous crustal transition is that the gravity high may, as a result of the re-

moval of less dense rock by deep erosion, reflect the Arctic source postulated for the wedges of coarse clastic sedimentary rocks formed in northern Alaska in the Late Devonian and in the Permian and Triassic (Churkin, 1969). Basement ridges such as the ridge along the southern margin of the Canada basin are common along continental margins elsewhere (Burk, 1968; Emery, 1968) and could reflect continental separation.

A series of crustal cross sections made by Demenitskaya *et al.* (1968) shows different transitions between the Eurasian continent and the Arctic Ocean (Fig. 5). One section in Figure 5 illustrates the crust from the Baltic shield across the Barents Sea and into the Eurasian basin. The part extending from the Baltic shield to Franz Josef Land is shown as continental crust with a thick sedimentary cover in the Barents Sea. The Gakkel Ridge has a crustal structure typical of a midocean ridge and is underlain by a layer in which compressional wave velocities are in the order of 7.5 km/sec—supposedly indicating a mixture of mantle and crustal material (Demenitskaya *et al.*, 1968). The abyssal plains on both sides of the Gakkel Ridge have a thin crust that appears to be typically oceanic.

From the north side of the Kolyma massif across the New Siberian Islands and along the Lomonosov Ridge, the crust gradually thins into the Lomonosov Ridge to provide a seismic layer of "subcontinental" crust (Fig. 5).

Figure 6 compares the crustal profiles of the Eurasian basin with those of the Canada basin. The transition from continental to oceanic crust off the Barents shelf is abrupt, as is that off northern Alaska. The transition is more gradual across the East Siberian Sea and the Mackenzie delta, where the abrupt transition has been modified by thick deposits of sediments.

MESOZOIC AND CENOZOIC GEOLOGIC FEATURES

The Canada basin is discontinuously rimmed by coastal-plain deposits. In northern Alaska the coastal plain is masked by Quaternary deposits which lie in places on nearly undeformed Upper Cretaceous rocks and, in other places, on Tertiary strata (Fig. 7). The Cretaceous marine deposits slope landward from the coast and thicken into a foredeep along the north front of the Brooks Range, where their nonmarine equivalents are complexly folded and faulted (Brosgé and Tailleur, 1970).

A minimum estimate of the age of the Canada basin north of Alaska is Late Cretaceous because a submarine canyon leading into the basin east of Barrow had been cut to a depth of more than 4,500 ft (1,370 m) and filled with sediments during the Late Cretaceous (Collins and Robinson, 1967, p. 183, Pl. 7). The modern Canada basin probably originated in either Late Jurassic or earliest Cretaceous time when clastic sediments were shed northward into the basin from uplifts in the Brooks Range. In the late Paleozoic and Triassic, the land and sea shifted to opposite positions, and detritus was shed from uplifts along the margins of the basin south toward the interior of Alaska (Brosgé and Tailleur, 1970).

Farther east, another segment of the Arctic coastal plain includes the region of the delta of the Mackenzie River where a mantle of Cenozoic deposits is underlain by a thick wedge of Cretaceous rocks (Fig. 7). On Banks Island and parts of Prince Patrick Island, thin coastal-plain deposits of late Tertiary and Pleistocene age lie unconformably on gently folded rocks of Early Cretaceous and early Tertiary age; these latter rocks, in turn, lie unconformably on more highly deformed Devonian and Precambrian rocks (Thorsteinsson and Tozer, 1962). Farther northeast, the Quaternary and late Tertiary coastal-plain deposits lie on deformed Mesozoic and early Tertiary strata along the northern edge of the Sverdrup basin (Tozer, 1960).

On the other side of Alaska, Arctic coastal-plain deposits are present on northern Wrangel Island (Ostrov Vrangelya), toward the Canada basin (Fig. 7). The Arctic coast of Wrangel Island has a thin veneer of Quaternary sediments

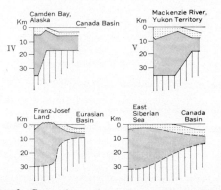

Fig. 6—Comparisons of crustal transition along continental margins of Arctic Ocean (Camden Bay and Mackenzie River profiles after Wold et al., 1970; Franz Josef Land and East Siberian Sea profiles after Demenitskaya et al., 1968). See Figure 5 for explanation of patterns.

and nearly flat-lying Upper Triassic rocks that lie unconformably on folded Carboniferous rocks. West of Wrangel Island the shelf of the Arctic Ocean increases to as much as 400 mi (600 km) in width in the East Siberian Sea. Farther west, the DeLong Islands, nearest the edge of the Canada basin, have mildly deformed Cambrian and Ordovician strata that are overlain by flat-lying Cretaceous rocks (Vol'nov et al., 1970).

These generally undeformed deposits rimming the Canada basin indicate that no major compression occurred along the continental margins of the Canada basin during the Cenozoic or, in many places, during the Mesozoic. Undeformed Mesozoic strata penetrated in boreholes in northernmost Alaska nearest the edge of the deep Canada basin (Rickwood, 1970) support this conclusion and suggest that there has been no motion between the floor of the Canada basin and Alaska since at least Early Cretaceous time. However, folds developed in Tertiary and older deposits of the Sverdrup basin lie at right angles to the margin of the Canada basin (Fig. 7). These Tertiary structures and comparable structures in northeast Greenland and Spitsbergen may have been related to northward drift of Greenland against Ellesmere Island (Harland, 1969) and to opening of Baffin Bay (Kerr, this volume).

On the European side of the Lomonosov Ridge, a very broad shelf including the Laptev, Barents, and Kara Seas borders the deep Eurasian basin. Fold belts involving rocks of mainly Paleozoic age are exposed on Spitsbergen, Novaya Zemlya, and Severnaya Zemlya. Besides these fold belts, whose trends appear to be truncated by the deep Eurasian basin, there is a broad platform of flat-lying Mesozoic strata which is centered on Franz Josef Land and includes parts of Spitsbergen and Severnaya Zemlya (Atlasov, 1964; Sidorenko, 1970). As in the case of the Canada basin, the existence of undeformed Mesozoic and Cenozoic strata along the edges of the Eurasian basin indicates a long history of little tectonic activity along its margin. If any sea-floor spreading occurred, the continents moved with the ocean floor, as is the case in the modern Atlantic.

Mesozoic Reconstruction of the Arctic

Figure 8 is a reconstruction of the Arctic as it may have been in the Late Cretaceous. Deep parts (> 1 km) of the modern Atlantic Ocean and the Eurasian basin part of the Arctic Ocean have been removed, along with their midocean ridges. Closing the Eurasian basin

FIG. 7—Major tectonic features of Arctic. Postulated faults between Ellesmere Island and Greenland and west of Novaya Zemlya should be omitted.

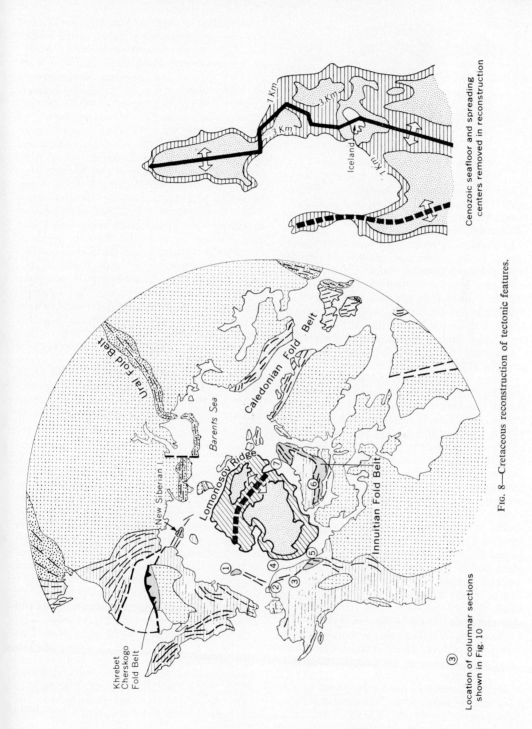

FIG. 8—Cretaceous reconstruction of tectonic features.

Fig. 9—Major crustal plates.

brings the continental margin of Eurasia against the Lomonosov Ridge, and closing the North Atlantic brings together parts of the Caledonian fold belt.

In attempts to reconstruct how drift has occurred, North America is considered a separate block from the Eurasian block, and differential movement between the two blocks is postulated to have resulted from sea-floor spreading of the Atlantic basin. The Mid-Atlantic Ridge and its northern extension across the Arctic Ocean— the Gakkel Ridge—are generally accepted as representing the eastern boundary of North America (Morgan, 1968; Fig. 9).

In the Pacific realm the position of the boundary separating North America from Eurasia is less certain. It has been placed in the Bering Sea region (LePichon, 1968; Hamilton, 1970); however, if there has been a separation of the two continents, it probably was within the Yakutia region of the USSR rather than in the Bering Strait. Across the Bering Strait, similar sequences of Paleozoic carbonate rocks overlying Precambrian metamorphic basement show a close correlation, even in the oldest rocks (Churkin, 1973). Most authors, in agreement with the latter interpretation, have placed the western boundary of the American plate within the Verkhoyansk Mountains of western Yakutia (Wilson, 1963; Heezen and Tharp, 1965; Morgan, 1968). I believe, instead, that the boundary separating the Cherskiy mountain system in eastern Yakutia (Fig. 7) from the Verkhoyansk Mountains farther west marks a more fundamental change in geology and has some of the features characteristic of fossil plate boundaries.

Mesozoic rocks of the Verkhoyansk geosyncline on the west are faulted against a Paleozoic geosyncline in the Cherskiy Mountains which passes eastward into platform deposits of the Kolyma massif (Bogdanov, 1963). Most of the faults are large thrusts that not only bring

Paleozoic rocks against Mesozoic rocks, but also displace sedimentary facies in the Paleozoic rocks. High-pressure metamorphic minerals are developed along these faults in wide zones of breccia and mylonite (Dobretzov et al., 1966). Along this zone of regional faults is a belt 1,000 km long which contains granitic batholiths of mainly Early Cretaceous age.

Much farther west, the more intensely studied Urals have been interpreted as a subduction zone along which the Paleozoic ocean floor moved, bringing the Russian and Siberian platforms closer together (Hamilton, 1970). Thus, the Arctic part of the Eurasian continent seems to be a composite of at least three separate subcontinents with Precambrian nuclei and Paleozoic platform covers—the Russian platform, the Siberian platform, and the Kolyma massif —that were separated by wide Paleozoic seaways. Deposits of geosynclinal proportions developed along the margins of these subcontinents. These geosynclinal strata were later deformed into fold belts as the seaways closed between the leading edges of the approaching Eurasian and North American plates. The boundary between the Cherskiy and Verkhoyansk fold belts seems to mark the suture of the Eurasian and North American continental plates, which collided in Early Cretaceous time, perhaps as a consequence of opening of the Atlantic.

PALEOZOIC GEOLOGIC FEATURES

Reconstruction of the Paleozoic history of the Arctic Ocean region depends mainly on interpretations of the land geology bordering the Arctic Ocean basin. Within the basin itself, thick Cenozoic and, in some areas, Mesozoic sedimentary units presumably blanket any older features so that even their geophysical characteristics seem to have been obscured. Moreover, the process of sea-floor spreading is supposed to sweep the sea floor beneath the continental margins, thereby removing the oldest sedimentary rocks from direct observation.

Paleozoic rocks around the edges of the Canada basin are generally much more deformed than are those of Cenozoic age, and they form discontinuously exposed fold belts (Churkin, 1973). By contrast, no Paleozoic fold belts are known to parallel the edges of the Eurasian basin. Instead, within the continental framework of Eurasia, the Ural and Cherskiy fold belts trend into the Eurasian basin and appear to end abruptly at its edge (Fig. 8).

Late Paleozoic

The southern end of the Canada basin was rimmed by an early Paleozoic geosynclinal belt (Churkin, 1969; Fig. 10). In the Late Devonian, uplifts in this belt, accompanied by granitic intrusions, produced a wedge of coarse clastic sediments that spread southward onto adjoining areas of Alaska, Canada, and Siberia (Brosgé and Tailleur, 1970; Trettin, 1967; Churkin, 1969). In both northern Alaska and the Canadian Arctic Islands, thick sequences of late Paleozoic and younger strata were deposited unconformably on the rocks of the early Paleozoic geosyncline in a series of successor basins. In the Brooks Range, the base of the Carboniferous section becomes progressively younger; the entire late Paleozoic section has more terrigenous detritus in the northern parts of the range (Armstrong et al., 1970). This northward transgression, plus the fact that the unconformably overlying Permian exposed in boreholes north of the Brooks Range is a chert-pebble conglomerate, suggests that a source area existed farther north during the late Paleozoic, as it did during the Late Devonian.

On Wrangel Island the Mississippian rocks and the underlying Upper Devonian rocks are very similar to, but thicker than, those in the Brooks Range. Permian and Triassic rocks, which are mainly clastic, unconformably overlie the Mississippian and also are similar to Permian and Triassic rocks of the Brooks Range (Bogdanov and Tilman, 1964). In the Canadian Arctic Islands an even thicker sequence of Carboniferous and younger rocks, lying unconformably on the older Paleozoic rocks of the Franklinian geosyncline, fills the Sverdrup basin (Thorsteinsson and Tozer, 1960; Fig. 10).

If the Arctic Ocean basin is a relatively young feature, the Ural fold belt originally may have extended into the Arctic Islands of Canada and northern Greenland (Atlasov, 1964; Hamilton, 1970). However, the major period of folding, accompanied by plutonic activity, occurred in the northern part of the Innuitian fold belt in the Late Devonian, and somewhat less intense deformation affected its southern part in the Early Mississippian (Stockwell, 1968; King, 1969). During the Late Carboniferous and Permian, when the Hercynian disturbances affected the Urals, sedimentation was nearly uninterrupted on the eroded Innuitian fold belt in the Sverdrup basin (Fig. 11). A former connection between the Ural and the Innuitian fold belts, therefore, seems unlikely.

Early Paleozoic

In Alaska, highly deformed and mildly metamorphosed, predominantly siliceous rocks are exposed in the northeastern Brooks Range and the British Mountains of northern Yukon Territory (Churkin, 1969; Figs. 8, 10). Originally, this fold belt and similar rocks penetrated in boreholes along the Arctic coast were considered as mainly Precambrian, belonging to a craton or platform that extended still farther north into what is now the Canada basin (Payne et al., 1952; Brosgé et al., 1962). However, I have interpreted these same rocks as part of an early Paleozoic geosyncline that rimmed the southern margin of the Canada basin (Churkin, 1969). More recently, the discovery of Cambrian trilobites (J. T. Dutro, W. P. Brosgé, and H. N. Reiser, written commun. and unpub. data, 1971), recognition of substantial amounts of mafic volcanic rocks, and dating of granitic rocks within the fold belt as Silurian (Reiser, 1970) have lent support to the idea that the fold belt represents, not a Precambrian craton, but an early Paleozoic geosyncline that was deformed in the middle Paleozoic.

West of the northeastern Brooks Range this fold belt seems to continue underneath the Arctic coastal plain. Slate, argillite, and graywacke in the bottoms of boreholes in the Prudhoe Bay oil field (Rickwood, 1970) and farther west at Point Barrow (Payne et al., 1952) probably represent continuations of the fold belt. These rocks form the basement of the Barrow arch, a broad structure of Mesozoic age that parallels the Arctic coast of Alaska.

Similar rocks affected by the same Late Devonian orogeny form the Innuitian fold belt in the Canadian Arctic Islands (Trettin, 1967), but, where the fold belts approach each other, their direct continuity is obscured by the Mackenzie River delta.

Structures in the Alaskan and Canadian parts of this fold belt generally parallel the edge of the Canada basin. On northern Ellesmere Island, however, a belt of Paleozoic rocks has greatly divergent north-trending structures that align with the trend of the submarine Lomonosov Ridge (Trettin, 1969; Fig. 8).

At the opposite end of the Lomonosov Ridge, on the New Siberian Islands, a Paleozoic fold belt is exposed which seems to trend into the Lomonosov Ridge on the north and the Cherskiy fold belt on the south (Fig. 8). The New Siberian Island fold belt has thus been in-

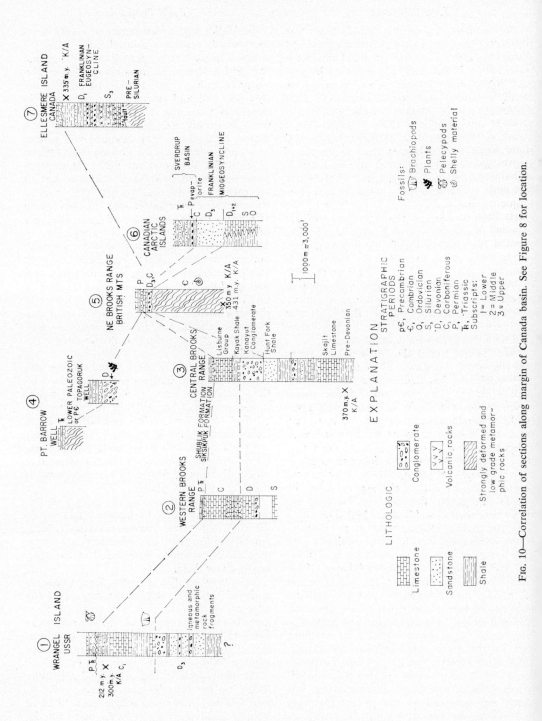

Fig. 10—Correlation of sections along margin of Canada basin. See Figure 8 for location.

terpreted as a link between the widely sepa-
rated fold belts (Bogdanov, 1963). If the Lo-
monosov Ridge is a Paleozoic fold belt split off
Eurasia, then the Canada basin was ringed by
Paleozoic fold belts prior to the opening of the
Eurasian basin.

Orogeny in the Caledonian fold belt of the
northern Atlantic—in the British Isles, East
Greenland, and Spitsbergen—appears to have
climaxed in the Silurian, earlier than the orogenic climax in the Innuitian fold belt. The
Late Cretaceous reconstruction (Fig. 8) re-
moves the Cenozoic Eurasian basin and brings
Ellesmere Island close to Spitsbergen, so that
the north-trending fold belt in northernmost Ellesmere Island (Trettin, 1969) that underwent
early Paleozoic movements lies near the northern end of the Caledonian fold belt. The Caledonian fold belt may have had an extension
along the Lomonosov Ridge–Barents Sea margin, but it also could have ended at the edge of
a proto–Canada basin. The zone of structural
intersection of the Innuitian fold belt with the
north-trending fold belt in northernmost Ellesmere Island is marked by an Early Devonian
ultramafic belt and a Tertiary graben (Trettin,
1969). Farther east, the Innuitian fold belt off
the northeast corner of Greenland may cut
across the Caledonian trend of East Greenland;
still farther east, it may be related to the Svalbardian fold belt in Spitsbergen (Harland,
1969).

Fig. 12—Early Paleozoic paleogeography.

The various fold belts, composed mainly of
geosynclinal deposits that both parallel and
trend into the Arctic Ocean, provide much evidence that the Arctic has been a major center
of marine sedimentation since at least the early
Paleozoic (Fig. 12). In general, the Paleozoic
marine faunas of Arctic North America
strongly resemble those of both Asia and Europe. Among the fossils from Alaska which
have been demonstrated to have a close similarity to those in parts of Eurasia are the following: Precambrian stromatolites; Cambrian trilobites; Ordovician, Silurian, and Early Devonian graptolites; Devonian tentaculitids; and
Paleozoic corals, foraminifers, and brachiopods
(Churkin, 1973). Most of these fossils probably had a planktonic stage in their life cycles,
and their distribution patterns seem to reflect
former trans-Arctic marine connections rather
than geographic proximity.

SUMMARY

An examination of the geologic history of
the Arctic strongly suggests that the Arctic has
been a center of marine sedimentation and an
avenue for polar migration of faunas since at
least the early Paleozoic. The fact that fold
belts are easily correlated around the edges of
the Arctic, but not across it, suggests that the
Arctic basin as a whole is not a feature developed within a continental framework across
which fold belts of different trends can be
matched; rather, it indicates that the basin represents a series of openings and, perhaps, clos-

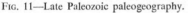

Shelf and land areas   Oceanic areas with geosynclines

Successor basins   B-Brooks
                   S-Sverdrup

Fig. 11—Late Paleozoic paleogeography.

	STAGE	TECTONICS	GEOLOGIC RECORD
CAMBRIAN TO DEVONIAN	PROTO CANADA BASIN	GEOSYNCLINAL SUBSIDENCE ALONG CONTINENTAL MARGINS	FRANKLINIAN GEOSYNCLINE IN CANADIAN ARCTIC ISLANDS AND PRE-LATE DEVONIAN GEOSYNCLINE IN NE BROOKS RANGE-BRITISH MOUNTAINS
LATE DEVONIAN AND EARLY MISSISSIPPIAN	CLOSING(?)* OF PROTO-CANADA BASIN	DEFORMATION, PLUTONIC ACTIVITY AND ACCRETION OF GEOSYNCLINES TO CONTINENT MAJOR UPLIFT	INNUITIAN AND NE BROOKS-BRITISH MOUNTAINS FOLD BELTS, PENETRATIVE STRUCTURES, METAMORPHISM, AND GRANITE INTRUSION. WEDGES OF CLASTIC SEDIMENTS SHED FROM UPLIFTS WITHIN FOLD BELTS TOWARD CONTINENTAL INTERIOR AND LATER SHALLOW MARINE LIMESTONE, RED BEDS, AND EVAPORITE SEDIMENTATION TO FORM SVERDRUP AND BROOKS BASINS
MISSISSIPPIAN TO TRIASSIC	SUCCESSOR BASINS DEVELOPED ON ROOTS OF EARLIER GEOSYNCLINES	RESTRICTED MARINE BASIN DEVELOPED WITHIN CONTINENTAL FRAMEWORK	
LATE JURASSIC OR EARLY CRETACEOUS	OPENING OF MODERN CANADA BASIN	SEA-FLOOR SPREADING	CLASTIC SEDIMENTS SHED FROM CONTINENT TOWARD BASIN
LATE CRETACEOUS	DEEP CANADA BASIN	DORMANT	TURBIDITES, SUBMARINE CANYON AND DELTA DEPOSITS LEADING INTO BASIN
CENOZOIC	OPENING OF EURASIA BASIN	SEA-FLOOR SPREADING	GAKKEL SPREADING CENTER

* CLOSING DOES NOT NECESSARILY IMPLY CONTINENTAL COLLISION AND MAY REFLECT ONLY INTERRUPTION AND UPLIFT OF EARLIER GEOSYNCLINAL CYCLES.

FIG. 13—Stages in development of Arctic Ocean basin.

ings of ocean basins that extended at least into early Paleozoic time.

Figure 13 shows stages in the development of the Arctic that seem best to fit the available data.

SELECTED REFERENCES

Armstrong, A. K., B. L. Mamet, and J. T. Dutro, Jr., 1970, Foraminiferal zonation and carbonate facies of the Mississippian and Pennsylvanian Lisburne Group, central and eastern Brooks Range, Arctic Alaska: Am. Assoc. Petroleum Geologists Bull., v. 54, no. 5, p. 687–698.

Atlasov, I. P., ed., 1964, Tektonicheskaya karta artiki i subartiki (Tectonic map of the Arctic and Subarctic): Leningrad, Scientific Research Inst. of Geology of Arctic, scale 1:5,000,000.

Barnes, D. F., 1970, Gravity and other regional geophysical data from northern Alaska, in W. L. Adkison and M. M. Brosgé, eds., Proceedings of the geological seminar on the North Slope of Alaska: Los Angeles, Pacific Sec. Am. Assoc. Petroleum Geologists, p. I1–I20.

Beloussov, V. V., and I. P. Kosminskaya, 1968, Structure and development of transition zones between the continents and oceans: Canadian Jour. Earth Sci., v. 5, p. 1011–1026.

Bogdanov, N. A., 1963, Tektonicheskoye razvitye v Paleozoye Kolymskovo Massiva i vostochnoi Arktiki (Tectonic development of the Kolyma massif and eastern Arctic during the Paleozoic): Akad. Nauk SSSR, Geol. Inst. Trudy, v. 99, 237 p.

——— and S. M. Tilman, 1964, Obshchchiye cherty razvitye Paleozoiskikh struktur ostrova Wrangelia i zapadnoi chasti Khrebta Bruksa (Alyaska) (General features in the development of Paleozoic structures of Wrangel Island and the western part of the Brooks Range [Alaska], in Soveschaniye po problem tektoniki, Moskva, 1963, skladchatye oblasti evrazii, materialy: Moscow, "Nauka," p. 219–230.

Brosgé, W. P., and I. L. Tailleur, 1970, Depositional history of northern Alaska, in W. L. Adkison and M. M. Brosgé, eds., Proceedings of the geological seminar on the North Slope of Alaska: Los Angeles, Pacific Sec. Am. Assoc. Petroleum Geologists, p. D1–D18.

——— et al., 1962, Paleozoic sequence in eastern Brooks Range, Alaska: Am. Assoc. Petroleum Geologists Bull., v. 46, p. 2174–2198.

Burk, C. A., 1968, Buried ridges within continental margins: New York Acad. Sci. Trans., ser. 2, v. 30, no. 3, p. 397–409.

Carey, S. W., 1955, Orocline concept in geotectonics, part I: Royal Soc. Tasmania Papers and Proc., v. 89, p. 255–288; Tasmania Univ. Dept. Geology Pub. 28.

Churkin, M., Jr., 1969, Paleozoic tectonic history of the Arctic basin north of Alaska: Science, v. 165, p. 549–555.

——— 1970, Fold belts of Alaska and Siberia and drift between North America and Asia, in W. L. Adkison and M. M. Brosgé, eds., Proceedings of the geological seminar on the North Slope of Alaska: Los Angeles, Pacific Sec. Am. Assoc. Petroleum Geologists, p. G1–G17.

——— 1973, Paleozoic and Precambrian rocks of Alaska and their role in its structural evolution: U.S. Geol. Survey Prof. Paper 740, 64 p.

Collins, F. R., and F. M. Robinson, 1967, Subsurface stratigraphic, structural and economic geology, northern Alaska: U.S. Geol. Survey Open-File Rept., 252 p.

Demenitskaya, R. M., and A. M. Karasik, 1969, The active rift system of the Arctic Ocean: Tectonophysics, v. 8, p. 345–351.

——— et al., 1968, The transition zone between the Eurasian continent and the Arctic Ocean: Canadian Jour. Earth Sci., v. 5, p. 1125–1129.

Dobretsov, N. L., et al., 1966, Karta metamorficheskikh Fatziy SSSR (Metamorphic facies map of the USSR): Moscow, Ministry of Geology, scale 1: 7,500,000.

Eardley, A. J., 1961, History of geologic thought on

the origin of the Arctic basin, *in* G. O. Raasch, ed., Geology of the Arctic, v. 1: Toronto, Univ. Toronto Press, p. 607–621.

Emery, K. O., 1968, Shallow structure of continental shelves and slopes: Southeastern Geology, v. 9, p. 173–194.

Hall, J. K., 1973, Geophysical evidence for ancient sea-floor spreading from Alpha Cordillera and Mende-leyev Ridge: this volume.

Hamilton, W., 1970, The Uralides and the motion of the Russian and Siberian platforms: Geol. Soc. America Bull., v. 81, p. 2553–2576.

Harland, W. B., 1969, Contribution of Spitsbergen to understanding of tectonic evolution of North Atlantic region, *in* Marshall Kay, ed., North Atlantic—geology and continental drift: Am. Assoc. Petroleum Geologists Mem. 12, p. 817–851.

Heezen, B. C., and M. Ewing, 1961, The mid-oceanic ridge and its extension through the Arctic basin, *in* G. O. Raasch, ed., Geology of the Arctic v. 1: Toronto, Univ. Toronto Press, p. 622–642.

—— and M. Tharp, 1965, Tectonic fabric of the Atlantic and Indian Oceans and continental drift: Royal Soc. London Philos. Trans., ser. A, v. 258, no. 1088, p. 90–106.

Hunkins, K., 1961, Seismic studies of the Arctic Ocean floor, *in* G. O. Raasch, ed., Geology of the Arctic, v. 1: Toronto, Univ. Toronto Press, p. 645–665.

—— and H. Kutschale, 1965, Quaternary sedimentation in the Arctic Ocean, *in* M. Sears, ed., Progress in oceanography: New York, Pergamon Press, v. 4, p. 89–104.

Kerr, J. W., 1973, North Canada rift system: this volume.

King, P. B., compiler, 1969, Tectonic map of North America: Washington, D.C., U.S. Geol. Survey, scale 1:5,000,000.

Lachenbruch, A. H., and B. V. Marshall, 1969, Heat flow in the Arctic, *in* U.S. Naval Arctic Research Lab. dedication symposium, Fairbanks, Alaska, 1969, Proc.: Arctic, v. 22, no. 3, p. 300–311.

Larson, R., H. W. Menard, and S. Smith, 1968, Gulf of California, a result of ocean floor spreading and transform faulting: Science, v. 161, p. 781–784.

LePichon, X., 1968, Sea-floor spreading and continental drift: Jour. Geophys. Research, v. 73, p. 3661–3697.

Lyubimova, E. A., *et al.*, 1969, Izmerenie teplovogo potoka cherez dno Svernogo Ledovitogo okeana v oblasti sredinnogo khrebta Gakkelya (Heat flow measurements across the bottom of the Arctic Ocean in the region of the Gakkel mid-ocean ridge): Akad. Nauk SSSR Doklady, v. 186, p. 1318–1321.

Meyerhoff, A. A., 1970, Continental drift, II; high-latitude evaporite deposits and geologic history of Arctic and North Atlantic Oceans: Jour. Geology, v. 78, p. 406–444.

Morgan, W. J., 1968, Rises, trenches, great faults, and crustal blocks: Jour. Geophys. Research, v. 73, p. 1959–1982.

Ostenso, N. A., 1968, Geophysical studies in the Greenland Sea: Geol. Soc. America Bull., v. 79, p. 107–132.

—— and R. J. Wold, 1973, Aeromagnetic evidence for origin of Arctic Ocean basin: this volume.

Payne, T. G., *et al.*, 1952, Geology of the Arctic Slope of Alaska: U.S. Geol. Survey Oil and Gas Inv. Map OM-126, scale 1:1,000,000.

Pushcharovsky, Yu. M., 1960, Nekotorye obshchiye problemy tektoniki artiki (Some general problems of the tectonics of the Arctic): Akad. Nauk SSSR Izv.

Ser. Geol., no. 9, p. 15–28.

Reiser, H. N., 1970, Northeastern Brooks Range—a surface expression of the Prudhoe Bay section, *in* W. L. Adkison and M. M. Brosgé, eds., Proceedings of the geological seminar on the North Slope of Alaska: Pacific Sec. Am. Assoc. Petroleum Geologists, p. K1–K14.

Rezanov, I. A., 1964, Voprosy noveishei tektoniki Severo-Vostoka SSSR (Questions of the modern tectonics of North-East USSR): Akad. Nauk SSSR Mezhduvedomstv. Geofiz. Byull., 148 p.

Rickwood, F. K., 1970, The Prudhoe Bay field, *in* W. L. Adkison and M. M. Brosgé, eds., Proceedings of the geological seminar on the North Slope of Alaska: Los Angeles, Pacific Sec. Am. Assoc. Petroleum Geologists, p. L1–L11.

Shatsky, N. S., 1935, O tektonike Arktiki (Tectonics of the Arctic), *in* Geologiya i poleznye iskopaemye Severa SSSR: Glavsevmorputi, v. 1, Geologiya.

Sidorenko, A. V., chief ed., 1970, Ostrova Sovetskoy arktiki (Soviet Arctic Islands), Geologiya SSSR, v. 26: Moscow, Ministry of Geology, "Nedra," 548 p.

Sobczak, L. W., and J. R. Weber, 1973, Crustal structure of Queen Elizabeth Islands and polar continental margin: this volume.

Stockwell, C. H., chm., 1968, Tectonic map of Canada: Canada Geol. Survey Map 1251A, scale 1: 5,000,000.

Sykes, L. R., 1965, The seismicity of the Arctic: Seismol. Soc. America Bull., v. 55, p. 501–518.

Tailleur, I. L., and W. P. Brosgé, 1970, Tectonic history of northern Alaska, *in* W. L. Adkison and M. M. Brosgé, eds., Proceedings of the geological seminar on the North Slope of Alaska: Los Angeles, Pacific Sec. Am. Assoc. Petroleum Geologists, p. E1–E20.

Thorsteinsson, R., and E. T. Tozer, 1960, Summary account of structural history of the Canadian Arctic Archipelago since Precambrian time: Canada Geol. Survey Paper 60-7, 25 p.

—— and ——, 1962, Banks, Victoria, and Stefansson Islands, Arctic Archipelago: Canada Geol. Survey Mem. 330, 85 p.

Tozer, E. T., 1960, Summary account of Mesozoic and Tertiary stratigraphy, Canadian Arctic Archipelago: Canada Geol. Survey Paper 60-5, 24 p.

Trettin, H. P., 1967, Devonian of the Franklinian eugeosyncline, *in* D. H. Oswald, ed., International symposium on the Devonian System, v. 1: Calgary, Alberta Soc. Petroleum Geologists, p. 693–701.

—— 1969, A Paleozoic-Tertiary foldbelt in northernmost Ellesmere Island aligned with the Lomonosov Ridge: Geol. Soc. America Bull., v. 80, p. 143–148.

Vogt, P. R., and N. A. Ostenso, 1970, Magnetic and gravity profiles across the Alpha Cordillera and their relation to Arctic sea-floor spreading: Jour. Geophys. Research, v. 75, p. 4925–4937.

—— —— and G. L. Johnson, 1970, Magnetic and bathymetric data bearing on sea-floor spreading north of Iceland: Jour. Geophys. Research, v. 75, p. 903–920.

Vol'nov, D. A., *et al.*, 1970, Novosibirskiye Ostrova (The New Siberian Islands), *in* A. V. Sidorenko, chief ed., Ostrova Sovetskoy Arktiki, Geologiya SSSR, v. 26: Moscow, Ministry of Geology, "Nedra," p. 324–374.

Wilson, J. T., 1963, Hypothesis of earth's behaviour: Nature, v. 198, p. 925–929.

Wold, R. J., T. L. Woodzik, and N. A. Ostenso, 1970, Structure of the Beaufort Sea continental margin: Geophysics, v. 35, p. 849–861.

Cretaceous–Early Tertiary Rift Basin of Baffin Bay—Continental Drift Without Sea-Floor Spreading[1]

RUDOLF MARTIN[2]

Calgary, Alberta, Canada

Abstract The Cretaceous to Eocene sedimentary-volcanic sequence of the Disko Island area and southern Baffin Island indicates that the opening of Baffin Bay, which resulted when Greenland and North America drifted apart, involved the following historical sequence: (1) the presence of a land-locked rift valley filled with terrestrial deposits—Barremian to Turonian; (2) widening of the valley and occurrence of intermittent marine connections, plus the first volcanic activity—late Turonian to Danian; restricted bottom circulation with deposition of bituminous shales—Santonian through Danian; (3) deepening of the rift, opening of magma chambers, and effusion of basaltic lavas—Paleocene and Eocene (limited to Davis Strait area); (4) widening and deepening of the rift valley to the present Baffin Bay and Davis Strait and deposition of a very thick, young sedimentary sequence in the deepest part of the graben. Baffin Bay shows no evidence of sea-floor spreading or of a mid–Baffin Bay ridge. In this respect, it appears similar to several other deep marine basins which are believed to be due to continental drift. Furthermore, the tectonic-depositional-volcanic histories of the Rhine Valley and East African rift systems closely parallel the first three stages of Baffin Bay's evolution. Rifting and continental drift apparently can occur independent of sea-floor spreading (which would be the last phase of the sequence). In Baffin Bay, the sedimentary units predate the volcanic deposits by about 50 m.y., which would not be the case if sea-floor spreading had created Baffin Bay; nor would the volcanic rocks be so limited in area. Sea-floor spreading in the Atlantic began only about 60 m.y. ago, long after the initial (Jurassic) phase of sedimentation.

Practical implications to the petroleum industry of considering rifting to be the primary cause of continental drift are that (1) the same sedimentary sequence is common to many coasts broken by drift—e.g., the oil provinces of western Africa; this sequence includes both source rocks and thick reservoir rocks; (2) the antithetically rotated fault blocks and crossfaults caused by rifting created suitable structural traps; (3) little danger of volatilization of hydrocarbons existed because volcanism started only at the end of the sequence; and (4) the central depression, representing the last stage of rift widening, was filled with thick clastic sediments without hydrocarbon source beds.

Introduction

Thick (approximately 6,500 ft or 1,980 m) Barremian to Eocene clastic sedimentary beds which occur on and north of Disko Island on the west coast of Greenland are matched by small inliers of sandstone and shale (up to 500

[1] Manuscript received, September 21, 1971.

[2] Deceased, April 18, 1972.

ft or 150 m thick) of similar age along the shores of Baffin Bay on southern Baffin Island and adjacent small islands (Kidd, 1953; Wilson and Clarke, 1965). The thick clastic sequence and the inliers lie on eroded and deeply weathered Precambrian rocks. At the base of the sequence in the Disko Island area (Henderson, 1969) are terrestrial sandstones and coal seams of Barremian to Coniacian age; some marine intercalations are present from the upper Turonian upward. These beds are succeeded by a mixed terrestrial-marine clastic sequence from the lower Santonian through the lower Tertiary that includes bituminous shales from the lower Santonian to the upper Danian.

The basaltic lava flows that have been mapped in the Disko Island area, as well as in the vicinity of Cape Dyer, Baffin Island, overlie the bulk of these sedimentary rocks (Fig. 1). They overstep the old Precambrian surface farther inland on both sides of Baffin Bay. Some clastic beds are intercalated between the basalt flows. Detailed dating of the Greenland flows has established a Paleocene-Eocene age for these lavas. The only older evidence of volcanic activity is tuffs (ashbeds) of Danian age, which have an andesitic to andesitic-basaltic composition (Munck and Noe-Nygaard, 1957).

Based on the Geological Society of London (1964) Phanerozoic time scale, the Baffin Bay sequence described above can be subdivided as shown in Table 1.

Precambrian

Structural movements during the Cretaceous and Tertiary were predominantly in the form of block faulting, accompanied by a certain amount of tilting. The principal movements took place at the beginning of the Danian and of the Paleocene; both intervals are represented by thick conglomerates. Beneath the more or less flat-lying Tertiary, the Cretaceous of the Disko Island area dips 10–15° to the northeast. One of the major faults, with a throw of approximately 2,000 m, traverses the Nûgssuaq Peninsula from north to south. The oldest member of the stratigraphic sequence, the Barremian-Aptian Kome Beds, is present exclusively on the upthrown (east) side of this fault (Munck and Noe-Nygaard, 1957).

Subsequent to the termination of deposition of the sedimentary-volcanic sequence, the areas on both sides of Baffin Bay were uplifted to considerable height. Both Greenland and Baffin Island now tilt slightly away from Baffin Bay (Fig. 2). Because some of the lava flows are of submarine origin and all those now on land occur at considerable elevations, the amount of uplift is at least 240–440 m on Baffin Island (Kidd, 1953) and much more on the Greenland side. The top of the basalt flows now is more than 900 m above sea level on Baffin Island and nearly 2,000 m above sea level in the Disko Island area.

Presumably, during and after this phase, the Baffin Bay rift opened to its present width and the graben deepened to its present depth. In the northern and most depressed area, the water depth now reaches nearly 2,400 m. Murray *et al.* (1970) have calculated magnetic basement depths as great as 18,000 m along the west side of Baffin Bay (Fig. 3) and thicknesses of sedimentary rocks in excess of 9,000 m.

The opening of the Baffin Bay rift as a result of the drifting apart of Greenland and North America has been sequential (Fig. 4).

1. A land-locked rift valley was filled with fluvial, lacustrine, and other terrestrial deposits (Kome Beds).

Table 1. Baffin Bay Sequence

Million Years B.P.		Age	Rock Types		
45		Eocence	Plateau basalts		
54	TERTIARY	Paleocene	Marine and terrestrial units, some basalt		
65					
		Danian	Marine and terrestrial units with some andesitic-basaltic tuffs		
70		Maestrichtian	Marine and terrestrial deposits	Intercalated bituminous shales	
		Campanian			
76	CRETACEOUS	Santonian		Marine intercalations	
82		Coniacian			
88		Turonian	Terrestrial deposits		
94		Cenomanian			
100		Albian			
106		Aptian	Terrestrial deposits (Kome Beds) (only east of Nugssuaq fault)		
112		Barremian			
118					

2. Widening of the rift occurred, along with renewed terrestrial deposition in the newly-formed central graben.

3. Deepening of the graben took place and intermittent connections with the open sea were formed. During this interval there was restricted bottom circulation leading to deposition of bituminous shales.

4. Deepening of the rift, opening of magma chambers, and extrusion of andesitic and andesitic-basaltic tuffs occurred.

5. Effusion of basaltic lava flows followed.

6. Widening and deepening of the rift valley to the present Baffin Bay and Davis Strait took place, and a very thick, young clastic sedimentary sequence was deposited in the deepest part of the graben.

In terms of duration, based on the same time

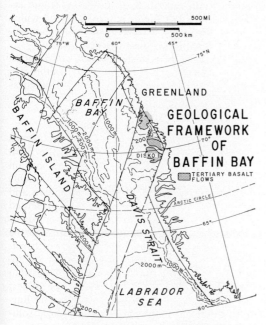

FIG. 1—Geologic framework of Baffin Bay.

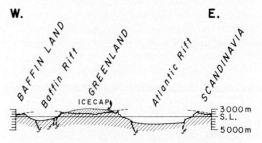

FIG. 2—Schematic cross section from Baffin Island through Greenland to Scandinavia. Vertical scale greatly exaggerated; length of section, approximately 3,500 km. After A. L. DuToit (1937).

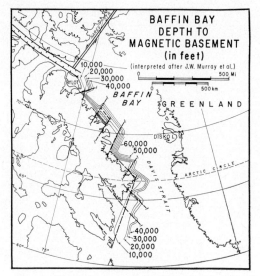

 BAFFIN BAY
DEPTH TO
MAGNETIC BASEMENT
(in feet)

(interpreted after J.W. Murray et al.)

FIG. 3—Depth to magnetic basement, west side of Baffin Bay (in feet). Interpreted from data by J. W. Murray *et al.* (1970).

scale as shown in Table 1, these various stages covered a considerable span of time:

Millions of Years		Stage
?	Uplift and block faulting	6
9	Plateau basalts	5
12	Marine and terrestrial sediments. Andestitic-basaltic ash layers	4
13	Restricted marine deposits	
12	Some marine intercalations	3
52	15 Nonmarine deposits in new central graben	2
	12 First nonmarine deposits on (later) flank blocks	1

The Tertiary volcanic rocks represent only the last stage in this sequence. Their occurrence is limited to the Disko Island area of western Greenland and the Cape Dyer area of Baffin Island, on either side of Davis Strait. No lavas have been reported north of a line from Cape Searle Island to Pröven, Greenland. Although there is no conclusive evidence of sea-floor spreading in Baffin Bay, the shallow (630+ m) Davis Strait passage may well be underlain entirely by plateau basalts that might have preserved a record of such spreading. No mid–Baffin Bay ridge has been observed that might be correlated with the submerged ridge beneath the Labrador Sea (Drake *et al.*, 1963; Hood and Godby, 1964; Kerr, 1967a). Although new data to the contrary may become available in the future, several other deep marine basins that generally are believed to be

caused by continental drift have not, to date, yielded evidence of sea-floor spreading and/or midbasin ridges—*e.g.*, the Mozambique Channel, the Red Sea, the Gulf of Mannar (Ceylon), the Coral Sea–Tasman Sea, and the rift between the Faeroe Plateau and the British Isles. Furthermore, the tectonic-depositional-volcanic histories of the Rhine Valley and East African rift systems closely parallel the first three stages of Baffin Bay's geologic history.

There thus appear to be strong arguments in favor of the view that rifting and continental drift can take place independent of sea-floor spreading, and that sea-floor spreading, wherever it does occur, is the seventh and last phase of the sequence. If sea-floor spreading had caused the formation of Baffin Bay, the sedimentary sequence would not predate the volcanic rocks as it does (by about 50 m.y.), nor would the latter be limited to a small area around Davis Strait. In addition, it is significant that the first volcanic units are andesitic tuffs, indicating the presence of a sialic crust and the occurrence of explosive volcanic vents that opened only rarely—in contrast to the subsequent more or less continuous flow of basaltic lavas.

Without in any way denying the reality of sea-floor spreading in areas where it has been proved, the writer considers it erroneous to credit this phenomenon as being the driving force in continental drift. It is obvious from the geologic history of Baffin Bay that a rift started to open, then widened and deepened, long before any basaltic magma was extruded. It also appears that the locus of the extrusion which did

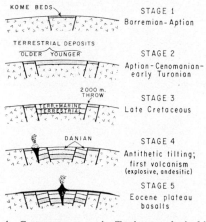

FIG. 4—Cretaceous to early Tertiary geologic history of Baffin Bay rift (schematic).

take place was very limited in area and, therefore, that it could not have been responsible for the formation of the entire Baffin Bay rift.

On a much larger scale, the Atlantic Ocean must have started to open at least 170 m.y. ago, because Bajocian sedimentary samples were recovered in a core taken north of Flemish Cap, off Newfoundland (Laughton *et al.*, 1970), and other occurrences of Jurassic rocks are known from various parts of this ocean. Yet the evidence of sea-floor spreading in the Atlantic does not reach farther back than about 60 m.y. It would appear, therefore, that much of the theorizing during the past decade with respect to the causes of continental drift should be reexamined. A thorough study of the geologic field evidence should result in a better understanding of the problem.

Baffin Bay, although it appears to be a northerly extension of the Labrador Sea, is, in reality, narrower and is separated from the latter by the Davis Strait and the adjacent volcanic extrusions. A reconstruction in which Nares Strait (the Kennedy Channel) is considered to be a transform fault (Wegener fault; Wilson, 1965) shows that Baffin Bay may be virtually closed by moving the 200-m depth lines on both sides together, but that the same amount of translation still leaves a major gap in the Labrador Sea (Fig. 5). If it is assumed that the shallow Davis Strait area is filled with volcanic

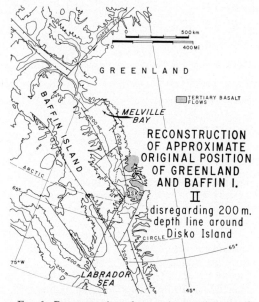

FIG. 6—Reconstruction of approximate original position of Greenland and Baffin Island, II. Disregarding 200-m depth line in area of Disko Island.

deposits that are related to the rifting, and if the 200-m depth line is disregarded in that area, the Labrador Sea gap still persists (Fig. 6). This gap may correspond, wholly or in part, to the mid–Labrador Sea ridge (Kerr, 1967a). Additional gaps correspond to Melville Bay—the widest part of Baffin Bay—which eventually may be found to have an interesting history of its own. In the opinion of Kerr (1967b), the displacement of Greenland along the Nares Strait fault is considerably less than is generally assumed, in which case the Melville Bay gap would have been much more extensive.

An attempt has been made on Figures 1 and 6 to show some of the possible rift faults (parallel with Baffin Bay), transform faults (Nares Strait—separation between Baffin Bay and the Labrador Sea), and crossfaults that have affected the area. It is evident from Figure 3 that the real number of crossfaults is considerably greater. Detailed magnetic maps reveal additional longitudinal faults as well as crossfaults (Geological Survey of Canada, 1970). Wilson and Clarke (1965) noted several large normal faults striking parallel with the coast at Cape Searle and on Padloping Island; the coastal blocks are downfaulted. On Greenland's west coast, normal faults parallel with, as well as at an angle to, the coast have been mapped trend-

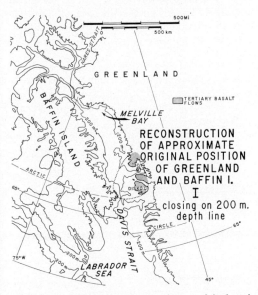

FIG. 5—Reconstruction of approximate original position of Greenland and Baffin Island, I. Closing on 200-m depth line.

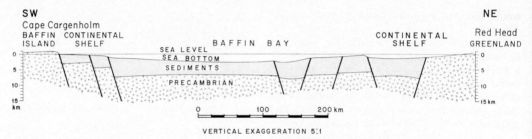

FIG. 7—Schematic geologic cross section of northern Baffin Bay. Interpreted after
P. J. Hood and M. E. Bower (1970).

ing north-northwest and northeast, respectively
(Grønlands Geol. Undersøgelse, 1970). That
some of these faults are very recent was shown
by Grant (1970).

Although several aeromagnetic and some
seismic refraction profiles have been published
for the Labrador Sea (Manchester, 1964;
Godby et al., 1966), only one profile across
(northern) Baffin Bay had been published in
part at the time this paper was written (Hood
and Bower, 1970). An attempt to interpret this
profile from the corresponding text was made
in Figure 7, but the depth of magnetic basement as shown in Figure 3 is much greater than
that shown on the section. For comparison, a
refraction profile (Mayhew et al., 1970) of the
Labrador Sea has been shown at the same vertical exaggeration (5 to 1) in Figure 8. It is evident that the older sedimentary units occur (or
are thickest) only in the fault blocks closest to
the shore—primarily the area underlying the
continental shelf—whereas the youngest sedimentary sequences are thickest in the deep-water area far offshore.

IMPLICATIONS TO PETROLEUM EXPLORATION

The practical implications to the petroleum
industry of viewing rifting as the primary cause

of continental drift and the opening of such basins as Baffin Bay, and of considering sea-floor
spreading as a secondary effect, are numerous.

1. The sedimentary sequence of Baffin Bay
is common to many coasts that are broken by
continental drift—e.g., the west coast of Africa
and the east coast of South America—and a
comparison of Baffin Bay with the rich oil
provinces of both sides of the South Atlantic is
thus warranted.

2. This sedimentary sequence includes both
hydrocarbon source rocks and great volumes of
clastic reservoir rocks derived from the adjacent landmasses during the initial stages of
their separation. Because of later widening of
the rift, these promising sedimentary rocks now
underlie the fault blocks closest to the shoreline, i.e., primarily the continental shelf.

3. The fault blocks broken off by the rifting
invariably have been rotated antithetically. This
movement, in combination with crossfaulting,
has created suitable structural traps for hydrocarbons.

4. The fact that lava flows occurred only after the sedimentary series had been laid down
limits the danger of volatilization of hydrocarbons to the immediate vicinity of volcanic
pipes. If sea-floor spreading were the primary
cause of continental drift, volcanic extrusions

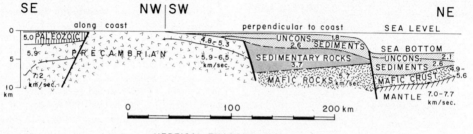

VERTICAL EXAGGERATION 5:1

FIG. 8—Seismic refraction profile transverse to Labrador Shelf. After M. A. Mayhew et al. (1970).

would have adversely affected all sedimentary deposits.

5. The central depression which formed the last stage of widening of the rift was filled with a thick sequence of young clastic sedimentary units. These beds are not underlain by any older sedimentary rocks such as those that include source rocks. Their locus roughly coincides with the deepest offshore waters.

SELECTED REFERENCES

Bartlett, G. A., and D. L. Smith, 1970, An outline of the Canadian Atlantic continental margin: Oilweek, v. 21, no. 12, May 11, p. 54–56.

Canada, Geological Survey of, 1970, Aeromagnetic series, Baffin Island, District of Franklin: Various sheets, scale 1–63,360.

Drake, C. L., et al., 1963, A mid–Labrador Sea ridge: Nature, v. 200, no. 4911, p. 1085–1086.

DuToit, A. L., 1937, Our wandering continents. An hypothesis of continental drifting: New York, Hafner, p. 259.

Godby, E. A., et al., 1966, Aeromagnetic reconnaissance of the Labrador Sea: Jour. Geophys. Research, v. 71, no. 2, p. 511–517.

Grant, A. C., 1966, A continuous seismic profile on the continental shelf off northeast Labrador: Canada Jour. Earth Sci., v. 3, no. 5, p. 725–730.

——— 1970, Recent crustal movements on the Labrador Shelf: Canada Jour. Earth Sci., v. 7, no. 2, p. 571–575.

Grønlands Geologiske Undersøgelse (Geological Survey of Greenland), 1970, Tectonic/geological map of Greenland: scale 1:2,500,000.

Henderson, G., 1969, Oil and gas prospects in the Cretaceous-Tertiary basin of West Greenland: Grønlands Geol. Undersøgelse Rap. 22, 63 p.

Hood, P. J., and M. E. Bower, 1970, Aeromagnetic profile from Cape Cargenholm, Baffin Island, to Red Head, West Greenland, in Report of activities, Part B, Nov. 1969–March 1970: Canada Geol. Survey Paper 70-1B, p. 37–39.

——— and E. A. Godby, 1964, Magnetic anomalies over the mid–Labrador Sea ridge: Nature, v. 202, no. 4937, p. 1099.

——— M. E. Bower, and E. A. Godby, 1969, Aeromagnetic reconnaissance of the North Atlantic Ocean, Labrador Sea and Baffin Bay: Geol. Assoc. Canada and Mineralog. Assoc. Canada Ann. Mtg., Abstracts, p. 63; also published in Abstracts of publications in scientific journals by officers of Geological Survey of Canada, April, 1969–March, 1970: Canada Geol. Survey Paper 70-4, p. 18.

——— P. Sawatzky, and M. E. Bower, 1967, Progress report on low-level aeromagnetic profiles over the Labrador Sea, Baffin Bay, and across the North Atlantic Ocean: Canada Geol. Survey Paper 66-58, 11 p.

Johnson, G. L., A. W. Closuit, and J. A. Pew, 1969, Geologic and geophysical observations in the northern Labrador Sea: Arctic, v. 22, no. 1, p. 56–68.

Kerr, J. W., 1967a, A submerged continental remnant beneath the Labrador Sea: Earth and Planetary Sci. Letters, v. 3, no. 2, p. 283–289.

——— 1967b, Nares submarine rift valley and the relative rotation of North Greenland: Bull. Canadian Petroleum Geology, v. 15, no. 4, p. 483–520.

Kidd, D. J., 1953, Geology, in P. D. Baird et al., Baffin Island expedition, 1953: preliminary field report: Arctic, v. 6, no. 4, p. 240–243.

Koch, B. E., 1964, Review of fossil floras and non-marine deposits of West Greenland: Geol. Soc. America Bull., v. 75, no. 6, p. 535–548.

Laughton, A. S., et al., 1970, Deep Sea Drilling Project, leg 12: Geotimes, v. 15, no. 9, p. 10–14.

London, Geological Society of, 1964, The Phanerozoic time scale: Geol. Soc. London Quart. Jour., v. 120, supp., p. 260–262.

Manchester, K. S., 1964, Geophysical investigations between Canada and Greenland: Halifax, Dalhousie Inst. Oceanography, Dalhousie Univ., M.S. thesis, 62 p.

Mayhew, M. A., C. L. Drake, and J. E. Nafe, 1970, Marine geophysical measurements on the continental margins of the Labrador Sea: Canada Jour. Earth Sci., v. 7, no. 2, pt. 1, p. 199–214.

Munck, S., and A. Noe-Nygaard, 1957, Age determination of the various stages of the Tertiary volcanism in the West Greenland basalt province, in Vulcanologia del Cenozoico, v. 1: 20th Internat. Geol. Cong., Mexico (Trabajos), Sec. I, p. 247–256.

Murray, J. W., W. G. Libby, and R. L. Chase, 1970, Baffin continental shelf, potential oil and gas source: Oilweek, v. 21, no. 12, p. 50–52, 54.

Rosenkrantz, A., and T. C. R. Pulvertaft, 1969, Cretaceous-Tertiary stratigraphy and tectonics in northern West Greenland, in Marshall Kay, ed., North Atlantic—geology and continental drift: Am. Assoc. Petroleum Geologists Mem. 12, p. 883–898.

Siegel, F., 1970, Cumberland, another Gippsland: Oilweek, v. 20, no. 52, p. 8–11, 32.

Wegener, A., 1924, The origin of continents and oceans: New York, E. P. Dutton & Co.

Wilson, J. T., 1965, A new class of faults, and their bearing on continental drift: Nature, v. 207, no. 4995, p. 343–347.

——— and D. B. Clarke, 1965, Geological expedition to Cape Dyer and Searle, Baffin Island, Canada: Nature, v. 205, no. 4969, p. 349–350.

Aeromagnetic Evidence for Origin of Arctic Ocean Basin[1]

NED A. OSTENSO[2] and RICHARD J. WOLD[3]

Arlington, Virginia, and Milwaukee, Wisconsin

Abstract   Aeromagnetic data have been used as a basis for making inferences about the geologic structure and evolution of the Arctic Ocean basin. The Alpha and Nansen ridges produce magnetic profiles which show axial symmetry and appear to correlate with profiles from the flanks of other well-documented ridges in the Greenland and Norwegian Seas. A quantitative attempt has been made to verify these correlations, which infer that the Alpha Cordillera became inactive 40 m.y. ago, when the locus of rifting shifted to the Nansen Ridge. The lack of magnetic disturbance associated with the Lomonosov Ridge is interpreted to indicate a section of the former Eurasian continental margin that was translated into the Arctic basin by sea-floor spreading along the Nansen Ridge axis. Within the Canada basin there is a thickening of sedimentary rocks from the Asian continental margin toward the Canadian Arctic Archipelago. Thickness of the sedimentary sequence in the Makarov basin is estimated to be approximately 1 km—almost twice that of the younger Fram basin.

Introduction

Aeromagnetic data collected over the Arctic Ocean by Ostenso and Wold (1971) have been used to construct a residual map of the Arctic Ocean basin (Fig. 1) and to calculate the depths to anomaly sources for various physiographic provinces (Fig. 2). The most salient observation from these figures is the presence of a zone of high magnetic disturbance that parallels the axes of the Alpha-Mendeleyev and Nansen ridges and that contrasts with the zone of magnetic quiescence along the Lomonosov Ridge. The southeastern part of the Canada basin is mainly undisturbed, but anomalies increase to the north and west. The anomalies over the Alpha-Mendeleyev and Nansen ridges appear to originate from or near the ridge surfaces, in contrast to the few anomalies from the Lomonosov Ridge, which have sources at greater depth. The Fram basin, lying between the Nansen and Lomonosov Ridges, appears to contain very few sedimentary rocks. The Makarov basin, lying between the Lomonosov and Alpha-Mendeleyev ridges, appears to contain a sedimentary sequence on the order of 1 km in thickness—twice that of the Fram basin sedimentary sequence. In the Canada basin the depth to anomaly sources has a rather wide variation. Not indicated in this presentation is the fact that the anomaly source deepens from west to east, *i.e.*, from Siberia toward the Canadian Arctic Archipelago.

The same aeromagnetic data were used in another kind of analysis—profile correlation and modeling. In this manner, Vogt et al. (1970) showed the relation of the Nansen Ridge to the complex spreading mechanism of the Greenland-Norwegian Seas and the North Atlantic (Fig. 3). The spreading rate for the Nansen Ridge is probably 1 cm/year or less. Similarly, Vogt and Ostenso (1970) showed that profiles across the Alpha Cordillera have a high degree of mutual correlation and biaxial symmetry over the ridge crest. Furthermore, the profiles appear to correlate with those from the flanks of other well-documented ridges in the Greenland and Norwegian Seas, and they can be matched with a sea-floor-spreading model over the paleomagnetic time span of 40–60 m.y. ago (Fig. 4). Vogt and Ostenso concluded that the cordillera may be an inactive midocean ridge that was spreading at a rate of 2 cm/year at least as early as 60 m.y. ago. Active spreading ended abruptly 40 m.y. ago, when a new locus of spreading started under what was then the Eurasian continental margin (Fig. 5). Spreading from this new locus—what is now the Nansen Ridge—sliced off a section of continental margin and translated it to the present location of the Lomonosov Ridge.

Evolution of Arctic Ocean Basin

These briefly summarized conclusions from aeromagnetic data were used as a framework to develop the hypothesis for the evolution of the Arctic Ocean basin that is presented in this paper. This hypothesis is designed to satisfy the following major criteria or constraints.

1. Until the late Paleozoic, Eurasia was two separate continental fragments—the Russian (European) and Siberian platforms. These two

[1] Manuscript received, September 21, 1971; revised, February 16, 1972.

The opinions in this paper are those of the authors. This research was sponsored, financially and logistically, by the Office of Naval Research through contract Nonr-1202(16) at the University of Wisconsin, Geophysical and Polar Research Center.

[2] Office of Naval Research.

[3] University of Wisconsin.

fragments converged during the middle Paleozoic and collided in the Permian or Triassic to form the Uralides (Hamilton, 1970).

2. There is evidence of geologic continuity between the North American and Siberian platforms at least as far back in time as the Paleozoic, and possibly the Precambrian (Churkin, 1970).

3. A source north of Alaska provided the sediments that flowed into a basin covering most of northern Alaska from the Devonian into the Jurassic (Brosgé and Tailleur, 1970).

4. The Arctic basin north of Alaska (roughly that part of the Canada basin underlying the Beaufort Sea) is a true, and probably a very ancient, ocean basin floored by oceanic crust and rimmed by an early Paleozoic geosynclinal belt (Churkin, 1969).

5. The Caledonides were formed by a mid-Paleozoic collision of the North American and European (Russian platform) plates. This orogenic belt later served as an axis of late Mesozoic rifting (Hamilton, 1970).

6. Large-scale thrusting of thin crustal sheets occurred in northwestern Alaska during the Early Cretaceous (Tailleur and Brosgé, 1970; Martin, 1970).

7. During Late Cretaceous and Tertiary time, folding occurred along a belt that forms the present Chukotskiy Mountains and Brooks Range and the associated foothills (Ostenso, 1968).

8. The Alpha Cordillera is a dormant axis of sea-floor spreading that was active at least 60 m.y. ago. Spreading ceased 40 m.y. ago when the locus of rifting bifurcated in the North Atlantic (Vogt and Ostenso, 1970). The new axis of Arctic spreading intersected the European continental margin, slicing off a section (analogous to Baja, California) that was translated northward to form the present Lomonosov Ridge (Ostenso and Wold, 1971).

9. The Alpha Cordillera is cut by numerous fractures that appear to be transform faults. The Siberian end of the cordillera (the Mendeleyev Ridge) underwent southerly displacement along an *en échelon* series of these faults (Hall, 1970).

Some of the references cited in the preceding criteria are recent summaries rather than original sources. All these references discuss at length the origin of the Arctic basin, each considering different data. Although the morphology developed here differs from most of these schemes, it satisfies nearly all of the factual framework established by the authors. Of equal

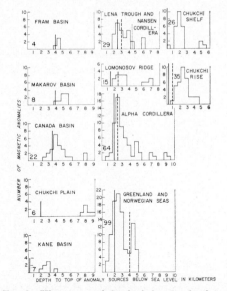

FIG. 2—Histograms of depths below sea level to top of anomaly sources (in kilometers) for various physiographic provinces. Solid vertical line represents water depths of shelves or basins and average elevation of ridge crests. Vertical dashed line represents main elevation of ridges and rises. Vertical dotted line represents depth of rift valley in Nansen Ridge. Numbers at left side of each histogram show total numbers of calculated depths (after Ostenso and Wold, 1971).

importance is the fact that this hypothesis is compatible with, although differing in detail from, other reconstructions of global tectonics based on magnetic data from more southern latitudes (*e.g.*, the reconstruction by Dietz and Holden, 1970).

RECONSTRUCTIONS

A series of drawings illustrating this hypothesis for the evolution of the Arctic Ocean basin through geologic time is shown in Figures 6–10. In the interest of clarity, and to emphasize the principal features of this scheme, much known detail is omitted from these figures. For instance, sea-floor spreading in the Norwegian and Labrador Seas is much more complicated than shown schematically in Figure 9 (Vogt et al., 1970).

Because the dynamic processes at work involved considerable tectonic deformation (both compressional and tensional), the continental plates are but roughly outlined. For reference purposes the present borders of Alaska, eastern Siberia, and the Scandinavian Peninsula are included in all the figures. The gross directions of plate motions are shown by open arrows and the axes of sea-floor spreading are heavy lines,

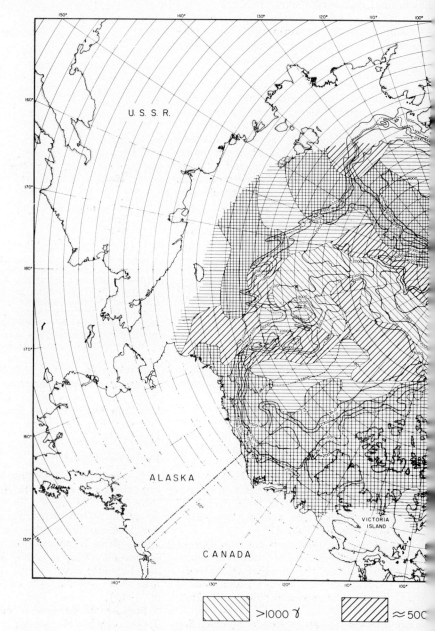

Fig. 1—Map showing zones of dominant magnetic profile

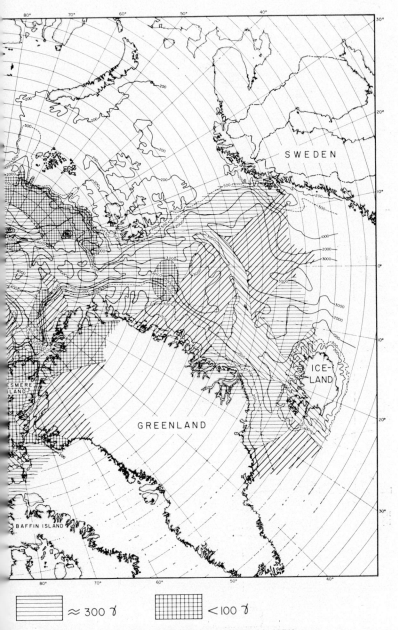

basin. Bathymetry is in meters (after Ostenso and Wold, 1971).

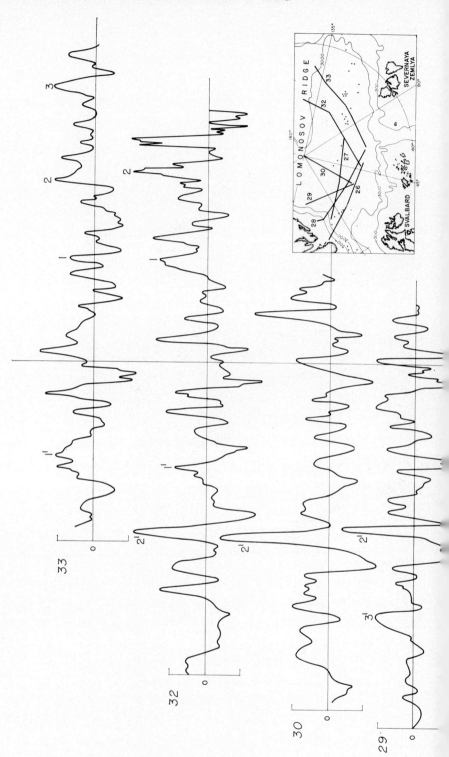

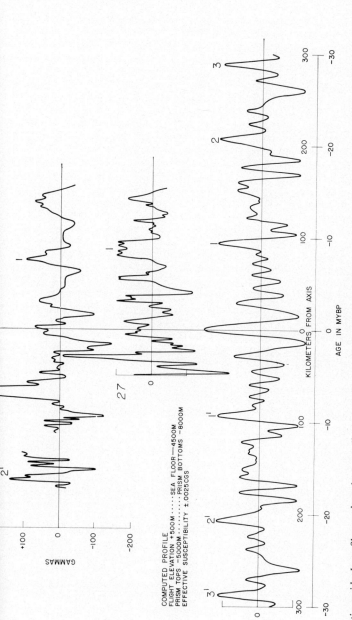
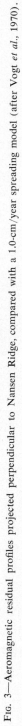

Fig. 3—Aeromagnetic residual profiles projected perpendicular to Nansen Ridge, compared with a 1.0-cm/year spreading model (after Vogt *et al.*, 1970).

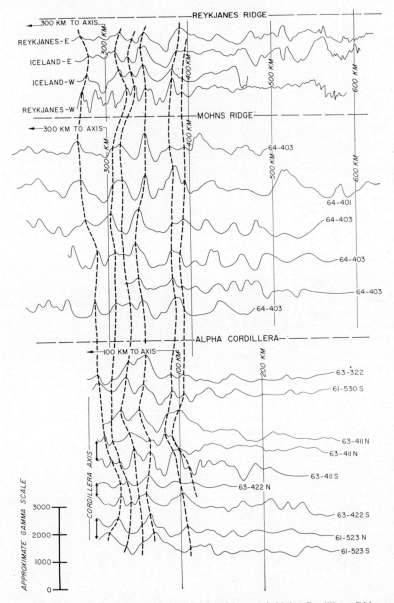

FIG. 4—Magnetic profiles across Reykjanes and Mohns Ridges and Alpha Cordillera. Ridge axes are to left at distances indicated by vertical lines. Profiles have been contracted by cos x, where x is angle between strike of flight track and the ridge axes. Alpha Cordillera profiles connected by heavy arrows have been "folded" at topographic axis to show bilateral symmetry. Dashed lines connect probable anomaly correlations between profiles (after Ostenso and Wold, 1971).

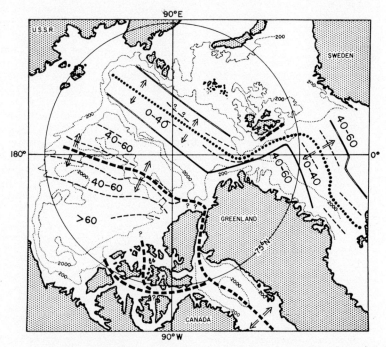

FIG. 5—Estimated age of Arctic Ocean floor in millions of years before present (after Vogt and Ostenso, 1970).

whereas transform faults are schematically shown by lighter lines. Subduction of oceanic crust is indicated by the solid arrows.

Figure 6 shows the Northern Hemisphere as it may have appeared in the early Paleozoic. Because North America and the Siberian platform are joined, sediments could have been transported "southward" into the geosyncline that covered northern Alaska and the Chukotsk Peninsula. The thesis that the Siberian platform is, and has been, part of the North American plate is one of the most important elements in this reconstruction. To refer to the single landmass by the rather well-established term "Laurasia" would be misleading, as that would involve the quite different concept of considering North America and all of Eurasia (exclusive of India) as a single unit. To avoid such ambiguity, the term "Ameria" is suggested to describe the North American–Siberian plate.

The ancient ocean basin—called here the "Hyperborean sea"—that was later to become part of the Canada basin, may or may not have been connected with the proto–Atlantic ocean. The Russian platform is being translated northward, where it will impinge first upon the North American–Greenland edge of America and then be deflected to rotate into the Siberian edge of Ameria.

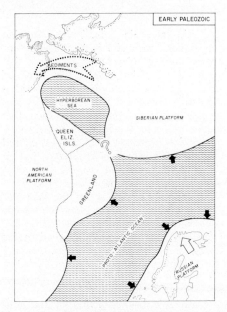

FIG. 6—In early Paleozoic time, Russian platform is approaching North American–Greenland plate; oceanic crust is being subducted under edges of all platforms as indicated by solid arrows. It is not known whether ancient Hyperborean sea was isolated or connected to proto–Atlantic ocean. Sediments were transported "southward" from Siberian platform into northern Alaska.

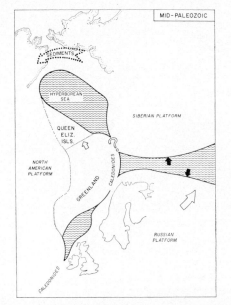

FIG. 7—In middle Paleozoic time, Russian platform collides with North American–Greenland plate, causing Caledonian orogeny along edges of the two plates and orthogonal folding in northern Greenland. Russian platform is then deflected relatively eastward toward Siberian platform, causing incipient opening of present Atlantic Ocean.

In the mid-Paleozoic (Fig. 7) the Russian platform collided with North America–Greenland, producing the Caledonian orogeny that affected the edges of both plates. The angle of the impacting plates was such that, in addition to compressive stresses at their edges, there was a tangential stress on the protuberance that would later become Greenland (see arrow). This tangential stress could have (1) caused the folding in northern Greenland that is roughly orthogonal to the main Caledonides structures of eastern Greenland; (2) promoted the major zone of weakness—the Wegener fault—along which the Queen Elizabeth Islands and Greenland later would undergo some differential movement; and (3) established strains that set the stage for separation of Greenland from North America proper. Presumably, all of these strains were manifested along zones of natural relative weakness.

Any reasonable reconstruction of the contacts between the North American and Russian plates leaves a hole between southeastern Greenland and the North Sea. This lack of contact between the two plates may account for the absence of Caledonian orogeny along this section of the Greenland coast. After the initial

impact with North America–Greenland, the Russian plate is deflected as indicated by the arcuate open arrow, and a second impact occurs along the Siberian edge of Ameria. This separation of the Russian platform from North America–Greenland marks the beginning of the modern Atlantic Ocean basin in the early Mesozoic.

By early Mesozoic time the Russian platform had collided with the Siberian platform (Fig. 8). Deformation at the edges of these two plates formed the Uralides. Either the impact of this collision or forces deep within the earth caused the Arctic to swing open during the late Mesozoic. This motion caused North America

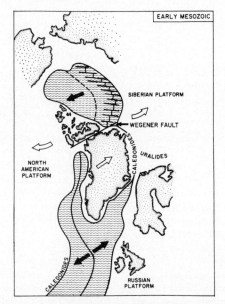

FIG. 8—In early Mesozoic time, Russian platform collides with Siberian platform to form Eurasian continent. Deformation along line of contact formed the Uralides. Continued northward thrusting of Russian platform causes a rotational movement of Eurasia relative to North America and an opening of present Atlantic Ocean–Labrador Sea about 180 m.y. ago. Alaskan orocline is initiated, and associated complex bending of structures in Alaska, eastern Siberia, and Bering–Chukchi Sea region occurs. As process continues, "southward" flow of sediments into Alaska ceases. An incipient Chukchi plateau is seen forming at northern edge of Chukchi shelf.

Crustal spreading that is opening Arctic Ocean–Labrador Sea is also opening Arctic Ocean along complexly offset axes of Alpha Cordillera. Greenland is laterally displaced relative to Queen Elizabeth Islands along Wegener fault. The islands themselves were formed by shattering of landmass lying north of Greenland. Lateral spreading from ridge axes caused further bending of Alaskan oroclinal system and subduction of Hyperborean sea crustal plate.

and the Siberian-Russian platforms (now united as Eurasia) to rotate slightly relative to each other. This rotation resulted in the initiation of the Alaskan orocline and its associated complex of deformations in Alaska, the Bering and Chukchi Seas, and eastern Siberia. This rotation caused tension on the northern edge of the Chukchi shelf and set the stage for the Chukchi Rise to be left behind as a remnant of continued rotation.

At this stage the Atlantic basin is growing by the process of sea-floor spreading away from the axis of an oceanic ridge that extends through what is now the Labrador Sea. Greenland is being separated from Canada. The exact connection between the Labrador Ridge and the Alpha Cordillera is still not clear. It is undoubtedly complex and probably, at some time, contributed to the "shattering" of the Queen Elizabeth Islands. The peculiar nature of the small displacements between the islands relative to the total spreading of the Labrador–Alpha-Mendeleyev ridge system suggests that this fracturing occurred in a late stage of the ridge when cooling "locked" spreading mantle to the underside of the continental crust.

Sea-floor spreading is orthogonal to the axes of the ridges, indicated by the heavy lines. Known and inferred fracture zones along the Labrador–Mid-Atlantic ridge system are not shown. The *en échelon* series of transform faults along the Alpha Cordillera is a schematic representation of Hall's (1970) model. A consequence of spreading from this configuration of ridge axes is further opening of the Arctic basin and continual rotation of North America relative to Eurasia, ultimately cutting off the "northern" supply of sediments. The southern edge of the ancient Hyperborean sea basin concurrently is subducted under northern Alaska and Canada. This underthrusting caused large thrust sheets to form in northern Alaska during the Early Cretaceous.

During Tertiary time, and presumably about 0 m.y. ago, there was a bifurcation of the axis of active spreading in the North Atlantic (Fig. 9). The Labrador Ridge–Alpha Cordillera system became dormant, and the new locus of spreading ran between Greenland and Europe and under the edge of the continental margin of Arctic Eurasia.

During this tectonic readjustment, there would have been a temporary halt or a substantial reduction in relative rotation of Eurasia about North America and a resultant period of quiescence throughout the Alaskan-Siberian

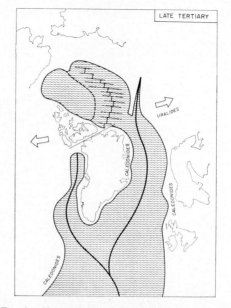

FIG. 9—About 40 m.y. ago, spreading ceased along Labrador and Alpha-Mendeleyev ridges, and locus of continued spreading ran between Greenland and Europe and under continental margin of Eurasia. A slice of the continental margin was translated northward to form present Lomonosov Ridge.

oroclinal system. As spreading continued along this new axis, the following events occurred: (1) a slice of the continental margin was translated northward to form ultimately the present Lomonosov Ridge; (2) the Arctic Ocean was enlarged by the formation of the Eurasian basin; (3) the Greenland and Norwegian Seas were enlarged, as was the Atlantic Ocean; (4) rotation of North America relative to Eurasia continued, but at a reduced rate; and (5) underthrusting of the Hyperborean sea floor under North America ceased. Another major manifestation of this new tectonic framework was deformation of the Brooks basin and the Chukotsk geosyncline.

Figure 10 shows the Arctic Ocean basin and environs as they are today. Active spreading, at a rate on the order of 1 cm/year, is still occurring orthogonal to the axis of the Mid-Atlantic–Nansen ridge system. The degree to which continued sea-floor generation contributes to widening of the ocean basins, and to further relative rotation between North America and Eurasia versus subduction at continental margins, has yet to be demonstrated. However, available tectonic evidence indicates that

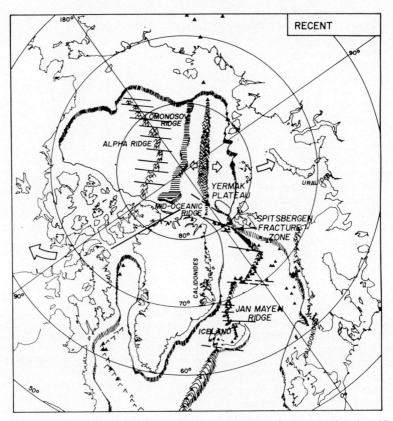

Fig. 10—Arctic Ocean basin as it appears today; active crustal spreading is still occurring along Nansen Ridge.

crustal underthrusting, if it is occurring at all, is a minor factor.

REFERENCES CITED

Brosgé, W. P., and I. L. Tailleur, 1970, Depositional history of northern Alaska, *in* W. L. Adkison and M. M. Brosgé, eds., Proceedings of the geological seminar on the North Slope of Alaska: Los Angeles, Pacific Sec. Am. Assoc. Petroleum Geologists, p. D1–D18.

Churkin, M., Jr., 1969, Paleozoic tectonic history of the Arctic basin north of Alaska: Science, v. 165, no. 3893, p. 549–555.

——— 1970, Fold belts of Alaska and Siberia and drift between North America and Asia, *in* W. L. Adkison and M. M. Brosgé, eds., Proceedings of the geological seminar on the North Slope of Alaska: Los Angeles, Pacific Sec. Am. Assoc. Petroleum Geologists, p. G1–G17.

Dietz, R. S., and J. C. Holden, 1970, Reconstruction of Pangaea: breakup and dispersion of continents, Permian to present: Jour. Geophys. Research, v. 75, no. 26, p. 4939–4956.

Hall, J. K., 1970, Arctic Ocean geophysical studies: the Alpha Cordillera and Mendeleyev Ridge: Palisades, New York, Lamont-Doherty Geol. Observ. Trans., no. 2, p. 125.

Hamilton, W., 1970, The Uralides and the motion of the Russian and Siberian platforms: Geol. Soc. America Bull., v. 81, p. 2553–2576.

Martin, A. J., 1970, Structure and tectonic history of the western Brooks Range, De Long Mountains and Lisburne Hills, northern Alaska: Geol. Soc. America Bull., v. 81, p. 3605–3622.

Ostenso, N. A., 1968, A gravity survey of the Chukchi Sea region, and its bearing on westward extension of structures in northern Alaska: Geol. Soc. America Bull., v. 79, p. 241–254.

——— and R. J. Wold, 1971, Aeromagnetic survey of the Arctic Ocean: techniques and interpretations: Marine Geophys. Research, v. 1, no. 2, p. 47–88.

Tailleur, I. L., and W. P. Brosgé, 1970, Tectonic history of northern Alaska, *in* W. L. Adkison and M. M. Brosgé, eds., Proceedings of the geological seminar on the North Slope of Alaska: Los Angeles, Pacific Sec. Am. Assoc. Petroleum Geologists, p. E1–E19.

Vogt, P. R., and N. A. Ostenso, 1970, Magnetic and gravity profiles across the Alpha Cordillera and their relation to Arctic sea-floor spreading: Jour. Geophys. Research, v. 75, no. 26, p. 4925–4937.

——— ——— and G. L. Johnson, 1970, Magnetic and bathymetric data bearing on sea-floor spreading north of Iceland: Jour. Geophys. Research, v. 75, no. 5, p. 903–920.

Crustal Structure of Queen Elizabeth Islands and Polar Continental Margin, Canada[1]

L. W. SOBCZAK and J. R. WEBER[2]

Ottawa, Ontario, Canada

Abstract Free-air and Bouguer anomaly maps have been compiled from about 9,000 gravity measurements made throughout the Canadian Arctic Archipelago and the Arctic Ocean. These measurements form part of a major survey of the Arctic being carried out by the Canadian government.

Correlation of Bouguer anomalies with geologic and physiographic features shows that negative anomalies generally occur over sedimentary basins and mountainous regions and positive anomalies occur over fold belts and the ocean basin.

The major feature of the free-air anomaly map is a series of large, positive, elliptically shaped anomalies overlying the continental margin and striking parallel with the continental break. These anomalies, which are approximately 120 km in width and between 150 and 300 km in length, have amplitudes greater than 100 mgal and regional horizontal gradients as large as 2.5 mgal/km. Interpretation of the gravity data, using seismic and geologic data for control, indicates that these anomalies can be explained best by a composite structure consisting of a sedimentary layer up to 10 km in thickness and a crust which thins by as much as 17 km.

The average free-air anomaly of the relatively flat archipelago (mean elevation of 15 m) west of 90°W long. is about 7 mgal; this value indicates that the region is in approximate isostatic equilibrium.

INTRODUCTION

Prior to 1957, very few gravity measurements were made in the Arctic Archipelago, even though the first measurements of gravity in Canada were made on Melville Island during the Parry expedition of 1819–1820. In 1957, systematic gravity surveys were initiated by the Earth Physics Branch (formerly Dominion Observatory) of the Canada Department of Energy, Mines and Resources by extending the gravity control network from Churchill, Manitoba, to various weather stations at Resolute Bay, Eureka, Mould Bay, and Alert. With the formation in 1958 of the Polar Continental Shelf Project (P.C.S.P.) in this department to coordinate most of the scientific studies carried out in the Arctic by the Canadian government, systematic regional gravity coverage of the Arctic became part of a continuous program. In cooperation with the P.C.S.P. and the Canadian Hydrographic Service, the Earth Physics Branch has established more than 9,000 gravity observations at a grid interval of about 10 km covering nearly 1,000,000 sq km of the Canadian Arctic.

In this paper we discuss the geophysical implications of gravity, seismic, and aeromagnetic data collected over the western part of the Queen Elizabeth Islands and the continental margin west of long. 90°W. Emphasis is placed on an interpretation of the gravity data in terms of deep-seated structures along two north-south profiles across the Arctic Archipelago and the continental margin.

GRAVITY RESULTS

Geologic Setting

The general structural-stratigraphic divisions in the Queen Elizabeth Islands proposed by Thorsteinsson and Tozer (1960) are shown in Figure 1. The *Precambrian shield* is exposed to the south and east of the region. To the north and west the shield underlies a relatively thin belt of late Precambrian and Paleozoic rocks which form the *Arctic lowlands*. Farther north and west the Paleozoic marine formations thicken considerably and become, in most of the region, miogeosynclinal in character. These formations make up the *Franklinian geosyncline,* which underwent major orogenic disturbances between Late Devonian and Middle Pennsylvanian time, producing first the north-trending Cornwallis fold belt along the northern extension of the Boothia uplift and, second, the Parry Islands and Central Ellesmere fold belts which parallel the geosynclinal axis. Trettin (1970; this volume) proposes an axial trough instead of a eugeosyncline in the northeastern part of Ellesmere Island, east of Lake Hazen. To the north and west the Paleozoic formations are overlain unconformably by a very thick sequence of shallow-water clastic deposits ranging in age from Permo-Carboniferous to early Tertiary and forming the *Sverdrup basin.* Deformation of these rocks in Late Cretaceous and Tertiary times resulted in a great variety of north-trending structures such as the Eureka Sound fold belt and the Prince Patrick

[1] Manuscript received, September 21, 1971.

[2] Canada Department of Energy, Mines and Resources, Earth Physics Branch.

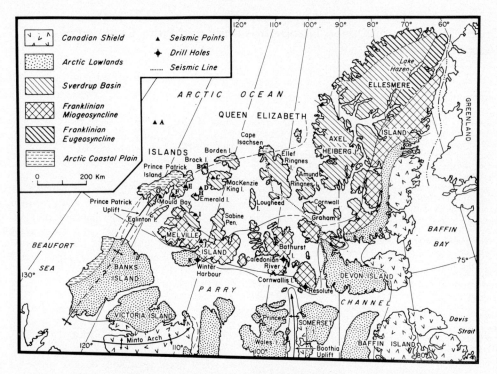

FIG. 1—Geologic sketch map outlining structural elements of Canadian Arctic Archipelago, and also showing location of drillholes and seismic stations.

uplift. On the northwest, the Sverdrup basin is bounded by the *Arctic coastal plain,* a narrow belt of unconsolidated sand and gravel which extends to the inner part of the continental shelf.

Bouguer Anomalies

The Bouguer anomalies (Fig. 2) have a range of more than 330 mgal—from less than −70 mgal south of Eureka on Ellesmere Island to more than 260 mgal over the ocean of the Canada basin where the water depth is greater than 3,500 m. The anomaly map shows the following characteristics: positive anomalies along moderately folded regions, negative anomalies over basin and mountainous areas, and large positive anomalies over the ocean. A steep gravity gradient (3.2 mgal/km) occurs along the continental slope. The archipelago region, which is topographically flat (the mean elevation of 4,000 stations west of long. 90°W is 15 m), is also gravitationally flat; most of the Bouguer anomalies range between ±20 mgal. The mean value of the regional Bouguer anomalies for the archipelago region west of long. 90°W is 6.0 mgal, which indicates that the re-

gion is near isostatic equilibrium.

On the islands, eight major anomaly lows are underlain by basins containing up to 10 km of clastic rocks. These gravity lows are separated by positive anomaly belts over Early Devonian to Tertiary fold belts.

The high values of the Bouguer anomaly field over the ocean deep merely reflect the water depths and obscure the anomalous features which are better represented by the free-air anomaly field.

Free-Air Anomalies

Free-air anomalies (Fig. 3) have a range of 185 mgal—from less than −70 mgal south of Eureka on Ellesmere Island to more than +115 mgal along the continental break where water depths are about 600 m. The mean value of the regional free-air anomalies for the archipelago region west of long. 90°W is 7.3 mgal; for the continental shelf region from Meighen Island to the west side of Prince Patrick Island the value is 27 mgal. The mean depth for the shelf region is about 400 m. Figure 3 reveals that the free-air anomaly field over the island and inter-island areas is similar to the Bouguer

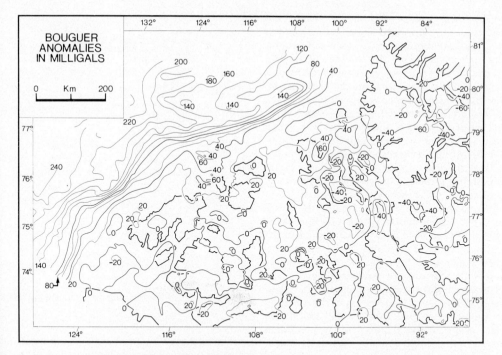

FIG. 2—Bouguer anomaly map of Queen Elizabeth Islands, continental margin, and Arctic Ocean. C.I. = 20 mgal.

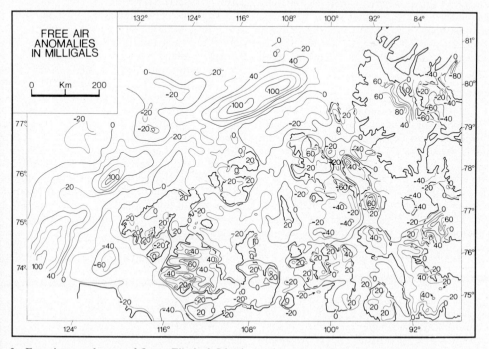

FIG. 3—Free-air anomaly map of Queen Elizabeth Islands, continental margin, and Arctic Ocean. C.I. = 20 mgal.

anomaly field except that the anomalies are more extensive and more negative over the basin areas and more positive over topographically high areas. Along the continental margin, a series of large elliptically shaped anomalies occurs over the continental break. These anomalies have been mapped southwestward from the offshore area of Ellef Ringnes Island along the continental shelf to the Beaufort Sea, where two additional pronounced elliptical anomalies have been found (Ostenso, 1962; Hornal *et al.*, 1970; Wold *et al.*, 1970). Off the Queen Elizabeth Islands these anomalies are approximately 120 km wide and between 150 and 320 km long, and have amplitudes greater than 100 mgal. The largest anomaly, north of Borden Island, is 130 km wide and 320 km long; it has a maximum value of 115 mgal and a steep horizontal gradient of 2.5 mgal/km. This anomaly lies obliquely across the continental break; the northeastern end overlies the continental shelf where water depths are less than 500 m, and the southwestern end overlies the continental slope where water depths are greater than 1,500 m. A second anomaly, which is northwest of Prince Patrick Island, is narrow and has an amplitude of 110 mgal; it overlies the continental slope where water depths are greater than 2,000 m. Farther to the southwest a third anomaly, west of M'Clure Strait, has a maximum value of 100 mgal; it straddles the continental break, which is at a depth of about 500 m.

AEROMAGNETIC RESULTS

A residual-magnetic-anomaly map (Fig. 4) was obtained by removing the regional field from the observed field using a crossover-point method; the regional field was given by the high-level, total-magnetic-field chart published by the Observatories Branch (now Earth Physics Branch) in 1965. This residual map generally shows a relatively flat magnetic field which ranges between ±100 gammas. No obvious correlation between these anomalies and the major structural subdivisions of the region is known. Bhattacharyya (1968) also derived a magnetic-residual-anomaly map by approximating the regional field to a quadratic surface computed by the method of least squares. By using the greater number of measurements and concentrating on the smaller anomalies, Bhattacharyya was able to provide greater resolution and show some continuity of the smaller anomalies, which readily correlate with mafic rock intrusions.

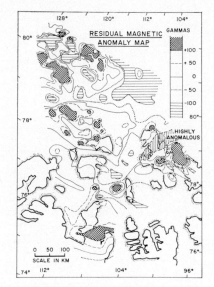

FIG. 4—Simplified residual total-magnetic-intensity map, in gammas.

The results of Bhattacharyya's analysis of the residual anomalies are shown as an isopach map of the strata overlying the magnetic basement (Fig. 5). There are two areas where gravity and magnetic anomalies are opposite in sign. Interpretation of a north-south magnetic low over Prince Gustaf Adolf Sea, west of Ellef Ringnes Island, suggests a linear, narrow trough with strata 7–8 km thick. Such a feature should correspond to a negative gravity anomaly of about 50 mgal, but the gravity anomaly is positive in this area. This paradox may be explained by the presence of a broad sheet of mafic rock which is exposed on Ellef Ringnes Island and thins gradually westward in accord with the decrease in the Bouguer anomaly field in that direction. Alternatively, the magnetic low may reflect the absence of mafic rocks within this part of the Sverdrup basin. In the second area, Bhattacharyya (1968) suggested that a broad, linear magnetic low parallel with the continental break is caused by a deep, linear sedimentary trough with a rock sequence up to 19 km thick. However, the freeair anomalies in this area are strongly positive and, thus, do not support Bhattacharyya's interpretation.

Worzel (1968), in a review of world continental margins, concluded that the magnetic studies provide information on the intrabasement changes and contribute little to structural studies of the overlying sedimentary cover—a

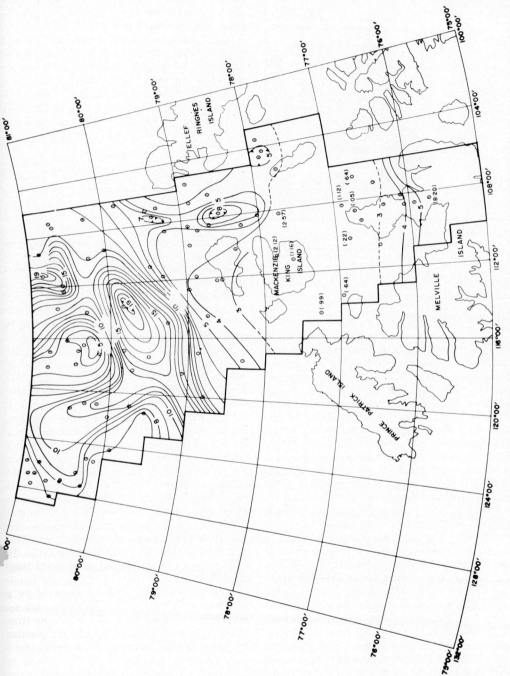

Fig. 5.—Contoured map of depths, in kilometers, to top of magnetized bodies.

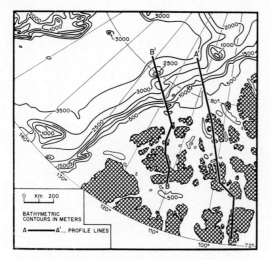

FIG. 6—Location map showing regional bathymetry, in meters, and location of profiles *A-A'* and *B-B'*.

conclusion which appears to be confirmed in the Queen Elizabeth Islands.

Hydrographic Results

Hydrographic data obtained by the P.C.S.P. to 1967 are shown in a bathymetric chart of the Arctic Ocean and vicinity (Fig. 6). Around the islands, water depths are fairly uniform, generally less than 500 m. A few northwest-trending channels on either side of Ellef Ringnes Island and to the west of Lougheed Island have water depths greater than 700 m. The continental margin northwest of the Queen Elizabeth Islands is relatively undisturbed. Beyond the continental margin lies the Canada basin, a uniform abyssal plain more than 3,500 m deep. Between Prince Patrick Island and Ellef Ringnes Island, the continental shelf has a gradient of about 0.25° and widens from 110 to 160 km. The continental break is 500–650 m deep; its gradient decreases from 1½° to 1° and its width increases from 110 to 160 km. Farther northeast, this slope continues to widen and appears to merge with the Alpha Cordillera, which crosses the Arctic Ocean northwestward from Ellesmere Island. On the southwest, the continental margin in the Beaufort Sea region is similar to that off the Queen Elizabeth Islands, except that the continental break is at a shallower depth of about 200 m. Off the coast of Alaska the continental margin has a narrow shelf of about 70 km, a very steep slope of about 4½°, and a continental break at about 200 m (Wold *et al.*, 1970). Inasmuch as conti-

nental shelves for other areas in the world are generally shallow (Worzel, 1968), these observations suggest that the continental margin has been depressed by about 300 m northwest of Prince Patrick Island and 450 m northwest of Ellef Ringnes Island. Such subsidence is also supported by geologic evidence; subaerial deposits are found at depths as great as 370 m below present sea level (Pelletier, 1964). Pelletier estimated from physiographic and geologic evidence that as much as 450 m of drowning may have taken place.

Structural Interpretation

Crustal models which best explain the gravity field by using the available geological and geophysical information have been derived along two north-south profiles. Profiles *A-A'* and *B-B'* (Figs. 7, 8) show the generalized geology, topography, residual magnetic anomalies, seismic refraction velocities, observed and computed gravity anomalies, and proposed crustal sections. The gravity effects of the structural sections were computed by a line-integral, two-dimensional method (Nagy, 1964). The models were compared to a standard five-layer crust, 40 km thick, with a density distribution defined as follows: 0 to 10 km, 2.79 g/cm³; 10–20 km, 2.86 g/cm³; 20–30 km, 2.92 g/cm³; 30–37 km, 2.98 g/cm³; and 37–40 km, 3.40 g/cm³. The density distribution is based on a straight-line velocity-density relationship $\rho = 1.46 + 0.233\ V$ (Smith *et al.*, 1966), where ρ is the density in g/cm³ and V is the velocity in km/sec. The velocity distribution is based on seismic results in this region. The thickness of the crust under the Queen Elizabeth Islands is considered to be 37 km, the mean value of seismic results in the region (Sander and Overton, 1965; Utsu, 1966; Overton, 1970). This standard column is comparable to that used by Kutschale (1966) for the "Siberia" basin (now called Makarov basin) and that used by Worzel and Shurbet (1955) for the Atlantic continental shelf.

In this study, compressional wave velocities of 6.0 and 6.2 km/sec are assumed to indicate crystalline basement rock of mid-Paleozoic age or older, and velocities of 8.2 km/sec represent the upper mantle. Because of the similarities in bulk densities, variations in the thickness of the carbonate rocks overlying crystalline rocks are not reflected in the gravity anomalies (Sobczak *et al.*, 1970). Thus, although Thorsteinsson and Kerr (1968) suggested a structural relief of more than 7 km between Early Ordovician and

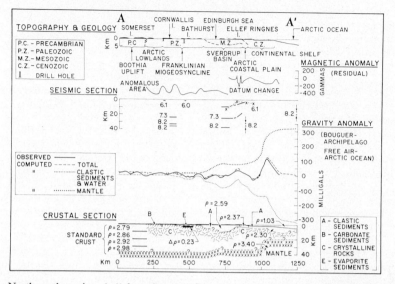

FIG. 7—North-south section *A-A'* from Somerset Island to Arctic Ocean. See Figure 6 for location.

Early Devonian carbonate rocks in the eastern and central parts of Cornwallis Island, the gravity record there is relatively featureless. Sander and Overton (1965) were also unable to detect the base of the carbonate rocks northeast of Cornwallis Island because the propagation velocities of the carbonate rocks were similar to those of the basement.

In profiles *A-A'* and *B-B'* the combined gravity effect of the water and the clastic sedimentary sequence is shown by the lower dotted curve, and the effect of crustal thinning is shown by the upper dotted curve (Figs. 7, 8). The sum of these effects is the total gravitational effect of the model which fits the observed gravity values.

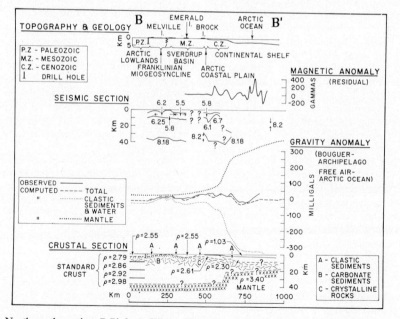

FIG. 8—North-south section *B-B'* from Winter Harbour to Arctic Ocean. See Figure 6 for location.

Seismic and geologic evidence indicates a clastic sequence at least 10 km thick in the Sverdrup basin near King Christian Island, east of the south end of Ellef Ringnes Island (Sander and Overton, 1965), and a clastic sequence about 5 km thick below the continental shelf north of Ellef Ringnes Island (Hobson and Overton, 1967). On Axel Heiberg Island a sedimentary section of approximately 12.4 km has been measured (Fortier et al., 1963). Studies of rock density (Sobczak et al., 1970) suggest that anomalies of -80 and -100 mgal should occur in the island and ocean areas. The fact that anomalies of this magnitude are not observed suggests some form of compensation at depth. On the basis of the available geophysical information, the discrepancy may be explained either (1) by assuming the presence of a lower basaltic crustal layer of varied thickness or (2) by considering the total crust to be thinner and neglecting any possible variations in upper-mantle density.

The first alternative is supported by the presence of a layer with velocity of 7.3 km/sec south of Ellef Ringnes Island at a depth of about 25 km below sea level. Sander and Overton (1965) interpreted this refractor as the upper surface of a lower basaltic crustal layer. Variations in the thickness of such a layer could compensate for the mass deficiency of the basin. However, this layer was not found below Hecla and Griper Bay near Emerald Island, where a thick clastic sequence is present and good seismic refraction data are available (Overton, 1970). Furthermore, a varied thickness of basaltic crust would not account for the gravity anomalies and the mass deficiency of the water and the clastic sequence at the continental margin.

The second, and the more likely, explanation is to consider the total crustal thickness to be varied but thinner, possibly including a variable basaltic layer. Crustal thinning of approximately 5 km below the Sverdrup basin near King Christian Island, a further thinning of 14 km below the continental shelf and slope, and a sedimentary sequence thickening by 5 km below the slope can easily account for the anomalies. Preliminary seismic results show that the depth to the mantle is 32–35 km at Haughton Head and 15–19 km over the continental slope (Berry and Barr, 1971). If these mantle depths are projected to profiles A-A' and B-B' at points of equivalent water depth (indicated by arrows in the diagram), they agree to within 1 km with the crustal models. A seismic profile along profile B-B' that extends for 175 km northwest from Brock Island (Overton, 1970) indicates that the depth to the mantle decreases from 42 to 32 km where the transition from continental to probably oceanic crust occurs. Overton (1970) stated that, if the crust-mantle boundary is inclined, a much shallower depth of 17 km is obtained. Similarly, if an inclined Mohorovičić discontinuity is assumed, the seismically determined crustal thickness near the north end of Ellef Ringnes Island could be reduced to 33 km, as indicated in the model of Figure 7 (A. Overton, personal commun.). Wold et al. (1970) concluded from their analysis of the gravity data in the Beaufort Sea region that the crust thins from an assumed continental level of 35 km to 17 km north of Alaska and to 22 km west of Banks Island. Geophysical data along the Canadian and Alaskan continental margins tend to support a thinning of the crust in the transition zone similar to that found at the Atlantic continental margin by Worzel and Shurbet (1955).

Worzel (1968), in a review of continental-margin structures of the world, found that the transition from continental crust to oceanic crust occurs in a zone between 50 and 300 km wide bisected by the 2,000-m isobath, and that the structures are generally in isostatic equilibrium. However, the continental margin northwest of the Queen Elizabeth Islands does not fit this general pattern. The anomalies associated with the transition zone generally occur along the continental break, which is at a water depth of about 500–650 m, and the transition zone is only 25 km wide. Wold et al. (1970) found similar results in the Beaufort Sea region, where the transition zone is 55–90 km wide. This departure from Worzel's general pattern is explained by the presence of a much greater seaward accumulation of sediments than is normally found at other continental margins (Wold et al., 1970).

The mean value of free-air anomalies found over the continental margin northwest of the Queen Elizabeth Islands is about $+27$ mgal. Such a value suggests that the continental margin is not in isostatic equilibrium. The reason might be the rapid rate of sedimentary deposition. If isostatic compensation is achieved by horizontal transfer of mantle material of density 3.4 g/cm^3, then the continental margin should sink nearly 200 m more. The drowning of the continental margin in this region may indicate that some isostatic adjustment has already taken place.

SUMMARY

The Bouguer anomalies throughout the Queen Elizabeth Islands correlate well with the geology. Lows are associated with low-density clastic and evaporite strata in basins; highs are correlated with fold belts and may be explained by the combined effects of dense carbonate rocks within the clastic sequences, variation in the lithology of the basement rocks, and intrusions of mafic rocks (Sobczak, 1963; Berkhout and Sobczak, 1967; Sobczak and Weber, 1970). The free-air anomalies over the Queen Elizabeth Islands indicate that the region is nearly in isostatic equilibrium; in contrast, the continental margin is not in equilibrium and should sink an additional 200 m. The positive, elliptically shaped free-air anomalies along the continental break are attributed to the transition from continental to oceanic crust; they may be explained by assuming an abrupt crustal thinning of 14 km in a distance of 25 km on the landward side of the anomaly and a 5-km thickening of low-density strata on the seaward side.

REFERENCES CITED

Berkhout, A. W. J., and L. W. Sobczak, 1967, Preliminary investigations of gravity observations in the Somerset and Prince of Wales Islands, Arctic Canada, with map: Dominion Observatory Ottawa Gravity Map Series, no. 81.

Berry, M. J., and K. G. Barr, 1971, A seismic refraction profile of Prince Patrick Island, Queen Elizabeth Islands: Canadian Jour. Earth Sci., v. 8, no. 3, p. 347–360.

Bhattacharyya, B. K., 1968, Analysis of aeromagnetic data over the Arctic Islands and continental shelf of Canada: Canada Geol. Survey Paper 68–44.

Fortier, Y. O., et al., 1963, Geology of the north-central part of the Arctic Archipelago, Northwest Territories (Operation Franklin): Canada Geol. Survey Mem. 320.

Hobson, G. D., and A. Overton, 1967, A seismic section of the Sverdrup basin, Canadian Arctic Islands, in A. W. Musgrove, ed., Seismic refraction prospecting: Tulsa, Oklahoma, Soc. Exploration Geophysicists, p. 550–562.

Hornal, R. W., et al., 1970, Preliminary results of gravity surveys over the Mackenzie Basin and Beaufort Sea, with maps: Earth Physics Branch Ottawa Gravity Map. Ser., nos. 117–119.

Kutschale, H., 1966, Arctic Ocean geophysical studies —the southern half of the Siberian basin: Geophysics, v. 31, no. 4, p. 683–710.

Nagy, D., 1964, The gravitational effect of two-dimensional masses of arbitrary cross section: Dominion Observatory Ottawa, Gravity Div., unpub. ms.

Ostenso, N. A., 1962, Geophysical investigations of the Arctic Ocean basin: Wisconsin Univ. Geophys. and Polar Research Center Research Rept. 62-4, 124 p.

Overton, A., 1970, Seismic refraction surveys, western Queen Elizabeth Islands and polar continental margin: Canadian Jour. Earth Sci., v. 7, no. 2, p. 346–365.

Pelletier, B. R., 1964, Development of submarine physiography in the Canadian Arctic and its relation to crustal movements: Bedford Inst. Oceanography Rept. 64-16.

Sander, G. W., and A. Overton, 1965, Deep seismic refraction investigations in the Canadian Arctic Archipelago: Geophysics, v. 30, no. 1, p. 87–96.

Smith, T. J., J. A. Steinhart, and L. T. Aldrich, 1966, Lake Superior crustal structure: Jour. Geophys. Research, v. 71, no. 4, p. 1141–1172.

Sobczak, L. W., 1963, Regional gravity survey of the Sverdrup Islands and vicinity, with map: Dominion Observatory Ottawa Gravity Map Ser., no. 11.

—— and J. R. Weber, 1970, Gravity measurements in the Queen Elizabeth Islands, with maps: Earth Physics Branch Ottawa Gravity Map Ser., nos. 115, 116.

—— and E. F. Roots, 1970, Rock densities in the Queen Elizabeth Islands, Northwest Territories: Geol. Assoc. Canada Proc., v. 21, p. 5–14.

Thorsteinsson, R., and J. W. Kerr, 1968, Cornwallis Island and adjacent smaller islands, Canadian Arctic Archipelago: Canada Geol. Survey Paper 67–64.

—— and E. T. Tozer, 1960, Summary account of structural history of the Canadian Arctic Archipelago since Precambrian time: Canada Geol. Survey Paper 60–7.

Trettin, H. P., 1970, Ordovician-Silurian flysch sedimentation in the axial trough of the Franklinian geosyncline, northeastern Ellesmere Island, Arctic Canada: Geol. Assoc. Canada Spec. Paper No. 7, p. 13–35.

Utsu, T, 1966, Variations in spectra of P-waves recorded at Canadian Arctic seismograph stations: Canadian Jour. Earth Sci., v. 3, no. 5, p. 597–622.

Weber, J. R., 1963, Gravity anomalies over the Polar continental shelf: Dominion Observatory Ottawa Contr., v. 4, no. 17, p. 3–10.

Wold, R. J., T. L. Woodzick, and N. A. Ostenso, 1970, Structure of the Beaufort Sea continental margin: Geophysics, v. 35, no. 5, p. 849–861.

Worzel, J. L., 1968, Advances in marine geophysical research of continental margins: Canadian Jour. Earth Sci., v. 5, no. 4, p. 963–983.

—— and G. L. Shurbet, 1955, Gravity anomalies at continental margins: Natl. Acad. Sci. Proc., v. 41, p. 963–983.

Probable Rift Origin of Canada Basin, Arctic Ocean[1]

IRVIN L. TAILLEUR[2]

Menlo Park, California 94025

Abstract Formation of the Canada basin by post-Triassic rifting seems the most workable and logical hypothesis on the basis of available information. Speculated counterclockwise rotation of the Alaska-Chukchi continental edge best rationalizes the complex geology of northern Alaska, whereas the assumption that a single continental block was present before the Jurassic makes the best palinspastic fit for Arctic America.

The Arctic Ocean is the focus of present-day spreading and probably was the focus of earlier stages of spreading in which spread of the Canada basin would have been an initial stage. Spread of the Canada basin is probable if the Atlantic formed by sea-floor spreading, because analogies between the Arctic and Atlantic edges indicate a common origin for the ocean basins.

Late Cretaceous and younger deflections of the cordillera in the Arctic and diabasic emplacements in the northern Arctic Islands may reflect later stages of spreading. Pre-Mesozoic plate tectonism may be represented by the widespread Proterozoic diabasic emplacements in the Canadian Arctic and by the Franklinian-Innuitian tract, where the volcanogenic rocks and deformation resulted not from a classical eugeosyncline-miogeosyncline couple, but from the junction of a mid-Paleozoic continental edge and another plate on closure of a pre–Arctic Ocean.

INTRODUCTION

Unlike many other speculations, the contention that the important Canada basin element of the Arctic formed by sea-floor spreading is not based on, or constrained by, a great amount of data. Instead, its bases are mainly onshore geology and common sense—*i.e.*, the geology of Arctic North America seems to be explained best by the speculation that the edges of the basin rifted and rotated apart in the Mesozoic. The better paleogeographic fit between Arctic Alaska and Arctic Canada became apparent in 1967, and indications supporting it have accumulated since then. The speculation is workable—and, in one instance (Rickwood, 1970), has been applied to explain the entrapment of Prudhoe Bay oil.

The better paleogeographic fit between Arctic Alaska and Arctic Canada with Carey's (1958) sphenochasm restored was realized when preparing for the International Symposium on the Devonian System in Calgary, 1967.

[1] Manuscript received, September 21, 1971. Publication authorized by the Director, U.S. Geological Survey.

[2] U.S. Geological Survey.

Devonian clastic wedges on the Amerasian continental edge and in the Canadian Arctic Archipelago seemed much more likely to have been shed off opposite flanks of a single linear uplift than off the southern flank of a 3,500-km-long semicircular uplift whose northern flank was an ocean deep.

Almost concurrently, Hamilton's (1967) conjecture that the Chukchi shelf was drifting past the Siberian mainland as part of complex rifting in the Arctic introduced the possibility of plate tectonics in northern Alaska. The drift that he postulated could be accommodated in Alaska in the strong deflections—*i.e.*, shortening—in the cordilleran front. Prior counterclockwise rotation of a northern Alaska plate, out of the Canada basin, could have caused the large-scale dislocations in the Brooks Range fold belt (Tailleur and Snelson, 1969).

Since 1968, suggestion of a two-stage spreading history for the rest of the Arctic Ocean has been considered. It now appears that spread of the Canada basin logically could be the initial stage of a three-stage spreading history. Mirror imagery between the Arctic and Atlantic coasts, across the North American craton, suggests a common origin for the continental edges and also suggests that the Canada basin formed by rifting and sea-floor spreading, if the Atlantic has rifted and spread.

A trip through the North American Arctic in 1970 impressed me with the probability of a long history of plate tectonics in that area. The American Arctic may record spreading beginning in the late Precambrian, plate collision ending in the Devonian, and current plate motion beginning after the Triassic.

GENERAL SPECULATIONS

Three fundamental aspects of the Canada basin are equivocal or unknown: its nature, age, and origin.

The nature of the ocean deep—whether it is oceanic, continental, or hybrid—has not been determined. However, growing evidence (Churkin, 1969) in favor of oceanic crust supports the assumption that the Canada basin is a true, but small, ocean deep.

Less evidence is available for the age of the Canada basin than for its nature. If the deep is oceanic, an age older than Mesozoic would be unique because no present oceanic basin is known to be as old as the Paleozoic. An ancient ocean ringed by mid-Paleozoic orogenic belts, as advocated by Churkin (1969) until recently, creates the additional problem of incorporating into oceanic crust the considerable amount of continental material represented by the poleward flanks of the belts and the detritus shed from them. Hall's (1970) suggestion of possible Permo-Carboniferous spreading in the southern Canada basin—and the resultant oceanic crust of the same age—is unsupported by the nonorogenic sedimentary records for that time interval in northern Alaska and the Arctic Archipelago. In comparison, it seems reasonable to assign a Jurassic to mid-Cretaceous age to the rifting and spreading, as speculated below.

The origin of the Canada basin also is entirely speculative. The hypothesis of rifting and spreading of the Canada basin briefly discussed in the following section seems the most workable of the several, in part mutually exclusive, hypotheses for the basin's genesis. It provides the energy, as well as the mechanism of underthrusting on a leading plate edge, to account for the gross dislocations in northern Alaska. Furthermore, assuming the Canada basin to have been closed during the Late Devonian to Triassic interval provides a better explanation of the geology and geologic relations of the Chukchi shelf–northern Alaska, Yukon Territory, and the Arctic Islands.

GEOLOGIC FIT

The generalized tectonics of the Brooks Range are related to northern Alaska's counterclockwise rotation out of the Canada basin (Figs. 1A, B). The map units are generalizations of different Devonian to Cretaceous facies and stratigraphic successions described elsewhere (Tailleur et al., 1966; Tailleur and Snelson, 1968a; Snelson and Tailleur, 1968; Martin, 1970). Superposed "thrust-together" sequences are fairly well defined in the western Brooks Range but are partially inferred in the east. Contrasts in facies are marked. For example, Devonian carbonate beds in map unit III contrast with Devonian clastic beds in unit II; Jurassic ophiolites are abundant in unit III, whereas only minor mafic rocks are present in the other units; and the earliest Cretaceous is represented by wacke in unit III, by a con-densed shale and coquina sequence in unit II, and by b sinal shale in unit I. Although the units have been thrust together, as shown in Figure 1A, they were deposited in regions that originally were widely separated, as shown in Figure 1B.

The Brooks Range orogen in northern Alaska (Fig. 1A) was constructed from an old sedimentary basin. Stable sedimentation offshore in this Arctic Alaska basin (Tailleur and Brosgé, 1970; Brosgé and Tailleur, 1970) was first interrupted by the intrusion of shallow diabase sills in unit II at the beginning of the Jurassic. In unit III, during the Middle Jurassic, ultramafic complexes were emplaced in what seems to have been an ocean-deep environment that had succeeded a continental-slope environment. In the earliest Cretaceous, a foredeep with a volcanic provenance on the south formed in unit III. The large-scale flat thrusts, which foreshortened the orogenic welt by more than 200 km, formed in Aptian and Albian time. They preceded and accompanied uplift of an ancestral Brooks Range geanticline and depression of flanking troughs filled with flysch deposits. Deformation continued in subsequent episodes—and perhaps is still active to some extent—but mid-Cretaceous and later sedimentation into successor basins on either flank of the present Brooks Range geanticline was postorogenic in character.

At least two phenomena in the Brooks Range orogenic history appear to be missing from the history of the foreland belt of the cordillera on the south: (1) foreshortening by about 50 percent during the middle, perhaps the culmination, of the orogeny, and (2) intrusion and extrusion of abundant mafic igneous rocks near the beginning.

The concept of sea-floor spreading and plate tectonics is invaluable to interpretation of these phenomena. It provides, in my opinion, the only credible energy source and mechanism for the gross dislocations in the Brooks Range, and it is compatible with the development of a continent-ocean boundary on a continental plate.

Accounting for the stacked thrust sheets by northward gravitational sliding seems impossible, if for no other reason than that there is no known paleo-uplift to the south from which the sheets could slide. Northward compressional overthrusting is no better an explanation; it seems precluded by the inherent weakness of sheets thousands of square kilometers in extent but generally less than 2 km thick.

In contrast, a southward-drifting continental

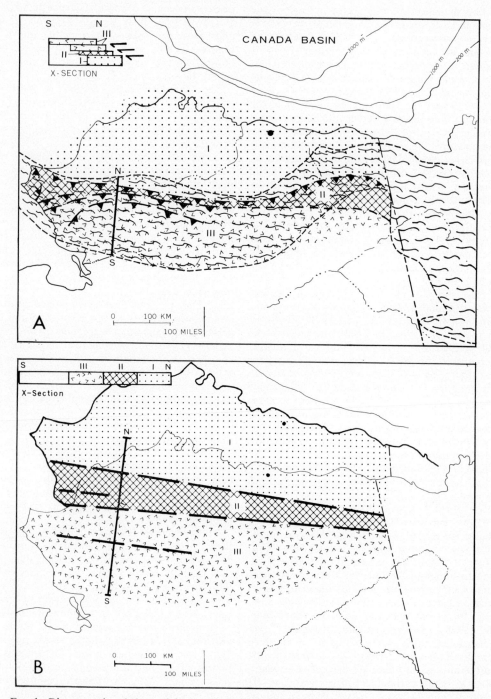

FIG. 1—Diagrammatic relations of large-scale thrusting and counterclockwise rotation in Arctic Alaska. **A.** Generalized map and section of thrusts and map units. Dashed lines mark boundary of Brooks Range orogen and its eastward continuation. **B.** Minimum extent of units before underthrusting.

plate seems capable of thrusting the sheets successively under one another. The energy available certainly would be sufficient. Thin sheets of the earth's skin need not have been very strong for the upper ones to have remained in place while the lower ones were carried under by the moving crustal plate. Thus, the stacked thrust sheets in the Brooks Range could have been produced by underthrusting as the northern Alaska plate drifted southward, rotating counterclockwise out of the Canada basin.

The Jurassic igneous activity far offshore in the Arctic Alaska sedimentary basin may be evidence of a spreading Canada basin. The igneous rocks, particularly 160-m.y.-old mafic-ultramafic complexes along the south palinspastic limit of the basin (Fig. 1B), appear to be ophiolitic. In the concept of plate tectonics, these ophiolites mark the boundary or leading edge of an active plate. Plate-edge conditions along the south side of the Brooks Range are also indicated by the presence of glaucophane. Thus, northern Alaska may have had a leading edge on the south; such a situation would be another indication of rotation out of the Canada basin.

Figure 2 demonstrates the paleogeographic fit based on the assumption that the Canada basin was not open before the Jurassic. Sedimentation in the Arctic would have been an extension of the cordilleran sedimentation in the south (Fig. 2B). "Barrovia" (named for Point Barrow), the provenance for the old Arctic Alaska sedimentary basin (Tailleur and Brosgé, 1970), and "Innuitia," the tectonic land that lay off the archipelago (Fig. 2A), would have formed a single linear positive element. Such a reconstruction seems particularly appropriate for the Late Devonian, when post-orogenic clastic wedges were shed off both flanks, and probably off the end of the Innuitian orogen, while carbonate sediments were being deposited farther offshore (Fig. 2B). Another significant factor is that Devonian to Jurassic deposition in northern Alaska and the Yukon would have been in more or less co-linear belts. Rocks of the Devonian, Mississippian, Permian, and Triassic Systems at the intersection of the Yukon River and the International Boundary, in northern Alaska, and on Wrangel Island (Ostrov Vrangelya) are all so similar that deposition in continuous environments seems required. At present, these environments are traced concentrically around a 90° bend into Alaska (Fig. 2A); the essentially linear traces subparallel with the reconstructed Innuitia in Figure 2B seem much more natural.

ANALOGICAL FIT

Figure 3 shows analogies between the Canada and Atlantic basins which suggest they had a common origin.

Basically, the Arctic seems to be the mirror image of the Atlantic seaboard across the craton or continental nucleus. Probably the most important element of similarity is the presence of tectonic landmasses seaward of Devonian clastic wedges in the Canadian archipelago and along the Atlantic. Similar Devonian wedges and seaward provenances in Wrangel Island and northern Alaska seem analogous to those of the Devonian in Europe. The vertical tectonics that probably controlled the Sverdrup basin in late Paleozoic and Triassic times are comparable with the vertical and extensional tectonics and sedimentation along the Atlantic coast during the same time. The 200-m.y.-old sills in northern Alaska may be synchronous with the Palisades sill and other mafic rocks on the east coast of North America, and possibly with mafic rocks on the African coast. In Mesozoic time, provincial sediment-transport directions were reversed in northern Alaska, the northwest flank of the Sverdrup basin, and the Appalachians so that detritus was carried toward the present oceans; deposition on the continental shelves continued thereafter. A gravity high occurs along the continental slopes of the Canada basin, and another gravity high occurs along the Atlantic coast. The mirror imagery persists to the present in the filling of the Canada basin from the continent in much the same way that the Gulf of Mexico is being filled.

If it is acceptable to reconstruct the pre-Jurassic Atlantic as shown in Figure 3B—with Devonian clastic wedges shedding from a single fold belt that subsequently was rifted—there should be little difficulty in accepting the analogous reconstruction of the Arctic that is shown.

Furthermore, the reconstruction results in analogies far to the south in the cordillera. As shown in Figure 3B, the Innuitian orogen would have been the counterpart of the Antler tectonic element. The restored front of the foreland belt along the craton is far enough to the east that all the present foreshortening in the belt can be accounted for, as in northern Alaska, by drift of the "stable" plate.

FIT WITH ARCTIC SPREADING

The foregoing arguments for spread of the Canada basin are by no means conclusive; they would have little value if spreading of the Canada basin did not fit into the geologic frame-

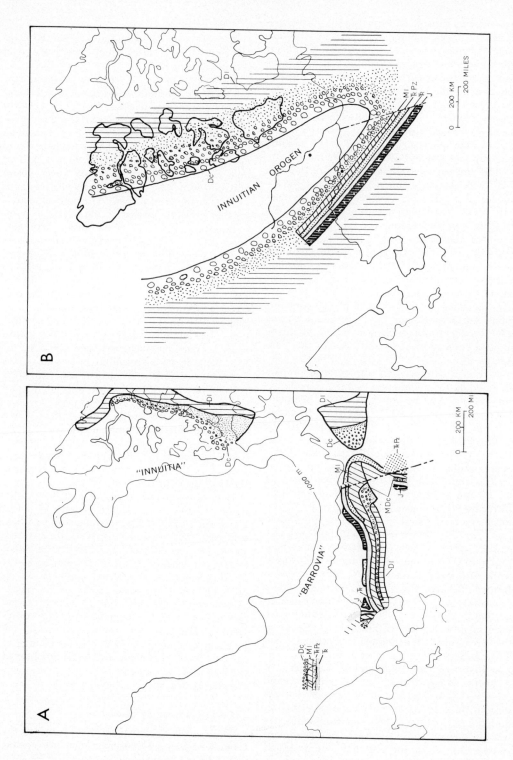

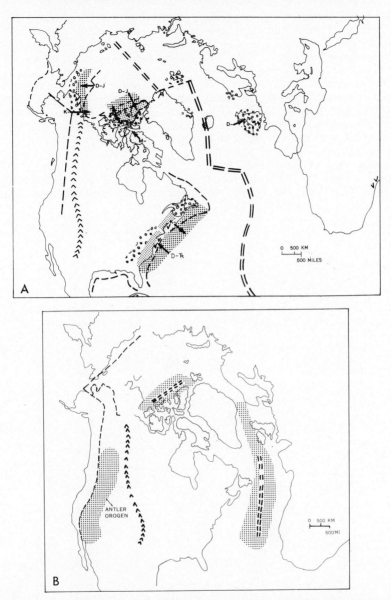

FIG. 3—Analogies between Canada and Atlantic basins that suggest a common origin of the two ocean deeps. (Computer-plotted projection centered in Hudson Bay.) **A.** Present geography. Thick lines, Atlantic rift system and inferred transform faults or sutures; dashed lines offshore, basin margins; inverted *v*'s, cordilleran front; circles and stippling, Devonian clastic wedges and offshore provenances; medium dots, late Paleozoic to Triassic basins; systemic symbols and arrows, age and direction of sediment transport. **B.** Pre-drift geography. Devonian orogens (stippled) and margin of Arctic basin are diagrammatic. Atlantic margin is from Bullard *et al.* (1965). Cordilleran front is palinspastic; Pacific margin is not. Symbols are same as in **A.**

FIG. 2—Sketch maps of Amerasian Arctic. **A.** Present occurrences of coeval and lithogenetically similar rocks and their inferred provenances "Barrovia" and "Innuitia." **B.** Palinspastic geology and geography based on assumption that Canada basin was not open before Jurassic. Dl, Devonian carbonate deposits; MDc, Mississippian and/or Devonian clastic deposits; Ml, Mississippian carbonate deposits; ℞Pz, Triassic to latest Paleozoic nearshore deposits; ℞, Late Triassic condensed deposits; and J, Jurassic distal deposits.

work of the Arctic Ocean. Logic suggests, though, that spread of the basin could have been the initial stage of sea-floor spreading in the Arctic, as shown in Figure 4.

Spreading, which is currently focused along the Gakkel Ridge, appears to have shifted in the mid-Tertiary from a focus along the Alpha Cordillera (Vogt and Ostenso, 1970; Hall, 1970). Thus, spreading in the Arctic seems to show one shift in focus with time. A prior shift to the Alpha Cordillera from a focus along the inferred spreading axis in the Canada basin (Fig. 4)—from which the Chukchi shelf–northern Alaska plate and the Arctic Ar-

chipelago plate rotated apart during Jurassic to mid-Cretaceous time—seems likely. A reconstruction involving three foci of spreading works out fairly well, as shown in Figure 3B. It seems logical at the present time to assume that Atlantic rifting and spreading were focused in the Canada basin during the Jurassic and Cretaceous, on the Alpha Cordillera during the Cretaceous and Tertiary, and on the Gakkel Ridge subsequently.

SUMMARY

The foregoing is a brief description of the circumstantial and intuitive evidence that

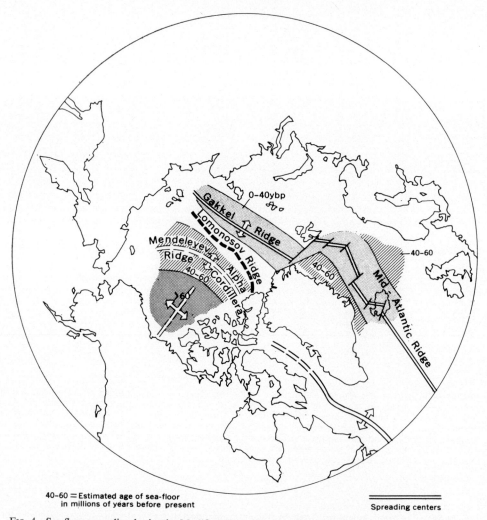

40–60 = Estimated age of sea-floor
in millions of years before present

Spreading centers

FIG. 4—Sea-floor spreading in Arctic. Modified from Churkin (this volume). Current spreading from Gakkel Ridge presumably shifted from a focus along Alpha Cordillera in Tertiary; logically, spread from Alpha axis could have shifted from focus (inferred) in Canada basin in Cretaceous.

spreading is the most workable explanation for the origin of the Canada basin. Spreading best accounts for the tectonics of the Brooks Range; palinspastic portrayals of spreading make the best paleogeographic fit within the Amerasian Arctic and between it and the cordillera to the south; analogies between the Canada and Atlantic basins suggest that they formed in the same manner; and the Canada basin is the logical initial (Jurassic to Cretaceous) focus of spreading. The test of this hypothesis should be whether the Canada basin shows the magnetic print of a spreading ridge, whether the continental crust can be traced to edges under the shelf deposits, and whether a JOIDES hole through the icepack penetrates Jurassic or Cretaceous mafic rocks. The questions are more than academic, because the petroleum potential of the vast continental shelf northwest of Alaska may depend on the origin of the Canada basin.

OTHER ARCTIC SPREADING

If the Canada basin originated by sea-floor spreading, the Amerasian Arctic may record several other episodes of spreading.

Strong deflections can be seen in the trace of the front of the cordillera in the Arctic and along its eastward continuation (Fig. 5A)—the Chukchi syntaxis between Siberia and Alaska and the syntaxial pair near the boundary between Alaska and Canada. These deflections may be due to lateral foreshortening in response to the southeastward drift of the Siberian-Chukchi shelf. The Arctic plate would be decoupled from the crustal plate to the south along the Kaltag-Porcupine and Tintina faults. Motion should not have begun before the latest Cretaceous, and the right-hand separation is continuing on the Kaltag fault segment (Patton and Hoare, 1968). This motion would explain the discordant folds in the floor of the Chukchi Sea (Grantz et al., 1970) and the tectonics in northwestern Canada (Cook and Aitken, this volume).

Another possible record of late sea-floor spreading is in the high Arctic Archipelago. Tertiary deformation there has been of mountain-building magnitude. This orogeny, together with the abundant mid-Cretaceous mafic intrusive rocks in the region, suggests that the tectonics are related to a shifting plate edge.

A continental edge or some other plate-tectonic element may also account for the volumes of late Precambrian mafic and ultramafic rocks

on the Canadian shield. Although the setting of these rocks seems unusually atectonic, mafic igneous activity is coupled so conceptually to current sea-floor spreading that some such association appears likely in Precambrian time as well.

The final suggested spreading requires substantial change in interpretation of the Paleozoic Franklinian geosyncline in the Arctic Archipelago (Fig. 5B). Instead of considering it as a classical eugeosynclinal-miogeosynclinal pair, I suggest that the miogeosynclinal deposits may be merely continental-shelf accumulations or buildups into a pre-Arctic Ocean, and the eugeosynclinal rocks and subsequent deformation may have resulted from the collision of two continental plates on closing of the pre-Arctic Ocean during middle Paleozoic time. A similar closing of a pre-Atlantic Ocean has been suggested by Wilson (1966) and others. In fact, Wilson (1968, p. 314) has wondered whether the Arctic Islands represent closure of a former ocean in the Arctic. Besides following the new reasoning that the eugeosynclinal-miogeosynclinal concept may be generally invalid, this suggestion explains why basement rocks east and west of the Mackenzie delta are different and why no Archaeozoic crystalline basement has been found in northern Alaska: the Devonian or older Neruokpuk Formation and other sub-Mississippian basement rocks of the western American Arctic were originally part of another continent. Perhaps the suture between two old continental plates will eventually be traced through its distortions in Alaska into the collision zone between continental plates that may exist near the Pacific coast to the south.

These last observations are permissive only, but they serve as interesting, perhaps profitable, alternate bases for speculation.

CONCLUSION

Regardless of whether the principles of plate tectonics and sea-floor spreading are valid, the possible movements focus in the Arctic so that global treatment of the concepts, such as reproduced in Figure 6, are incomplete without consideration of the Arctic. Although the existence of some sort of "sinus Borealis" in Pangaea cannot be disproved, certainly none existed between Siberia and Alaska. Plate tectonicists and, particularly, oceanographers must widen their perspective to include the area above the Arctic Circle and also take into account what is known about Arctic geology.

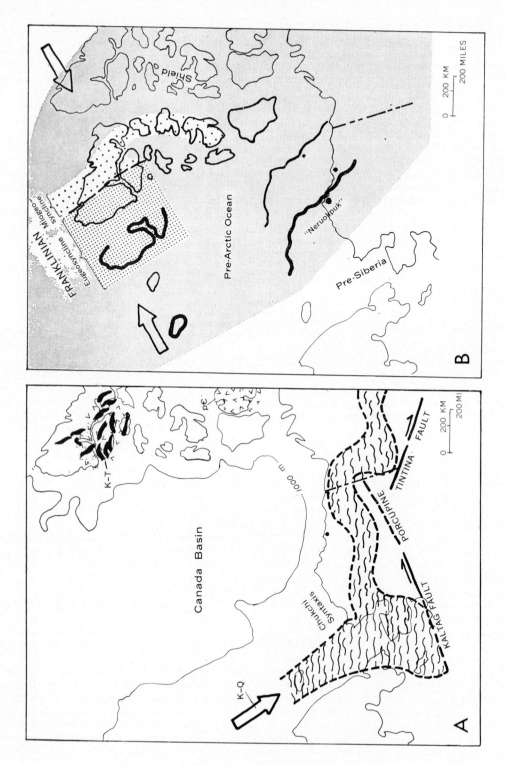

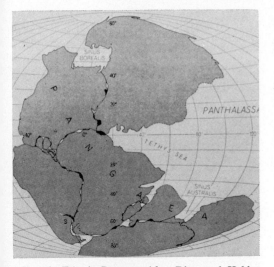

FIG. 6—Triassic Pangaea. After Dietz and Holden (1970); published with permission of *Scientific American*. An example of untenable reconstruction of the Arctic. At minimum, any "sinus Borealis" would have been separated from Pacific basin by join between northern Alaska and easternmost Siberia in existence since late Paleozoic.

SELECTED REFERENCES

Brosgé, W. P., and I. L. Tailleur, 1970, Depositional history of northern Alaska, *in* W. L. Adkison and M. M. Brosgé, eds., Proceedings of the geological seminar on the North Slope of Alaska: Los Angeles, Pacific Sec. Am. Assoc. Petroleum Geologists, p. D1–D17.

Bullard, Edward, J. E. Everett, and A. G. Smith, 1965, The fit of the continents around the Atlantic, *in* A symposium on continental drift: Royal Soc. London Philos. Trans. 1088, p. 41–51 (esp. Fig. 8).

Carey, S. W., convener, 1958, Continental drift, a symposium: Hobart, Univ. Tasmania Geology Dept., 375 p.

Churkin, Michael, Jr., 1969, Paleozoic tectonic history of the Arctic basin north of Alaska: Science, v. 165, August 8, p. 549–555.

—— 1973, Geologic concepts of Arctic Ocean basin: this volume.

Cook, D. G., and J. D. Aitken, 1973, Tectonics of northern Franklin Mountains and Colville Hills, District of Mackenzie, Canada: this volume.

Dietz, R. S., and J. C. Holden, 1970, The breakup of Pangaea: Sci. American, v. 223, no. 4, p. 30–41

(esp. p. 34).

Grantz, Arthur, *et al.*, 1970, Reconnaissance geology of the Chukchi Sea as determined by acoustic and magnetic profiling, *in* W. L. Adkison and M. M. Brosgé, eds., Proceedings of the geological seminar on the North Slope of Alaska: Los Angeles, Pacific Sec. Am. Assoc. Petroleum Geologists, p. F1–F28.

Hall, J. K., 1970, Arctic Ocean geophysical studies: the Alpha Cordillera and Mendeleyev Ridge: Lamont-Doherty Geol. Observatory (U-2-70) Tech. Rept. No. 2, 115 p.

Hamilton, Warren, 1967, Continental drift in the Arctic (abs.), *in* Symposium on continental drift, Abstracts: Montevideo, 1967.

Martin, A. J., 1970, Structure and tectonic history of the western Brooks Range, De Long Mountains and Lisburne Hills, northern Alaska: Geol. Soc. America Bull., v. 81, p. 3605–3621.

Patton, W. W., Jr., and J. M. Hoare, 1968, The Kaltag fault, west-central Alaska, *in* Geological Survey research, 1968: U.S. Geol. Survey Prof. Paper 600-D, p. D147–D153.

Rickwood, F. K., 1970, The Prudhoe Bay field, *in* W. L. Adkison and M. M. Brosgé, eds., Proceedings of the geological seminar on the North Slope of Alaska: Los Angeles, Pacific Sec. Am. Assoc. Petroleum Geologists, p. L1–L11.

Snelson, Sigmund, and I. L. Tailleur, 1968, Large-scale thrusting and migrating Cretaceous foredeeps in western Brooks Range and adjacent regions of northwestern Alaska (abs.): Am. Assoc. Petroleum Geologists Bull., v. 52, no. 3, p. 567.

Tailleur, I. L., and W. P. Brosgé, 1970, Tectonic history of northern Alaska, *in* W. L. Adkison and M. M. Brosgé, eds., Proceedings of the geological seminar on the North Slope of Alaska: Los Angeles, Pacific Sec. Am. Assoc. Petroleum Geologists, p. E1–E19.

—— and Sigmund Snelson, 1968, Large-scale flat thrusts in the Brooks Range orogen, northern Alaska (abs.): Geol. Soc. America Spec. Paper 101, p. 217.

—— and ——, 1969, Large-scale thrusting in northwestern Alaska possibly related to rifting of the Arctic Ocean (abs.): Geol. Soc. America Spec. Paper 121, p. 569.

—— B. H. Kent, and H. N. Reiser, 1966, Outcrop geologic maps of the Nuka-Etivluk region, northern Alaska: U.S. Geol. Survey Open-File Rept., 5 sheets, map scale 1:63,360.

Vogt, P. R., and N. A. Ostenso, 1970, Magnetic and gravity profiles across the Alpha Cordillera and their relation to Arctic sea-floor spreading: Jour. Geophys. Research, v. 75, p. 4925–4937.

Wilson, J. T., 1966, Did the Atlantic close and then re-open?: Nature, v. 211, p. 676–681.

—— 1968, Static or mobile Earth: the current scientific revolution: Am. Philos. Soc. Proc., v. 112, no. 5, p. 309–320.

FIG. 5—Evidence of other drift in Amerasian Arctic. **A.** Deflections (shortening) in trace of fold belt and right-hand dislocations in response to Cretaceous to Holocene southeastward drift of Chukchi shelf. Note Cretaceous mafic rocks (v) and Tertiary deformation (spindles) in high Arctic (Axel Heiberg and Ellesmere Islands) and late Precambrian mafic rocks (v) on edge of North American craton. **B.** Suggested Paleozoic plate tectonism. Franklinian "miogeosyncline" is on continental slope of North American craton; "Neruokpuk" sedimentary basin on pre-Siberian continent; and Franklinian "eugeosyncline" along plate junction in pre–Arctic Ocean.

Geologic Structure of Baffin Bay and Davis Strait as Determined by Geophysical Techniques[1]

K. S. MANCHESTER[2] and **D. B. CLARKE**[3]

Dartmouth, Nova Scotia, and Halifax, Nova Scotia

Abstract   Analysis of magnetic and bathymetric data recently collected by Canadian research ships gives no indication of a median ridge or valley in Baffin Bay. However, the shallow depth of the mantle in the center of the bay suggests that the crust is oceanic and may have been created by sea-floor spreading. Tertiary basalts in Davis Strait also could be related to a spreading event. Rapid sedimentation in the basin has obscured basement structures. Magnetic data at present are insufficient to determine the extent and direction of possible spreading.

Seismic profiles on both sides of the bay show horst-and-graben structures which may indicate that the area began to form in the Precambrian and opened primarily during Tertiary time.

The Melville Bay graben may contain a thick section of Cretaceous-Tertiary rocks related to those of the Disko Island area.

INTRODUCTION

The purpose of this short note is to report some of the findings of the last 10 cruises by Canadian ships that have carried out geological and geophysical research in the eastern Arctic area. The location, type, and density of data recorded are shown in Figure 1. Lower density of ship tracks in some areas is generally attributable to bad ice conditions.

Maximum water depth in Baffin Bay is 2,400 m. Baffin Bay is separated from the deeper water of the Labrador Sea by a shallow sill (maximum depth 650 m) in Davis Strait (Fig. 2). That Baffin Bay once was a spreading center is not indicated by either a median ridge or valley.

CENTRAL PROFILE

A profile across central Baffin Bay from just south of Bylot Island, Canada, to Svartenhuk

[1] Manuscript received, September 20, 1971.

[2] Marine Geophysics Section, Bedford Institute.

[3] Department of Geology, Dalhousie University.

We wish to thank D. L. Barrett, C. E. Keen, D. I. Ross, and many others at the Bedford Institute and M. J. Keen, J. Johnson, I. Park, and R. Hyndman at Dalhousie University for assisting in collecting or in supplying unpublished data for use in this paper. We also wish to thank the officers and crews of the Department of Energy, Mines and Resources and of the Department of Transport ships that were used in collecting these data.

Peninsula, West Greenland, is shown in Figure 3. The seismic reflection profile shows a basement rise on the continental shelf offshore from Baffin Island. Large positive gravity and magnetic anomalies are associated with this rise. This may be an offshore horst, related and similar to the horst-and-graben structures described on northern Baffin Island by Jackson (1969). The attitude of the shelf and slope sedimentary units is typically prograding, but some slump features possibly are present. The character of the West Greenland continental slope is similar.

In the deep part of Baffin Bay, the reflection profile shows 3 seconds of water (two-way time), 2 seconds of flat-lying sedimentary beds, and indications of a rough reflecting surface at 5-seconds penetration. Data from a refraction line near the center of the bay (Barrett et al., 1971) agree well with the reflection data. Results of this investigation are included in Figure 3. On the basis of these refraction seismic data, the crust has been interpreted as oceanic in character.

In the central profile (Fig. 3) there is a small 200-gamma anomaly on the Baffin Island side which may correspond to the boundary of continental and oceanic crust. The gravity profile also shows a typical continental-shelf-edge anomaly in approximately the same position.

MAGNETIC PROFILES

Selected magnetic-anomaly profiles from various cruises are shown in Figure 4. These shipboard magnetic-anomaly profiles show the low-frequency, low-amplitude character of the magnetic field over the central part of Baffin Bay, larger amplitude anomalies associated with the continental margin (500 gammas), and high-amplitude, high-frequency anomalies associated with the Tertiary basalt region in the Davis Strait area. A more complete discussion of this latter type of anomaly is given by Park et al. (1971). Magnetic lineations in central Baffin Bay have not been identified with any certainty by use of the present data, but more data may make it possible to correlate the lineations in the west-central part of the bay. A

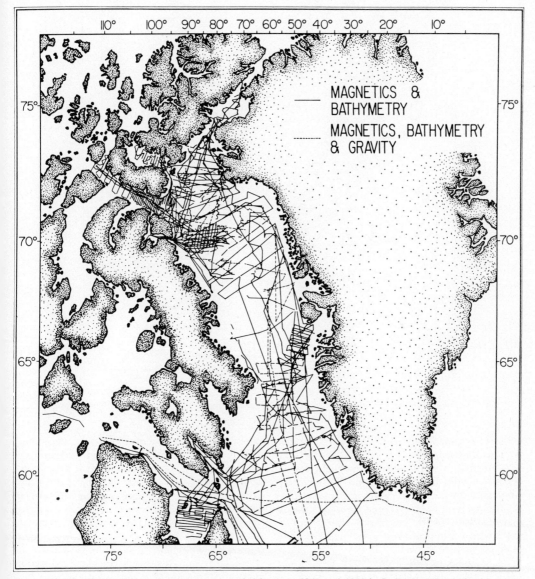

FIG. 1—Location of marine geophysical data recorded between 1963 and 1970 in Baffin Bay–Davis Strait region.

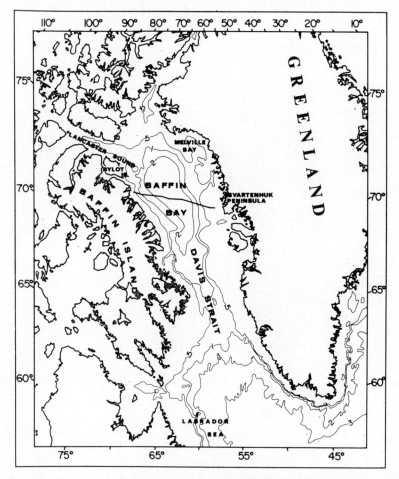

FIG. 2—General bathymetry, in kilometers. Heavy line across Baffin Bay is location of Figure 3 profile.

tentative correlation of three magnetic profiles is shown in Figure 4.

A persistent, broad, negative magnetic anomaly in Melville Bay parallels the West Greenland coast approximately as far north as lat. 72° N. The location of this anomaly corresponds to that of a bathymetric depression shown in Figure 2 which is indicative of a sedimentary basin (Barrett and Manchester, 1969). From aeromagnetic data in this area, Hood and Bower (1970) calculated that the magnetic basement may be buried beneath as much as 20,000 ft (6,100 m) of strata.

NORTHERN PROFILES

Three profiles in the northern part of Baffin Bay are shown in Figure 5. Profile *A* is a seismic reflection profile recorded across part of

Melville Bay by Johnson (1971). As noted, this region is a bathymetric and magnetic depression on the Greenland shelf; it may represent a downfaulted block of continental crust. The record shows approximately 150 m of acoustically almost transparent strata overlying an erosional surface. The underlying sedimentary rocks are folded and faulted; their age is unknown. Perhaps this basin is related to the subsidence and deposition in the Cretaceous-Tertiary province of West Greenland, in which case these rocks might be of late Mesozoic age.

Although profiles *B* and *C* are not continuous, they do give a representative section across Baffin Bay. In profile *B* the magnetic and gravity profiles show a shelf-edge anomaly near the eastern end of the line and a possible indication of a buried median structure near the structural

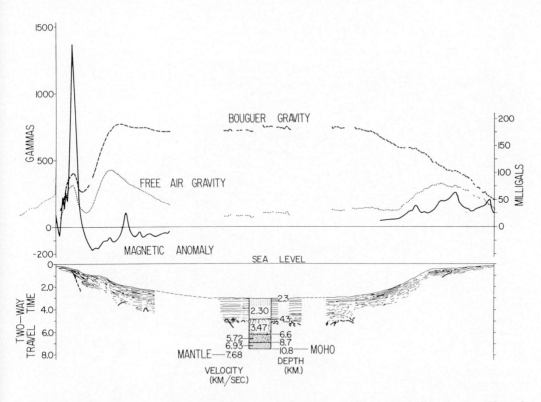

Fɪɢ. 3—Composite profile across Baffin Bay showing magnetic, gravity, and seismic reflection data (see Figure 2 for location). Included also are data from a transverse refraction line near center of bay.

center of the western half of the bay. The asymmetric bathymetric profile probably reflects the large amount of sediment contributed from Lancaster Sound; this sedimentary cover completely blankets any basement structure.

Profile *C* shows the magnetic, gravity, and bathymetric profiles over approximately the same feature as profile *A*—*i.e.*, the magnetic-bathymetric depression of Melville Bay which is shown in the inset map by dashed lines. The negative gravity anomaly agrees with the predicted thick sedimentary cover in this region.

Davis Strait

The most important factor in the development of Davis Strait has been the copious outpouring of basalt in early Tertiary time (Clarke and Upton, 1971). These basalts are present on land on both sides of the strait (Clarke, 1970), and may be shown to extend well offshore on the Greenland side (Park *et al.*, 1971). The basalts may be related to an early phase of a sea-floor-spreading event about 60 m.y. ago (LePichon *et al.*, 1971).

Conclusions

The shallow depth to mantle in the center of Baffin Bay suggests that the crust is oceanic and possibly was created during a sea-floor-spreading event. Rapid sedimentation in the restricted basin thus formed has, as shown by the seismic profiles, obliterated most of the features associated with this spreading.

The seismic profiles on the continental shelves on both sides of Baffin Bay show tensional structures—*e.g.*, the horsts and grabens of the northeastern Baffin Island shelf and the large sediment-filled graben in Melville Bay. These structures may indicate that the area began to form in the Precambrian (Fahrig *et al.*, 1970), and the sedimentary record may indicate that the major opening took place in the Tertiary (LePichon *et al.*, 1971).

Magnetic lineations are indicated in the west-central part of Baffin Bay, but more magnetic data are required in order to determine the extent and spreading direction of the oceanic crust.

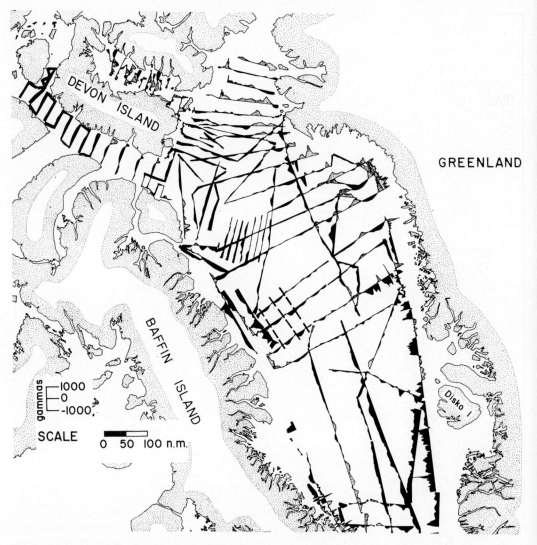

Fig. 4—Selected magnetic-anomaly profiles. Stippled profiles are positive anomalies and solid profiles are negative anomalies. Dashed lines indicate tentative correlation of three magnetic-anomaly profiles.

The Melville Bay graben may contain very thick Cretaceous-Tertiary sedimentary rocks that are correlative with strata in possibly related structures on land in the Disko Island area, as outlined by Henderson (1969).

REFERENCES CITED

Barrett, D. L., and K. S. Manchester, 1969, Crustal structure in Baffin Bay and Davis Strait from magnetometer surveys: Am. Geophys. Union Trans., v. 50, no. 4, p. 135.
———— et al., 1971, Baffin Bay—an ocean: Nature, v. 229, no. 5286, p. 551–553.

Clarke, D. B., 1970, Tertiary basalts of Baffin Bay—possible primary magma from the mantle: Contr. Mineralogy and Petrology, v. 25, p. 203–224.
———— and B. G. J. Upton, 1971, Tertiary basalts of Baffin Island: Canadian Jour. Earth Sci., v. 8, no. 2, p. 248–258.
Fahrig, W. F., E. Irving, and G. D. Jackson, 1970, Franklin igneous events, tension faulting, and possible Hadrynian opening of Baffin Bay, Canada (abs.): Am. Assoc. Petroleum Geologists Bull., v. 54, no. 12, p. 2480.
Henderson, G., 1969, Oil and gas prospects in the Cretaceous-Tertiary basin of West Greenland: Grønlands Geol. Undersøgelse Rap. No. 22.
Hood, G., and M. E. Bower, 1970, Aeromagnetic pro-

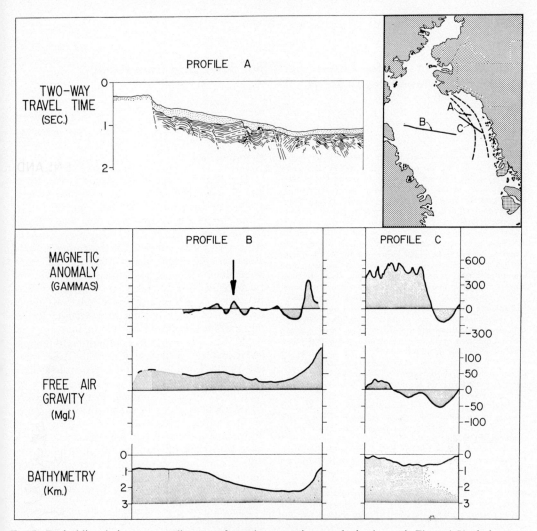

Fɪɢ. 5—Dashed lines in inset map outline area of negative magnetic anomaly that is seen in Figure 4. Vertical arrow in profile *B* indicates location of a possible buried median structure.

file from Cape Cargenholm, Baffin Island, to Red Head, West Greenland, *in* Report of activities, part B, November 1969 to March 1970: Canada Geol. Survey Paper 70–1.

Jackson, G. D., 1969, Reconnaissance of north-central Baffin Island (27C-G, 37C-H, 38A-C, parts of 48A), *in* Report of activities, part A, April to October, 1968: Canada Geol. Survey Paper 69–1.

Johnson, J. S., 1971, A contribution to the structural

geology of northern Baffin Bay and Lancaster Sound: Halifax, Nova Scotia, Dalhousie Univ., unpub. M.S. thesis.

LePichon, X., R. D. Hyndman, and G. Pautot, 1971, Geophysical study of the opening of the Labrador Sea: Jour. Geophysical Research, v. 76, p. 4724–4743.

Park, I., *et al.,* 1971, Seaward extension of the West Greenland Tertiary volcanic province: Earth and Planetary Sci. Letters, v. 10, no. 2, p. 235–238.

Geophysical Evidence for Ancient Sea-Floor Spreading from Alpha Cordillera and Mendeleyev Ridge[1]

JOHN K. HALL[2]

Palisades, New York 10964

Abstract Geophysical data from Fletcher's Ice Island (Station T-3) for the period mid-1962 to mid-1970 show that, during this time, the ice station traversed the Chukchi Rise; portions of the Alpha Cordillera and Mendeleyev Ridge; and the Chukchi, Mendeleyev, and Canada plains. The geophysical findings, together with pertinent observations from older investigations, support the suggestion of earlier investigators that the Alpha Cordillera is an inactive center of sea-floor spreading. Several fractures are shown to cut the Mendeleyev Ridge and Alpha Cordillera, and many other closely spaced fractures are suggested by topographic, magnetic, and gravity trends. These fractures appear to parallel the 142°W meridian. Seismic reflection profiles show a buried topography similar to that of the Mid-Atlantic Ridge. Offsets in the apparent axial rift suggest that the fractures are traces of transform faults. The angular relation between the Mendeleyev Ridge and the Alpha Cordillera appears to result from a southerly displacement of the cordillera crest along numerous en échelon transform faults. Magnetic anomalies are consistent with the sea-floor-spreading hypothesis. A crustal gravity model based on a continuous 600-km-long gravity and bathymetric profile and on one unreversed refraction measurement from Station Alpha shows the observed gravity to be consistent with a section of East Pacific Rise type; a 5-km-thick oceanic layer overlies 27 km of "anomalous" mantle ($\rho = 3.15$).

A proposed history for the Amerasian basin since late Precambrian time suggests that the basin was affected by spreading at least once in the Paleozoic and again in the late Mesozoic and early Tertiary. The early Paleozoic episode is thought to be related to the opening and closing of a proto-Atlantic ocean and the development of the Appalachian-Caledonian orogen. It is concluded that the oceanic crust beneath the Beaufort Sea is Permo-Carboniferous or older.

Seismic reflection profiles show more than 2 km of sedimentary rocks beneath the Mendeleyev and Canada plains, but no basement reflections have been recorded. Pronounced reflectors may represent major climatic or depositional changes. The sedimentary cover on the Alpha Cordillera and the Mendeleyev Ridge ranges from several hundred meters to more than 1 km. Sedimentary ridges (sand waves) up to 55 m high are abundant on the crestal plateau of the Alpha Cordillera; they appear to be the result of currents which transported sediment across the ridge from northwest to southeast. This process is presently inactive, and may have terminated with the initiation of continental glaciation, perhaps as early as late Miocene time. Similar sedimentary features 700 m beneath the Mendeleyev plain suggest a strong bottom circulation in the past. A zone of bottom erosion along the Mendeleyev Ridge flank may reflect a circulation of water through Cooperation Gap, a trough which appears to cross the ridge. Two buried channels extending to subbottom depths of 700 m were observed between the Mendeleyev fracture zone and the Mendeleyev plain.

INTRODUCTION

The deep portions of the Arctic Ocean form an almost rectangular basin approximately 1,800 km wide and 2,500 km long (Fig. 1). Three subparallel ridges cross this basin along its minor axis. The central Lomonosov Ridge is the narrowest and highest of these, and is both aseismic and magnetically quiet. On the Eurasian side of this ridge lies the Arctic midocean ridge (called the "Nansen" or "Gakkel" Ridge by some), a seismically active belt considered to be an extension of the Mid-Atlantic Ridge and a center of present sea-floor spreading. The Alpha Cordillera and its southern continuation—Mendeleyev Ridge—lie on the Amerasian side of the Lomonosov Ridge. When first identified in 1957, this feature was thought to be of fault-block origin (Hunkins, 1961). However, more recent analysis of submarine bathymetric profiles (Beal, 1968) and later aeromagnetic and gravity data (Vogt and Ostenso, 1970) have led to the suggestion that the Alpha Cordillera is an inactive or fossil center of sea-floor spreading. Vogt and Ostenso (1970) compared the magnetic anomalies over the Alpha Cordi-

[1] Manuscript received, September 20, 1971. Lamont-Doherty Geological Observatory Contribution No. 1978. This investigation was conducted under contracts Nonr-266(82) and N00014–67–A–0108–0016 with the Office of Naval Research. The opinions expressed in this paper are the writer's and do not represent those of the Navy Department or the U.S. Government.

[2] Lamont-Doherty Geological Observatory. Present address: Geological Survey of Israel, Jerusalem, Israel.

The data used in this study were obtained by approximately 40 scientists of the Lamont-Doherty Geological Observatory over a period of more than 8 years. Their contribution is gratefully acknowledged. The Naval Arctic Research Laboratory in Barrow, Alaska, maintained the camp on Station T-3 and provided the support so necessary to this work. Allan Gill provided the magnetic measurements obtained during the winter by the British Trans-Arctic Expedition. This study was accomplished under the supervision of Kenneth L. Hunkins and John E. Nafe. Discussions with Bruce C. Heezen, M. Talwani, H. Kutschale, W. Pitman, X. LePichon, J. I. Ewing, and R. W. Fairbridge were extremely helpful.

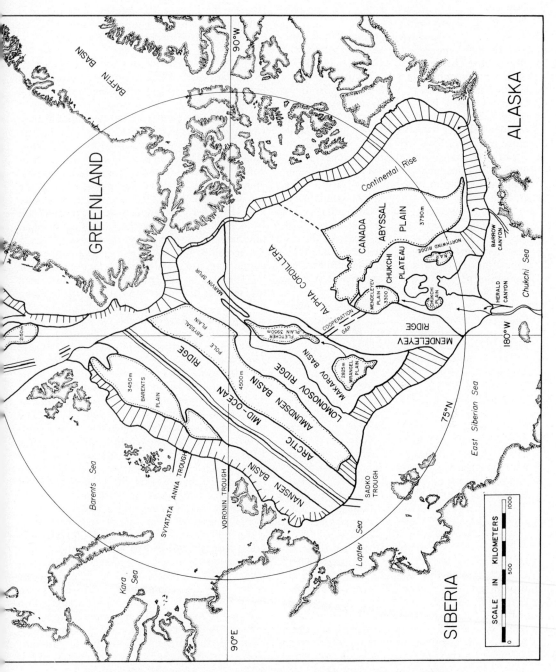

FIG. 1—Physiographic diagram of Arctic Ocean, modified from Hunkins (1968).

llera with those on the flanks of the Reykjanes Ridge and suggested that the Alpha Cordillera may have become inactive in the Tertiary, possibly about 40 m.y. ago.

As part of a long-term program to investigate the more inaccessible parts of the Arctic Ocean through the use of drifting scientific ice stations, personnel of the Lamont-Doherty Geological Observatory, with the support of the Office of Naval Research, have carried out a geophysical and geological research program on Fletcher's Ice Island (Station T-3) since its reoccupation in May 1962. This program, consisting of navigation, depth soundings, and gravity and magnetic observations—plus supplemental seismic reflection measurements, coring, and bottom photography—continues to the present time with numerous additions and refinements. During the period 1962–1970, Station T-3 drifted over large parts of the Alpha Cordillera and the Mendeleyev Ridge (Fig. 2), permitting the first detailed geophysical examination of one of the largest features in the Arctic basin.

This paper briefly summarizes the principal findings of these investigations, which are available in more complete form in the writer's Ph.D. dissertation (Hall, 1970).

The present findings are wholly consistent with the suggestion of Beal (1968) and Vogt and Ostenso (1970) that the Alpha Cordillera is an inactive midoceanic ridge. The principal evidence for this conclusion is the identification of at least five fracture zones that cut the cordillera, as well as apparent offsets of the ridge axis in the crestal region. Bathymetric data suggest the presence of other fractures, and seismic reflection studies suggest a buried basement topography similar to that found on the Mid-Atlantic Ridge. The magnetic and gravity data support the idea of such a topography and also suggest the existence of other fractures.

Bottom currents appear to control sedimentation over a large part of the area studied. Elongate sedimentary ridges (sand waves) are widespread over the crestal plateau, but they are blanketed with a uniform cover of pelagic sediment, suggesting that they have been inactive for a considerable period of time. These features are apparently the result of a strong paleocirculation, similar to the weak one found today, which transported sediment across the ridge from northwest to southeast. Along the eastern flank of the Mendeleyev Ridge, a region of submarine erosion apparently is maintained by a strong flow of water through Coop-

eration Gap, from the Makarov basin to the Canada basin. A zone of sand waves observed beneath the present Mendeleyev plain indicates that bottom currents have apparently been an effective agent of deposition in the past.

DATA REDUCTION

All data used in this study were reduced and processed with the aid of an electronic digital computer.

Navigation—Two types of navigational fixes were used to prepare the T-3 drift track in Figure 2. Positions prior to April 1967 were determined through celestial navigation with a theodolite, whenever visibility permitted. A maximum error of ±1 km was possible when the sun was used, and ±0.5 km when stars were used. In general, positions after April 1967 are from satellite fixes using the U.S. Navy Navigation Satellite System. Errors in excess of ±0.25 km are unlikely because of the high rate of accurate fixing at polar latitudes and because of the low rate of ice drift. Wind data were used to compute the most probable drift between fixes.

Depth soundings—Beginning in June 1963, depth soundings were made almost continuously with a Precision Depth Recorder (PDR). The records were digitized at short intervals (0.1–0.5 km) and at all slope changes to allow accurate interpolations. The echo-distance error due to timing in the recorder and reading of the records was about 0.0025 sec (±2 m). The soundings have been corrected for vertical variations in the sound velocity. Prior to June 1963, a total of 617 spot soundings was obtained using explosive charges and a geophone receiver. These soundings have been corrected in the same manner as the PDR data.

Gravity measurements—Gravity measurements were made several times daily with a Lacoste & Romberg Model G (No. 27) geodetic gravity meter. More than 8,000 of the 12,000 observations obtained are reported here. Instrumental drift was determined 25 times over the period through comparison measurements at the University of Wisconsin pendulum station at Barrow, Alaska. The observations have been reduced to sea level and corrected for instrumental drift and accelerations due to east-west motions of the ice (Eötvös correction). Maximum errors are considered to be less than 1 mgal for most observations, but possibly may have been as much as 5 mgal during the severest storms.

An additional 150 gravity measurements ob-

refer to more detailed maps given in Hall (1970).
Approximately 18,000 km of track is shown here. Average daily drift was 5.2 km. *A-A'* is location of profile in Figure 10.

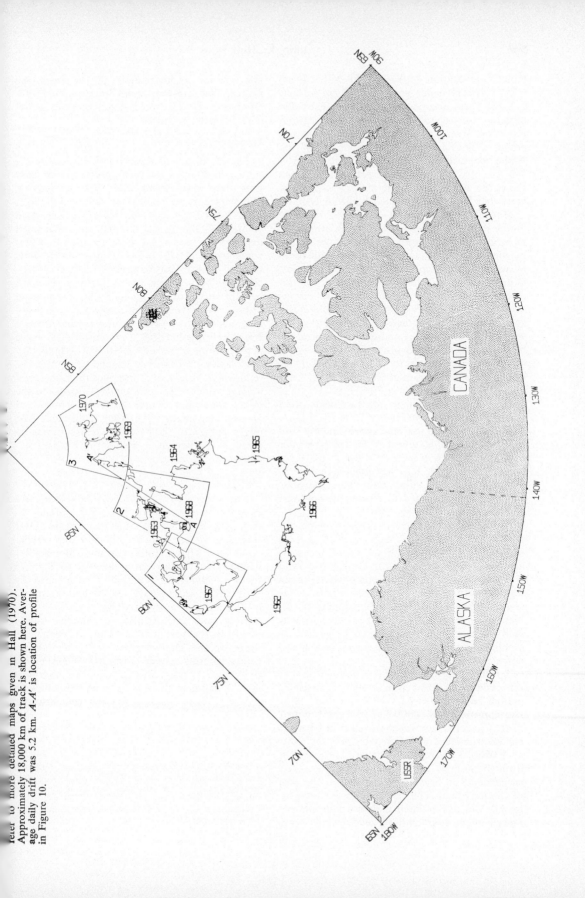

tained from Station Alpha in 1958 with a Frost C-1-15 gravity meter were used to aid in contouring. These observations are of limited value because the abandonment of the station, following 7 months of measurements, did not permit a final calibration. Comparison of the Alpha measurements with those from Station T-3 at five Alpha–T-3 track intersections shows the Alpha data to be about 15 mgal too high; they have been adjusted accordingly.

Magnetic measurements—The total intensity of the earth's magnetic field was measured almost continuously with a proton precession magnetometer. The accuracy of the individual measurements is greater than ±10 gammas. Diurnal variations were reduced, if not eliminated, by averaging the hourly observations over 24-hour periods. Magnetic total-intensity anomalies were obtained by subtracting the value of the earth's regional field as determined by a Taylor series expansion of third degree, fitted by least squares to the regional field in this area by the Dominion Observatory of Canada (Haines, 1967).

Supplemental magnetic measurements were made by the British Trans-Arctic Expedition (BTAE) from an ice floe approximately 140 km northwest of Station T-3 during the winter of 1968–1969. A Varian M-49 portable magnetometer, with an accuracy greater than ±20 gammas, was read every hour when possible, and the data were used to fill out the contours in the area over the ridge crest.

Airborne total-intensity measurements reported by Ostenso and Wold (1971) were a useful aid to interpretation. These measurements were made at an altitude of 450 m with a proton precession magnetometer. No attempt was made to reduce these observations to sea level—a change of less than 20 gammas. A correction for temporal variations in the magnetic field was not considered necessary, because all flights through these areas were of less than 2 hours' duration.

Seismic reflection measurements—A seismic reflection profiler was in operation for extended periods between February 1967 and June 1970, and approximately 4,000 km of track was profiled. The sound source consisted of a triggered capacitor bank from a sonar "boomer" with a 9,000-joule storage capacity, discharging through a single underwater spark transducer suspended 8 m below the sea ice near the edge of the ice island. The reflected signals were received by two flexural-disk hydrophones, placed 30 m apart and suspended 4 m below

the sea ice approximately 25 m from the source. The received signals were amplified, filtered, and recorded on a modified 19-inch (48 cm) drypaper recorder.

GEOPHYSICAL DATA

The highlights of the geophysical results are shown in Figures 3–10. Figures 3–5 are contour maps of the bathymetry, free-air gravity, and magnetic anomalies for the overall area. Data from additional sources have been used where available to fill out the areas. Detailed maps of the inset areas were included in a previous paper (Hall, 1970). Figures 6–10 show selected profiles across various features. Wherever possible, sections of interesting track have been projected onto a plane by the computer in order to remove the constantly varying headings and vertical exaggerations which result from the irregular drift. In these profiles, water depths are in corrected meters and sedimentary thicknesses are based on a sound velocity in the sedimentary rocks of 2 km/sec; thus, the sedimentary thickness in kilometers is equal to the travel time in seconds. Areas interpreted as acoustic basement have been blackened. The upper surface of the basement is usually recognized as the beginning of a series of large hyperbolas.

DISCUSSION

From the above geophysical data, a picture emerges of an oceanic ridge very similar to those presently acting as centers of sea-floor spreading in other areas, but with one exception. The Alpha Cordillera and Mendeleyev Ridge appear to have been dormant or inactive for a relatively long period, as evidenced by their thick sedimentary cover and complete lack of current seismic activity.

How does one identify an inactive ridge? Probably the best way is to see if it matches some of the characteristics of other known ridges without actually displaying signs of activity such as numerous earthquakes, high heat flow, a sediment-free axis, *etc.* In the following sections, newly observed features which appear

———————————————————

≫≫→

Fig. 3—Bathymetric map showing location of inferred fracture zones (lines 1–24). Depths are in corrected meters; C.I. = 100 m. Includes data from Black and Ostenso (1962), Cabaniss (1962), Cabaniss *et al.* (1965), and Somov (1955). Generalized 500-m contours are from DeLeeuw (1967).

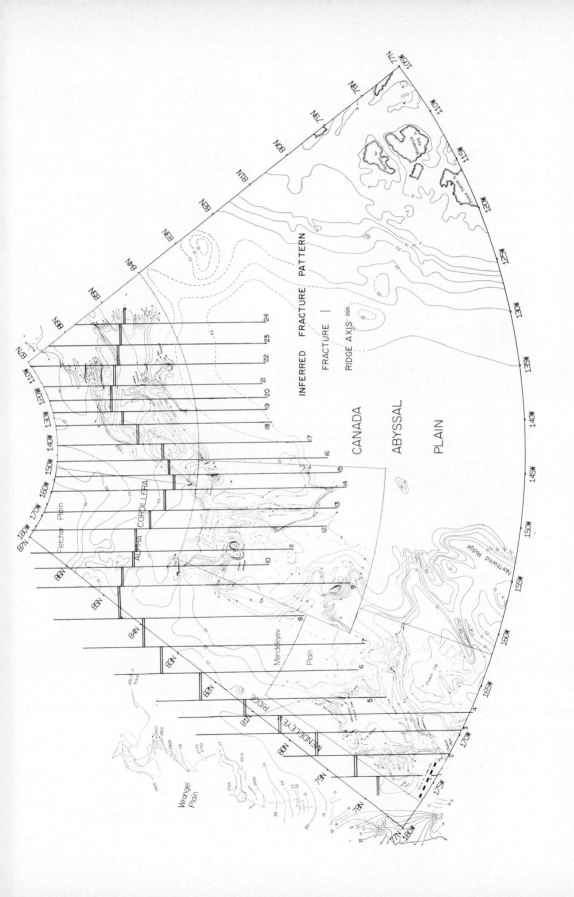

to match these characteristics will be discussed within this framework, and other known features will be reinterpreted.

Fracture zones, lineations, and ridge offsets —The principal evidence for suggesting a center of sea-floor spreading is the observation of numerous lineations extending from the ridge crest in what appears to be a more or less systematic pattern. The inferred pattern, based on these lineations and all other lines of evidence, is shown as an overlay on the contour maps in Figures 3–5. In this pattern there is no evidence to suggest that the fractures are subparallel, because all the features from which relatively accurate orientations can be obtained— spread out along more than 500 km of the ridge—indicate a direction paralleling the 142° W meridian. For ease of reference, this is approximately the orientation of the Alaska-Yukon boundary.

The strongest evidence for the existence of fracture zones cutting the Alpha Cordillera is found along the southern flank of the Mendeleyev Ridge (Fig. 3, line 5), where the ridge is paralleled by a prominent 600-m-high scarp. This feature, named the "Mendeleyev fracture zone," was crossed three times within a distance of approximately 80 km. Data from these crossings (Fig. 6), projected onto a plane normal to the strike of the feature (parallel with the 142°W meridian), show that the fracture disappears into the ridge northwestward, although it maintains its identity in the magnetic and gravity anomalies and appears as a distinct scarp in the acoustic basement.

This fracture zone appears to exert an influence on sedimentation in the area. An analysis of the seismic reflection records, as well as bottom photographs, sediment cores, and bottom-current measurements, suggests that sedimentation in this area is complex. West of the scarp (profile B-B' in Fig. 6) is an elevated area where the sea floor has been deeply eroded. Bottom photographs of this area reveal the only known basement outcrops in the Canada basin (Hunkins et al., 1970), and bottom-current measurements (Hunkins et al., 1969) suggest that bottom-current erosion and deposition are taking place. On the east side of the trough, the seismic reflection data (Hall, 1970) suggest that, despite uniform pelagic(?) sedimentation, bottom currents have maintained a scarp long after the original basement ridge was buried. One possible explanation for these currents might be the presence and proximity of Cooperation Gap. The reported 2,700-m depth (Be-

lov and Lapina, 1958) and the presumed orientation (Fig. 1) of this feature might suggest that it is connected with the Mendeleyev fracture zone. Such a connection would allow bottom water in the basins across the ridge to pass through the ridge. The erosional effects could be expected to be strongest where the current is confined to such a narrow gap.

Other strong indications of lineation paralleling the Mendeleyev fracture zone are found farther northeast. On the west side of an elevated rectangular region is a narrow ridge which rises to a depth of less than 2,900 m. Named the "Lamont Ridge" by DeLeeuw (1967), this narrow ridge is seen clearly in profiles of seven crossings (Fig. 7) spaced over a distance of 200 km. Farther northeast, isolated Crary Seamount was delineated when the ice island followed an N-shaped track. Steep sides were observed on the northeast and southeast sides of the flat-topped structure (as shown in projected profile C-D in Figure 7), suggesting that it is bounded on the east by another fracture (line 15, Fig. 3) striking in the direction of a very steep valley observed to the north by Hunkins (1961) from Station Alpha. Still farther northeast, another pronounced and extended lineation (line 21, Fig. 3) appears to cross the ridge axis. Valleys on both ridge flanks of this lineation suggest a small offset, as indicated. Just east of the valley on the southern flank is Ostenso Seamount, extending nearly a kilometer above the surrounding topography. A depression at the summit suggests that this seamount is volcanic, and it is possibly associated with the fracture inferred nearby.

On the north of the Mendeleyev Ridge, Kutschale (1966) observed a steeply dipping basement ridge beneath the Wrangel plain; this ridge has served as a dam to separate the sediments of the Wrangel plain from those of the deeper Fletcher plain. This basement ridge parallels the other major lineations on the southern ridge flank, suggesting continuity of this pattern for a great distance across the ridge. The location of the high basement block east of the fracture trace (Kutschale, 1966) is in agreement with the inferred offsets, and it appears

---

                                                      »»»→

Fig. 4—Alpha Cordillera free-air gravity map showing location of inferred fracture zones. C.I. = 5 mgal. Data from Cabaniss (1962) and Kutschale (1966) are included.

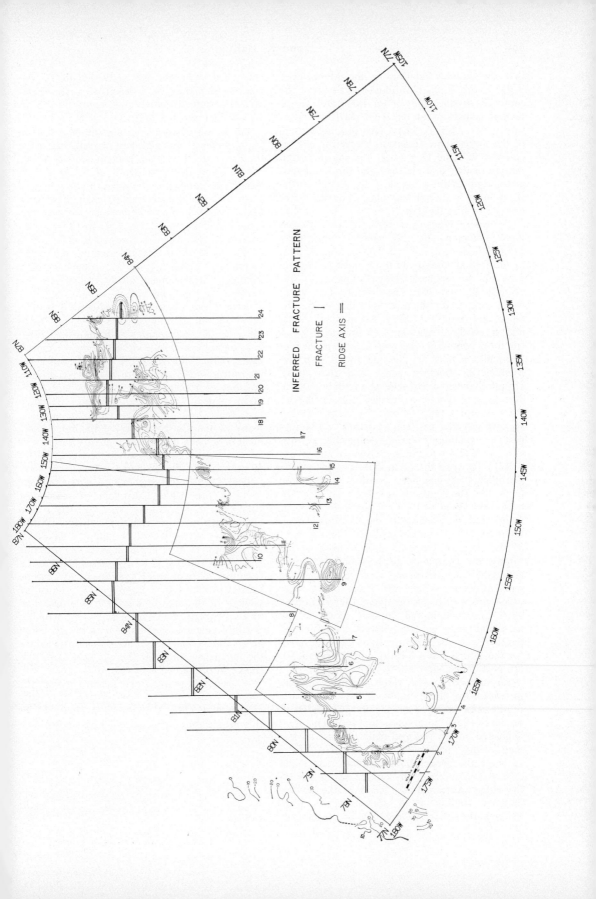

INFERRED FRACTURE PATTERN

FRACTURE |

RIDGE AXIS ═

that the angular relation of the Mendeleyev Ridge to the Alpha Cordillera is a result of the southerly displacement of the ridge crest along several transform faults. This particular fracture (line 4, Fig. 3) may have produced some of the topographic features observed in the vicinity of Charlie Gap—e.g., the sharp eastern margin of the "T-3 plateau" and the southwestern margin of the Chukchi Cap, as well as the sharp bend in the abyssal channel at the southern end of Charlie Gap.

Elsewhere, other fractures have been inferred from lineations in the general bathymetry (Fig. 3, lines 1, 2, 7, 9, 10, 12, 14, 16, and 24), in the free-air gravity (Fig. 4, lines 6, 18, and 20), and the magnetics (Fig. 5, lines 6, 11, 14, 16, 17, 20, and 24). These inferred fractures were compared, wherever possible, with Ostenso and Wold's (1971) aeromagnetic data, and a good correlation was found. Inferred fractures commonly are associated with abrupt anomalies similar to the one found over the Mendeleyev fracture zone, and they mark abrupt changes in the general anomaly pattern. The large magnetic anomalies associated with these fractures (Fig. 6) and the average 50-km spacing inferred between fractures would suggest an explanation for the somewhat permissive correlation found by Ostenso and Wold (1971) between the commonly oblique Alpha Cordillera aeromagnetic profiles and those from the Reykjanes Ridge flank. Where Ostenso and Wold's (1971) flight lines lie away from, and parallel with, the fractures (e.g., flight 61-523, which bisects lines 7 and 8 south of the ridge and lines 6 and 7 north of the ridge), the anomalies display good symmetry about the ridge. However, an abrupt change in pattern occurs where the ridge offset, here based on the gross topography (after DeLeeuw, 1967), is encountered. Similar offsets in the ice-island magnetic data, viewed in a projection parallel with the fracture trend, are the basis for the inferred axis locations in the northeastern part of the survey area.

Physiography—The ridge structure appears to control the physiography of the central parts of the Amerasian basin. On the basis of Kutschale's (1966) observation that sediments were deposited on the Wrangel plain because a basement ridge prevented the sediments from reaching the deeper Fletcher plain, one might expect similar situations on the south side of the ridge. As noted, the bend in the abyssal channel leading from the Chukchi plain through the Charlie Gap may be structurally controlled, whereas the great length of the Charlie Gap may be a result of a set of descending steplike barriers presented by the inferred fractures 3–5 (Fig. 3).

Below the Charlie Gap lies the Mendeleyev plain, which is mapped here in some detail for the first time. This plain has gradients of about 1:1,000 and lies at a depth of 3,300 m. Although the connection between the Mendeleyev plain and the deeper Canada plain has never been surveyed, one might expect to find another broad steplike descent governed by a succession of offsetting fractures such as lines 7–9 (Fig. 3). South of Crary Seamount, the broad rectangular uplift may be a consequence of a southerly displacement of the ridge axis between long. 130° and 170°W, as indicated.

A very rough basement physiography is indicated in the seismic profiles over the ridge (Figs. 8, 9). It compares with the rough ridge physiography presently observed on the crestal areas of the Mid-Atlantic Ridge. For instance, in profile *BCDE* of Figure 8, one can discern portions of Heezen et al.'s (1959) high fractured plateau, rift-mountain, and rift-valley provinces. As can be seen from the profiles, many of the characteristics of the ridge basement have been masked by a greatly varied sedimentary cover which is rarely thinner than 100 m and may be thicker than 1,200 m.

Beal (1968) was the first to note the presence on the Alpha Cordillera of seamounts with central depressions; he suggested a volcanic origin for the seamounts. In this investigation, six seamounts were mapped. Of these, four appear to have depressions on the summits and are presumed to be volcanoes lying along fractures. Wilkins and Harris Seamounts can be seen in profile *A-B* of Figure 7. They lie in the vicinity of the area of low heat flow discussed by Lachenbruch and Marshall (1966). Another possibly volcanic seamount, partially obscured by a thick sedimentary cover, was observed on the northern margin of the Chukchi Cap; it is shown in profile *XYZ* of Figure 7.

A general geophysical profile across the southern flank of the Alpha Cordillera along section *A-A'* (Fig. 2) is shown in Figure 10. In this profile the Alpha Cordillera is shown as a

Fig. 5—Alpha Cordillera magnetic-anomaly map showing location of inferred fracture zones. C.I. = 100 gammas.

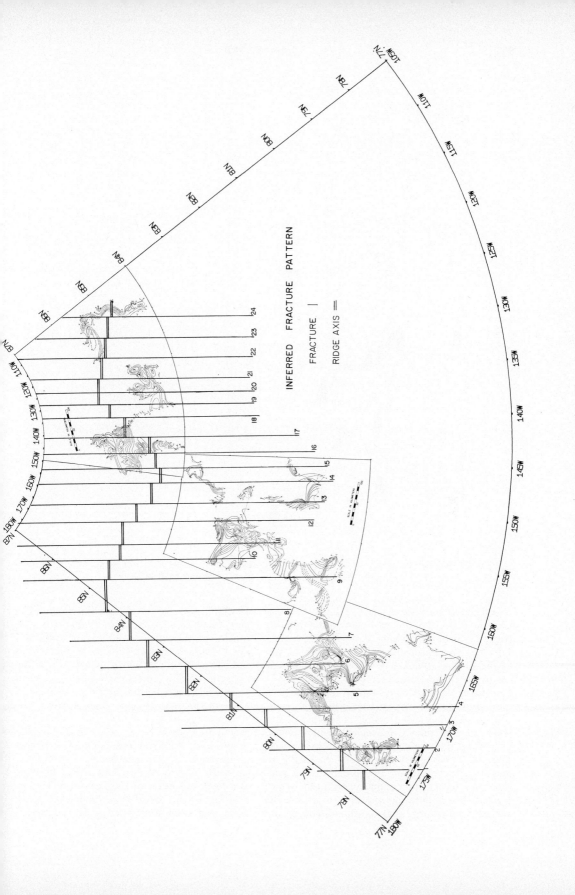

INFERRED FRACTURE PATTERN

FRACTURE |

RIDGE AXIS ═

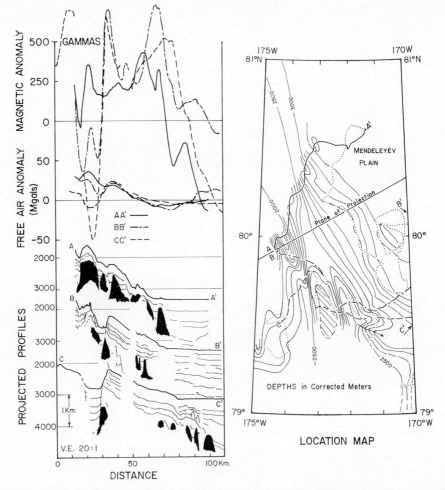

FIG. 6—Projected geophysical profiles across Mendeleyev fracture zone. Reflection profiles are based on assumed sound velocity of 2 km/sec within sediment.

rounded feature rising nearly 2 km above the Canada plain. To the east the crestal regions rise still higher, reaching depths of less than 1,100 m. In this profile the overall inclination of the southern flank is 0°23′, which is identical to the inclination observed by Beal (1968) from an analysis of nine submarine crossings of the cordillera.

Two steep-sided depressions as deep as 1 km were traversed in the northeastern part of the area. Step faults bound these depressions, and there is some suggestion (Fig. 9, profiles *V-W* and *A-S*) that the floors of the depressions contain thick sedimentary sequences which are also faulted. The fault traces appear to extend to the surface, suggesting that tensional forces are

continuing to act on the cordillera. In this region the free-air anomalies change from +80 mgal over the crest to −30 mgal in less than 30 km. Although the cause of these depressions is unknown, it appears likely that they are related either to nearby crustal movements or, perhaps, to readjustments within the ridge itself.

Sediment distribution—The seismic reflection profiles show a distinct difference between the sedimentary cover over the Mendeleyev Ridge and that over the Alpha Cordillera. A comparison of the profiles in Figure 6 with those in Figure 8 illustrates these differences. With the exception of the bottom erosion zone and the scarp face of the Mendeleyev fracture zone, the Mendeleyev Ridge is covered by a

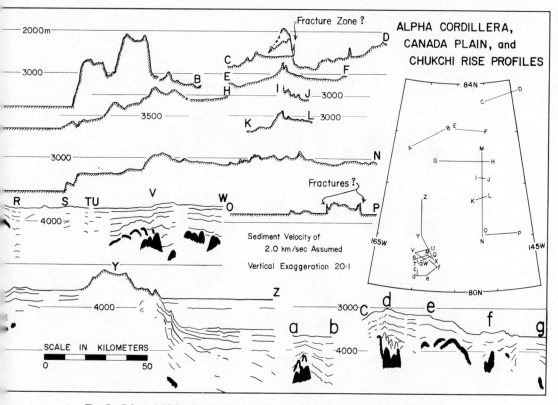

FIG. 7—Selected Alpha Cordillera, Canada plain, and Chukchi Rise seismic profiles.

300-m-thick layer of conformal sedimentary units suggestive of pelagic sedimentation. The bottom surface is acoustically smooth and produces a characteristically strong, uniform echo on the sounding record. Beneath this conformal layer lie generally horizontal to subhorizontal reflectors which are similar to those found on the Alpha Cordillera, and which in some areas (Fig. 6, profile A-A′) show the existence of an erosional stage prior to the deposition of the overlying conformal layer. In contrast, the crestal regions of the Alpha Cordillera (Fig. 8) are characterized acoustically by a series of overlapping hyperbolic echoes representative of a highly corrugated sea floor. After an analysis of data obtained from numerous camera stations, bottom-current measurements, nephelometer stations, and a few short cores, and from the distribution of hyperbola amplitudes as seen on the echo sounder, Hall (1970) concluded that these features reflected the presence of elongate sedimentary structures formed by the bottom-current-related transport of fine sediment across the crest of the Alpha Cordillera from northwest to southeast. However, the weakness of the observed currents, the uniform sedimentary cover thought to blanket these features, the random distribution of ice-rafted debris in the numerous bottom photographs, and the low strength of the turbidity of the observed bottom nepheloid layer—together these indicate that this process is presently inactive. However, the present circulation inferred from the bottom currents and the nepheloid-layer measurements appears to be capable of producing the observed hyperbolization with considerably increased currents. It is tempting to speculate that such an increase in circulation, without appreciable change in pattern, would attend an ice-free ocean where greater interaction between the atmosphere and the ocean was possible. The thin veneer of sediment overlying these sedimentary ridges suggests that these conditions might have prevailed around 10 m.y. ago.

Another region of hyperbolization observed beneath the Mendeleyev plain suggests that similar bottom-current activity occurred in the

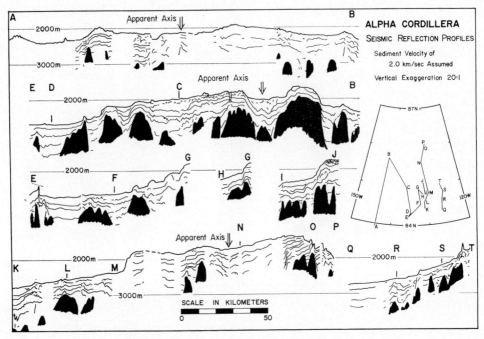

FIG. 8—Selected Alpha Cordillera seismic profiles, western section.

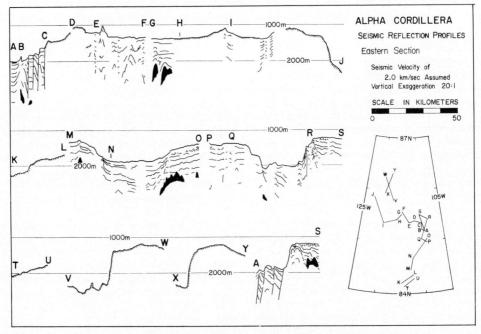

FIG. 9—Selected Alpha Cordillera seismic profiles, eastern section.

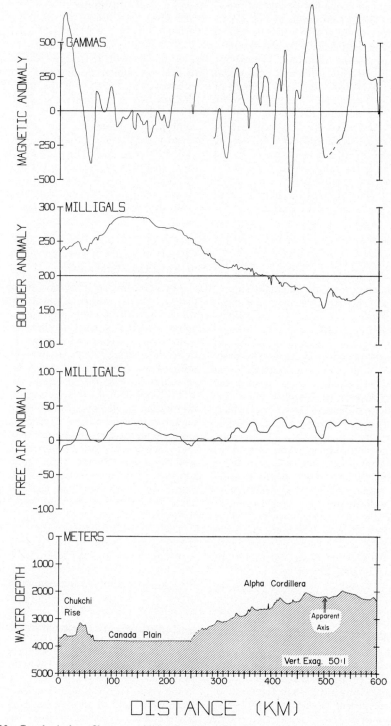

Fig. 10—Geophysical profile across Alpha Cordillera. See Figure 2 (*A-A'*) for location of profile.

distant past for an extended period of time. This region is seen as two sequences of hyperbolic reflections extending from 550 to 850 m below the surface of the plain. If a sedimentation rate of 1 cm/1,000 years is assumed for the overlying sedimentary cover, one might speculate that this hyperbolization is a result of a strong bottom circulation brought about by the opening of the Atlantic about 60 m.y. ago.

Two buried channels were observed leading down from the backslope of the Mendeleyev fracture zone to the Mendeleyev plain. In the seismic profiles these channels are impressed upon the sedimentary interfaces to a maximum depth of 700 m. Two periods of channel usage are suggested by changes in the character of the channel fillings and by a northward migration of about 1 km in one channel. This migration corresponds roughly in time to a zone of enhanced hyperbolization within the adjacent plain sediments and suggests a possible relation. In all three channel crossings the right side of the channel floor (facing downstream) is topographically higher.

Seismic reflection profiles over the Mendeleyev and Canada plains reveal more than 2 km of sedimentary beds and no indication of basement. Kutschale's (1966) measurement of at least 3.5 km of sedimentary units beneath the Wrangel plain, across the Mendeleyev Ridge, suggests that the sedimentary cover is considerably thicker. As might be expected, the seismic and bathymetric profiles suggest a much greater supply of terrestrial sediment in the vicinity of the southern terminus of the Mendeleyev Ridge and the eastern terminus of the Alpha Cordillera, where a great thickness of sedimentary units is observed over the crestal regions and—in the case of the Mendeleyev Ridge—where there is a smooth transition between the ridge and the adjacent plains. In contrast, the transition between the Canada plain and the Alpha Cordillera and Chukchi Rise is very abrupt.

Crustal gravity model—A two-dimensional crustal gravity model was fitted to the geophysical profile shown in Figure 10 by using the procedures outlined by Talwani et al. (1959). Seismic control was available on the cordillera crest in the form of an unreversed refraction station obtained by Hunkins (1961) from Station Alpha. This profile shows a 290-m sedimentary thickness and a 2.80-km thickness of 4.70-km/sec "basement" material overlying an "oceanic" layer of 6.44-km/sec compressional wave velocity. The presence of this oceanic layer near the apparent axis of the ridge suggests a structure similar to that of the East Pacific Rise. Accordingly, a crustal model with interfingering of "anomalous" mantle ($\rho = 3.15$) beneath the ridge flanks and an anomalous root beneath the ridge crest was used; the model was similar in shape to that shown by Talwani et al. (1965) for the East Pacific Rise and was found to satisfy the observed free-air gravity data. For densities of 2.30 g/cc for a combined sedimentary-basement layer, 280 g/cc for the presumed 5-km-thick oceanic layer, and 3.15 g/cc and 3.40 g/cc for the "anomalous" mantle and normal mantle, respectively, this model shows a 27-km-thick root of "anomalous" mantle to be required. Over the ridge crest the total crustal thickness is about 35 km.

SPECULATIONS CONCERNING ALPHA CORDILLERA AS AN INACTIVE CENTER OF SEA-FLOOR SPREADING

The preceding sections have presented bathymetric, gravity, seismic, and magnetic data which support the contention of earlier investigators that the Alpha Cordillera is an inactive center of sea-floor spreading. Furthermore, these data suggest that, in the vicinity of the crest of the Alpha Cordillera at least, sea-floor spreading has occurred parallel with the present 142°W meridian. In this section, these findings are related to geologic events along the continental margins, within the framework of lithosphere-plate–continental-margin tectonics (Bird and Dewey, 1970). A model is proposed which suggests that the Alpha Cordillera represents the northernmost segment of an oceanic ridge which was active at least twice—in the early Paleozoic and from the late Mesozoic to the early Tertiary.

The rationale for this model is as follows. If the opening motions of the Atlantic Ocean, the Eurasian basin, and the Labrador Sea over the past 80 m.y. are reversed, without accounting for similar motions in the Amerasian basin, we arrive at a continental configuration similar to that shown in Figure 11. In this configuration it is obvious that, even with further closing along the strike of the inferred fracture zones to reverse the early Tertiary spreading suggested by Vogt and Ostenso (1970)—most likely accomplished at the expense of the basin boundaries in the vicinity of northern Greenland and Ellesmere Island and of an area somewhere between Siberia and the Verkhoyansk Mountains—a relatively deep and rectangular ocean basin remains. Most significantly, this early basin is

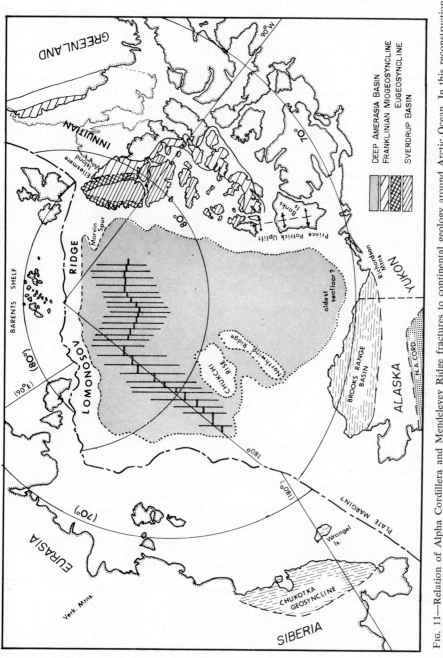

FIG. 11—Relation of Alpha Cordillera and Mendeleyev Ridge fractures to continental geology around Arctic Ocean. In this reconstruction of approximate configuration about 80 m.y. ago, the Atlantic Ocean, Labrador Sea, and Eurasian basin have been closed. Fictitious separation between Alaska and Siberia is shown in lieu of unknown deformations between Verkhoyansk Mountains and Siberia.

bordered on the south and east by folded Paleozoic geosynclinal belts that indicate a depositional and deformational history quite similar to that of the Caledonian-Appalachian belts to the south, which Dewey (1969) and Bird and Dewey (1970) have related to an opening and closing of a proto–Atlantic ocean in the late Precambrian and early Paleozoic.

Are these Paleozoic belts, the Innuitian fold system on the northern margin of Greenland and along the Canadian Archipelago, and the Brooks Range orogen of northern Alaska and its probable western continuation—the Chukotsk geosyncline of northeastern Siberia—part of this same Caledonian-Appalachian system? This model would suggest that they are, because removal of the effects of Greenland's northerly movement in the Tertiary makes the belts appear to have been far more linear and continuous. As can be seen in Figure 11, the results of Greenland's 500-km movement north (LePichon et al., in prep.), while maintaining contact with Ellesmere Island across the Robeson Channel as required by Kerr (1967), would be to produce a reverse-Z bending of the belts. Keen et al. (1969) have cited examples of extensive folding, thrusting, and diapirism along the inferred axis of compression within the Sverdrup basin as evidence for one such bend. Presumably, the other bend occurs in the northeastern corner of Greenland where the belts of northern and eastern Greenland meet at nearly right angles. This inferred hinge or pivot may lie beneath the sea somewhere north of Kronprins Christian Land or, preferably, near the ice-covered area at the end of Hagens Fjord (Mylius Ericksens Land), whereas the areas of compressional deformation implicit in this interpretation should be concealed beneath the permanent ice cover of Greenland.

In summary, this rationale suggests that, in about late Mesozoic time and the beginning of the Tertiary—prior to the northward movement of Greenland—the Amerasian basin was the northernmost extension of an opening Atlantic Ocean and was the site of sea-floor spreading from the present Alpha Cordillera. An earlier spreading episode in this basin, in late Precambrian and early Paleozoic time, was linked in much the same way (around the northern tip of Greenland) with the spreading ridge system in the proto-Atlantic. In the early Paleozoic, however, this southern ocean was closed by subduction along underthrust Benioff zones and there was accompanying develop-

ment of geosynclinal belts along the continental margins. Subduction within the southern Amerasian basin was probably along two such zones—one beneath the Innuitian belts in the Canadian Arctic and a second beneath northern Alaska and Siberia. Between these two zones, from Prince Patrick Island to the Yukon, the spreading and subducting sea floor probably paralleled the continental margin. The rough parallelism between the present Atlantic and the proto-Atlantic suture (the Caledonian-Appalachian belts)—and between the present inferred Amerasian basin fracture pattern and this older, undeformed margin—suggests that the spreading in this earlier episode was not appreciably different. The Amerasian basin probably remained open following the closure of the southern proto-Atlantic along a line from Florida to northern Ellesmere Island.

Proposed model—A more detailed discussion of the proposed model has been given by the writer (Hall, 1970). For this brief presentation, it is appropriate to note that this model has benefited from ideas, arguments, and earlier models set forth by Wilson (1966), Harland (1965), Churkin (1969), and Tailleur (1969). For a geologic description of the areas considered, the reader is directed to summary articles elsewhere in this volume. The model is as follows.

1. Prior to the early Tertiary, the Caledonian-Appalachian orogen extending from Florida to Spitsbergen continued northwest and west through the Innuitian fold system in northern Greenland and Ellesmere, forming a continuous, relatively smooth, arcuate belt around eastern and northern North America. West of Prince Patrick Island, another belt continued through the Yukon and northern Alaska, and perhaps across northeastern Siberia along the Chukotsk geosyncline.

2. Following the model of Bird and Dewey (1970), I propose that, between late Precambrian and Ordovician time, a proto–Atlantic ocean opened along the full length of the Caledonian-Appalachian orogen. The Amerasian basin may have existed prior to this opening. This opening was accomplished through plate accretion (sea-floor spreading) along a fracture in an older North American–African–European continent; it was accompanied by subsidence of the separating continental margins and by generally uninterrupted sedimentation.

3. This ocean began to close during the Ordovician. Oceanic-plate subduction was accom-

plished through the development of marginal trenches and underthrusting along Benioff zones. This underthrusting and associated granitization produced the Caledonian orogeny.

4. Closing continued until the Devonian, when a collision of the continents, probably as far north as eastern Ellesmere Island, produced the late Caledonian "spasms" (Haller and Kulp, 1962) in the Greenland and Innuitian fold belts and the Acadian orogeny to the south.

5. Minor movements occurred along the belts in late Paleozoic and early Mesozoic time; these movements may have been precursory to the present opening of the Atlantic Ocean. Some spreading may have occurred in the Amerasian basin.

6. In Jurassic and Cretaceous time, the Brooks Range geanticline was produced as a result of the Nevadan orogeny along the Western cordillera. At about the same time, opening of the Atlantic began in the far south, and by Late Cretaceous time it had progressed as far north as Greenland.

7. Between 80 and 60 m.y. ago, Greenland became separated from Labrador, rotating approximately 11°E about an apparent pole on Ellesmere Island (LePichon et al., in prep.).

8. From sometime before 60 m.y. ago until 40 m.y. ago, spreading occurred on the Alpha Cordillera (Vogt and Ostenso, 1970) parallel with the present 142°W meridian. The amount of spreading may have exceeded the opening of the basin, producing compressional structures in the marginal geosynclines south of the Alpha Cordillera.

9. Between 60 and 40 m.y. ago, Greenland (excluding the northern Greenland belt) also moved north approximately 500 km about an apparent pole of rotation in the vicinity of Hudson Bay (LePichon et al., in prep.). This predominantly strike-slip motion occurred along the Davis Strait. This northward movement resulted in the deformation of the eastern Franklinian geosyncline and the northern Greenland Caledonian belt, through a kinking of the belt about two hinges or pivots in northeastern Greenland and the Sverdrup basin. Bending of the Sverdrup basin produced folding transverse to the earlier Paleozoic and early Tertiary folds, thrusts, and zones of diapirism (Keen et al., 1969). The latter part of this northward movement resulted in the accretion of the northern Greenland Caledonian belt to the central and southern parts of Greenland

and in the effective closing off of the Amerasian basin. The northward movement possibly was accommodated through deformation of the Greenland end of the Lomonosov Ridge, which was then the outer margin of the Barents shelf, and may have produced the Marvin Spur.

10. Approximately 40 m.y. ago, the movements of Greenland ceased, except for slight rifting along the Robeson Channel (Kerr, 1967). Spreading ceased on the Alpha Cordillera about this time (Vogt and Ostenso, 1970) and was replaced by opening of the Greenland Sea and the Eurasian basin.

This proposed model has the merits of (1) providing a rather simple explanation for the geometric relations of the geosynclinal belts in the Amerasian Arctic, (2) explaining the ubiquitous Middle to Upper Devonian clastic wedges of northern provenance (Churkin, 1969) in terms of detritus shed from a marginal mountain range just landward of the trench (mountains which since have been eroded and remnants of which are probably seen presently in the argillaceous Barrow arch beneath the northern coast of Alaska), (3) providing an explanation for the marked geologic contrast between the Brooks Range orogen and the northern Yukon in terms of greatly differing distances from their respective subduction zones, and (4) explaining the occurrence of granitic plutons in northern Alaska and the formation of uplifts and arches in the Canadian Arctic Archipelago as a result of emplacement of magmas from underlying Benioff zones. Furthermore, the model suggests (1) that the Richardson Mountains in the northern Yukon may represent the relatively undisturbed constituents of the ancestral Brooks Range which have been shielded from the effects of deformation, uplift, and erosion by their much greater distance from a Benioff zone, and (2) that the Barents shelf (and the Lomonosov Ridge) on the far side of the basin may be an analogue of the geosynclinal belts considered here.

Age of Canada basin—The proposed history of the Amerasian basin indicates that it is very old—and that it might also contain very old sea floor. Speculations of how old, of course, will depend on the interpretation of events around the basin. However, the inferred direction of spreading and the location of the ridge axis (Fig. 11) suggest that, in the absence of any appreciable change in spreading direction during or between spreading episodes, the oldest oceanic crust should be located near the Mackenzie delta in the Yukon, approximately 1,700 km from the present ridge crest. A simple calculation shows that this older sea floor is probably a product of an earlier episode of spreading. A visual inspection of the correlated Alpha Cordillera–Reykjanes Ridge magnetic profiles (Ostenso and Wold, 1971) shows that the anomaly wavelengths and, therefore, the spreading rates are similar. A conservative spreading rate of 2 cm/year, which is considerably higher than the actual figure for the Reykjanes Ridge, would require 85 m.y. to produce this 1,700 km of crust. However, the geologic and aeromagnetic data suggest that the most recent (late Mesozoic–early Tertiary) spreading episode perhaps lasted only half that time (20–40 m.y.), so at least another 850 km of crust would have to have formed in an earlier episode.

When was that episode? Until there is drilling in the area, one can only speculate about earlier spreading. However, in addition to the evidence of angular unconformities and mild folding in the Permo-Carboniferous of the outer Sverdrup basin (Thorsteinsson and Tozer, 1961), perhaps suggestive of some mild tectonic activity, the geologic history accords with Precambrian-Cambrian spreading. The existence of such ancient sea floor, making the Arctic Ocean truly unique, should not be entirely dismissed.

The magnetic data tend to support a conclusion that the basin is quite old. Ostenso and Wold (1971) showed, in a figure presenting the overall physiography of the magnetic field based on their extensive aeromagnetic data, that the magnetic field becomes very subdued for a distance of up to 800 km from the Alaskan continental margin. This subdued zone generally parallels the ridge axis shown in Figure 11; it was observed from Station T-3 during the 1964–1966 drift over the Canada plain. In this zone, anomalies are less than 100 gammas. It is possible that this quiet zone represents an elevation of the Curie-point isotherm resulting from the thick sedimentary cover, but such a situation is considered unlikely in view of the large anomalies observed on the thickly blanketed Mendeleyev and Wrangel plains. Instead, the subdued field may reflect long periods of constant polarity such as those in the late Paleozoic or middle Mesozoic, or perhaps an even older period when the area was situated much closer to the magnetic equator.

SELECTED REFERENCES

Beal, M. A., 1968, Bathymetry and structure of the Arctic Ocean: Corvallis, Oregon State Univ., Ph.D. dissert., 204 p.

Belov, N. A., and N. N. Lapina, 1958, Bottom sediments in the central portion of the Arctic Ocean: Leningrad, Arctic Geology Institute Trans., v. 85.

Bird, J. M., and J. F. Dewey, 1970, Lithosphere plate–continental margin tectonics and the evolution of the Appalachian orogen: Geol. Soc. America Bull., v. 81, p. 1031–1060.

Black, D. J., and N. A. Ostenso, 1962, Gravity observations from Ice Island Arlis II, 6 October, 1961 to 8 April, 1962: Univ. Wisconsin Geophys. and Polar Research Center Research Rept. No. 62-8, 26 p.

Cabaniss, G. H., 1962, Geophysical data from U.S. Arctic drifting stations, 1957–1960: Air Force Cambridge Research Lab., U.S.A.F., Research Note AFCRL-62-683, 234 p.

——— K. L. Hunkins, and N. Untersteiner, 1965, US-IGY Drifting Station Alpha, Arctic Ocean, 1957–1958: Office of Aerospace Research, U.S.A.F., AFCRL-65-848, Special Rept. No. 38, 336 p.

Churkin, M., Jr., 1969, Paleozoic tectonic history of the Arctic basin north of Alaska: Science, v. 165, no. 3893, p. 549–555.

DeLeeuw, M. M., 1967, New Canadian bathymetric chart of the western Arctic Ocean, north of 72°: Deep-Sea Research, v. 14, no. 5, p. 489–504.

Dewey, J. F., 1969, Evolution of the Appalachian/Caledonian orogen: Nature, v. 222, p. 124–129.

Drake, C. L., et al., 1963, A mid-Labrador Sea ridge: Nature, v. 200, p. 1085–1086.

Haines, G. V., 1967, A Taylor series expansion of the geomagnetic field in the Canadian Arctic: Dominion Observatory Ottawa Pubs., v. 35, no. 2, p. 119–140.

Hall, J. K., 1970, Arctic Ocean geophysical studies; the Alpha Cordillera and the Mendeleyev Ridge: New York, Columbia Univ., Ph.D. dissert., 125 p.

Haller, J., and J. L. Kulp, 1962, Absolute age determinations in East Greenland: Medd. om Grønland, v. 171, no. 1, 77 p.

Harland, W. B., 1965, Discussion of the tectonic evolution of the Arctic–North Atlantic region: Royal Soc. Philos. Trans., ser. A, v. 258, p. 59–75.

Heezen, B. C., M. Tharp, and M. Ewing, 1959, The floors of the oceans, I, The North Atlantic: Geol. Soc. America Spec. Paper 65, 122 p.

Hunkins, K. L., 1961, Seismic studies of the Arctic Ocean floor, in G. O. Raasch, ed., Geology of the Arctic, v. 1: Toronto, Univ. Toronto Press, p. 645–665.

——— 1968, Geomorphic provinces of the Arctic Ocean, in J. E. Sater, ed., Arctic drifting stations: Montreal, Arctic Inst. North America, p. 365–376.

——— E. M. Thorndike, and G. Mathieu, 1969, Nepheloid layers and bottom currents in the Arctic Ocean: Jour. Geophys. Research, v. 74, no. 28, p. 6995–7008.

——— et al., 1970, The floor of the Arctic Ocean in photographs: Arctic, v. 23, no. 3, p. 175–189.

Keen, M. J., et al., 1969, The continental margin of eastern Canada—Nova Scotia to Nares Strait: Unpub. ms.

Kerr, J. W., 1967, Nares submarine rift valley and the relative rotation of Greenland: Bull. Canadian Petroleum Geology, v. 15, no. 4, p. 483–520.

Kutschale, H. W., 1966, Arctic Ocean geophysical studies—the southern half of the Siberia basin: Geophysics, v. 31, no. 4, p. 683–710.

Lachenbruch, A. H., and B. V. Marshall, 1966, Heat flow through the Arctic Ocean floor—the Canada basin–Alpha rise boundary: Jour. Geophys. Research, v. 71, no. 4, p. 1223–1248.

LePichon, X., R. D. Hyndman, and G. Pautot, in prep., A geophysical study of the opening of the Labrador Sea: Jour. Geophys. Research.

Ostenso, N. A., and R. J. Wold, 1971, Aeromagnetic survey of the Arctic Ocean—techniques and interpretations: Marine Geophys. Research, v. 1, no. 2, p. 178–219.

Somov, M. M., 1955, Observational data of the scientific research drifting station of 1950–1951, v. I–III: Morskoi Transport 1954–1955 (translated by the American Meteorological Soc., ASTIA Doc. 117–133).

Tailleur, I., 1969, Rifting speculation on the geology of Alaska's North Slope; Part II: Oil and Gas Jour., September 29, 1969, p. 128–130.

Talwani, M., J. L. Worzel, and M. Landisman, 1959, Rapid gravity computations for two-dimensional bodies with application to the Mendocino submarine fracture zone: Jour. Geophys. Research, v. 64, no. 1, p. 49–59.

————— X. LePichon, and M. Ewing, 1965, Crustal structure of the mid-ocean ridges, 2. Computed model from gravity and seismic refraction data: Jour. Geophys. Research, v. 70, no. 2, p. 341–352.

Thorsteinsson, R., and E. T. Tozer, 1961, Structural history of the Canadian Arctic Archipelago since Precambrian time, in G. O. Raasch, ed., Geology of the Arctic, v. 1: Toronto, Univ. Toronto Press, p. 339–360.

Vogt, P. R., and N. A. Ostenso, 1970, Magnetic and gravity profiles across the Alpha Cordillera and their relation to Arctic seafloor spreading: Jour. Geophys. Research, v. 75, no. 26, p. 4925–4937.

Wilson, J. T., 1966, Did the Atlantic close and then reopen?: Nature, v. 211, p. 676–681.

Origin of Arctic and North Atlantic Oceans[1]

A. A. MEYERHOFF[2]
Tulsa, Oklahoma 74101

Abstract Late Proterozoic through Early Permian evaporite deposits are widespread in northern Canada, Greenland, and northern Eurasia. All of these evaporites are found today on the Atlantic Ocean, Eurasia, and Canada sides of the Lomonosov Ridge and its extensions into northern Siberia and northern Canada. No evaporites are known to be present on the Pacific side of the Lomonosov Ridge or north of its extensions into Siberia and Canada. This fact alone suggests that the Atlantic Ocean has been open into the Arctic since middle to late Proterozoic time; it further suggests that the Lomonosov Ridge and its continental extensions were in existence by late Proterozoic time. Hence, the distribution pattern indicates that the evaporites were brought in by, and precipitated from, marine waters entering via the present location of the Atlantic Ocean and the Lena Trough. Geologic data from Iceland, new geophysical data from the North Atlantic Ocean, and physical continuity of the Proterozoic Lomonosovides around the Canadian basin of the Arctic Ocean lend strong support to the interpretation given here.

Post-Devonian evaporite deposits in the Arctic are scarce, and their depocenters generally are farther south than those of Devonian and pre-Devonian times. The locations of the post-Devonian evaporite depocenters appear to be related to the formation of two sills across the present North Atlantic: the Franz Josef sill between Novaya Zemlya and Spitsbergen, separating the Arctic from the North Atlantic, and the Faeroe-Greenland sill extending from Scotland to southeastern Greenland.

Because the known evaporite-distribution patterns show such close relations among the present North Atlantic and Arctic Oceans; the present continental positions; and the existing sites of the Lomonosov Ridge, the Franz Josef sill, and the Faeroe-Greenland sill, postulation of plate-tectonic models for the formation of the North Atlantic and Arctic is unnecessary. In fact, no plate-tectonic or polar-wandering mechanism yet proposed explains the orderly geometric relations between the evaporite deposits and the observed geographic-topographic features. Hence, sea-floor spreading, plate motions, and polar wandering—if they ever took place in the North Atlantic–Arctic region—were pre–late Proterozoic events.

INTRODUCTION

General

The presence of extensive evaporite deposits of Proterozoic and Paleozoic ages in the circum-Arctic and circum–North Atlantic regions long has been cited as evidence for continental drift, sea-floor spreading, and polar wandering. The rationale for this conclusion is that evaporite precipitation and deposition require the presence of a hot climate in which evaporation exceeds total water input, and that such conditions can occur only in the torrid zone near the equator.

At the heart of such reasoning is one of geology's great foibles—"the present is the key to the past." The present is *not* the key to the past; at the very best it is a useful guideline for interpreting past earth history.

Evaporite Maxima and Minima

For example, most geologic literature leads one to believe that the present climatic zones existed at all times in the past—which is untrue. In previous papers (Meyerhoff, 1970a, b), I attempted to show that great worldwide warm periods (evaporite maxima) alternated through time with great worldwide cool periods (evaporite minima = glacial maxima; Fig. 1). During an evaporite-maximum period, only two climatic zones are present on the earth: a very broad torrid zone as wide as 120° of latitude and two temperate zones, one centered at each pole. Thus, during evaporite maxima, the temperate zones are at the poles and frigid zones do not exist. During such maxima, thick evaporite deposits can form at high latitudes.

In contrast, during evaporite-minimum periods, three different climatic zones develop, as today: a restricted torrid zone approximately straddling the equator, but in fact offset slightly northward; two temperate zones paralleling the torrid zone; and, at the poles, two frigid zones. Glacial conditions can and do develop during evaporite minima, not only near the poles, but also at much lower latitudes.

The evidence supporting these statements was published in a series of maps by Meyerhoff (1970a). These maps show evaporite distribution since middle Proterozoic time and coal distribution since Devonian time. Without exception, most of the coal is in latitudinal belts poleward from the evaporite deposits of the same ages. The evaporite belt straddles the equator, but the center of the evaporite belt, like the center of the present torrid zone, is off-

[1] Manuscript received, March 21, 1973.

[2] The American Association of Petroleum Geologists.

I thank Amy Lee Brown, Kathryn Meyerhoff, Peter Misch, Peggy Rice, Carol Thompson, and Deborah Zikmund for help during various phases of the preparation of this paper.

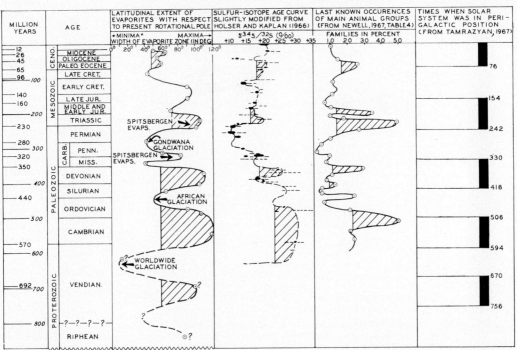

FIG. 1—Curves showing evaporite-maximum and evaporite-minimum periods (from Meyerhoff, 1970a, b; 1973); changes in S³⁴/³² ratios in salt deposits through time (modified from Holser and Kaplan, 1966); faunal extinctions (based on Newell, 1967); and vibrational-orbital periods of the solar system in our galaxy (from Tamrazyan, 1967). Republished with permission of Canadian Society of Petroleum Geologists.

set northward from the equator. The more poleward positions of the coal belts are proof that coal deposition takes place under cooler temperature conditions than does evaporite deposition. The widths of the evaporite and coal belts fluctuate episodically, possibly periodically, through time. Thus, the evaporite zone was 90–120° wide during the early Vendian (Proterozoic, approximately 690 m.y. ago), Cambrian, Devonian, Bashkirian (earliest Pennsylvanian), Late Permian–Triassic (Figs. 2, 3), and latest Jurassic–Early Cretaceous. The evaporite zone was only 50–80° wide during Mississippian–Early Permian (Fig. 4), Early and Middle Jurassic, and Late Cretaceous–early Eocene times.

Evaporite-minimum periods after Silurian time are easy to identify, because coal and tillite deposition was exceptionally widespread during such periods. Evaporite-minimum periods before Devonian time (before coal formation was possible) can be identified mainly on the basis of the presence of tillites, as, for example, late Vendian (600 m.y.) and latest Ordovician times. Widespread glaciation also is a

feature of latest Pennsylvanian–Early Permian and late Miocene–present times (Fig. 1).

Northern and Southern Evaporite Depositional Patterns—Contrasts

Evaporite depositional patterns contrast sharply between the Northern and Southern Hemispheres. This contrast is quite natural if one considers the fact that 60 percent of the Northern Hemisphere is land area, whereas only 20 percent of the Southern Hemisphere is land area. This fact possibly is the basis for Shepard's (1973, p. 101) statement that the unsolved evaporite problem "seems to be a minor point" insofar as the new global tectonics is concerned. Yet the contrasts between the two hemispheres involve two more facts that are not given sufficient consideration by geologists and geophysicists.

First is the fact that, in Antarctica, evaporites are unknown except in four very small saline lakes (McLeod, 1964). This is not to say that none will be found in Antarctica, but, in my opinion, the likelihood of finding large evaporite deposits there is remote. A few gyp-

PERMIAN

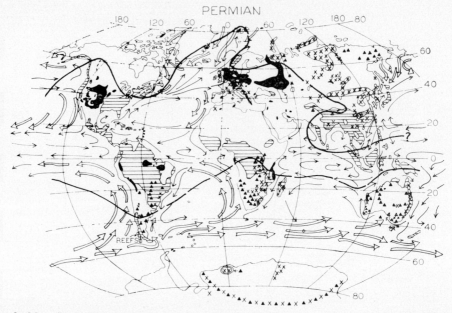

FIG. 2—Map showing Permian evaporite, coal, and tillite distributions. Modified somewhat from Meyerhoff (1970a). X = coal; solid black = evaporites; solid triangles = tillite; predominantly coal areas are separated from predominantly evaporite areas by heavy black lines (note northward deflection in area of modern Gulf Stream–North Atlantic Drift. Present warm ocean currents shown by single-line arrows; present cold ocean currents shown by double-line arrows. Horizontally ruled areas are those areas which today receive more than 1,000 mm of annual rainfall. Reproduced with permission of University of Chicago Press.

TRIASSIC

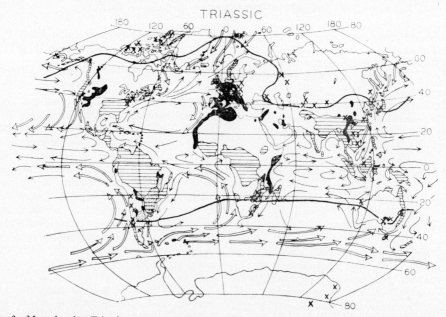

FIG. 3—Map showing Triassic evaporite, coal, and eolian sandstone distributions. Triassic was an evaporite-maximum period. Modified somewhat from Meyerhoff (1970a). Symbols are same as for Figure 2, with two exceptions: (1) there are no known Triassic tillites and (2) eolian and partly eolian sandstone deposits are shown by stippled pattern. Note great width of evaporite zone. Reproduced with permission of University of Chicago Press.

MISSISSIPPIAN

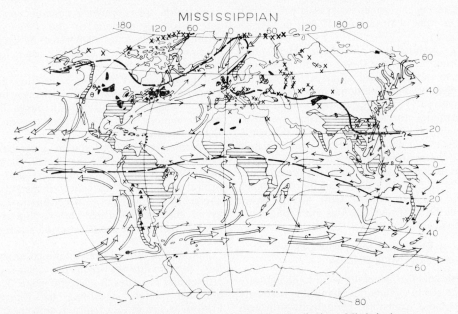

Fig. 4—Map showing Mississippian evaporite, coal, and tillite distributions. Mississippian was an evaporite-minimum period. Modified somewhat from Meyerhoff (1970a). Symbols are same as for Figure 2. Note narrow width of evaporite zone. Reproduced with permission of University of Chicago Press.

sum and anhydrite beds ultimately may be found in pre-recent Antarctic deposits, but I predict that the volume of such strata will be miniscule.

The second consideration is the latitudinal distribution of the evaporites in the two hemispheres. The most northerly evaporites known in the Northern Hemisphere are at 83°N lat. on the Arctic coast of Ostrov Vrangelya (Wrangel Island), and evaporite deposits south of 83°N are extensive. In contrast, evaporite deposits in the Southern Hemisphere are unknown south of 40°S lat. (Argentina), except for the four existing saline lakes described by McLeod (1964) in Antarctica.

An explanation for this distribution of evaporites might be found in the facts that (1) two of the southern continents taper southward, so that the available land area for evaporite deposition is very small, and (2) one continent, Australia, does not reach farther south than about 39°S lat., except in Tasmania. The argument that the fourth continent, Antarctica, is at latitudes too high for evaporite deposition is without substance. Large areas—in fact most—of Antarctica are between 60° and 83°S lat., the same latitude in which more than 2,000,000 km³ of evaporites are found in the Northern

Hemisphere (Meyerhoff, 1970b, p. 434). Antarctica has been explored sufficiently that some hint of the presence of large evaporite deposits (of the magnitude of those in the Northern Hemisphere) probably would have been found by now.

The absence of evaporites in Antarctica is explained easily if it is assumed that the continent has remained in its present position throughout geologic history. If it has, the West Wind Drift–Roaring Forties belt would have isolated Antarctica, and the northward offset of the meteorologic equator would have inhibited evaporite deposition at high southern latitudes. In fact, the known stratigraphic history of Antarctica—particularly of East Antarctica—is explained best if the continent is considered to have remained in its present location. The reconstructions of Antarctica's former positions, such as that by Irving (1964, p. 270), ignore the sedimentary records of the southern continents. The Irving postulate, for example, requires that Australia was as far north as 28°S lat. during Triassic and Permian times. If so, where are the Triassic and Permian evaporites of Antarctica? They have not been found. Instead, coals of these ages are extensive in Antarctica, a fact which shows that Antarctica was in one of the coal zones for at least part of past geologic time (Meyerhoff, 1970a, p. 26–28; Figs. 2, 3).

The high-latitude Northern Hemisphere evaporites do not owe their latitudinal positions solely to the northward offset of the meteorologic equator. Two additional important factors are involved: (1) the evaporites at high northern latitudes formed only during evaporite-maximum periods (Fig. 1), and (2) the northernmost evaporites show a close spatial relation among the positions of the various trans-Arctic and trans–North Atlantic sills, the present positions of the Arctic Ocean and North Atlantic Ocean, and the modern Gulf Stream–North Atlantic Drift. These relations are brought out in subsequent sections.

CAUSE OF EVAPORITE-MAXIMUM AND EVAPORITE-MINIMUM PERIODS

Earth scientists generally seem to be unaware that the global climate has changed episodically —and more probably periodically—through time, and that "polar regions" can be regions of temperate, moist climate with luxuriant vegetation and abundant animal life. They long have assumed that the 6-month period of darkness in polar regions eliminates the possibility for rich floral and faunal assemblages to flourish there. One only needs to look at the large trees buried in the snow of the Sierra Nevada 4 months each year, or to note the thick stands of taiga forest at 71°N lat. in Siberia, to realize the error of this assumption.

The following are but a few of those who have presented various hypotheses for worldwide climatic change: Brooks (1926, 1949), Fairbridge (1961), Schindewolf (1963), Bloch (1964), Ewing (1964, 1971), Flohn (1964), van der Hammen (1964), Lamb (1964), Schove (1964), Wundt (1964), Donn (1967), Newell (1967), Steiner (1967), Tamrazyan (1967), Billings (1968), Broecker (1968), Damon (1968), Donn and Ewing (1968), Mitchell (1968), Suess (1968), Weyl (1968), and Meyerhoff (1973). A very complete list of recent summaries of the problem was published by Mitchell (1968). Suffice it to say here that volcanic ash, CO_2 and other gases in the atmosphere, compositional changes of the hydrosphere and of seawater, orogeny, continental drift, eustatic changes in sea level, cosmic effects (sun spots, galactic cycles, etc.)—all these have been invoked to explain climatic changes. In a paper published this year (Meyerhoff, 1973), I concluded that the most sound

explanation for worldwide climatic change is one involving motions of the solar system within the galaxy, as elaborated in detail by Tamrazyan (1967). The basic reasons for my conclusions are shown on Figure 1.

Figure 1 shows a close correlation among evaporite maxima and minima, changes in S^{34}/S^{32} ratios in marine salt deposits, times of faunal extinctions, and the different positions of the solar system within our galaxy (Fig. 5).

Specifically, the solar system undergoes two types of motions within the galaxy (Bok and Bok, 1957; Trumpler and Weaver, 1962). Its orbital period about the center of the galaxy is about 220 m.y. (212 m.y., according to Tamrazyan). Because the orbital path is elliptical, the solar system has an apogalactic and a perigalactic (Fig. 5).

The second motion is a vibrational or oscillatory period during which the solar system crosses and recrosses the galactic plane. The vibrational period, according to Tamrazyan (1967), is 176 m.y., a figure in agreement with that of 160–180 m.y. reported by Hatfield and Camp (1970).

Because of the oscillatory motions across the galactic plane, Hatfield and Camp (1970) postulated that magnetic forces probably concentrated within the plane cause maximal cosmic radiation close to and within the plane. They thus reasoned that faunal extinctions should be greatest when the solar system is crossing the plane.

Therefore, during those times when the solar system is (1) crossing the galactic plane and (2) close to the perigalactic, heat production should be greatest and evaporite-maximum periods should occur. Conversely, cosmic radiation and heat production should be least when the sun is (1) farthest from the galactic plane and (2) near the apogalactic. At such times, evaporite-minimum conditions should exist and periods of glaciation would be possible. This process is not, strictly speaking, periodic, because of the difference between the galactic orbital period (212 m.y.) and the vibrational period (176 m.y.).

Regardless, Figure 1 shows some striking correlations among several events. The data on the figure, especially the galactic data, require far more intensive study for verification, but the preliminary correlations appear to be too good to be coincidental.

In summary, there have been periods in the earth's history when the earth was much warmer than today and evaporite deposition

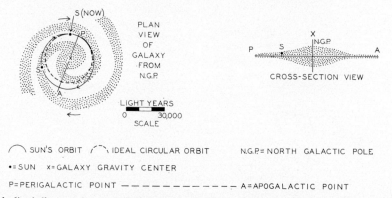

Fɪɢ. 5—Idealized diagrams based on Bok and Bok (1957), Trumpler and Weaver (1962), Tamrazyan (1967), and Meyerhoff (1973). Left sketch shows plan view of our galaxy from North Galactic Pole; cross-section view is shown at right. Dashed circle at left is circular orbital path through galaxy; solid circle is actual orbital path of sun (black dot) through galaxy. At right, sun is shown above galactic plane. In its galactic orbit of about 212 m.y., sun passes up and down through galactic plane in vibrational or oscillatory orbit of about 176 m.y. When sun (= solar system) is in galactic plane, solar system undergoes maximum cosmic radiation and heating. Possible interrelations between galactic motions of solar system and phenomena observed on earth are shown in Figure 1. Republished with permission of Canadian Society of Petroleum Geologists.

was possible at very high northern latitudes, not only because of the northward offset of the meteorologic equator, but also because of the probable entrance of Gulf Stream waters into the Arctic. These periods alternated with periods when the earth was much cooler, as today, and glaciation occurred on many parts of the earth. The decreasing importance of high-latitude evaporite deposition in the Northern Hemisphere after Devonian time and the absence of such deposition in Arctic regions after Triassic time are phenomena related to the increasing effectiveness as barriers of the various transoceanic sills in the Arctic and North Atlantic since middle Proterozoic or earlier time. The evidence for this statement, discussed by Meyerhoff (1970b), is reviewed briefly in subsequent pages.

ORIGIN OF ARCTIC OCEAN

Previous Hypotheses

Hypotheses for the origin of the Arctic Ocean can be grouped naturally into three categories. The first is the "fixist" or the "permanence" model advocated by most geologists until the advent of the new global tectonics, and supported most recently in one of my papers (Meyerhoff, 1970b). The second is the "foundering" or "subsidence" model, ranging from true foundering of continental crust (Shatsky, 1935; Eardley, 1948, 1961; E. King et al., 1966) to oceanization (Beloussov, 1962; Bogdanov and Til'man, 1964). The third category

includes a variety of "mobilist" hypotheses, ranging from rifting by earth expansion (e.g., Carey, 1958) to rifting by sea-floor spreading (e.g., Wilson, 1963; Johnson and Heezen, 1967; Ostenso, 1968; Churkin, 1969; Grantz, 1969; Harland, 1969; Tailleur, 1969; Vogt and Ostenso, 1970; Harland and Gayer, 1972; see also the papers in this volume for a wide variety of mobilist concepts and hypotheses, some of which are mutually exclusive).

I refer the interested reader to the publications cited for further details. Much of the remainder of this paper is a discussion of the facts which appear to support a fixist or permanence model.

Problems of Origin

Has an Arctic Ocean existed?—Before any model can be adopted for the Arctic area, the existence of an Arctic Ocean in pre-Tertiary time should be established. The geologic data are quite clear on this point: a sea has existed in the area of the present Arctic Ocean during many periods of time since the early to middle Proterozoic. This conclusion is based on the numerous paleogeographic maps of the area (e.g., Zhamoyda, 1968; Harland, 1969; Callomon et al., 1972) and on fossil distribution (Mamet and Belford, 1968; Mamet, 1970, 1972). The distribution of Arctic evaporites also supports the conclusion that a sea has been present in the area of today's Arctic Ocean since middle Proterozoic or earlier time.

Fig. 6—Index map to principal geographic features mentioned in text. Bathymetric contours in meters.

Is the modern Arctic an ocean?—Major disagreements exist concerning the origin of the Canadian basin of the Arctic Ocean (Fig. 6), but almost all Arctic specialists have concluded that the Eurasian basin of the Arctic is oceanic (*compare* Wilson, 1963; E. King *et al.,* 1966; Churkin, 1969; Harland, 1969; Vogt and Ostenso, 1970). Regardless of the origin of the Canadian basin, it is safe to conclude that at least the Eurasian basin of the Arctic Ocean is oceanic.

Therefore, the real question is whether the Arctic should be considered as a separate ocean basin. In my earlier paper (Meyerhoff, 1970b, p. 415–417), I concluded that the Arctic is a part of the Atlantic having mediterranean-like characteristics. I have nothing to add to this opinion, except to observe that possibly the Arctic should be considered, in certain respects, as similar to a "small ocean basin" as used by Menard (1967). Only the presence of a mid-ocean ridge (Gakkel Ridge) in the Eurasian basin distinguishes the Arctic from a small ocean basin and in turn suggests that it is the

geologic-geographic continuation of the North Atlantic Ocean.

Conclusions—The Arctic Ocean appears to be a polar extension of the Atlantic that has been partially separated from the Atlantic by transoceanic sills, or barriers, of continental crust—the Lomonosov Ridge, the Franz Josef sill, and the Faeroe-Greenland sill. The Arctic —geologically and bathymetrically—is totally separate from the Pacific. The Pacific entrance to the Arctic is a 1,350-km-wide continental shelf, 60 m or less deep, that is part of the North American and Eurasian continents. In fact, the Alaska–eastern Siberia area is a Proterozoic platform and shelf area which Nikolaev (1959) termed the "Paleo-Bering continent." The Arctic, therefore, cannot have opened into the Pacific since early Proterozoic or later time, except through shallow seaways. The Canadian basin of the Arctic seems to be underlain by "modified" or transitional crust, intermediate between continental and oceanic, whereas the Eurasian basin is underlain by truly oceanic crust.

Fundamental Facts

A valid hypothesis will not be contradicted by important new data. A hypothesis or theory which is contradicted by new data must be abandoned, and a new hypothesis or theory must be sought to replace it. The purpose of this section is to seek a hypothesis for the origin of the Arctic Ocean which takes into account all of the facts and which avoids speculation as much as possible.

Large features of Arctic geology—Geosynclines, now fold belts, surround most of the present Arctic Ocean. These belts occupy the present Brooks and Chukotsk Ranges, the Canadian Arctic Islands and northern Greenland (Franklinian geosyncline), the Taymyr and Ural ranges via Novaya Zemlya and Pay-Khoy, East Greenland, and a fold belt from Ireland to Spitsbergen—the Caledonides (Fig. 7). The Lomonosov Ridge appears to have been a former geosynclinal site or island arc; today, it is a partially submerged pre–Middle Ordovician fold belt with at least one radiometrically dated suite of rocks 550 m.y. old (Trettin, 1969). Study of Figure 7 shows that the Canadian basin of the Arctic is completely surrounded by fold belts which were deformed at different times since early Paleozoic or older time. I have called these the "Lomonosovides" (Meyerhoff, 1970b). The Eurasian basin and the Atlantic north of Iceland also have deformed geosynclines along most of their margins.

Wherever great epeiric seas invaded Western Canada, the Hudson Bay region, Scandinavia, northern European Russia, and northern Siberia, the invasion was from the north. The proof for such a statement can be seen on the paleogeographic maps cited and has been reviewed by Meyerhoff (1970b). Two examples may be cited where evaporite depocenters show salt-distribution patterns that are predicted by evaporite-basin theory (R. H. King, 1947; Scruton, 1953; Busson, 1968; Fuller and Porter, 1969) —*i.e.*, the sulfate salts are closer to the proximal side of the basin and the heavier salts are near the distal side. Specifically, in the late Proterozoic–Cambrian evaporite basin of the Irkutsk amphitheater (Fig. 7), anhydrite and gypsum are more abundant in the proximal, or northern, margins of the epeiric basin, whereas halite and heavier salts are more abundant farther from the present Arctic Ocean in the distal, or southern, regions of the former epeiric sea (Yanshin, 1962; Karpyshev, 1965; Komar and Semikhatov, 1965; Menner, 1965; Zhar-

kova, 1965; Pisarchik *et al.*, 1968; and many others). The same is true of the Devonian evaporite basin of Western Canada (Fuller and Porter, 1969; Klingspor, 1969).

The main lessons to be learned from the large geosynclines surrounding the Arctic and North Atlantic are that their histories were quite dissimilar, and that the source of the waters which filled these geosynclines was, in large part, from the north. Study of Haller's (1971) description of the East Greenland geosyncline and comparison of it with Holtedahl's (1960) and Harland's (1961, 1969) descriptions of the Caledonides extending from southern Norway to Spitsbergen make it apparent that these geosynclinal areas never were joined. The same is true of the other areas postulated by some to have been joined. For example, it is difficult to find much in common between the Lomonosov Ridge (Trettin, 1969) and the Franz Josef sill (see Meyerhoff, 1970b, for list of references), which are alleged by some to have been joined (*e.g.*, Harland and Gayer, 1972). Similarly, the Franklinian geosyncline (Douglas, 1970) has very little in common with either the Brooks-Chukotsk geosyncline or the Taymyr and Ural fold belts (Spizharskiy, 1968).

The sedimentary sequences of the former epeiric seas are just as instructive, because they exhibit many differences. In almost every case, a northern source for marine invasions—specifically, the area of the present Arctic Ocean—is demonstrable. The geologic facts simply do not justify postulations that the marine invasions of the circum-Arctic epeiric seas of the past came from a sea now occupied by the Uralides (a former plate junction, according to Hamilton, 1970), or from a seaway between the present Verkhoyansk and Cherskiy Ranges (Churkin, 1972). This statement is demonstrated in a subsequent section.

Bering-Chukotsk shelf—The largest barrier between the Arctic and the world ocean is the Bering-Chukotsk shelf, 1,350 km wide, separating the Canadian basin of the Arctic from the Pacific Ocean. The antiquity of this "Paleo-Bering continent" (Nikolaev, 1959) is well established; it includes rocks as old as early Proterozoic (Verechtchagin, 1959; Spizharskiy, 1967; Glushkov, 1968; Smirnov, 1968; P. B. King, 1969). The area of this shelf is, in essence, a broad continental landmass which is an integral part of both North America and Eurasia, a fact elaborated by Churkin (1972, p. 1028, 1030).

Lomonosov Ridge—Poleward from the Bering-Chukotsk shelf is the Proterozoic (and pos-

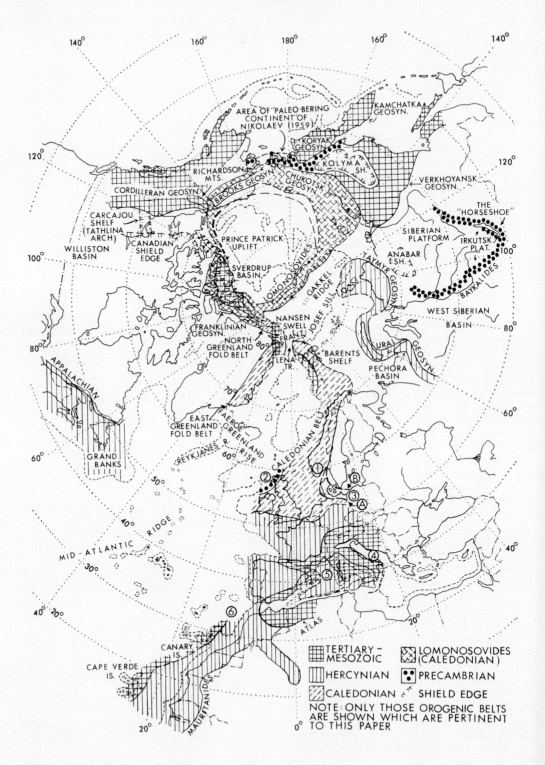

sibly older) Lomonosov Ridge, which strikes almost in a straight line across the Arctic Ocean (Figs. 6, 7), subparallel with the 40°W-140°E meridian, and intersects the north geographic pole. The ridge is underlain by continental crust (Ostenso, 1962; Demenitskaya *et al.,* 1968; Trettin, 1969; Karasik *et al.,* 1971; and others). Where the Lomonosov Ridge intersects the Canadian Arctic Archipelago (Franklinian geosyncline), deformed late Proterozoic–Cambrian and Early to early Middle Ordovician rocks on the ridge's landward extension are overlain unconformably by nearly horizontal late Middle Ordovician sedimentary rocks (Trettin, 1969, p. 145). Radiometric dates from the Proterozoic metamorphic rocks of northern Ellesmere Island, near the point where the Lomonosov Ridge intersects the Canadian Arctic Archipelago, yield an age of 550 m.y. (Trettin, 1969, p. 143). Trettin (p. 145) wrote that the Lomonosov Ridge (where it joins Ellesmere) formed an upland in Middle Ordovician time.

The Lomonosov Ridge extends inland on both the Siberian and Canadian sides of the Arctic and appears to form a metamorphosed fold belt around the entire present-day Canadian basin (Churkin, 1969). This fold belt was termed by me the "Lomonosovides" (Meyerhoff, 1970b); its position is shown on Figure 8. The belt yields radiometric dates from granitic intrusions ranging from 310 to 419 m.y. (Silurian, Devonian). By Middle Devonian time, almost the entire Lomonosovides were exposed, and they shed terrestrial debris southward (toward the continent; Krylova *et al.,* 1967; Trettin, 1967; Rzhonsnitskaya, 1968; Churkin, 1969). Terrestrial Devonian deposits are common around the margin of the Canadian basin, as well as around the Eurasian basin and the margins of the North Atlantic. The uplift of the Lomonosovides effectively isolated the present

area of the Canadian basin from the rest of the present Arctic and the North Atlantic.

Significance of Lomonosovides—The Lomonosovides (Fig. 8) form a circle around the Canadian basin of the Arctic Ocean. The apparent overall continuity of this circular orogen, as demonstrated first by Churkin (1969), means simply that the present Canadian basin area was *not* formed by sea-floor spreading. Foundering and basification are not eliminated, nor is the possibility that the area may have been an ocean basin throughout its history. The apparent continuity of the Lomonosovides also rules out the possibility that the Lomonosov Ridge was rafted by sea-floor spreading from the Franz Josef sill.

Franz Josef sill (Figs. 6, 7)—This sill is the northern edge of the Barents Sea, a broad epicontinental shelf sea occupying the northwestern corner of the European continent. This continental shelf (Demenitskaya *et al.,* 1968; Emelyanov *et al.,* 1971; Shimarayev *et al.,* 1971), on the basis of evidence published from the Franz Josef Islands and Spitsbergen (Dibner, 1957; Harland, 1961, 1969; Dibner and Krylova, 1963; and many others), has been exposed many times since the middle Proterozoic, but it became most effective as a barrier during the Devonian uplift that raised the Lomonosovides and other orogenic zones around and near the present Arctic margins. The Franz Josef sill is broken only between Spitsbergen and Greenland, by the Lena Trough, where a 75-km gap (between the 2,000-m isobaths) may be oceanic (Ostenso, 1968).

Faeroe-Greenland sill—This southernmost sill joins the Faeroe Islands with Greenland via Iceland. Meyerhoff (1970b) presented evidence to show that the sill is at least as old as the Permian, but most earth scientists regard this sill as a Tertiary or Late Cretaceous feature. Hernes (1966) listed the reasons why the Faeroe-Greenland sill is older than the Mid-Atlantic Ridge. The geophysical studies of Pálmason (1965, 1967, 1971) showed that the crust beneath Iceland and the Faeroe-Iceland part of the Faeroe-Greenland sill is anomalous; it resembles crust of a type which is intermediate between oceanic and continental crust. However, more recent studies conducted in 1972 by I. P. Kosminskaya, and interpreted by her and G. B. Udintsev (oral commun. from I. P. Kosminskaya, August 4, 1972; oral commun. from G. B. Udintsev, March 11, 1973), indicate that the structure of the Faeroe-Greenland Ridge, including the entire Iceland Pla-

←〜〜

FIG. 7—Index map of major geologic-tectonic features of Arctic and lands surrounding it. European and North African data compiled with help of Peter Misch. 1 = area where Caledonian rocks are absent and believed to have been removed by erosion; 2 = Lewisian rocks; 3 = area between lines *A* and *B; A* is one possible boundary of Caledonides; *B* is alternate possibility; 4 = Adriatic "spur"—a structural peninsula of African foreland; 5 = western Mediterranean internal massif; 6 = northernmost proved limit of Cape Verde–Canaries belt; northward connections, if any, are unknown. Republished with permission of University of Chicago Press.

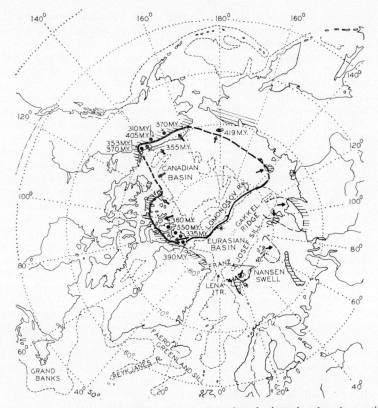

FIG. 8—Lomonosovides (heavy black line) and Late Devonian clastic-wedge deposits continentward from Lomonosovides (diagonal shading = Late Devonian terrestrial debris eroded from Lomonosovides). Arrows show inferred directions of transport of sediments. Compiled from Harland (1961, 1969), Markov *et al.* (1967), Gnibidenko (1968), Rzhonsnitskaya (1968), Churkin (1969), and Trettin (1969). Note general regional uplift of northern rim of Lomonosovides. Sources of dates: 419 m.y., Wrangel I.—Gnibidenko (1968); 317 m.y., Mt. Doonerak (Brooks Range)—Churkin (1969); 310 and 405 m.y., Romanzof Mts.—Churkin (1969); 355 m.y., Mt. Sedgwick, N.W.T.—Churkin (1969); 353 and 370 m.y., Mt. Fitton, N.W.T.—Churkin (1969); 360 m.y., Axel Heiberg I.—Churkin (1969); 335 m.y., Ellesmere I.—Churkin (1969); 390 and 550 m.y., Ellesmere I.—Trettin (1969). Sources of radiometric dates are given in bibliographies of each reference cited here.

teau, is continental, not oceanic. Depths to the Mohorovičić discontinuity range from 28 to 40 km (G. B. Udintsev, oral commun., March 11, 1973). Kosminskaya and Udintsev believe that the sill is a continental mass which extends unbroken from the Faeroe and New Hebrides Islands on the southeast to Greenland on the northwest. This interpretation supports Hernes' (1966) conclusions about the relative age of the sill. A sea-floor-spreading model is thus eliminated in the North Atlantic.

Kosminskaya and Udintsev's interpretation is reinforced by Grønlie and Ramberg's (1970) gravity study of the Norwegian Sea. They showed that the Norwegian Sea–Vøring Plateau is underlain by a minimum of 7 km of sedimentary and layered rocks above Layer 3 —and more likely by 9 to 11 km of sedimen-

tary and layered rocks. This great thickness (Figs. 9, 10) onlaps the Mid-Atlantic Ridge just east of Jan Mayen Island. According to Udintsev (oral commun., March 11, 1973), the crustal structure of the Jan Mayen Ridge between Iceland and Jan Mayen also is typically continental, as is the crustal structure beneath the Vøring Plateau.

Iceland—The geology of Iceland has puzzled most earth scientists who advocate plate tectonics, because its geology is not that predicted by the new global tectonics. In fact, as Tr. Einarsson (1960, 1965) and Th. Einarsson (1967) have shown for many years, Iceland is a 100,000-sq km island which straddles the Mid-Atlantic Ridge and is underlain by numerous northeast- to north-trending anticlines and synclines paralleling the ridge (Fig. 11). The anti-

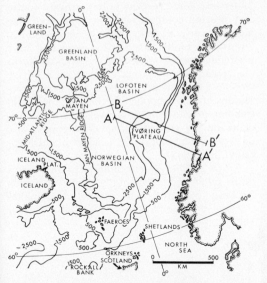

FIG. 9—Index map, North Atlantic Ocean, showing location of two lines of Figure 10 from Grønlie and Ramberg (1970).

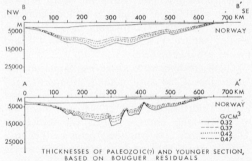

THICKNESSES OF PALEOZOIC(?) AND YOUNGER SECTION, BASED ON BOUGUER RESIDUALS

FIG. 10—West-east gravity profiles A-A' and B-B' (Fig. 9) from Grønlie and Ramberg (1970). Thickness of stratified rocks underlying Vøring Plateau is shown using four assumed density contrasts. Minimum thickness of section in thickest part is 7 km; maximum is 11 km. Note that profiles run to foot of Jan Mayen Ridge, which, according to Kosminskaya and Udintsev (oral commun.; see text), is continental crust. According to Udintsev, Vøring Plateau also is continental or near-continental crust. Implications for sea-floor spreading need no elaboration.

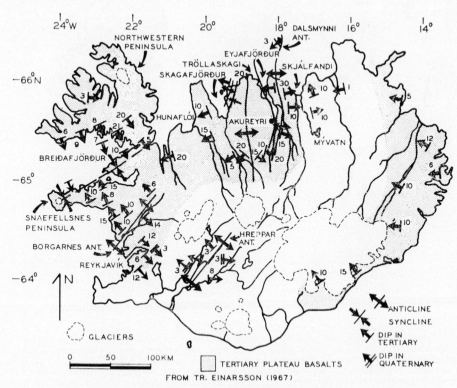

FIG. 11—Structure map of Iceland (from Tr. Einarsson, 1967, and modified by Tr. Einarsson and Meyerhoff, in press).

clines range in length from about 60 to 120 km
and, in width, from about 2 to 60 km. They are
parallel to subparallel, forming an inter-anasto-
mosing pattern. Flank dips range up to 45° and
locally are overturned.

There are numerous strike-slip faults on Iceland. One of the most notable groups of such
faults is in the northern part of the island
where a north-south-striking set of straight 60-
to 80-km-long faults parallels the anticlines.
The anticlines and synclines formed either in a
vertical stress field or in a compressive stress
field. The presence of north-south-striking
wrench faults in association with the northeast-
and north-trending anticlines suggests that the

faults and folds formed in a northwest-south-
east-directed compressive stress field accompanied by vertical uplift. The various so-called
"transform faults" striking east-west that have
been reported in numerous geophysical works
on Iceland simply do not exist; at least, I have
seen no field evidence for their existence in two
seasons of field mapping. In contrast, the north-
trending wrench faults are very much in evidence on the ground, on air photographs, and
on topographic maps (Tr. Einarsson and Meyerhoff, in press).

North polar magnetic map—Figure 12 is a
north polar projection of the globe on which
Archean platforms and magnetic anomalies

FIG. 12—North Polar projection showing Archean shields and magnetic anomalies. This map shows that
magnetic anomalies of ocean basins are traceable onshore where they are approximately concentric about Archean
shields. Magnetic anomalies with very different patterns are present in Archean-shield interiors and are not shown
for sake of clarity. Implications for sea-floor spreading model are serious, because no current model of sea-floor
spreading explains geometric relations between Archean shields and magnetic anomalies shown on this figure.
Onshore projections are based mainly on Karasik *et al.* (1971), Solov'yev (1971), and Riddihough (1972). A
total of 39 references was used to compile figure. References used are given in Meyerhoff *et al.* (1972, p. 678).

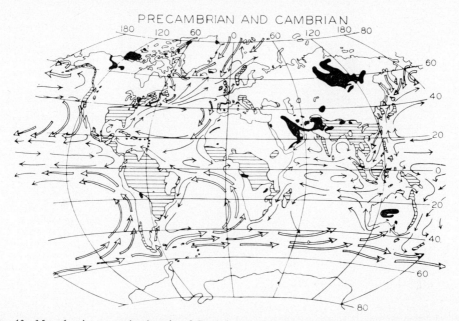

PRECAMBRIAN AND CAMBRIAN

FIG. 13—Map showing evaporite deposits of Cambrian and Vendian (late Proterozoic). Some Riphean (early to middle Proterozoic) localities are included. Most evaporite is late Vendian and Early Cambrian. Symbols are explained in caption for Figure 2. Modified from Meyerhoff (1970a). Republished with permission of University of Chicago Press.

have been plotted. This map, first published by Meyerhoff *et al.* (1972, p. 678), is a very critical illustration for interpreting the significance of the magnetic anomalies. The important points are that (1) the magnetic anomalies strike onshore into the continents and (2) they are approximately concentric about Archean continental nuclei. These facts suggest that the anomalies are unrelated to sea-floor spreading and that the Archean nuclei have held approximately the same positions with respect to one another since Archean time.

In my opinion, this map destroys modern concepts of plate tectonics. Dating of various anomaly sources on land shows that most of them are mafic to ultramafic rocks of Proterozoic and Paleozoic ages (Karasik *et al.*, 1971; Solov'yev, 1971). The possibility that similar ages are equally valid for the oceans is supported by several Proterozoic dates found in the ocean basins. One of these, described by Wanless *et al.* (1968), is at "Bald Mountain," just west of the central rift area at 45°N lat. There, the dated rocks range in age from 787 m.y. to 1,690 m.y. Much farther south, west of the Mid-Atlantic Ridge crest at the equator, Melson *et al.* (1971) dated St. Paul's rocks at 835 m.y. Paleozoic trilobite localities also are

known from the flanks of the Mid-Atlantic Ridge (Furon, 1949). All ancient rock localities known to me are summarized by Meyerhoff and Meyerhoff (1972) and by H. A. Meyerhoff (1972). The increasing number of ancient dates that are being found seems to reduce considerably the likelihood that the oceans are geologically young. Even the evidence in Iceland is against drift, where the oldest dated rocks from near the central rift are late Miocene (Tr. Einarsson and Meyerhoff, in press).

Patterns of evaporite deposition—Figures 13 and 14 show high-latitude evaporite distribution for late Proterozoic–Cambrian and Devonian times, respectively. Both were evaporite-maximum periods. The principal point of these figures is to demonstrate the effectiveness of the Lomonosov Ridge as a sill from at least late Proterozoic time onward. All evaporites deposited in the Arctic are on the Atlantic side and south of the Lomonosov Ridge and its continental extensions into Siberia and Canada. There are no evaporites inside the Lomonosovides—*i.e.*, on the Pacific side of the Lomonosov Ridge.

After Devonian time, the Franz Josef sill was an effective barrier to the flow of the warm saline water of the Gulf Stream–North Atlan-

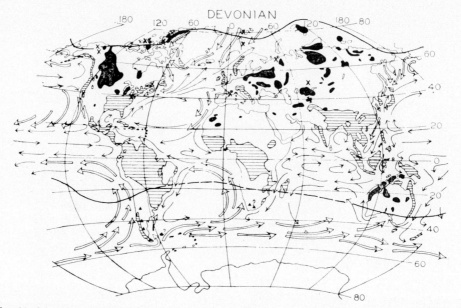

Fig. 14—Map showing Devonian evaporite, coal, and tillite deposits. Symbols are same as for Figure 3. Modified from Meyerhoff (1970a). Republished with permission of University of Chicago Press.

tic Drift into the Arctic Ocean. Almost all evaporite deposition in Europe and North America after Devonian time was south of the Franz Josef sill (Figs. 2, 3). After Permian time, there was almost no evaporite deposition north of the Faeroe-Greenland sill. This fact is the basis for my statement (Meyerhoff, 1970b) that the Faeroe-Greenland sill is at least as old as the Late Permian. If Kosminskaya and Udintsev's new seismic interpretations are correct and the Faeroe-Greenland sill is continental, then it probably predates the Permian and may be Precambrian.

Hamilton's hypothesis—A warm climate and a plentiful supply of saline water are the principal requirements for circum-Arctic evaporite deposition. Conceivably, if sea-floor spreading has taken place, there could have been other entrances to the Arctic. The Bering-Chukotsk shelf area is eliminated. Therefore, it is necessary to examine Hamilton's (1970) hypothesis that the Siberian and European continents were propelled toward one another during late Precambrian and Paleozoic times and collided in Permian and Triassic times. If this hypothesis is correct, the ocean basin supposedly separating the European and Asian continents would have been a logical entryway to the Arctic.

Hamilton's hypothesis is beset by serious difficulties. He ignored the significance of the Lomonosovides, which Churkin (1969) had al-

ready described; moreover, he ignored the pattern of evaporite distribution in the East Greenland area, as well as in the Canadian Arctic Archipelago (which is outside the Lomonosovides) and in Spitsbergen, Pechora, Siberia, and neighboring areas. Even if these facts somehow could be reconciled, the unexplained fact remains that certain structures and rock formations of the Timan region west of the Urals continue beneath the Urals and reappear under the West Siberian basin *east* of the Urals (Dedeyev *et al.,* 1962; Gafarov, 1970). This fact alone eliminates Hamilton's hypothesis from further consideration.

However, one additional point should be noted. Tamrazyan (1964, 1971) recognized the essential continuity of the Russian and Siberian platforms and postulated that they have drifted apart—not together. Ironically, he used many of the same data as Hamilton to arrive at an opposite conclusion. Tamrazyan also had the advantage of having worked personally on the terrane.

Churkin's hypothesis—Churkin postulated that the region between the Verkhoyansk Range (Fig. 6) on the west and the Cherskiy Range, just east of the Verkhoyansk Range, is a Jurassic–Early Cretaceous geosuture along which the Eurasian and North American plates collided. The area is located where waters from the Pacific could enter into the Eurasian basin, on the Atlantic side of the Lomonosov Ridge. However, Churkin's hypothesis also is contradicted by the presence of evaporites along East Greenland, in Spitsbergen, and in the Pechora region. Churkin leaves open the question of the circular, undisplaced Lomonosovides. He apparently was unaware of the study by Tuchkov *et al.* (1968), who published several paleogeographic maps of the northeastern USSR showing the continuity of rock formations from the Verkhoyansk into the Cherskiy Range from Devonian time through the Cretaceous.

An even more difficult problem for Churkin's hypothesis is that of mechanics. The Americas plate allegedly is separating from the Eurasian plate along the Mid-Atlantic and Gakkel Ridges. Yet the Gakkel epicenter belt continues into the region between the Verkhoyansk and Cherskiy Ranges. The conclusion is that an extensional zone (Gakkel Ridge) is transformed into a compressional zone as the epicenter belt passes onto the Eurasian mainland from the Gakkel Ridge. Furthermore, the implication of Churkin's scheme is that the Eurasian plate is colliding with the North American plate as it tears away from it in the Atlantic and the Arctic. How can a so-called "rising" mantle create new crust along one part of an epicenter belt, yet subduct the crust in northeastern Siberia, farther along the same epicenter belt?

Fixist Model

That the North Atlantic and Arctic Oceans have been in their present positions since middle Proterozoic or earlier time is indicated by the following: (1) dissimilar geosynclines which (in plate-tectonic theory) would have to have been adjacent to one another, (2) the circular Lomonosovides, (3) the absence of evaporites within the Canadian basin area, (4) the evidence that most epeiric sea invasions of Eurasia and Canada came from the region of the present Arctic, (5) the distribution of late Proterozoic and younger evaporites on the Atlantic and southern sides of the Lomonosovides, (6) the fact that Europe nearly touches Greenland across the Lena Trough, (7) the extension of continental crust from the Faeroe Islands to Greenland, (8) the faunal continuity from Asia to Canada and Alaska, (9) the faunal discontinuity between Europe and North America (Mamet and Belford, 1968; Meyerhoff and Meyerhoff, 1972; Teichert and Meyerhoff, 1972), (10) the presence of evaporites along the shores of the North Atlantic (evaporites of the same ages as those in northern Canada and northern Eurasia), (11) the evidence for compressional structures in Iceland, (12) the thick blanket of bedded rocks from the Jan Mayen Ridge to Norway, (13) the landward extension of the oceanic magnetic anomalies, and (14) the increasing discoveries of Proterozoic rocks in the ocean basins. No other tectonic model of the Arctic explains all of these very large-scale phenomena. I conclude that a fixist model, modified repeatedly by vertical and compressional tectonics, most completely explains the geology of the North Atlantic and Arctic regions.

ECONOMIC SIGNIFICANCE OF EVAPORITE MAXIMA AND MINIMA

The economic importance of the concept of changing world climates cannot be overemphasized. For example, the Mississippian Period (Fig. 4) was a time of widespread deposition of commercial coal deposits; in contrast, economic Triassic coals are scarce and are found mainly near the polar regions (Fig. 3). Another interesting facet of the Triassic evaporite maximum is the concentration of major petroleum deposits of that period in high southern and northern latitudes (Fig. 15). Triassic oil and gas deposits are known in lower latitudes—as, for example, in the Dnepr-Donets graben of the southern Ukraine, in local deposits of the southern Volga-Urals district and the Emba salt basin around the northern part of the Caspian Sea, and in similar local deposits in the western United States (Vasil'yev, 1968a, b; Cram, 1971). It is true that North Rankin, offshore from the northern part of Western Australia (Anonymous, 1972a, b; Challinor *et al.*, 1972; Martison *et al.*, 1973), has reserves of 5.0 to 10.5 trillion cu ft of natural gas and 1.5–4.0 million bbl of condensate in Late Triassic sandstone. However, there is no assurance that the hydrocarbons originated in rocks of the same age as the reservoir. Another apparent exception may be Hassi R'Mel in Algeria, which has proved reserves of 35 trillion cu ft of natural gas and 1.4 billion bbl of condensate (Halbouty *et al.*, 1970; Magloire, 1970). Almost all geologists familiar with Hassi R'Mel agree that the reservoir is Permo-Triassic sandstone, probably Triassic. However, these same geologists maintain that the source of the hydrocarbons is the underlying marine Paleozoic.

Therefore, Figure 15 shows the location of indigenous Triassic oil and gas field areas. From west to east, the Northern Hemisphere

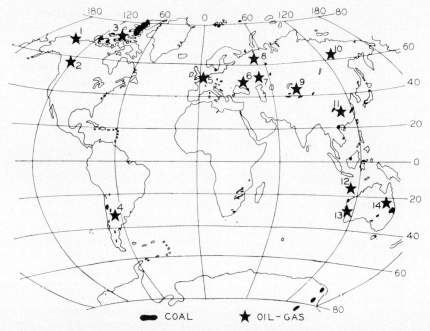

FIG. 15—Triassic oil, gas, and coal deposits. Note their concentration in high northern and southern latitudes. Median position is at about present-day 20°N lat., or close to present meteorologic (heat) equator. This fact also suggests that Triassic distribution of continents and ocean basins was about the same as that today. Compiled from Vasil'yev (1968a, b), Douglas (1970), Meyerhoff (1970c), Halbouty et al. (1970), Anonymous (1972a, b), Challinor et al. (1972), and Martison et al. (1973). 1 = Prudhoe Bay area, Alaska; 2 = production from Baldonnel and Halfway Formations, British Columbia, and Halfway, Montney, and Charlie Lake Formations, Alberta; 3 = Ellef Ringnes, Kristoffer Bay, Dome Bay, etc. (Heiberg production), of Canadian Arctic Archipelago; 4 = Mendoza Province fields, Argentina; 5 = North Sea; 6 = Dnepr-Donets graben, USSR; 7 = Emba salt basin and southern Volga-Urals district, USSR; 8 = Pechora basin, USSR; 9 = Dzungaria basin, Sinkiang, China; 10 = Vilyuy basin, eastern Siberia, USSR; 11 = Szechwan basin, China; 12 = North Rankin, offshore shelf, Australia; 13 = Dongara, Perth basin, Australia; 14 = Cooper basin and Moonie areas, eastern Australia. Republished with permission of Canadian Society of Petroleum Geologists.

productive areas are the Prudhoe Bay field of Alaska, the Canadian Arctic Islands (King Christian, Kristoffer Bay, etc.), Pechora basin (northern European Russia), Vilyuy basin (north-central Siberia), Dzungaria basin (northwestern China), and Szechwan basin (east-central China). In the Southern Hemisphere, sizable Triassic fields are found in Mendoza Province (western Argentina), Western Australia (Dongara), and possibly elsewhere in Australia. The fact that the Southern Hemisphere fields are closer to the equator than the Northern Hemisphere fields is related, in my opinion, to the northward offset of the earth's heat equator (Meyerhoff, 1970a, b; Meyerhoff and Teichert, 1971; Meyerhoff and Harding, 1971) and to the deflection of the Gulf Stream–North Atlantic Drift into the Arctic Ocean. In fact, the distribution of the fields suggests that the ocean basin–continent distribution in Triassic time had to be nearly the

same as it is now. This conclusion also is supported strongly by the distribution of vertebrate faunas of the Triassic (Meyerhoff and Meyerhoff, 1972, p. 292).

The principal economic lesson to be learned from this study is that the most favorable giant petroleum and coal accumulations of a particular age are related to the configuration of the climatic zone during that age. Therefore, a thorough understanding of evaporite maxima and minima, and of global climatic history, is prerequisite to intelligent exploration for fossil-fuel reserves. These statements apply not only to petroleum and coal, but also to tar sand and oil shale.

CONCLUSIONS

The Arctic Ocean is a mediterranean-like extension of the Atlantic Ocean. Both the North Atlantic and the Arctic have had their present positions and width since middle Proterozoic or earlier time. The geological and geophysical data support this interpretation and rule out sea-floor spreading and plate tectonics in the North Atlantic–Arctic area since middle Proterozoic time. The magnetic data (Fig. 12) seem to preclude drift since late Archean or very early Proterozoic time. The tectonic model published by Meyerhoff *et al.* (1972) seems to fit all the facts presented here; the new-global-tectonics model and its many variants do not. The Meyerhoff *et al.* (1972) model may *not* eliminate continental drift during Archean time when the earth was cooling. In fact, as pointed out by de Sitter (1956) and Jeffreys (1970), some type of convective phenomenon must have characterized the earth's early cooling history, and it is only by such early convection and placing of continental nuclei that the antipodal relations between continental and oceanic crust, as well as many other global phenomena, can be explained.

REFERENCES CITED

Anonymous, 1972a, Gas strikes rekindle Aussie shelf: Oil and Gas Jour., v. 70, no. 5 (Jan. 31), p. 54–55.
——— 1972b, Les réserves australiennes de gaz: Paris, Pétrole Informations, no. 1256 (Dec. 22), p. 75.
Beloussov, V. V., 1962, Basic problems in geotectonics: New York, McGraw-Hill Book Co., 816 p.
Billings, D. E., 1968, Note on solar variability and climatic change, *in* J. M. Mitchell, Jr., ed., Causes of climatic change: Am. Meteorological Soc., Meteorological Mon., v. 8, no. 30, p. 144–145.
Bloch, M. R., 1964, Die Beeinflussung der Albedo von Eisflächen durch Staub und ihre Wirkung auf Ozeanhöhe und Klima: Geol. Rundschau, Band 54, Heft 1, p. 515–522.
Bogdanov, N. A., and S. M. Til'man, 1964, Obshchiye chertiy razkhitiya paleozoyskikh struktur ostrova Vrangelya i zapadnoy chasti khrebta Bruksa (Alyaska, *in* M. V. Muratov, ed., Soveshchaniye po problemi tektoniki, Moskva, 1963, Skladchatye oblasti Eurazii, materialy: Moscow, Izd. "Nauka," p. 219–230.
Bok, B. J., and P. F. Bok, 1957, The Milky Way: Cambridge, Mass., Harvard Univ. Press, 269 p.
Broecker, W. S., 1968, In defense of the astronomical theory of glaciation, *in* J. M. Mitchell, Jr., ed., Causes of climatic change: Am. Meteorological Soc., Meteorological Mon., v. 8, no. 30, p. 139–141.
Brooks, C. E. P., 1926, Climate through the ages: New Haven, Conn., Yale Univ. Press, 439 p.
——— 1949, Climate through the ages, revised ed.: New York, McGraw-Hill Book Co., 395 p.
Busson, G., 1968, La sédimentation des évaporites: Paris, Muséum Natl. d'Histoire Naturelle, n.s., sér. C, t. 19, fasc. 3, p. 125–169.
Callomon, J. H., D. T. Donovan, and R. Trümpy, 1972, An annotated map of the Permian and Mesozoic formations of East Greenland: Copenhagen, Medd. om Grønland, v. 168, no. 3, 35 p.
Carey, S. W., 1958, The tectonic approach to continental drift, *in* S. W. Carey, ed., Continental drift, a symposium: Hobart, Univ. Tasmania, p. 177–355.

Challinor, A., *et al.*, 1972, Seismic work paid off well on northwest Australia's shelf: Oil and Gas Jour., v. 70, no. 38 (Sept. 18), p. 146–148.
Churkin, M., Jr., 1969, Paleozoic tectonic history of the Arctic basin north of Alaska: Science, v. 165, no. 3893, p. 549–555.
——— 1972, Western boundary of the North American continental plate in Asia: Geol. Soc. America Bull., v. 83, no. 4, p. 1022–1036.
Cram, I. H., ed., 1971, Future petroleum provinces of the United States—their geology and potential: Am. Assoc. Petroleum Geologists Mem. 15, 1496 p.
Damon, P. E., 1968, The relationship between terrestrial factors and climate, *in* J. M. Mitchell, Jr., ed., Causes of climatic change: Am. Meteorological Soc., Meteorological Mon., v. 8, no. 30, p. 106–111.
Dedeyev, V. A., *et al.*, 1962, Stroyeniye dosredney yuroskogo fundamenta Zapadno-Sibirskoy nizmennosti v svete novykh dannykh (Structure of the pre-Middle Jurassic basement of the West Siberian Lowland in the light of new data): Sovetskaya Geologiya, no. 7, p. 26–40 (Engl. transl. by Am. Geol. Inst., 1964, Internat. Geology Rev., v. 6, no. 2, p. 277–286).
Demenitskaya, R. M., *et al.*, 1968, The transition zones between the Eurasian continent and the Arctic Ocean: Canadian Jour. Earth Sci., v. 5, no. 4, pt. 2, p. 1125–1129.
de Sitter, L. U., 1956, Structural geology, 1st ed.: New York, McGraw-Hill Book Co., 552 p.
Dibner, V. D., 1957, Geologicheskoye stroyeniye zemli Frantsa Iosifa. Geologicheskoye stroyeniye ostrova Viktoriya, *in* F. G. Markov and D. V. Nalivkin, eds., Geologiya sovetskoy Arktiki: Leningrad, Nauchno-Issled. Inst. Geologii Arktiki Trudy, v. 81, 520 p.
——— and N. M. Krylova, 1963, Stratigraficheskoye polozheniye i veshchestvennyy sostav uglenosynkh otlozheniy i ugol'nykh plastov na ostrovakh zemli Frantsa Iosifa (Stratigraphic composition and material composition of coal measures in Franz Josef Islands): Sovetskaya Geologiya, no. 7, p. 77–89 (Engl. transl. by Am. Geol. Inst., 1965, Internat. Geology Rev., v. 7, no. 6, p. 1030–1038).
Donn, W. L., 1967, Causes of the ice ages: Sky and Telescope, v. 33, no. 4, p. 3–7.
——— and M. Ewing, 1968, The theory of an ice-free Arctic Ocean, *in* J. M. Mitchell, Jr., ed., Causes of climatic change: Am. Meteorological Soc., Meteorological Mon., v. 8, no. 30, p. 100–105.
Douglas, R. J. W., ed., 1970, Geology and economic minerals of Canada, 5th ed.: Canada Geol. Survey, Economic Geology Rept. No. 1, 838 p.
Eardley, A. J., 1948, Ancient Arctica: Jour. Geology, v. 56, no. 5, p. 409–436.
——— 1961, History of geologic thought on the origin of the Arctic basin, *in* G. O. Raasch, ed., Geology of the Arctic: Univ. Toronto Press, v. 1, p. 607–621.
Einarsson, Th., 1967, The extent of the Tertiary basalt formation and the structure of Iceland, *in* S. Björnsson, ed., Iceland and mid-ocean ridges: Soc. Sci. Islandica, v. 38, p. 170–177.
Einarsson, Tr., 1960, The plateau basalt areas in Iceland, *in* J. Askelsson *et al.*, eds., On the geology and geophysics of Iceland: Norden, 21st Internat. Geol. Congress, 1960, Guide to Excursion no. H-2, p. 5–20.
——— 1965, Remarks on crustal structure in Iceland: Royal Astron. Jour., Geophys. Jour., v. 10, no. 3, p. 283–288.
——— 1967, Early history of the Scandic area and

some chapters on the geology of Iceland, *in* S. Björnsson, ed., Iceland and mid-ocean ridges: Soc. Sci. Islandica, v. 38, p. 13–28.

—— and A. A. Meyerhoff, in press, Continental drift, VI: tectonic features of Iceland: Jour. Geology.

Emelyanov, E. M., *et al.,* 1971, The geology of the Barents Sea, *in* F. M. Delany, ed., The geology of the East Atlantic continental margin, 2, Europe: London, Natural Environment Research Council, Inst. Geol. Sci., Rept. No. 70/14, ICSU/SCOR Working Party 31 Symposium, p. 1–15.

Ewing, M., 1964, Comments on the theory of glaciation, *in* A. E. M. Nairn, ed., Problems in Palaeoclimatology: London, Interscience Publishers, p. 348–353.

—— 1971, The late Cenozoic history of the Atlantic basin and its bearing on the cause of the ice ages, *in* K. K. Turekian, ed., The late Cenozoic glacial ages: New Haven, Conn., Yale Univ. Press, p. 565–573.

Fairbridge, R. W., 1961, Convergence of evidence on climatic change and ice ages: New York Acad. Sci., v. 95, art. 1, p. 542–579.

Flohn, H., 1964, Grundfragen der Paläoklimatologie im Lichte einer theoretischen Klimatologie: Geol. Rundschau, Band 54, Heft 1, p. 504–515.

Fuller, J. G. C. M., and J. W. Porter, 1969, Evaporite formations with petroleum reservoirs in Devonian and Mississippian of Alberta, Saskatchewan, and North Dakota: Am. Assoc. Petroleum Geologists Bull., v. 53, no. 4, p. 909–926.

Furon, R., 1949, Sur les trilobites dragués à 4255 m de profondeur par le Talisman (1883): Acad. Sci. Paris, t. 228, no. 19, p. 1509–1510.

Gafarov, R. A., 1970, O glubinnom stroyenii fundamenta v zone sochleneniya Vostochno-Yevropeyskoy platformy i Urala (Abyssal structures of the basement in zone of articulation of the East European platform with the Urals): Akad. Nauk SSSR Izv. Ser. Geol., no. 8, p. 3–14 (Engl. transl. by Am. Geol. Inst., 1971, Internat. Geology Rev., v. 13, no. 4, p. 520–529.

Glushkov, A. P., 1968, Skladchatye oblasti Severo-Vostoka, proterozoy, p. 214–215, *in* A. I. Zhamoyda, ed., Geologicheskoye stroyeniye SSSR, t. 1, Stratigrafiya: Moscow, Izd. "Nedra," 711 p.

Gnibidenko, G. S., 1968, Novyye dannyye po stratigrafii paleozoya ostrova Vrangelya (More information on the Paleozoic stratigraphy of Wrangel Island): Akad. Nauk SSSR Doklady, v. 179, no. 2, p. 407–409 (Engl. transl. by Am. Geol. Inst., 1968, Acad. Sci. USSR Doklady, v. 179, p. 37–39).

Grantz, A., 1969, Strike-slip faults in Alaska (abs.): Geol. Soc. America Spec. Paper 121, p. 117.

Grønlie, G., and I. B. Ramberg, 1970, Gravity indications of deep sedimentary basins below the Norwegian continental shelf and the Vøring Plateau: Norsk Geol. Tidsskr., v. 50, p. 375–391.

Halbouty, M. T., *et al.,* 1970, World's giant oil and gas fields, geologic factors affecting their formation, and basin classification, *in* M. T. Halbouty, ed., Geology of giant petroleum fields: Am. Assoc. Petroleum Geologists Mem. 14, p. 502–555.

Haller, J., 1971, Tectonic map of East Greenland (1:500,000): Copenhagen, Medd. om Grønland, Bind 171, nr. 5, 286 p.

Hamilton, W., 1970, The Uralides and the motion of the Russian and Siberian platforms: Geol. Soc. America Bull., v. 81, no. 9, p. 2553–2576.

Hammen, T. van der, 1964, Paläoklima, stratigraphie

und evolution: Geol. Rundschau, Band 54, Heft 1, p. 428–441.

Harland, W. B., 1961, An outline structural history of Spitsbergen, *in* G. O. Raasch, ed., Geology of the Arctic: Univ. Toronto Press, v. 1, p. 68–132.

—— 1969, Contribution of Spitsbergen to understanding of tectonic evolution of North Atlantic region, *in* Marshall Kay, ed., North Atlantic—geology and continental drift: Am. Assoc. Petroleum Geologists Mem. 12, p. 817–852.

—— and R. A. Gayer, 1972, The Arctic Caledonides and earlier oceans: Geol. Magazine, v. 109, no. 4, p. 289–314.

Hatfield, C. B., and M. J. Camp, 1970, Mass extinctions correlated with periodic galactic events: Geol. Soc. America Bull., v. 81, no. 3, p. 911–914.

Hernes, I., 1966, History of the Atlantic Ocean and the Scandinavian Caledonian chain: Nature, v. 212, no. 5065, p. 911–912.

Holser, W. T., and I. R. Kaplan, 1966, Isotope geochemistry of sedimentary sulfates: Chem. Geology, v. 1, no. 2, p. 93–135.

Holtedahl, O., ed., 1960, Geology of Norway: Oslo, Norges Geologiske Undersøkelse, 540 p.

Irving, E., 1964, Paleomagnetism and its application to geological and geophysical problems: New York, John Wiley and Sons, 399 p.

Jeffreys, H., 1970, The earth, 5th ed.: Cambridge Univ. Press, 525 p.

Johnson, G. L., and B. C. Heezen, 1967, Morphology and evolution of the Norwegian-Greenland Sea: Deep-Sea Research, v. 14, p. 755–771.

Karasik, A. M., *et al.,* 1971, Nekotorye osobennosti glubinnogo stroyeniya i proiskhozhdeniya khrebta Lomonosova po aeromagnitnym dannym, *in* R. M. Demenitskaya *et al.,* eds., Geofizicheskiye metody razvedki v Arktike (sbornik statey), vyp. 6: Leningrad, Nauchno-Issled. Inst. Geologii Arktiki, p. 9–19.

Karpyshev, V. S., 1965, O vzaimootnoshenii mezhdu galogenno-karbonatnoy i krasnosvetnoy formatsiyami kembriya v zapadnoy chasti Irkutskogo amfiteatra (Relationship between the halite-carbonate and Cambrian redbed formations in the western part of the Irkutsk amphitheater): Akad. Nauk SSSR Doklady, v. 160, no. 2, p. 425–428 (Engl. transl. by Am. Geol. Inst., 1965, Acad. Sci. USSR Doklady, v. 160, p. 10–12).

King, E. R., I. Zietz, and L. R. Alldredge, 1966, Magnetic data on the structure of the central Arctic region: Geol. Soc. America Bull., v. 77, no. 6, p. 619–646.

King, P. B., comp., 1969, Tectonic map of North America: U.S. Geological Survey, 2 sheets, scale, 1: 5,000,000.

King, R. H., 1947, Sedimentation in the Permian Castile Sea: Am. Assoc. Petroleum Geologists Bull., v. 31, no. 3, p. 470–477.

Klingspor, A. M., 1969, Middle Devonian Muskeg evaporites of Western Canada: Am. Assoc. Petroleum Geologists Bull., v. 53, no. 4, p. 927–948.

Komar, V. A., and M. A. Semikhatov, 1965, K geologicheskoy istorii Sibirskoy platformy v pozdnem dokembrii (Geologic history of the Siberian platform in the late Precambrian): Akad. Nauk SSSR Doklady, v. 161, no. 2, p. 421–424 (Engl. transl. by Am. Geol. Inst., 1965, Acad. Sci. USSR Doklady, v. 161, p. 42–45).

Krylova, A. K., *et al.,* 1967, Devonian of the Siberian platform, *in* D. H. Oswald, ed., International symposium on the Devonian System: Calgary, Alberta Soc. Petroleum Geologists, v. 1, p. 473–482.

Lamb, H. H., 1964, The role of atmosphere and oceans in relation to climatic changes and the growth of ice-sheets on land, in A. E. M. Nairn, ed., Problems in palaeoclimatology: London, Interscience Publishers, p. 332–348.

Magloire, P. R., 1970, Triassic gas field of Hassi er R'Mel, Algeria, in M. T. Halbouty, ed., Geology of giant petroleum fields: Am. Assoc. Petroleum Geologists Mem. 14, p. 489–501.

Mamet, B. L., 1970, Carbonate microfacies of the Windsor Group (Carboniferous), Nova Scotia and New Brunswick: Canada Geol. Survey Paper 70–21, 121 p.

——— 1972, Un essai de reconstitution paléoclimatique basé sur les microflores algaires du Viséen: Montréal, 24th Internat. Geol. Cong., 1972, sec. 7, p. 282–291.

——— and D. J. Belford, 1968, Carboniferous Foraminifera, Bonaparte Gulf basin, northwestern Australia: Micropaleontology, v. 14, no. 3, p. 339–347.

Markov, F. G., S. V. Cherkesova, and I. S. Gramberg, 1967, Devonian of the Soviet Arctic, in D. H. Oswald, ed., International symposium on the Devonian System: Calgary, Alberta Soc. Petroleum Geologists, v. 1, p. 503–515.

Martison, N. W., D. R. McDonald, and P. Kaye, 1973, Exploration on continental shelf off northwest Australia: Am. Assoc. Petroleum Geologists Bull., v. 57, no. 6, p. 972–989.

McLeod, I. R., 1964, The saline lakes of the Vestfold Hills, Princess Elizabeth Land, in R. J. Adie, ed., Antarctic geology: Amsterdam, North-Holland Publishing Co., p. 65–72.

Melson, W. G., S. R. Hart, and G. Thompson, 1971, St. Paul's Rocks, equatorial Atlantic: petrogenesis, radiometric ages, and implications on sea-floor spreading: Woods Hole Oceanographic Inst. Tech. Rept., ref. no. 71–20, 38 p. (reprinted in Geol. Soc. America Mem. 132, Hess Volume).

Menard, H. W., 1967, Transitional types of crust under small ocean basins: Jour. Geophys. Research, v. 72, no. 12, p. 3061–3073.

Menner, V. V., 1965, O raspredelenii evaporitov v srednepaleozoyskikh otlozheniy severnoy Sibiri (Distribution of evaporites in the middle Paleozoic of northern Siberia): Akad. Nauk SSSR Doklady, v. 161, no. 3, p. 666–669 (Engl. transl. by Am. Geol. Inst., 1965, Acad. Sci. USSR Doklady, v. 161, p. 52–65).

Meyerhoff, A. A., 1970a, Continental drift: implications of paleomagnetic studies, meteorology, physical oceanography, and climatology: Jour. Geology, v. 78, no. 1, p. 1–51.

——— 1970b, Continental drift, II: high-latitude evaporite deposits and geologic history of Arctic and North Atlantic Oceans: Jour. Geology, v. 78, no. 4, p. 406–444.

——— 1970c, Developments in Mainland China, 1949–1968: Am. Assoc. Petroleum Geologists Bull., v. 54, no. 8, p. 1567–1580.

——— 1973, Mass biotal extinctions, world climate changes, and galactic motions: possible interrelations, in A. Logan and L. V. Hill, eds., The Permian and Triassic Systems and their mutual boundary: Calgary, Canadian Soc. Petroleum Geologists Spec. Pub. 2, p. 745–758.

——— and J. L. Harding, 1971, Some problems in current concepts of continental drift: Tectonophysics, v. 12, no. 3, p. 235–260.

——— and H. A. Meyerhoff, 1972, "The new global tectonics": major inconsistencies: Am. Assoc. Petroleum Geologists Bull., v. 56, no. 2, p. 269–336.

——— and C. Teichert, 1971, Continental drift, III: late Paleozoic glacial centers and Devonian-Eocene coal distribution: Jour. Geology, v. 79, no. 3, p. 285–321.

——— H. A. Meyerhoff, and R. S. Briggs, Jr., 1972, Continental drift, V: proposed hypothesis of earth tectonics: Jour. Geology, v. 80, no. 6, p. 663–692.

Meyerhoff, H. A., 1972, "The new global tectonics": major inconsistencies (reply): Am. Assoc. Petroleum Geologists Bull., v. 56, no. 11, p. 2294–2295.

Mitchell, J. M., Jr., 1968, Concluding remarks, in J. M. Mitchell, Jr., ed., Causes of climatic change: Am. Meteorological Soc., Meteorological Mon., v. 8, no. 30, p. 155–159.

Newell, N. D., 1967, Revolutions in the history of life, in C. L. Albritton et al., eds., Uniformity and simplicity: Geol. Soc. America Spec. Paper 89, p. 63–91.

Nikolaev, A. A., 1959, Nord-est, p. 275–276, in Système ordovicien; p. 318–320, in Système silurien; and p. 392–395 in Système devonien, in N. K. Ovechkin, ed., Structure géologique de l'U.R.S.S., t. 1, Stratigraphie, fasc. 3, Paléozoique: Paris, Centre Natl. Recherche Sci., p. 185–503.

Ostenso, N. A., 1962, Geophysical investigations of the Arctic Ocean basin: Wisconsin Univ. Geophys. and Polar Research Center Rept. 62–4, 124 p.

——— 1968, Geophysical studies in the Greenland Sea: Geol. Soc. America Bull., v. 79, no. 1, p. 107–131.

Pálmason, G., 1965, Seismic refraction measurements of the basalt lavas of the Faeroe Islands: Tectonophysics, v. 2, no. 6, p. 475–482.

——— 1967, Upper crustal structure in Iceland, in S. Björnsson, ed., Iceland and mid-ocean ridges: Reykjavík, Soc. Sci. Islandica, v. 38, p. 67–79.

——— 1971, Crustal structure of Iceland from explosion seismology: Reykjavík, Soc. Sci. Islandica, v. 40, 187 p.

Pisarchik, Ya. K., M. A. Minayeva, and G. A. Rusetskaya, 1968, Paleogeograficheskaya kharakteristika Sibirskoy platformy v kembriyskoye vremya, in A. K. Bobrov et al., eds., Geologicheskoye stroyeniye i neftegazonosnost' vostochnoy chasti Sibirskoy platformy i prilegayushchikh rayonov: Moscow, Izd. "Nedra," p. 81–90.

Riddihough, R. P., 1972, Regional magnetic anomalies and geology in Fennoscandia: a discussion: Canadian Jour. Earth Sci., v. 9, no. 3, p. 219–232.

Rzhonsnitskaya, M. A., 1968, Kratkaya kharakteristika paleogeografii i paleobiogeografii, p. 358–362, in A. I. Zhamoyda, ed., Geologicheskoye stroyeniye SSSR, v. 1, Stratigrafiya: Moscow, Izd. "Nedra," 711 p.

Schindewolf, H., 1963, Neokatastrophismus?: Zeitschr. Deutsch. Geol. Gesell., Jahrg. 1962, Band 114, Heft 2, p. 430–445.

Schove, D. J., 1964, Solar cycles and equatorial climates: Geol. Rundschau, Band 54, Heft 1, p. 448–477.

Scruton, P. C., 1953, Deposition of evaporites: Am. Assoc. Petroleum Geologists Bull., v. 37, no. 11, p. 2498–2512.

Shatsky, N. S., ed., 1935, Geologiya i poleznye iskopayemyi severa SSSR: Moscow, Geologorazvedochnaya Konferentisiya, I, Trudy, t. 1, p. 149–168.

Shepard, F. P., 1973, Submarine geology, 3d ed.: New York, Harper and Row, 517 p.

Shimarayev, V. N., *et al.*, 1971, Vyyavleniye osobennostey glubinnogo stroyeniya yugo-vostochnoy chasti Barentseva morya po aeromagnitnym dannym, *in* R. M. Demenitskaya *et al.*, eds., Geofizicheskiye metody razvedki v Arktike (sbornik statey), vyp. 6: Leningrad, Ministerstva Geologii SSSR, Nauchno-Issled. Inst. Geologii Arktiki, p. 51–54.

Smirnov, A. M., 1968, Role of the Precambrian basement in structural evolution of the Pacific mobile belt (particularly its north-western section), *in* M. Minato *et al.*, eds., Pacific geology—1: Tokyo, Tsujika Shokan Publishing Co., p. 145–165.

Solov'yev, N. M., ed., 1971, Karta anomal'nogo magnitnogo polya territorii SSSR: Moscow, Vses. Nauchno-Issled. Geol. Inst. (VSEGEI), scale, 1: 10,000,000.

Spizharskiy, T. N., ed., 1967, Tektonicheskaya karta SSSR, 1966: Vses. Nauchno-Issled. Geol. Inst. (VSEGEI), 2 sheets and legend sheet, scale 1: 7,500,000.

—— ed., 1968, Geologicheskoye stroyeniye SSSR, t. 2, Tektonika: Moscow, Izd. "Nedra," 535 p.

Steiner, J., 1967, The sequence of geological events and the dynamics of the Milky Way galaxy—the present cosmic year: a preliminary study: Geol. Soc. Australia Jour., v. 14, p. 99–131.

Suess, H. E., 1968, Climatic changes, solar activity, and the cosmic-ray production rate of natural radiocarbon, *in* J. M. Mitchell, Jr., ed., Causes of climatic change: Am. Meteorological Soc., Meteorological Mon., v. 8, no. 30, p. 146–150.

Tailleur, I. L., 1969, Speculations on North Slope geology: Oil and Gas Jour., v. 67, no. 38, p. 216–226; v. 67, no. 39, p. 128–130.

Tamrazyan, G. P., 1964, Printsipial'noye razlichiye teplovogo rezhima nedr Yevropeyskoy chasti i sopredel'nykh oblastey Aziatskoy chasti SSSR (Fundamental difference between the temperatures at depth in the European USSR and adjacent Asiatic regions): Akad. Nauk SSSR Doklady, v. 157, no. 2, p. 337–340 (Engl. transl. by Am. Geol. Inst., 1965, Acad. Sci. USSR Doklady, v. 157, p. 11–14).

—— 1967, The global historical and geological regularities of the earth's development as a reflection of its cosmic origin (as a sequence of galactic movement in the solar system): Ostrava, Czech., Sborník Vedeckých Prací Vysoké Skoly Bánské v Ostrave, Rocník 13, Rada Horniko-Geologiká, Clánek 182, v. 1, p. 5–24.

—— 1971, Siberian continental drift: Tectonophysics, v. 11, no. 6, p. 433–460.

Teichert, C., and A. A. Meyerhoff, 1972, Continental drift and the marine environment: Montréal, 24th Internat. Geol. Cong., sec. 7, p. 339–349.

Trettin, H. P., 1967, Devonian of the Franklinian eugeosyncline, *in* D. H. Oswald, ed., International symposium on the Devonian System: Calgary, Alberta Soc. Petroleum Geologists, p. 693–701.

—— 1969, A Paleozoic-Tertiary fold belt in northernmost Ellesmere Island aligned with the Lomonosov Ridge: Geol. Soc. America Bull., v. 80, no. 1, p. 143–148.

Trumpler, R. J., and H. F. Weaver, 1962, Statistical astronomy: New York, Dover Publishers, Inc., 644 p.

Tuchkov, I. I., *et al.*, 1968, Istoriya razvitiya i paleogeograficheskiye usloviya nakopleniya neftegazonosnykh otlozheniy na territorii Yakutii, *in* A. K. Bobrov *et al.*, eds., Geologicheskoye stroyeniye i neftegazonosnost' vostochnoy chasti Sibirskoy platformiy i prilegayushchikh rayonov: Moscow, Izd. "Nedra," p. 25–41.

Vasil'yev, V. G., 1968a, Geologiya nefti, spravochnik, tom 2, kniga 1, neftyanye mestorozhdeniya SSSR: Moscow, Izd. "Nedra," 764 p.

—— 1968b, Gazovye mestorozhdeniya SSSR, spravochnik: Moscow, Izd. "Nedra," 688 p.

Verechtchagin, V. N., 1959, Nord-est, p. 164–166, *in* N. K. Ovechkin, ed., Structure géologique de l'U.R.S.S., t. 1, Stratigraphie, fasc. 2, Précambrien: Paris, Centre Natl. Recherche Sci. p. 69–185.

Vogt, P. R., and N. A. Ostenso, 1970, Magnetic and gravity profiles across the Alpha Cordillera and their relations to Arctic sea-floor spreading: Jour. Geophys. Research, v. 75, no. 26, p. 4925–4937.

Wanless, R. K., *et al.*, 1968, Age determinations and geological studies, K-Ar isotopic ages, report 8: Canada Geol. Survey Paper 67–2, pt. A, 141 p.

Weyl, P. K., 1968, The role of the oceans in climatic change: a theory of the ice ages, *in* J. M. Mitchell, Jr., ed., Causes of climatic change: Am. Meteorological Soc., Meteorological Mon., v. 8, no. 30, p. 37–62.

Wilson, J. T., 1963, Continental drift: Sci. American, v. 208, p. 86–100.

Wundt, W., 1964, Die Bedeutung der Stahlungskurve nach den Anschauunger von Bacsák im Zusammenhang mit den Untersuchungen von Milankovitch und Woerkom: Geol. Rundschau, Band 54, Heft 1, p. 478–486.

Yanshin, A. L., 1962, Perspektivy otkrytiya mestorozhdeniy kaliynykh soley na territorii Sibiri (Potassium salt prospects in Siberia): Novosibirsk, Akad. Nauk SSSR Sibirskoy Otdeleniye, Geologiya i Geofizika, no. 10, p. 3–22 (Engl. transl. by Am. Geol. Inst., 1964, Internat. Geology Rev., v. 6, no. 12, p. 2132–2147).

Zhamoyda, A. I., ed., 1968, Geologicheskoye stroyeniye SSSR, t. 1, Stratigrafiya: Moscow, Izd. "Nedra," 711 p.

Zharkova, T. M., 1965, Karnallit v kamennoy soli kembriyskikh otlozheniy Sibirskoy platformy (Carnallite in rock salt from Cambrian sediments of the Siberian platform): Akad. Nauk SSSR Doklady, v. 164, no. 1, p. 1771–178 (Engl. transl. by Am. Geol. Inst., 1966, Acad. Sci. USSR Doklady, v. 164, p. 144–145).

Test of Nature and Extent of Continental Drift as Provided by Study of Proterozoic Dike Swarms of Canadian Shield[1]

W. F. FAHRIG,[2] E. IRVING,[3] and G. D. JACKSON[2]

Ottawa, Ontario, Canada

Abstract The Franklin intrusions are an extensive swarm of late Hadrynian (latest Proterozoic) diabase dikes that are present in an arc from Great Bear Lake eastward to Melville Peninsula, Baffin Island, and northern Ungava Bay. They are chemically and petrologically classified as tholeiites and are probably comagmatic. Paleomagnetic pole positions and numerous whole-rock K-Ar age determinations indicate that the dikes were emplaced at low latitudes 650 m.y. ago. They intrude Hadrynian sedimentary sequences that contain features indicative of depositon under warm climatic conditions.

The Baffin dikes are subparallel with the northeast coastline of Baffin Island and with a pronounced northwest-trending fault system. Intermittent, mainly normal movement along these faults persisted from the Helikian to the Quaternary and produced a series of graben structures which may be due to the same regional tension as the dikes. Thus, Baffin Bay and Davis Strait may have begun to form as early as the late Hadrynian, and they may contain Paleozoic strata.

INTRODUCTION

During the Phanerozoic, episodes of igneous activity have produced extensive arrays of mafic extrusive and hypabyssal rocks which are characterized by internal uniformity of general composition and by similarity in K-Ar ages and paleomagnetic directions. Examples are the Tasmanian dolerite of Australia (McDougal, 1961; Irving, 1963), the Ferrar dolerite of Antarctica (McDougal, 1963; Bull et al., 1962), and the Karroo dolerite and the Drakensburg Volcanics of southern Africa (Graham and Hales, 1957; McDougal, 1963; van Zijl et al., 1962; McElhinny and Jones, 1965).

The Canadian shield contains similar widespread diabase swarms and related extrusive rocks of many different ages that show promise of being differentiable into a series of discrete igneous episodes which will provide important Precambrian chronostratigraphic markers.

MACKENZIE AND FRANKLIN IGNEOUS EVENTS

We now have information indicating at least two episodes of basic igneous activity in the Canadian shield which will be useful as chronostratigraphic markers (Figs. 1, 2). The first episode involves the Mackenzie igneous events, which were discussed by Fahrig and Jones (1969) and by Robertson (1969). These events have been dated at about 1,200 m.y.; included are the emplacement of the Muskox intrusion, the outpouring of the Coppermine lavas, and the formation of northwest-trending dike swarms in the District of Mackenzie, northern Manitoba, and the Sudbury area. During these events, the geomagnetic field for the western and central Canadian shield had a characteristic direction defined by pole 5 (Fig. 3); there were no polarity reversals during this magnetic interval.

The second episode involves the Franklin igneous events (Fahrig et al., 1971; Jackson, 1966, 1971). These events have been dated at about 675 m.y.; they include the emplacement of a spectacular swarm of diabase dikes that crop out in a huge arc extending from Great Bear Lake and Coronation Gulf on the west, eastward to Boothia and Melville Peninsulas, Baffin Island, and northern Ungava Bay. During the time of emplacement, the geomagnetic field for the northern and northeastern Canadian shield had a characteristic direction de-

[1] Manuscript received, September 20, 1971.

[2] Geological Survey of Canada.

[3] Canada Department of Energy, Mines and Resources, Earth Physics Branch.

FIG. 1—Distribution of Mackenzie igneous rocks (shown by thin lines) in Canadian shield.

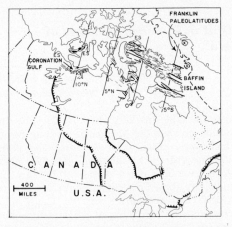

Fig. 2—Distribution of Franklin igneous rocks in Canadian shield. Thin lines and blobs are mafic igneous rocks, thick lines are faults. **ES** represents evaporites and stromatolites; dashed line shows Greenland fitted to North America along 500-fm contour (after Bullard *et al.*, 1965); and **x** indicates Disko Island.

fined by pole 1 (Fig. 3); during this magnetic interval there was at least one polarity reversal. Although the Mackenzie and Franklin poles are not a great distance apart, there is a very large polar loop between them which (on the present geographic grid) sweeps north from the equator at 150°W toward North America and curves west and south to the equator at 170°E (Fig. 3). This effect, discovered by Dubois (1962), has now been documented in some detail by Robertson and Fahrig (in press), who have officially named it the "Logan Loop."

TECTONIC SPECULATIONS

Diabase dike swarms indicate crustal tension, and it is of interest to relate them to other geologic events or features of similar ages. The Bathurst Trench, which probably originated before emplacement of the Mackenzie dikes, extends from Coronation Gulf along Bathurst Inlet and southeastward. Formation of graben structures predates the emplacement of the Mackenzie dikes in the southern part of the trench, and normal faulting is known to postdate the dikes in the northern part (J. A. Fraser, personal commun.). Therefore, it is likely that normal faulting occurred along the Bathurst Trench during emplacement of the 1,200-m.y.-old Mackenzie dikes, which are parallel with the trench.

The magnetic inclinations of the Franklin diabases are low, indicating that they were emplaced at low latitudes. This conclusion is supported by evidence of warm depositional conditions; gypsum, anhydrite, and stromatolites are present in thick late Proterozoic sequences that occur as erosional remnants in an elongate area from Amundsen Gulf to northern Baffin Island (Fahrig *et al.*, 1971). It seems likely that these strata are only slightly older than the Franklin dikes that intrude them.

The Franklin diabases are particularly evident on Baffin Island, where they are subparallel with a pronounced northwest-trending fault system and with the island itself (Fig. 2). The movement on most of the faults has been normal, and has resulted in the development of a series of grabens. Trettin (1969) argued that the central Borden fault zone of northwest Baffin Island was an important hinge line during Helikian sedimentation, and that basement gneisses along the zone were elevated to the level occupied by the Helikian strata prior to early Paleozoic sedimentation. Trettin also suggested that the zone was weakly active during early Paleozoic sedimentation and was reactivated in post-Silurian time. Evidence of the latter activity is well documented in the southeast extension of the zone in the Mary River region (Jackson, 1966). The Helikian strata referred to by Trettin may actually be Hadrynian, so that the formation of the northwest-trending Baffin dikes and the northwest-trending graben zones may be roughly concordant and may be the result of the same regional tensions. Jackson *et al.* (in prep.) have suggested that some of the graben zones north of the central Borden fault zone may actually have been active during Helikian-Hadrynian sedimentation. These factors suggest the possibility that the present Davis Strait was a rift zone in very late Pre-

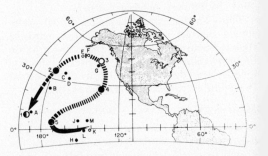

Fig. 3—Mean paleomagnetic poles of some Proterozoic rocks; also shown is Logan Loop. 1. Franklin pole position; 5. Mackenzie pole position. Points between 1 and 5 represent rocks 675–1,200 m.y. old, and points **H** to **M** represents rocks 1,300–1,400 m.y. old. (Figure is from Robertson and Fahrig, in press.)

cambrian time and therefore may contain Paleozoic strata. The very much later Cenozoic separation of Baffin Island and Greenland indicates tension similar in direction to that indicated by the late Precambrian dikes and the normal fault systems of Baffin Island. Thus, northeast-southwest tensions may have recurred several times in the Canadian shield, the major culminations occurring in the western shield about 1,200 m.y. ago and in the northeastern shield about 675 m.y. ago and again about 60 m.y. ago.

It would be very significant if an extension of the Franklin diabases could be identified positively in western Greenland. Their presence only along the southwest edge of Greenland might suggest that Greenland and Baffin Island have maintained much the same relative positions since the end of the Proterozoic. Presence of Franklin diabase near or south of Disko Island might be taken to indicate that Greenland has moved away from Canada in Phanerozoic time.

It is also interesting to note that these late Precambrian paleomagnetic data provide a means for studying the Paleozoic history of the Atlantic. The deep-water deposits of the Caledonian geosyncline of northwestern Europe and their equivalents in eastern North America indicate the presence during the early Paleozoic of an ocean, which closed in the middle Paleozoic during the Caledonian orogeny and reopened in the Mesozoic to form the present Atlantic Ocean (Wilson, 1966). It would appear that the best test of these ideas would be paleomagnetic studies on rocks of the orogenic belts themselves. However, such rocks generally have been extensively remagnetized (Chamalaun and Creer, 1964; Roy et al., 1968), and there is little hope of obtaining a sufficient quantity of reliable information. A procedure which is accessible is comparison of Proterozoic polar sequences from the Canadian and Baltic shields, which have formed the marginal cratons and which supposedly have been carried along in this "to and fro" motion. If a wide early Paleozoic ocean did not exist, then equivalent poles will agree if the continents are restored to their late Paleozoic positions. Now that paleomagnetic data from the Baltic shield are available (Neuvonen and Grundström, 1969), it should soon be possible to make a decisive test. Results regarding the age range between the Franklin and Mackenzie intervals will be of particular interest, because the Franklin-Mackenzie polar loop should be identifiable in both shields if the current interpretation according to plate tectonics is incorrect.

SELECTED REFERENCES

Bull, C., E. Irving, and J. Willis, 1962, Further palaeomagnetic results from South Victoria Land, Antarctica: Royal Astron. Soc. Geophys. Jour., v. 6, p. 320–336.

Bullard, E. L., J. E. Everitt, and A. G. Smith, 1965, The fit of the continents around the Atlantic: Royal Soc. London Philos. Trans., Ser. A, v. 258, p. 41–51.

Canada Geological Survey, 1969, Geological map of Canada: Canada Geol. Survey Map 1250A, scale 1: 5,000,000.

Chamalaun, F. M., and K. W. Creer, 1964, Thermal demagnetization studies on the Old Red Sandstone of the Anglo-Welsh cuvette: Jour. Geophys. Research, v. 69, p. 1607–1616.

Douglas, R. J. W., 1969, Orogeny, basement, and the geological map of Canada, in Age relations in high-grade metamorphic terrains: Geol. Assoc. Canada Spec. Paper 5, p. 1–6.

Dubois, P. M., 1962, Palaeomagnetism and correlation of Keweenawan rocks: Canada Geol. Survey Bull. 71.

Fahrig, W. F., and D. L. Jones, 1969, Paleomagnetic evidence for the extent of Mackenzie igneous events: Canadian Jour. Earth Sci., v. 6, p. 679–688.

——— E. Irving, and G. D. Jackson, 1971, Paleomagnetism of the Franklin diabases: Canadian Jour. Earth Sci., v. 8, p. 455–467.

Graham, K. W. T., and A. T. Hales, 1957, Paleomagnetic measurements on Karroo dolerites: Advances in Physics, v. 6, p. 149–161.

Irving, E., 1963, Paleomagnetism of the Marrabeen Chocolate Shale and the Tasmanian dolerite: Jour. Geophys. Research, v. 68, p. 2283–2287.

——— and W. A. Robertson, 1969, Test for polar wandering and some possible implications: Jour. Geophys. Research, v. 74, no. 4, p. 1026–1036.

Jackson, G. D., 1966, Geology and mineral possibilities of the Mary River region, northern Baffin Island: Canadian Mining Jour., v. 87, no. 6, p. 57–61.

——— 1971, Operation Penny Highlands, south-central Baffin Island: Canada Geol. Survey Paper 71–1, part A, p. 138–140.

——— W. C. Morgan, and A. Davidson, in prep., Regional geology of north-central Baffin Island (Operation Bylot): Canada Geol. Survey Paper.

McDougall, I., 1961, Determination of the age of a basic igneous intrusion by the potassium-argon method: Nature, v. 190, p. 1184–1186.

——— 1963, Potassium-argon age measurements on dolerites from Antarctica and South Africa: Jour. Geophys. Research, v. 68, no. 5, p. 1535–1545.

McElhinny, M. W., and D. L. Jones, 1965, Paleomagnetic measurements on some Karroo dolerites from Rhodesia: Nature, v. 206, p. 921–922.

Neuvonen, K. J., and L. Grundström, 1969, Paleomagnetism of the dike systems in Finland: Geol. Soc. Finland Bull., no. 41, p. 57–63.

Robertson, W. A., 1969, Magnetization directions in the Muskox intrusion and associated dykes and lavas: Canada Geol. Survey Bull. 167, 52 p.

——— and W. F. Fahrig, in press, The great Logan paleomagnetic loop—the polar wandering path from Canadian Shield rocks during the Helikian era: Canadian Jour. Earth Sci.

Roy, J. L., N. D. Opdyke, and E. Irving, 1968, Further paleomagnetic results from the Bloomsburg Formation: Jour. Geophys. Research, v. 72, p. 1–12.

Trettin, H. P., 1969, Lower Paleozoic sediments of northwestern Baffin Island, District of Franklin: Canada Geol. Survey Bull. 157, 70 p.

Wilson, J. T., 1966, Did the Atlantic close and then reopen?: Nature, v. 211, p. 676–677.

Zijl, J. S. V. van, K. W. T. Graham, and A. L. Hales, 1962, The paleomagnetism of the Stromberg lavas of South Africa: Geophys. Jour. Royal Soc., v. 7, p. 23–39.

Canadian Arctic Rift System—A Summary[1]

J. Wm. KERR[2]

Calgary, Alberta, Canada

The Canadian Arctic rift system is a branch of the Mid-Atlantic Ridge that extends 3,000 mi (4,800 km) into the North American continent. It is an incipient structure that diminishes in degree of development northwestward, bifurcates at the head of Baffin Bay, and disappears into the Canadian Arctic Islands. The rift system is mainly an extensional structure, which has allowed Greenland and Canada to rotate apart and form intervening seaways.

The rift system initially developed in passive response to external forces. The general location of the rift system thus was determined largely by the initiating regional forces. The detailed path, however, was guided by anisotropic trends of the crust—mainly the gneissic grain of the Precambrian shield and, to a lesser degree, the structures of the sedimentary cover—that interacted with the initiating stress system. Once established, the rift system probably became an active structure that propagated its own development.

Four stages of rift-ocean development can be recognized in different parts of the Canadian Arctic rift system. They are represented by (1) an extension fault (many examples), (2) a rift valley (Jones Sound), (3) a proto-ocean (Baffin Bay), and (4) an incipient ocean (Labrador Sea). The sedimentary record of each stage contains relicts of the earlier stages.

Simultaneous with extension of the rift system, and partly as a result of that extension, the Eureka Sound fold belt was deformed by compression. These two features are diametrically opposed parts of a couple; they are separated by a broad intervening pivotal area where extensional structures merge northward into compressional structures. It appears that the couple resulted because a pronounced crosswise gneissic trend impeded the northwestward advance of the rift system and localized the pivot.

The rift system began to form with an initial rift along the site of the present Labrador Sea, probably in latest Triassic or Early Jurassic time. The principal movements took place in Cretaceous and Tertiary time, and substantial deformation occurred on Ellesmere Island as late as the Oligocene. Presently, the rift system apparently is dormant, except for minor adjustments that are indicated by occasional earthquakes in Baffin Bay and the Labrador Sea (Kerr, 1970).

REFERENCE CITED

Kerr, J. Wm., 1970, Today's topography and tectonics in northeastern Canada, in Symposium on recent crustal movements: Canadian Jour. Earth Sci., v. 7, no. 2, pt. 2, p. 570.

[1] Manuscript received, September 20, 1971.

[2] Institute of Sedimentary and Petroleum Geology.

Reconnaissance Geophysical Studies in Barents and Kara Seas—Summary[1]

P. R. VOGT[2] and N. A. OSTENSO[3]

Washington, D.C. 20390, and Arlington, Virginia 22217

Abstract A reconnaissance geophysical survey of the Barents and Kara Seas, conducted from icebreakers in 1965 and 1966, consisted of about 10,000 line-km of bathymetric-magnetic data, 57 gravity measurements, and two short end-to-end seismic refraction profiles. Magnetic data do not support a continuation of Caledonian or Precambrian basement structures under the Barents Sea at shallow depth. A broad 400-gamma anomaly, the source of which lies about 20 km below sea level, strikes north-northwest between Norway and Bear Island. Magnetized basement approaches the sea floor only near Bear Island and 74.5°N, 33°E. Free-air anomalies in the northeast Barents Sea are within 30 mgal of zero. Magnetic anomalies in the Kara Sea parallel, but do not connect, tectonic structures of Taymyr and Novaya Zemlya. Magnetic basement is deep in the southwestern Kara Sea but shoals northeast of a line connecting northern Novaya Zemlya with the Yeniseyskiy Zaliv (estuary). Thus, primarily vertical movement is suggested along the line. Anomalies with amplitudes greater than 500 gammas occur only near the pre-Mesozoic outcrops on the Izvestiy Ts.I.K. Islands. The East Novaya Zemlya Trench is slightly undercompensated, having a median free-air gravity of −9 mgal and extremes of −33 and +11. Two refraction measurements in the eastern Barents Sea showed 400 m of unconsolidated sediments overlying a 3.1-km/sec basement and 700–1,100 m of 2.8-km/sec sediment overlying a 4.1-km/sec basement. The basement is probably Paleozoic sandstone or shale.

Introduction

During the summers of 1965 and 1966, research cruises were made into the Barents and Kara Seas by the USCGC *Northwind* and the USS *Atka*. Widely spaced magnetic, gravity, and seismic refraction data (Fig. 1) provided a preliminary geophysical picture of this vast region. This paper summarizes the most significant results; a more comprehensive treatment will be published later. In condensing the manuscript to this form, we have included as many data as possible, at the expense of interpretation.

Previous work in this area has included seismic refraction (Ewing and Ewing, 1959; Kvale et al., 1966); aeromagnetic surveys (Volk, 1964; Demenitskaya, 1967); and Soviet geologic work (Nalivkin, 1960; Markov and Nalivkin, 1957). Bathymetry obtained from the *Northwind* has been published by Johnson and Milligan (1967). Hamilton (1970) correlated geologic and magnetic data in an evolutionary model for northwestern Siberia.

Regional Magnetic Surveys

Magnetic data were obtained with a digitally recording nuclear precession magnetometer (Wold, 1964). The sensing head was towed 200 m behind the ships, and operations had to be suspended when crossing the ice pack. Total field data in selected portions of the surveyed region (Fig. 1) are shown in graph form along the ship tracks in Figures 2–5.

Contour maps of the residual total field in the areas of best coverage (southwestern Barents Sea and northern Kara Sea, Figs. 6, 7) were constructed by graphical subtraction of a linear regional field.

From Figures 2 and 6, the following observations can be made. The Barents Sea is not a submerged extension of the Baltic shield as depicted by some writers (Kummel, 1961). If Precambrian rocks of the shield were near the sea floor, the magnetic profiles should be highly disturbed, as they are over the sea floor just south and west of the Baltic shield of southern

[1] Manuscript received, September 20, 1971.

Icebreaker support for the magnetic and bathymetric profiling, gravity stations, and seismic refraction lines was furnished by the USCGC *Northwind* in 1965, Captain K. M. Ayres commanding. In 1966, support for the same research was provided by the U.S. Navy icebreaker *Atka*, Captain J. S. Blake commanding. Leonard Johnson, of the U.S. Naval Oceanographic Office, kindly provided reprints and charts of his latest research in the Arctic seas. The authors are further indebted to J. A. Andrew, D. Nelson, R. Wanous, and R. Wold, all of the Geophysical and Polar Research Center, University of Wisconsin, for support in various phases of the research. Without the able assistance and cooperation of officers and men of the USCGC *Northwind* and USS *Atka*, this study could never have been completed. Computer facilities were furnished by the University of Wisconsin Computing Center. This study was completed under Office of Naval Research Contract Nonr-1202(29), and one of the authors, P. R. Vogt, was supported by a National Science Foundation graduate fellowship. Financial assistance was also provided by Army-Navy Service Contract DA-49018-eng-3219.

The opinions and assertions presented in this paper are those of the authors personally and are not to be considered as official or as reflecting the view of the U.S. Department of Defense.

[2] U.S. Naval Oceanographic Office.

[3] Office of Naval Research.

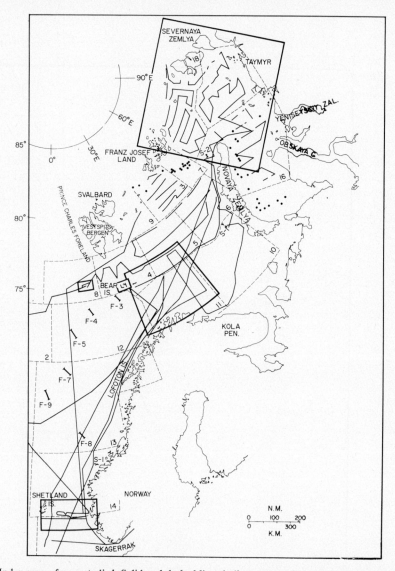

Fig. 1—Index map of area studied. Solid and dashed lines indicate magnetic tracks from *Northwind* and *Atka*, respectively. Tracks are discontinuous because magnetometer sensor could not be towed through pack ice. Heavy rectangles delineate areas of contoured magnetic data. Dots show locations of gravity observations. Bars schematically show location and orientation of seismic refraction profiles. Prefix F designates data from Ewing and Ewing (1959); B, Kvale *et al.* (1966); and S, this study.

Norway (Fig. 2) and west of central Norway (Fig. 3). Rather, the magnetic field over the Barents Sea is subdued, in some places resembling that over a thick sedimentary basin. We found no obvious linear trends of magnetic anomalies in the Barents Sea, although Volk (1964) has noted an east-west orientation based on unpublished Soviet data. The Caledonian structure, in particular, does not appear to extend northward into the Barents Sea at shallow depths, and only two small (<2 km wavelength) features were found. The magnetic field within 50 km of northern Norway is almost undisturbed by local anomalies. There are several broad magnetic highs which may reflect extensive ultramafic or mafic intrusions into the upper lithosphere, similar to the intrusion proposed for western Finnmark by Brooks (1970; Fig.

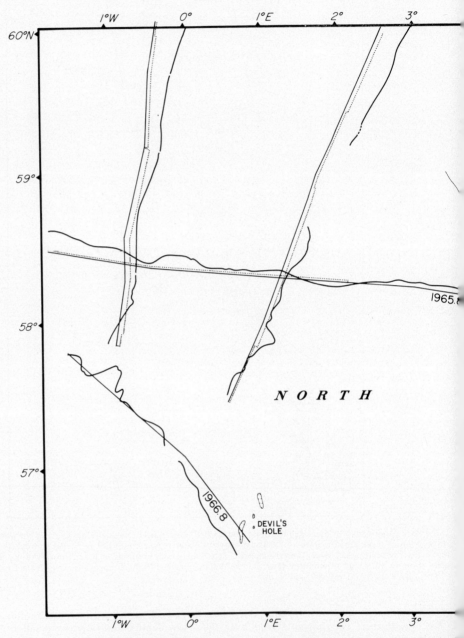

FIG. 2—Total magnetic field and bathymetric profiles south of Norway. Graph a
anomalies within 50 km of Precambrian

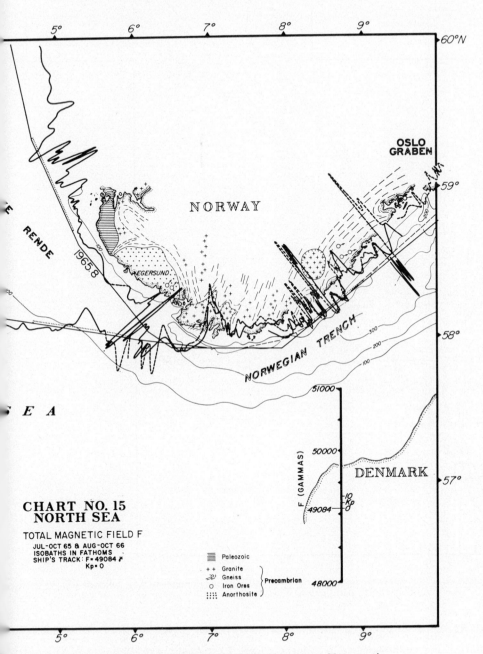

CHART NO. 15
NORTH SEA

TOTAL MAGNETIC FIELD F
JUL-OCT 65 & AUG-OCT 66
ISOBATHS IN FATHOMS
SHIP'S TRACK: F = 49084 M
Kp = 0

≣ Paleozoic
+ + Granite
〰 Gneiss
○ Iron Ores   } Precambrian
⫶⫶⫶ Anorthosite

p tracks indicates *K*-indices from Göttingen Magnetic Observatory. Note erratic
aleozoic igneous and metamorphic complexes.

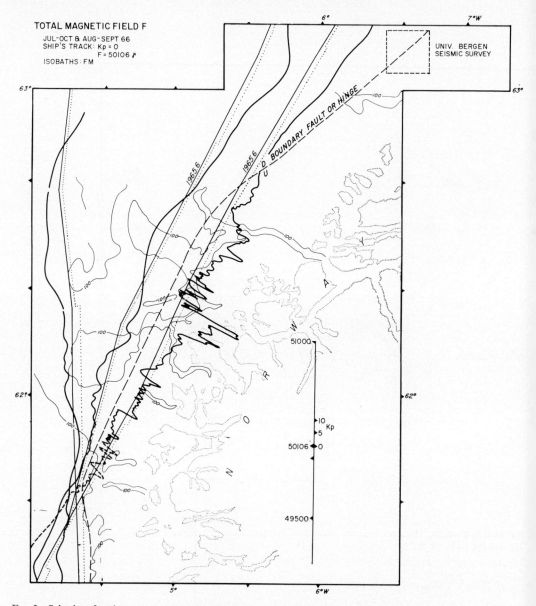

FIG. 3—Seismic refraction survey reported by Kvale *et al.* (1966). Same conventions were followed as in Figure 2. Heavy, abruptly curved line suggests seaward edge of shallow magnetized basement.

6). The magnetic anomalies apparently do not continue southward into Norway, however.

We estimated the depth of several prominent features by the approximate half-slope method of Peters (1949). Shallow sources (0.5–2 km) indicating basement domes were found only within 30 km of Bear Island and near 74.5°N, 33°E. Five-kilometer-deep sources are indicated in the region north of 72°N lat., between 33° and 45°E long. (Fig. 6). A complex anomaly near 73°N, 36°E yielded a deeper source level. Four depths ranged from 14 to 21 km. In the eastern Barents Sea, six sources ranged in depth from 7 to 10 km; one depth was 15 km. A broad 400-gamma feature striking north-northwest between Norway and Bear Island reflects a source about 20 km deep.

In the Kara Sea, magnetic-source depths are

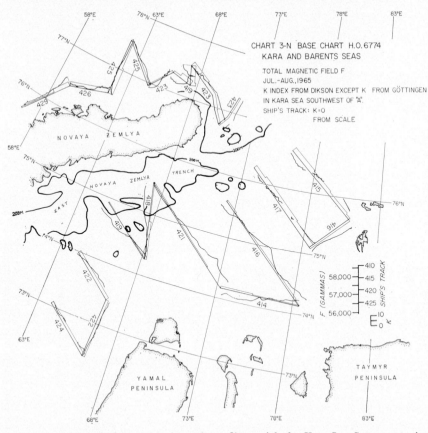

FIG. 4—Total magnetic field and bathymetric profiles, mainly for Kara Sea. Same conventions were followed as in Figure 2.

more varied, although the broad anomalies have a better-defined trend. Wavelengths of a few kilometers and amplitudes of 50 to several hundred gammas appear over most of the northern and central Kara Sea (Figs. 4, 5), indicating a shallow magnetic basement. In contrast, the southern Kara Sea, between Novaya Zemlya and the mainland, is rather smooth magnetically (Fig. 4). A series of anomalies with amplitudes of several hundred to 1,000 gammas and wavelengths of 10–100 km appears to trend east-northeastward across the central Kara Sea (Fig. 7). If these long-wavelength anomalies reflect the tectonic grain of the deep crust, then this grain parallels the tectonic trends and topographic features of Novaya Zemlya and the Taymyr Peninsula. Thus, the Novaya Zemlya structure apparently does not turn south-southwestward across the Kara Sea to connect with the Taymyr ranges. Nor does it appear that Novaya Zemlya was offset

in a right-lateral sense by transcurrent faulting as suggested by Hamilton (1970). A hypothesis consistent with geologic and magnetic data is that the Novaya Zemlya structure continues toward Severnaya Zemlya, remaining parallel with the Taymyr structures, with which it is probably contemporaneous. The magnetic data (Figs. 4, 5) further show that the basement shoals relatively abruptly northeast of a line connecting the Yeniseyskiy Zaliv (estuary) with the northern tip of Novaya Zemlya. This shoaling of the magnetic basement is revealed not only by the appearance of short-wavelength anomalies, but also by the steep gradients of broader features. Near 76.5°N, 83°E, there are intense anomalies with amplitudes exceeding 1,000 gammas, suggesting a shoaling of the Paleozoic or Precambrian basement in the vicinity of the Izvestiy Ts.I.K. Islands, on which are outcrops of rocks of that age.

Further evidence for the abrupt downwarp-

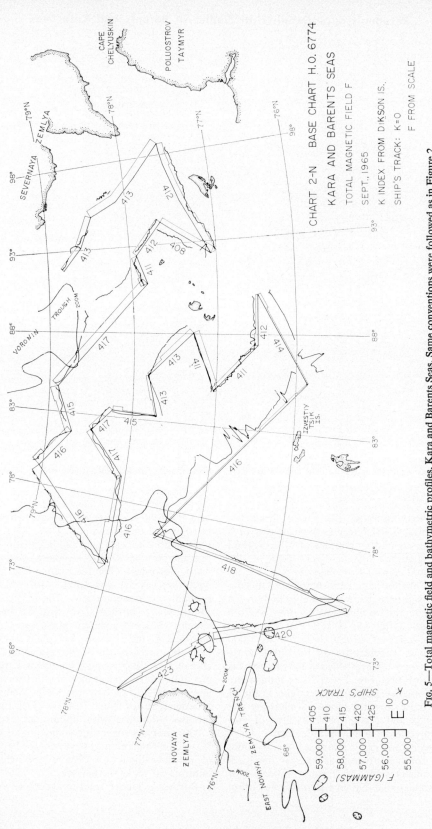

FIG. 5—Total magnetic field and bathymetric profiles, Kara and Barents Seas. Same conventions were followed as in Figure 2.

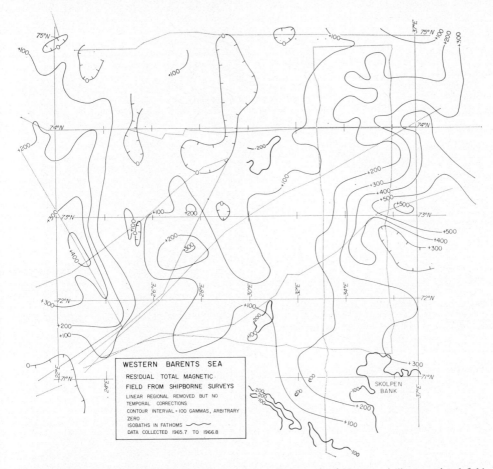

FIG. 6—Contoured residual magnetic field and measurement lines north of Norway. A linear regional field was removed graphically. Temporal variations were ignored, although no magnetic storms are represented.

ing of the magnetic basement is found around the Yenisey estuary. Paleozoic and Precambrian sedimentary and intrusive rocks are exposed on the rugged east bank of the estuary, whereas the flat west bank—*i.e.,* the coast of the Yamal Peninsula—is underlain by 1 km of sedimentary beds which thicken farther southwest to 4 km in a distance of less than 100 km. Soviet geologists have reported a huge oil deposit just north of the Yamal Peninsula which is believed to be large enough to supply the Soviet Union's petroleum needs for the next 50 years (American Polar Society, 1967). The structural lineament apparently reflected by the Yenisey estuary is co-linear with the northeastern tip of Novaya Zemlya.

On the basis of the preceding observations, we propose primarily vertical faulting or flexing

between the north tip of Novaya Zemlya and the Yenisey estuary (Fig. 7). Near Novaya Zemlya the southern block was uplifted, whereas the movement was reversed near the mainland. This interpretation contrasts with the 500-km strike-slip movement proposed by Hamilton (1970).

GRAVITY AND SEISMIC REFRACTION MEASUREMENTS

In heavy pack ice it was possible to read a special overdamped version of the LaCoste & Romberg gravimeter either above the ship's center of gravity or on the sea ice. In this manner, it was possible to obtain 33 stations in the Barents Sea and 24 in the Kara Sea (Fig. 8). Gravimeter readings were generally repeatable to within 2 or 3 mgal but were too widely scat-

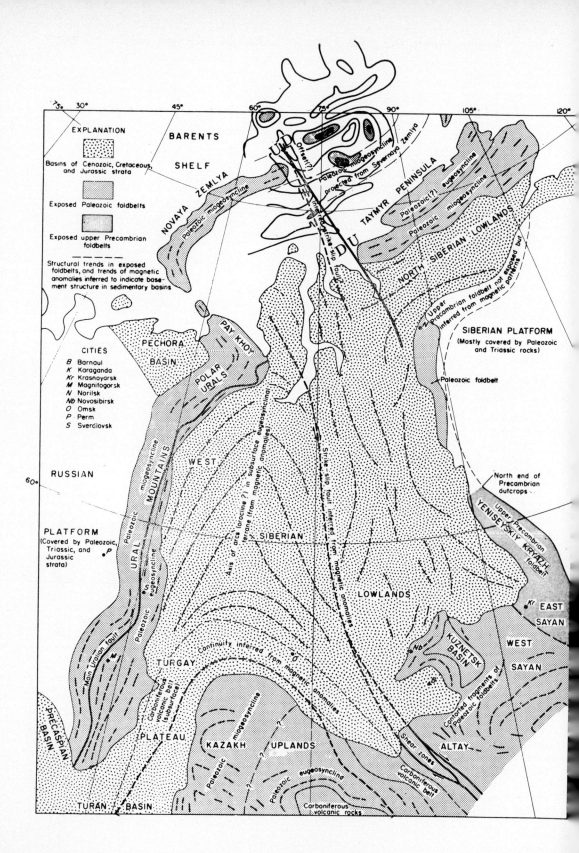

EXPLANATION

Basins of Cenozoic, Cretaceous, and Jurassic strata

Exposed Paleozoic foldbelts

Exposed upper Precambrian foldbelts

Structural trends in exposed foldbelts, and trends of magnetic anomalies inferred to indicate basement structure in sedimentary basins

CITIES

B Barnaul
K Karaganda
Kr Krasnoyarsk
M Magnitogorsk
N Norilsk
Nb Novosibirsk
O Omsk
P Perm
S Sverdlovsk

BARENTS SHELF

NOVAYA ZEMLYA

Paleozoic miogeosyncline

TAYMYR PENINSULA

Paleozoic miogeosyncline projected from Severnaya Zemlya

Paleozoic (?) eugeosyncline

Paleozoic miogeosyncline

NORTH SIBERIAN LOWLANDS

Upper Precambrian foldbelt not exposed but inferred from magnetic pattern

SIBERIAN PLATFORM
(Mostly covered by Paleozoic and Triassic rocks)

Paleozoic foldbelt

PECHORA BASIN

PAY KHOY

POLAR URALS

WEST

SIBERIAN

LOWLANDS

North end of Precambrian outcrops

YENISEYSKIY KRYAZH

Upper Precambrian foldbelt

RUSSIAN

PLATFORM
(Covered by Paleozoic, Triassic, and Jurassic strata)

• P

URAL MOUNTAINS

Paleozoic miogeosyncline

Paleozoic eugeosyncline

• S

Main Uralian fault

Axis of arca (orocline?) in subsurface eugeosyncline (?) terrane (from magnetic anomalies)

Strike-slip fault inferred from magnetic anomalies

EAST SAYAN

• Kr

WEST SAYAN

KUZNETSK BASIN

Continuity inferred from magnetic anomalies

TURGAY

• O

Carboniferous volcanic belt (subsurface)

• Nb

Contorted fragments of Paleozoic foldbelts

PRECASPIAN BASIN

PLATEAU

KAZAKH   UPLANDS

Paleozoic miogeosyncline

Paleozoic eugeosyncline

Shear zones

ALTAY

Carboniferous volcanic belt

TURAN   BASIN

Carboniferous volcanic rocks

75°   30°   45°   60°   75°   90°   105°   120°

60°

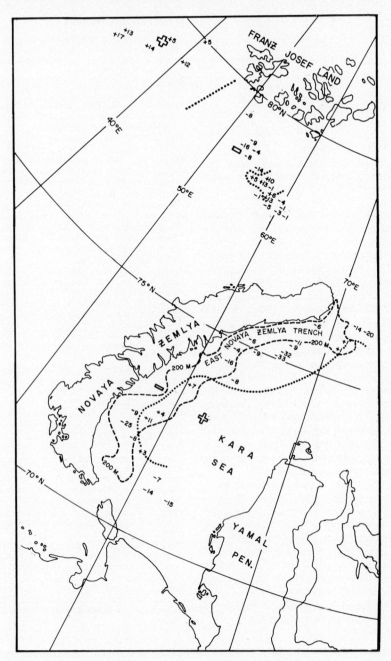

FIG. 8—Observed free-air gravity anomalies in Barents and Kara Seas. East Novaya Zemlya Trench is delineated by dashed 200-m isobath. Regions of positive and negative anomalies are separated by dotted lines.

FIG. 7—Residual contours in Kara Sea (from Figs. 4, 5) are superimposed on regional geologic interpretation of Hamilton (1970). Heavy black lines show writers' preference for hinge fault or flexure rather than Hamilton's inferred fault.

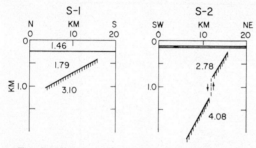

FIG. 9—Upper crustal structure deduced from seismic refraction lines S-1 and S-2, west of Novaya Zemlya (Fig. 1). Velocity in each layer is in km/sec.

tered to warrant detailed calculations of possible crustal structures. In general, the free-air anomalies are small, indicating that the region is in approximate isostatic balance. The range of values (Fig. 8) is comparable to that observed over many stable continental shelves, inland from their edges—for example, the shelf northwest of Alaska (Ostenso, 1968) or the Skagerrak (Anderson, 1966). There is no apparent relation between water depth and free-air anomalies for the Barents Sea stations.

The few gravity stations in the Barents Sea suggest the existence of broad anomalies with dimensions of several tens to 100 km and amplitudes within 10 or 20 mgal of zero. The free-air gravity in the Kara Sea shows a similar scatter of values, although the average is about 10 mgal lower. The East Novaya Zemlya Trench and surrounding parts of the Kara Sea seem to be slightly undercompensated.

Two relatively crude seismic refraction measurements were made in the eastern Barents Sea. Navigation and ice were major problems; water-wave arrivals were used to establish range. The interpretation (Fig. 9) suggests that a Paleozoic sedimentary basement, such as that cropping out on Novaya Zemlya, lies below 0.5–1 km of unconsolidated or semiconsolidated sediment. By comparison, Ewing and Ewing (1959) found 0.3 km of unconsolidated sediment in the western part of the sea.

SELECTED REFERENCES

Alberta Society of Petroleum Geologists, 1960 (1962), Geological map of the Arctic: Calgary, Alberta, scale 1:7,500,000 (prepared for 1st Internat. Symposium on Arctic Geology).

American Polar Society, 1967: Polar Times, v. 65, p. 28.

Anderson, O. B., 1966, Surface-ship gravity measurements in the Skagerrak, 1965–1966: Copenhagen, Geodaetisk Inst. Medd., no. 42.

Atlas USSR, 1962, Atlas of the USSR: Moscow, USSR.

Brooks, M., 1970, A gravity survey of coastal areas of West Finnmark, northern Norway: Geol. Soc. London Quart. Jour., v. 125, p. 172–192.

Demenitskaya, R. M., 1967, Kora i mantiya Zemli: Moscow, Izd. "Nedra," 279 p.

Ewing, J., and M. Ewing, 1959, Seismic refraction measurements in the Atlantic Ocean basin, in the Mediterranean Sea, on the Mid-Atlantic Ridge, and in the Norwegian Sea: Geol. Soc. America Bull., v. 70, p. 291–318.

Hamilton, W., 1970, The Uralides and the motion of the Russian and Siberian platforms: Geol. Soc. America Bull., v. 81, p. 2553–2576.

Johnson, G. L., and D. B. Milligan, 1967, Some geomorphological observations in the Kara Sea: Deep Sea Research, v. 14, p. 19–28.

Kummel, B., 1961, History of the earth—an introduction to historical geology: San Francisco, W. H. Freeman & Co., 610 p.

Kvale, A., M. Sellevoll, and H. Gammelsaeter, 1966, Seismic refraction measurements on the Norwegian continental shelf at 63°N, 06°30'E: Univ. Bergen, Seismol. Observatory.

Markov, F. G., and D. V. Nalivkin, eds., 1957, Geologiya Sovetskoi Arktiki: Nauchno-Issled. Inst. Geologii Arktiki, 520 p.

Nalivkin, D. V., 1960, The geology of the USSR: New York-London, Pergamon Press, 170 p. (in English).

Ostenso, N. A., 1968, A gravity survey of the Chukchi Sea region, and its bearing on westward extensions of structures in northern Alaska: Geol. Soc. America Bull., v. 79, p. 241–254.

Peters, L. J., 1949, Direct approach to magnetic interpretation and its applications: Geophysics, v. 14, p. 290–320.

Volk, V. E., 1964, Application of airborne magnetic survey data in studying the Arctic basin of the earth's crust: Sovetskaya Geologiya, no. 2, p. 117–120 (transl. by W. L. Burton).

Wold, R. J., 1964, The Elsec Wisconsin digital recording proton magnetometer system: Univ. Wisconsin Geophys. and Polar Research Center Rept. No. 64-4.

Tectonic Evolution of the Barents Shelf and Related Plates[1]

W. B. HARLAND[2]

Cambridge, England

Abstract In order to reconstruct successively earlier configurations of lithosphere plates and their constituent parts, as related to the Barents shelf, a brief investigation of some possible past relations between Spitsbergen and the northwestern Eurasian plates, Greenland, the Canadian Arctic Islands, and the intervening seas and ocean basins is necessary.

Working backward in time, I have "reversed" the late Phanerozoic spreading of the Norwegian and Greenland Sea basins of the Atlantic Ocean and the Eurasia basin of the Arctic Ocean. The results are familiar reconstructions of Triassic-Permian paleogeology that show Spitsbergen adjacent to North Greenland and Ellesmere Island.

The restoration of Paleozoic displacements depends mainly on different interpretations of the Caledonian orogeny (especially the amount of closing and the amount of sinistral transcurrent movement involved). Relations between these structures, the North Greenland and Innuitian fold belts, the Lomonosov Ridge, and the Uralides, for instance, are critical.

Precambrian movements and the development of the North Atlantic geosyncline are related both to alternative models for a proto–Atlantic ocean basin and to late Precambrian diastrophism as variously inferred.

INTRODUCTION

The purpose of this paper is to further understanding of the tectonic evolution of the Arctic region by drawing attention to the stratigraphic and structural information obtained from the archipelago of Svalbard (whose largest island is known as Spitsbergen). These islands occupy the northwestern edge of the European continental platform and, together with other islands to the east, mark its (upturned) edge, which divides the Barents Sea from the Arctic and North Atlantic Oceans. The rocks that are exposed range in age from late Precambrian to Holocene; few stratigraphic gaps are evident. Thus, the study area offers a sample history of a key sector of the lithosphere, from which detailed evidence can be obtained for a long history of horizontal and vertical movements. The evidence also supplements that gained from studies of the ocean floors.

The major movements concerned are those of the lithosphere plates, whose shape and identity evolved as the movements took place. At any one time, apart from slow subsidence or uplift within the plates, relatively rapid diastrophism is concentrated in the mobile belts where the plates join and where movements take the form of extension, compression, "transtension," and "transpression" (Fig. 1). The record in the lithosphere is commonly long and complex, combining a sequence of movements of different orientations. There is evidence of tectonic events which took place long before those for which we have evidence from the ocean floors.

Plate motion is inferred through different and quite distinct arguments. Direct evidence is of three kinds: (1) observed motion (flux) is necessarily limited to recent time; (2) interpretation of paleolatitude and paleoazimuth (fix) require motion, possibly differential motion, on a globe of known radius; (3) the structure of the crust points to differential motion to account for lithogenesis and tectogenesis (froth). Indirect evidence is circumstantial, and the arguments use likelihood of past reconstructions to explain observed configuration of all kinds of characters and parameters (fit).

The completeness of the stratigraphic record in Svalbard permits its structural and circumstantial evidence (froth and fit) to be used to test critically most models of Phanerozoic movement in the plates (of the present Arctic). Indeed, the facts that the earth is a closed system and that lithosphere plates apparently behave with little internal distortion lead to the hope that presently available evidence from the oceans and continents can be used to set such constraints on palinspastic mapping that a few

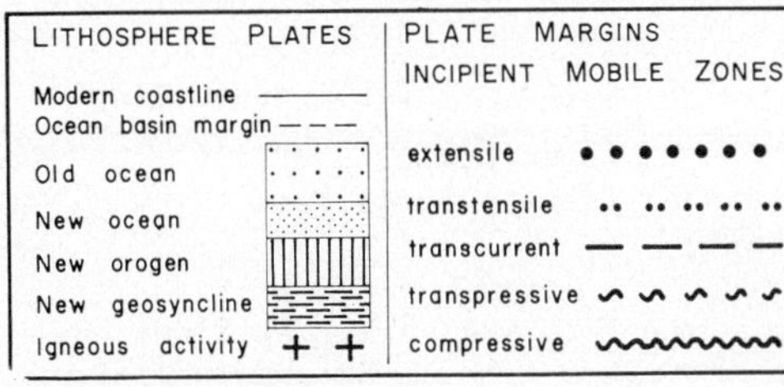

[1] Manuscript received, September 20, 1971. (*Note:* Original manuscript submitted in February 1971; revised manuscript received by Editor in April 1971.)

[2] Department of Geology, University of Cambridge, Sedgwick Museum.

LITHOSPHERE PLATES		PLATE MARGINS INCIPIENT MOBILE ZONES	
Modern coastline	———		
Ocean basin margin	– – –		
Old ocean		extensile	● ● ● ● ● ● ●
New ocean		transtensile	●● ●● ●● ●●
New orogen		transcurrent	— — — —
New geosyncline		transpressive	⌢⌢ ⌢⌢ ⌢⌢
Igneous activity	+ +	compressive	⌢⌣⌢⌣⌢⌣⌢⌣

FIG. 1—Legend for Figures 2–8. Modern coastline is used for identification of plates and has no other significance.

clear alternative models will emerge for further testing.

In this paper, an attempt is made to reconstruct plate positions backward through time, and only brief comment is made on the evidence where it is well known. The maps were projected (orthographically) from curved plates on a hemisphere.

Geographic names—The Lomonosov Ridge divides the Arctic basin into the Amerasia and the Eurasia basins. Beal *et al.* (1966) proposed names that have been generally followed for the Amerasia basin, but their nomenclature for the Eurasia basin is incomplete and is in conflict with the common Russian usage which has been adopted here (as shown broadly in Table 1 and Fig. 2).

"Spitsbergen" has recently been officially designated to refer only to the island formerly known as "Vestspitsbergen"; it does not now include Nordaustlandet or other islands. This change affects the nomenclature used here. We may now unambiguously refer to the "West Spitsbergen orogeny," characteristic of western Spitsbergen, without fear of confusion with the name "Vestspitsbergen." Less helpfully, the area of Ny Friesland previously covered north-central Spitsbergen but now is referred to as "northeast Spitsbergen." Usage throughout this paper follows current Norwegian recommendations and therefore may not match previous usage.

Compass directions are used to refer to present-day relations of the areas discussed and have no paleogeographic significance.

FIG. 2—Present Arctic. Area of this and subsequent maps approximates area within Arctic Circle. Ocean-ridge features are distinguished as follows:

1. Alpha Cordillera
2. Lomonosov Ridge
3. Gakkel Ridge
4. Spitsbergen fracture zone
5. Hovgard fracture zone
6. Atka Ridge
7. Greenland fracture zone
8. Mohns Ridge
9. Jan Mayen fracture zone
10. Jan Mayen Ridge

POST-DEVONIAN HISTORY

Cenozoic

Recent mobility—Seismic and volcanic evidence identifies the current mobile zone of extension and transcurrence along the continuation of the Mid-Atlantic Ridge north of Iceland

Table 1. Geographic Names in a Traverse from Alaska to Spitsbergen

	Beal et al. (1966)	Russian Usage	Johnson (1969)
Amerasia* basin	(Canada basin* etc. ((large and complex) (Alpha Cordillera* (Makarov basin	 Makarov basin*	
	Lomonosov Ridge*		
Eurasia* basin	(Fram basin (Nansen Cordillera (−	Amundsen basin* Gakkel Ridge* Nansen basin* Litke Trough	Pole Abyssal Plain Mid-Oceanic Ridge Barents Abyssal Plain (with Fram Deep)
	Yermak Rise* Barents shelf*		

*Names adopted here.

through the Jan Mayen Ridge, Mohns Ridge, Atka Ridge, the Spitsbergen fracture zone (de Geer megashear), and Gakkel Ridge (Sykes, 1965; Horsfield and Maton, 1970; Vogt *et al.,* 1970).

Late Quaternary or Holocene volcanoes and recent hot springs are known in the northwest corner of Spitsbergen. Plateau basalts (possibly Tertiary) cap many table mountains there (Harland, 1969a; this volume).

Iceland–Gakkel Ridge phase of spreading (Fig. 3)—The locus of current seismic and volcanic events fits well (1) the required zone of extension along the Jan Mayen and Mohns Ridges that generated the Norwegian and Greenland basins between Iceland and Spitsbergen; (2) the zones of transtension along the Atka Ridge; (3) the zone of transcurrence along the Spitsbergen fracture zone (a part of the great de Geer lineament; parallel with the Hovgard and Greenland fracture zones); and (4) the zone of extension along the Gakkel Ridge that generated the Nansen and Amundsen basins. This pattern has emerged in a succession of papers published since 1960 (*e.g.,* Heezen and Ewing, 1961; Heezen, 1962; Johnson and Heezen, 1967; Demenitskaya and Karasik, 1969).

From magnetic signatures of the ocean floor, Vogt and Ostenso (1970) have estimated that spreading in the Nansen-Amundsen basin, and in an equivalent central zone of the Norwegian-

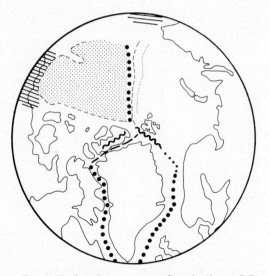

FIG. 4—Region shown at approximately 60 m.y. B.P. Laurasian plate is continuous in Arctic and is about to divide.

Greenland basin, took place in approximately the last 40 m.y. They also tentatively suggested from similar evidence that the marginal parts of the basins off Greenland and Scandinavia might have opened between 60 and 40 m.y. ago. This hypothesis is based on an analysis of discontinuities and timing of the separation between (1) Greenland and Labrador, (2) Greenland and Europe, and (3) North America and Europe (Vogt *et al.,* 1969) as follows. At 60 m.y. B.P., spreading of 0.6 cm/year occurred between Greenland and Labrador, 0.98 cm/year between Greenland and Europe, and 1.16 cm/year between North America and Europe; there was uniform extension and transtension. At 42 m.y. B.P., the reversal rate increased and spreading between Greenland and Labrador decreased from 0.6 cm/year to zero; stepped transtension occurred between Greenland and Europe at rates between 0.8, 0.6, and 0.8 cm/year, and extension occurred at the same rates between North America and Europe. Then, at 20 m.y. B.P., spreading occurred only between Greenland and Europe and North America and Europe; uniform extension and transtension resulted in magnetic striping.

Alpha Cordillera–Labrador phase of spreading (Fig. 4)—The Alpha Cordillera appears to have the same properties as a midoceanic zone of spreading. It is not now active. Vogt and Ostenso (1970) suggested that the Alpha Cordillera and the Makarov basin—and an equivalent

FIG. 3—Region shown at approximately 40 m.y. B.P. Reconstructed by closing Eurasian basin and juxtaposing Lomonosov Ridge and Barents shelf.

part of the Canada basin on the other side—
were generated in the same time interval (60–
40 m.y. ago). They also suggested (as did M. A.
Beal, independently) a connection between
the Alpha spreading and the opening of Baffin
Bay, Davis Strait, and the Labrador Sea. If the
Alpha spreading were directly connected with
the Labrador Sea–Baffin Bay spreading, it
would have died out slowly between 40 and 20
m.y. ago. The main Atlantic opening, however,
can be traced back to 220 or 240 m.y. ago
from evidence off the Atlantic seaboard of the
United States (Vogt *et al.,* 1969). It seems that
the Labrador spreading was initiated about 60
m.y. ago, and it would thus be difficult to argue
an earlier formation of the Alpha Cordillera
from the Mesozoic spreading in the Atlantic. It
seems simplest to assume a model which relates
the Alpha spreading to the early Cenozoic
phase on both sides of Greenland, and to assume the later Cenozoic phase as initiating
spreading on the other side of the Lomonosov
Ridge (splitting it from the Barents and Kara
shelves) and being connected with Atlantic
spreading only east of Greenland through Jan
Mayen and Iceland. By using a rigid plate
model, I previously had concluded that the Alpha Cordillera must have spread at some time
corresponding to formation of the oceanic gap
that remains on either side of Greenland when
the Eurasia basin has been closed.

*West Spitsbergen and Sverdrup Basin oroge-
nies* (Fig. 4)—A compressive phase with
thrusting and folding (systematically toward
the east) affected the west coast of central and
southern Spitsbergen (Harland and Horsfield,
in press). Post-tectonic graben strata are not
well dated but appear to be Oligocene (Livshitz, 1965) or near Oligocene; the youngest deformed strata are proved Paleocene (Vonderbank, 1970). I used such evidence (Harland,
1969b) to argue a Tertiary initiation of Atlan-
tic-Arctic opening, in opposition to the suggestion by Johnson and Heezen (1967) of an earlier opening in Cretaceous time. Later oceanic
estimates now confirm that the West Spitsbergen orogeny probably preceded the Gakkel
phase of opening and coincided with a phase of
compression and/or transpression which may
be correlated with opening of the Labrador
Sea.

This orogenic episode would appear to be a
relatively superficial plate-collision effect between Greenland and the Barents shelf. There
is little evidence of Tertiary metamorphism in

outcrops, and the whole orogen has been peneplaned, uplifted, and dissected so as to be almost topographically indistinguishable from the
Caledonian orogen, along which it lies.

The Tertiary folding of the Canadian Arctic
Islands and North Greenland are probably related. I suggested (Harland, 1965) that the
northward movement of Greenland rotated
Ellesmere Island "anticlockwise" and so caused
the north-south Tertiary folds in the Sverdrup
basin.

It is not clear, however, how these orogenies,
which might have taken place between 40 and
60 m.y. ago, could accompany the Alpha phase
of opening. I suggested (Harland, 1965) that
this orogenic phase, caused by a collision with
northeast Greenland, accompanied the opening
of the Davis Strait and that the orogenic movements possibly were compressive movements
combined with early transcurrence along the
Spitsbergen fracture zone. If so, a transpressive
model would allow the overthrusting to the east
only in the earliest phase of movement. This
condition could be accommodated if a relatively short-lived collision tectogenesis occupied
a short time interval about 50 m.y. ago. Assumption of this model is stretching the evidence, but it is consistent with Spitsbergen and
Canadian stratigraphy.

Carboniferous to Cretaceous

Barents shelf (Fig. 5)—Some Mesozoic geology is summarized in another contribution to
this symposium (Harland, this volume) and,
together with late Paleozoic history, in two
other recent papers (Harland, 1969a, b). A
history of gentle net subsidence during which
about 5 km of sediment accumulated shows
greater mobility toward the beginning and end
of this depositional sequence. Albian subsidence appears to have accelerated, and a Late
Cretaceous hiatus reflects uplift. Early Cretaceous basin volcanism, sill intrusion, and faulting are matched in the Canadian Arctic (Blackadar, 1964) and suggest the beginning of a
new thermal pattern in the mantle.

Earlier Mesozoic and Permian strata suggest
stable conditions, whereas evidence of slight igneous activity, coarser sediments, and a record
of differential subsidence and faulting on a
small scale distinguish Early Carboniferous
time.

Lomonosov Ridge—It has been generally assumed that the Lomonosov Ridge, having non-
oceanic magnetic characteristics, was sepa-

FIG. 5—Region shown at approximately 350–100 m.y. B.P. Arctic plate is continuous sialic lithosphere. Alaska is tentatively restored to position shown, as suggested by R. Stoneley (in press).

rated by the Gakkel fission from the north of the Barents shelf (Heezen and Ewing, 1961; Wilson, 1963; Harland, 1965). Although little is known of the patterns of Carboniferous to Cretaceous sedimentation in Svalbard, there is some evidence to suggest a clastic provenance at times from the north. Such evidence is consistent with the existence of a high area north of the Barents shelf and suggests that, whether or not the far (Pacific) side of the Lomonosov Ridge was then ocean, the watershed may have approximated the Lomonosov range as it then was.

Alaskan orocline–Canada basin spreading— Carey's (1958) prophetic tectonic analysis led him to suppose a rotation of the Alaskan orogenic belt. Recent studies in Alaska have suggested a rotation of about 70°, so as to bring northern Alaska from a position against the Canadian Arctic Islands (Tailleur and Snelson, 1968; Tailleur and Brosgé, 1970; Churkin, 1970; Stoneley, in press) via the opening of the larger part of the Canada basin. Other papers in this volume discuss this matter fully. Certainly, the suggestion (which I cannot judge but am ready to accept) contradicts my own previous assumption (Harland, 1969) that the larger part of the Canada basin could have been an ancient ocean—an idea also favored by Churkin (1969, 1970). Late Mesozoic tectogenesis along the Brooks Range is consistent with a

zone of opening possibly paralleling the present north Canadian continental slope, and with the Cretaceous magmatism referred to here. My own independent reconstructions with plates on a globe show this model to be geometrically possible for the Arctic side, but I draw no conclusions between several hypotheses on the kinematic history of Alaska.

Early Cretaceous magmatism (Fig. 5)—I attempted (Harland, 1969a, b) to explain the Early Cretaceous volcanicity and dolerite intrusion of Svalbard, Franz Josef Land, and the Canadian Arctic Islands as the results of early heating of the mantle prior to the Iceland-Gakkel phase of opening. This same evidence, together with Blackadar's (1964) evidence from the Canadian islands, might be better used to postulate a hot zone parallel with the initial spreading that originated the Canada basin.

*Verkhoyansk orogen—*It would seem reasonable to relate this Mesozoic orogeny to the Alaskan orocline rather than to the Gakkel spreading (*cf.* Wilson, 1963).

*Uralides—*Hamilton's (1970) analysis of the Uralides demonstrated that movement in the Ural Mountain system continued through much of Paleozoic time and that early reconstructions must allow greatly increased distances between the Siberian and Russian platforms. Thus, an ocean thousands of kilometers wide may have closed along two symmetrical subduction zones; only the closing stages of the orogeny would correspond to the age for the Uralian orogeny, widely recognized as late Paleozoic. The Siberian plates thus cannot be related to the Fennoscandian-Russian plate, as they have been, except during Mesozoic and Cenozoic time. However, the best-known miogeosynclinal sequences of the Urals show fairly continuous sedimentation throughout Paleozoic time and do not reveal the earlier mobility.

Arctic plate (Fig. 5)—Restoring these postulated movements results in a continuous continental plate connecting the Barents shelf and the Lomonosov range to North America, Greenland, and northern Europe. The whole Arctic Ocean was generated within this plate from Cretaceous through Cenozoic time, and the Early Cretaceous magmatism was a portent of this movement. Movement appears to have been localized along the old Innuitian-Lomonosov line. Some slight mobility was evident along the zone where continued subsidence of the Franklinian geosyncline extended from the platform deposits of the Barents shelf.

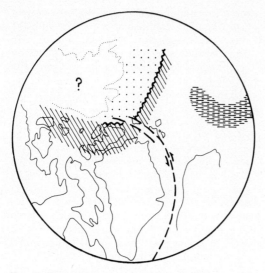

FIG. 6—Region shown at approximately 350 m.y. B.P.
Svalbardian-Innuitian phase.

MID-PALEOZOIC HISTORY

Devonian

Arctic Caledonian platform (Fig. 5)—The Carboniferous to Cretaceous and later Tertiary sediments were deposited on a platform with a predominantly shallow-marine environment and intermittent continental phases (*e.g.,* Tournaisian, Rhaetian-Liassic, Barremian). The sedimentary patterns fit such an extended Arctic platform, relating the deposits of the Barents shelf to the Canadian Arctic in particular. These sedimentary beds cover a platform of denudation developed during the intense Devonian erosion. The basement had been deformed by mid-Paleozoic orogenic activity of the Caledonian and Innuitian phases.

Svalbardian transcurrence (Fig. 6)—Svalbardian folding and faulting, of Late Devonian age, are well established. I proposed this Svalbardian orogeny to be part of a phase of extensive sinistral transcurrent movement (Harland, 1965) and later summarized further arguments (Harland, 1969a). Some strike-slip movement is structurally demonstrated. The larger amount proposed to restore eastern Spitsbergen to a position nearer to central East Greenland is based on general stratigraphic and tectonic arguments. This hypothesis has unavoidable consequences for other pre-Devonian relations in the Arctic. This zone of transcurrence (Fig. 6) would have provided a zone of mobility traversing this Arctic platform and also would

have provided a zone of weakness for the Cretaceous and later fission.

Innuitian tectogenesis—The Innuitian orogeny of the Canadian Arctic Islands can only be dated as post–middle(?) Devonian and pre–Late Mississippian. It is thus probably related to the Svalbardian rather than to the earlier main Caledonian orogeny.

North Greenland fold belt—Little is published about the age of this orogeny, except that it appears to be post-Silurian and therefore is probably part of the Innuitian system rather than the main Caledonian system.

Forlandsundet orogenic phase—The west-coast belt of central and southern Spitsbergen is the site of the Tertiary West Spitsbergen orogeny and also of the more intense and extensive Caledonian orogeny; the latter orogeny deformed younger rocks in this region than it did in eastern Spitsbergen. The deformed sedimentary sequence includes Late Ordovician and possibly Silurian strata. No Devonian rocks are known in the area, and a Late Silurian or Devonian orogenic phase possibly occurred here. The name "Forlandsundet phase" is introduced here to refer to the latest Caledonian deformation—whatever its age—of western Oscar II Land and Prins Karls Forland. The contrast in several respects between these west-coast Caledonian rocks and the eastern (Ny Friesland) sequence is consistent with sinistral transcurrent faulting along the Billefjorden lineament, because, if the effects of such faulting are removed, eastern Spitsbergen is restored to a position far south of western Spitsbergen in pre-Devonian time. Western Spitsbergen would thus lie in an intermediate position between eastern Spitsbergen and Peary Land or near Peary Land (Harland, 1969c).

Central East Greenland diastrophism—Whereas Lower and Middle Devonian deposits in western Spitsbergen are relatively undisturbed, several distinct phases of diastrophism have been established in a Middle and Upper Devonian sequence in central East Greenland (Bütler, 1959). The Devonian graben in Spitsbergen lies west of the boundary fault; on the basis of the foregoing hypothesis, the graben would have formed far north of the East Greenland Devonian deposits.

Ordovician-Silurian Diastrophism

Main Caledonian orogeny (Fig. 7)—The main tectogenesis that constructed the orthotectonic belt of Svalbard, East Greenland, western Scandinavia, the northern British Isles, and the

Appalachians began in some areas in Cambrian time but was most active in Ordovician and continued through Silurian time. The marine environment in which the extensive North Atlantic geosyncline existed was thereby converted into the Caledonides, which generated Old Red Sandstone sedimentation. The whole of Svalbard appears to have been affected by orogenesis at this time; to distinguish this phase of Caledonian movements in Svalbard from others, the term "Ny Friesland orogeny" has been used (the youngest known undeformed rocks are late Arenigian and the fold structures are cut by granites dated at about 380 m.y. B.P.). Widespread apparent ages of 380 to 420 m.y. are found throughout the metamorphic terrane of Svalbard (Gayer *et al.*, 1966). Evidence of a corresponding orogeny is apparent also in central East Greenland.

I have postulated (Harland, 1965) that, prior to the Svalbardian movements, eastern Spitsbergen was situated nearer to central East Greenland and so belonged to the American side of the North Atlantic geosyncline; this conclusion is based on the stratigraphic sequence and sedimentary facies. The earlier time of diastrophism and the marked north-south strike of the structures also would be difficult to fit, at that time, somewhere off Peary Land.

In contrast, the north Scandinavian structures swing around northern Norway to the east and clearly belong to the European side,

where earlier diastrophism is evident (Pringle and Sturt, 1969). The significance of the difference between these sides depends on the width of the sea or ocean between them. If there is an important tectonic discontinuity, it could cut obliquely across the Barents shelf separating Norway and Spitsbergen. The problems of this earlier history relate to the nature of the geosyncline from which the Caledonides were formed. However, whatever the earlier history, the major part of the Barents shelf seems to have been affected by orogenesis so as to become a part of Laurasia that subsequently developed as a platform through post-Devonian time.

Early Uralian orogeny—Although the paratectonic phase of Uralian orogeny clearly belongs to late Paleozoic time, Hamilton (1970) has argued for earlier oceanic subduction zones of early Paleozoic age in the area. To what extent the closing of such a Uralian ocean paralleled the main Caledonian closing of the North Atlantic geosyncline is not clear, but extensive plate movement appears to have taken place around Ordovician time, presumably involving substantial ocean spreading somewhere outside the study area. The islands of Novaya Zemlya are a part of the Uralides, and they record sedimentation throughout Paleozoic time. This region thus escaped the main mid-Paleozoic orogeny, but the recurrent clastic sequence there indicates that the region was not far removed from diastrophism at any time throughout the Paleozoic Era.

Cornwallis folding—The main Innuitian orogen strikes approximately east-west and includes lower Paleozoic through Silurian strata. Cutting across this orogen with north-south strike is an earlier fold structure—the Cornwallis fold belt. I have compared the age and strike of the Cornwallis fold belt with those of the main Caledonian orogen farther east, and find the Cornwallis fold belt is isolated from the Caledonian belt (Harland, 1965). A connection with the developing Uralides may be considered, but I have not analyzed the available evidence.

Lomonosov Range

I use the term "ridge" for the present bathymetric feature, and "range" for the postulated mountain belt that bordered the Barents shelf before the Gakkel spreading. I tentatively adopt the view (Tailleur and Brosgé, 1970; Hamilton, 1970; Stoneley, in press) that the Lomonosov range, in later Paleozoic time, was

Fig. 7—Region shown at approximately 450–400 m.y. B.P. Main Caledonian movements are occurring, and Cornwallis fold belt is evident.

bounded on the Pacific side by lithosphere that later evolved and rotated into present-day Alaska. The ridge was suggested by Carey (1958) to be an extension feature (nematath) which developed at the same time that his "Alaskan orocline" formed by the opening of the (Canada basin) sphenochasm. I prefer to regard the ridge as an orogen resulting from compression or transpression.

Hypotheses depending on Svalbardian transcurrence—Svalbardian transcurrence would bring the Lomonosov range at its time of formation from a position originally oriented toward northeast Greenland. There is as yet only circumstantial evidence as to its age. I postulate it to be of mid-Paleozoic age and consider subsidiary hypotheses. Tectonic maps of Greenland show both the Caledonian and the Innuitian belts turning out to sea toward the northeast, and my alternative hypotheses (given in the following paragraphs) allow the Lomonosov range to have been a continuation of one or the other of them, or both.

A. *Lomonosov range of approximately Devonian-Carboniferous age*—This hypothesis would continue the Innuitian and North Greenland fold belts into the Lomonosov range. Compressive orogeny would not be far removed in time from Late Devonian transcurrence. It is not impossible that western Spits·bergen is a link in this mountain chain subsequently displaced by faulting. I prefer this hypothesis.

B. *Lomonosov range of approximately Ordovician-Silurian age*—This hypothesis would reconstruct the main Caledonian orogen so that its western margin would have passed from central East Greenland through eastern Spitsbergen, turning east through the Lomonosov range, whereas the eastern margin would have followed along Scandinavia and turned east around the north of the Fennoscandian shield. Thus, western Spitsbergen would either be a link in this chain, or it would lie north of the orogen and be related to the North Greenland fold belt.

A proposed hypothesis that the later stages of the Ny Friesland orogeny passed from compression to sinistral transpression (Harland, 1971) would allow the Lomonosov range to have formed by compressive components. This hypothesis would accommodate the zig-zag zone of orogeny. I do not favor it, however, because Devonian sedimentation in northern Spitsbergen shows evidence of rivers flowing north to the sea, in which case a Silurian Lo-

monosov range should have developed offshore(?) as an island-arc system.

Hypothesis accepting present relation to Axel Heiberg Island—Trettin's (1969; this volume) observation of evidence suggesting a structural trend in northern Axel Heiberg Island relating to the Lomonosov Ridge would challenge the preceding hypotheses, but the argument has not been sufficiently developed to be conclusive. It will be discussed elsewhere.

LATE PRECAMBRIAN AND EARLY PALEOZOIC HISTORY

Geosynclines

North Atlantic geosyncline (Fig. 8)—The main Caledonian orogen is composed of thick sequences of upper Precambrian to lower Paleozoic strata. In eastern Spitsbergen, the Hecla Hoek geosyncline comprises about 15 km of Precambrian and 3 km of Cambrian and Ordovician strata. In East Greenland, the Greenlandian Eleonore Bay Formation is about 12 km thick and is overlain by a similar lower Paleozoic sequence. In northern Norway, the nearest equivalent sequence is the Barents Sea Group —a similar geosynclinal sequence (Siedlecka and Siedlecki, 1968). Similar thicknesses are evident farther south. All these geosynclinal sequences are similar enough in time range, thickness, and tectonic sequence to justify the unifying term "North Atlantic geosyncline"

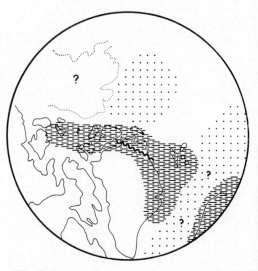

FIG. 8—Region shown at approximately 1,000–500 m.y. B.P. North Atlantic geosyncline with Carolinidian(?) phase.

(the geosyncline also extends through Britain, Newfoundland, and at least to New York).

Innuitian–North Greenland geosyncline—The beginning of this geosyncline is not so well known, but a major part of its known history and of its strata is Paleozoic.

Uralian geosyncline—With little exception, it appears that all Paleozoic systems are represented in this vast geosyncline or complex.

Diastrophism

East Spitsbergen—There is no evidence of significant diastrophism within the Hecla Hoek geosyncline of Ny Friesland—spanning perhaps hundreds of millions of years.

Northwest Spitsbergen—In the Raudfjorden area, only rocks correlated with the Lower Hecla Hoek (metamorphosed and migmatized) are unconformably overlain by the Siktefjellet Group (Late Silurian?) and the Red Bay Formation (earliest Devonian). In this area, as in some others, radiometric ages of approximately 600 m.y. B.P., as well as typical Caledonian ages, are known. I propose to label this the "Raudfjorden event," whose exact age is extremely difficult to interpret (Gayer *et al.,* 1966). Similar age problems and records of possibly similar events are found in areas of southern Spitsbergen and Nordaustlandet.

Carolinidian orogeny—Much literature on this orogeny stems from the relatively few observations reported by Haller (1955). If, indeed, the significance is as stated, a Precambrian geosyncline existed in northeast Greenland distinct from, and predating, the Greenlandian geosyncline to the south and the Innuitian–Peary Land geosyncline to the north. I have suggested that this Carolinidian orogeny (or phase) might correspond in time, or might be structurally analogous to, the Raudfjorden event in northwest Spitsbergen. This relation is another reason for associating northwest Spitsbergen with Peary Land rather than with eastern Spitsbergen. However, the interpretation of thermal events in early stages in orogenic sequences is not yet satisfactory.

Earlier Oceans

Among the thick (geosynclinal) sequences, it may not be easy to identify thinner (oceanic) sequences that could have been concentrated by subductive scraping.

Proto-Atlantic ocean (Fig. 8)—The concept that an earlier extensive marine geosyncline closed to form the Caledonian Appalach-

ian belt before reopening as the Atlantic was first advanced by van der Gracht (1928). Wilson (1966) argued for an extensive ocean basin with relatively narrow geosynclinal areas, and I (Harland, 1967) criticized his reconstruction because it allegedly divided Spitsbergen from Nordaustlandet. Any division within Spitsbergen should coincide instead with the transcurrent fault belt, but what is exposed has the characteristics only of a transcurrent fault with no obvious oceanic features—except, perhaps, in earlier (Precambrian) time. An ocean basin, if it existed, more probably separated Svalbard from Norway, because there is close similarity between eastern Spitsbergen and East Greenland.

Proto–Uralian ocean—Hamilton (1970) argued for an extensive oceanic area which in Precambrian time could have completed the northern encirclement of the Fennoscandian shield and the Russian platform (Fig. 8).

Proto–Arctic ocean—Alternatively, either of the above postulated oceans might have extended into the present Arctic basin area, presumably along the main North Canadian–North Greenland suture—the precursor of the de Geer line.

Conclusion

Because no direct evidence is known from Svalbard that can contribute to a picture of earlier Precambrian configurations, this speculation ceases its backward track at this point.

I have focused on Spitsbergen and speculated less reliably with increasing distance from it. However, because we each contribute a different perspective and adjust our weak areas to the strong points of others, this symposium will yield more than the sum of its parts.

Selected References

Atlasov, I. P., *et al.,* 1964, Tectonic map of the Arctic and Subarctic, scale 1:5,000,000: Akad. Nauk. SSSR Doklady, v. 156, no. 6, p. 1341–1342; translation 1970, by E. R. Hope (DRB Canada), A new tectonic chart of the Arctic.

Beal, M. A., *et al.,* 1966, The floor of the Arctic Ocean —geographic names: Arctic, v. 19, no. 3, p. 215–219.

Blackadar, R. G., 1964, Basin intrusions of the Queen Elizabeth Islands, District of Franklin: Canada Geol. Survey Bull. 97.

Bütler, H., 1959, Das Old Red-Gebiet am Moskusoksefjord: Medd. om Grønland, v. 160, no. 4, p. 1–188.

Carey, S. W., 1958, The tectonic approach to continental drift, *in* Continental drift—a symposium: Hobart, Univ. Tasmania, Geol. Dept., p. 177–355.

Churkin, M., Jr., 1969, Paleozoic tectonic history of the Arctic basin north of Alaska: Science, v. 165, p. 549–555.

———— 1970, Fold belts of Alaska and Siberia and drift between North America and Asia, *in* W. L. Adkison and M. M. Brosgé, eds., Proceedings of the geological seminar on the North Slope of Alaska: Los Angeles, Pacific Sec. Am. Assoc. Petroleum Geologists.

Demenitskaya, R. M., and A. M. Karasik, 1969, The active rift system of the Arctic Ocean: Tectonophysics, v. 8, no. 4–6, p. 345–351.

Gayer, R. A., *et al.*, 1966, Radiometric age determinations on rocks from Spitsbergen: Norsk Polarinst. Skr., no. 137, 39 p.

Haller, J., 1955, Der "Zentrale Metamorphe Komplex" von NE-Grønland: Medd. om Grønland, v. 73, no. 3, p. 1–174.

Hamilton, W., 1970, The Uralides and the motion of the Russian and Siberian platforms: Geol. Soc. America Bull., v. 81, p. 2553–2576.

Harland, W. B., 1965, Tectonic evolution of the Arctic–North Atlantic region: Royal Soc. London Philos. Trans., v. 258, p. 59–75.

———— 1967, Early history of the North Atlantic Ocean and its margins: Nature, v. 216, no. 5114, p. 464–466.

———— 1969a, Contribution of Spitsbergen to understanding of tectonic evolution of North Atlantic region, *in* Marshall Kay, ed., North Atlantic—geology and continental drift: Am. Assoc. Petroleum Geologists Mem. 12, p. 817–851.

———— 1969b, Mantle changes beneath the Barents shelf: New York Acad. Sci. Trans., ser. 2, v. 31, no. 1, p. 25–41.

———— 1969c, *in* Discussion of Soper: Geol. Soc. London Proc., December.

———— 1970, The Mesozoic geology of Svalbard (abs.): Am. Assoc. Petroleum Geologists Bull., v. 54, no. 12, p. 2484.

———— 1971, Tectonic transpression in Caledonian Spitsbergen: Geol. Mag., v. 108, no. 1, p. 27–41.

———— 1973, Mesozoic geology of Svalbard: this volume.

———— and R. A. Gayer, 1972, The Arctic Caledonides and earlier oceans: Geol. Mag., v. 109, no. 4, p. 289–314.

———— and W. T. Horsfield, in press, West Spitsbergen orogen, *in* Data for orogenic studies: Geol. Soc. London Spec. Pub. 4.

Heezen, B. C., 1962, The deep-sea floor, *in* S. K. Runcorn, ed., Continental drift: New York, Academic Press, p. 235–288.

———— and M. Ewing, 1961, the Mid-oceanic ridge and its extension through the Arctic basin, *in* G. O. Raasch, ed., Geology of the Arctic: Toronto, Univ. Toronto Press, v. 1, p. 662.

Horsfield, W. T., and P. I. Maton, 1970, Transform faulting along the de Geer line: Nature, v. 226, p. 256–257.

Johnson, G. L., 1969, Morphology of the Eurasian Arctic basin: Polar Record, v. 14, no. 92, p. 619–628.

———— and B. C. Heezen, 1967, The morphology and evolution of the Norwegian-Greenland Sea: Deep-Sea Research, v. 14, p. 755–771.

Livshitz, Yu. Ya., 1965, Tectonics of central Vestspitsbergen, *in* Materiali po geologii Spitsbergen: Inst. Geologii Arktiki Inf. Byull., p. 55–70 (translation by J. E. Bradley, W. B. Harland, ed., 1970, Geology of Spitsbergen: Natl. Lending Library Science and Technology, Boston Spa., Yorkshire, England.

Pringle, I. R., and B. A. Sturt, 1969, The age of the peak of the Caledonian orogeny in west Finnmark, north Norway: Norsk Geol. Tidsskr., v. 49, p. 435–436.

Siedlecka, Anna, and S. Siedlecki, 1968, Some new aspects of the geology of Varanger Peninsula (northern Norway): Norges Geol. Undersøkelse Prelim. Rept. No. 247, p. 288–306.

Stoneley, R., in press, Discussion of paper on Alaska: Geol. Soc. London Quart. Jour.

Sykes, L. R., 1965, The seismicity of the Arctic: Seismol. Soc. America Bull., v. 55, no. 2, p. 519–536.

Tailleur, I. L., and S. Snelson, 1969, Large-scale thrusting in northwestern Alaska possibly related to rifting of the Arctic Ocean (abs.): Geol. Soc. America Spec. Paper 121, p. 569.

———— and W. P. Brosgé, 1970, Tectonic history of northern Alaska, *in* W. L. Adkison, and M. M. Brosgé, eds., Proceedings of geological seminar on the North Slope of Alaska: Los Angeles, Pacific Sec. Am. Assoc. Petroleum Geologists, p. E1–E19.

Trettin, H. P., 1969, A Paleozoic-Tertiary fold belt in northernmost Ellesmere Island, aligned with the Lomonosov Ridge: Geol. Soc. America Bull., v. 80, p. 143–148.

———— 1973, Early Paleozoic evolution of northern parts of Canadian Arctic Archipelago: this volume.

van der Gracht, W. A. J. M. van Waterschoot, 1928, The problem of continental drift, and Remarks, *in* Theory of Continental Drift, a symposium: Am. Assoc. Petroleum Geologists, p. 1–75; 197–226.

Vogt, P. R., and N. A. Ostenso, 1970, Magnetic and gravity profiles across the Alpha Cordillera and their relation to Arctic sea floor spreading: Jour. Geophys. Research, v. 75, p. 4925–4937.

———— ———— and G. L. Johnson, 1970, Magnetic anomalies and sea-floor spreading north of Iceland: Jour. Geophys. Research, v. 76, p. 903.

———— *et al.*, 1969, Discontinuities in sea floor spreading: Tectonophysics, v. 8, no. 4–6, p. 286–317.

Vonderbank, K., 1970, Geologie und Fauna der Tertiären Ablagerungen Zentral-Spitsbergens: Norsk Polarinst. Skr. 153, 119 p. (Engl. abs.).

Wilson, J. T., 1963, Continental drift: Sci. American, April, p. 86–100.

———— 1966, Did the Atlantic close and then re-open?: Nature, v. 211, p. 676–681.

Economics of Petroleum Exploration and Production in the Arctic

Supply and Demand Applied to North American Arctic[1]

HENRY B. STEELE[2]

Houston, Texas

Abstract The economic potential of petroleum production from Alaska and other possibly productive areas in the North American Arctic regions is significant. There are basic distinctions between economic and geologic potential, and between exploration, development, and production costs for petroleum. Further distinctions exist between fixed and variable costs, between short-run and long-run costs, and between those expenditures which represent outlays for the purchase of actual goods and services (labor, materials, capital goods) and those expenditures which do not (lease bonuses and rentals, royalties, and various taxes). Projected production levels for North American Arctic oil for 1920 range from 5.2 million bbl per day at a price of $2.30 per barrel to 9.9 million bbl per day at a price of $4.44 per barrel.

Introduction

In comparison with the subject matter of the more technical disciplines of the natural sciences, the subject matter of economics appears rather simple and pedestrian. However, oversimplification of economic problems should be avoided. The more one substitutes "common sense" for genuine economic analysis, the greater is the likelihood that one's conclusions will be disoriented with respect to market realities. The purpose of this paper is to adapt the supply-and-demand framework, as generally understood, to the very special circumstances of the petroleum industry in the North American Arctic regions.

Everyone "knows" that prices are determined by supply and demand. The assumptions implicit in most popular discussions of market behavior seem to be the following: (1) Prices result from supply being "equated" with demand. (2) Supply depends upon the average cost of production, which is usually assumed to be constant under most circumstances, and is the same from company to company—and, hence, is the same for the entire industry or for any producer considered individually. (3) Demand, however, does vary, as between the total market demand and the demand for the output of any given company. Total industry demand is regarded as a given magnitude, in effect a constant, which does not actually vary with prices charged. The demand for the production

of an individual firm is regarded as independent of the output of the firm, so that each firm is seen as being able to sell as much as it can at the existing level of market price. (4) Consequently, with constant prices and constant production costs, a firm's profit is equal to its constant unit profit multiplied by its output rate. (5) To provide greater incentive for production, all that is necessary is a higher price, which will increase unit profits and motivate producers to sell more units in order to increase profits in both directions.

The inadequacies of the oversimplified frame of reference as applied to North American Arctic oil can be summarized under the following headings: (1) Total oil demand is not a fixed amount, but is a function of market price. (2) Production costs are not constant, but vary enormously from field to field and from well to well. (3) Total outlays of the oil industry are not identical with total production costs. (4) Actual interaction between price, demand, production rates, and the various components of "costs" is rather complex. There exists, at any given level of production, a *maximum* price, which is the highest price that could possibly be exacted from the buyer. At this price the buyer would be substantially indifferent to buying the goods or doing without them. For the same level of production there also exists a *minimum* price, which is the lowest price the seller could possibly be persuaded to accept in exchange for his production. At this price the seller would be substantially indifferent to making the sale and remaining in business as a going concern or leaving the industry.

The maximum price essentially reflects consumer demand. A buyer will never pay more for goods than the full value of what they are worth to him, although he will gladly pay less. The minimum price essentially measures minimum production cost, assuming maximum producing efficiency and the earning of the minimum competitive rate of return on investment necessary to keep the producer in the industry. In the long run, a seller will never produce any output for sale at a lower price, although he will gladly charge more.

In a purely competitive market, the maxi-

[1] Manuscript received, September 20, 1971.

[2] University of Houston.

mum and minimum prices are the same. But in all other markets, and particularly in oil and gas, there is an appreciable gap between maximum demand price and minimum supply price. This gap tends to be filled by such levies as taxes, royalties, bonuses, and rentals; by profits higher than the necessary minimum rate (so-called "economic profits"); and by production costs at levels higher than the efficient minimum. These outlays, not being a part of necessary production costs in an economic sense, do not determine prices; instead, they are, themselves, determined by the circumstance that prices lie above the level of minimum necessary production costs.

Why do prices lie above this level? In general, the answer is that there are imperfections in the competitive process which prevent all production from being supplied at minimum supply cost and marketed directly to buyers, who, themselves, would have to purchase competitively. In the case of oil, it is clear that the existing price has been determined by other elements than demand and minimum production costs. These elements include a congeries of historical factors, ranging from such private-market determinants as the traditionally strong market positions of some individual companies in certain regions, to public policies embodying official solicitude for such objectives as security of supply and conservation of oil as a physical stock. Nevertheless, although such concerns may, from time to time, have been influential in establishing crude oil prices at levels higher than could be explained on the basis of minimum production cost, the industry has been surprisingly competitive in reacting to price levels and changes in price levels.

ECONOMIC ANALYSIS OF ARCTIC OIL POTENTIAL

Hence, to analyze the economic potential of North American Arctic oil, we must sort out the various elements determining market prospects. These prospects depend primarily upon net profiles to producers after all production costs and noncost levies have been deducted from wellhead netbacks.[3] To assess these prospects, one must first focus attention upon well-

[3] A *netback price* is "the price realized by the producer or seller resulting from the use of the computed price; it may be more or less than the base price depending on the formula used and the location of the purchaser." Definition from *A Dictionary for Accountants,* 3d ed. (Eric L. Kohler, 1953: New York, Prentice-Hall, p. 22).

head prices and the factors influencing wellhead netbacks. Efforts must be directed next toward the study of the necessary costs of exploration, development, and production of the oil.

After having estimated probable levels for wellhead prices and for production costs, it becomes germane to consider what disposition will be made of the gap between the two. How much will be appropriated by various levels of resource-ownership interests, public and private? How much will remain with the producing companies? How are they likely to channel these funds between reinvestment in production and other applications?

In succeeding paragraphs, an estimate is made of the long-run supply response to the probable net price incentives faced by producers. Fundamental to this discussion is the distinction between economic and geologic potential in a given region. Attention must also be paid to the cost diversity of production from fields with varying reserves and locational advantages or disadvantages. The paper concludes with estimates of long-run relations between United States domestic crude oil price and total production from the North American Arctic regions for the years 1980, 1985, and 1990.

Net-Price Incentives for Producers

Wellhead netbacks—Crude oil prices at the wellhead depend on three major factors: (1) the quality of the oil, (2) the existing price at the market which is chosen as the reference point for wellhead pricing, and (3) the assigned transportation cost from the wellhead to the market which is chosen for reference pricing. All three of these factors are, to some extent, flexible in certain circumstances.

The actual magnitude of wellhead netbacks can be only very roughly approximated at the present time, because nothing is yet known about actual transportation costs from the North American Arctic regions to consuming markets, and because it is additionally necessary to forecast market prices ahead for the mid-1970s in order to anticipate the expected dates at which the Arctic oil will become available. If we take current prices after the 25¢-per-barrel increase recently posted as an estimate of mid-1970 prices, we are probably underestimating future prices. Nevertheless, by taking these prices in conjunction with the transportation cost estimates presented in the report of the Cabinet Task Force on Oil Import Control (1970), we can arrive at rough estimates of wellhead netbacks. For shipments to

Los Angeles, transport costs would be about $1.00 per barrel (75¢ for the Trans-Alaskan Pipeline and 25¢ for tanker shipment using U.S. flagships). Deducting this cost from an expected price of about $3.35, the wellhead netback is $2.35 per barrel. For shipments to the midwest via a pipeline up the Mackenzie Valley, transport costs are estimated at about $1.15–$1.25 per barrel. If prices in the Chicago area are about $3.60, then Chicago-area sales netbacks would be $2.35–$2.45 per barrel. Shipments to the East Coast via the Northwest Passage are of doubtful economic feasibility at present. The Task Force estimated pipeline costs from the North Slope to the East Coast as approximately $1.40–$1.50 per barrel. If an East Coast price of $3.85 is assumed, wellhead netbacks to this market would be $2.35–$2.45. Hence, United States netbacks all lie within about the same range. It is possible that these transport costs are underestimated, but, because it is likely that prices are also underestimated, the two sources of error will tend to cancel out.

Production costs—What production costs should be deducted from wellhead netbacks? There are few, if any, industries for which cost analysis is more difficult than for oil and gas. Among the major reasons for this are uncertainty in exploration, joint costs, and the very long time range for the composite process by means of which oil is discovered, developed, and produced. What is usually termed "production" cost for oil should be divided into separate cost categories—exploration, development, and field production (in the narrower sense of extraction).

In the long run, the minimum supply price for oil would be the sum of the necessary long-run exploration, development, and production costs per barrel, where these costs are computed to include the minimum rate of return on investment necessary to compensate investors for risks. In the oil industry, the necessary rate of return on risky operations may be relatively high. However, actual prices paid for oil may be well above minimum competitive supply price based on total long-run production costs. The reason for this, as suggested earlier, is that noncost items may readily fill the gap between maximum demand price and minimum production cost.

For example, any goods which cost relatively little to produce and are of great value to the buyer offer considerable profit potential to someone. In world oil markets, there are at least four major groups typically in contention:

resource owners, producing companies, consumers, and governments. Very little oil is produced from lands held in fee simple by oil companies; almost all oil comes from lands owned either privately or by state or national governments. If total producing costs are low and market prices are potentially quite high, the "surplus" over cost can be appropriated, in varying degrees, by landowners (particularly if the land is held by the governments of producing companies [ignoring inter-industry problems arising from varying degrees of vertical integration among firms and assuming, for simplicity, all companies to be fully integrated from oil and gas production through transportation, refining, and marketing]), by the governments of consuming countries, or conceivably even by the consumers themselves, who might combine and exert organized pressure to lower prices.

If producing companies are monopolistic, and consumers, landowners, and governments are passive, the surplus between production cost and maximum price might be appropriated by the companies as monopoly profits. If private landowners were the only actively monopolistic parties, the surplus would be dissipated through high lease bonuses and royalties. If public landowners were involved, the surplus might take the form of a host of various contributions to governments, including not only bonuses and royalties but also production and income taxes. If the governments of consuming countries were the only active agents, high taxes on consumption—particularly sales and excise taxes—would absorb the economic surplus. Finally, if producers were highly competitive and all other parties were passive, consumer prices would be based only on production costs, and the disappearance of the surplus would mean that the buyer was the beneficiary.

The gap between price and production cost is called "economic rent" by economists. In economic theory, economic rent is a surplus return which is susceptible to full confiscation without impairing the producer's ability to supply a commodity. In the case of minerals production, however, it is probably preferable to regard part of this surplus as a quasi-rent, at least to the extent that depletable resources must be replaced if the producer is to remain in business as a viable economic agent. Pure economic rent is a return which accrues only to resources which are absolutely fixed in supply and are hence undepletable.

The distinction between true production

costs and noncost levies ordinarily is not made in the day-to-day operations of oil companies. To them, royalties and taxes appear to be the same sort of expenses as drilling and development costs, because they all have the same negative effect on the cash flow. The basic distinction is that noncost levies are, in principle, negotiable, whereas true production costs are not. If production costs on a particular lease increase to the point where it is no longer profitable to continue production if a given percentage royalty is paid, negotiations may be undertaken to reduce the royalty rate rather than have production cease; but there is no way that producers can "negotiate" with the earth's crust in order to reduce the cost of drilling a given well. Although levies which are negotiable in principle may not be regarded as negotiable in practice, the fact remains that there is a basic difference between costs imposed by nature and payments contrived by human arrangement. (Recognition of this difference is not to argue that all taxes, for example, are in the nature of arbitrary tribute. State production taxes may in part constitute a mechanism for charging an industry for the true social costs incurred by the state for real public costs generated by oil development. Furthermore, higher-than-minimal operating costs imposed by regulations to protect natural environments may be justified on grounds that the true net social cost of oil production includes all costs of maintaining environments in their initial condition prior to oil development.)

With these distinctions in mind, let us attempt to estimate the true long-run production costs of oil produced at the wellhead in major fields in the North American Arctic. Many estimates of such costs have already been made on the basis of preliminary knowledge. M. A. Adelman (1971) has estimated the costs of Prudhoe Bay oil from 18¢ to 26¢ per barrel; the higher cost includes a 20-percent rate of return on investment. Charles Norman (1969) estimated that the costs would be between 23.5¢ and 27¢ per barrel, including a normal rate of return on investment. The Cabinet Task Force on Oil Import Control (1970) estimated economic costs at 28¢ per barrel, exclusive of an allowance of 8¢ per barrel for noncost levies such as production taxes and royalties. From this evidence, it appears reasonable to draw the conclusion that true production costs for the giant Prudhoe Bay field will be no more than about 30¢ per barrel, after allowing about

20 percent as a minimum rate of return on investment.

Wellhead netbacks versus minimum production cost—It therefore appears that, for the Prudhoe Bay field, the gap between wellhead netbacks of about $2.35–$2.45 and the minimum production cost of 30¢ leaves about $2.05–$2.15 to be contested between companies, landowners, governments, and perhaps even consumers. In Alaska, royalties and production taxes together are already greater than production costs, and there is every reason to expect continuing pressure for increases in these levies. If we assume a wellhead price of $2.40, a minimal 12.5 percent royalty amounts to 30¢ per barrel, and the contemplated 8-percent severance tax which will be applied to the most prolific wells will add another 19.2¢ per barrel. A so-called "disaster tax" of 1 percent adds another 2.4¢, making a total of 51.6¢ per barrel.

It is unlikely that all fields to be found in the North American Arctic will be as large as Prudhoe Bay. Some industry spokesmen express hope that several equally large, or even larger, fields will be found as other Alaskan and Canadian areas are explored; others pessimistically assume that Prudhoe Bay will be the only large field found in these regions. The former group points to the Middle East and notes the extremely favorable geology of other parts of the Western Hemisphere Arctic, especially the Canadian Arctic Islands. The latter group points to the East Texas field and notes that it is the only giant field found in that general area—or anywhere in the conterminous United States. It is certain that smaller fields will have higher production costs, and that the more remote fields will have higher transport costs to market.

Long-Run Supply Response to Net Price Incentives for Producers

In order to estimate the long-run supply schedule for North American Arctic oil, it is necessary to project the relations over time between crude oil prices in consuming markets and the amount of production which these prices will elicit, after allowing for the cost of transporting Arctic oil to the market. It is difficult enough to make such estimates for the Prudhoe Bay field, about which much already is known—but, in order to make 10- or 20-year projections, one must estimate the size and location and the production and other costs for an unknown number of undiscovered fields. A large part of such a projection is an exercise in sheer speculation.

In making supply-schedule projections, it is a mistake to assume mechanically that demand for oil increases autonomously at a given percentage rate per year, regardless of the price of oil. Although the demand for oil is not very sensitive to price levels, it is not wholly insensitive. More will be demanded at low prices than at high prices. If it proves increasingly expensive to find and produce oil, oil prices may rise relative to prices of other energy sources such as coal and nuclear power. Demand will be less at relatively high prices for oil, because some users will switch to other fuels. Thus, although one can project an estimated demand schedule for some future year which relates millions of barrels of oil demanded to the price per barrel, one cannot predict exactly how much oil will in fact be demanded—and supplied—until it is known how much can be produced at a given price, including all costs and levies. Hence, the role which Arctic oil—and oil in general—will play in energy markets of the future depends to a large extent on the success which the oil industry and its geologists encounter in Arctic exploration in the coming years.

The writer is currently participating in a study of United States oil and gas supply and demand during the period 1970–1990 (Steele et al., 1971). In this study, demand is projected to increase strongly throughout the period, even if prices reach levels substantially higher than those previously experienced. Oil and gas production is foreseen as responding very significantly in the long run to either price increases or decreases, all in Western Hemisphere areas, including Alaska and Canada. Price is taken as a variable, and supply and demand analyses are made of each area which can be expected to export oil to the United States. Spe-

cial cases are developed in which price is assumed to be (1) $2.30 per barrel—a price which is taken as corresponding with the Cabinet Task Force (1970) case, in which a liberalizing of import controls reduces prices by 80¢ per barrel; (2) $3.10 per barrel—the existing price before the recent price hike; and (3) the price necessary to keep United States imports from the Eastern Hemisphere down to a level of 10 percent of total domestic demand—the security objective specified by the Cabinet Task Force (1970). In none of these three cases was projected available supply from the North American Arctic great enough to prevent needs arising for reliance upon foreign imports from overseas sources to the extent of 20 percent or more of domestic demand, even if domestic prices were assumed to rise sharply.

In part, this forecast implies a less buoyant projection of American Arctic production by 1990 than others may be predicting. Even so, it is based on estimates that several other very large fields will be found in Alaska and Canada in the next 20 years, although it is not assumed that any of them will be larger than Prudhoe Bay.

Table 1 shows that, in 1980, total North American Arctic oil production is assumed to be quite responsive to the expected price level. If a constant price of $2.30 is expected to prevail during the entire period, total supply will be only 3.4 million bbl per day; if a steady price level of $4.44 is expected, output will be 4.8 million bbl per day. Over this price range, Alaskan production is foreseen to increase from 1.8 to 2.5 million bbl per day, and Arctic Canadian production is projected to increase from 1.6 million to 2.3 million bbl per day. As the time range increases, supply becomes steadily more responsive to price levels. By 1990, total production is seen to range from 5.2 to 9.9 million bbl per day at the two extremes of the

Table 1. Projected Production Levels for Crude Oil, at Various Prices, North American Arctic Regions—1980, 1985, 1990 (million bbl/day)

Price ($) 1970	1980			1985			1990			Cumulative Reserves Found (billion bbl)
	Alaska	Arctic Canada	Total	Alaska	Arctic Canada	Total	Alaska	Arctic Canada	Total	
2.30	1.8	1.6	3.4	2.2	2.8	5.0	2.3	2.9	5.2	21
3.10	2.0	1.8	3.8	3.0	3.0	6.0	3.7	3.7	7.4	29
3.85	2.2	2.0	4.2	3.6	3.2	6.8	4.7	4.2	8.9	36
4.44	2.5	2.3	4.8	4.1	3.5	7.6	5.3	4.6	9.9	41

Source: Author's own estimates; see text.

indicated price range. At the lowest price, it is estimated that total reserves of 21 billion bbl will have been proved, cumulatively, through 1990, whereas 41 billion bbl will have been proved at the highest price. At the lowest price, it is assumed that exploration efforts will be diverted in considerable measure from the conterminous United States to Canada and Alaskan exploration will remain at about the same level. At higher prices, it is assumed that expanded exploration will occur in all areas—including Canada, Alaska, and the conterminous United States.

CONCLUSIONS

In the market for crude oil, supply and demand are not fixed magnitudes. Instead, each is a function of the price level. For the large oil fields, price may be much higher than production cost, but there is a tendency for noncost levies to fill the gap. Supply prospects depend upon net price incentives to producers; these incentives are a function of wellhead netbacks, production costs, and noncost levies. Although the economic potential of North American Arctic oil is less than its sheer geologic potential, the true economic potential should not be underestimated. Projected production levels in 1990 range from 5.2 million bbl per day at a price of $2.30 per barrel to 9.9 million bbl per day at a price of $4.44 per barrel.

REFERENCES CITED

Adelman, M. A., 1971, Significance of shifts in world oil supplies, in Alaskan oil-cost and supply: New York, Praeger (Adelman, Bradley & Norman).

Cabinet Task Force on Oil Import Control, 1970, The oil import question: Washington, D.C. (esp. p. 48, 49, 226, 227).

Norman, C. A., 1969, Economic analysis of Prudhoe Bay oil field, Alaska: Cambridge, Mass., Massachusetts Inst. of Technology, M.A. thesis.

Steele, H. B., J. H. Lichtblau, and D. V. Rustow, 1971, Economic and political aspects of United States oil import control policies: New York, Petroleum Industry Research Found., Inc. (tentative title; manuscript still in preparation).

Arctic Oil and the World—One Perspective[1]

DANIEL C. ION[2]

London, England

Abstract The Arctic is the latest "accretion" to the prospective petroliferous area of the world which, historically, has grown in steps as new areas have come within reach through technical and economic breakthroughs.

The production of Arctic oil will depend on the effort expended. Historically, though total world oil supply and demand have increased smoothly and exponentially, individual-country production and demand have moved in steps as the effort expended has varied with the presence or absence of restrictions, self or externally imposed.

Resulting world oil-supply patterns over the past 30 years also have shown some marked and varied changes.

On the basis of presently indicated reserves, it appears that North American Arctic oil will be used in the U.S.A. However, the predicted world supply pattern in 1985 probably would be changed significantly if the North American Arctic had proved to be equal to the Middle East in size of reserves.

Introduction

The Arctic is the lastest "accretion" to the prospective petroliferous area of the world which, historically, has grown in steps. These steps have resulted from (1) expanding geologic concepts—*e.g.,* the shift from Iran to Arabia in the early 1930s and the shift from land to offshore exploration in the early 1950s; (2) the development and application of new exploration tools—*e.g.,* geophysical techniques in the U.S. Gulf Coast in the 1920s; (3) the adaptation of techniques to overcome hostile environments as economic and political factors opened up new areas for exploration—*e.g.,* North Africa and the Arctic.

Expanding Geologic Concepts

Redwood (1896) illustrated the known world petroleum deposits and indications of petroleum, and, even from the time of publication of the fourth edition of his map (1922) to 1970, it is surprising how few other major accumulations have been reported on land. However, the pace of exploitation has been dependent partly on breakthroughs in geologic thinking.

For example, in the 1920s the general geologic opinion regarding the Middle East was that only heavy oils were likely to be found on the Arabian foreland. This opinion seemed confirmed by the discovery of heavy oil in Kuh-i-Mund on the Persian side in 1931 (Emmons, 1931, Fig. 395, p. 668). However, in 1932 came the discovery of oil by the first well drilled on the Bahrain Island anticline. This discovery altered the picture completely, and the whole of the Arabian side of the gulf became prospective. It was in fact a major breakthrough, which was followed by the discoveries in 1936 at Dammam, Saudi Arabia, in 1938 at Burgan, Kuwait, and in 1939 at Dukhan, Qatar. These discoveries within 7 years outlined the great potential of the Middle East, which now has about 62 percent of the published proved reserves of the world.

Another example of a significant breakthrough is that regarding offshore potential. In 1947, the prospective areas of the world (Weeks, 1947) were limited to land area. One evaluation (World Oil Atlas, 1947) of these areas was, in part, that petroleum potential of Alaska and Australia was small, and that of Africa, including Libya, was poor.

In 1954, the AAPG review of the world's prospects included the continental-shelf areas (Hedberg, 1954). This recognition, not only of the offshore potential but of the technical possibilities of exploration and exploitation, was a major leap forward—the biggest in the last 30 years.

In 1957 there was activity off only five countries; in 1963 there was activity off 56 countries and 12 percent of the world's proved reserves were estimated to be offshore; in 1970, almost 20 percent of the world's production was from offshore areas. In 1963, one estimate was that 20 percent of the world's proved reserves were offshore (Weeks, 1963); indeed, the in-place oil of offshore areas may be a much higher proportion of the world's resource base.

The 1970 map on this aspect (International Petroleum Encyclopedia, 1970, p. 28–29) is interesting because the offshore areas are drawn much more diagrammatically, implying that the continental slopes and rises cannot now be ex-

[1] Manuscript received, October 18, 1971.

Permission to publish this paper has been given by the British Petroleum Co., Ltd.

[2] British Petroleum Co., Ltd.

cluded from the prospective areas. This reevaluation was the outcome of a breakthrough in knowledge and thinking about the ocean floors, the revival and modification of scientific ideas about continental drift, new concepts of plate tectonics, and other innovations which are increasing the prospective areas offshore. Some think that small ocean basins may be the next and most important additions to prospective areas.

The application of these new ideas of crustal deformation and their causes are amending classic ideas on the growth of major structural land features that may well have practical implications on land prospects for petroleum.

In the past, the communication of new ideas and their cross-fertilization, acceptance, and application by science and industry in different areas were slow, and, even with hindsight, it is difficult to pinpoint certain scientific breakthroughs (Dott and Reynolds, 1969; Hubbert, 1966).

An example is that the first major field in the Middle East, Masjid-i-Sulaiman, was discovered by the first well on May 26, 1908, but not until 1919 was the reservoir rock identified as the Asmari Limestone by S. J. Shand; and it was another 4 years before this identification was accepted. G. A. Alexin (1962) also illustrated, with many examples from the USSR, the slow development and acceptance of new ideas in petroleum exploration.

NEW EXPLORATION TOOLS

Many of the prospective areas in the United States thought to be unfavorable in 1931 (Arnold and Kemnitzer, 1931) had been explored and found productive of oil by 1963 (Weeks, 1963), mainly because of the geophysical breakthrough in the 1920s, particularly in the U.S. Gulf Coast (Halbouty and Hardin, 1955). The surge in production is shown by the steep rise, from 1925 to 1933, from 145 to 403 million bbl. To this surge, of course, the East Texas field contributed from 1928 onward.

Geophysical methods have continued to improve (Link, 1966; Dobrin, 1970), and the interdependence of the geologist and geophysicist has become increasingly obvious (Ion, 1958).

Increasingly in the future, one can expect new scientific concepts and new technology to be much more rapidly and universally adopted. However, although they are very important factors in pushing back the frontiers, they are not the only ones, nor indeed have they ever been.

TECHNICAL ADAPTATION AND ECONOMIC AND POLITICAL FACTORS

The expansion of the prospective area in North Africa (Weeks, 1947; Heatzig and Michel, 1969) was the result of several factors:

1. The North African campaigns of World War II both reduced the mystery of the Sahara (a psychological factor) and provided the means to explore by land, using half-tracks and camel-foot tires, etc., and from the air, with the development of aerial photography, interpretation, and mapping of desert areas.

2. Incentive was given to French exploration by the desire of the French government for more oil from their own controlled territories, and the Bureau des Recherches des Pétroles was established as the instrument of their financial support.

3. Changes in scientific ideas about the geology of the North African basins occurred, although there was strong advocacy by only a few enthusiasts.

Hence, there were technologic, politico-economic, and scientific factors leading to the discoveries in 1956 of Edjeleh, Hassi Messaoud, and Hassi R'Mel—which put Algeria, and thus North Africa, on the map.

The subsequent fast development of North Africa, particularly Libya, was predominantly due to politico-economic factors: the French troubles in Algeria; the U.S.A. conditions which encouraged U.S. independents to "go foreign"; and the Suez 1956 incident, which gave potential North African oil added value because it was on a short haul to Europe, which had a fast-rising demand.

Exploration in the Arctic leading to the Prudhoe Bay discovery was not the result of a new geologic concept, a new tool, or a new adaptation. The basic technology, at least for exploring and drilling in the "dry" Arctic areas, had been built up gradually over the past 15 years. The main drive was increasing politico-economic incentives caused by the increasing lack of success to meet U.S. demand with U.S. oil.

EXPLORATION-DEVELOPMENT EFFORT

This lack of success in the U.S. has many causes. In 1967 the National Petroleum Council (1967a) listed 15 major factors—geological technological, economic, and political—which affected operations during the period of 1946–1965, but considered that "... the various factors affecting petroleum operations are so interrelated that their influence cannot be measured separately in most cases. Economic conditions often serve to stimulate technology and policy changes. Similarly technology and policies influence costs and prices."

Their view that "additional resources remain to be found" has had recent confirmation (NPC, 1970; see also Cram, 1971); however, as this latest report notes, ". . . the trend for expenditures that do the work (geology, geophysics, drilling and completing wells, *etc.*) has remained practically flat since 1958." The report further stresses that this trend ". . . is inimical to the development of the country's enormous petroleum resources," particularly as "new exploratory ideas and concepts more frequently spring from the results of drilling." There can be no quarrel with such opinions.

Strong arguments, however, have arisen (1) as to whether increased domestic production is essential for economic and security reasons or is unessential on one or both counts; (2) as to the means whereby the optimum supply pattern, whatever it may be, can be achieved; and (3) as to whether to give industry incentive and freedom or to increase government control and management. There probably has never been an argument so well documented as that regarding the importance of the domestic oil industry. However, I wish to stress, as others have, that the oil industry is not monolithic. Every company has its own motivations; the public as well as the governments in most countries is increasingly interested, educable, and important, and no country can consider its oil problems in isolation from the rest of the world (Ion, 1970). These points can be illustrated from events in other countries.

The history of the Mexican oil industry illustrates the complexity of the factors which govern the production curve of any single country. Although one might have thought at first that expropriation was a self-imposed restriction on production, that generalization is too simple. Expropriation did not come in 1921 and cause the dramatic fall in production from 193 to 32 million bbl in 1932; it came in 1938. The phenomenal rise of production from 64 million bbl in 1918 to the 1921 peak was due to development of flush production in the Tampico–Golden Lane areas; the slightly less rapid decline to 50 million bbl in 1928 was partly due to the depletion of the known pools, but also to other external and internal factors, many rooted in history, with importance varying according to the different protagonists in the argument (Serrocold, 1938; Marrett, 1939; Powell, 1965).

Many problems beset the industry in the 10 years to 1938, and many more unforeseen ones arose after expropriation, which was imposed for complex, and even mutually incompatible, reasons. Since 1945, however, production has increased steadily to the present figure of more than 164 million bbl per annum.

One specific point has general significance— that of available alternative supply sources. The troubles in Mexico in the early 1930s were paralleled by growing awareness of the richness of Venezuela regarding petroleum potential, and considerable exploratory effort was diverted to that country.

Indonesia also has had a troubled history. The more or less steady increase in production from 1918 was drastically halted by World War II and the resulting oocupation by the Japanese. Recovery after 1946 was retarded, from 1960 to 1966, by the new legislation aimed at nationalization and restructuring onto a contract basis for foreign participation. Indonesia long has been considered a particularly rich oil province, and it will be most interesting to see what results arise from the increasing recent efforts to attract exploration.

The period 1951–1957 in Iran provides an illustration of the complexity of factors governing the petroleum industry. Production fell from more than 242 million bbl in 1950 to 7.8 million bbl in 1952, and only in early 1957 was the 1950 rate restored.

Venezuela has a different history. Whereas in Iran the self-imposed restriction was short term and, since 1957, there has been increasing pressure to increase production, in Venezuela there has in fact been a long-term restriction. The petroleum economic policy of the Venezuelan government was described (Martinez, 1963) as one of maintaining the production rate at the current level or allowing for a 4 percent yearly increase in order to conserve the oil, which is a nonrenewable resource, and preserve the price structure in the world crude market. Martinez forecast a maximum rate of production in 1973 at 1,400 million bbl on a calculated petroleum resource or ultimate recoverable reserves of 69.2 billion bbl. That forecast may well be close to the actual because of consistent government action.

In Canada there was a rapid rise in production rate from 1950. Canadian production was helped by the demands on the U.S.A. created by the Korean war (1950–1954) and, in 1956, by the closing of the Suez Canal. However, from 1957 to 1960, production was restricted by the imposition of import controls by the U.S.A. Increase resumed as agreement was reached between Canada and the U.S., but U.S. imports again were subject to restriction imposed in March 1970. In essence, Canadian producers consider that their reserves potential would, without restriction, have enabled production to continue on the 1950–1956 curve projection. The agreement announced in November 1970 between the U.S. and Canada should allow a much easier flow of oil in the future.

In Libya, the tremendous surge of production from its start in 1961 to the end of 1969 is unrivaled in the oil industry; but in 1970 most of the producing companies were cut back by the government, officially in the cause of conservation of resources to prevent overexploitation of the reservoirs. At the end of 1969, according to the Oil and Gas Journal, the proved reserves of Libya were about 35 billion bbl. How these reserves will grow and what production will materialize will depend on the presence or absence of constraints internally or externally imposed on exploration and development.

These examples in the fluctuations in individual-country productions are important in considering the possible trends in production from the Arctic, because they show how seriously one must weigh the factors other than the potential resource base, the various costs, and market demand.

Historically, these fluctuations have been masked in the smooth and exponential increase in total world supply and demand, but they have affected the world supply patterns and they should be considered before looking to the future.

WORLD SUPPLY PATTERNS

By 1955 the pattern of the main oil movements by sea had recovered from the dislocation of World War II and was from the three major producing areas (the U.S.A., the Caribbean, and the Middle East) to the two major consuming areas (the U.S. East Coast and Europe). Basically, the movement was from the U.S. Gulf Coast to the U.S. East Coast, from the Caribbean to the U.S. East Coast, and from the Middle East to Europe via the Suez Canal (British Petroleum, 1955)

In the 15-year period to 1970, the chief points about the pattern of the main oil movements by sea have been the following.

1. The dramatic changes effected by the two closures of the Suez Canal, short-lived in 1956 and longer in 1967; but the economic effect was lessened by the development for the long haul around the Cape of Good Hope of very large tankers, which will henceforth be a permanent feature of sea transportation. There could be no more striking illustrations of the flexibility of the noncommunist world oil industry.

2. The growth of the major new supply sources of North and West Africa and, particularly in 1967, the importance of the former.

3. The changed position of the U.S.A., from export of approximately 136 million bbl and import of 440 million bbl in 1955, to export of 63 million bbl and import of approximately 1,140 million bbl in 1969.

4. The growth of demand in North America, northwest Europe and, most spectacularly, Japan.

FUTURE OF ARCTIC OIL

The prospective area of the Arctic is merely the latest, and probably by no means the last, of the "accretions" to the areas of the world which are prospective for oil. However, its development and that of future areas will depend on the effort applied, and that cannot be assessed only on U.S. domestic circumstances.

Milton Lipton (1969) considered North Slope oil as pivotal to U.S. oil policy—by keeping the options open and leaving room for a "more comfortable choice" in deciding a balance between domestic, Canadian, and offshore crudes through the 1970s.

However, if one adds to the 30–40 billion bbl of oil from the North Slope—taken as the "high" figure by Milton Lipton—an equal amount from the Canadian Arctic as being proved by 1980 and a total of 150 billion bbl indicated by 1990, what would be the position?

Many people believe that trying to forecast so far ahead is moving into the realm of fantasy. M. A. Adelman, when making a long-term oil-price forecast, refused in November 1969 to look beyond 1985 because ". . . what happens after that has such a low present value that ignorance of it can be borne."

However, I believe that a look ahead can have value if one appreciates that it is only an exercise; it can help to keep all options open and prevent hasty, irrevocable decisions on currently known facts by emphasizing that these facts are still only a small part of the eventual.

In such an exercise, the assumptions may be as important as the results; unfortunately, however, it is common for the results to be remembered and the assumptions ignored. Generally, this oversight is because the assumptions are not given or they are given only in very broad terms because of space limitations. This exposition suffers from the latter problem.

General Qualitative Assumptions for Period 1970–1990

1. There is no world war.

2. The momentum of the politico-social forces of the past 100 years will be sufficient to carry on for another 20 years the same broad energy requirements and production, despite increasing questioning of the desirability of an industrialized society as the goal of mankind and increasing awareness of the fragility of the physical environment and the interdependence of its many aspects. This opinion presupposes that there will be no major social revolution and that, through increased knowledge of the environment, methods will be developed to maintain or achieve acceptable qualities of environment. These qualities may vary with locality but in total must also be acceptable (Chapman, 1970).

3. The momentum of the politico-economic forces, evolving particularly over the past 20 years, will continue to develop and react in such a way as to ensure that total costs will be covered by prices sufficient to insure the employment of adequate capital. The relative roles and involvement of producing governments, consuming governments, and large and small companies in the industry may well change, but it is assumed that basic, normal economics will still guide.

It is in this last area that probably the greatest changes will occur, because the physical costs of practical exploration, refining, transportation, and marketing "are only a fraction of current prices" (Adelman, 1969). The great flexibility is in the monies taken by the producing and consuming countries, each of which has its own individual motivations and methods of achieving the revenues which it considers to be required.

There are basically only two overriding principles: oil has no value without a market and there is no oil market without oil. In practice, even these may be ignored in certain circumstances—e.g., as the first principle was in Iran in 1951. However, with time and greater sophistication, the so-called market forces are being used to effect truly competitive supply. Libya in 1970 is a good example. The problem

is that oversimplification, as noted with Mexican expropriation, can lead to wrong thinking.

1990 World Supply-Demand Exercise

The numbers in Table 1 are *not* intended to be forecasts; they are reasonable in only my personal view, but they do not knowingly offend any known current thinking on the order of possibilities. The big hypothetical assumption is in the reserves figures for Alaska and the Canadian Arctic beyond the 40 billion bbl each which some have already suggested.

The resulting supply pattern implies that North America would, in quantity, be almost balanced; in effect, 2.0 million bbl/day of oil would be imported by the U.S. from the Eastern Hemisphere (let us assume from Africa and Indonesia equally). In the Eastern Hemisphere, as now, Western Europe and Japan would be the deficit areas. One would assume that Western Europe would be supplied broadly as to 13 million bbl/day from Africa, 7 million bbl/day from the USSR, and 19 million bbl/day from the Middle East. Japan would take preferably 11 million bbl/day from "other Eastern Hemisphere," predominantly Indonesia and offshore eastern and southern Asia; 10 million bbl/day from the Middle East; and 5 million bbl/day from the eastern USSR.

The supply pattern also implies an average annual addition of about 1 million bbl/day in the Arctic, the USSR, the Middle East, and the rest of the Eastern Hemisphere. To the development costs must be added the costs of finding the new oil in these and the other areas, particularly in Africa and the rest of the Western Hemisphere. The total is obviously enormous. Indeed, it is the magnitude of this sum to be provided over the next 20 years—not any shortage of the oil resource base—that may cause some to doubt whether a demand of 150 million bbl/day could be met in 1990.

Assuming this demand figure is more or less correct, any shortfall under 20 million bbl/day from the Arctic would have to be met by greater production elsewhere.

In 20 years time in the U.S. and Canada, probably only production from nonconventional oil (coal, tar sands, oil shales) would be capable of major increase. Mexico is considered as self-supporting though with a much increased consumption. In Venezuela, at 2.5 million bbl/day, a declining production from about 1980 is assumed. South America has already been given an increase from 1.4 to 5 million bbl/day, but this may well be an underesti-

Table 1. 1990 World Supply-Demand Exercise
(million bbl/day)

	Demand	Supply	Surplus	(Deficit)	Hemisphere Balance	Notes
U.S.A. (Lower 48)	32.5	8		(24.5)		(1)
Canada	5	4		(1.0)		
Arctic	0	20	20			(2)
Venezuela	2.5	2.5				
Other W. Hemisphere	4.5	5	.5			
Nonconventional crudes		3	3			
TOTAL W. HEMISPHERE	44.5	42.5	23.5	(25.5)	(2)	
W. Europe	40	1		(39.0)		(3)
Communist area	21	33	12			(4)
Africa	6	20	14			
Middle East	3	32	29			(5)
Japan	27	0.5		(26.5)		(6)
Other E. Hemisphere	8	20.5	12.5			(7)
TOTAL E. HEMISPHERE	105	107	67.5	(65.5)	2	
ROUNDED TOTAL WORLD	150	150	91	(91.0)	0	(8)

Source: Author's own estimates.
Notes:

(1) Implied demand increases 5½ percent in 1969–80 and 5 percent in 1980–90; U.S. demand for 1980 is considered to be 20 million bbl/day. (Emerson [1970] gives 25 million bbl/day, and API [1970] gives 20 million bbl/day.)

(2) Implied production for 1980 at 8 million bbl/day. *Cf.* Lipton (1969) high estimate 1980 at 5 million bbl/day and Emerson (1970), 2.5 million bbl/day for Alaska. Implied proved reserves as of 1980 at 80 billion bbl; as of 1990, 150 billion bbl.

(3) European Economic Community (1970) estimate of 20 million bbl/day, to which U.K. and rest of Europe demand has been added.

(4) U.S. Bureau of Mines (1970) demand forecast, 6.84 million bbl/day for 1980 for USSR.

(5) Implied proved reserves as of 1990 at 175 billion bbl.

(6) Ministry of International Trade and Industry (1970) forecast for 1980 at 17 million bbl/day increased at 10 percent per annum to 1990.

(7) Including SE Asia at 10+ million bbl/day.

(8) Moody (1970) estimated 98 million bbl/day for noncommunist world.

mate if the eastern offshore possibilities materialize.

In the Eastern Hemisphere, the Middle East is the obvious known large producer. The published proved reserves are approximately 332 billion bbl (Oil and Gas Jour., 1969), and an average production over 20 years of more than 20 million bbl/day entails the use of approximately 140 billion bbl; hence, 32 million bbl/day of production in 1990 gives a production-reserves ratio of approximately 1/16—without any new discoveries. Another possibility is the USSR; there is no doubt that its potential is very large indeed. Hendricks (1965, Table 7) estimated for the USSR, China, and Mongolia approximately 2,900 billion bbl of oil in place and 1,800 billion bbl expected to be discovered. Moody (1970) estimated the undiscovered potential of the USSR and satellite nations as 350 billion bbl, about 40 percent of the world's total undiscovered potential. Hence, if the logistic and physical problems of the exploitation of petroleum, mainly in Siberia, offshore and onshore, can be overcome, the weight of such re-

serves may in fact already have predetermined a 1990 production of more than the 25 million bbl/day allowed in Table 1 from the planned 10 million bbl/day in 1975.

Conclusions

It is again stressed that this exercise in forecasting is based on some very major assumptions which must not be ignored. It should be possible to judge, on the basis of the increase in available facts from this symposium, whether the major assumption of a potential Arctic production of 20 million bbl/day in 1990 is reasonable. It might even be possible to computerize the facts, factors, and probabilities, and possibly even the costs.

However, the following broad conclusions are unlikely to be changed.

1. By 1990 the world may well be in a tight supply position even if (a) the Arctic is producing 20 million bbl/day, which will be required in the U.S., and (b) considerable exploration effort and resulting discoveries have occurred around the world, including the USSR.

2. Increasing volumes will make more difficult the loss of any major source; and a balanced supply-demand pattern, even at a level lower than 150 million bbl/day, can only be achieved if there are minimum constraints consistent with reasonable attention to conservation of the environment.

Selected References

Adelman, M. A., 1969, A long term price forecast: Jour. Petroleum Technology, v. 21, p. 1515–1520.

Alexin, G. A., 1962, in Proceedings of United Nations inter-regional seminar on techniques of petroleum development, January 23–February 21, 1962: New York, United Nations Dept. Econ. and Social Affairs, 1964.

American Petroleum Institute, 1970: Petroleum Intelligence Weekly, June 15, 1970.

Arnold, R., and W. J. Kemnitzer, 1931, Petroleum in the United States and possessions . . . : New York, Harper & Bros., 1052 p.

British Petroleum Company, 1955, Statistical review, Annual Series: London, British Petroleum Co.

Chapman, P. F., 1970, Energy production—a world limit: New Sci., v. 720, p. 634–636.

Cram, I. H., ed., 1971, Future petroleum provinces of the United States—their geology and potential: Am. Assoc. Petroleum Geologists Mem. 15, 1496 p.

Dobrin, M., 1969, Evaluation of marine reconnaissance techniques: Houston, Texas, 1st Ann. Offshore Tech. Conf., May 18–21, 1969, Preprints, v. 1, p. 375–386.

Dott, R. H., Sr., and M. J. Reynolds, 1969, Sourcebook for petroleum geology: Am. Assoc. Petroleum Geologists Mem. 5, 471 p.

Emerson, J., 1970: Oil and Gas Jour., June.

Emmons, W. H., 1931, Geology of petroleum, 2d ed.: New York, McGraw-Hill, 736 p.

European Economic Community, 1970: Petroleum Press Service, July.

Halbouty, M. T., and G. Hardin, 1955, New geological studies result in discoveries of large gas and oil reserves from salt dome structures in the Texas Louisiana Gulf Coast: Rome, Italy, 4th World Petroleum Cong. Proc., v. 2, sec. 1.

Heatzig, G., and R. Michel, 1969, Petroleum developments in North Africa in 1968: Am. Assoc. Petroleum Geologists Bull., v. 53, no. 8, p. 1700–1727.

Hedberg, H., 1954, World oil prospects—from a geological viewpoint: Am. Assoc. Petroleum Geologists Bull., v. 38, p. 1714–1724.

Hendricks, J., 1965, Resources of oil, gas, and natural gas liquids in the United States and the world: U.S. Geol. Survey Circ. 522, 22 p.

Hubbert, M. K., 1966, History of petroleum geology and its bearing upon present and future exploration: Am. Assoc. Petroleum Geologists Bull., v. 50, no. 12, p. 2504–2518.

International Petroleum Encyclopedia, 1970: Tulsa, Oklahoma, Petroleum Publishing Co., 400 p.

Ion, D. C., 1958, Interdependence in world-wide oil exploration: Geophysics, v. 23, p. 318–328.

———— 1970, Communication problems in reserve concepts and in environmental control, in Exploration and economics of the petroleum industry, new ideas, new methods, new developments: New York, Mathew Bender, v. 8, p. 31.

Link, W. C., 1966, An expert gives a geological approach to reserve ultimate of the U.S.: Oil and Gas Jour., August 22, p. 150–151.

Lipton, M., 1969, Implications of the North Slope for North American oil: Jour. Petroleum Technology, v. 21, p. 1511–1514.

Marrett, R. H. K., 1939, An eyewitness of Mexico: London, Oxford Univ. Press.

Martinez, A. R., 1963, Estimation of the magnitude and duration of oil resources: Frankfurt, Germany, 6th World Petroleum Cong. Proc., sec. 8, paper 17, p. 133–148.

Ministry of International Trade and Industry (Japan), 1970: Platts Oilgram, June.

Moody, J. D., 1970, Petroleum demands of future decades: Am. Assoc. Petroleum Geologists Bull., v. 54, no. 12, p. 2239–2245.

National Petroleum Council, 1967a, Factors affecting U.S. exploration, development and production—introduction: Washington, D.C.

———— 1967b, The impact of new technology on the U.S. petroleum industry, 1946–1965: Washington, D.C.

———— 1970, Future petroleum provinces of the United States, a summary: Washington, D.C., 138 p.

Oil and Gas Journal, 1969: December 12.

Powell, J. R., 1965, The Mexican petroleum industry—1938–1950: Los Angeles, Univ. California Press.

Redwood, Boverton, 1896, A treatise on petroleum, 1st ed.: London, Chas. Griffin & Co.

———— 1922, A treatise on petroleum, 4th ed.: London, Chas. Griffin & Co.

Serrocold, J., 1938, Oil in Mexico: London, Chapman & Hall.

U.S. Bureau of Mines, 1970: World Petroleum, August.

U.S. Geological Survey, 1922, The oil supply of the United States: Am. Assoc. Petroleum Geologists Bull., v. 6, no. 1, p. 42–46.

Weeks, L. G., 1947, Highlights on development in foreign petroleum fields: Am. Assoc. Petroleum Geologists Bull., v. 31, p. 1135–1193.

———— 1963, World wide review of petroleum exploration: Frankfurt, Germany, 6th World Petroleum Cong. Proc., p. 231–233.

Winger, J., 1970, The petroleum situation: New York, Chase Manhattan Bank, Monthly Review, November (also other writings).

World Oil Atlas, 1947: Oil Weekly, June, p. 15.

Exploration and Production in Canadian Arctic Archipelago[1]

A. N. EDGINGTON, D. L. CAMPBELL, and N. A. CLELAND[2]

Calgary, Alberta, Canada

Abstract The Canadian Arctic Archipelago includes all islands north of the Canadian mainland and west of Greenland, extending north from the mainland a distance of 1,400 mi (2,255 km) and having a maximum east-west extent of approximately 1,500 mi (2,415 km). The climate is characterized by long cold winters, short cool summers, and very low precipitation.

The remote location, the dearth of permanent settlements and service facilities, and the extremely harsh climate pose many problems for those engaged in exploration work and will contribute peculiar difficulties for future exploitation of the area's immense mineral resources.

There are unusual problems which have been or will be encountered when operating in the Arctic, but techniques have been developed to overcome them. Despite these adverse factors, it appears that the potential rewards of Arctic exploration are commensurate with the risks.

INTRODUCTION

The Northwest Territories of Canada compose most of Canada north of 60°N lat. and are divided for practical administrative purposes into three provisional districts: Keewatin, Mackenzie, and Franklin. The District of Franklin, covering nearly 550,000 sq mi (884,990 km^2), includes the Hudson Straits Islands, Boothia and Melville Peninsulas, and the Arctic Archipelago. The Canadian Arctic Archipelago extends from 61°N lat. at the southern tip of Resolution Island, just south of Baffin Island, to 83°N lat. at the northern extremity of Ellesmere Island, a distance of approximately 1,400 mi (2,255 km); the maximum east-west extent is slightly greater.

Recorded exploration of the Arctic Islands commenced approximately 450 years ago with the search for the Northwest Passage and resulted in such place names as Davis Strait, Baffin Bay, Hudson Bay, and Frobisher Bay. Polar exploration was further advanced by whaling and sealing enterprises and the fur trade, to which the Hudson Bay Company has devoted 3 centuries of corporate effort. The efforts of many expeditions to reach the North Pole, continuing attempts to find the Northwest Passage, and eventually the search for the lost Franklin Expedition established the basic cartography of the islands but yielded only a smattering of geologic knowledge from widely separated points.

The first geologic map was compiled by Haughton (1859) in 1854. This map offered a broad interpretation of the few facts that were provided by the earlier expeditions of Captains Belcher, Kellett, Collinson, and M'Clure. It was not until the post-war years in the late 1940s that the first long-range, systematically planned geologic exploration of the islands was commenced by the Canadian government when the Geological Survey of Canada started an extensive reconnaissance program. This work was fundamental to the opening of the Arctic Islands territory to oil and gas exploration; however, the value of the Geological Survey's contribution is not limited to geology; its operations on the islands also provided the basic knowledge of how to live and work in this remote and inhospitable area.

EXPLORATION

Shortly after the war, trimetrogon photography was flown for all of northern Canada; it was followed, between 1958 and 1962, by vertical photography covering much the same area. Once these aerial photographs became available, it was apparent to geologists who examined them that the Canadian Arctic Islands included not only a considerable thickness of sediments, but also many very large-scale fold and piercement-type structures that might be conducive to the trapping of oil and gas. By the late 1950s, enough was known of the geology of the area to attract the attention of industry. In February 1959, several companies and individuals applied to the Canadian government for petroleum and natural gas permits. Formal regulations were promulgated by the Canadian government in June 1960 covering petroleum and natural gas rights in the Arctic Islands, and more than 40 million acres of oil and gas permits were issued within a relatively short time thereafter.

The Canadian Arctic Islands were referred to by the late J. C. Sproule as an "open geological book," because of the excellent exposures

---

[1] Manuscript received, October 18, 1971.
[2] J. C. Sproule and Associates Ltd.

which permit ready field study of an apparently complete stratigraphic section and of many structural features. The widespread exposures permit relatively inexpensive acquisition of first-rate structural and stratigraphic data through the study of aerial photographs.

Photogeology, although an invaluable tool in the early phases of exploration anywhere, is never a substitute for surface geologic investigations. The remoteness of the area, the shortness of the field season, and the fact that field crews must have air support result in very high per-diem costs. Fortunately, these high per-diem costs are offset to a large extent by the quantity and quality of geologic information that can be obtained in a short time.

Geophysical operations, including gravity surveys and reflection and refraction seismic work, have also been undertaken in the islands, but they, too, are costly because of the environmental conditions.

Typical exploration costs are outlined below.

Geologic field party: Approximately $80,000-plus per month for a party consisting of four to six geologists supported by helicopter and fixed-wing aircraft.
Gravity survey: Approximately $50,000 per month for a two-man party using a helicopter.
Seismic survey: $300,000 to $400,000 per month; approximately $4,000 per mile.

PETROLEUM PROSPECTS

The oil and gas potential of the Canadian Arctic Islands has been demonstrated by the numerous occurrences of hydrocarbons in outcrop and by the results of exploratory drilling. Surface indications of the presence of hydrocarbons are common on the islands, mostly in beds of Paleozoic age. Bituminous shales are widespread. The largest surface occurrences of hydrocarbons have been found as grahamite in Silurian beds on eastern Bathurst Island and as extensive oil sands containing heavy oil in the Lower Triassic of northwest Melville Island.

Minor gas shows were encountered in the Dome *et al.* No. 1 Winter Harbour well drilled on southern Melville Island in 1961, but none were potentially commercial. The original Panarctic Drake Point well—drilled on Sabine Peninsula, Melville Island, in 1969—penetrated high-pressure gas zones and blew out of control. Attempts to control the well were not successful, and a new well, the Panarctic Drake Point K-67A, was started nearby and drilled to a total depth of 10,671 ft (3,253 m). Large gas flows were obtained from several sandstones between 3,600 and 4,800 ft (1,097 to 1,463 m), and shows of oil and of gas-condensate

were also reported in deeper zones. The well location is on a large anticlinal structure recognized on the surface. Panarctic's recent well, on King Christian Island, blew out of control on October 25, 1970, and caught fire; it was out of control for 3 months. The flow from this well is reported to be from a Triassic sandstone at rates in excess of 40 million cu ft/day. This well is also located on a large anticlinal structure.

Potential hydrocarbon traps in the Canadian Arctic Archipelago include almost all types of structural and stratigraphic traps. Facies changes associated with the predominant sandstone and shale sequence in the Sverdrup basin, as well as the interfingering carbonate and shale units and reef deposits in the Franklinian geosyncline, provide an abundance of stratigraphic-trapping possibilities. Conditions for structural trapping are favorable, as the result of folding and faulting during various periods and of diapiric action. Many of the structural trends that have been formed are of spectacular development as, for example, those in the Parry Island fold belt. Thick rock units containing good porosity and permeability are present in the Paleozoic as well as in the Mesozoic succession; in places, these potential reservoir zones are several thousand feet thick.

DRILLING OPERATIONS

The first well in the Arctic Islands was drilled at Winter Harbour on southern Melville Island during the winter of 1961–1962. Drilling of the well demonstrated that, despite the location, operations could be successfully undertaken on a year-round basis. All wells have been wildcat tests. To date, 10 dry holes have been drilled; twin wells on Melville Island's Sabine Peninsula have been completed as potential gas wells; one gas discovery has recently been brought under control on King Christian Island, and two relief wells have been completed and three wildcats are presently drilling ahead. Well depths have ranged from 4,000 to 12,500 ft (1,219–4,810 m).

The severity of the Arctic environment raises the cost of all operations, many of which affect drilling. Factors which combine and compound to impose very high drilling costs include: the expensive transport of equipment and supplies to, and within, this remote area; the cost of establishing service facilities that are normally close at hand in southern areas; the shortage of water for drilling; and the more elaborate drilling program required for each wildcat.

Deep wildcats drilled through permafrost and high-pressure formations require extra casing strings and, consequently, large-diameter holes, which are slow to drill. Conductor pipe must be cemented to a depth of 500 ft (152 m) for blowout control, and the surface casing must be set through the layer of permafrost and cemented well into the unfrozen section, regardless of whether the wildcat is to be deep. It is commonly necessary to install pilings, cribbing, and insulation with a drilling foundation to preclude thawing and softening of the surface soil.

Special high-gypsum cements or high-alumina cements are used to cement through permafrost zones. Substantial extra costs also may be incurred in hauling seawater or melting snow for drilling water made necessary by the frozen desertlike conditions that prevail over most of the prospective island areas. The problem of permafrost thawing after production begins has two possible solutions. One method is to circulate a refrigerated fluid in the surface-casing annulus and the other is to insulate the production casing through the permafrost zone.

The first exploratory wells in the Arctic Islands (1961 to 1964), were drilled with conventional rigs which were transported by ship, offloaded on the islands, and transported overland to drillsites. Since that time, there has been a steady evolution to more portable rigs. All rigs now operating on the islands have been designed or modified to varied degrees of portability for transport in fixed-wing aircraft or by helicopter.

An even more portable rig is now being utilized on the Arctic mainland. This drilling rig evolved from the necessity of using diamond drill bits to accomplish the hard drilling. It has great potential in exploratory drilling because of its extreme portability.

Average drilling costs in the Arctic Islands will be in the order of $200 per foot—more than 10 times the average cost in the western provinces of Canada. The wide spacing for wildcat wells and the special drilling requirements have contributed to the substantially higher costs. Production wells will probably be drilled directionally from widely spaced drillsites, and average well costs should be substantially reduced when extensive production drilling operations are under way.

Production

There is as yet no production of oil or gas from the Canadian Arctic; in fact, there have been no discoveries of oil in Canada's Arctic Islands. However, the dramatic discovery of huge oil and gas reserves at Prudhoe Bay on the Alaskan North Slope and Panarctic's gas discoveries on the Sabine Peninsula and King Christian Island demonstrate the tremendous potential of the area, and production will inevitably follow these discoveries.

Field production operations will certainly be planned to take maximum advantage of automation techniques and remote supervisory control systems.

On the basis of published information for proposed North Slope operations, it is probable that production from the Canadian Arctic will be controlled on a flow-station basis. The number of wells tied into each of the several flow stations in a particular field will be fixed by the average producing rates expected from the individual wells. Inlet manifolds at each flow station will direct well streams into high-pressure group separators, and provision will be made for a test separator to handle flow from wells on test. The crude oil from the separators will flow through atmospheric surge tanks to automatic custody transfer-units and on to the oil-gathering system. Gas will be dehydrated and gathered for conservation. All equipment will be housed against the elements in separate buildings.

The per-well cost of producing oil in the Arctic will no doubt be high, but the required productivity for economic operation is sufficiently great that the per-barrel cost will be reasonable in comparison with normal U.S. and Canadian costs. It is our opinion that the cost will be on the order of 20 cents per net barrel at a rate of 5,000 bbl/day per well.

Transportation

Of all the items that affect any development in the Arctic, and especially the development of natural resources, transportation is easily the most important. All equipment, materials, supplies, and personnel will require transportation to the area of exploration and development. The outputs of raw or partially processed materials and products, in order to be useful, will need to be exported to the world's markets. Reliable and economical transportation is absolutely necessary if a competitive position is to be obtained.

Because of the unique location and climate of the Arctic Islands, the principal transportation methods of immediate interest are those involving aircraft, sea-going vessels, and pipelines. Land transport is essentially restricted to specialized movement on the various islands.

Aircraft—The great advantage of Arctic air transportation is its relative independence from movement on a seasonally changing surface. Only at the terminal sites are the inherent problems of the Arctic surface encountered. These, as related to aircraft, are seldom of major proportions and, in the case of helicopters, are practically negligible. Aircraft, therefore, can reach many areas with relative ease in comparison to other transportation modes.

Aircraft are most useful in transportation of people, perishables, and high-priority cargoes. They are of particular importance where the loss of an operating season precludes the use of cheaper, slower means or where access is required to otherwise isolated areas—and, of course, where emergency service is required on short notice. Aircraft, including helicopters, usually offer the best system for exploration and survey work.

Costs for operating aircraft in the Canadian Arctic range from about 20 cents per ton-mile for the Hercules to more than $1.50 per ton-mile for smaller aircraft such as the Twin Otter and Otter.

Marine vessels—Generally, where surface ships can be used, freight in large quantities can be transported by ships at far less cost than by any other means.

The annual sealift to the Canadian Arctic is currently restricted to a few weeks in the summer when cargo vessels accompanied by ice-breakers are able to reach such points as Resolute on southern Cornwallis Island and Eureka on the western part of Ellesmere Island with goods and supplies. The *Manhattan* evaluation by Humble demonstrated the operational feasibility of moving ice-breaking tankers through the Northwest Passage to Prudhoe Bay on the Alaskan North Slope; however, the economics of the venture were not considered to be competitive with the proposed pipeline across Alaska.

The 95th meridian, which passes through Resolute, represents an Arctic divide with respect to severity of ice conditions. To the east, 1-year ice is common which would probably permit access on a year-round basis to large ice-breaking vessels. To the west, multiyear ice —hummocky, commonly ridged and rafted by pressure—constitutes a potentially severe transportation problem. Thus, extended-season operations, at least in the eastern part of the Arctic Islands, utilizing improved ice-breaker

and shipping designs and techniques would appear to be considerably more practical than operations utilizing the Northwest Passage to Alaska.

Captain Thomas C. Pullen, the Canadian representative on board the S.S. *Manhattan*, has suggested that the minimum suitable tanker for operations in the Canadian Arctic would be an ice-breaking vessel of 200,000 deadweight tons capable of carrying 1.5 million bbl.

A fleet of such tankers would be required to provide year-round operations, and each vessel probably would cost roughly $50,000,000. Estimates have been presented suggesting that the costs of oil movement by tanker from the North Slope to the U.S. eastern seaboard might be on the order of $1.00 per barrel. Concern for the effect of crude oil spills on the delicate ecological balance requires that extreme measures be taken to avoid spills; thus, pollution-control regulations and measures will undoubtedly add significantly to these transportation costs.

Development of a fleet of ice-breaking bulk carriers capable of operating on a year-round basis into the Canadian Arctic Islands would also substantially reduce the costs of operation and development in the area by providing relatively low-cost, flexible year-round service for supplies, equipment, and parts.

Pipelines—At the present time, four groups are conducting comprehensive research programs designed to evaluate the equipment and techniques necessary to provide a safe and efficient pipeline system for transportation of oil and gas up the Mackenzie River valley for access to southern markets.

The great distance between the Arctic and present market areas rules out the economic validity of all but the very large-diameter pipelines. The cost of a large-diameter pipeline up the Mackenzie to markets in the Chicago area has been estimated to be in excess of $2 billion. The staff of the U.S. Cabinet Task Force (1970), which examined U.S. oil-import controls, estimated pipeline tariff costs of approximately $1.25 per barrel to move crude oil by pipeline from the Arctic across Canada to markets in the Chicago area.

Special problems arising from scouring due to ice movement in shallow water and the presence of deep channels and irregular bottom topography will complicate the use of underwater pipelines in the Arctic.

Land transportation—The complete absence of roads in the Arctic Islands limits transportation on land to specialized vehicles designed for off-road use.

Tracked vehicles have been developed which are capable of hauling complete drilling rigs and seismic equipment, together with associated supplies and camps, over muskeg and other northern terrain; the development of newer big-wheel vehicles, which have lower maintenance costs and do less damage to the terrain, promise improved systems for this purpose. The more sophisticated air-cushion vehicle undoubtedly will be applied to many off-road situations as its fuel-payload-distance relationship improves and the cost benefits can be demonstrated.

ECONOMICS

The profitability of developing oil reserves in the Arctic Islands is a matter of considerable concern; the following example shows the economics that would be associated with a successful exploration program on permits totaling 3,000,000 acres in the islands.

An exploration program to evaluate the permits would begin with photogeologic and surface mapping followed by geophysical surveys to obtain supporting subsurface information. This work would lead to the selection of drilling locations. Because of the relative ease of interpreting the geology in the area, a discovery was assumed to occur with the drilling of four wildcats.

The capital costs associated with such an exploration program leading to a major oil discovery would be in the order of $15,000,000.

The reservoir was postulated to contain 5 billion bbl of recoverable oil reserves, which represents the lower limit of the initial estimate of the Prudhoe Bay reserves.

The average rate of oil production from wells is expected to be 5,000 bbl/day, and the development spacing is considered to be 320 acres per well. Enhanced recovery will require one injection well for each producing well, so that a total of 200 wells will be drilled. There will be 100 producing wells, setting the production level at 500,000 bbl/day.

Development wells will be drilled over a 5-year period at an average cost of $1,000,000

per well. Production and secondary-recovery facilities will require an additional investment of $60,000,000 over a 4-year period, at a cost of $300,000 per well. Total investment in producing facilities is estimated as approximately $260,000,000.

Oil from the Arctic will probably be sold on the North American east coast at a projected price of $3.50 per barrel. Transportation by ice-breaking tanker from dock facilities in the Arctic is expected to cost $1.50 per barrel; thus, the value at the loading point in the Arctic Islands should be in the order of $2.00 per barrel. The cost of transporting from the field by pipeline to the dock facilities and then loading onto tankers was estimated to be 30 cents a barrel, giving a wellhead value of $1.70 per barrel. Operating costs were conservatively estimated to be $400 per well per day for both production and injection wells; under the assumed conditions, this figure yields an operating cost of 16 cents per barrel over the producing life of the reservoir.

The costs, values, and production developed herein were used to prepare a cash-flow forecast, which was then discounted to provide the present worth of future income.

Based on the 15-percent present worth of future income, before taxes, this postulated reservoir would have a value in the order of $550,000,000. If the risk associated with the venture is taken into account by arbitrarily taking only 20 percent of this value, the reservoir is worth in excess of $100,000,000, which is equivalent to $33 per acre for the total permit acreage assumed.

Even if the wellhead price is reduced by a further 70 cents to $1.00 per barrel, the values are still about 50 percent of those quoted above. Thus, although the costs and risks are high in the Arctic, the potential rewards certainly appear to be commensurate.

REFERENCES CITED

Cabinet Task Force on Oil Import Control, 1970, The oil import question: Washington, D.C.
Haughton, Samuel, 1859, Geological account of the Arctic Archipelago, in F. L. McClintock, The voyage of the Fox in the Arctic seas; a narrative of the discovery of the fate of Sir John Franklin and his companions: London, p. 372–399.

Economics of Prudhoe Bay Field—A Comparison with Bell Creek Field[1]

CHARLES A. NORMAN[2]

Denver, Colorado

Abstract An economic model of Prudhoe Bay field based on the discounted cash-flow method uses the following assumptions: (1) 7.5 billion bbl of recoverable oil, (2) an average initial producing rate of 4,000 bbl per well per day, (3) a peak production rate of 1.6 million bbl per day, and (4) a discount factor of 15 percent. The model gives a producing cost (no exploratory or lease costs included) of $0.28/bbl. A similar economic model for the Trans-Alaskan Pipeline gives a pipeline cost of $0.45/bbl for transport from Prudhoe Bay to Valdez. Tanker costs from Valdez to Los Angeles are estimated at $0.30/bbl.

For comparative purposes, a model of Bell Creek field, Montana, was made along the same lines as the Prudhoe Bay model. Actual producing rates of Bell Creek field were used, and the expected ultimate recovery was assumed to be 150 million bbl. The model gives a cost of production at Bell Creek of $0.58/bbl.

INTRODUCTION

Statements have been made in the press estimating the cost of production of Prudhoe Bay crude oil at figures from 18 cents to $2.10 per barrel. Part of the reason for the wide range of estimates obviously is due to honest differences of opinion, but a large part is due to differences in the definition of cost. Therefore, a definition of cost of production as used here seems in order.

The *cost of production* is defined as the minimum price which the operator could receive for the oil at the wellhead and just break even over the life of the project. "Break even" means making no profit except the required rate of return on invested capital.

This cost of production does not include exploration costs; nor does it include lease-bonus costs and state severance taxes. It does include all development and operating costs over the life of the field with a return on investment of 15 percent per annum after federal income taxes.

PRUDHOE BAY FIELD MODEL

Costs are derived by establishing a model which incorporates the best estimates of all cash outlays and incomes over the life of the field. The following are the major assumptions of the model for Prudhoe Bay field.

[1] Manuscript received, October 18, 1971.

[2] Continental Oil Company.

1. The field contains 7.5 billion bbl of recoverable reserves, of which 12½ percent goes to the state of Alaska as landowner's royalty.

2. The average initial potential of all field wells will be 4,000 bbl per day.

3. Production will begin in mid-1972,[3] and peak production of the field will reach 1,600,000 bbl per day 4 years after initial production.

4. Cost of development wells on 640-acre spacing is $850,000 each.

5. An annual rate of return of 15 percent after federal income taxes is required for all investments in the field.

6. Federal-income-tax rate is 50 percent.

Figure 1 lists the postulated expenditures and production by year for the field model, and Figure 2 shows expenditures and production in graphic form. On the basis of the above assumptions and by use of the discounted cash-flow methods, a cost of 28 cents per barrel is derived for the cost of production.

Sensitivity Analyses

How sensitive is the cost of production to various changes in the field model? Almost all of the assumptions incorporated in the model are open to question; in fact, the assumption that production will begin in mid-1972 is almost certainly wrong. Simple sensitivity analyses (varying one parameter while holding all others constant) on the model help put the cost of production in better perspective.

First, let us examine the effect on the cost of production caused by a delay in the starting of production. Delay in getting the pipeline started means a corresponding delay in production for the field. I have assumed an initial production of 500,000 bbl per day for the field, starting in the middle of 1972. It now appears that production will not get started before mid-1973 at the earliest. If we assume that development of the field proceeds so that the field is ready and capable of production of 500,000 bbl per day in mid-1972, but that actual production is delayed for one reason or another until mid-1973, the delay of 1 year in the start of production raises the cost of production 4

[3] *Editor's Note:* This assumption obviously was not met; thus, some adjustment in the model is necessary. See the writer's further comments under "Sensitivity Analyses."

	68	69	70	71	72	73	74	75	76	77	78	79	80	81	82	83	84	85	86	87	88	89	90	91	92	93	94	95	96	97	98	Totals
Rig Mobilization Cost	2.0	1.8																														4.2
Producing Wells	2.0	12.8	29.8	50.1	54.4	56.8	55.2	56.0	20.0	16.0	7.2	8.0	8.0																			376.3
Injection Wells		1.7	1.7	1.7	1.7	1.6	.8	.8																								10.7
Dry & Junked Wells	4.0	1.2	1.6	1.2	1.6	1.6	1.6	1.6	.8	.4	.4	.4																				12.4
Camp, Dock & Airstrip	3.2	4.2	12.4																													19.8
Vehicles	2.0	2.0	2.0	2.0	.3	.3	.3	.3	.1			.1		.1		.1		.1		.1		.1		.1		.1		.1				10.2
Power Plant		.5	1.5																													2.0
Automation Equip.			1.3																													1.3
Storage Tanks			5.0																													5.0
Gathering System			8.5	2.0	2.0	2.0	2.0																									16.5
Gasoline Plant			10.0	10.0	6.0																											26.0
Gas Injection System		5.0	15.0	20.0	20.0	20.0	20.0							20.0																		120.0
Artificial Lift Equipment													3.5	3.5	3.5	3.5																14.0
Storm Losses			5.0	5.0			5.0			5.0					5.0					5.0			5.0		5.0			5.0				45.0
Well Workovers												3.0	3.0	3.0	3.0	3.0	2.0	2.0	2.0	2.0	2.0	2.0	2.0	1.5	1.5	1.5	1.0	1.0	1.0	1.0		41.0
Field Operating Cost			2.5	5.5	9.0	10.4	10.8	11.0	11.0	11.0	11.0	11.0	11.0	11.0	11.0	11.0	11.0	11.0	10.8	10.7	10.5	10.3	10.1	10.1	10.0	10.0	10.0	10.0	10.0	10.0	10.0	279.6
Annual Oil Production			95	295	400	490	560	560	560	560	560	520	458	403	355	312	275	242	213	187	165	145	128	113	99	87	77	68	60	53		7480

FIG. 1—Expenditures (millions of dollars) and crude oil production (millions of barrels) by year for Prudhoe Bay field model.

cents a barrel in the field model—to 32 cents per barrel—if all other factors remain the same. Thus, the "break-even" point for production of all 7.5 billion bbl of oil in the field model is raised 4 cents a barrel if initial production is delayed 1 year. This increase of 4 cents a barrel respresents a maximum increase, because it is derived under the assumption that the operators of the field do not delay capital investment in the field in anticipation of a delay in initial production. A second year's delay in the start of production would raise the cost of production an additional 4.6 cents per barrel (each year's delay raises the cost approximately 4 cents per barrel, with interest compounded at 15 percent per year).

Second, let us look at how much the cost of production is affected if there is a significant difference in the amount of capital needed to develop the field from what I have assumed for the model. Costs of development wells, gas-injection facilities, gathering systems, and many other items may turn out to be significantly higher or lower than have been estimated; but, for the sake of analysis, let us assume that in 1972 development costs amount to $100 million more than I have estimated. An additional capital investment of $100 million in 1972 (roughly equivalent to adding $250,000 to the cost of each producing well in the field) raises the cost of production 6 cents a barrel, to 34 cents per barrel.

So, a combination of two adverse factors applied to the model—a production delay of 1 year and an additional investment of $100 million in 1972—would raise the cost of production to about 38 cents per barrel.

One feature of the model should be noted especially. The largest part of the cost of production is dependent on the combination of well costs and average initial production per well. For purposes of economic evaluation, neither the cost of an individual well nor its daily capacity is critical by itself, but the combination of the two values is very critical. This model assumes a well cost of $850,000 per well and an average initial capacity of 4,000 bbl per day, or a value of $212.50 for the well cost of each barrel per day of initial capacity. Penttila (1970) has estimated the average initial potential of Prudhoe Bay wells at 5,500 bbl per day. If Penttila's well-capacity figure were used in this model, the cost of each well in the model could be increased by $319,000 and the cost of production still would be 28 cents per barrel.

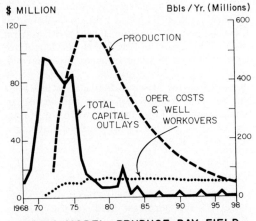

BASIC MODEL - PRUDHOE BAY FIELD

Fig. 2—Graph showing gross expenditures (millions of dollars) and production (millions of barrels) by year for Prudhoe Bay field model.

PIPELINE COSTS

A model also has been set up for the pipeline from Prudhoe Bay to Valdez. The major assumptions for this model are the following.

1. The initial cost of the pipeline with a capacity of 500,000 bbl per day is $900 million.
2. The total cost for a capacity of 1.6 million bbl per day is $1.3 billion.
3. A discount factor of 7 percent after taxes is used. Because pipelines are traditionally financed by a large portion of debt capital (the interest on which is tax deductible), a discount factor of 7 percent is assumed to be adequate.
4. Direct operating costs of 6 cents a barrel are predicted when the pipeline is operating at a capacity of 1.6 million bbl per day.
5. Additional oil from the North Slope will be available to the pipeline so that it will carry 1.6 million bbl per day throughout its 30-year life (after reaching capacity in 1976), for a total throughput of 14.3 billion bbl.

Such a model gives a cost of 41 cents per barrel for transporting crude from Prudhoe Bay to Valdez.

We can now take a look at how sensitive this figure is to increased costs. If an additional $200 million is required for investment in 1971 (making the original investment equal to $1.1 billion instead of $900 million, and final investment equal to $1.5 billion rather than $1.3 billion), the effect is to increase the transport cost from 41 cents per barrel to 46 cents per barrel.

TOTAL COSTS

The basic models give costs of 28 cents per barrel and 41 cents per barrel for production and transport, respectively. If we allow for a 1-year delay in production and an addition of $200 million to pipeline investment, we get costs of 32 cents and 46 cents per barrel for production and pipeline transport, respectively, or a total cost for crude oil at Valdez of 78 cents per barrel. If we "round off" at 80 cents per barrel and allow 30 cents per barrel for tanker costs to Los Angeles, we have a total cost of $1.10 per barrel for Prudhoe Bay crude delivered to Los Angeles.

COMPARISON WITH BELL CREEK FIELD

Bell Creek field was discovered in June 1967. It lies on the northeast flank of the Powder River basin in Powder River County, Montana. It produces from a stratigraphic trap in the Muddy Sandstone (Lower Cretaceous) at an average depth of about 4,500 ft (1,372 m). Ultimate production is estimated at between 115 and 150 million bbl (Oil and Gas Jour., 1971). It is one of the largest oil fields, if not the largest, discovered onshore in the "lower 48" during the past 5 years.

The principal assumptions in the model of Bell Creek field are:

1. Ultimate production of 150 million bbl.
2. Well costs for pumping wells of $65,000 each and average reserves of 375,000 bbl per well (400 wells in the field).
3. Average initial potential of 300 bbl per well.
4. Average field operating costs of 15 cents per barrel (vs. 4 cents per barrel at Prudhoe Bay).

In short, Bell Creek is a very profitable field,

the kind that any U.S. oil company would be pleased to find.

The interesting question now is: what is the cost of production at Bell Creek field compared with that at Prudhoe Bay? By using a model for Bell Creek based on actual costs and production to date, and discounting future cash flows at 15 percent after taxes, a cost of production of 58 cents per barrel is derived.

In comparison, we see that, although the cost of production at Prudhoe Bay is significantly cheaper than at Bell Creek field, when the pipeline cost to Valdez is added to Prudhoe Bay costs, the cost of North Slope crude oil F.O.B. Valdez is higher than Bell Creek oil in southeastern Montana.

By taking a very simple view of both fields, it is obvious why Prudhoe Bay production costs are so low. By dividing the 7.5 billion bbl of oil in the Prudhoe Bay model by the cost of drilling the 454 producing wells (at $850,000 each), we get a well cost per barrel of reserves of 5 cents. At Bell Creek, if we divide the 150 million bbl by the cost of the 400 producing wells (at $65,000 each), we get a well cost per barrel of reserves of 17 cents. Thus, the low cost of production at Prudhoe Bay results from the economies of scale associated with huge reservoirs.

REFERENCES CITED

Oil and Gas Journal, 1971, Where are the reserves around the United States?: v. 69, no. 4, p. 123.

Penttila, Bill, 1970, Sadlerochit reservoir at Prudhoe Bay, Alaska (abs.): Am. Assoc. Petroleum Geologists Bull., v. 54, no. 12, p. 2500.

Two Stochastic Models Useful in Petroleum Exploration[1]

GORDON M. KAUFMAN[2] and PAUL G. BRADLEY[3]

Cambridge, Massachusetts, and Vancouver, British Columbia, Canada

Abstract   What probability law characterizes the *spatial* distribution of oil and gas fields in a petroleum province? How does the probability that a wildcat well will penetrate a reservoir change (if at all!) as the history of a basin unfolds?

The answers to these questions are important inputs to any model of the process of exploring for oil and gas. Some attention has been devoted to these questions, but there are deficiencies in the treatments of each.

Our objective is twofold: (1) to posit a reasonable model of the spatial distribution of petroleum reservoirs that conforms to several empirically observed facts about such distribution; and (2) to examine a simple first-order model of the exploration process that allows one to test empirically the hypothesis that, at an early stage in the exploration of a basin, the process behaves like sampling without replacement.

The techniques of inference outlined will be useful in predicting properties of an unexplored region.

Introduction

The process of exploring for oil and gas involves many uncertainties. Any attempt to forecast returns to investment in exploration must take the uncertainties into account in a systematic way. Inferences about the important uncertain quantities characterizing the exploration process should be based on a mathematical model whose parameters may be estimated coherently from observable data. Thus, at the root of any useful model of the exploration process is a set of assumptions that clearly delineate the probability law governing the generation of observable data.

Our first objective is to construct a model of the exploration process that allows us to test empirically the hypothesis that, at an early stage in the exploration of a basin, the process behaves like sampling without replacement. The model we posit is parsimonious—based on a small number of assumptions and indexed by only five parameters. The set of assumptions on which it is based

[1] Manuscript received, October 18, 1971.

This work was supported in part by a grant from Resources for the Future. A portion of G. M. Kaufman's support came from NASA Contract No. NGL-22-009-309, Integrated Planning and Control Systems. P. G. Bradley was the holder of a Canada Council Postdoctoral Fellowship.

[2] Sloan School of Management, Massachusetts Institute of Technology.

[3] Department of Economics, University of British Columbia.

reflects at least two qualitative assertions commonly made by oilmen: the "big ones" tend to be found first, and the size distribution of fields is highly skewed. We may use this model to compute answers to two questions of paramount importance in designing exploration strategy: (1) How does the probability that a wildcat well will find a reservoir change (if at all!) as the history of a basin unfolds? (2) What is the probability that a yet-to-be-drilled wildcat well will find a reservoir of a specified size, or greater, at a given time in the development of a basin?

Our second objective is to posit a reasonable model of the *spatial* distribution of petroleum reservoirs which conforms to several empirically observed facts about such distribution, but which does not possess three unrealistic attributes that characterize models of spatial occurrence appearing in the literature: dependence of the model on arbitrary subdivision of a basin into units of subspace; the assumption of spatial homogeneity of the stochastic process operating within each such unit, as well as across units; and conceptualization of a reservoir as a *point* (in the plane) rather than as an object with positive *area* (see Uhler and Bradley, 1970; Allais, 1957; Engel, 1957).

The first model we propose differs significantly from those postulated by Arps and Roberts (1956), and by Kaufman (1963). In an explicit and intuitively meaningful way, it accounts for the impact of exploration technology on the probability of discovering a new reservoir. It is structured so that inferences about parameters not known with certainty may be made in accordance with well-understood statistical principles. In particular, the assumption that the probability of discovering a reservoir is proportional to its size strongly biases any "usual" estimator where the sample size is small, so we have developed methods for coping with this complicating feature of the data-generating process.

Our spatial model has not yet been subjected to empirical validation. However, its structure is sufficiently flexible to warrant the conjecture that it will prove to be a reasonable characterization of a process that is spatially inhomogeneous—*i.e.*, fields tend to cluster rather than to be spread evenly throughout a basin. Under the direction of one of the authors, Golovin (1970) has programmed versions of this model and done computational exploration of some of its features. We shall draw heavily on his work in our discussion.

MODEL OF DISCOVERY PROCESS

Nomenclature

The technology available for identifying potential oil- and/or gas-bearing structures is not perfect. We shall assume that application of this technology to the entire areal extent of a generic basin will delineate M distinguishable prospects. We label them "1, 2, $\cdots$, M" and call "$\mathfrak{M} = \{1, 2, \cdots, M\}$" the *label set* for the population of prospects in this basin. Each prospect is or is not a *field;* by "field" we mean a hydrocarbon-bearing reservoir or a collection of contiguous reservoirs. (Precision in defining "field" is not important at this juncture.) If it is a field, the field has many characteristics of interest; momentarily, we focus on only one—the *areal extent.*
Let

$$x_i = \begin{cases} 1 & \text{if the } i^{\text{th}} \text{ prospect is a field} \\ 0 & \text{otherwise,} \end{cases}$$

and define

$$A_i = \text{areal extent of } i^{\text{th}} \text{ prospect.}$$

Then (x_i, A_i) for $i \epsilon \mathfrak{M}$ is a characteristic of the ith population element. We do not know $\theta_M \equiv \{(x_i, A_i) | i \epsilon \mathfrak{M}\}$ with certainty, prior to beginning exploration of the basin. One of our objectives is to make inferences about θ_M as prospects are delineated and fields discovered. In particular, we wish to know which elements of θ_M have $x = 1$, since the ith prospect is by definition a field if, and only if, $x_i = 1$.

At the outset of exploration, the exploration process will generate only a small subset of potential prospects in the basin—perhaps $n < M$ of them with population labels $i_1, \cdots, i_n$. Only a subset of $k < n$ of these prospects will have been drilled. Hence, a *sample* of size n is an ordered sequence of n of the population elements $(i_1, \cdots, i_n)$ with $i_l \epsilon \mathfrak{M}$ for $l = 1, 2, \cdots, n$, together with an ordered n-tuple of observed characteristics. For example:

$$(i_1, \cdots, i_n); (x_{i_1}, A_{i_1}), A_{i_2}, A_{i_3}, (x_{i_4}, A_{i_4}), \cdots,$$
$$(x_{i_k}, A_{i_k})].$$

There will be no loss in generality in the context of the model we deal with here if we relabel those prospects that have been drilled in the order in which they were drilled and reorder as follows:

$$[(i_1, \cdots, i_n); (x^{(1)}, A^{(1)}), \cdots, (x^{(k)}, A^{(k)}),$$
$$A_{i_2}, A_{i_3}, \cdots)].$$

In fact, our model will allow us to ignore the

ordering of areas A_{i_j} of prospects that have been generated at a given point in time but not drilled, so we define a sample as:

$$H_{n,k}^r = [(i_1, \cdots, i_n); (x^{(1)}, A^{(1)}), \cdots,$$
$$(x^{(k)}, A^{(k)}); \{A_{ij}\}],$$

where it is understood that the element $\{A_{i_j}\}$ is the set of areas of undrilled prospects generated by the exploration process at the instant when the $(k+1)^{\text{st}}$ well is to be drilled; r is $\sum_{t=1}^{k} x^{(t)}$, the number of fields found by the first k wells. We shall use "$H_{n,k}^r$" as shorthand for a complete description of a sample where no ambiguity will arise.

In order to describe the assumptions on which our model is based, we need the following notational array.[4]

$I_N = \{i | i \epsilon \mathfrak{M} \text{ and } x_i = 1\}$, the label set of *fields* in the basin,

$S_N = \sum_{i \epsilon I_N} A_i$, the total area of N *fields* in the basin,

$R_M = \sum_{i=1}^{M} A_i$, the total area of M *prospects* in the basin,

$J_k = \{t | x^{(t)} = 1 \text{ for } t = 1, 2, \cdots, k\}$, the label set of successful wells among the first k wells drilled,

$\bar{J}_k = \{t | x^{(t)} = 0 \text{ for } t = 1, 2, \cdots, k\}$, the label set of unsuccessful wells among the first k wells drilled,

$s_k = \sum_{t \epsilon J_k} A^{(t)}$, the total area of fields discovered by the first k wells, and

$u_k = \sum_{t=1}^{k} A^{(t)}$, the total area of prospects drilled by the first k wells.

Data-Generating Model

We shall assume that the process generating observable data has the following properties:

1. *Constant technology*—Given S_N and R_M, and conditional on observing a sample $H_{n,k}^r$ yielding statistics s_k and u_k,

$$P(\tilde{x}^{(k+1)} = 1 | H_{n,k}^r) = \frac{S_N - s_k}{R_M - u_k}.$$

This assumption says that the probability that the $(k+1)^{\text{st}}$ well will discover a field changes in a "hypergeometric-like" fashion with changes in s_k and u_k. The ratio S_N/R_M does not depend on either s_k or u_k; it is a rough measure of technologic efficiency and hence is labeled "constant technology."

2. *Probabilistic proportionality*—Given $\{A_i | i \epsilon \mathfrak{M}$ and $x_i = 1\}$, and conditional on observing $H_{n,k}^r$ and $\tilde{x}^{(k+1)} = 1$, the probability that the $(k+1)^{\text{st}}$ well will discover a field of areal extent A is

[4] A summary of symbols is given at the end of the paper in Appendix 1.

$$P(\tilde{A}^{(k+1)} = A \mid \tilde{x}^{(k+1)} = 1, H_{n,k}^r)$$

$$= \begin{cases} \dfrac{A}{S_N - s_k} & \text{if } A\epsilon\{A_i \mid x_i = 1 \text{ and } i \notin J_k\} \\ 0 & \text{otherwise.} \end{cases}$$

Assumptions 1 and 2 formalize the idea that the probability of discovering a field of areal extent A is proportional to A, because, given R_M and S_N,

$$P(\tilde{A}^{(k+1)} = A, \tilde{x}^{(k+1)} = 1 \mid H_{n,k}^r)$$

$$= \begin{cases} \dfrac{A}{R_M - u_k} & \text{if } A\epsilon\{A_i \mid x_i = 1 \text{ and } i \notin J_k\} \\ 0 & \text{otherwise.} \end{cases}$$

Both assumptions ignore the information content of the statistic $\{A_{i_j}\}$—the set of areas A_{i_j} of prospects generated prior to drilling the $(k+1)^{\text{st}}$ well but as yet undrilled—and exploit only the information generated by the outcome of drilling the first k wells. In order to exploit all information in $H_{n,k}^r$, we would have to build a model of the process generating prospects as well as one generating discoveries. We have chosen to suppress this complicating feature in our preliminary investigation.

3. *Probability law of* $\{\tilde{A}_i \mid i\epsilon I_N\}$—The parameter $\{\tilde{A}_i \mid i\epsilon I_N\}$ is a set of mutually independent, identically distributed, random variables, each characterized by a density $f(\cdot \mid \theta)$ concentrated on $(0, \infty)$ and indexed by a parameter θ.

Likelihood Function

The likelihood function generated by observation of a sample $H_{n,k}^r$ is (defining $u_o = 0$ and $s_o = 0$)

$$L(N, R_M, \theta, S_N \mid H_{n,k}^r)$$

$$\propto \prod_{t=1}^{k} \left(\frac{S_N - s_{t-1}}{R_M - u_{t-1}}\right)^{x^{(t)}}$$

$$\cdot \left(1 - \left[\frac{S_N - s_{t-1}}{R_M - u_{t-1}}\right]\right)^{1-x^{(t)}}$$

$$\cdot \prod_{t\epsilon J_k} \left[\frac{A^{(t)}}{S_N - s_{t-1}}\right] f(A^{(t)} \mid \theta) \tag{1.1}$$

$$\cdot f^{*N-r}(S_N - s_k \mid \theta),$$

where f^{*N-r} is the $(N-r)$-fold convolution of f with itself. The appearance of the term

$$\text{``} f^{*N-r}(S_N - s_k) \text{''}$$

may be explained as follows. The process of generating observations does so in two stages. First, nature generates N values $\{A_i \mid i\epsilon I_N\}$. Then the observables are generated in a way that depends, probabilistically, on $S_N = \sum_{i\epsilon I_N} A_i$. Consequently, S_N is a parameter of the observational process (1 and 2) and, at the same time, a statistic from the vantage point of the process generating field areas (3). If we wish to make inferences about

N, R_M, θ, and S_N jointly, then S_N appears in both roles.

The likelihood function (1.1) may be rewritten as proportional to:

$$\prod_{t\epsilon J_k} \left(1 - \left[\frac{S_N - s_{t-1}}{R_M - u_{t-1}}\right]\right)^{1-x^{(t)}}$$

$$\cdot \prod_{t\epsilon J_k} \left(\frac{A^{(t)}}{R_M - u_{t-1}}\right) f(A^{(t)} \mid \theta) \tag{1.2}$$

$$\cdot f^{*N-r}(S_N - s_k \mid \theta).$$

Approximation of likelihood function—In general, working directly with $L(N, R_M, \theta, S_N \mid H_{n,k}^r)$ is difficult. However, where $N-r$ is very large, we can apply the (equal components) *central limit theorem*—i.e., if f has mean $m\epsilon(-\infty, +\infty)$ and bounded variance v, then, as $N-r$ increases, f^{*N-r} becomes more accurately approximated at each value of its domain by a normal density $f_N(\cdot \mid m[N-r], v[N-r])$ with mean $m[N-r]$ and variance $v[N-r]$.[5]

Here we are interested in the behavior of L when f is a lognormal density with parameter $\theta = (\mu, \sigma^2)$:

$$f(x \mid \theta) = f_L(x \mid \mu, \sigma^2)$$

$$= \begin{cases} \dfrac{1}{\sqrt{2\pi\sigma^2}} e^{-\frac{1}{2}(\log_e x - \mu)^2 / \sigma^2} \dfrac{1}{x} & \text{if } x > 0, \\ 0 & \text{otherwise.} \end{cases} \tag{1.3}$$

Combining the normal approximation suggested above with f as in (1.3), that portion of (1.1) involving μ and σ^2 may be written as proportional to

$$\sigma^{-r} e^{-\frac{1}{2}k(g-\mu)^2/\sigma^2 - \frac{1}{2}v/\sigma^2}$$

$$\cdot (v[N-r])^{-\frac{1}{2}} e^{-\frac{1}{2}([S_N - s_k] - m[N-r])^2/v(N-r)}, \tag{1.4}$$

where

$$m = \exp\{\mu + \tfrac{1}{2}\sigma^2\}, \qquad v = m^2[\exp\{\sigma^2\} - 1],$$

$$g = \frac{1}{r} \sum \log A_i, \qquad v = \sum (\log A_i)^2 - rg^2.$$

Maximum likelihood estimation—It will be convenient to work with m in place of μ in the sequel. To find a maximum likelihood estimator (MLE) of parameters m, σ^2, N, R_M, and S_N where the likelihood function is of the form (1.1) is analytically difficult. We employ the following procedure:[6]

---

[5] Provided $\int \mid f(\xi \mid \theta) \mid^2 d\xi < \infty$.

[6] In practice we have utilized the gradient method developed by Goldfeld et al. (1966) to estimate simultaneously μ (or m) and σ conditional upon the pair (N, S_N). This creates the tableau described in step 4. It may prove possible to employ this method to estimate all parameter values simultaneously, thus eliminating the search procedure of steps 4–7. Using data

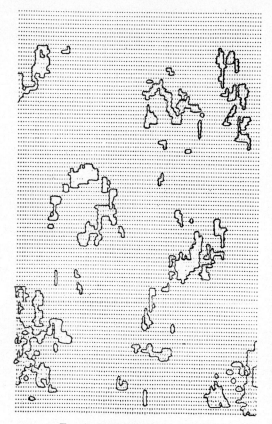

FIG. 1—Spatial stochastic model.

1. Fix the value of R_M.

2. Find an MLE $m^*(\sigma, N, S_N)$ of m for fixed σ, N, and S_N.

3. Holding N and S_N fixed, substitute $m^*(\sigma, N, S_N)$ for m in (1.4); find MLE's of m and σ^2 by searching (1.4) over $\sigma^2 \epsilon (0, \infty)$. Call this pair "$[m_*(N, S_N), \sigma_*^2(N, S_N)]$."

4. Repeat step 3 for a large set of values of the ordered pair (N, S_N), and tabulate the value of log likelihood for each (N, S_N) at $[m, \sigma^2] = [m_*(N, S_N), \sigma_*^2(N, S_N)]$.

5. Search tabulated values of the log likelihood for an approximate maximizer $(N^*, S_N^*, m_*[N^*, S_N^*], \sigma_*^2[N^*, S_N^*])$ of (1.1), given R_M.

6. Repeat steps 2 through 5 for a set of values of R_M.

7. Search log likelihood values for an approximate (joint) MLE of all parameters.

on exploratory drilling in Alberta, we have estimated parameters for several regions. The data support the hypothesis that the sizes of discoveries tend to decrease over time; but, although the estimates appear reasonable, we regard them as too tentative to be published at this time.

SPATIAL MODEL

By a *spatial model* of petroleum deposits, we mean a stochastic process generating values of a sequence of random variables in a way that jointly simulates the frequency distribution of areal extent, the geographic location, and the shape of these deposits. The first approaches that present themselves are incorrect. For example, viewing the process generating the *number* of fields per unit area A as a spatially homogeneous Poisson process is incorrect. Randomizing the parameter $\lambda(A)$ of such a process by assuming that $\lambda(A)$ is a random variable with gamma density (Uhler and Bradley, 1970) leads to a better approximation, but it still is deficient in the tails—that is, a negative binomial distribution does not fit well in the right tail. In addition, a compound Poisson process, or a (randomized) modification of it, does not really explain the "clustering close together" that one observes when examining a map pinpointing oil and gas fields in a well-explored basin.

The model we propose here is conceptually simple, extremely flexible, and easily modified in many ways. We replace the two-dimensional continuum with the *lattice* $L = \{(i, j) | i, j \text{ integer}\}$ of ordered pairs of integers and equip it with the simplest of probabilistic laws of motion: a symmetric random walk. We then define an imbedded process that lays down a 1 or a 0 at first (or subsequent) passage of the random walk through a lattice point. The assumptions we detail soon lead to pictures such as that shown in Figure 1 (Golovin, 1970, p. 17).

Distinguishing features of the model used to generate Figure 1 are that reservoirs have positive area, there is a cluster effect, and the frequency histogram of area extents is, aside from a truncation effect induced by clustering, asymptotically lognormal.

Basic Definitions and Properties

The model is composed of three basic objects: a symmetric random walk on L, a random process superposed on the path taken by the random walk, and a stopping rule.

Let $[i, j; t]$ denote the position on L of the random walk at trial t, $t = 0, 1, 2, \cdots$, and define

$$\delta(i, j) = \begin{cases} 1 & \text{if } (i, j) \text{ has been assigned a 1 at} \\ & \text{some } t' \leq t, \\ 0 & \text{if } (i, j) \text{ has been assigned a 0 at} \\ & \text{some } t' \leq t. \end{cases}$$

If the random walk has not passed through (i, j) at some $t' \leq t$, then $\delta(i, j)$ is left undefined. We set

$$I(t) = \{(i, j) | \delta(i, j) = 1 \text{ at trial } t\}, \text{ and}$$
$$J(t) = \{(i, j) | \delta(i, j) = 0 \text{ at trial } t\},$$

and define the *state* S_t of the process at trial t as a triplet consisting of the location $[i, j; t]$ of the random walk at the end of trial t, the set $I(t)$, and the set $J(t)$; that is, $S_t = ([i, j; t], I(t,) J(t))$. Let h_t be the smallest nonnegative integer such that $[i, j; t+h_t] \notin I(t) \cup J(t)$; $t+h_t$ is the first trial following trial t at which first passage through an unassigned point occurs. Set $t_0 = 0$, $t_k = \sum_{i=1}^{k} h_i$, $k \geq 1$, and define on $t_0, t_1, \cdots, t_k, \cdots$ a sequence $\{\tilde{\xi}_{t_k}, k = 1, 2, \cdots\}$ of mutually independent random variables with common probability function

$$P\{\tilde{\xi}_{t_k} = j\}$$

$$= \begin{cases} 1-\mu & \text{if } j = 0; \\ \mu \begin{pmatrix} m \\ r \end{pmatrix} \rho^r (1-\rho)^{m-r} & \text{if } j = 2^r, r = 0, 1, 2, \cdots, m; \\ 0 & \text{otherwise}; \end{cases}$$

with m a positive integer and $0 < \rho < 1$. The value ξ_{t_k} of $\tilde{\xi}_{t_k}$ may be interpreted as a "chain" of ones that the process will attempt to lay down on points in the complement of $I(t)$ in L. Upon termination of the assignment of ones that begins at $[i, j; t_k]$, the random walk continues with no assignments made until, at the (random) trial $\tilde{t}_{k+1} = t_k + \tilde{h}_{k+1}$, a lattice point $[i, j; \tilde{t}_{k+1}] \notin I(t_k) \cup J(t_k)$. A value $\xi_{t_{k+1}}$ of $\tilde{\xi}_{t_{k+1}}$ is generated, and the assignment of ones begins anew as described above.

Assignment of ones is governed by the following rules, where we let

$$N([i, j; t_k]) \equiv \{(i+x, j+y) \,|\, x = \pm 1, y = \pm 1\},$$

the set of nearest neighbors to $[i, j; t_k]$ in L.

1. If no element of $N([i, j; t_k])$ is in $I(t_k)$, set $\delta([i, j; t_k]) = 1$.

2. If at least one element of $N([i, j; t_k])$ is in $I(t_k)$, set $\delta([i, j; t_k]) = 0$ and terminate the assignment of ones (from the "chain" of ξ_{t_k} ones).

3. If $\delta([i, j; t_k]) = 1$, let the random walk continue, repeating step 1 until either:

(a) ξ_{t_k} ones have been assigned to $[i, j; t_k], \cdots, [i, j; t_k + \xi_{t_k}]$, or

(b) a position $[i, j; t_k + l]$, $l < \xi_{t_k}$ is reached, for which at least one element of $N([i, j; t_k + l])$ is in $I(t_k)$. Then terminate the assignment of ones from the "chain" of ξ_{t_k} ones.

Clearly, the random time $\tilde{h}_t = \tilde{t}_{k+1} - t_k$ depends on the state S_{t_k} of the process at trial t_k.[7] The number of ones assigned to lattice points from the "chain" $\tilde{\xi}_{t_k} = \xi_{t_k}$ of ones depends, in a very compli-

cated way, on $S_{t_k}, S_{t_{k+1}}, \cdots, S_{t_{k+l}}$, where l is the first integer such that $([i, j; t_{k+l}]) = 0$. In probabilistic parlance, the rule for generating a value of h_t and that for the assignment of ones to lattice points are called *stopping rules*.

REFERENCES CITED

Allais, M., 1957, Method of appraising economic prospects of mining exploration over large territories— Algeria Sahara case study: Management Sci., p. 285–347.

Arps, J. J., and T. C. Roberts, 1958, Economics of drilling for Cretaceous oil on the east flank of Denver-Julesburg basin: Am. Assoc. Petroleum Geologists Bull., v. 42, no. 11, p. 2549–2566.

Engel, J. H., 1957, Use of clustering in mineralogical and other surveys, *in* Proceedings of 1st international conference on operations research: Baltimore, Operations Research Soc. America, p. 176–192.

Goldfeld, S. M., R. E. Quandt, and H. F. Trotter, 1966, Maximization by quadratic hill-climbing: Econometrica, p. 541–551.

Golovin, L., 1970, Two mathematical models for oil and gas disposition: Cambridge, Sloan School Management, Massachusetts Inst. Technology, unpub. M.S. dissert., 65 p.

Kaufman, G. M., 1963, Statistical decision and related techniques in oil and gas exploration: Englewood Cliffs, New Jersey, Prentice-Hall, 307 p.

Uhler, R. S., and P. G. Bradley, 1970, A stochastic model for determining the economic prospects of petroleum exploration over large regions: Jour. Am. Stat. Assoc., p. 623–630.

Appendix 1. Summary List of Symbols

Model of Discovery Process

A_i	surface area of ith reservoir
k	number of wildcats drilled, *i.e.*, number of prospects observed
M	number of prospective drilling sites
N	number of reservoirs in the basin
r	number of successful wildcats
R_M	total area of M prospects in the basin
s_k	total (cumulative) area of reservoirs discovered by k wildcats
S_N	total area of N reservoirs in the basin
θ	parameter set for the density function of A_i; $\theta = (\mu, \sigma^2)$
u_k	total (cumulative) area of prospects drilled by k wildcats
x_i	outcome of ith wildcat well ($x_i = 1$ where well is a success, 0 otherwise)

Spatial Model

$\delta(i, j)$	state of point (i, j); 0 or 1, where 1 signifies presence of petroleum
$I(t)$	petroleum areas: set of 1-points, $I(t) = [(i, j) \,|\, \delta(i, j) = 1]$
$J(t)$	nonpetroleum areas (or unassigned): set of 0-points, $J(t) = [(i, j) \,|\, \delta(i, j) = 0]$
L	spatial location: lattice of ordered pairs, $L = [(i, j) \,|\, i, j \text{ integer}]$
N	set of nearest neighbor points to point $(i, j; t_k)$: $N[(i, j; t_k)] = \{(i+x, j+y) \,|\, x = \pm 1, y = \pm 1\}$
ξ_{t_k}	chain of ones laid down from point $(i, j; t_k)$ subject to prescribed stopping rules
S_t	state of the process at trial t: $S_t = [(i, j; t), I(t), J(t)]$

---

[7] There is no semantic confusion in using "time" h_{k+1} to denote number of trials between $t_{k+1} - t_k$, and we shall do so.

Reward and Uncertainty in Exploration Programs[1]

PAUL G. BRADLEY[2] and GORDON M. KAUFMAN[3]

Vancouver, British Columbia, Canada, and Cambridge, Massachusetts

Abstract The attractiveness of a petroleum exploration program depends on the expected return and the associated risk. Previous analyses of drilling programs have dealt with particular aspects of uncertainty. The variable which has received the most attention has been size of reservoirs. Various skewed probability density functions have proved consistent with empirical observation. Estimates of the expected value and variance of this variable have been casually interpreted as measures of the economic reward and the degree of risk, respectively, of specific exploration programs. The size of reservoir found, however, is only one aspect of the uncertainty in exploratory drilling. Among the other variables which have an important bearing on the economics of the program are the probability of making a discovery, the depth of the producing formation, and the productivity of the wells. The possible stochastic descriptions of the most significant variables have combined effects on the attractiveness of a venture.

Introduction

In our preceding paper (Kaufman and Bradley, this volume), we constructed a model to describe the results of wildcat drilling. Given the existence in nature of a set of targets of differing characteristics—in this case the variable considered is areal extent—we specified the process by which information about the targets would be accumulated. The model permits predictions about the success ratio and the size of discoveries for successive increments of drilling. Knowledge of the probability laws governing the results of petroleum exploration would make it possible to characterize the economic risks involved, but would entail a more elaborate model than the one we have proposed. It would be necessary, utilizing information obtained from wells already completed, to specify the joint probability distribution governing the entire set of variables which determine the economic return from subsequent drilling.

Previous analyses of exploratory drilling programs have emphasized particular aspects of

uncertainty. The variable which has received the most attention is size of reservoirs (Allais, 1957; Arps and Roberts, 1958; Arrington, 1960; Kaufman, 1963). Estimates of the expected value and standard deviation of reservoir size have been casually interpreted as measures of the economic reward and the degree of risk, respectively, of particular exploration programs. The size of reservoir found is, of course, only one aspect of the uncertainty of exploratory drilling. Among the other variables that have an important bearing on the economics of the program are the probability of making a discovery, the depth of the producing formation, and the productivity of the wells.

In this paper we select a set of variables which are crucial to the economic results of petroleum exploration. These are treated as random variables; the values they assume indicate the number of successes that occur in a drilling program and determine, for a particular discovery, the unit production cost and net economic return if that reservoir is developed. In specifying the joint probability law for these variables, we are forced to make extreme and probably unrealistic assumptions. In particular, we assume the different random variables to be independently distributed, and we do not take into account changes that may occur in the probability distributions as exploration proceeds. This latter simplification, of course, ignores the thrust of our previous model, which describes a depletion process by which the largest pools, having been found first, are "used up," and hence cease to be possible targets. We are conscious of these limitations, and we are prepared to adopt any better data-generating models that may be devised.

The values of the independent random variables affect the economic return to exploration in relatively complicated ways. As a consequence, the probability functions that govern the pertinent economic measures cannot be deduced directly from knowledge of the joint probability distribution of the physical variables. Instead, we must rely on a Monte Carlo type of simulation procedure. Using postulated probability functions and specified parameters, we generate values for selected random variables, such as reservoir size. From this set of values, we compute the economic magnitudes of interest: net return and unit pro-

[1] Manuscript received, October 18, 1971.

This work was supported in part by a grant from Resources for the Future. A portion of G. M. Kaufman's support came from NASA Contract No. NGL-22-009-309, Integrated Planning and Control Systems. P. G. Bradley was the holder of a Canada Council Postdoctoral Fellowship.

[2] Department of Economics, University of British Columbia.

[3] Sloan School of Management, Massachusetts Institute of Technology.

duction cost. This process constitutes a single trial, and the procedure is repeated many times. The resulting histograms approximate the probability density functions of the variables which describe the economic results of an exploratory drilling program.

In the next section, we specify the set of physical variables whose values are critical to the economic success or failure of an exploration venture. We then present (1) a model which relates the expenditures needed to develop and produce a crude oil reservoir to this set of variables, and (2) a model which relates the output of the developed reservoir to certain of the variables. Utilizing these models, we can compute unit production cost and total value, or net economic return, for the reservoir; the latter is conditional upon the wellhead price at which the crude oil can be sold.

A Model of Returns to Exploration

In Table 1 we define the variables that will be employed in computing the returns when a reservoir is discovered. We distinguish among three classes of variables:

1. Physical variables, which are observable upon completion of the wildcat well;

2. Certain economic variables, which we postulate to be known with certainty; and

3. Dependent variables, whose values we will compute. These variables take on a particular set of values for each wildcat well.

The expenditure required to produce a reservoir is resolved into four components, of which the first three compose what is usually termed "development investment":

I_1 = drilling investment;
I_2 = investment in surface gathering and processing facilities;
I_3 = camp investment, required in remote locations; and
I_4 = capitalized operating costs.

Based on Fisher's (1964) investigation of drilling costs, we assume that well cost increases exponentially with depth and that:

$$\tilde{I}_1 = N\beta_{11}(e^{\beta_{12}d} - 1) + \tilde{\epsilon}_1, \tag{1}$$

where $\tilde{\epsilon}_1$ is an error term. In a similar vein, it has been shown that the relation between investment and capacity in a chemical process plant commonly may be well approximated by the so-called "six-tenths factor" (Chilton, 1950; Williams, 1947). Using this factor, we specify the investment for surface equipment to be:

$$\tilde{I}_2 = \beta_{21}(Nq_o)^{\beta_{22}} + \beta_{23}N + \tilde{\epsilon}_2. \tag{2}$$

The first term on the right-hand side, with $\beta_{22} = 0.6$,

Table 1. Definitions of Variables

Physical Variables

v	oil in place in reservoir (bbl)
d	mean well depth (ft)
q_o	mean initial well productivity (bbl/day/well)

Economic Variables

D	ratio of initial developed production capacity of reservoir to total proved reserves (or production-decline rate)
p	expected price, assumed constant (dollars/bbl)
r	discount (interest) rate
T	economic time horizon (years)

Dependent Variables

W	cost of an exploratory well (dollars)
N	number of development wells drilled
G	gross value of reservoir (present-value dollars)
I	total expenditure required to establish and maintain production, *i.e.*, development investment and operating costs (present-value dollars)
Y	net value of reservoir (present-value dollars)
X	unit production cost (dollars/bbl)

represents investment which is dependent on the scale of operations, or throughput. The second component relates to expenditures which are dependent on the number of development wells, such as roads, gathering lines, and drilling pads, all of which are costly under Arctic permafrost conditions. Assuming that investment in a field base camp is allocated to individual pools in proportion to their developed capacity, we have:

$$\tilde{I}_3 = \beta_{31}(Nq_o) + \tilde{\epsilon}_3. \tag{3}$$

Capitalized operating costs are assumed to be represented by:

$$\tilde{I}_4 = \beta_{41} + \beta_{42}N + \tilde{\epsilon}_4. \tag{4}$$

Equation 4 resolves total operating costs into a component which depends on the number of development wells and a component which is constant for the reservoir.

Summing the various investment components, we have:

$$\begin{aligned}
\tilde{I} = N[\beta_{11}(e^{\beta_{12}d} - 1) + \beta_{23} + \beta_{42}] \\
+ \beta_{21}(Nq_o)^{\beta_{22}} + \beta_{31}(Nq_o) + \beta_{41} \\
+ \tilde{\epsilon}_1 + \tilde{\epsilon}_2 + \tilde{\epsilon}_3 + \tilde{\epsilon}_4.
\end{aligned} \tag{5}$$

We assume that, over several reservoirs, the individual error terms compose a sequence of mutually independent random variables, identically distributed according to a known probability law. Writing $\tilde{u} = \tilde{\epsilon}_1 + \tilde{\epsilon}_2 + \tilde{\epsilon}_3 + \tilde{\epsilon}_4$ in Equation 5 yields:

$$\begin{aligned}
\tilde{I} = N[\beta_{11}(e^{\beta_{12}d} - 1) + \beta_{23} + \beta_{42}] \\
+ \beta_{21}(Nq_o)^{\beta_{22}} + \beta_{31}(Nq_o) + \beta_{41} + \tilde{u}.
\end{aligned} \tag{6}$$

The output which can be obtained from a given

reservoir is directly related to the volume of reserves that can be proved, V. Postulation that the mean recovery factor, F, is known with certainty results in:

$$V = Fv. \qquad (7)$$

Several models describing the production-decline behavior of a reservoir have been studied, and the most notable of these are exponential decline and hyperbolic decline. We use the former, because it appears to describe output over time sufficiently well for our purposes, and because it is mathematically convenient. Consequently, cumulative production, Q, at any given time is:

$$Q_t = \int_o^t N_t q_t dt = Nq_o \int_o^t e^{-Dt} dt, \qquad (8)$$

where D is the production-decline rate. The term at the extreme left incorporates the assumption that installed capacity is not increased at later stages in the productive life of the pool.

Integration of Equation 8 yields:

$$Q_t = \frac{Nq_o}{D}(1 - e^{-Dt}). \qquad (9)$$

If we consider a long period of time, such that proved reserves are essentially recovered ($Q_t \to V$, $t \to \infty$), Equation 9 becomes:

$$V = \frac{Nq_o}{D}. \qquad (10)$$

Hence, for a specified decline rate, D, initial producing capacity can be related to reservoir size by applying Equations 10 and 7:

$$Nq_0 = DFv. \qquad (11)$$

In addition, it can readily be seen that the number of development wells drilled depends on reservoir size and the mean initial capacity (or productivity) of a well:

$$N = DF \frac{v}{q_o}. \qquad (12)$$

Equation 6, in conjunction with Equations 11 and 12, relates the investment required to produce the crude oil in a reservoir to the set of physical parameters which describe that reservoir, as listed in Table 1.

We can now compute the economic return that will be gained by developing the newly discovered reservoir. On the basis of output as described by Equation 8 and the use of continuous discounting, gross revenue must be:

$$G = pNq_o \int_o^T e^{-(D+r)t} dt. \qquad (13)$$

Integration yields:

$$G = pNq_o \left[\frac{1 - e^{-(D+r)T}}{D + r} \right]. \qquad (14)$$

Representing the factor in brackets by A makes the expression for gross revenue:

$$G = pNq_o A. \qquad (15)$$

Net revenue, or the economic return resulting from the discovery of the reservoir, is the difference between gross revenue and total investment:

$$\tilde{Y} = \tilde{G} - \tilde{I}. \qquad (16)$$

Our basic model for the returns to exploration thus consists of Equations 6, 11, 12, 15, and 16. This model relates the economic payoff of a discovery to the set of observable physical parameters in Table 1. When a wildcat is dry, the direct payoff is zero. The required economic parameters (Table 1) are assumed to be determined exogenously, to be known with certainty, and to be fixed for all reservoirs discovered by a series of wildcat wells. At the outset of exploration in a region (and therefore before the development of any producing capacity), the vector β of parameters as well as the probability law governing $\tilde{u}$ would not be known; they would have to be estimated from sample data.

Before discussing applications of this model, it will be useful to describe the final dependent variable listed in Table 1—unit production cost, denoted by X. This variable will be particularly useful in our analysis because it is not dependent on economic expectations; specifically, it is calculated without reference to expected wellhead price. By focusing on cost we properly restrict ourselves to geological and technical forms of risk.[4] We define unit cost, X, as the amount that must be realized on each barrel of crude oil produced in order to recover the investment in the reservoir, including capitalized operating costs.[5] In the notation we have used:

$$\tilde{X} = \frac{\tilde{I}}{Nq_o A}. \qquad (17)$$

[4] Adelman (1966) has distinguished among commercial, geological, engineering, and political risks. Changes in selling price would represent commercial risk, narrowly defined. Our estimates of expected return and variability of returns neglect the risk of possible changes in selling price and hence may be misleading. We have not treated political risk here, but would do so through the revenue side—for example, by specifying the probability of getting any returns after a given year.

[5] This measure of cost has been used elsewhere in analyzing crude oil production. See Adelman (1966) and Bradley (1967).

Because the denominator of Equation 17 represents discounted or present-value output (measured in barrels), unit cost depends on the investment needed to obtain production and on the resulting pattern of output over time.

APPLICATION OF MODEL TO THE ARCTIC

In using this model to gain insights into the economics of Arctic exploration, we encounter formidable problems. At the outset we noted the need to specify the probability laws governing petroleum exploration in order to use properly the data which are collected to make inferences about the underlying parameters. As a makeshift substitute for a more comprehensive model, we have postulated probability functions for the independent random variables. In the case of reservoir size, it is possible to employ a hypothesis which has been tested considerably in the literature;[6] in other cases we were compelled to perform our own rough tests on the selected probability functions. Once the required probability functions are specified we need estimates of parameters which characterize the Arctic area. Since we have not had access to information on which such estimates could be based, we conjecture possible values. It is also necessary to know the vector of cost parameters which determine investment, denoted β in the previous sections. To meet this need we have

[6] Two examples are in Kaufman (1963) and Mc-Crossan (1969).

made some rough calculations which employ the estimates of C. A. Norman (this volume).

The probability functions and parameters for variables used in the simulations are summarized in Table 2. Parameter estimates are based on data describing petroleum occurrence in the Province of Alberta, except for initial well productivity, for which the Alberta data were not appropriate to our needs. After inspecting data for Algeria, Iran, and Libya, we based our rough estimates of productivity parameters on the Libyan information. Certainly, our hypotheses about the distributions of the depth and productivity variables require further testing. It would be of great interest to test for possible correlation between these variables. The important figures used in computing the cost parameter, β, are listed in Table 3.

With this background information, we shall consider the model of the previous section. The outcome of drilling a wildcat well is determined (1) by whether the well is a success—that is, whether it finds crude oil—and, if it does, (2) by the observed values of the variables v, d, and q_o. Considering for the present only successes, we simulate wildcat drilling by treating v, d, and q_o as random variables, recognizing this distinction by the notation $\tilde{v}$, $\tilde{d}$, and $\tilde{q}_o$. A single outcome is evaluated by generating values for $\tilde{v}$, $\tilde{d}$, and $\tilde{q}_o$ according to the probability density functions and parameters shown in Table 2, and then by computing—with the use of Equations 6, 11, 12, 15, and 16—the corresponding values for the depen-

Table 2. Probability Functions and Parameters for Independent Random Variables

Variable	Probability Density Function	Parameter Values[1]		Source of Parameter Values
		μ	σ	
Depth of well, $\tilde{d}$	Normal	5610	1615	Estimated by authors from data on 106 light and medium crude reservoirs in Alberta (Oil and Gas Conservation Board, 1968).
Volume of crude discovered, $\tilde{v}$	Lognormal	(1) 16.15	2.14	Uhler and Bradley (unpub.) estimated $\mu = 16.15$, $\sigma = 2.14$ for limestone-reef
		(2) 16.84	2.14	pools in Alberta (143 pools, 1968 data). Item (2) is parameter set where
		(3) 17.54	2.14	pools are postulated to be twice as big, i.e., $(v_i)_2 = 2(v_i)_1$.
		(4) 18.23	2.14	Items (3) and (4) represent successive doubling of pool size.
Mean initial well productivity, $\tilde{q}_o$	Lognormal	7.51	1.18	Estimated by authors from data on 25 reservoirs in Libya (Oil and Gas Journal, 1969).[2]
Error of estimate in investment function (development), $\tilde{u}$	Normal	0	44000	Estimated by authors. Standard error of estimate in regression relating expenditures to footage of development drilling: Alberta, British Columbia, Saskatchewan, Manitoba.

[1] For $\tilde{y}$ normally distributed, density function is:

$$f = \frac{1}{\sigma \sqrt{2\pi}} exp \left[-\frac{1}{2\sigma^2} (y - \mu)^2 \right].$$

For $\tilde{x}$ lognormally distributed:

$$f = \frac{1}{x\sigma \sqrt{2\pi}} exp \left[-\frac{1}{2\sigma^2} (\log x - \mu)^2 \right].$$

[2] Data could not be obtained for Alberta. Because of prorationing, initial reported production would understate true potential production for Alberta pools.

Table 3. Components of Cost Parameters[1]

I_1 Investment in producing wells:

    (a) Drilling costs, per well — $C_1 = \beta_{11}(e^{\beta_{12}d}-1)$, where $\beta_{11}=119{,}000$, $\beta_{12}=.0002$ (cost of drilling only, 9,000-ft development well, estimated to be $600,000)

    (b) Cost increment for slant drilling of development wells, per well — $75,000

    (c) Cost of drilling pad, per well — $50,000

    (d) Cost of connecting roads, per mile — $200,000

I_2 Investment in surface facilities:

    (a) Processing plant (including oil and gas separation, gas compression for reinjection) — $C_2 = \beta_{21}(Nq_0)^{\beta_{22}}$, where $\beta_{21}=291$, $\beta_{22}=0.6$ (cost of plant with 100,000 bpd capacity estimated to be $8.62 million)

    (b) Cost of injection wells, per well — $I_1(a, c, d)$ above

    (c) Cost of gathering lines, per mile — $120,000

I_3 Operating costs, per well per year — $E_1 = \gamma_1 + \gamma_2/N$, where $\gamma_1 = 6000$, $\gamma_2 = 554{,}000$, and N = number of developmental wells

I_4 Camp investment (assumed to serve several reservoirs in field and allocated to a given reservoir according to share of field output over production period) — $24,300,000

---

[1] Derived from estimates of various expenditures required to produce crude at Prudhoe Bay made by Norman (this volume). We are not aware of any other estimates available to the public which are as carefully detailed. In adapting the original figures to obtain the ones shown here and to calculate our β, we have combined categories and made simplifying assumptions for which the author of the original estimates should not be held responsible.

---

dent variables listed in Table 1. For each set of conditions examined, 2,000 outcomes were evaluated. The results were displayed in the form of histograms, two of which are illustrated in Appendix A. In the next section, we describe the results of this procedure where the underlying physical and economic parameters were chosen to represent Arctic conditions.

SIMULATION RESULTS

For the probability functions specified in Table 2, the expected values for depth and well productivity are, respectively, 5,610 ft (1,710 m) and 3,640 bbl per well per day. The latter figure is near the 4,000 bbl per well per day postulated by Norman (this volume); apparently the discoveries at Prudhoe are deeper than the footage value used, however. Suppose it were known with certainty that all Arctic discoveries would be at about this depth and wells would flow at this output

rate. The returns in such a situation were simulated in the method described, and the results are reported in Table 4. Discoveries under these conditions were uniformly profitable at a wellhead price of $1.00 per barrel.

Examination of Table 4 shows that the rows correspond to progressively more optimistic assumptions about the size of reservoirs. At the low end, the postulated lognormal distribution of reservoir sizes yields pools whose median size is around 10 million bbl (oil in place), a figure which corresponds to past experience with the attractive Devonian reefs in Alberta. At the high end, the postulated distribution yields pools whose median size is about eight times as big—a very generous assumption indeed. Production costs vary between 60 and 80 cents a barrel. The principal cause of cost variation lies with economies of scale in surface facilities. This effect would be stronger were it not for the fact that the calculations permitted a

Table 4. Expected Returns to Development Where Reservoir Size is Variable and Depth and Mean Initial Well Productivity Are Fixed

Reservoir Size,[1] $\tilde{v}$ (millions bbl of oil in place) Median	Production Cost,[2] $\tilde{X}$ (dollars/bbl)			Net Returns,[2] $\tilde{Y}$ (millions of present-value dollars)			
	Mean	Standard Deviation	Coefficient of Variation	Mean	Standard Deviation	Coefficient of Variation	Fraction with Positive Return
(1) 10.3	.791	.817	103	8.23	39.9	485	1.00
(2) 20.6	.724	.765	106	19.4	118.	608	1.00
(3) 41.4	.669	.721	108	42.7	405.	948	1.00
(4) 82.6	.585	.650	111	77.4	455.	588	1.00

[1] Reservoir recovery factor $(F) = 0.35$.

[2] The following economic variables are treated as known with certainty.

    (a) decline rate $(D) = 8$ percent per year;

    (b) discount rate $(r) = 15$ percent per year;

    (c) economic time horizon $(T) = 25$ years;

    (d) expected wellhead price $(p) = \$1.00$.

Table 5. Expected Returns to Development Where Reservoir Size and Mean Initial Well Productivity Are Variable and Depth Is Fixed

Reservoir Size,[1] $\tilde{v}$ (millions bbl of oil in place) Median	Production Cost,[2] $\tilde{X}$ (dollars/bbl)			Net Returns,[2] $\tilde{Y}$ (millions of present-value dollars)			
	Mean	Standard Deviation	Coefficient of Variation	Mean	Standard Deviation	Coefficient of Variation	Fraction with Positive Return
(1) 10.3	1.79	2.89	161	6.92	25.7	371	.449
(2) 20.6	1.56	2.42	155	13.8	57.2	414	.523
(3) 41.4	1.33	1.95	147	44.1	597.	1354	.552
(4) 82.6	1.15	1.75	152	69.7	471.	676	.637

[1] Reservoir recovery factor (F) =0.35.

[2] The following economic variables are treated as known with certainty:
  (a) decline rate (D) =8 percent per year;
  (b) discount rate (r) =15 percent per year;
  (c) economic time horizon (T) =25 years;
  (d) expected wellhead price (p) =$1.00.

sharing of the costly items included under the category of base-camp expenditures (camp, airstrip, vehicles, power plant, rig mobilization) with other pools assumed to exist in the field. Net returns increased as would be expected, roughly in proportion to the volume of reserves discovered.

We now consider the situation where it is not certain that the development wells in the pools discovered will produce initially at 3,600 bbl per day. We postulate this to be the expected rate, but permit the degree of dispersion in rates which we observed in the Libyan data. The simulated outcomes of exploratory drilling are displayed in Table 5. A striking feature of this new situation is that not all the discoveries are commercial—defined under our assumptions as being capable of producing profitably at a wellhead price of $1.00 per barrel. The percentage of fields with positive returns is under 50 for the most conservative assumption about reservoir sizes, which means

that production cost was found to be under $1.00 per barrel less than half the time; the corresponding mean production cost is about $1.80. As would be expected, the dispersion of outcomes is much greater than in the preceding example, as can be seen by comparing the coefficients of variation (defined as the standard deviation measured as a percentage of the mean).

In Table 6 we postulate reservoir size, depth, and well productivity all to be variable, defined by the corresponding probability functions shown in Table 2. The differences between Tables 5 and 6 are not very pronounced. The coefficients of variation in Table 6 are generally higher; the fact that they are not universally higher suggests that we should increase the number of trials evaluated under each set of conditions beyond 2,000. The observed moments of the outcome distributions are not quite stable—a consequence of the extreme skewness of the distributions. The means and standard deviations in the initial row of Table

Table 6. Expected Returns to Development Where Reservoir Size, Depth, and Mean Initial Well Productivity Are Variable

Reservoir Size,[1] $\tilde{v}$ (millions bbl of oil in place) Median	Production Cost,[2] $\tilde{X}$ (dollars/bbl)			Net Returns,[2] $\tilde{Y}$ (millions of present-value dollars)			
	Mean	Standard Deviation	Coefficient of Variation	Mean	Standard Deviation	Coefficient of Variation	Fraction with Positive Return
(1) 10.3	1.83	2.78	152	6.83	28.7	420	.435
(2) 20.6	1.67	2.78	166	16.8	150.	893	.481
(3) 41.4	1.37	2.35	172	30.3	247.	815	.568
(4) 82.6	1.19	1.99	167	87.2	1168.	1339	.643

[1] Reservoir recovery factor (F) =0.35.

[2] The following economic variables are treated as known with certainty:
  (a) decline rate (D) =8 percent per year.
  (b) discount rate (r) =15 percent per year.
  (c) economic time horizon (T) =25 years,
  (d) expected wellhead price (p) =$1.00.

6 are computed from the histograms shown in Appendix A.

The results just considered were conditional upon the discovery of oil by the exploratory well. In order to compute expected returns before drilling begins, these figures must be modified to take into account the probability that the well will be successful. In our preceding paper (Kaufman and Bradley, this volume), we describe a model which provides one approach to specifying the probability that, given a sequence of wildcat wells, the next one will be a success. It should also be noted that the net-return figures we have computed relate to development investment and operating costs, and do not include the cost of exploratory wells, which have been reported to range from $2 million to $3 million or higher on the North Slope. It therefore appears from Table 6 that, with the figures we have used, some combination of very favorable success ratio and large median reservoir size (high mean of the distribution of v) is needed to make expected returns to a sequence of wildcats positive. Given the skewness of the distributions, there will, of course, be some very profitable discoveries even where the expected return is low.

With regard to the need to find large reservoirs, we might expect the initial finds to be relatively large for any existing distribution of pool sizes in nature. This line of reasoning is formalized by the model in our preceding paper—that the probability of finding a large pool in the Arctic is higher than the probability of finding a small one. However, this probability is modified by better knowledge about the geology of the region, acquired as data accumulate from exploration. This increased knowledge might permit better selection among available prospects in later periods.

The results presented in this paper are intended to be only speculative. They cannot be treated as conclusive because we have not had Arctic data from which to derive the parameter estimates, and thus have relied on possible similarities with developed producing regions. We believe that it will be necessary to make progress along the lines suggested in the preceding paper before we can confidently characterize the uncertainties of the exploration process.

REFERENCES CITED

Adelman, M. A., 1966, Oil production costs in four areas: Proc. Council of Economics, Am. Inst. Min., Metall., Petroleum Engineers Ann. Mtg., p. 96–211.

Allais, M., 1957, Method of appraising economic prospects of mining exploration over large territories—Algeria Sahara case study: Management Sci., p. 285–347.

Arps, J. J., and T. G. Roberts, 1958, Economics of drilling for Cretaceous oil production on the east flank of Denver-Julesburg basin: Am. Assoc. Petroleum Geologists Bull., v. 42, no. 11, p. 2549–2566.

Arrington, J. R., 1960, Predicting the size of crude reserves is key to evaluating exploration programs—and here's a practical way to evaluate reserves: Oil and Gas Jour., v. 158, no. 9, p. 130–132.

Bradley, P. G., 1967, The economics of crude petroleum production: Amsterdam, North Holland, 149 p.

Chilton, C. H., 1950, Six tenths factor applies to complete plant costs: Chem. Eng., April, 1950, p. 112–114; also *in* C. H. Chilton, ed., 1960, Cost engineering in the process industries: New York, McGraw-Hill.

Fisher, F. M., 1964, Supply and costs in the U.S. petroleum industry: Baltimore, Maryland, Johns Hopkins Univ., Resources for the Future, 177 p.

Kaufman, G. M., 1963, Statistical decision and related techniques in oil and gas exploration: Englewood Cliffs, New Jersey, Prentice-Hall, 307 p.

—— and P. G. Bradley, 1973, Two stochastic models useful in petroleum exploration: this volume.

McCrossan, R. G., 1969, An analysis of size frequency distribution of oil and gas reserves of Western Canada: Canadian Jour. Earth Sci., v. 6, no. 2, p. 201–211.

Norman, C. A., 1973, Economics of Prudhoe Bay—comparison with Bell Creek field: this volume.

Williams, R., Jr., 1947, Six tenths factor aids in approximating costs: Chem. Eng., p. 124–125; also *in* C. H. Chilton, ed., 1960, Cost engineering in the process industries: New York, McGraw-Hill.

APPENDIX A

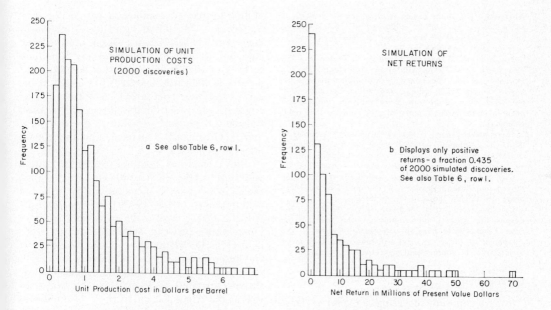

Arctic Geopolitics[1]

HOWARD A. MEYERHOFF[2] and A. A. MEYERHOFF[3]

Tulsa, Oklahoma 74101

Abstract The Arctic region is all of the earth north of 60°N lat.—an area of 14 million sq mi (36.4 million sq km), or 7 percent of the world's surface area and 14 percent of its land area.

Russia fronts 52 percent of the Arctic Ocean and has jurisdiction over 70 percent of the continental shelves. Moreover, of the approximately 256 million persons living in the six Arctic nations, 244 million are citizens of the USSR. It is plain from these statistics that Russia's position in the Arctic is not just predominant; it is overwhelming.

The same statement is true of the mineral resources of the Arctic. Although not well explored, Russia's nonhydrocarbon mineral wealth probably is proportionate to her Arctic area. Russia's hydrocarbon reserves are far out of proportion to the area controlled; for example, proved plus probable reserves in the West Siberian basin alone are double those of the entire U.S.

Control of the Arctic, therefore, is vital to Russia, but despite her much greater population, she does not yet have manpower to develop and control the Arctic. Development of Arctic resources will take place best in an atmosphere of international peace and cooperation.

INTRODUCTION

In a symposium covering a region as large and as imperfectly known as the Arctic, emphasis inevitably falls on limited but significant facets of its parts. Obviously, it will take years of laborious field studies before the parts add up to the whole; yet, even at this early stage of exploration and development, a regional pattern can be discerned. It is a composite of geography, geology, economics, and demography that can be projected into the future with some confidence. A generation ago the term "geopolitics" would have embraced this composite concept. Stripped of some of its Teutonic overtones, it is still a useful designation, and we venture to apply it to the following overview of the Arctic.

Development of the Arctic is dependent on the subarctic hinterland, with which the region north of the Arctic Circle interfingers and merges. The gross area of land and sea north of 60°N lat. measures approximately 14 million sq mi (36.4 million sq km). It includes 3.66

[1] Manuscript received, January 5, 1972.

[2] GeoSurveys, Inc., and Professor Emeritus, The University of Pennsylvania.

[3] The American Association of Petroleum Geologists.

million sq mi (9.51 million sq km) of the Arctic Ocean, 1.78 million sq mi (4.62 million sq km) of the North Atlantic Ocean north of Iceland, and roughly 8.5 million sq mi (22 million sq km) of islands and bordering continents (7 percent of the earth's surface; 14 percent of the earth's exposed land area). Frontage on the Arctic Ocean is as follows: Russia, 52 percent; Canada, 24 percent; Norway, 9 percent; Denmark's Greenland, 8 percent; and the United States, 7 percent.

With a length of 2,000 mi (3,200 km) and a width of 1,600 mi (2,560 km), the Arctic Ocean is an ocean in name only. It is, in fact, a mediterranean (Pratt, 1947, p. 659) arm of the Atlantic Ocean with a single oceanic entry— Lena Strait—between Spitsbergen and Greenland (Fig. 1). Bering Strait is merely a shallow and geologically ephemeral opening on a 900-mi-wide (1,350 km) continental shelf. Shallow shelves surround these narrow entryways, as well as the Arctic Ocean; of the 5.44 million sq mi (14.1 million sq km) covered by water, about 2 million sq mi (5.2 million sq km) consists of continental shelves. Political jurisdiction of the shelf areas has assumed increasing importance in recent years as their hydrocarbon potential has been revealed, and in this respect Russia is especially fortunate. Approximately 70 percent of the 2 million sq mi (5.2 million sq km) of shelves fringe the USSR, in contrast to 10 percent for Norway, 5 percent for Denmark, 7 percent for Canada, and 8 percent for the United States. Although information regarding prospective oil and gas reserves is far from definitive, the potential for each of the Arctic political units appears to be proportionate to the land and shelf area controlled.

ARCTIC OCEAN

The Arctic mediterranean consists of two distinct basins, separated by the Lomonosov Ridge. Although the ridge does not surface, it rises more than 10,000 ft (3,000 m) above the Eurasian basin on its Atlantic side and approximately 7,000 ft (2,120 m) above the shallower Canadian basin on the Pacific side. The ridge extends without a break from the central Siberian shelf to the North American shelf off Ellesmere Island. There, it swings westward and parallels the outer margin of other Canadian Arctic Islands. It is composed of continental crust, 450 mi (720 km) wide, with a core of Precambrian rocks that were folded into a linear mountain chain as early as Proterozoic time and were folded again during the early Paleozoic (Fig. 2; Spizharskiy, 1967; Trettin, 1969; Meyerhoff, 1970a, b; Meyerhoff and Meyerhoff, 1971). Its age and the nature of its ties with the two continents bespeak the permanence of the Arctic Ocean and offer no support to the notion advanced by some advocates of continental drift that the ridge severed original ties with northwestern Europe and migrated westward to its present position.

The Lomonosov Ridge has long functioned as a sill, separating the waters of the two basins

(Meyerhoff, 1970b). The deeper Eurasian depression, which is underlain by oceanic crust, has maintained a connection with the North Atlantic at least since late Proterozoic time. Chemical analyses have shown Atlantic affinities of the waters as far east as the Laptev Sea on the Atlantic side of the ridge, in contrast to the more sluggish Pacific waters in the Canadian basin on the opposite side of the ridge (von Arx, 1962). To enter the Canadian basin, water from the Pacific must cross 900 mi (1,350 km) of shelf that shallows to a 60-ft (18 m) depth, whereas the Gulf Stream and North Atlantic Drift propel warm saline waters through the Lena Strait and across the 700-ft (212 m) depth in the Barents Sea. The climatic effects on land and sea (Worthington, 1970) had significance in the conduct of World War

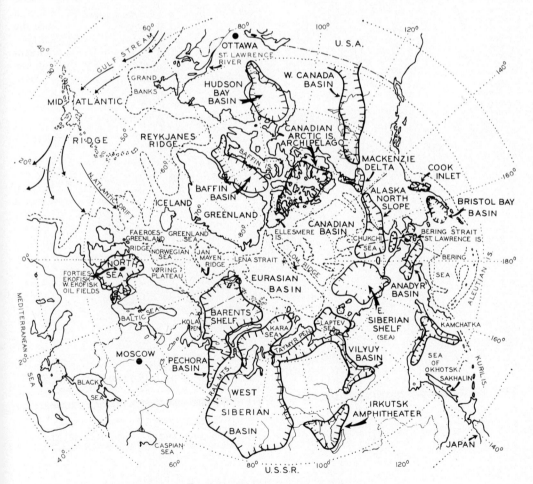

FIG. 1—Index map of Arctic region.

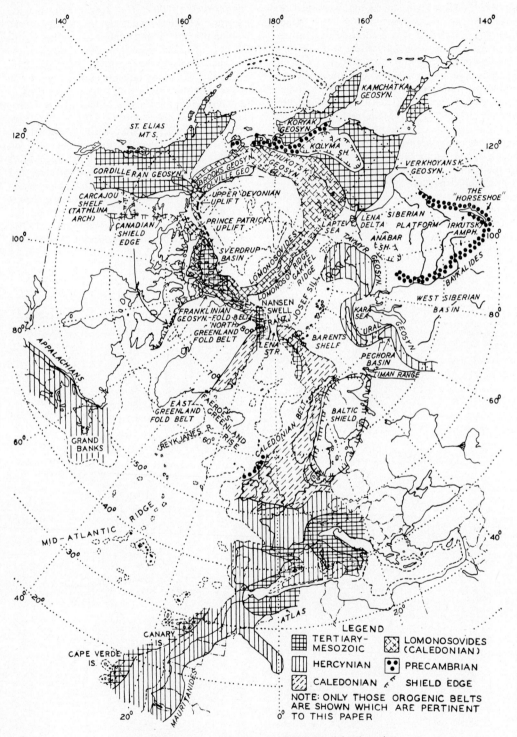

Fig. 2—Main geologic provinces and fold belts of Arctic region.

II. Germany's conquest of Norway in no small measure was designed to assure year-round shipments of Sweden's iron ore from Kiruna via the open Norwegian port of Narvik (Fig. 3). Open water at Murmansk provides Russia with its single perennial commercial harbor on the Arctic. As spectacular and historic as the voyage of Esso's *Manhattan* may have been, it did little more than prove what already was known—that the Canadian Arctic and Alaska (and Siberia east of the Laptev Sea and the Lomonosov Ridge) are not beneficiaries of climatic ameliorization. Pack ice clogs the Canadian basin, which overlies a crust that apparently is neither oceanic nor continental (E. King *et al.*, 1964, 1966; Vogt and Ostenso, 1970).

MARGINAL LANDS

Political Geography

The nations with Arctic frontage have markedly contrasted relations and interests with respect to the Polar region. Iceland, with a population of 210,000 persons of mainly Norse descent, lies wholly within the Arctic as defined herein. For more than a millennium it has subsisted on a meager economy and in geopolitical and geological obscurity. Its obscurity, however, is now threatened—geologically, because its 40,000 sq mi (104,000 sq km) lie athwart, and probably terminate, the Mid-Atlantic Ridge; geopolitically, because of its strategic position in the North Atlantic corridor to the Arctic. Its volcanic origins severely restrict the economic potential, but its location on one of the earth's major structures has brought it into scientific prominence. The size of the USSR Embassy in the capital city, Reykjavík, shows that Russia is cognizant of that key geographic location in the main entrance to the Arctic.

Spitsbergen (Svalbard), which commands the eastern side of the Lena Strait, is a dependency of Norway. Its "permanent" population is given as 3,000, but it, too, has a transient Russian population exploiting coal and other mineral deposits under license from the Norwegian government. On the west side of Lena Strait, 37,000 inhabitants live on the fringes of Denmark's 840,000-sq mi (2,184,000 sq km) ice-capped island of Greenland. Its geologic affinities are with the North American continent, from which it is separated by the frigid waters of Davis Strait and Baffin Bay (Fig. 4). In the north, only a narrow channel separates it from Ellesmere Island.

Ellesmere Island lies at the northern apex of Canada's Arctic Archipelago, which forms a fragmented triangle extending 1,000 mi (1,600 km) north of the nearest point on the mainland, to lat. 83°. On the south, in the Northwest Territories and in Labrador's Ungava Peninsula, the Precambrian shield forms the undulate surface of the mainland and the Precambrian rocks extend into the islands. There, however, they are partly covered by a flat-lying Paleozoic sedimentary sequence, which abuts a complex fold-mountain range along the Arctic margin. The fold belt was formed from Proterozoic to Devonian sedimentary rocks.

If the 60th parallel is accepted as the southern boundary of the subarctic zone, Yukon and the Northwest Territories and part of the Ungava Peninsula are entirely within Canada's "frozen North." Workers who winter in the mining camps of northern Labrador, Quebec, Manitoba, Saskatchewan, and British Columbia, or in the oil and gas fields of northern Alberta, might argue for a 55°N-lat. boundary, but, even without this southerly extension, 42 percent of Canada lies in the Arctic or subarctic. Of Canada's 21,000,000 inhabitants, fewer than 50,000 live north of the 60th parallel. Even with generous allowance for the oil and gas explorationists now probing the Arctic Archipelago, the population along the broad expanse of the Arctic Ocean numbers less than 5,000. Except for the Dew Line installations, government outposts have policing rather than military functions. Canadians, however, recognize the fact that their future economic development depends largely on the use they make of the North, and a commission is concentrating on the multiple possibilities. Likewise, the government is a major participant in the Panarctic consortium currently carrying on geological, geophysical, and other exploratory activity, primarily for oil and gas, in the Mackenzie delta and the archipelago. A major gas discovery (5 trillion cu ft-plus = 150 billion m^3-plus) was made during 1970 in Triassic sandstone at King Christian Island (Fig. 1), and additional unevaluated discoveries have been made since, both in the delta and in the archipelago (Porth and Tafel, 1970; Anon., 1971a, b, c, 1972a, b, c, d, e; Bourne and Pallister, 1972; Chilton, *et al.*, 1972; Cleland, 1972; Heise, 1972; R. E. King, 1972).

The Arctic Slope of Alaska has been of concern to the U.S. government only sporadically. Exploration by government geologists in the 1930s led to the creation of a Naval Oil Reserve, and the empty spaces of the North and

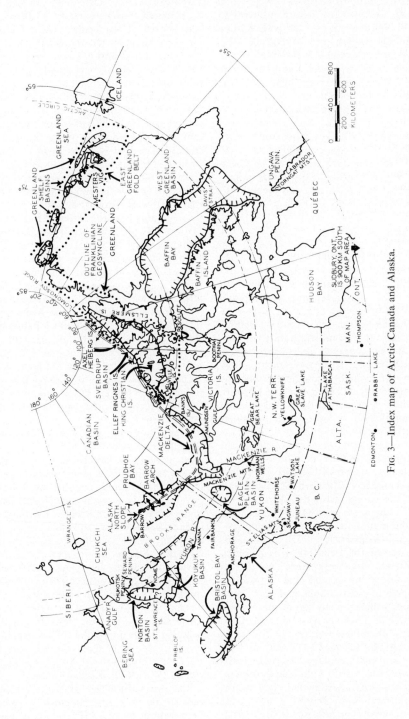

Fig. 3.—Index map of Arctic Canada and Alaska.

in the Aleutians were a cause for worry during World War II. Yet the base at Barrow is dismantled, as though a United States presence on the Arctic is of secondary importance. Even the 1968 discovery of oil at Prudhoe Bay has been regarded officially with annoyance and indifference, it would appear, on the basis of the 4–5 year delay in reaching an obvious and urgent decision with reference to pipeline transportation. The hypothetical inconvenience to a small fraction of Alaska's wildlife and possible environmental modification of 0.001 percent of the state's 580,000 sq mi (1,500,000 sq km) apparently weighs more heavily than the need for oil and gas in the other 49 petroleum-short states and more heavily than the loss of tax revenues, not to mention the losses sustained by the petroleum companies during the several years of suspended activity.

Russia has no illusions about the importance of its Arctic and subarctic terrane. It is pushing north as rapidly as limited manpower and financial resources will permit, and perhaps faster than they warrant. Ignorance of the effects of gas-field development on the permafrost environment resulted in the complete loss of one giant gas field (Taz, with an original recoverable reserve of 41 trillion cu ft—Vasil'yev, 1968a, b; Omen, 1973) and the destruction of vegetation over many square miles of countryside. The catastrophe was an object lesson in environmental control from which the engineering profession will profit worldwide. The Russians, however, have almost no other place to go. Approximately 90 percent of their 8,600,000 sq mi (22,360,000 sq km) lies north of the latitude of the United States–Canada border, and more than half is north of the 60th parallel. A large part of the southern USSR, east of the Caspian Sea (Kazakhstan, Turkmeniya, Uzbekistan) is inhospitable desert; hence, conquest of the north is vital to Russia's future. Temporarily, however, as a result of the 24th Communist Party Congress directives of 1971, the Russian government has given priority to development of its southern territories over the Arctic—largely because of the costly logistics problems found in the far North.

Regardless, more progress has been made by Russia in utilizing the Arctic than has been

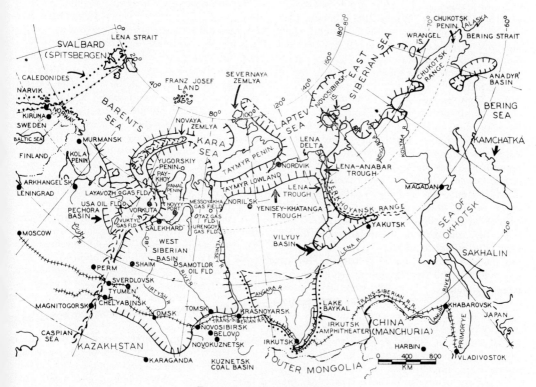

Fig. 4—Index map of Eurasia.

made in North America, although there still are hundreds of thousands of square kilometers of almost uninhabited forest land or taiga that remain but partly explored. Yet, along the endless stretch of Arctic coast, minute inspection of an up-to-date map reveals only two sections more than 100 mi (160 km) long which lack the name of an outpost or settlement of some kind.

Physical Geography

Climate—In the Köppen-Trewartha climate classification (Trewartha, 1968), almost the entire region herein referred to the "Arctic" has a polar or subarctic climate. A "polar climate" is one where tundra or ice cap prevails throughout the year. Precipitation is low—less than 20–22 in. (508–559 mm) per year—and generally is in the 1–12-in. (25–305 mm) range. Ice caps dominate Greenland, parts of Baffin and Ellesmere Islands (Fig. 3), and local areas of Spitsbergen and Iceland. Small mountain glaciers furrow almost all mountain ranges near coasts. A "subarctic climate" belongs to the humid class of climates—cool humid, with precipitation generally in the 12–30-in. (305–762 mm) range, but locally up to 40–60 in. (1,016–1,565 mm). Where the Japanese Current abuts the southern Alaska coast and where the Gulf Stream reaches Iceland and western Norway, annual rainfall up to 120 in. (3,130 mm) is common, and locally it exceeds 200 in (5,588 mm).

The Gulf Stream–North Atlantic Drift system is highly beneficial to Iceland, the coast of Norway, and northwestern Russia adjacent to Norway. Murmansk is the only major Russian Arctic port which is ice free 365 days a year. A permanent polar pack ice blankets the entire Arctic Ocean. Winter pack ice covers almost all of the Barents Sea and the western North Atlantic to the southern tip of Greenland. The eastern North Atlantic remains ice free.

On the continents of North America and Eurasia, the influence of the Arctic air masses is modified by other climatic factors. In Eurasia the mountain barrier extending from the Alps to the Himalayas blocks the summer monsoon winds and rains from the south. The result is that summer and winter precipitation is scant and no section of subarctic Siberia, except the higher mountain ranges, receives more than 20 in. (508 mm) of rain; the Arctic rim receives 10 in. (254 mm) or less. In European Russia the westerly winds from the Atlantic lose their moisture as they pass over Western Europe,

and only a relatively small wedge east of the Baltic Sea in the vicinity of Leningrad gets more than 20 in. (508 mm). Temperatures are affected by the immense size of the continent, and in the Lena River basin the annual temperature variation is 160° or 170°F (71° or 77°C). The mean average January temperature is −40°F (−40°C) or less. Although the communists may have made life in Siberia respectable, they have not made it comfortable.

The Western cordillera of North America likewise is a deterrent to the passage of moist winds from the Pacific into the interior, and the patterns of precipitation in the Arctic and subarctic regions of Canada and Alaska closely parallel those of the USSR. Only in southern Greenland, where the cold dry winds from the ice cap meet the warm moist air from the Atlantic, is there heavy precipitation. Although the smaller size of North America is less conducive to such extremes of temperature as are known in Siberia, the difference is one of degree. A short stretch of Alaska's Pacific coast north of the 60th parallel is favored with more clement weather as a result of the warming—and rainy—influence of the Japanese Current.

Geomorphology—Scarcely a major event in the course of geologic history skipped the Arctic; hence the variety of landforms is as great as it is in more southerly latitudes. The only obvious differences are attributable to the climate. Physical processes of weathering predominate over chemical decay; static snow and ice and permafrost have created many of the surficial features, and the mobile ice of glaciers has left fresh scoured and pitted surfaces wherever Holocene melting has exposed the underlying bedrock. The tundra has established itself over large areas, and the kinds of vegetation increase southward into the subarctic, much of which is heavily forested where climatic conditions permit.

Canada, northwest Europe, and parts of central and most of eastern Siberia are underlain by Precambrian shields and old mountain systems. In fact, a substantial fraction of the Arctic rim consists of Proterozoic and middle Paleozoic fold mountains that were formed by compression directed from the Arctic basin (Fig. 2); the submerged Lomonosov Ridge, which belongs to this group of tectonic features, crosses the entire Arctic Ocean and is joined to orogenic structures of the same age and origin in Canada and Siberia (Spizharskiy, 1967; Trettin, 1969). The Arctic basin obviously has functioned as an oceanic basin at least since middle Proterozoic time, and no variety of plate-tectonic prestidigitation can account for its geologic borders.

The only active volcanic region is Iceland, on the subarctic fringe of the region. It can be described with some oversimplification as a block-faulted lava plateau which is under compressional stress (Einarsson, 1965; Einarsson and Meyerhoff, 1974). The lavas have been folded, and flank dips range from 10° to 45°. Locally, the lavas have been folded to the limits of cohesion in competent basalt, and the notion that the tension on the Mid-Atlantic Ridge is pulling the island apart appears baseless. Comparison with the Harney section of the Columbia Plateau discloses many similiarities.

In Eastern Canada the Precambrian extends from the St. Lawrence River northward through all of the Ungava Peninsula and reappears in Baffin Island. Precambrian rocks probably underlie much of Greenland's ice cap, and an imperfectly known sedimentary basin lies between Greenland and the mainland in Davis Strait and Baffin Bay (Fig. 3). The shield also stretches from Lake Superior north-northwestward, west of Hudson Bay, to the channels separating the mainland from the archipelago; a salient forms the core of Boothia Peninsula. The Ungava Peninsula is a flat upland that rises in elevation toward the Quebec-Labrador boundary, where local elevations are as high as 7,000 ft (2,210 m) in the Torngat Mountains. West of Hudson Bay the elevation is low, and in the bay it drops below sea level; in the south a basinal structure contains an Ordovician-Devonian stratigraphic section. Mining is the only basis for settlement on the heavily glaciated surface; a mining camp, Yellowknife, serves as the capital of the Northwest Territories.

West of the shield, flat-lying Paleozoic sedimentary rocks form a low plain drained by the Mackenzie River (Figs. 1, 2). Northwest Canada's three great lakes—Athabasca, Great Slave, and Great Bear—which feed the Mackenzie, lie along the unconformable Paleozoic-Precambrian contact. The Mackenzie River is seasonally navigable, and its lowland is the site of numerous settlements and of increasing exploratory activity for oil and gas. Mesozoic rocks cover areas that increase in size northward toward and beneath the Mackenzie delta in the Arctic Ocean, and westward along parts of the Rocky Mountain front. On the west the Mackenzie Mountains and the Rocky Mountain system form the boundary of the lowland, and they, with the Pacific mountain system and in-

termontane lowland drained by the Yukon River, compose the whole of Yukon Territory and adjacent sections of southeastern Alaska (Fig. 3).

The Arctic Archipelago is a composite geomorphic region, merging on the south with mainland geology but dominated by a thickened platform sequence of Paleozoic rocks, extensively covered northward and westward by a Mesozoic section. The platform sequence merges with the thick section of the folded Franklinian geosyncline of the central part of the archipelago (Fig. 2). The folding originated by pressure from the Arctic Ocean; hence the deformation is more subdued southward, and in the western islands the orogenic structures are now covered in part by a late Tertiary and Quaternary coastal plain. Elsewhere the Franklinian fold belt borders the ocean as far east as northern Greenland (Fig. 2).

Although confirmation currently is lacking, the Franklinian structures may continue westward beneath the Mackenzie delta, to emerge in the Brooks Range of Alaska. The Brooks Range has a core of folded Proterozoic to Middle Devonian rocks that trend east-west, parallel with the Arctic coast. Devonian and pre-Devonian compression was from the north, but Laramide compression was from the south. A flexure in Laramide structures occurs along the Yukon-Alaska boundary, in approximate alignment with the so-called orocline of the St. Elias Mountains in the Pacific Mountain system (Fig. 3). South of the Brooks Range the Yukon River drains a complex intermontane belt. On the North Slope (Alaska north of the Brooks Range), Laramide fold-fault structures diminish in size northward and form a foothill zone with some Appalachian-type topography. Toward the coast a thickened Mesozoic section is buried beneath a thin and broken Tertiary cover and a Quaternary coastal plain that broadens westward toward Barrow. Reconnaissance geophysical work has identified Brooks Range structures submerged and buried in the Chukchi Sea,[4] extending toward the Chukotsk Range of Siberia.

Northeastern Siberia is a mountainous coun-

[4] Geophysical surveys by the U.S. Geological Survey during parts of 1969, 1970, and 1971, partly in the USGS cutter *Storis,* revealed that the Brooks Range structures continue eastward beneath the Chukchi shelf toward the Mackenzie delta, and westward into Siberian waters (USGS news releases first appeared December 5, 1969).

try with southwest-northeast *en échelon* ranges extending to the coast as far west as the Kolyma River (Fig. 4), which drains a sizable north-facing basin. Westward, a coastal plain fringes the coastal area as far as the Lena River, which reaches the Arctic through a rather narrow, highland-flanked valley (Fig. 4). Mountainous terrain of the Taymyr Peninsula also extends to the coast and into the off-lying Severnaya Zemlya islands; from the Yenisey valley westward to the Baltic shield, however, a vast plain is broken only by the Ural Mountains, which loop into the Yugorskiy Peninsula and thence into Novaya Zemlya. West of the Urals the plain is drained by relatively short streams—the Dvina and Pechora. In western Siberia, however, the Ob', Irtysh, and Yenisey Rivers rise far south of the Arctic coast in the well-watered mountains of the Chinese and Outer Mongolian borders. In the south the spring thaw begins in April, and floodwaters pour into the still-frozen North in such volume that as much as 200,000 sq mi (520,000 sq km) of the West Siberian plain may be flooded in any year. River navigation is uncertain and hazardous, and ground transportation, as well as habitation, is nearly impossible over large areas.

Thus, the mountainous eastern region and the flooded western region severely restrict development of vast segments of the Siberian Arctic. Neither the north-flowing Mackenzie in Canada nor the northwest-flowing Yukon poses comparable problems in North America—but neither do these regions contain three of the world's largest oil and gas basins, as does Russia's problem area.

MINERAL RESOURCES

It is evident from the geography of Arctic and subarctic regions that the only comfortably habitable areas are the islands and coastal margins that are warmed by the Gulf Stream–North Atlantic Drift and the Japanese Current. The beneficiaries are Iceland, coastal Norway, the Murmansk patch of northwestern Russia, and a small segment of Alaska within the latitudinal limits under consideration. Even in these restricted localities, the climate might more accurately be described as tolerable rather than comfortable. Significantly, these are the only places where fishing acquires economic importance. Elsewhere there are but two possible reasons for settlement and development—economic and military. In the subarctic, hunting and lumbering have some economic

potential, but the major economic attractions are the nonrenewable mineral resources (Quineau, 1961). Although the airplane has transformed the accessibility of the entire Arctic, it has had little effect on exploitation of bulk materials such as the base and ferrous metals, coal, and petroleum—all of which depend on ground transportation. Gold and platinum and, more recently, uranium are almost the only products valuable enough to pay for the air freight. Water transportation is available the year round in the restricted "comfortable" localities listed. Elsewhere it is available for the short summer season, and even then it generally is hazardous. Technology is beginning to expand the possibilities of mineral exploitation. Nearby coal deposits, especially in Siberia, have made it possible to reduce bulk ores to the metal content by concentration and refining. Oil and gas within pipable distance of large mineral deposits now are offering the same opportunity for bulk reduction. The recent development of outsize freight planes has cut the cost of air transport materially. Even so, mineral deposits—whether metal or hydrocarbon—must be of great size to defray the heavy costs of exploration, development, processing, shipping, and manning, and still yield a profit. Ample illustration can be found in the story of Yellowknife, or in the less remote INCO nickel operation at Thompson, or the iron ore developments along the Quebec-Labrador boundary where the ore moves by rail to ports on the St. Lawrence estuary. It is a safe guess—if one may paraphrase the playwright and poet Goldsmith—that many a mineral deposit exists with boom unseen, to waste its value on the Arctic air.

Mineral Resources Other than Hydrocarbons

Canada—Canada's mineral industry, which grosses more than $4 billion annually, makes a 7 percent contribution to her export trade (Engineering and Mining Jour., 1969a). Of the $2 billion of metals mined, approximately three fourths comes from the Precambrian shield (Lang *et al.*, 1970), but the recently published mineral map (Douglas, 1970) of the country shows and lists a scant 11 present (and past) mining operations in the Northwest Territories with annual output worth approximately $125 million (Fig. 3). All mines are metal producers, and the assortment is large—gold, uranium, silver, the base metals, tungsten, nickel, and some byproducts such as cadmium and cobalt. A group of four mines just south of the

NWT border on Lake Athabasca, Saskatchewan (Fig. 3), might be considered as one and added to make an even dozen. They produce uranium and gold. Except for a lone mining camp on Hudson Bay, every other operation is at or near the western margin of the Precambrian and has easy access to the three great Canadian lakes and/or the Mackenzie River. Although mineralization of the shield is zonal and large areas are barren, the low density of mining activities in the Northwest Territories stands in marked contrast to the numerous operations in Ontario and Quebec. Surely, the economics of accessibility is a dominant factor which causes the contrast. This statement is certainly true for a very large iron ore deposit that was discovered in 1962–1963 between Hudson Bay and the southern part of the Northwest Territories.

The second major mineral province is in the Western cordillera of the Yukon (Little et al., 1970), which has 10 mining camps. One produces asbestos and the others metals—primarily gold, but some silver, and one mine produces lead-zinc with the byproduct cadmium. Total annual value of the mine products is approximately $25 million. Nearly all gold was recovered from placers, but most of the dredging has been suspended or abandoned. Here, too, the density of mining activities contrasts markedly with the burgeoning activity south of the 60th parallel in British Columbia. One may suspect that accessibility and latitude are more potent factors than geology. Although mineralization has been reported in the Ungava Peninsula north of 60° latitude, exploratory work has not led to exploitation. The metals found in the archipelago remain undisturbed, but they include iron ore and zinc on Baffin Island, lead-zinc near Resolute, and copper on Victoria Island (Fig. 3; Engineering and Mining Jour., 1969a; Thorsteinsson and Tozer, 1970).

Reconnaissance surveys, including a continuing aeromagnetic survey, have not disclosed new ore bodies in large segments of the shield; nor have they deciphered all of the intricacies of Precambrian structure. The linear pattern of the paired gold belts, the unique occurrence of the Sudbury Ni-Cu-Ag complex, the hematitic ores in parts of the Proterozoic sequence—these and other types of mineralization in the southern part of the shield bespeak a variety of geologic situations that call for more definitive and sophisticated exploratory work. Gulf Oil's discovery of uranium on Rabbit Lake in northern Saskatchewan, not far from the boundary of the Northwest Territories, illustrates the point (Fig. 3). Having spent one long season in central Quebec looking for potentially economic mineral deposits, one of us (HM) has no illusions about the difficulties that discovery and development present. Foreseeable shortages will, in time, warrant a closer look.

Alaska—The gross mineral industry of Alaska is valued at approximately $300 million, of which all but $40 million is attributable to oil and gas production (U.S. Bureau of Mines, 1971). Approximately $27 million of the nonpetroleum output is in structural materials—sand, gravel, and stone. The rest of the industry can be characterized best as discouraging. Although gold production seems to be holding steady at 21,000 troy oz (600,000 g), this figure is a drop from the 250,000-oz (7,100,000 g) annual output 20 years ago. The decline began in the boom years of the late 1950s, and in 1964 one of us (HM) failed to find a single dredge in operation in the Nome, Tanana, and Yukon districts, although a few were manned by maintenance crews in a futile hope that gold might be revalued (Fig. 3).[5]

Persistent field studies by U.S. Geological Survey geologists over the years have uncovered many deposits of a large assortment of metals, and with every recent shortage of mineral raw materials there has been a surge of exploratory activity by private industry. In 1969, for example, 17 companies had field parties looking for, or testing, known copper deposits, one of them on the south flank of the Brooks Range; yet there was only one producer. Deposits of nickel, iron ore, and uranium were receiving exploratory attention, and efforts were being made to increase the number of operations already producing modest quantities of the platinum metals, tin, and mercury. Byproduct lead and antimony complete the list of metals in actual production, and the list can be supplemented by the nonmetal barite. Ironically, the strongest continuing stimulant to exploration and development is Japan, whose avid search for minerals is being furthered by cooperating American companies. Paradoxically, the coal-mining industry has held its own for several years, although at a level somewhat below its peak of 860,000 tons in the mid-1950s. Its potential market has been restricted and its future is uncertain as production and distribution of oil and gas increase within the

---

[5] The recent revaluations of U.S. currency may alter somewhat this last statement.

state; but in some localities coal will no doubt remain the most accessible fuel for some time to come.

Alaska's misfortune is its small population, together with a limited regional market and marginal location with respect to the 48 conterminous states. The long-range future is brighter, because Alaska's mineral wealth will be in demand as shortages and international competition for raw materials grow.

Western Europe—The Baltic shield has many of the characteristics of Canada's Precambrian shield, but it is not as extensive or as highly mineralized. It flanks and underlies the Baltic Sea, extending northward into Sweden, part of Norway, all of Finland, and the Kola Peninsula of the USSR (Fig. 4). Compared with the Canadian shield, it is densely settled, geologically better known, and more intensely exploited. The mining industry is nearly 3 centuries old. Among Norway's numerous mines, the ilmenite-magnetite mine in the southwestern part of the country probably is the largest, and the seemingly inexhaustible high-grade iron ore extracted at Kiruna, Sweden, has long been prized as a "sweetener" for the low-grade ores native to Great Britain, Germany, and Luxembourg. Finland has the largest copper deposit in Europe, but her valuable nickel deposit in the Kola Peninsula was lost as a result of the Russo-Finnish war early in World War II. She does, however, share the iron ores of the Kola Peninsula with her Russian neighbor. The Caledonian range that forms Norway's northwestern coast has yielded few minerals, but in Spitsbergen coal has been mined for at least half a century—at present, mostly under license by Russia. In Denmark's Greenland, the most important commercial operation terminated when the vein deposits of the sodium aluminum fluoride, cryolite, were finally mined out. It was the world's only known commercial cryolite ore body (other commercial deposits may have been discovered recently in the USSR), but was no match for other ores used by the burgeoning aluminum industry, which even now is having trouble finding sufficient fluorspar for a flux. A lead-zinc deposit, which has been mined at Mesters Vig, Greenland (Fig. 3), suggests the likelihood of inaccessible mineral wealth in the Precambrian rocks buried under the ice cap.

Russia—Although the threat of German conquest of Russia east of the Urals in World War II gave considerable impetus to the development of Siberia, the region west of the Urals still is the most densely populated and intensely industrialized segment of this vast country (Fig. 4). Its mineral resources are not fully known, much less appraised, especially in the Arctic and subarctic parts. In European Russia, industry long depended on coal and lignite for energy, although some hydropower was used. Limited transportation facilities and technology retarded conversion to oil and natural gas, but contracts for pipe with Western European countries—notably Germany—are speeding the changeover. Nonetheless, the USSR is still the world's largest producer and consumer of coal and lignite.

One of the gravest problems the Russians have had to face is the physical separation of coal and iron ore—in northern Europe, the Ural region, and Western Siberia. For example, the iron and steel complex at Cherepovets (not far from Leningrad) uses iron ore from the Kola Peninsula, 900 mi (1,350 km) north, and coking coal from Vorkuta, 1,700 mi (2,700 km) northeast in the Pechora basin on the west flank of the Polar Urals. The Kola Peninsula also supplies apatite, which is Russia's principal raw material for its superphosphate plants, as well as much of its nickel from the nickel-copper-cobalt deposits taken from Finland. Aluminum production is dependent on nephelite to supplement limited reserves of bauxite. Whether because of deficiencies in mineralization or exploration, the Ural Mountains north of the broad pass between Perm' and Sverdlovsk (Fig. 4) contribute little mineral wealth to the Russian economy. Peak elevations generally are below 6,000 ft (1,800 m), but at this latitude the range is a southern peninsula of the Arctic tundra with average winter temperatures of $-40°F$ ($-40°C$).

The region which most Westerners call "Siberia" is divided by Russians into four separate areas (Fig. 5). The first is Soviet Central Asia, south of the Urals but including Kazakhstan, as well as the neighboring so-called autonomous Moslem republics of the USSR. Western Siberia is the vast lowland north of Karaganda, east of the Urals, south of the Arctic Ocean, and west of the Yenisey River. What the Russians call "Eastern Siberia" is the region north of Mongolia, east of the Yenisey River, west of the Lena River, and south of the Arctic Ocean. The region east of the Lena River is known as the Soviet Far East and Maritime Region. The Russians do not include Soviet Central Asia, the Soviet Far East, or the Maritime Region within Siberia. Soviet Central Asia is excluded

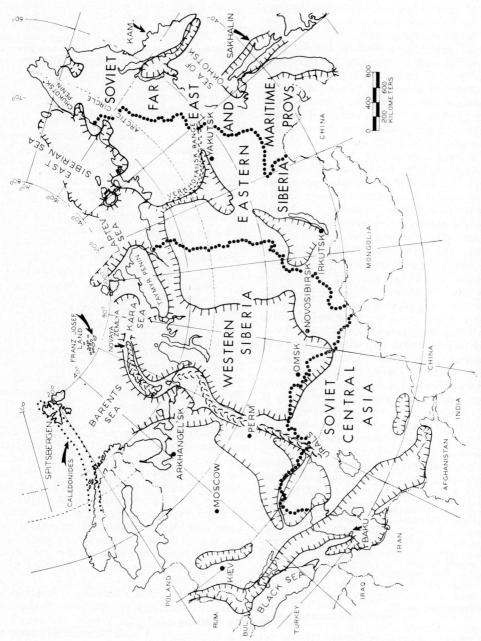

Fig. 5—Four main geographic subdivisions of Siberia. Subdivision boundaries are shown by black dots.

from detailed discussion here, because no part of it lies in the Arctic or subarctic.

In Western Siberia (Fig. 4), the development of mineral resources for heavy industry until the early 1960s was centered almost entirely in the Kuznetsk basin, one of Russia's principal coking coal producers. The Kuznetsk basin is east and southeast of Novosibirsk, a city of nearly 1,000,000 inhabitants at 55°N lat. Industrialization began with a coke-chemical industry, and a zinc refinery was added at Belovo in 1930. In 1932 an integrated iron and steel plant began operation at Novokuznetsk (then known as Stalinsk), but the iron ore had to be shipped 1,100 mi (1,760 km) from the southern Urals (Fig. 4). Construction of a direct rail line from Magnitogorsk to Novokuznetsk to relieve pressure on the more devious Trans-Siberian Railway brought to light the Karaganda coal basin, midway between the two terminals (Fig. 4). Karaganda, now a city of 500,000, has become a secondary industrial center, but Karaganda coal, which lacks coking characteristics, did not meet any of the needs of the iron and steel industry. The economics of the latter was relieved partly by rail transport of iron ore to Novokuznetsk and of coking coal to Magnitogorsk on the return trip. Post–World War II growth has added ferrous alloy and aluminum reduction plants and a second iron and steel mill. During the past decade the discovery of vast oil and gas pools in the West Siberian basin was followed by the delivery of oil in 1964, and gas in 1966, to the Sverdlovsk-Chelyabinsk industrial area, and of oil and gas in 1969–1971 to the Kuznetsk sector.

Obviously, Western Siberia is destined for rapid industrial growth in these areas, but north of 60°—even 57°—the outlook is far from good. D. V. Belorusov tells why (1967 [1969]):

Almost 40% of the West Siberia plain is covered with forest. The middle Ob' basin has an extensive swamp cover, and in West Siberia as a whole, swamps account for 40%–50% of the total area. Our limited knowledge about the region and the extensive swamp cover greatly hamper . . . development. . . . The climate is characterized by extreme continentality—a harsh winter and a relatively warm summer. . . . While the mean annual temperatures, say, are −6.7°C at Salekhard (on the Ob' at the Arctic circle) and −9.1° at Novyy Port (on the Ob' estuary at 68°), they rise substantially toward the south: −0.4° at Shaim (60°N) and +1.6° at Tyumen' (57°N).

The region is characterized by poor transport development, especially year-round services. . . . There are very few motor roads. . . . The few that do penetrate northward are not adapted to heavy loads. . . . They are out of action during the spring and autumn mud season.

The principal means of transportation at the present time is the stream network made up of the Ob' and Irtysch and their tributaries. . . . Both in spring flooding and during periodic summer freshets, the rivers often flood their banks and merge with lakes and swamps. The middle course of the Ob' then reaches a width of 100 km. . . . The absence of year-round transport services and the difficulty of building roads, communication lines, poor transmission lines and pipelines in the swampy terrain greatly complicate the development of the region.

Like Western Siberia, Eastern Siberia (Fig. 4) is well supplied with energy resources, especially brown coal, which is mined by stripping and is burned in mine-site thermal power plants. Supplementary energy comes from hydroelectric generators on the Yenisey River and its major tributary, the Angara. Much of this region is mountainous, and power sites are numerous. The Angara drains Lake Baykal (Fig. 4), the deepest freshwater body in the world. The lake lies close to the drainage divide with the Lena River, which appears to have captured some of the Yenisey's regional headwaters. The highlands along the Mongolian border still supply the lake and the Angara with a large volume of water, and the topography between Irkutsk (population, 425,000) and Krasnoyarsk (population, 575,000) provides excellent power sites. Most of Eastern Siberia's population is concentrated in these two industrial centers on the Trans-Siberian Railroad, and the natural resources of the region are funneled into them for processing and transportation. Both cities are south of 60°N lat., but settlements north of the rail line, with the exception of Yakutsk on the Lena River, are mostly small mining and lumber camps. One of the largest and oldest is the Noril'sk district, just east of the Yenisey River at 68°N (Fig. 4). Now a community of 175,000 inhabitants, it is a major supplier of nickel, copper, titanium, vanadium, platinum metals, and a variety of minor metals. Long dependent on local coal deposits, its recent growth has been accelerated by natural gas supplied from the vast nearby gas fields (mainly Messoyakha field) in the West Siberian basin.

Eastern Siberia is essentially a highland of complex mountains and plateaus, flanked on the west and east by the Yenisey and Lena Rivers, respectively. A broad lowland just north of 70° extends across the entire east-west width of the region, but its central or Taymyr section is separated from the Arctic Ocean by a mountain range that also forms the Severnaya Zemlya archipelago, which ends at 82°N lat. The geology of the region south of the Taymyr lowland, unlike that of Western Siberia, is that of a shield rather than a basin area, and favors mineralization rather than hydrocarbon accumulation. The assortment of metals mined in the Noril'sk district is merely a sample of what the region as a whole contains. Elsewhere gold, iron, molybdenum, zinc, lead, antimony, tungsten, asbestos, and rare earths augment the list; yet, from its very nature, the country is but fractionally explored to the point of resource evaluation, and even less of it is developed.

The Soviet Far East (Fig. 4) in many ways resembles Eastern Siberia. South of the upper Lena River a jumbled series of ranges rises along the boundary with eastern Outer Mongolia, and with the Inner Mongolian and Manchurian sections of China, without actually defining the border. The Amur River separates Russia and China as far south and east as the city of Khabarovsk, where the Amur turns northeast into Russian territory (Fig. 4). The boundary turns south at Khabarovsk, and the Russians occupy a lowland south to Vladivostok and the coastal mountain range of the Primor'ye region east of the lowland. East of the middle and lower Lena River, a broad belt belonging to the Circum-Pacific mountain system extends unbroken to the Bering Strait and Sea in the north, although it is penetrated southward from a narrow Arctic coastal plain by the broad valleys of the Indigirka and Kolyma Rivers. Farther south, the mountain belt terminates at the Sea of Okhotsk, which separates it from the mountainous Kamchatka Peninsula. Offshore from the Vladivostok extension, Sakhalin Island forms a narrow closure for a northern triangular bight of the Sea of Japan.

A recent visitor to this part of the USSR aptly called it "Russia's Wild East." From Lake Baykal to Khabarovsk, a distance of 1,500 mi (2,400 km), there are numerous grim frontier towns spaced along the Trans-Siberian Railroad, which now follows the long loop around the China border; conflicting ideologies caused the closing of the shortcut to Vladivostok through Harbin in Manchuria. Irkutsk, at 62°N lat., is connected with the railroad by a poor 600-mi (960 km) road, and with Magadan, on the Sea of Okhotsk, by 1,500 mi (2,400 km) of very poor road. Except for these railroads and for a limited road network radiating from Irkutsk, this part of the USSR is a trackless wilderness with some seasonal river transportation and tenuous ties by air with the south. Yet it has been explored superficially, and some of the larger mineral deposits are being exploited.

Of special interest are tin and diamond deposits in the Soviet Far East. Following the early development of the tin mines, Russia threatened to disrupt the International Tin Council by flooding the western market. Suddenly realizing that the tin was needed in her domestic market, Russia since has absorbed nearly all production. According to well-founded reports, Russia cherished some hope of cracking the diamond trade after the diamond mines were in production, but most of the output was industrial and, cannily, the Russians made a deal with the DeBeers' interests to handle whatever gem diamonds are recovered. This region as a whole has much the same mineral potential as Eastern Siberia, but manpower for development is more than scarce; people are reluctant to settle in a rugged, isolated country that has the dubious distinction of having the coldest winter temperature ever officially recorded outside of Antarctica.

Almost all of Russia's northern regions have been explored, at least superficially. At one time the government reported as many as 1,000 parties in the field. Although the inventory of mineral resources is by no means complete, the Russians have a fair knowledge of the potential wealth which the tundra and taiga contain. Development, however, has suffered from several handicaps. The severest, without question, is manpower. In a country of 8.65 million sq mi (22.36 million sq km), an evenly spread population of 244 million is only 28 inhabitants per square mile (11 per sq km). Actually, more than three quarters of the population live west of the Urals, and about 30 percent of the total is urban, living in cities of 200,000 or more. The only settlements north of 60° that attain urban stature are Irkutsk, at the west end of Lake Baykal, and Murmansk and Arkhangel'sk, in European Russia (although the population of Leningrad at 59°55'N is 4,000,000). The number of workmen and supervisory personnel available for activities in the north is small, and it will continue to fall far short of the region's potential for years to come.

Even socialism requires capital for development—a point which Lenin repeatedly emphasized. However, Russian capital has been directed so completely into heavy industry, armament, and space projects that simple consumer needs have had low priority, and development of the North now is even lower on the waiting list. Specific government objectives have prompted the intensive development of specific districts—*e.g.,* the tin and diamond deposits of the Far East (and far North!). Siberia's resources, known and unknown, exceed the needs of Russia's comparatively low population-to-area ratio. Currently, development seems to be geared to specific areal growth and to national requirements for specific raw materials. Utilization of the swamplands of Western Siberia and their underlying oil and gas fields, and of the taiga uplands as well as the frigid mountains of Eastern Siberia and the Far East, probably will await more critical needs for their mineral wealth.

HYDROCARBON RESOURCES

Petroleum is an old story in the Arctic and subarctic of North America. It was discovered at Norman Wells (Fig. 3) in the Mackenzie lowland in 1920, but transportation problems confined its use to the sparsely settled surroundings until World War II. Then, to meet military needs, the Canol pipeline was built to a refinery at Whitehorse, and the refined oil was piped to Skagway and Fairbanks, and to Watson Lake airfield in Yukon Territory (Fig. 3). Government exploration of Alaska's North Slope led to the creation of a large U.S. Naval Reserve east of Barrow in 1937, and to small local production for use at Barrow. Except for the World War II emergency, the demand-supply situation scarcely warranted further development at that time. New exploration was not undertaken until the late 1950s, but the potential of the North was not fully appreciated for another decade.

Canada—The history of Canada's oil industry is coincident with that of the U.S., starting about the time of Drake's Titusville discovery, mostly in the Paleozoic fields of Ontario. It did not assume importance until the Leduc discovery near Edmonton, Alberta, in 1947. Since then intensive exploration has pushed north in the Prairie provinces, from the U.S. border into northeastern British Columbia, Yukon, and the Northwest Territories. In the Alberta or Western Canadian basin, proved reserves of oil and condensate now total 11 billion bbl (1.5 billion tons), and gas reserves total 55 trillion cu ft (1.6 trillion m^3).

Exploration continues there, but attention is also being directed northward, where a consortium of private companies is collaborating with government geologists in examining and testing the Mackenzie delta and the Arctic Archipelago (Fig. 3). The Mackenzie delta and the contiguous and related Amundsen Gulf cover an area of 64,000 sq mi (166,000 sq km). Seismic data indicate that part of this area is underlain by 33,000 ft (10,000 m) or more of sedimentary rocks, including both Paleozoic and Mesozoic sequences. One well has been drilled into the Cambrian, and Proterozoic-Cambrian evaporites are known to be present in the south (Bassett and Stout, 1967). These evaporites have formed anticlines, domes, and ridges. Subsurface relations with the structures of Alaska's Brooks Range, which plunges under the delta-floodplain from the west, and with the Franklin Mountains, which plunge from the north-northeast, are obscure. Drilling already has established the presence of gas, and Imperial Oil Ltd.'s H-25 Atkinson well encountered oil at 5,750 ft (2,360 m) in Lower Cretaceous sandstone (Porth and Tafel, 1970). Additional discoveries have been made in the delta—in strata of Tertiary, Late Cretaceous, and Early Cretaceous ages. Their size and commercial importance still are undefined. An estimate of 50 billion bbl (6.85 billion tons) of recoverable oil and 100 trillion cu ft (2.9 trillion m^3) of gas for this basin does not seem out of line on the basis of stratigraphic and structural data now available (Meyerhoff and Meyerhoff, 1971).

The Sverdrup basin (Figs. 2, 3) covers an area of approximately 125,000 sq mi (320,000 sq km) along the northwestern margin of the Arctic Archipelago. It is a smaller successor basin (Halbouty *et al.,* 1970) to the Franklinian geosyncline, which extended from Melville Island northeast of the Mackenzie delta to northeastern Greenland a distance of 1,100 mi (1,760 km; Fig. 2). The Franklinian geosyncline contains a Proterozoic through Late Devonian sedimentary sequence ranging from 36,000–39,000 ft (11,000–12,000 m) in the miogeosyncline to possibly 57,000 ft (18,000 m) in the eugeosynclinal section in Axel Heiberg and Ellesmere Islands. The Sverdrup basin, which is 600 mi (1,000 km) long and has a maximum width of 260 mi (430 km), contains an incomplete sequence, 46,000 ft (14,000 m) thick, of Mississippian–earliest Pennsylvanian (Bashkirian) through middle Eocene sedimentary rocks. Middle Eocene folding terminated basinal sedimentation. In a basin of this size and duration, considerable lateral and vertical variations in lithology are found, but the section in nearly all the systems represents a change from a shelf facies on the southeast to a basinal facies on the northwest. Numerous diapirs in the Sverdrup basin are believed to be formed from evaporites of Pennsylvanian age (Thorsteinsson and Tozer, 1970), although evaporites of Cambrian through Devonian ages also may have contributed to the diapirs. Eocene orogeny folded the late Paleozoic, Mesozoic, and early Tertiary rocks, and refolded the pre-Mississippian rocks on which the younger sequence lies unconformably. Prospecting has been extensive but drilling has been limited. A gas discovery in Triassic sandstone on King Christian Island (Fig. 3) suggests the presence of a field of 5 trillion cu ft (150 billion m³) or more, with possibly 1 billion bbl (0.14 billion tons) of liquid hydrocarbons; a subsequent 1971 discovery in Kristoffer Bay, Ellef Ringnes Island, 50 mi (80 km) farther north, in the same sandstone as that at King Christian, promises to be nearly as big (Heise, 1972). More recently, oil has been discovered in the Arctic Archipelago (Anon., 1972a).

The only other Arctic sedimentary basin in Canada that merits attention for petroleum exploration is the 40,000 sq mi (104,000 sq km) of Baffin Bay between the Ungava Peninsula and Greenland (Figs. 1, 3). Marginal outcrops, on islands and peninsulas fringing Greenland's ice cap and in southeastern Baffin Island, reveal the presence of a Late Cretaceous–early Tertiary stratigraphic section, mostly with Arctic faunal and floral affinities. Although the bay is shared by Canada and Denmark, the sedimentary rocks shelve off Greenland, in a bench 250 mi (400 km) long and 60 mi (100 km) or less wide. The possibility that a sedimentary basin is present in the deeper water of the bay has not been determined. Exploration on the shelf under concession from Denmark is in progress, but the results have not been publicized.

Greenland—Quite apart from the Baffin Bay shelf, Greenland's eastern margin ultimately may stir exploratory interest (Figs. 2, 3). This Atlantic border was active tectonically during Proterozoic and much of Paleozoic time (Haller, 1969, 1971). The geosynclinal Proterozoic sedimentary section is as thick as 30,000 ft (9,000 m). These rocks unconformably underlie an early Paleozoic sequence that was folded during the Caledonian disturbance. Devonian rifting produced grabens in which 20,000–25,000 ft (6,000–7,500 m) of continental "Old Red Sandstone" accumulated. Mild Acadian deformation was followed by late Paleozoic marine transgression from north to south, and by the deposition of a sequence of Mesozoic rocks. Sedimentation was intermittent; deformation—mostly faulting—was spasmodic, but marine deposition did not end until Campanian time. This sedimentary-rock section has aroused considerable scientific interest, and the post-Devonian sequence may have a hydrocarbon potential that merits testing. These rocks extend as much as 150 mi (260 km) offshore, where the exploratory environment leaves much to be desired, but where the possible rewards in Permian and Triassic terrigenous clastic, carbonate, and evaporite sections ultimately may counterbalance the physical and geological risks.

Alaska—In the opposite, or northwestern, corner of the North American continent, the presence of at least one giant field[6] is assured (Fig. 3). The Prudhoe Bay field was discovered in 1968. The trap is an unconformity trap, and the major reserves (20 billion bbl [2.7 billion tons] of oil and 26 trillion cu ft [710 billion m³] of gas) are in Early Cretaceous, Jurassic, Triassic, and Mississippian sandstones and carbonate rocks below transgressive Late Cretaceous units. The stratigraphic section is sufficiently well known and thus is not described here (Rickwood, 1970; Morgridge and Smith, 1972). The North Slope coastal plain offers good prospects for extended discoveries, but the future, like the present, is fraught with problems.

At present, environmental faddists are effectively blocking production and transportation. It is a safe prediction that, in the future, equally strenuous objections will be raised to development of the Naval Reserve west of Prudhoe Bay and of the Wild Life Preserve that lies east of the field and extends to the Yukon boundary. Apparently, the coexistence of the scant native population, the birds and beasts, and oilmen cannot be visualized by zealots who believe that their plan for protecting the environment should prevail, and to whom dependence on undependable petroleum supplies from remote and temperamental foreign sources appears preferable to economic development of Alaska and of a strategic coastline. Whatever the reserves of the North Slope—20 billion bbl (2.7 billion tons) at Prudhoe Bay alone, and probably more elsewhere—they are needed now, because foreign suppliers are tak-

[6] In this paper we use the term "giant field," adopting the definitions of Halbouty *et al.* (1970) for giant fields: 500 million bbl or larger (70 million tons) for oil; and 3.5 trillion cu ft (100 billion m³) for gas.

ing advantage of increasing demand and existing shortages.

Despite the promise of the North Slope, the area of the fold belt and adjoining continental shelf is limited by natural and political boundaries. However large, the hydrocarbon reserves are finite and will have a short life in meeting projected domestic requirements of the United States. The rest of onshore Alaska offers some, but severely restricted, possibilities for discoveries and production. More alluring, because of size and, perhaps, lack of definitive data, are the widening shelves on the west, shared with the USSR. The Chukchi shelf facing the Arctic and the Bering shelf fronting the North Pacific Ocean are connected by the shallow waters of Bering Strait. In combination they cover more than 300,000 sq mi (780,000 sq km). Geophysical studies, in part by the U.S. Geological Survey, have traced the Brooks Range structures and Colville geosyncline into the Chukchi Sea, where their trend suggests that they may extend to Wrangel Island or beyond, into the East Siberian Sea (Fig. 2). Whether petroleum-bearing strata will be found in the structures is unknown. Preliminary studies by Scholl and Hopkins (1969) have outlined a large Tertiary sedimentary basin just south of the Seward Peninsula on the Bering shelf. Named the "Norton basin" from Norton Sound, it extends westward, passes north of St. Lawrence Island, and terminates against the Chukotsk Peninsula in Siberia (Figs. 1–3). Approximately 7,500–8,000 ft (2,300–2,500 m) of sedimentary rocks is present above acoustic basement. Two basins have been identified south and west of the Pribilof Islands (Grantz et al., 1970). They may be similar to the Bristol Bay basin, where nine wells, drilled in an 18,000-ft (5,500-m) sedimentary section, penetrated Paleocene through Pliocene continental strata with only one show of oil (Figs. 1–3; Hatten, 1971).

To borrow (and corrupt) a line, we might summarize the hydrocarbon outlook for Arctic and subarctic North America by saying that, from Greenland's icy mountains to Alaska's frigid shores, the prospects of finding several giant fields are good. Anything below giant size is economically worthless until—and unless—it can be tied into an existing nearby transportation system. Hence it is likely that many small fields will go undeveloped, regardless of domestic or world demands. The modern and ancient shelves and the hinge lines where they merge with sedimentary basins or defunct geosyn-

clines, as well as the less severely deformed—and generally younger—stratigraphic sections in the fold and fault mountain belts, present a recurrent series of hydrocarbon habitats from northern Greenland to the Bering Strait and the Chukchi Sea. The Mackenzie delta, which breaks the continuity of the Arctic mountain border, does not interrupt prospective hydrocarbon reservoirs. On the contrary, it adds one more type of favorable habitat. The immediate problem is the climate—primarily the socio-political climate and, secondarily, the weather.

Eurasia—A tour across Arctic Eurasia from west to east is a trip from the partly known into the unknown. Yet the fragmentary knowledge currently available reveals a hydrocarbon potential, partially proved, that may rival that of the Middle East. There are at least a dozen areas of interest between Spitsbergen and the Chukchi-Bering Sea, all but one of them under Soviet jurisdiction. The exception is Norway's Spitsbergen and adjacent waters.

Norway-Spitsbergen—The indiscriminate use of the word "sea" for water bodies, shallow or deep, with or without closure, is peculiar to Eurasian geography. In Western Europe, for example, the counterpart of Hudson Bay is the Baltic Sea. The shallow epeiric North Sea opens northward into the deep oceanic Norwegian Sea, which is separated from the North Atlantic Ocean by the Faeroe-Iceland Ridge or sill, from the contiguous oceanic Greenland Sea by Jan Mayen Ridge, and from the relatively shallow (less than 100 fm [180 m]) Barents Sea by the shallow shelf off southern Spitsbergen.

Because of their depth and the underlying oceanic crust fringed with narrow sedimentary slopes, the Norwegian and Greenland Seas offer few prospects for hydrocarbon discoveries, except (1) beneath the Vøring Plateau west of Norway, where 30,000 ft (9,000 m) of Permian(?)-Quaternary section is present (Grønlie and Ramberg, 1970), and (2) between Jan Mayen Island and Greenland, where another thick section may be present (Figs. 1, 4).

The shallow North Sea, in contrast, appears to have recoverable reserves of 120 trillion cu ft (3.43 trillion m³) of gas and more than 20 billion bbl (2.8 billion tons) of oil. The more recent discoveries (Forties field, *etc.*) have extended the known reserves into waters under Norwegian jurisdiction (Ekofisk and West Ekofisk field, *etc.;* Fig. 1). The Vøring Plateau appears to be a large basin contiguous with the North Sea sedimentary sequence off the Norwegian coast.

More promising, however, is the Barents Sea, the western 40,000 sq mi (100,000 sq km) of which belongs to Norway (Fig. 4). The western margin from the mainland through Bear Island is part of the Silurian Caledonides (Fig. 2; Czarniecki, 1969). The large area east of the fold belt extends to the Hercynian Ural–Novaya Zemlya orogenic belt, and the entire shelf sea is underlain by continental crust with an unexplored sedimentary overburden (Demenitskaya et al., 1968; Eldholm and Ewing, 1971). In Svalbard, which includes Spitsbergen and nearby islands in the northwestern Barents Sea, Caledonian folding was followed by Devonian block faulting and the deposition of "Old Red Sandstone" in grabens (Harland, 1969). Marine Devonian rocks eastward in the Pechora basin of northern European USSR suggest that the continental redbeds grade into a marine facies, possibly correlative with the marine Devonian of Novaya Zemlya (Vasil'yev, 1968b). In Svalbard, Early Carboniferous continental strata are overlain by Late Carboniferous and Permian marine beds, and the proportion of carbonate rocks increases in the Permian; the Late Triassic, Jurassic, and Early Cretaceous continental and marine strata have been identified on the island of Franz Josef Land, and a thin Late Cretaceous section is present in Svalbard (Dibner and Krylova, 1963; Escher, 1965; Klubov, 1965; Nalivkin, 1967; Sokolov and Pchelina, 1967; Sosipatrova, 1967; Kopik, 1968; Czarniecki, 1969; Harland, 1969). It is probable that rocks of these ages extend across much of the submerged basin (Eldholm and Ewing, 1971).

The structure beneath the Barents Sea is unknown, but the possibility of the existence of basins, faults, and even orogenic deformation to explain the Triassic conglomerates in Franz Josef Land is good in so large a shelf area, three quarters of which is shared by Russia. Obviously, conjecture can be set at rest only by a program of systematic geophysical exploration.

Russia—In addition to the Barents Sea, Arctic and subarctic Russia contains a dozen sedimentary basins, not including parts of the Chukchi and Bering shelves shared with Alaska (Figs. 1, 2, 4). From west to east they are the Pechora basin, Kara Sea, West Siberian basin, Yenisey-Khatanga trough, Laptev Sea and Lena delta, Lena Trough, Lena-Anabar trough, Irkutsk amphitheater, Vilyuy basin, East Siberian Sea, Sea of Okhotsk, and Anadyr' basin (Meyerhoff and Meyerhoff, 1971). Platform basins may be present in an area as large as the Barents shelf, the margins of which were deformed orogenically, but most of which appears to have escaped deformation between the Caledonian fold belt on the west and the Hercynian Ural–to–Novaya Zemlya orogenic zone on the east. Post-Caledonian block faulting during Devonian time and a strong middle Eocene thrust from the Atlantic added structural complications in central and western Svalbard but left the broad platform unaffected. In the absence of geophysical exploration, the detailed structure of the platform is unknown.

The Pechora basin (Fig. 4) is flanked on the east by the northern Urals and Pay-Khoy and on the southwest by the Timan Range. On the north and northeast it opens into the Pechora Sea reentrant of the Barents Sea. Although covered by a veneer of Jurassic and Cretaceous rocks, it is a Paleozoic extension of the pre-Ural foredeep. It contains 20,000 ft (6,000 m) or more of Silurian through Permian strata, which underwent structural deformation from tectonic movements in both the Timan Range and the Ural Mountains. Oil was found in the basin in 1929 and gas in 1935; subsequently, 43 structures have been proved to contain commercial oil and/or gas (Vasil'yev, 1968a, b). Among them are the giant Layavozh and Vuktyl' gas fields and the Usa oil field. All the Paleozoic systems from Silurian through Permian are productive. Known reserves are estimated at 10 billion bbl (1.4 billion tons) of oil and 45 trillion cu ft (1.3 trillion m³) of gas; but the basin has a potential 10 times greater than these conservative figures.

From Novaya Zemlya to the islands of Severnaya Zemlya on the east, the Kara Sea covers a shallow platform with unknown possibilities (Fig. 4). Its western area appears to be an extension of the West Siberian basin. Its northeastern section is believed to contain 18,000–20,000 ft (5,500–6,000 m) of Jurassic and Cretaceous sedimentary rocks, overlying a deformed Paleozoic and Precambrian basement. If this section has been correctly reported, it is correlative with the prolific sedimentary sequence in the West Siberian basin, but its hydrocarbon potential is untested and unknown.

The West Siberian basin, by way of contrast, is being explored and exploited actively (Fig. 4;

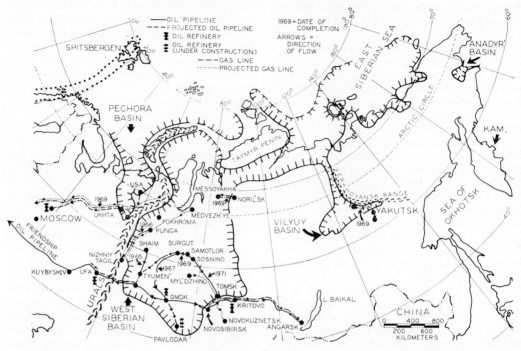

FIG. 6—Pipeline map of Siberia.

Vasil'yev, 1968a, b; Nesterov et al., 1971). Although production began only 10 years ago, more than 205 fields and potential fields have been identified in its 700,000-sq mi (1,750,000 sq km) area—30 or more of them giants (Halbouty et al., 1970; Nesterov et al., 1971). Known and probable reserves of 79 billion bbl (11 billion tons) of oil and 787 trillion cu ft (22.5 trillion m³) of gas undoubtedly will be increased 3- or 4-fold as exploration continues. The productive section is a terrigenous sequence of terrestrial and marine Jurassic and Cretaceous rocks that filled a subsiding intraplatform basin. The sediments were deposited on a complex basement which was converted to horst and graben structures by post-Hercynian block faulting. These structures provided ideal sites for hydrocarbon accumulation in the 7,000- to 20,000-ft (2,100 to 6,000 m) Mesozoic succession, and a Late Cretaceous shale formed a seal. The entire region has been stable since Jurassic time, and its low elevation has prevented erosion that would have facilitated the escape of gas and oil. Transportation problems retarded the development of this immense province, and initially (1964) the oil was barged on the Ob' River. A 600mi (1,000 km) pipeline was completed to the refinery at

Omsk in 1967, and another tied the fields with Tomsk in 1969 (Fig. 6). The result was an increase in output from 1,400,000 bbl (192,000 tons) in 1964 to 14,000,000 bbl (1,920,000 tons) in 1969. This amount will be increased greatly during 1971–1975 with a planned increase to 730–876 million bbl (100–120 million tons) per year by 1975 (Dikenshteyn, 1971). The principal gas fields are north of the oil fields, and their development proceeded more slowly, but pipeline transport from some fields now is available to Sverdlovsk and other Ural industrial centers (Fig. 6; Meyerhoff and Meyerhoff, 1971). The largest oil field in Russia is in the middle Ob' region—the Samotlor field (Figs. 7, 8), with recoverable reserves of 15.1 billion bbl (2.1 billion tons; Halbouty et al., 1970). The world's largest gas field is in the northern part of the basin near the Arctic coast —Urengoy field (Figs. 9, 10), with proved plus probable gas reserves of 175 trillion cu ft (5.0 trillion m³) and proved, probable, and potential reserves of 210 trillion cu ft (6 trillion m³; Remejew and Ostrowskaja, 1969; Nesterov et al., 1971). Condensate reserves are more than 5 billion bbl (684 million tons).

East of the West Siberian basin between the Taymyr fold mountains on the north and the

Anabar shield on the south, the Yenisey-Khatanga trough (Figs. 1, 2, 4) contains up to 20,000 ft (6,000 m) of Jurassic and Cretaceous sedimentary rocks that have large gas accumulations. A small quantity of heavy oil has been tapped in underlying Triassic and Permian strata near Nordvik, at the northeast end of the trough (Meyerhoff and Meyerhoff, 1971), where a Devonian salt-dome province is located (Kornev et al., 1966). North of the Taymyr range, the coastal area and shelf of the Laptev Sea, as well as the Lena delta farther east, are almost unexplored, although reconnaissance mapping and surveying, begun about 1969, increased steadily during 1970. Overall, there has been little exploration eastward along the Arctic Slope across the East Siberian Sea to the Chukchi Sea between Arctic Siberia and Alaska, but this situation will change markedly during the next few years. The breadth of the shelf and the onshore geology suggest hydrocarbon possibilities which probably will not be realized for some time to come.

Not much more is known of the Lena-Anabar trough and the Lena Trough (Figs. 1, 2, 4). but the ties of the former with the Khatanga trough and of the latter with the Vilyuy basin suggest petroleum possibilities that undoubtedly will receive attention in the future. In the Vil-

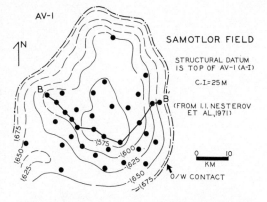

FIG. 7—Samotlor oil field, West Siberian basin, USSR. Location of Figure 8 is shown. Field location is shown on Figure 4.

yuy intracratonic basin, centered at the confluence of the Lena and Vilyuy Rivers (Fig. 4), two giant gas fields and four smaller gas producers have been discovered in Permian, Triassic, and Jurassic sandstone (Vasil'yev, 1968b; Fradkin, 1969). Production comes from cupola-like structures on the crest of an east-west arch—130 mi (210 km) long, 35 mi (56 km) wide—with closure of nearly 5,000 ft (1,500 m). The productive domed structures range in

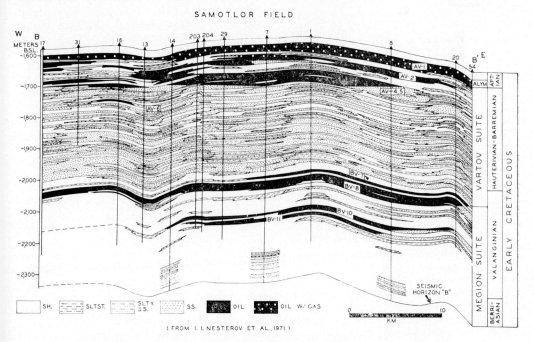

FIG. 8—West-east structural cross section of Samotlor field. Location is on Figure 7.

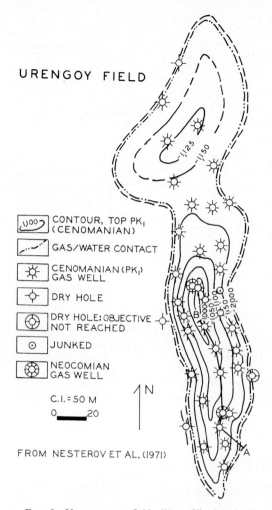

URENGOY FIELD

- $\sqrt{1100}$ CONTOUR, TOP PK₁ (CENOMANIAN)
-   GAS/WATER CONTACT
-   CENOMANIAN(PK₁) GAS WELL
-   DRY HOLE
-   DRY HOLE: OBJECTIVE NOT REACHED
-   JUNKED
-   NEOCOMIAN GAS WELL

C.I.= 50 M

0   20

↑N

FROM NESTEROV ET AL. (1971)

Fig. 9—Urengoy gas field, West Siberian basin, USSR. Location of Figure 10 is shown. Field location is shown on Figure 4.

length from 15 to 25 mi (24–40 km). Although most have been drilled, development awaits transportation and markets. Proved plus probable reserves are about 70 trillion cu ft (2 trillion m³); ultimate reserves are estimated to be more than 200 trillion cu ft (6 trillion m³) plus about 2 billion bbl of condensate (Fradkin, 1969).

Beyond the Lena River in the Soviet Far East, exploration has been limited, but some oil and natural gas have been found in Proterozoic rocks in the intracratonic basins within the subarctic Irkutsk amphitheater—a platform bounded by the U-shaped Precambrian (Riphean) Baykalides orogenic belt (Fig. 4; Trofi-

muk *et al.*, 1964; Vasil'yev, 1968a, b). Of greater significance, if only because of its location, is the recent (1969) discovery of gas in the Anadyr' basin on the west side of the Bering Sea (Dolzhanskiy *et al.*, 1966; Burlin, 1967; Belyayev *et al.*, 1970; Demenitskaya, 1971; Meyerhoff *et al.*, 1971; Trofimuk, 1971). The basin is a small area of infolded Cretaceous and Tertiary sedimentary rocks. The gas is in a Miocene sandstone reservoir (Vostochno-Ozero). Unfortunately, this and a subsequent discovery are noncommercial. Nevertheless, production here and in Sakhalin no doubt will lead to more widespread exploration in the Maritime Region. Inland, however, Russia's Eastern or Pacific cordillera is not conducive to early settlement or intensive resource development. The geology, in any case, favors mineralization rather than hydrocarbon accumulation, except in local basins described by Avrov *et al.* (1969), Eremenko *et al.* (1970), and Trofimuk (1971).

Arctic Outlook

A simple inspection of a map of the Arctic (Fig. 1) demonstrates Russia's primary interest in this polar sector of the earth. Its Arctic frontage far exceeds Canada's, and the other national territories bordering the northern oceans offer no comparison. Areally, the region north of the Arctic Circle comprises a major part of the Soviet domain, and its development must be a project of prime importance. To a degree, Canada faces the same prospect and has even farther to go. If Canada's 21.4 million inhabitants were spread evenly over its territory, the density would be but 6 people per square mile, in contrast to 28 for Russia. From a purely occupational standpoint, Arctic Alaska, Greenland, and Spitsbergen are of no importance to the populations of their respective nations.

Accessibility offers a complex set of problems. Norway and Russia enjoy some advantages because the warm current from the Atlantic provides Spitsbergen and European Russia as far east as Murmansk with open water the year round. Water access to the rest of the Arctic coastal areas is seasonal and, even then, uncertain. Widely spaced rivers—only the Mackenzie in North America, and the Ob', Yenisey, and Lena in Siberia—offer usable waterways and valleys for inland access during short seasons. Vital as the airplane is, it cannot provide economic bulk transport for the mineral commodities most likely to lure local or regional settlement. Roads, railroads, and piplines pre-

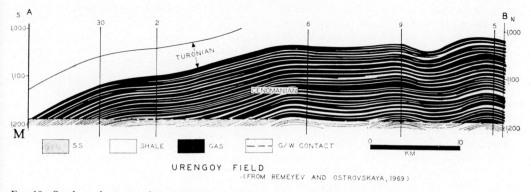

URENGOY FIELD
(FROM REMEYEV AND OSTROVSKAYA, 1969)

FIG. 10—South-north structural cross section of southern part of Urengoy field. Only Cenomanian reservoirs are shown; deeper Neocomian reservoirs not shown. Location is on Figure 9.

sent soluble but expensive engineering problems.

Nonetheless, as this summary has shown, the Russian, Canadian, and Alaskan Arctic—and possibly the Norwegian Arctic—contain resources which these countries and the rest of the world cannot do without. The mineral wealth still is imperfectly known, but the immediate need for Alaskan oil is obvious to all but the most rabid conservationists. There is less immediate pressure for Canadian hydrocarbons and metals, and only regional demands currently for Soviet oil and gas, although this situation in Russia is changing as plans for oil export proceed. Domestic requirements for certain metals found only in the Arctic have been more urgent in Russia, but neither domestic nor world demand for oil would justify the early development of her huge reserves north of the Arctic Circle. However, these reserves, which may rival those in the Persian Gulf, will give Russia control of a major source of world supply in the not-too-distant future. The reserves already proved are double the known reserves in the more thoroughly explored United States, and none of the broad shelf areas extending 6,000 mi (10,000 km) from the Barents Sea to the Chukchi Sea have been probed.

The immediate importance of Alaska's North Slope is evident, but it pales in comparison with the long-range significance of Russia's Arctic lands and shelves. Realization of the region's potential presents problems that are massive, if not insuperable. The terrain and the climate can be managed—at a price. Time no doubt will see the development of engineering competence which at present is not equal to the demands of the region. So far as we can see,

little intelligent, coordinated planning is being done to overcome the two most difficult problems—manpower and capital. Much of Russia's capital is being expended on nonproductive military hardware while she barters for foreign pipe and other types of sophisticated Western equipment. Low productivity in agriculture and industry, not to mention the loss of manpower to bureaucratic, political, and military establishments, place severe limits on the development of the North by a population that is thin by any standard in so large a country. The situation will endure as long as the Russians cherish their xenophobic regard for foreign men and money. Until the Russian outlook broadens —as it may now be doing (July, 1972)[7]— many of the assets of the Russian Arctic, like the ocean they border, will remain frozen or, at best, will undergo a "slow thaw." It will take many people and a huge investment for the Russians to radiate outward from the heartland to the marginal northland.

Whatever the problems that must be solved, the resources of the Arctic and subarctic north of 60° must be used. The region comprises 14 percent of the land surface of the earth, and it is a safe guess that the Arctic regions contain a larger percentage of the world's metallic and industrial wealth. Even in our ignorance we can hazard a "guesstimate" that 30–35 percent of the world's untapped hydrocarbon resources

[7] On July 19, 1972, Occidental Petroleum Co., a California-based company, signed an agreement with the USSR to supply to the Russians "a wide range of scientific and technical services" (Assoc. Press). Other foreign firms, particularly from Japan and the United States, were discussing additional possible contracts with the USSR.

are in Arctic and subarctic Russia, and the potential along Canada's Arctic fringe is unknown. Ironically, but perhaps causally, the North is in the political hands of underpopulated nations. Whether population pressures for lebensraum from the overpopulated countries will threaten the inhospitable north is problematic. China has not forgotten its territorial losses to Russia, and China's northwest still can accommodate more people.

If pressure comes, it is likely to be for access to the mineral wealth of the North. Russia senses this prospect and, as noted, is already seeking control of the main entry to the Arctic from the Atlantic. Her obsession for control of strategic waterways has sought military solutions, currently in naval strength. Military control is illusive, and will prove inimical to demographic and economic development. Even in an age of nuclear weapons, the North is indefensible, especially in an area as sprawling as Siberia or northern Canada. Effective utilization of these vast regions will require the manpower and monetary resources that can so easily be squandered on nonproductive policing. Development calls for international cooperation in a climate of peace.

SELECTED REFERENCES

Anonymous, 1971a, Imperial hits again in Canadian Arctic: Oil and Gas Jour., v. 69, no. 20, p. 86.
——— 1971b, Canada's Tuk area gets two new strikes: Oil and Gas Jour., v. 69, no. 26, p. 32–33.
——— 1971c, Panarctic scores third Arctic gas strike: Oil and Gas Jour., v. 69, no. 51, p. 39.
——— 1972a, First free crude hit in Arctic Islands: Oil and Gas Jour., v. 70, no. 2, p. 62.
——— 1972b, Odds improve for Mackenzie Valley gas line: Oil and Gas Jour., v. 70, no. 9, p. 28.
——— 1972c, Imperial confirms 2,000 bopd flow from Arctic wildcat: World Oil, v. 174, no. 4, p. 71, 75.
——— 1972d, Panarctic has new oil, gas zones in two Arctic wildcats: Oil and Gas Jour., v. 70, no. 18, p. 82.
——— 1972e, Panarctic extends Drake Point 6 miles: Oil and Gas Jour., v. 70, no. 24, p. 60.
Arx, W. S. von, 1962, An introduction to physical oceanography: Reading, Mass., Addison-Wesley Publishing Co., 422 p.
Avrov, V. A., et al., 1969, Karta perspektiv neftegazonosnosti SSSR (Map of oil-gas prospective areas of USSR): Ministerstvo Geologii SSSR, Ministerstvo Neftedobyvayushchey Promyshlennosti SSSR, and Ministerstvo Gazovoy Promyshlennosti SSSR, scale 1:5,000,000, 4 sheets.
Azis, A., G. S. Barry, and I. Haugh, 1972, The undiscovered mineral endowment of the Canadian shield in Manitoba: Canada Dept. Energy, Mines and Resources Mineral Resources Br. Mineral Inf. Bull. MR 124 and Manitoba Dept. Mines, Resources and Environmental Management Pub. 72-1, 42 p.
Bakirov, A. A., and G. E. Ryabukhin, eds., 1969, Nef-

tegazonosnye provintsii i oblasti SSSR (Oil and gas provinces and districts of USSR): Moscow, "Nedra," 478 p.
Bassett, H. G., and J. G. Stout, 1967, Devonian of Western Canada, in Symposium on the Devonian System, v. 1: Calgary, Alberta Soc. Petroleum Geologists, p. 717–752.
Bateman, A. M., 1950, Economic mineral deposits, 2d ed.: New York, Wiley & Sons, Inc., 916 p.
Belorusov, D. V., 1969, Specific peculiarities of the West Siberia complex: Soviet Geog., Review and Translation, v. 10, no. 6, p. 271–285 (original Russian article in Problemy Severa, 1967, no. 12, p. 124–136).
Belyayev, I. V., et al., 1970, Glubinnoye stroyeniye Anadyrskogo neftegazonosnogo basseyna po geofizicheskim dannym (Deep structure of Anadyr' oil-gas basin, from geophysical data): Akad. Nauk SSSR Sibirskoye Otdeleniye, Geologiya i Geofizika, no. 5, p. 113–118.
Bourne, S. A., and A. E. Pallister, 1972, New industry, government data stimulates Arctic Islands interest: Oil and Gas Jour., v. 70, no. 17, p. 108–110.
Burlin, Yu. K., 1967, Vozmozhnye ploshchadi neftegazonakoplennya v Anadyrskoy vpadine na Chukotke (Possible oil- and gas-bearing features of Anadyr' basin of Chukotka): Moscow Univ. Vestnik, no. 1, p. 51–58.
Chilton, J. R., E. D. Bietz, and C. A. S. Bulmer, Jr., 1972, Four discoveries highlight Arctic Islands exploration: World Oil, v. 174, no. 5, p. 53–56.
Cleland, N. A., 1972, The Canadian Arctic: costs, potential high: Oil and Gas Jour., v. 70, no. 12, p. 94, 97–98, 100–101.
Czarniecki, S., 1969, Sedimentary environment and stratigraphical position of the Treskelodden beds (Vestspitsbergen): Polska Akad. Nauk, Prace Muzeum Ziemi, nr. 16, p. 201–336.
Demenitskaya, R. M., ed., 1971, Geofizicheskiye metody razvedki v Arktike (sbornik statey) (Geophysical reconnaissances of Arctic: symposium), v. 6: Leningrad, Ministerstva Geologii SSSR, Nauchno-Issled. Inst. Geologii Arktiki, 134 p.
——— et al., 1968, The transition zone between the Eurasian continent and the Arctic Ocean: Canadian Jour. Earth Sci., v. 5, no. 4, p. 1125–1129.
Dibner, V. D., and N. M. Krylova, 1963, Stratigraficheskoye polozheniye i veshchestvenny sostav uglenosnykh otlozheniy i ugol'nykh plastov na ostrovakh zemli Frantsa Iosiva (Stratigraphic position and material composition of carbonate rocks and coal deposits of Franz Josef Land): Sovetskaya Geologiya, no. 7, p. 77–89.
Dikenshteyn, G., 1971, Der gegenwärtige Stand der Erdöl- und Erdgas ressourcen in der UdSSR: Berlin, Zeitschr. für angewandte Geologie, Band 17, Heft 4, p. 114–117.
Dolzhanskiy, B. G., et al., 1966, Novyye dannyye o glubinnom stroyenii tsentral'noy chasti Anadyrskoy vpadiny (New data on deep structure of central part of Anadyr' basin): Geologiya Nefti i Gaza, no. 10, p. 15–21.
Douglas, R. J. W., ed., 1970, Geology and economic minerals of Canada, ed. 5: Canada Geol. Survey Econ. Geology Rept. No. 1, 2 vol., 838 p.
Einarsson, Tr., 1965, Remarks on crustal structure in Iceland: Royal Astron. Soc. Geophys. Jour., v. 10, no. 3, p. 283–288.
——— and A. A. Meyerhoff, 1974, Continental drift,

VI: tectonic features of Iceland: Jour. Geology, v. 82, in press.

Eldolm, O., and J. Ewing, 1971, Marine geophysical survey in the southwestern Barents Sea: Jour. Geophys. Research, v. 76, no. 17, p. 3832–3841.

Engineering and Mining Journal, 1969a, Canada's nationwide intensified exploration program pushes northward: v. 170, no. 4, p. 120.

———— 1969b, Canada's dynamic mining industry: v. 170, no. 9, p. 97–202.

Eremenko, N. A., et al., 1970, Karta perspektiv neftegazonosnosti shel'fa SSSR (Map of oil-gas prospective area of shelves of USSR): Akad. Nauk SSSR, Ministerstvo Geologii SSSR, Ministerstvo Neftyanoy Promyshlennosti SSSR, and Akad. Nauk Azerbaydzhan SSR, scale 1:5,000,000, 3 sheets.

Escher, E. F., 1965, Geological sketch of Svalbard Islands (Spitsbergen): Geol. Mijnbouw, 44e jaarg., nr. 8, p. 285–294.

Fagerderg, B., and P. H. Fahlstrom, 1969, Crushing and grinding practice in Sweden: Mining Eng., v. 21, p. 61–65.

Fradkin, G. S., ed., 1969, Leno-Vilyuyskaya neftegazonosnaya provintsiya (Lena-Vilyuy oil and gas province): Moscow, "Nauka," 279 p.

Grantz, A., et al., 1970, Reconnaissance geology of the Chukchi Sea as determined by acoustic and magnetic profiling, in W. L. Adkison and M. M. Brosgé, eds., Proceedings of the geological seminar on the North Slope of Alaska: Los Angeles, Pacific Sec. Am. Assoc. Petroleum Geologists, p. F1–F28.

Grønlie, G., and I. B. Ramberg, 1970, Gravity indications of deep sedimentary basins below the Norwegian continental shelf and the Vøring Plateau: Norsk Geol. Tidsskr., v. 50, p. 375–391.

Halbouty, M. T., et al., 1970, World's giant oil and gas fields, geologic factors affecting their formation, and basin classification, in M. T. Halbouty, ed., Geology of giant petroleum fields: Am. Assoc. Petroleum Geologists Mem. 14, p. 502–555.

Haller, J., 1969, Tectonics and neotectonics in East Greenland—review bearing on the drift concept, in Marshall Kay, ed., North Atlantic—geology and continental drift: Am. Assoc. Petroleum Geologists Mem. 12, p. 852–858.

———— 1971, Tectonic map of east Greenland (1: 500,000). An account of tectonism, plutonism, and volcanism in east Greenland: Medd. om Grønland, Bind 171, nr. 5, 286 p.

Harland, W. B., 1969, Contribution of Spitsbergen to understanding of tectonic evolution of North Atlantic region, in Marshall Kay, ed., North Atlantic—geology and continental drift: Am. Assoc. Petroleum Geologists Mem. 12, p. 817–851.

Hatten, C. W., 1971, Petroleum potential of Bristol Bay basin, Alaska, in I. H. Cram, ed., Future petroleum provinces of the United States—their geology and potential: Am. Assoc. Petroleum Geologists Mem. 15, v. 1, p. 105–108.

Heise, H., 1972, Arctic Islands gas reserve ballooning: Oil and Gas Jour., v. 70, no. 2, p. 36–38.

Holtedahl, O., ed., 1960, Geology of Norway: Norges Geol. Undersøkelse Skr., nr. 208, 540 p. and folio volume.

Il'in, K. B., 1968, Karta osnovnyky metallogenicheskikh zon territorii of SSSR, 1967 (Map of principal metallogenic zones of USSR, 1967): Moscow, Ministerstvo Geologii SSSR, Vses. Nauchno-Issled. Geol. Inst., 2 sheets and legend, scale 1:7,500,000.

Ivanov, A. A., and Yu. F. Levitskiy, 1960, Geologiya galogennykh otlozheniy (formatsiy) SSSR (Geology of salt formations of USSR): Vses. Nauchno-Issled. Geol. Inst. Trudy, n.s., t. 35, 424 p.

King, E. R., I. Zietz, and L. R. Alldredge, 1964, Genesis of the Arctic Ocean basin: Science, v. 144, no. 3626, p. 1551–1557.

———— ———— and ———— 1966, Magnetic data on the structure of the central Arctic region: Geol. Soc. America Bull., v. 77, no. 6, p. 619–646.

King, R. E., 1972, Canada is focal point of 1972 exploration interest: World Oil, v. 174, no. 5, p. 47–50.

Klubov, B. A., 1965, Ob ustanovlenii permskikh otlozheniy na ostrove Barentsa (arkhipelag Shpitsbergen) (Discovery of Permian strata on Barents Sea islands, Spitsbergen archipelago): Akad. Nauk SSSR Doklady, v. 152, no. 3, p. 629–631.

Kolgina, L. P., et al., 1971, Litologiya porod-kollektorov mela Surgut-Ust'-Balykskogo neftenosnogo regiona Zapadnoy Sibiri (Lithology of Cretaceous reservoirs in Surgut-Ust'-Balyk oil-bearing region of West Siberia): Moscow, "Nauka," 168 p.

Kopik, J., 1968, Remarks on some Toarcian ammonites from the Hornsund area, Vestsptisbergen, in Geological results of the 1957–1958, 1959, 1960 Spitsbergen Expeditions: Studia Geol. Polonica, v. 21, p. 33–52.

Kornev, B. V., et al., 1966, O perspektivakh i osnovnykh napravleniyakh neftegazopoiskovykh rabot v Noril'skom rayone (Prospects and directions of trends in oil and gas exploration work in Norilsk area): Geologiya Nefti i Gaza, no. 1, p. 10–15.

Kulling, O., and P. Geijer, 1960, The Caledonian mountain chain in the Torneträsk-Ofoten area, northern Scandinavia; The Kiruna iron ore field, Swedish Lapland: 21st Internat. Geol. Cong., Copenhagen 1960, Guides to Excursions A25, C20, 76 p.

Lang, A. H., et al., 1970, Economic minerals of the Canadian shield, in Geology and economic minerals of Canada: Canada Geol. Survey Econ. Geology Rept. No. 1, p. 151–226.

Little, H. W., et al., 1970, Economic minerals of western Canada, in Geology and economic minerals of Canada: Canada Geol. Survey Econ. Geol. Rept. No. 1, p. 489–546.

L'vov, M. S., 1969, Resursy prirodnogo gaza SSSR (Resources of natural gas in USSR): Moscow, "Nedra," 224 p.

Magnusson, N. H., 1965, The Precambrian history of Sweden: Geol. Soc. London Quart. Jour., v. 121, pt. 1, p. 1–30.

McCaslin, J. C., 1969, A look down under up north: Oil and Gas Jour., v. 67, no. 50, p. 107.

Meyerhoff, A. A., 1970a, Continental drift: implications of paleomagnetic studies, meteorology, physical oceanography, and climatology: Jour. Geology, v. 78, no. 1, p. 1–55.

———— 1970b, Continental drift, II: high-latitude evaporite deposits and geologic history of Arctic and North Atlantic Oceans: Jour. Geology, v. 78, no. 4, p. 406–444.

———— and H. A. Meyerhoff, 1971, Terre polari, in Enciclopedia del petrolio e del gas naturale: Rome, Ente Nazionale Idrocarburi, Casa Editrice Carlo Colombo, v. 8, p. 1108–1126.

———— I. A. Mamantov, and T. Shabad, 1971, Russian Arctic boasts big potential: Oil and Gas Jour., v. 69, no. 43, p. 122–126.

Modelevskiy, M. Sh., and N. S. Tolstoy, 1970, Geologiya i neftegazonosnost' arkticheskikh i subarkticheskikh rayonov mira (Geology and oil and gas accumulations in Arctic and subarctic areas of the world): Moscow, Ministerstvo Neftyanoy Promyshlennosti, Vses. Nauchno-Issled. Inst. Organizatsii, Upravleniya i Ekonomiki Neftegazovoy Promyshlennosti, 116 p.

Morgridge, D. L., and W. B. Smith, Jr., 1972, Geology and discovery of Prudhoe Bay field, eastern Arctic slope, Alaska, *in* R. E. King, ed., Stratigraphic oil and gas fields—classification, exploration methods, and case histories: Am. Assoc. Petroleum Geologists Mem. 16 and Soc. Explor. Geophysicists Spec. Pub. 10, p. 489–501.

Nalivkin, D. V., ed., 1967, Geologicheskaya karta SSR, 1966 (Geologic map of USSR, 1966): Ministerstvo Geologii SSSR, Vses. Nauchno-Issled. Geol. Inst., 2 sheets and legend, scale, 1:7,500,000.

Nesterov, I. I., F. K. Salmanov, and K. A. Shpil'man, 1971, Neftyanye i gazovye mestorozhdeniya Zapadnoy Sibiri (Oil and gas fields of West Siberia): Moscow, "Nedra," 464 p.

Owen, E., in press, Trek of the oil finders: a history of exploration for petroleum: Am. Assoc. Petroleum Geologists Mem. 6.

Pershina, A. I., *et al.*, 1971, Biostratigrafiya siluriyskikh i devonskikh otlozheniy Pechorskogo Urala (Biostratigraphy of Silurian and Devonian of Pechora Urals): Leningrad, Izd. "Nauka," Akad. Nauk SSSR, Leningradskoye Otdel., Komi Filial, Inst. Geologii, 130 p.

Porth, H., and W. D. Tafel, 1970, Erdöl und Erdgas in der Arktis: Hamburg, Oeh, Zeitschr. für Mineralölwirkschaft, Heft. 7, p. 201–208.

Pratt, W. E., 1947, Petroleum on continental shelves: Am. Assoc. Petroleum Geologists Bull., v. 31, no. 4, p. 657–672; 1972, reprinted *in* AAPG Reprint Ser. No. 3, p. 40–55.

Quineau, P. E., 1961, Mining in the Arctic: Mining Engineering, v. 4, p. 694–699.

Rankama, K., ed., 1963, The Precambrian, I; Fennoscandian shield: New York, Interscience Pub., 279 p.

Remejew, O. A., and K. W. Ostrowskaja, 1969, Urengoj —die grösste Erdgaslagerstätte der Welt: Berlin, Zeitschr. fur Angewandte Geologie, Band 16, Heft 6, p. 297–300.

Rickwood, F. K., 1970, The Prudhoe Bay field, *in* W. L. Adkison and M. M. Brosgé, eds., Proceedings of the geological seminar on the North Slope of Alaska: Los Angeles, Pacific Sec., Am. Assoc. Petroleum Geologists, p. L1–L11.

Rutten, M. G., 1969, The geology of western Europe: Amsterdam, Elsevier Pub. Co., 520 p.

Sarkisyan, S. G., ed., 1968, Geologiya i neftegazonosnost' tsentral'noy chasti Zapadno-Sibirskoy nizmennosti (Geology and oil and gas accumulations of central part of West Siberian lowland): Moscow, "Nauka," 144 p.

Scholl, D. W., and D. M. Hopkins, 1969, Newly discovered Cenozoic basins, Bering Sea shelf, Alaska: Am. Assoc. Petroleum Geologists Bull., v. 53, no. 10, p. 2067–2078.

Semenov, A. I., and A. D. Shcheglov, eds., 1968, Geologicheskoye stroyeniye SSSR, t. IV, Osnovnye zakonomernosti razmeshcheniya mestorozhdeniy poleznykh isokopalyemykh na territorii SSSR (Geologic

structure of USSR, v. IV, Basic regularities in distribution of commercial mineral deposits of USSR): Moscow, "Nedra," 504 p.

Shabad, T., 1969, Basic industrial resources of the U.S.S.R.: New York, Columbia Univ. Press, 393 p.

Siedlecka, A., 1968, Lithology and sedimentary environment of the Hyrnfjellet beds and the Treskelodden beds (late Palaeozoic) at Treskelen, Hornsund, Vestspitsbergen, *in* Geological results of the Polish 1957–1958, 1959, 1960 Spitsbergen Expeditions, pt. VI: Studia Geol. Polonica, v. 21, p. 53–96.

Simonen, A., 1960, Petrographic provinces of the plutonic rocks of the Svecofennides of Finland: 21st Internat. Geol. Cong., Copenhagen 1960, Rept. 13, p. 28–38.

Sokolov, V. N., and T. M. Pchelina, 1967, O nizhnem i srednem triase zemli serkap na Zapadnoy Shpitsbergena (Lower and Middle Triassic of Sörkapp Land, Vestspitsbergen): Akad. Nauk SSSR Doklady, v. 176, no. 6, p. 1374–1377.

Sosipatrova, G. P., 1967, Kompleksy foraminifer iz verkhnego paleozoyskikh otlozheniy Shpitsbergena (Foraminiferal complexes in upper Paleozoic strata of Spitsbergen): Akad. Nauk SSSR Doklady, v. 176, no. 1, p. 182–185.

Spizharskiy, T. N., ed., 1967, Tektonicheskaya karta SSSR, 1966 (Tectonic map of USSR, 1966): Ministerstvo Geologii SSSR, Vses. Nauchno-Issled. Geol. Inst., 2 sheets and legend, scale 1:7,500,000.

Thorsteinsson, R., and E. T. Tozer, 1970, Geology of the Arctic Archipelago, *in* Geology and economic minerals of Canada: Geol. Survey Canada, Econ. Geol. Rept. No. 1, p. 547–590.

Trettin, H. P., 1969, A Paleozoic-Tertiary fold belt in northernmost Ellesmere Island aligned with the Lomonosov Ridge: Geol. Soc. America Bull., v. 80, no. 1, p. 143–148.

Trewartha, G. T., 1968, An introduction to climate, 4th ed.: New York, McGraw-Hill Book Co., 408 p.

Trofimuk, A. A., ed., 1971, Neftegazonosnye basseyny Dal'nego Vostoka SSSR (Oil-gas basins of Far Eastern USSR): Moscow, Izd. "Nedra," 183 p.

———— *et al.*, 1964, Main problems of prospecting the Markovo oil field in eastern Siberia: Geologiya Nefti i Gaza (Engl. transl. *in* Petroleum Geology, McLean, Va., v. 8, no. 1 [May 1969], p. 13–18).

U.S. Bureau of Mines, 1971, Mineral production in Alaska in 1970: Juneau, Alaska, Area Rept. A-35, 4 p.

U.S. Geological Survey–State of Alaska, 1964, Mineral and water resources of Alaska: U.S. Geol. Survey– State of Alaska Dept. Natural Resources, 179 p.

Vasil'yev, V. G., ed., 1968a, Geologiya nefti, spravochnik, t. 2, kniga 1, Neftyanye mestorozhdeniya SSSR (Geology of oil, sourcebook, v. 2, book 1, Oil fields of USSR): Moscow, "Nedra," 764 p.

———— ed., 1968b, Gazovye mestorozhdeniya SSSR, spravochnik (Gas fields of USSR, sourcebook): Moscow, "Nedra," 688 p.

Vogt, P. R., and N. A. Ostenso, 1970, Magnetic and gravity profiles across the Alpha Cordillera and their relation to Arctic sea-floor spreading: Jour. Geophys. Research, v. 75, no. 26, p. 4925–4937.

Worthington, L. V., 1970, The Norwegian Sea as a mediterranean basin: Deep-Sea Research, v. 17, no. 1, p. 77–84.

Index

This index consists of three sections, which appear in the following order:

(1) Title Index (in order of appearance)
(2) Author Index (alphabetical)
(3) Keyword Index (alphabetical).

The *title index* is a listing of the titles in the order published.

The *author index* is arranged alphabetically according to each author's last name. For papers by more than one author, each author's name appears in the index in alphabetical order. The appearance of an author's name followed by the title of an article does not mean that he is the only author of that article. He may be one of two or more authors of the paper whose title follows his name. The author index does *not* show multiple authors in any single listing.

To locate a reference in the *keyword index,* the reader should begin by thinking of the significant words. Then he should look in the index for the keyword entry for each of those words. The reference codes will direct him to the pages.

The columns on the right-hand side of the keyword index give the page number and a code number (1 or 3) indicating the nature of the source. The code is:

(1) for phrase from title; and
(3) for phrase from abstract, text, table, figure, or figure caption.

The keyword for each entry is located at the left-hand side of the page. The ($>$) sign indicates the first word in each title or key phrase. The ($<$) sign indicates the end of the title or key phrase.

Title Index

Author Index

Keyword Index